THE PROPERTIES OF GASES AND LIQUIDS

THE SERIES

THE PROPERTIES OF GASES AND LIQUIDS

Their Estimation and Correlation

ROBERT C. REID

Professor of Chemical Engineering
Massachusetts Institute of Technology

THOMAS K. SHERWOOD

Professor of Chemical Engineering
Massachusetts Institute of Technology

SECOND EDITION

McGRAW-HILL BOOK COMPANY

New York   St. Louis   San Francisco   Düsseldorf   London
Mexico   Panama   Sydney   Toronto

THE PROPERTIES OF GASES AND LIQUIDS

PREFACE TO SECOND EDITION

Information regarding the properties of materials is essential to the planning and building which are the business of engineers. An enormous amount of such data has been collected and tabulated over the years, but the rapid advance of technology into new fields seems always to maintain a gap between the demand for basic data and its experimental determination. The engineer is required to rely on common sense, experience, and methods of estimating physical properties in developing new machines and processes.

A very large number of methods have been proposed for the estimation of physical properties of materials. This book presents a critical review of the various estimation procedures for a limited number of properties of gases and liquids—critical properties, P-V-T and thermodynamic properties, vapor pressures, latent heats, heats of formation, free energies of formation, heat capacities, surface tensions, viscosities, thermal conductivities, and diffusion coefficients. Comparisons of experimental and estimated values are usually shown in the form of tables in order to indicate the degree of reliability of the methods discussed. The procedures evaluated are necessarily limited to those which appeared to the authors to be of the greatest practical use and validity. Recommendations are made regarding the best methods of estimating each property and of extrapolating available data.

The book is intended to serve the practicing engineer, especially the process or chemical engineer. Because the subject matter is tied closely to basic theory, the book should also interest the student of molecular physics.

The first edition of this book was published early in 1958 though actual writing ceased in late 1956. In the eight years since its publication, a large number of papers have been published which purport to correlate various physical properties of gases and liquids. Many new methods have appeared; the present half-life of an existing correlation or estimation method is now about four years. Thus in the past eight years, only a fraction of the estimation techniques recommended in the first edition have withstood the test of time; many have been supplanted by newer, more accurate methods.   It is interesting to note, however, that even now, most of the new methods are still largely empirical.   The rigorous approach to calculation of most physical properties is still unattainable since the fundamental laws describing forces between molecules are not clearly established and, even if they were, the mathematics required for a solution is often nearly intractable.

In revising the book we have reluctantly decided to delete the chapter on Vapor-Liquid-Equilibrium, as this area has now grown to such a degree as to demand a separate volume.   We have, however, added chapters dealing with surface tension, thermodynamic properties, and equilibrium properties of mixtures, besides expanding and bringing up to date all the remaining chapters.   Every chapter has been completely rewritten except Chapter 1, which, though changed slightly, still accurately reflects our opinion on the subject of the estimation of the properties of gases and liquids.   A set of Appendixes has been introduced to summarize material referred to in several chapters or for material of a very detailed nature.   Appendix A, for example, lists for convenient reference a consistent, complete set of critical and other useful pure-component properties for compounds and the common elements; Appendix G provides a consistent set of Lennard-Jones constants.

Although the final decision as to the choice of the recommended methods rests solely with ourselves, we wish to express our appreciation to many individuals who kindly read rough drafts and made valuable comments and criticisms.   Dr. Arnold Bondi and Dr. Bernard Kouzel have been very helpful in all areas.   Dr. Donald Miller has graciously reviewed and made several valuable analyses of data for vapor pressures and heats of vaporization.   Others to whom special thanks are due are Dr. Richard Heitman, Professors Charles Hill, George Thodos, John Prausnitz, Otto Redlich, and Wayne Edmister.

Simultaneously with the revision we have had the good fortune to be associated with an A.I.Ch.E. project to develop a program to allow computer estimation of many of the same physical properties as discussed in this book.   The discussion and assistance of the A.I.Ch.E. subcommittee of E. L. Meadows, T. L. Leininger, G. E. Jones, R. R. Hughes, L. Friend, C. D. Alstad, W. M. Carlson, and B. J. Price is gratefully acknowledged.

Paul S. Shapiro, E. Ma, and T.-S. Lee were of great assistance in many of the calculations and literature searches.   The manuscript was typed primarily by Janine Levitch, Sheila Scanlon, and Ann Flynn, and it is due to their diligence, patience, and skill that our rough drafts were translated into readable form.

Most of the tedious job of proofreading and searching for bibliographical references fell to Nancy Reid, and her patience and constant encouragement cannot be fully acknowledged.   Donald and Ann Christine Reid collated drafts, indexed literature references, and were helpful in many other ways, down even to keeping the pencils sharp. It is hoped that the close proximity to the chores necessary in writing a book will not have deterred them in any way from their present desire to write and publish their own books.

Robert C. Reid
Thomas K. Sherwood

Preface to Second Printing

We should like to thank those who kindly pointed out errors in the first printing. These have been corrected. Also, as the contents of this book deal with liquids and gases, we would like to recommend the valuable new book by Arnold Bondi which allows us to estimate similar properties for molecular crystals, high-molecular-weight liquids, and glasses.*

Robert C. Reid
Thomas K. Sherwood

* Arnold Bondi, "Physical Properties of Molecular Crystals, Liquids and Glasses," John Wiley & Sons, Inc., New York, 1968.

CONTENTS

Appendixes

THE PROPERTIES OF GASES AND LIQUIDS

CHAPTER 1

INTRODUCTION

"EVERYTHING IS KNOWN ABOUT MOLECULES"

Knowledge of the properties of materials is basic to engineering, since the cost and safety of structures are dependent on the strength and permanence of the materials of construction. Civil and mechanical engineers have long been concerned with the properties of steels, concrete, and other materials employed in various types of structures and machinery. With the development and growth of the process industries, it has become increasingly important to have information regarding the properties of gases and liquids, including many new chemical substances whose physical properties have never been measured experimentally. The design of a plant to manufacture butadiene, for example, requires knowledge of the properties of this material and related compounds, not only for the proper design of piping and pumps but for the design of heaters, coolers, and separation equipment.

The chemical or process engineer deals primarily with molecules, and his activities might be described as "molecular engineering." His basic need is knowledge regarding the behavior of molecules, in the form of reliable quantitative data on the chemical, physical, and thermodynamic properties of pure substances and mixtures. Much of the needed data exists, and modern molecular theory provides a sound basis for the prediction of some of the needed numbers. Indeed, in the view of the modern physicist, "everything is known about molecules." J. C. Slater, in his book "Modern Physics," states that "(in nuclear physics) we are still seeking the laws; whereas in the physics of atoms, molecules and solids, we have found the laws and are exploring the deductions from them." There is, unfortunately, a great gap between having the laws and having the numbers which the engineer and applied scientist need for design purposes.

The "International Critical Tables," "Landolt-Börnstein Tabellen," API and MCA data sheets, the Thermophysical Properties Research Institute books, and other such compilations provide much of the data needed by the process engineer, but frequently a desired property is not

1

to be obtained either from such sources or from the periodical literature. The present book is intended as a critical review of the many methods which have been proposed for the estimation of certain of the more important properties of gases and liquids in cases where experimental values are not to be found.

Prediction is usually based on correlations of known information, with interpolation or extrapolation as required. Correlations are of three types: purely empirical, partly empirical but based on some theoretical concept, and purely theoretical. The first is often unreliable and worthless, and the third is seldom adequately developed. Most of the useful correlations are of a form suggested in part by theory, with empirical constants based on experimental data.

Useful correlations are very often based on but a fragment of theory. The latent heats of vaporization of liquids (expressed as calories per gram) vary widely. Simple molecular theory suggests the qualitative concept that the latent heat is the energy required to separate the molecules of the liquid and to do the work of expanding the vapor. It follows that the latent heat should depend more on the number of molecules than on the mass of the substance; hence the molal latent heat might be suspected to be constant. Experimental data indicate this constant to be in the vicinity of 8000, and the rough rule that the molal latent heat of vaporization is 8000 cal/g mole at the normal boiling point (i.e., at 1 atm) may be taken as valid to ± 20 per cent for a very large number of substances. Much better correlations of latent-heat data are given in Chap. 4, but the point is that even an elementary theoretical concept may be extremely helpful.

In many cases, a simple theory which is only approximately correct may provide a useful correlation if the deviations from the theory are treated empirically. The ideal-gas law is valid at low pressures but represents poorly the P-V-T data on real gases at high pressures. Good correlations are obtainable by empirical treatment of the compressibility Z, which is defined by writing $PV = ZRT$ and which may be regarded as a correction factor in the ideal-gas law. Empirical correlations of Z, in turn based on the inexact theoretical concept of "corresponding states," are equivalent to empirical correlations of the deviations $(PV/RT - 1)$ of the data from the ideal-gas law. This procedure illustrates a very powerful method for the development of correlations of physical data as a basis for predictions.

Another method of developing useful correlations of physical data is to employ an equation based on theory, with the incorporation of empirical expressions for one or more of the required terms. The Clapeyron equation, for example, is a simple and valid basis for calculation of the latent heat of vaporization from vapor-pressure data. It requires, however, that the volume increase on vaporization be known. The incorporation of an empirical expression for volume increase into the theoretical Clapeyron equation provides a useful correlation of latent heats of vaporization in terms of vapor pressures.

In spite of the feeling on the part of modern physicists that "everything is known about molecules," there are almost no purely theoretical expressions for the physical properties in which the engineer is interested. Perhaps the nearest approach to a comprehensive picture of molecular behavior is the modern kinetic theory of gases. This is an extension of the simpler Maxwell theory, with allowance for the forces between molecules.

Molecules are assumed to repel each other when close together and to attract each other when far apart. The intermolecular potential is the quantitative relation between the potential energy of attraction and the distance between molecules. Various intermolecular potentials have been proposed, that of Lennard-Jones being perhaps best known. Once an intermolecular potential function is assumed, it is possible to develop theoretical expressions for various properties of dilute gases, including the second (and the third) virial coefficients, viscosity, thermal conductivity, molecular diffusivity, and thermal-diffusion coefficient. The constants (usually two in number) in the intermolecular potential function are specific to the chemical species and do not vary appreciably with temperature. The overall result of this approach is a basis for prediction with good precision of a few properties of gases. The predicted variation of these properties with temperature is often in excellent agreement with experimental data. These developments constitute a most important advance over the original kinetic theory.

It should be realized that this complex but successful theoretical development is basically empirical, in that the form of the intermolecular potential function is assumed and the potential parameters must be obtained from data on some property of the substance or must be estimated by the use of empirical rules. No satisfactory theory has been developed to describe quantitatively the forces or potentials between molecules.

Since a number of properties of a pure dilute gas may be calculated by an assumed molecular potential function involving two constants, it is evident that theory provides relations between any two of the properties. These are extremely useful but once again empirical in the sense that experimental data on one property must be known in order to calculate the values of the other. Though "everything is known about molecules," it would appear that the present state of molecular theory permits the prediction of a physical property of a substance only if data on some other physical property are available. Theoretical prediction based only on molecular structure is not yet feasible.

Though the theory of dilute gases is relatively advanced, the behavior of liquids is less well understood. The present book is restricted to methods of estimation of the physical properties of gases and liquids; polymers, solids, liquid metals, and salts are not considered. Furthermore, the treatment is confined to a limited number of properties, selected as being of most general interest to engineers. The discussion deals with the properties of pure substances and mixtures.

The properties of the substances are obviously dependent upon the nature of the atoms which constitute the molecule, and considerable success has been attained in expressing certain properties as additive functions of values assigned to the atoms, with allowance for molecular structure. For example, Lydersen's rule for additive volumes provides a fair basis for the estimation of the critical volume of many materials. Rules similar in form are available for estimating many other properties of pure substances. Mixtures are treated in many different ways. One common method is to consider a mixture as a hypothetical pure component and use pure-component correlations. In others, the constants in pure-component correlations are expressed in terms of composition. In the estimation of transport properties and certain equilibrium properties which can be treated by means of the virial equation, theory leads to a relation involving the composition.

Most of the properties to be discussed in subsequent chapters involve interaction between molecules. Heat and free energy of formation, however, depend primarily on molecular structure and the energies required to break the chemical bonds between atoms. Estimation of these properties requires knowledge of bond energies, and most methods are based on empirical rules with values assigned to different types of chemical bonds between atoms. The theory of such bond energy is even less well developed than that describing interactions between molecules.

The general pattern of the chapters to follow is a critical study of the most promising methods of estimation of each property considered, followed whenever possible by a recommendation as to the best methods. The literature suggests literally dozens of methods of correlation of many of the properties; two or more of the most promising are selected and compared with the experimental data. In most cases the comparison has been made with two to four times as many known values as shown in the abbreviated tables reproduced.

Tables are used in place of graphs for two reasons: to facilitate comparisons of the deviations with the type of compound (polar, halogen-containing, etc.) and to provide a collection of experimental values for convenient reference. No statistical analysis of the tabulated comparisons has been attempted, but simple arithmetic average errors (without regard to sign) are indicated in most instances.

The value of a correlation or estimation method depends on at least three things: its accuracy, its simplicity, and the type of information necessary for its use.   If sufficient information about the substance is available, it may be possible to predict the property quite accurately. If little but the chemical formula and perhaps the normal boiling point is known, it may be necessary to employ a less reliable procedure.   For these reasons, it has seemed desirable to offer several recommendations regarding the estimation methods for certain of the properties, the recommended procedures being dependent on the auxiliary information known about the substance.

It should be emphasized that reliable experimental data are always to be preferred over values estimated by any of the methods discussed. Eventually, the continued publication of experimental measurements and the developing theory of molecular behavior may make a book of this kind pointless.   In the meantime, the empirical and semitheoretical methods of estimation of the kinds discussed must be relied on in process-design calculations and for many other purposes in the fields of engineering and applied science.

CHAPTER 2

CRITICAL CONSTANTS AND OTHER CHARACTERISTIC
PARAMETERS FOR PURE MATERIALS

2-1 Scope

Most estimation techniques discussed in this book require the knowledge of certain parameters which are characteristic of the pure component of interest or of which a mixture is composed. The most common (and successful) example is the corresponding-state concept, where properties are compared at equal reduced states. This concept is discussed in detail in Chap. 3, and it is sufficient to note here that the application of the corresponding-state concept usually requires some knowledge of the component critical properties. Thus methods to estimate the critical properties of temperature, pressure, and volume are considered in detail in this chapter. In addition, it has been shown that estimation and correlation techniques may often be significantly improved if other characteristic parameters are taken into account. Those of most importance are the normal atmospheric boiling point, the critical compressibility factor, the acentric factor, and the Riedel factor. As values of these parameters are needed throughout the book, their estimation is also considered in this chapter. Finally, as in many of the theoretically based methods of estimation the Lennard-Jones intermolecular potential is assumed applicable, the methods of obtaining Lennard-Jones characteristic energy and distance parameters are discussed briefly.

A meaningful error involved in the estimation of any of these pure-component characteristics is extremely difficult to obtain. Each compound is a separate entity, and success with a few different families of materials by no means assures success with an untested family. Whenever possible, average deviations for each method are presented, but these should be treated with some caution, as averages give only an approximate idea of the validity of a method. For example, if a method for estimating critical temperatures should give accurate values when applied to esters but poor results when applied to alcohols, a statistical average of the errors would have little significance, especially when one wishes to apply it to pure esters or alcohols.

A very large number of relations have been proposed for estimating the

6

critical temperature, pressure, and volume, but only a few will be described here. The principal reasons for rejection of those not presented were (1) poor agreement between experimental and predicted values, and (2) limited applicability, i.e., accurate results are obtained with only a few species or a single homologous series. Each proposed method which could not be immediately rejected was tested by using it to predict the critical properties of a variety of organic and inorganic compounds whose critical properties had been well substantiated by experimental means. The method or methods that gave the best results in this testing scheme were selected for presentation. Appendix A contains a tabulation of the reported experimental values of the critical properties of many compounds and elements.

2-2 The Critical State

The critical temperature of a pure material may be defined as the maximum temperature at which liquid and vapor phases can coexist in equilibrium. The vapor pressure at this temperature is termed the critical pressure, and the volume per mole or unit mass, the critical volume.

An oversimplified picture of the critical point may be gained by a kinetic picture of the liquid phase. The potential energy of attraction between molecules, which is responsible for the liquid phase, is counterbalanced to some degree by the kinetic energy of the molecules. The latter tends to separate randomly all portions of the liquid. Thus vapor pressure is due to the tendency of some of the liquid molecules which have a sufficiently high kinetic energy to break away from the strong cohesive-force fields of the liquid. As temperature is raised in a liquid system, the kinetic energy of the molecules increases but there is little effect on the cohesive forces. The temperature at which the average molecular kinetic energy becomes equal to the negative of the potential energy of attraction is termed the *critical temperature* (73), since above this temperature no liquid phase is then possible.

Experimental studies of the critical region are numerous, but often conflicting interpretations of the data are given. The fact that, with increasing temperature, the liquid and vapor densities rapidly approach each other in this region is sometimes illustrated by the rapid development of a fog or opalescence near the liquid-gas interface. In such a case gravity effects or agitation often masks a smooth transition. There is also conflicting opinion as to whether or not there is a definite critical point or whether one might more appropriately speak of a region with a finite range of pressure, temperature, and volume. For the purposes of the present discussion such differences are, however, unimportant, since this range would be so small (e.g., the temperature range would be only a few hundredths of a degree) that one could still speak of a critical point.

From a mathematical sense, the important criteria of the critical point are

$$(dP/dV)_{T_c} = (d^2P/dV^2)_{T_c} = 0 \qquad (2\text{-}1)$$

Thus an isotherm at T_c undergoes a point of inflection at the critical pressure and volume on a P-V graph. Some authors have shown that it is reasonable to assume that the third and fourth derivatives of pressure with respect to volume at T_c are also zero [or at least very small (33)].

Theoretical treatments of the critical state have ordinarily chosen some molecular model such as the cell theory of liquids to allow a formulation of an equation of state relating liquid volumes to temperature and pressure. Then, by using Eq. (2-1), the critical constants may be found in terms of the parameters or constants contained in the equation of state. Such treatments have not as yet produced accurate methods for estimating the critical constants, and at the present time reliance must be placed on empirical methods.

An excellent review of the critical state has been given by Rice (49).

2-3   Estimation of Critical Temperatures

Modified Guldberg Rule.   Guldberg first noted that the ratio of the normal boiling point to the critical temperature was relatively constant for many organic and inorganic materials and approximately equal to $2:3$. Several authors (18, 31, 51, 55, 75) have significantly improved the rule by defining a parameter θ,

$$\theta = T_b/T_c \qquad (2\text{-}2)$$

where θ is calculated for any particular compound by summing up atomic and structural constants. There is often little choice among the methods of calculating θ if the criterion is based only on accuracy, but for applicability to more types of compounds, Lydersen's method (31) appears to be best. In this method,

$$\theta = 0.567 + \Sigma\Delta_T - (\Sigma\Delta_T)^2 \qquad (2\text{-}3)$$

where $\Sigma\Delta_T$ is obtained by summing the contributions listed in Table 2-1. Lydersen tested Eq. (2-3) for 244 compounds comprising a wide variety of types and found that only 27 showed errors greater than 2 per cent; the critical temperatures of most of these latter materials were based on old measurements which have never been verified. High-molecular-weight alkanes and esters have estimated critical temperatures consistently 1 to 2 per cent less than experimental values; the same trend was noted for alcohols above butanol, though errors up to 5 per cent were found. The method is illustrated in Example 2-1.

TABLE 2-1. LYDERSEN'S CRITICAL PROPERTY INCREMENTS*

	Δ_T	Δ_p	Δ_v
Nonring increments:			
—CH₃	0.020	0.227	55
—CH₂	0.020	0.227	55
—CH	0.012	0.210	51
—C—	0.00	0.210	41
=CH₂	0.018	0.198	45
=CH	0.018	0.198	45
=C—	0.0	0.198	36
=C=	0.0	0.198	36
≡CH	0.005	0.153	(36)
≡C—	0.005	0.153	(36)
Ring increments:			
—CH₂—	0.013	0.184	44.5
—CH	0.012	0.192	46
—C—	(−0.007)	(0.154)	(31)
=CH	0.011	0.154	37
=C—	0.011	0.154	36
=C=	0.011	0.154	36
Halogen increments:			
—F	0.018	0.224	18
—Cl	0.017	0.320	49
—Br	0.010	(0.50)	(70)
—I	0.012	(0.83)	(95)
Oxygen increments:			
—OH (alcohols)	0.082	0.06	(18)
—OH (phenols)†	0.031	(−0.02)	(3)
—O— (nonring)	0.021	0.16	20
—O— (ring)	(0.014)	(0.12)	(8)
—C=O (nonring)	0.040	0.29	60
—C=O (ring)	(0.033)	(0.2)	(50)
HC=O (aldehyde)	0.048	0.33	73
—COOH (acid)	0.085	(0.4)	80
—COO— (ester)	0.047	0.47	80
=O (except for combinations above)	(0.02)	(0.12)	(11)
Nitrogen increments:			
—NH₂	0.031	0.095	28
—NH (nonring)	0.031	0.135	(37)
—NH (ring)	(0.024)	(0.09)	(27)

TABLE 2-1. LYDERSEN'S CRITICAL PROPERTY INCREMENTS* (*Continued*)

	Δ_T	Δ_p	Δ_v
Nitrogen increments (*Cont.*)			
—N̶— (nonring)	0.014	0.17	(42)
—N̶— (ring)	(0.007)	(0.13)	(32)
—CN	(0.060)	(0.36)	(80)
—NO₂	(0.055)	(0.42)	(78)
Sulfur increments:			
—SH	0.015	0.27	55
—S— (nonring)	0.015	0.27	55
—S— (ring)	(0.008)	(0.24)	(45)
＝S	(0.003)	(0.24)	(47)
Miscellaneous:			
—S̶i̶—	0.03	(0.54)	
—B̶—	(0.03)		

NOTES
1. There are no increments for hydrogen.
2. All bonds shown as free are connected with atoms other than hydrogen.
3. Values in parentheses are based upon too few experimental values to be reliable.
4. From vapor-pressure measurements and a calculational technique similar to Fishtine (13) it has been suggested that the C̶—H ring increment common to two condensed saturated rings be given the value of $\Delta_T = 0.064$ (38).
* A. L. Lydersen, Estimation of Critical Properties of Organic Compounds, *Coll. Eng., Univ. Wisconsin, Eng. Expt. Sta. Rept.* 3, Madison, Wis., April, 1955.
† Ref. 1.

Forman and Thodos Method. Thodos and his coworkers at Northwestern have attempted to devise an accurate method to estimate critical properties by a technique which does not require knowledge of the normal boiling temperature. The technique seeks to estimate suitable van der Waals' constants a and b [see Eq. (3-48)]. From the criteria of an inflection point in the critical isotherm at the critical point [Eq. (2-1)] van der Waals' equation of state yields

$$T_c = 8a/27bR \qquad (2\text{-}4)$$
$$P_c = a/27b^2 \qquad (2\text{-}5)$$

The use of this method does not require that the material being tested follow van der Waals' equation; rather one may say that Eqs. (2-4) and (2-5) relate critical properties to two other parameters (a, b) which are more easily correlated with molecular structure.

Forman and Thodos's method is developed in a series of papers (15, 16, 68–69, 70). The method relates a and b to structure. The molecule is visualized as a number of units consisting either of carbon atoms (with any attached hydrogens) or of clearly identifiable functional groups (such as —OH, etc.). Each of these units contributes an increment, not to a or b, but to $a^{2/3}$ and $b^{3/4}$. The sum of all $a^{2/3}$ increments is then raised to the $3/2$ power to obtain a and the sum of all $b^{3/4}$ increments raised to the $4/3$ power to obtain b for use in Eqs. (2-4) and (2-5). The method is slightly more complicated than outlined, since double bonds, rings, isomerism, etc., must be allowed for. A routine is outlined in detail below to suggest a formal approach to the estimation of a and b for any specified compound. The procedure is to evaluate $\Delta a^{2/3}$ and $\Delta b^{3/4}$ contributions from an analysis of the structure of the molecule.

   a. *Saturated Aliphatic Hydrocarbon Portion.* Carbons in aliphatic hydrocarbons are divided into four *types:*

$$
\begin{array}{cccc}
1 & 2 & 3 & 4 \\
\\
-CH_3 & -CH_2- & -\overset{\displaystyle |}{\underset{\displaystyle |}{C}}-H & -\overset{\displaystyle |}{\underset{\displaystyle |}{C}}- \\
\end{array}
$$

The $\Delta a^{2/3}$ and $\Delta b^{3/4}$ contributions for each carbon are functions of the *type* of carbon and the value of n, the *total* number of carbon atoms and functional atoms (atoms other than hydrogen in such groups as —NH$_2$, —OH, —COOH). Table 2-2 lists these contributions.

TABLE 2-2. GROUP CONTRIBUTIONS $\Delta a^{2/3}$ AND $\Delta b^{3/4}$ FOR THE SATURATED ALIPHATIC HYDROCARBONS*

n	Type 1		Type 2		Type 3		Type 4	
	$\Delta a^{2/3}$	$\Delta b^{3/4}$	$\Delta a^{2/3}$	$\Delta b^{3/4}$	$\Delta a^{2/3}$	$\Delta b^{3/4}$	$\Delta a^{2/3}$	$\Delta b^{3/4}$
1								
2	15,577	11.453						
3	15,216	11.453	13,678	6.262				
4	15,035	11.453	13,678	6.262	12,567	2.064		
5	14,927	11.453	13,678	6.262	11,189	0.886	6,181	− 4.937
6	14,854	11.453	13,678	6.262	10,270	0.101	4,980	− 6.670
7	14,803	11.453	13,678	6.262	9,614	−0.460	4,123	− 7.909
8	14,764	11.453	13,678	6.262	9,122	−0.880	3,480	− 8.837
9	14,734	11.453	13,678	6.262	8,739	−1.207	2,979	− 9.559
10	14,710	11.453	13,678	6.262	8,433	−1.469	2,579	−10.337
11	14,690	11.453	13,678	6.262	8,182	−1.683	2,252	−10.160
12	14,674	11.453	13,678	6.262	7,974	−1.862	1,979	−11.004
13	14,660	11.453	13,678	6.262	7,797	−2.012	1,748	−11.337
14	14,648	11.453	13,678	6.262	7,646	−2.142	1,550	−11.623
15	14,638	11.453	13,678	6.262	7,514	−2.254	1,379	−11.870

* J. C. Forman and G. Thodos, *AIChE J.*, **4**:356 (1958).

To correct the total $\Delta a^{2/3}$ and $\Delta b^{3/4}$ for isomerism, the use of correction factors is recommended.

$$\Sigma \, \Delta a^{2/3} \text{ (corrected)} = f_a \Sigma \, \Delta a^{2/3} \text{ (calc.)} \qquad (2\text{-}6)$$

$$\Sigma \, \Delta b^{3/4} \text{ (corrected)} = f_b \Sigma \, \Delta b^{3/4} \text{ (calc.)} \qquad (2\text{-}7)$$

where $\quad f_a = \frac{1}{3}[W_i/W_s + 2 + 0.087m + 0.0045 \sum_{k=1}^{m} k(k-1)] \qquad (2\text{-}8)$

$\quad f_b = \frac{1}{2}[W_i/W_s + 1 + 0.101m - 0.005m^2] \qquad (2\text{-}9)$

$\quad m$ = total number of side chains attached to main carbon chain

$\quad W$ = Wiener number

W is calculated by multiplying the number of carbons on one side of any bond by the corresponding number on the other side and summing over all carbon-carbon bonds; subscript i refers to the isomer and s to the corresponding straight-chain compound.

For the octane isomer 2-methyl-3-ethylpentane, W_i is calculated as

$$\alpha: 1 \times 7 = 7$$
$$\beta: 1 \times 7 = 7$$
$$\gamma: 3 \times 5 = 15$$
$$\delta: 6 \times 2 = 12$$
$$\epsilon: 1 \times 7 = 7$$
$$\zeta: 2 \times 6 = 12$$
$$\eta: 1 \times 7 = 7$$
$$\overline{}$$
$$67 = W_i$$

whereas the value for the normal form of octane, W_s, is

$$\text{C—C—C—C—C—C—C—C}$$
$$\alpha \quad \beta \quad \gamma \quad \delta \quad \epsilon \quad \zeta \quad \eta$$

$$\alpha: 1 \times 7 = 7$$
$$\beta: 2 \times 6 = 12$$
$$\gamma: 3 \times 5 = 15$$
$$\delta: 4 \times 4 = 16$$
$$\epsilon: 3 \times 5 = 15$$
$$\zeta: 2 \times 6 = 12$$
$$\eta: 1 \times 7 = 7$$
$$\overline{}$$
$$84 = W_s$$

It may be noted that $W_s = \frac{1}{6}(N - 1)(N)(N + 1)$, where N is the number of carbon atoms.

b. Olefinic and Acetylenic Linkages. After determining the sum of $\Delta a^{2/3}$ and $\Delta b^{3/4}$ for the saturated hydrocarbon portion, double or triple bonds may be inserted in the correct locations and appropriate contributions added. These contributions are given in Table 2-3. In those cases where more than one double bond is present, it is often necessary to define a new type of carbon atom, that is, $=\overset{\mid}{C}-H$ is termed a 3_u type of carbon. For example, if the saturated parent is

$$
\begin{array}{ccccccc}
 & & & & C & & \\
 & & & & | & & \\
 & & & & C & & \\
 & & & & | & & \\
C & C & C & C & C & C & C \\
\end{array}
$$

and the first olefin substitution is

$$
\begin{array}{ccccccc}
 & & & & C & & \\
 & & & & | & & \\
 & & & & C & & \\
 & & & & | & & \\
C-C-C & = & C-C-C-C \\
\beta\ \ \alpha & & \gamma\ \ \delta\ \ \epsilon
\end{array}
$$

TABLE 2-3. DOUBLE- AND TRIPLE-BOND CONTRIBUTIONS IN FORMAN AND THODOS METHOD*

	$\Delta a^{2/3}$	$\Delta b^{3/4}$
First double bond:		
(1-1)	$-3,868$	-2.021
(2-1)	$-3,154$	-1.895
(2-2)	$-2,551$	-2.009
(3-1)	$-1,548$	-1.706
(3-2)	$-\ 928$	-1.820
(3-3)	$-\ 540$	-1.930
Second double bond:		
(3-1)	$-\ 828$	-1.259
(3-2)	$-\ 496$	-1.343
(3_u-1)	$-1,332$	-1.745
(3_u-2)	$-1,324$	-1.862
(3_u-3)	$-1,316$	-1.979
($3_u \leftarrow$ 2-1)	$-1,687$	-1.399
($3_u \leftarrow$ 2-2)	$-\ 910$	-1.485
Triple bond:		
(1-1)	$-4,269$	-3.680
(2-1)	$-1,934$	-3.008
(2-2)	$-1,331$	-3.122

NOTE: The arrow points away from the carbon atom involved in the formation of unsaturated bonds toward the type of carbon atom adjacent to it; to be used in conjugated systems only.

* J. C. Forman and G. Thodos, *AIChE J.*, **4**:356 (1958).

then the substitution would be of a (2-2) type.* If, then, another double bond were placed in the α position, the form would correspond to a $(3_u\text{-}2)$ type. If, instead, the substitution were in the β position, it would be a $(3_u \leftarrow 2\text{-}1)$ type, in the γ position a $(3_u\text{-}3)$ type, in the δ position a (3-2) type, and finally in the ϵ position a (2-1) type. In the last case, no contribution is listed for a (2-1) substitution of a second double bond so that a first-double-bond increment would be used.

    c. Naphthenic Forms. If the molecule contains one or more naphthenic rings, the ring carbons must be treated differently and separate contributions used. For such ring atoms, three new types of carbons are defined,

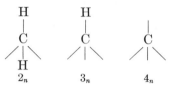

Contributions are listed in Table 2-4. Note that a separate contribution is necessary for the naphthenic ring, and also for multisubstitutions on the ring.

    d. Aromatic Forms. Aromatic forms are handled in a way similar to the naphthenes; the carbon types associated with such aromatics are defined as

The 3_a and 4_a types occur on single aromatic rings; the 4_p type allows fused ring systems to be treated. The contributions are listed in Table 2-4, and tri- or higher-substituted aromatics are handled in the same manner as described in the note under Table 2-4.

    e. Functional Groups. After calculating the carbon-hydrogen increments, functional groups are considered. The $\Delta a^{2/3}$ and $\Delta b^{3/4}$ values are different for each functional group and also depend upon n, the total number of *carbon atoms* and *functional atoms* present. The analytical forms are

$$\Delta a^{2/3} = q/n + k \qquad (2\text{-}10)$$
$$\Delta b^{3/4} = s/n + t \qquad (2\text{-}11)$$

where q, k, s, and t are tabulated in Table 2-5. It should be noted that, if the material contains more than one halogen attached to a single carbon atom, the lowest-atomic-weight halogen is considered first; then one

*Note that the designation (2-2) refers to the carbon types *before* the double bond is inserted. A similar comment holds for other types of designations used in this method.

proceeds to the next higher, etc. For example, in

$$
\begin{array}{c}
\text{F} \\
| \\
-\text{C}-\text{Cl} \\
| \\
\text{Cl}
\end{array}
$$

TABLE 2-4. NAPHTHENIC AND AROMATIC CONTRIBUTIONS IN FORMAN AND THODOS METHOD*

		$\Delta a^{2/3}$	$\Delta b^{3/4}$
Carbon type:			
	2_n	12,535	5.338
	3_n	9,910	0.023
	4_n	2,066	−8.094
	3_a	11,646	5.991
	4_a	11,144	1.043
	4_p	11,561	1.634
Naphthenic ring contribution		2,648	9.073
Aromatic ring contribution		0	0
Position contribution from multiple substitution:			
Naphthene rings			
cis-1,2		− 427	−0.866
1,3		−2,525	−1.493
trans-1,2		−2,525	−1.493
1,3		−4,195	−2.494
Aromatic rings			
	1-2	− 830	−1.253
	1-3	−1,597	−0.806
	1-4	155	0.212
	1-5	279	0.254
	1-6	488	0.525

NOTE: If several naphthenic rings are present in the same molecule, a "ring" contribution for each is to be made. If there is only a single substitution in the ring, no position contribution is necessary. Disubstitutions of the form (1,1), (1,4), (1,5), etc., are not defined, but it is recommended that the (1,3) contributions be used in these cases. Also trisubstitutions are undefined, but they may be approximated by using the disubstitution rules and proceeding around the molecule in a clockwise direction. Thus there would be three disubstitution contributions for a trisubstituted molecule, etc. For example, the cyclohexane derivative,

$$
\begin{array}{c}
\text{CH}_2 \ \text{CH}_2 \\
\text{CH}_3-\text{HC} \diagdown \diagup \text{CH}-\text{CH}_3 \\
\text{CH}_2 \ | \ \text{CH} \\
\text{CH}_3
\end{array}
$$

would have a (1,2), a (1,3), and a (1,4) [for the last, as explained above, use the (1,3) values] disubstitution contribution.

* J. C. Forman and G. Thodos, *AIChE J.*, **4**:356 (1958).

TABLE 2-5. CONSTANTS FOR EQUATIONS WHICH ESTABLISH FUNCTIONAL GROUP CONTRIBUTIONS FOR ORGANIC COMPOUNDS IN FORMAN AND THODOS METHOD*

	Functional group	$\Delta a^{2/3} = q/n + k$		$\Delta b^{3/4} = s/n + t$	
		q	k	s	t
Alcohols............	—OH	30,200	14,000	8.96	7.50
Phenols.............	—OH	0	8,500	0	4.19
Ethers (noncyclic)....	—O—	14,500	6,500	0	3.26
Ethers (cyclic)........	—O—	0	9,440	0	2.74
Ketones............	$\overset{\text{O}}{\overset{\|}{-\text{C}-}}$	62,800	16,700	27.20	4.55
Carboxylic acids......	$\overset{\text{O}}{\overset{\|}{-\text{COH}}}$	142,670	16,730	66.80	5.10
Acid anhydrides......	$\overset{\text{O O}}{\overset{\|\ \|}{-\text{COC}-}}$	0	43,880	0	14.78
Esters:					
Formates..........	$\overset{\text{O}}{\overset{\|}{\text{HCO}-}}$	35,140	26,800	2.29	15.80
Others.............	$\overset{\text{O}}{\overset{\|}{-\text{CO}-}}$	37,430	25,500	−3.00	12.20
Amines:					
Primary..........	—NH₂	4,800	18,900	0	10.15
Secondary........	$\overset{\text{H}}{\overset{\|}{-\text{N}-}}$	51,800	0	19.60	−1.10
Tertiary..........	$\overset{\|}{-\text{N}-}$	60,200	−4,300	29.20	−7.90
Nitriles............	—CN	86,000	25,900	39.70	12.10
Aliphatic halides:					
Fluorides.........	—F				
First............		2,420	12,240	−3.70	10.92
Second...........		−38,500	4,510	−48.50	12.86
Third...........		0	3,450	0	6.92
Chlorides.........	—Cl				
First...........		0	22,580	0	11.54
Second..........		66,000	−5,100	19.00	3.90
Third...........		−60,250	29,100	−40.80	19.40
Fourth..........		0	16,500	0	11.46
Bromides.........	—Br				
First...........		−2,720	23,550	−4.35	11.49
Second..........		0	20,860	0	5.37
Iodides............	—I				
First............		0	33,590	0	13.91
Aromatic halides:					
Fluoride..........	—F	0	4,210	0	7.22
Chloride..........	—Cl	0	17,200	0	10.88
Bromide..........	—Br	0	24,150	0	12.74
Iodide............	—I	0	34,780	0	15.22

* J. C. Forman and G. Thodos, *AIChE J.*, **6**:206 (1960).

the contribution would be a first fluoride, a second chloride, and a third chloride.

f. Tabulation. After all the $\Delta a^{2/3}$ and $\Delta b^{3/4}$ values are tabulated, the sums are raised to the $3/2$ and $4/3$ powers, respectively, to calculate a and b. The units of a are cm^6-atm/(g mole)^2 and of b cm^3/g mole; so R should be 82.06 to give T_c and P_c in degrees Kelvin and atmospheres, respectively, by use of Eqs. (2-4) and (2-5). Forman and Thodos claim that calculated critical temperatures of hydrocarbons are, on the average, in error by less than 1 per cent and, for compounds containing functional groups, by less than 2 per cent. The method is rather complex and not applicable for certain types of materials (see Recommendations) but certainly has the advantage that no additional physical data, such as a boiling point, are required. The method is illustrated in Example 2-1.

Example 2-1. Estimate the critical temperature of ethylpropyl ether by both Lydersen's and Forman and Thodos's method. The experimental value is 500.6°K (Appendix A).

Solution. *Lydersen.* The normal boiling point is 335°K.

$$\Delta_T = 2CH_3— + 3\overset{|}{C}H_2— + —O—$$
$$= 2(0.020) + 3(0.020) + 0.021$$
$$= 0.121$$

From Eq. (2-3)

$$\theta = 0.567 + 0.121 - (0.121)^2 = 0.673$$
$$T_c = 335/0.673 = 497.8°K$$
$$\text{Error} = [(497.8 - 500.6)/500.6] \times 100 = -0.6\%$$

Forman and Thodos.

$$n = 6$$

First consider the ether group,

$$\Delta a^{2/3} = q/n + k = 14{,}500/6 + 6{,}500 = 8{,}917$$
$$\Delta b^{3/4} = s/n + t = 0/6 + 3.26 = 3.26$$

Now tabulate the $\Delta a^{2/3}$ and $\Delta b^{3/4}$.

	$\Delta a^{2/3}$	$\Delta b^{3/4}$
2 type 1 carbons.........	2(14,854)	2(11.453)
3 type 2 carbons.........	3(13,678)	3(6.262)
Ether group.............	8,917	3.26
	79,659	44.952

Thus

$$a = (\Sigma \Delta a^{2/3})^{3/2} = (79{,}659)^{3/2} = 22.49 \times 10^6 \ cm^6\text{-atm}/(\text{g mole})^2$$
$$b = (\Sigma \Delta b^{3/4})^{4/3} = (44.952)^{4/3} = 159.8 \ cm^3/\text{g mole}$$

and from Eq. (2-4)

$$T_c = \frac{8a}{27bR} = \frac{(8)(22.49) \times 10^6}{(27)(82.06)(159.8)} = 508°K$$
$$\text{Error} = [(508 - 500.6) \times 100]/500.6 = +1.5\%$$

Estimation with Low-temperature Data. Experimental data on a property of a substance at conditions far removed from the critical state may be extrapolated by any one of several techniques to estimate the critical temperature. Most of the possibilities have never been thoroughly investigated, and it is difficult to assess the accuracy of those proposed in the literature. The few that are described below indicate the general method.

Critical Temperatures from Surface-tension Data. Values of surface tension are often related to temperature by the form (72) [see Eq. (8-2)]

$$\gamma = a_\gamma (1 - T/T_c)^{n_\gamma} \qquad (2\text{-}12)$$

In theory, values of surface tension at three temperatures determine the unknown constants a_γ, n_γ, and T_c. However, Simkin (59) has proposed a method using only two data points by the rearrangement

$$\gamma_2/\gamma_1 = [(T_c - T_2)/(T_c - T_1)]^{n_\gamma} \qquad (2\text{-}13)$$

The constant n_γ has been shown to be about $1\frac{1}{9}$ for simple liquids such as A, Ne, O_2, N_2 (22) but to be much lower for associated liquids such as the alcohols or glycols. Simkin related the constant n_γ to the entropy change ΔS_{sv} occurring when a mole of "surface-oriented" molecules is vaporized. To calculate ΔS_{sv} the Eötvös constant k_E (see next section) and the entropy of vaporization at the normal boiling point must be available.

$$\Delta S_{sv} = \Delta S_{v_b} - 2.02 k_E \qquad (2\text{-}14)$$

k_E is known for many molecules but can also be estimated by rearrangement of Eq. (2-16) (see Sec. 8-3),

$$k_E = (V_2^{2/3}\gamma_2 - V_1^{2/3}\gamma_1)/(T_1 - T_2) \qquad (2\text{-}15)$$

and in which liquid volumes must now be available. Figure 2-1 shows the variation of n_γ with ΔS_{sv} (59).

Thus, from values of surface tension at two temperatures, the entropy of vaporization at the normal boiling point, and liquid-density data, Simkin was able to estimate critical temperatures.

Application of Eq. (2-13) when *more* than two-temperature-surface-tension data points are available requires some mention. If the equation were exact, the same value of T_c would be obtained irrespective of what pair of γ-T values were chosen. Actually calculated values of T_c do differ somewhat with different γ-T pairs, but owing to the low power of n_γ the differences are small (usually of the order of 5°C or so) even when the γ-T pairs chosen are at widely different temperatures.

To increase the accuracy of the method, the surface-tension values used should be such that $\gamma_2/\gamma_1 < 0.9$, and if the vapor is associated, the entropy of vaporization must be corrected by the ratio $M_{\text{true}}/M_{\text{nonassociated}}$. Simkin demonstrated that this technique yields T_c values of the same order

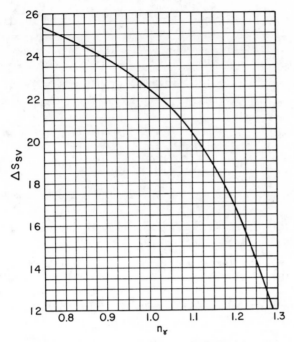

FIG. 2-1. n_γ as a function of ΔS_{sv} for Eq. (2-13). (*D. J. Simkin, paper presented at the national meeting of the American Institute of Chemical Engineering, Seattle, Wash., June 9–12, 1957.*)

of accuracy as Lydersen's method by testing it for some 33 diverse compounds. The real value of the technique, according to Simkin, is that it should prove applicable to very polar compounds (e.g., to glycerol or ethylene glycol) where structural contribution techniques are probably not valid. At present there are no experimental critical data for such compounds on which to base a detailed comparison, but one can see from Example 2-2 that the calculated values of T_c from the two methods differ considerably.

Example 2-2. Estimate the critical temperature of ethylene glycol by using the methods of Simkin and of Lydersen. There are no experimental critical properties with which to make a comparison.

Solution. *Simkin Method.* Necessary data (17):

	20°C	160°C
Surface tension, dynes/cm.......	48.43	35.97
Density, g/cm³.................	1.114	1.008
Molal volume, cm³/g mole......	55.72	61.58

Heat of vaporization at $T_b = 191.1$ cal/g $= 11,862$ cal/g mole
$$T_b = 197°C = 470°K$$

To determine the Eötvös constant, Eq. (2-15) is used.

$$k_E = (V_2^{2/3}\gamma_2 - V_1^{2/3}\gamma_1)/(T_1 - T_2)$$
$$= [(61.58)^{2/3}(35.97) - (55.72)^{2/3}(48.43)]/(-140) = 1.04$$

Then $\Delta S_{sv} = \Delta S_{v_b} - 2.02 k_E = 11{,}862/470 - (2.02)(1.04) = 23.1$

From Fig. 2-1, $n_\gamma = 0.96$

Lack of data prevents any corrections in ΔS_{v_b} for association in the gas phase. From Eq. (2-13)

$$(\gamma_2/\gamma_1) = [(T_c - T_2)/(T_c - T_1)]^{n_\gamma}$$
$$48.43/35.97 = [(T_c - 20)/(T_c - 160)]^{0.96}$$
$$T_c = 545°C = 818°K$$

Lydersen Method

$$\Sigma\Delta_T = 2\,(-\overset{|}{C}H_2) + 2\,(-OH) = 2(0.020) + 2(0.082) = 0.204$$

From Eq. (2-3)

$$\theta = 0.567 + 0.204 - (0.204)^2 = 0.729$$
$$T_c = T_b/0.729 = 470/0.729 = 645°K$$

The difference between the results from the two methods is 173°K; Simkin's method is probably preferable. If the value of ΔS_{v_b} were corrected for the ratio M (true)$/M$ (nonassociated), where this ratio is greater than unity, then the calculated value of T_c would be greater than 818°K; this value is evidently a lower limit by Simkin's method.

Critical Temperatures from Liquid-density Data. Smith, Greenbaum, and Rutledge (60) combined the Ramsay-Shields-Eötvös equation (see Sec. 8-3),

$$\gamma/\rho_L^{2/3} = k_E(T_c - T - 6) \tag{2-16}$$

with the definition of the parachor [Eq. (8-3), Table 8-1] $[P]$ (47), which is assumed to be independent of temperature,

$$[P] = \gamma^{1/4}M/(\rho_L - \rho_v) \tag{2-17}$$

to derive the relation

$$T_c = \frac{T_2 - T_1}{(\rho_{L_1}/\rho_{L_2})^{19/3} - 1} + T_2 + 6 \qquad \rho_L \gg \rho_v \tag{2-18}$$

By using Eq. (2-18), T_c may be estimated from a pair of $\rho_L - T$ data points. However, because of the large exponent on the density ratio and the approximate nature of Eq. (2-16), values of T_c from Eq. (2-18) are often inaccurate and are sensitive to the pair of $\rho_L - T$ values chosen.

Pitzer et al. (43, 44) present an iterative, empirical method for estimating T_c which requires knowledge of the normal boiling point, the boiling temperature at 100 mm Hg pressure, and at least one other liquid-density–temperature point. The method assumes that all materials with the same acentric factor (see Sec. 2-7) have a similar relation between V/V_c and T/T_c. A similar method could be proposed using Table 3-6 and relating reduced liquid density to the critical compressibility factor and T/T_c

$(= T_r)$. In the latter case $\rho_r = f(T_r, Z_c)$ and

$$V_1/V_2 = \rho_{r_2}/\rho_{r_1} = f(T_{r_1}, Z_c)/f(T_{r_2}, Z_c),$$

where the $f(T_r, Z_c)$ is tabulated in Table 3-6. Neither method appears to yield results of high accuracy.

Fishtine (13) has developed another iteration method by combining Eqs. (3-82), (3-85), and (4-6) to predict T_c from ΔH_v and a single liquid-density–temperature point. In this method P_c, V_c, and Z_c are also determined. Critical temperature estimates are fair (though poorer, in general, than those by Lydersen's method), but the errors in estimated critical volumes and pressures are high.

Cecil and Reed (8a) proposed a correlation between T_c (and also P_c, V_c, and Z_c) and the slope and intercept constants for the (almost) linear relation between the square of the saturated liquid density and the absolute temperature. The method was tested only on nonpolar materials and yielded errors in the same range as those noted above.

Critical Temperatures from Vapor-pressure Data. Chapter 4 presents a number of vapor-pressure correlations which could be useful in calculating critical pressures from critical temperatures, or vice versa. Only Stiel and Thodos (63) have utilized a vapor-pressure correlation to obtain the critical temperature directly. The Frost-Kalkwarf equation [Eq. (4-20)] was used. As described in Sec. 4-6, it is possible to determine the constants B and C by plotting Y versus X [where Y and X are defined in Eq. (4-21)] and noting that C is the slope and B the intercept of the straight line. The constant D $(= 0.1832 P_r/T_r^2)$ cannot be determined a priori since T_c and P_c are, of course, unknown. However, by assuming various values of D until Y versus X plots show minimum curvature, a line can be found from which to determine C and B. Stiel and Thodos found that T_c was related to the constants B and C by the equation

$$T_c = B/(0.5643C - 1.4520) \tag{2-19}$$

Considerable experimental data must be available, and the authors recommend that D be obtained by means of a least-mean-square computer program. The accuracy of the method is difficult to assess. Less than 1 per cent error is claimed for T_c if excellent vapor-pressure data are available which extend over a range of at least several atmospheres.

Critical Temperature from Other Correlations. Marschner (32) discusses in some detail the Guldberg rule at different pressures. Pilcher and Ward (42) have expanded Herzog's method (23) to make it more accurate. In the latter, the ratio T_b/T_c is correlated as a linear function of the parachor for many families. The fact that the parachor is an additive function of the structure makes the method similar in form to Lydersen's. The fact that materials with more than one functional group are not treated reduces the overall applicability. The parachor is also related to critical properties in special equations for alkanes by Nokay (40) and Gambill (18).

Several specialized estimation techniques have been developed, e.g., for saturated branched aliphatic hydrocarbons (64), for the phenolic type of materials (6), for high-boiling materials (3), and for straight-chain alcohols (58). For elements, Gates and Thodos (20) propose the simple form

$$T_c = 1.47 T_b^{1.03} \qquad (2\text{-}20)$$

which yielded an average error of about 1.4 per cent.

Many other methods could be mentioned (5, 9, 10, 12, 21, 30, 35, 36, 46, 48, 53, 54, 56, 71, 74, 76, 77), but their accuracy appears to be less than for those methods already described.

Recommendations. If the normal boiling point is available, use Lydersen's method [Eq. (2-3)] with Table 2-1. If no such point is available, use Forman and Thodos's method [Eq. (2-4)] with Tables 2-2 to 2-5. Lydersen's method is applicable to almost all types of organic molecules; Forman and Thodos's method cannot be used for aldehydes, sulfur compounds, or secondary or tertiary alcohols. For aliphatic branched-chain hydrocarbons, the special method of Stiel and Thodos (63) can be used, although Lydersen's method gives results of similar accuracy.

The errors to be expected in the estimation of T_c by these recommended methods are less than 2 per cent, except for particularly complex or very polar materials.

2-4 Estimation of Critical Pressures

The estimation of critical pressures by all methods proposed to date involves a greater degree of uncertainty than the corresponding estimation of critical temperatures. The errors in the critical-pressure estimations may run as high as 10 to 15 per cent for relatively simple nonpolar compounds; however, the error is usually only 3 to 4 per cent. No convenient parameter such as boiling point has been found on which to base the correlations, and there is a wide diversity in the types of methods proposed.

Of the many proposed methods, only two are considered in detail here. Others are less accurate or considerably less general in applicability (4, 20, 23, 39, 42, 44, 58, 64).

Riedel Method. Riedel (50) proposed a simple, rather accurate relationship between the critical pressure and structure. Structural parameters have been developed by Riedel and later by three others (18, 31, 75); all yield results of comparable accuracy. The values of Lydersen (31) are recommended primarily because more types of molecules may be treated.

$$P_c = M / (\Sigma \, \Delta_p + 0.34)^2 \qquad (2\text{-}21)$$

where P_c is in atmospheres. The values of Δ_p are tabulated in Table 2-1; M is the molecular weight. In testing with 172 compounds, an arithmetic average deviation of 3.8 per cent was noted.

Forman and Thodos Method. Equation (2-5) is applicable, with the values of a and b determined as described in Sec. 2-3, under Forman and Thodos Method.

Recommendations. Both Riedel's and Forman and Thodos's methods yield results of comparable accuracy, but in many cases large individual errors are noted. Riedel's method with Lydersen's Δ_p values is capable of being used for more types of compounds, is simpler to use, and is usually slightly more accurate. For these reasons it is recommended here. Forman and Thodos's method cannot be used for sulfur compounds, aldehydes, or secondary or tertiary alcohols. Lydersen's values of Δ_p lead to predicted critical pressures 2 to 6 per cent low for highly branched structures and high-molecular-weight alcohols; they also yield poor results for highly polar materials.

For hydrocarbons, errors of ± 1 to 3 per cent may be expected; for nonhydrocarbons, the errors vary but are usually less than 10 per cent. Neither method is applicable to glycols or other very polar materials. Both methods are illustrated in Example 2-3.

Example 2-3. Estimate the critical pressure of ethylpropyl ether both by Riedel's and by Forman and Thodos's methods. The experimental value is 32.1 atm (Appendix A).

Solution. *Lydersen.*

$$\Sigma \Delta_p = 2(\overset{|}{\text{C}}\text{H}_3) + 3(\overset{|}{\text{C}}\text{H}_2\text{---}) + \text{---O---} = 2(0.227) + 3(0.227) + 0.16 = 1.295$$

From Eq. (2-21), with $M = 88.15$,

$$P_c = 88.15/(0.34 + 1.295)^2 = 33.0 \text{ atm}$$
$$\text{Error} = [(33.0 - 32.1)/32.1] \times 100 = 2.8\%$$

Forman and Thodos. In Example 2-1, the parameters a and b were determined for ethylpropyl ether. Using these values and Eq. (2-5),

$$P_c = a/27b^2 = [(22.49 \times 10^6)/(27)(159.8)^2] = 32.6 \text{ atm}$$
$$\text{Error} = [(32.6 - 32.1)/32.1] \times 100 = +1.6\%$$

2-5 Estimation of Critical Compressibility Factors

The critical compressibility factor Z_c is defined as

$$Z_c = P_c V_c / R T_c \tag{2-22}$$

Values between 0.25 and 0.29 are found for most organic compounds, although lower values are found for polar compounds and slightly higher values for the light, inert gases. The characterization of a molecule by its Z_c value is a common technique, and later in the book there are presented many correlations which involve Z_c as a so-called "third correlating parameter," in addition to, for example, reduced temperature and pressure. Z_c can, of course, be determined from Eq. (2-22) with values of P_c, V_c, and T_c known. Often, however, one or more of such critical constants are either missing or in doubt; so it is valuable to have an independent way to estimate Z_c. Two such methods are presented below.

Lydersen Method. Lydersen (31) pointed out, with justification, that $1 - Z_c$ is a convenient measure of the nonideal behavior at the critical point. Such behavior is caused to a large degree by the intermolecular forces between molecules. Such forces are not easy to analyze theoretically, but it is logical that Z_c should be correlated with some other property which itself is a sensitive function of these same intermolecular forces. He chose, after some study, to use the molal latent heat of vaporization at the normal boiling point as a convenient property which

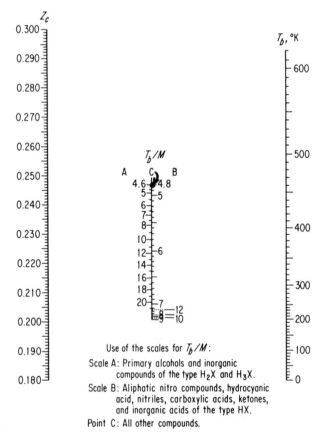

Use of the scales for T_b/M:

Scale A: Primary alcohols and inorganic compounds of the type H_2X and H_3X.

Scale B: Aliphatic nitro compounds, hydrocyanic acid, nitriles, carboxylic acids, ketones, and inorganic acids of the type HX.

Point C: All other compounds.

FIG. 2-2. Nomograph of the equation $Z_c = f(T_b) - g(T_b/M)$. (*G. J. García-Bárcena, S. B. thesis in chemical engineering, Massachusetts Institute of Technology, Cambridge, Mass., 1958.*)

is often known but which could be estimated by methods described in Sec. 4-21. The correlation obtained can be written,

$$Z_c = 1/[3.43 + (6.7)(10^{-9})(\Delta H_{v_b})^2] \qquad (2\text{-}23)$$

where ΔH_{v_b} is given in calories per gram mole.

Equation (2-23) is not recommended for polar compounds such as water, ammonia, nitriles, acids, acetone, or alcohols. In testing with some 128 nonpolar organic compounds, an average deviation of 3.1 per cent was found.

García-Bárcena Methods. García-Bárcena (19) suggested two different empirical methods to determine Z_c.

Boiling-point Correlation. It was noted that a functional equation of the form

$$Z_c = f(T_b) - g(T_b/M)$$

is applicable to a wide variety of compounds. This equation is shown as a nomograph in Fig. 2-2. The center scales (except pivot point C) are not used except for polar compounds; this results from the fact that $g(T_b/M)$ is defined as zero for nonpolar materials.

Additive Technique. A more accurate method, but one which is not applicable to polar compounds, aliphatic halides, or inorganic materials, uses an additive group technique and Eq. (2-24)

$$Z_c = 0.293 - \Sigma \Delta_Z \qquad (2\text{-}24)$$

where the Δ_Z values are tabulated in Table 2-6.

TABLE 2-6. ATOMIC AND STRUCTURAL CONTRIBUTIONS FOR Δ_Z*

Group ¶	Δ_Z†
—H	0.0000
—CH₃ or —CH₂—	
First 10 in the molecule	0.0046
Each after the tenth	0.0037
—CH or —C—	
First in the molecule	−0.0035
Each successive one	0.0042
—C—H in ring	0.0025
Ring closure:	
Three-membered ring	0.0152‡
Five-membered ring	−0.0057
Six-membered ring	−0.0057
Benzene ring (including atoms and bonds)	0.0178
Substitutional forms:	
Ortho	0.0122
Meta	0.0072
Para	0.0102
1,2,3	0.0184‡

TABLE 2-6. ATOMIC AND STRUCTURAL CONTRIBUTIONS FOR Δz^* (Continued)

Group ¶	Δz †
1,2,4	0.0054‡
1,3,5	0.0000‡
C=C bond:	
First	0.0133
Second	−0.0012‡
Isomerism:	
Cis	−0.0022‡
Trans	−0.0102‡
C≡C bond	+0.0183‡
—NH$_2$:	
Aliphatic	0.0097‡
Aromatic	0.0252‡
—NH aliphatic	0.0047‡
N— aliphatic	−0.0057
—SH	0.0110
—S—	0.0082
—O—	0.0076
—O— in ring	0.0136
HCOO— (formates):	
4 carbon atoms or less	$0.0360-0.0040N$ §
More than 4 carbon atoms	−0.0075
—COO— (esters):	
5 carbon atoms or less	$0.0360-0.0040N$ §
More than 5 carbon atoms	−0.0075
—F (aromatic)	0.0112
—Cl (aromatic)	0.0112
—Br (aromatic)	0.0112
—I (aromatic)	0.0112

* G. J. García-Bárcena, S.B. thesis in chemical engineering, Massachusetts Institute of Technology, Cambridge, Mass., 1958.

† The values of the contributions Δz are given to four decimal places, but when Δz is evaluated, it should be rounded off to three places.

‡ The value of Δz was obtained from a single compound.

§ N is the number of —CH$_3$ and —CH$_2$— groups in the molecule.

¶ The bonds indicated as open are joined to atoms other than hydrogen.

Figure 2-2 when tested with 155 compounds yielded an arithmetical average deviation of 2.7 per cent, while Eq. (2-24) yielded an error of 0.8 per cent for 111 compounds for which it was applicable.

Recommendations. Table 2-7 summarizes the arithmetic average errors in the estimation of Z_c for the compounds tested. Equation (2-24) should be used to estimate Z_c unless a polar compound, aliphatic halide, or thioether is involved. For the latter, Fig. 2-2 is recommended.

Example 2-4. Determine the critical compressibility of fluorobenzene. The normal boiling point is 358°K, and the latent heat of vaporization at this temperature is 7625 cal/g mole. The experimental value of Z_c is 0.263.

TABLE 2-7. COMPARISON OF ESTIMATION TECHNIQUES FOR Z_c

Type of compound	Eq. (2-23)		Fig. 2-2		Eq. (2-24)	
	No. tested	% dev.	No. tested	% dev.	No. tested	% dev.
Paraffins	50	1.4	49	1.4	50	0.8
Cycloparaffins	5	2.9	5	2.7	5	1.4
Olefins	7	2.1	7	2.1	7	0.5
Alkynes	0*	...	0*	...	1	0.0
Aromatic hydrocarbons	14	2.7	14	2.5	14	0.5
Amines	4	1.6	5	1.5	5	0.3
Mercaptans	2	2.2	2	0.5	2	0.4
Thioethers	2	2.9	2	3.3	2	3.7
Ethers	5	3.1	6	3.7	6	1.4
Esters	14	4.5	15	5.1	15	1.7
Halogenated hydrocarbons	16	4.6	18	4.4	4†	0.4
Alcohols	4	7.6	4	3.1	0‡	
Ketones	2	5.6	2	1.4	0‡	
Nitriles	0‡	...	2	1.2	0‡	
Organic acids	0‡	...	5	6.7	0‡	
Miscellaneous organic compounds	3	6.7	3	2.6	0‡	
Inorganic compounds	0§	...	16	1.8	0‡	
Total	128		155		111	
Average deviations		3.1		2.7		0.8

* Acetylene, the only alkyne for which the experimental value of Z_c is available, cannot exist in the liquid state under atmospheric pressure.
† The equation can be used only for aromatic halogen derivatives.
‡ The equation cannot be used for this type of compound.
§ Not calculated; the equation should not be used for inorganic compounds.

Solution. *Additive Group Method.* No data are required. From Eq. (2-24)

$$Z_c = 0.293 - \text{(benzene ring)} - \text{(aromatic fluorine)}$$
$$= 0.293 - 0.0178 - 0.0112 = 0.264$$
$$\text{Error} = [(0.264 - 0.263)/0.263] \times 100 = +0.4\%$$

Boiling-point Method. Fluorobenzene is nonpolar; so in Fig. 2-2 pivot point C is to be used. Thus $Z_c = 0.265$.

$$\text{Error} = [(0.265 - 0.263)/0.263] \times 100 = +0.8\%$$

Lydersen Method

$$Z_c = 1/[3.43 + (6.7)(10^{-9})(7,625)^2] = 0.262$$
$$\text{Error} = [(0.262 - 0.263)/0.263] \times 100 = -0.4\%$$

2-6 Estimation of Critical Volumes

No generally reliable estimation methods for the critical volume have been suggested. One reason for this is that there are just not many good experimental values upon which to base an estimating technique; conversely, those methods which have been suggested may appear better than they really are, since most of the known data were utilized to develop the correlations. Two very different methods are presented in detail below. In the light of the above comments, the accuracy is only fair.

Lydersen Method (31). The critical volume is determined by a simple additive group technique originally suggested by Schuster (57).

$$V_c = 40 + \Sigma\Delta_v \qquad (2\text{-}25)$$

where Δ_v values are listed in Table 2-1. Vowles has suggested a similar tabulation (75). Lydersen reports that, in testing with 144 compounds, the average deviation found was 2.3 per cent.

Critical Compressibility Method. Equation (2-22) may be arranged to determine the critical volume,

$$V_c = Z_cRT_c/P_c \qquad (2\text{-}26)$$

In this case the values of Z_c, T_c, and P_c must be either known or estimated by methods described earlier in this chapter. To test Eq. (2-26), critical volumes were estimated from values of Z_c, T_c, and P_c as calculated from Eqs. (2-2) and (2-3) for T_c, Eq. (2-21) for P_c, and Eq. (2-24) or, when not applicable, Fig. 2-2 for Z_c. The arithmetic average error was found to be 3.6 per cent for the same group of compounds used in testing Eq. (2-25). The accuracy of the method would be considerably improved if experimental values of T_c, and particularly P_c, could have been used.

Other Methods. Most other methods are considerably less accurate than the two suggested above. Many utilize the parachor (23, 27, 35, 42), while others use liquid-density data (5, 13, 26). Thodos (68–70) suggests another accurate estimation technique for hydrocarbon materials using van der Waals' b values determined in a somewhat different way from that discussed in Sec. 2-3. Gates and Thodos (20) suggest that V_c for the elements be determined with Eq. (2-26), where $Z_c = 0.29$.

Recommendations. If no experimental values of T_c and P_c are available, use the group-contribution technique of Lydersen [Eq. (2-25)], with Table 2-1. If experimental values of P_c and T_c are available, use Eq. (2-26), with Z_c determined by Eq. (2-24) and Table 2-6 or, when not applicable, from Fig. 2-2.

In the first case errors from 2 to 10 per cent are to be expected. In the latter case, errors less than 5 per cent are probable.

Example 2-5. Estimate the critical volume of ethylpropyl ether by Lydersen's method and Eq. (2-26). Compare with the experimental value of 339 cm³/g mole.
    Solution. *Lydersen's Method.* From Table 2-1,

$$\Delta_v = 2(-CH_3) + 3(\overset{\mid}{C}H_2-) + -O-$$

From Eq. (2-25),

$$V_c = 40 + 2(55) + 3(55) + 20 = 335 \text{ cm}^3/\text{g mole}$$
$$\text{Error} = [(335 - 339)/339] \times 100 = -1.2\%$$

Eq. (2-26). From Examples 2-1 and 2-3, the estimated values of T_c and P_c are 497.8°K and 33.0 atm. Equation (2-24) yields a value of $Z_c = 0.262$. Thus

$$V_c = (0.262)(82.07)(497.8)/33.0 = 324 \text{ cm}^3/\text{g mole}$$
$$\text{Error} = [(324 - 339)/339] \times 100 = -4.4\%$$

2-7 Acentric Factor

The acentric factor ω was introduced by Pitzer (43, 44) as a correlating parameter to characterize the acentricity of a molecule. It is used in many sections of this book to make reduced-state correlations more accurate for nonspherical molecules. The acentric factor is defined by the vapor-pressure curve, i.e.,

$$\omega \equiv -\log P_{vp_r} \text{ (at } T_r = 0.7) - 1.000 \qquad (2\text{-}27)$$

To obtain ω from Eq. (2-27), the reduced vapor pressure P_{vp_r} is plotted against either the reduced temperature T_r or $1/T_r$. The reduced vapor pressure at a reduced temperature of $T_r = 0.7$ is needed in Eq. (2-27); so vapor-pressure data in the range usually slightly above the normal boiling point are required. This particular method of defining ω results from the fact that for spherically symmetric molecules (e.g., argon) the value of P_{vp_r} at a T_r of 0.7 is very nearly 0.1; thus ω is zero. For most other materials this P_{vp_r} value is somewhat less than 0.1; so ω is positive and usually ranges from 0 to 0.4.

Edmister Method. There are several ways to estimate ω if vapor-pressure data are not available. The most accurate method was suggested by Edmister (11), who applied Eq. (4-3) at the normal boiling point and at the point where $T_r = 0.7$, eliminated B/T_c, and combined the result with Eq. (2-27) to yield

$$\omega + 1 = \tfrac{3}{7}[\theta/(1 - \theta)] \log P_c \qquad (2\text{-}28)$$

where $\theta = T_b/T_c$ and P_c is in atmospheres. Granting that Eq. (4-3) yields only approximate values of vapor pressures, Eq. (2-24) is relatively insensitive to this fact and yields reliable values of ω. The critical pressure must be known (or estimated), and the reduced boiling-point ratio can be obtained from experimental values of T_b and T_c or can be estimated directly from Eq. (2-3). Table 2-8 presents a random sample of experimental values of ω for 37 materials [from Eq. (2-27)], compared with values calculated by the use of Eq. (2-28). Experimental values of T_c, P_c, and T_b were used. Except in a few materials the error is less than 5 per cent.

It is often stated that Z_c and ω are related linearly as

$$Z_c = 0.291 - 0.080\omega \qquad (2\text{-}29)$$

TABLE 2-8. COMPARISON OF ACENTRIC FACTORS FROM EQ. (2-27) WITH THOSE CALCULATED FROM EQ. (2-28)

Compound	Acentric factor	
	Eq. (2-27)	Eq. (2-28)
Acetone	0.318	0.315
Acetylene	0.186	0.208
Ammonia	0.250	0.268
Argon	−0.002	−0.003
Benzene	0.215	0.215
n-Butane	0.201	0.206
Butanone	0.316	0.335
Butene-1	0.203	0.196
Butene-2 (cis)	0.273	0.265
Butene-2 (trans)	0.234	0.228
Carbon disulfide	0.123	0.135
Carbon monoxide	0.041	0.049
Cyclohexane	0.186	0.197
Cyclopentane	0.193	0.206
Ethane	0.105	0.103
Ethanol	0.635	0.648
Ethylene oxide	0.157	0.242
n-Heptane	0.352	0.352
n-Hexane	0.290	0.302
Hydrogen sulfide	0.100	0.106
Isobutane	0.192	0.190
Isobutene	0.201	0.201
Isopentane	0.206	0.224
Krypton	−0.002	+0.003
Methane	0.013	0.007
Methanol	0.556	0.563
Methylcyclopentane	0.234	0.239
Nitrogen	0.040	0.036
Neopentane	0.195	0.203
Oxygen	0.021	0.016
n-Pentane	0.252	0.255
Propane	0.152	0.159
n-Propanol	0.600	0.631
Propylene	0.143	0.148
Toluene	0.252	0.279
Water	0.348	0.365
Xenon	0.002	0.014

Such a relationship is not recommended for general use; at best it is only approximate, and Eq. (2-28) is to be preferred for the estimation of ω.

Recommendations. If the vapor-pressure data are available, Eq. (2-27) is convenient for the calculation of ω; critical properties may be estimated by the methods described in Secs. 2-3 and 2-4, or, preferably, experimental values can be used.   If no vapor-pressure data are available, Eq. (2-28) can be used, with either experimental or estimated values of P_c and θ.   Equation (2-27) is exact (by definition) if reliable reduced vapor pressures are employed; Eq. (2-28) is accurate in most cases to ± 5 per cent.

Example 2-6.   Estimate the acentric factor for toluene, and compare with the experimental value of 0.252.   For toluene, $P_c = 41.6$ atm, $T_c = 592°K$, and $T_b = 384°K$ (Appendix A).

Solution
$$\theta = {}^{384}\!\!/_{592} = 0.648$$
From Eq. (2-28), $\omega = \{ \tfrac{3}{7}[0.648/(1 - 0.648)] \log 41.6 \} - 1 = 0.275$

$$\text{Error} = [(0.275 - 0.252)/0.252] \times 100 = +9.1\%$$

2-8   Riedel Factor

Another characterizing parameter similar to the acentric factor was defined by Riedel (45, 52).   As this factor has been adopted for use in many correlations discussed later, its estimation is now considered.

This Riedel factor α_c is actually defined as

$$\alpha_c \equiv d(\ln P_{vp_r})/d(\ln T_r) \qquad \text{at the critical point} \qquad (2\text{-}30)$$

However, it is almost never calculated from this definition.   Riedel developed a generalized vapor-pressure equation [Eq. (4-14)] from which α_c is usually determined.   Equation (4-14) solved for α_c yields

$$\alpha_c = -[\log P_{vp_r} + \phi(T_r)]/\psi(T_r) + 7.00 \qquad (2\text{-}31)$$

where P_{vp} and T_r can be any reduced vapor-pressure–temperature datum point and the functions ϕ and ψ are read from Tables (4-1) and (4-2).   A convenient reference point is the normal boiling point, where $P_{vp_r} = 1/P_c$ and $T_r = T_b/T_c = \theta$ [see Eq. (2-3)].   Then Eq. (2-31) becomes, with P_c in atmospheres,

$$\alpha_c = [\log P_c - \phi(\theta)]/\psi(\theta) + 7.00 \qquad (2\text{-}32)$$

The similarity in form between Eq. (2-27) and (2-31) is striking; in fact, by eliminating P_{vp_r} and employing the fact that from Tables 4-1 and 4-2, $\phi\ (T_r = 0.7) = 1.242$ and $\psi\ (T_r = 0.7) = 0.203$, it is easily shown that

$$\omega = 0.203(\alpha_c - 7.00) + 0.242 \qquad (2\text{-}33)$$

Equation (2-33) is occasionally useful in obtaining ω from α_c, or vice versa.

Miller (37) suggests that the simple equation

$$\alpha_c = 0.9076[1 + (T_{br} \ln P_c)/(1 - T_{br})] \qquad (2\text{-}34)$$

predicts α_c within about 0.1 unit except for hydrogen, water, bromine, phenol, and aniline.

Example 2-7. Estimate the Riedel factor for toluene. Use the critical properties listed in Appendix A.

Solution. $\theta = 0.648$; thus, from Table 4-1, $\phi(0.648) = 1.586$, and from Table 4-2, $\psi(0.648) = 0.271$.

From Eq. (2-32),

$$\alpha_c = [(\log 41.6) - 1.586]/0.271 + 7.00 = 7.12$$

By Eq. (2-34),

$$\alpha_c = 0.9076[1 + (0.648 \ln 41.6)/0.352] = 7.21$$

2-9 Normal Boiling Temperatures

It is not often that one wishes to estimate the boiling temperature at 1 atm, since for most known compounds this physical property (or a boiling point at some lower pressure) is the first to be determined. The "Handbook of Chemistry and Physics" (25) and other reference handbooks list values of T_b.

Estimation techniques for T_b when no vapor-pressure data are available are all empirical. Burnop (2, 7, 8) estimated T_b for nonpolar materials from an additive group method, but the exponential form of the correlation makes it very sensitive to changes in the group sum.

Watson Method. Watson (77) related the boiling point and liquid volume; and a rearrangement of his equations yields

$$T_b = \frac{\theta}{V_b{}^{0.18}} \exp\left(\frac{2.77 V_b{}^{0.18}}{\theta} - 2.94\right) \tag{2-35}$$

where θ is T_b/T_c and may be estimated from Eq. (2-3). V_b is the molal volume of the saturated liquid at T_b. Usually, if T_b is not known, neither is V_b. However, the low exponent on V_b makes the estimation of T_b relatively insensitive to reasonable errors in V_b; thus it may be estimated by approximate methods such as those given in Sec. 3-18.

Lydersen-Forman-Thodos Method. In another technique T_b may be estimated by combining Lydersen's estimate of $T_b/T_c = \theta$ from Eq. (2-3) with Forman and Thodos's estimation of T_c [Eq. (2-4)] as

$$T_b = (\theta)(T_c) \tag{2-36}$$

Since there are errors in the estimation of both θ and T_c, the resulting value of T_b is not expected to be more accurate than 5 to 10°C.

In addition to the general estimation techniques, there are two less generally applicable methods for the estimation of T_b which are often surprisingly accurate.

Ogata and Tsuchida Method. Ogata and Tsuchida (41) employed the form

$$T_b = py + q \tag{2-37}$$

In this equation, y is determined by the hydrocarbon radical type and p and q by the functional group. Table 2-9 lists recommended values of

TABLE 2-9. TABULATION OF PARAMETERS FOR EQ. (2-37)*

RX	p	q	Groups, R, showing deviation $> 5°K$
RH	1.615	63.8	Me, t-Bu
RCl	1.348	179.7	
RBr	1.260	213.6	
RI	1.198	253.4	
ROH	0.896	277.6	Me, t-Bu
MeOR	1.217	191.2	Me
EtOR	1.137	221.8	
ROR	2.158	143.2	Me, Hep
PhOR	0.849	377.4	
$RONO_2$	1.016	280.5	
RSH	1.191	221.0	
RSMe	1.146	249.2	Me
RSEt	1.080	280.0	
RSR	1.937	214.4	Me, Hep
RNH_2	1.194	201.4	
RNHMe	1.180	215.2	
RNHEt	1.081	247.9	
RNHPr	0.991	282.8	
$RNMe_2$	1.193	218.7	Me
RNO_2	0.923	308.8	Me, Et
HCOR	1.140	233.8	
MeCOR	1.022	270.6	
EtCOR	0.918	302.2	
RCN	0.960	292.2	
RCOCl	1.040	267.9	
HCOOR	1.073	244.6	
MeCOOR	1.000	273.2	
EtCOOR	0.963	297.5	
PhCOOR	0.766	425.9	
RCOOH	0.903	342.4	
RCOOMe	1.000	273.2	
RCOOEt	0.963	297.5	
RCOOPr	0.911	323.4	
RCOOPh	0.766	425.9	
$(RCO)_2O$	1.286	337.7	Hep
$ClCH_2COOR$	0.721	359.6	
$Cl_2CHCOOR$	0.745	372.3	
$BrCH_2COOR$	0.745	374.4	
$NCCH_2COOR$	0.565	433.5	
$CH_2{=}CHCOOR$	0.918	302.2	

TABLE 2-9. TABULATION OF PARAMETERS FOR EQ. (2-37)* (*Continued*)

R	y	R	y
Methyl	55.5	t-Amyl	122.0
Ethyl	77.1	Neopentyl	125.0
n-Propyl	102.0	n-Hexyl	171.0
Isopropyl	92.0	Isohexyl	168.0
n-Butyl	124.5	n-Heptyl	191.5
sec-Butyl	118.0	n-Octyl	210.0
Isobutyl	116.5	Vinyl	71.0
t-Butyl	96.0	Allyl	104.0
n-Amyl	149.0	2-Butenyl	127.0
Isoamyl	140.5	Phenyl	197.0

* Y. Ogata and M. Tsuchida, *Ind. Eng. Chem.*, **49**:415 (1957).

y, p, and q.   In testing Eq. (2-37) with some 600 compounds, 80 per cent were found to be predicted within 2°K, 89 per cent within 3°K, and 98 per cent within 5°K.   Compounds with more than a single functional group cannot be treated.

Somayajulu and Palit Method.   A method of comparable accuracy was suggested by Somayajulu and Palit (61).

$$T_b = a(\Sigma Z)^c + b \qquad (2\text{-}38)$$

The constants a, b, and c are given for homologous series in Table 2-10. The term ΣZ is the atomic-number sum.

Example 2-8.   Estimate the value of T_b for ethyl bromide.   Compare with the experimental value of 311°K (38°C) (Appendix A).

Solution.   *Method of Ogata and Tsuchida.*   From Table 2-9, $y = 77.1$, $p = 1.260$, and $q = 213.6$.   From Eq. (2-37),

$$T_b = (1.260)(77.1) + 213.6 = 310.7°\text{K}$$

Method of Somayajulu and Palit.   From Table 2-10, $a = 57.54$, $b = -102.5$, $c = \frac{1}{2}$. $\Sigma Z = 2C + 5H + 1Br = (2)(6) + (5)(1) + (1)(35) = 52$.   From Eq. (2-38), $T_b = (57.54)(52)^{1/2} - 102.5 = 312°\text{K}$.

Method of Lydersen-Forman-Thodos.   From Table 2-1 and Eq. (2-3), $\theta = 0.567 + \Sigma \Delta_T - (\Sigma \Delta_T)^2$, where

$$\Sigma\Delta_T = (CH_3\text{—}) + (\text{—}CH_2\text{—}) + Br$$
$$= 0.020 + 0.020 + 0.010 = 0.050$$
$$\theta = 0.567 + 0.050 - (0.050)^2 = 0.614$$

T_c calculated by Forman and Thodos's method (Sec. 2-3) is 503°K.   From Eq. (2-36)

$$T_b = (\theta)(T_c) = (0.614)(503) = 309°\text{K}$$

Method of Watson.   To use Eq. (2-35), a value of V_b is required.   A rough estimate may be obtained from Schroeder's additive method (Table 3-4),

$$V_b = 7N_C + 7N_H + 31.5N_{Br}$$
$$= (7)(2) + (7)(5) + 31.5 = 80.5 \text{ cm}^3/\text{g mole}$$

TABLE 2-10. VALUES OF a, b, AND c FOR EQ. (2-38)*

Homologous series	a	b	c
n-Alkyl fluorides............	51.31	− 26.70	½
n-Alkyl chlorides...........	52.06	− 17.05	½
n-Alkyl bromides..........	57.54	−102.5	½
n-Alkyl iodides............	61.10	−164.0	½
n-Alkyl aldehydes..........	48.87	36.85	½
n-Alkyl ketones...........	44.11	67.20	½
n-Alkyl acids..............	36.17	188.0	½
n-Alkyl primary amines....	45.43	55.56	½
n-Alkyl secondary amines...	46.52	28.10	½
n-Alkyl tertiary amines.....	47.95	− 5.05	½
n-Alkyl benzenes..........	46.88	52.57	½
n-Alkyl cyclohexanes.......	49.54	9.16	½
n-Alkyl cyclohex-1-enes....	47.24	34.10	½
n-Alkanes.................	154.40	−223.90	⅓
n-Alk-l-enes..............	154.45	−222.10	⅓
n-Alk-l-ynes..............	144.44	−168.78	⅓
Normal alcohols..........	2.44	288.0	1
n-Alkyl ethers............	3.58	157.10	1
n-Alkyl acetates..........	2.76	220.80	1
n-Alkanethiols............	3.87	178.0	1

* G. R. Somayajulu and S. R. Palit, *J. Chem. Soc. (London)*, **1957**:2540.

From Eq. (2-35), and using $\theta = 0.614$,

$$T_b = \frac{0.614}{(80.5)^{0.18}} \exp\left[\frac{(2.77)(80.5)^{0.18}}{0.614} - 2.94\right] = 305°K$$

In addition to these methods, there have been two estimation techniques applicable only for certain classes of hydrocarbons.

Stiel and Thodos Method. Stiel and Thodos (64) propose that for *saturated aliphatic* hydrocarbons

$$T_{b_n} = 10^3[1.209 - 1.163/(1 + 0.0742N^{0.85})] \tag{2-39}$$

where T_{b_n} is the normal boiling point for a straight-chain hydrocarbon of N carbon atoms. The boiling point for any isomeric structure with the same N carbons is given as

$$T_{b\ isomer} = T_{b_n} - (96.52/N^2)(W_n - W_i) - 5.45(P_n - P_i) \tag{2-40}$$

In Eq. (2-40), W is the Wiener number as explained in Forman and Thodos's method to determine T_c and P_c (Sec. 2-3). The designation P is the polarity number and is defined as the number of pairs of carbon atoms separated by three single carbon-carbon bonds. For straight-chain paraffins, $P_n = N - 3$. P_i refers to the polarity number of an isomer. Tested with 148 paraffinic isomers up through C_{10}, Stiel and

Thodos found the average discrepancy between calculated and experimental values of T_b to be 0.45 per cent.

Kinney Method. In a quite different approach, Kinney (28, 29) expressed T_b for aliphatic hydrocarbons, olefins, and naphthenes by

$$T_b = 230.1Y^{1/3} - 270 \qquad (2\text{-}41)$$

Y is termed the *boiling-point number* and can be determined from the contributions in Table 2-11. In this method it is essential to calculate Y by first determining the longest chain of the molecule and designating it as the base group. Branching groups are then considered and olefinic groups next. If two equal chain lengths are possible as the base chain, the one containing the fewest unsaturated linkages is chosen. Rings are considered as side groups attached to a nonring carbon (as, for example, in methylcyclopentane or to hydrogen as in cyclopentane).

TABLE 2-11. ATOMIC AND GROUP BOILING-POINT NUMBERS*

Structural group	Value ΔY
Carbon, in the main chain...	0.8
Hydrogen, attached to the main chain..............................	1.0
Radicals, saturated, attached to the main chain or to cyclic rings:	
Methyl...	3.05
Ethyl..	5.5
Propyl...	7.0
Butyl..	9.7
2,2-Dimethyl grouping..	−0.4
Two or three alkyls attached to adjacent carbons of saturated main chains of 6 carbons or less....................................	+0.5
Four or more alkyls attached to adjacent carbons of saturated main chains of 6 carbons or less....................................	1.0
Type of olefinic linkage:	
$CH_2{=}CH_2$...	1.2
$RCH{=}CH_2$...	1.5
$RCH{=}CHR$...	1.9
$R_2C{=}CHR$...	2.3
$R_2C{=}CR_2$...	2.8
Radicals, unsaturated, attached to main chain:	
Methylene..	4.4
Ethylidene...	7.0
Vinyl..	5.4
Propylidene..	9.0
Butylidene...	10.4

* C. R. Kinney, *J. Am. Chem. Soc.*, **60**:3032 (1938); *Ind. Eng. Chem.*, **32**:559 (1940).

TABLE 2-11. ATOMIC AND GROUP BOILING-POINT NUMBERS* (*Continued*)

Structural group	Value ΔY
Type of acetylenic linkage:	
HC≡CH	4.0
RC≡CH	4.4
RC≡CCH₃	5.4
RC≡CR	4.8
Type of diolefin:	
Allenes	4.8
Conjugated, normal values of double bonds plus not conjugated, normal values of double bonds only	0.8
Type of triolefin:	
All bonds conjugated, normal values of double bonds plus	2.4
Two bonds conjugated, normal values of double bonds plus	0.8
No conjugation, normal values of double bonds only	
Type of diacetylene:	
1,3-Diacetylenes, normal values of triple bonds only	
All other conjugated, normal values of triple bonds plus	3.0
No conjugation, normal values of triple bonds only	
Type of enyne:	
Conjugated, normal values of bonds plus	0.8
No conjugation, normal values of bonds only	
Type of dienyne:	
Conjugated, normal values of bonds plus	2.4
No conjugation, normal values of bonds only	
Cyclic radicals. Add 0.8 for each carbon, 1.0 for each hydrogen, the normal values of any unsaturated linkages, and the following values for the ring:	
Type 1	
Cyclopropyl	2.1
Cyclobutyl	2.3
Cyclopentyl	2.5
Cyclohexyl	2.7
Type 2	
Cycloheptyl	3.4
Cyclooctyl	3.9
Cyclononyl	4.4
Cyclodecyl	4.9
Cyclohendecyl	5.4
Cyclododecyl	5.9
Cyclotridecyl	6.4
Cyclotetradecyl	6.9
Cyclopentadecyl	7.4
Cyclohexadecyl	7.9
Cycloheptadecyl	8.4

In testing with 762 hydrocarbons, the average deviation was 4°K, and in 92 per cent of the cases tested the calculated value of T_b was within $\pm 10°$K of the experimental value.

Example 2-9. Estimate the normal boiling point of 2,3,4-trimethylpentane. Compare with the experimental value of 386.6°K.

Solution. *Method of Stiel and Thodos.* For the parent straight-chain molecule, *n*-octane, Eq. (2-39) gives

$$T_{b_n} = 10^3\{1.209 - 1.163/[1 + 0.0742(8)^{0.85}]\} = 398.9°\text{K}$$

and the Wiener and polarity numbers

$$W_n = \tfrac{1}{6}(N + 1)(N)(N - 1) = \tfrac{1}{6}(9)(8)(7) = 84$$
$$P_n = N - 3 = 5$$

For the isomer, $W_i = 65$ (see Sec. 2-3).

To determine the polarity number for the isomer, the carbon atoms may be labeled as follows:

$$
\begin{array}{ccccc}
1 & 2 & 3 & 4 & 5 \\
\text{C} & \text{C} & \text{C} & \text{C} & \text{C} \\
 & | & | & | & \\
 & \text{C} & \text{C} & \text{C} & \\
 & 6 & 7 & 8 &
\end{array}
$$

The pairs separated by three carbon-carbon bonds are 1-4, 1-7, 2-5, 2-8, 4-6, 5-7, 6-7, 7-8; thus $P_i = 8$.

From Eq. (2-40), for the isomer,

$$T_{b_i} = 398.9 - 96.52[(84-65)/8^2] - 5.45(5-8) = 386.6°\text{K}$$
$$\text{Error} = 386.6 - 386.6 = 0°\text{K}$$

Method of Kinney. From Table 2-10, with the main chain of 5 carbon atoms and 12 hydrogens and with three methyl radicals attached to the main chain,

$$Y = (5)(0.8) + (12)(1.0) + (3)(3.05) + (0.5) = 25.65$$

(The last 0.5 is the contribution from 3 methyl radicals attached to adjacent carbon atoms.)

$$T_b = (230.1)(25.65)^{\frac{1}{3}} - 270 = 409°\text{K}$$
$$\text{Error} = 409 - 386.6 = 22.4°\text{K}$$

Recommendations. For saturated aliphatic hydrocarbons, use Eqs. (2-39) and (2-40). Errors less than ± 2 to 3°K are to be expected. For other compounds, the method of Ogata and Tsuchida, [Eq. (2-37) and Table 2-9] is recommended. Errors less than $\pm 5°$K are predicted; however, if this method is inapplicable, use Eq. (2-36), with θ determined from Eq. (2-3) and Table 2-1 and T_c from the estimation technique in Sec. 2-3. Errors in this latter case are usually $\pm 15°$K except for inorganic or highly polar compounds, in which cases considerably greater errors are possible.

2-10 Lennard-Jones Potential Parameters

The Lennard-Jones intermolecular potential-energy–distance relation is often employed to calculate properties such as virial coefficients, fugacities, and viscosities of nonpolar gases. The calculation techniques are discussed later. In this section methods are presented to estimate the Lennard-Jones values of ϵ_0, the minimum energy of attraction, and σ, the intermolecular distance when $\varphi(r)$ is zero [see Eq. (3-29) and Fig. 3-1]. Actually ϵ_0/k is the quantity estimated, where k is Boltzmann's constant. The dimensions of ϵ_0/k are degrees absolute temperature. The estimation of ϵ_0/k and σ for the Stockmayer potential is discussed in Sec. 3-13 (65).

The most complete tabulation of ϵ_0/k and σ values is given by Svehla (66). Many of these were obtained from experimental viscosity and thermal-conductivity data, but others were determined from empirical relationships, and many are only approximate. Flynn and Thodos (14) have also published a tabulation of ϵ_0/k and σ values obtained from viscosity data. Often these values differ greatly from those given by Svehla; e.g., for butane, Flynn and Thodos list $\epsilon_0/k = 208°K$, whereas Svehla suggests a value of $531.4°K$. Both these may be compared with the tabulation of Hirschfelder, Curtiss, and Bird (24), in which a value of $410°K$ is listed. In other comparisons, the differences are not so striking, but it is common to find them as great as $50°K$. Only two viscosity-temperature data points are needed to obtain numerical values of ϵ_0/k and σ. Flynn and Thodos obtained a set of ϵ_0/k values from various data-point pairs and then reported an average. Svehla developed a least-squares program to choose values of ϵ_0/k, σ which would allow him to reproduce the original viscosity-temperature with the least error. These different averaging procedures could lead to significant differences in the values of ϵ_0/k and σ selected.

It may be noted that the differences in the two sets of ϵ_0/k, σ values are not due to the use of different experimental data, as Svehla (67) has recently recalculated his values based on the same data used by Flynn and Thodos, and in most cases the original discrepancies remain. Also, it has been found that values of ϵ_0/k and σ values determined from viscosity data often differ from values determined from pressure-volume-temperature data; so this introduces an additional uncertainty in the values. Hirschfelder, Curtiss, and Bird (24) present a similar, but less comprehensive, tabulation of ϵ_0/k and σ in which the values determined by viscosity data and P-V-T data are tabulated separately.

Stiel and Thodos Method. Most of the estimation techniques for Lennard-Jones force constants relate ϵ_0/k and σ to liquid density (48a) or to some characteristic temperature and volume. Stiel and Thodos (62) have shown that, for many organic materials, the following relations may be employed:

$$\epsilon_0/k = 65.3 T_c Z_c^{18/5} \quad °K \tag{2-42}$$

$$\sigma = 0.1866 V_c^{1/3} Z_c^{-6/5} \quad A \tag{2-43}$$

or

$$\sigma = 0.812(T_c/P_c)^{1/3} Z_c^{-13/15} \quad A$$

In most cases, a more convenient form by which to express σ is that based on the so-called "hard-sphere volume" b_0, where

$$b_0 = \tfrac{2}{3}\pi N_0 \sigma^3 \tag{2-44}$$

N_0 is Avogadro's number. From Eq. (2-43), to express b_0 in cubic centimeters per gram mole, and where T_c, P_c are expressed as in degrees Kelvin and atmospheres,

$$b_0 = (0.676/Z_c^{2.60})(T_c/P_c) \tag{2-45}$$

If Z_c is assumed to be constant and equal to 0.288, Eqs. (2-42) and (2-45) reduce to the most common rules suggested by Svehla,

$$\epsilon_0/k = 0.75 T_c \tag{2-46}$$
$$b_0 = 17.28(T_c/P_c) \tag{2-47}$$

Equations (2-46) and (2-47) fit all the data in Appendix G somewhat better than Eqs. (2-42) and (2-43), but in both cases there is considerable scatter. At the same time, Eqs. (2-42) and (2-43) fit the ϵ_0/k, σ values recommended by Stiel and Thodos.

Example 2-10. Estimate the Lennard-Jones force constants ϵ_0/k, σ, and b_0 for propane. The critical constants are $T_c = 369.9°$K, $P_c = 42.0$ atm, $V_c = 200$ cm^3/g mole, $Z_c = 0.277$ (Appendix A). The reported values of ϵ_0/k and σ as determined from viscosity data are 237.1°K and 5.118 A (66).

Solution. From Eq. (2-42)

$$\epsilon_0/k = (65.3)(369.9)(0.277)^{3.6} = 237.1°\text{K}$$
$$\text{Error} = [(237.1 - 237.1)/237.1] \times 100 = 0\%$$

Equation (2-46) gives $\epsilon_0/k = 277°$K, a considerably less accurate value. From Eq. (2-43)

$$\sigma = (0.1866)(200)^{1/3}(0.277)^{-1.2}$$
$$= (0.812)(369.9/42.0)^{1/3}(0.277)^{-0.867} = 5.09 \text{ A}$$
$$\text{Error} = [(5.09 - 5.12)/5.12] \times 100 = -0.6\%$$

From Eq. (2-45)

$$b_0 = (0.676)(369.9/42.0)(0.277)^{-2.60} = 167 \text{ cm}^3/\text{g mole}$$

From Eq. (2-47)

$$b_0 = (17.28)(369.9/42.0) = 152 \text{ cm}^3/\text{g mole}$$

It may be noted that Flynn and Thodos (14) report values of $\epsilon_0/k = 206°$K and $\sigma = 5.24$ A for propane. With these values, errors are +15 per cent and -2.9 per cent, respectively. Svehla reports his best values as 237.1°K and 5.118 A, and in this case errors are 0 and -0.5 per cent.

Recommendations. A convenient set of values reported by Svehla, as calculated from experimental viscosity data, are tabulated in Appendix G. These should be used as a first choice. If the compound of interest is not tabulated, use Eqs. (2-42) and (2-43) or (2-45), or use

Eqs. (2-46) and (2-47). Do not estimate ϵ_0/k by one set and σ by the other.

The reported values of Lennard-Jones potentials ϵ_0/k and σ often differ. However, it is interesting to note that, between reported sets of potentials, usually if a large positive difference exists in, say, ϵ_0/k, then there is a large negative difference in the reported value of σ. This fact often causes calculated viscosities to be almost the same, as there is a compensation effect. Even in the case of n-butane, where, as noted above, Flynn and Thodos and Svehla tabulate very different ϵ_0/k and σ values, the calculated gas-viscosity curves (by methods described in Chap. 9), both sets of potentials being used, are only slightly different (67) (see Fig. 9-2).

NOMENCLATURE FOR CHAPTER 2

a = van der Waals' constant for Eqs. (2-4) and (2-5)
a = parameter in Eq. (2-38)
a_γ = constant in Eq. (2-12)
b = van der Waals' constant for Eqs. (2-4) and (2-5)
b = parameter in Eq. (2-38)
b_0 = hard-sphere volume, $\frac{2}{3}\pi N_0 \sigma^3$
B = constant for Eq. (4-16)
c = parameter in Eq. (2-38)
C = constant for Eq. (4-16)
D = constant for Eq. (4-16)
f_a, f_b = correction factors in Eqs. (2-8) and (2-9)
ΔH_v = enthalpy of vaporization, cal/g mole; ΔH_{v_b}, at the normal boiling point
k = parameter in Eqs. (2-8) and (2-10); Boltzmann's constant
k_E = Eötvös constant
m = total number of side chains in Eqs. (2-8) and (2-9)
M = molecular weight
n = total number of carbon atoms and functional groups; parameter in Eq. (2-10)
n_γ = constant in Eq. (2-12)
N = number of carbon atoms (or other atoms as noted by subscript)
N_0 = Avogadro's number
p = parameter in Eq. (2-37)
P = pressure, atm; P_c, critical pressure; P_{vp}, vapor pressure; P_r, reduced pressure P/P_c
P_n, P_i = polarity number [see Eq. (2-40)]
$[P]$ = parachor [see Eq. (2-17)]
q = parameter in Eq. (2-10); parameter in Eq. (2-37)
R = gas constant
ΔS_v = entropy of vaporization, cal/(g mole)(°K); ΔS_{v_b}, at the normal boiling point
t = parameter in Eq. (2-10)
T = temperature, °K; T_c, critical temperature; T_b, normal boiling point; T_r, reduced temperature T/T_c
V = volume, cm³/g mole; V_c, critical volume; V_b, at the normal boiling point; V_r, reduced volume V/V_c
W = Wiener number; W_s, for straight-chain hydrocarbon; W_i, for branched-chain hydrocarbon
y = parameter in Eq. (2-37)

Y = parameter in Eq. (2-41)
Z = compressibility factor PV/RT; Z_c, critical compressibility factor
Z = atomic number

Greek

α_c = Riedel factor [Eq. (2-31)]
γ = surface tension, dynes/cm
$\Delta_{p,T,v}$ = Lydersen increments in Table 2-1
Δ_Z = García-Bárcena increments in Table 2-6
ϵ_0 = Lennard-Jones parameter
$\theta = T_b/T_c$
ρ = molal density
σ = Lennard-Jones parameter
$\varphi(r)$ = interaction potential energy
ω = acentric factor

REFERENCES FOR CHAPTER 2

1. Ambrose, D.: *Trans. Faraday Soc.*, **59**:1988 (1963).
2. Banks, W. H.: *J. Chem. Soc.*, **1939**:292.
3. Barbuz, V. F.: *Trans. Gos. Inst. Prinkl. Khem.*, **49**:113 (1962); *Chem. Abstr.*, **60**:36 (1964).
4. Benko, J.: *Acta Chim. Acad. Sci. Hung.*, **34**:217 (1962).
5. Benko, J.: *Acta Chim. Acad. Sci. Hung.*, **35**:447 (1963).
6. Briggs, D. K., and W. D. Drake: *Nature*, **180**:1353 (1957).
7. Burnop, V. C. E.: *J. Chem. Soc.*, **1938**:826.
8. Burnop, V. C. E.: *J. Chem. Soc.*, **1938**:1614.
8a. Cecil, R. R., and T. M. Reed III: Paper submitted to *Ind. Eng. Chem. Fundamentals.*
9. Chen, Mei-Chio, and Dji-Bin Hu: *J. Chinese Chem. Soc.*, **10**:208, 210 (1943).
10. Corner, J.: *Trans. Faraday Soc.*, **36**:781 (1940).
11. Edmister, W. C.: *Petrol. Refiner*, **37**(4):173 (1958).
12. Elrod, H.: Estimation of the Critical Temperature and Pressure of Uranium, NDA-14-122, Feb. 1, 1956, A Method for the Estimation of Critical Temperatures and Pressures, NDA-14-121, Feb. 2, 1956, Nuclear Development Corporation of America, White Plains, N.Y.
13. Fishtine, S. H.: *Ind. Eng. Chem. Fundamentals*, **2**:149 (1963).
14. Flynn, L. W., and G. Thodos: *AIChE J.*, **8**:362 (1962).
15. Forman, J. C., and G. Thodos: *AIChE J.*, **4**:356 (1958).
16. Forman, J. C., and G. Thodos: *AIChE J.*, **6**:206 (1960).
17. Gallaugher, A. F., and H. Hibbert: *J. Am. Chem. Soc.*, **59**:2504 (1937).
18. Gambill, W. R.: *Chem. Eng.*, **66**(12):181 (1959); **66**(14):157 (1959).
19. García-Bárcena, G. J.: S. B. thesis in chemical engineering, Massachusetts Institute of Technology, 1958.
20. Gates, D. S., and G. Thodos: *AIChE J.*, **6**:50 (1960).
21. Grunberg, L., and A. H. Nissan: *Trans. Faraday Soc.*, **44**:1013 (1948).
22. Guggenheim, E. A.: *J. Chem. Phys.*, **13**:253 (1945).
23. Herzog, R.: *Ind. Eng. Chem.*, **36**:997 (1944).
24. Hirschfelder, J. O., C. F. Curtiss, and R. B. Bird: "Molecular Theory of Gases and Liquids," John Wiley & Sons, Inc., New York, 1954.
25. Hodgman, C. D. (ed.): "Handbook of Chemistry and Physics," 30th ed., Chemical Rubber Publishing Co., Cleveland, Ohio, 1948.

26. Khalivov, Kh. M.: *Isvest. Akad. Nauk Azerbaïdzhan S.S.R.*, *Ser. Fiz.-Tekh. i Khim Nauk*, **1958**(3):51.
27. Kharbanda, O. P.: *Ind. Chemist*, **32**:474 (1956).
28. Kinney, C. R.: *J. Am. Chem. Soc.*, **60**:3032 (1938).
29. Kinney, C. R.: *Ind. Eng. Chem.*, **32**:559 (1940).
30. Lewis, D. T.: *J. Chem. Soc.*, **1938**:261.
31. Lydersen, A. L.: Estimation of Critical Properties of Organic Compounds, *Coll. Eng.*, *Univ. Wisconsin*, *Eng. Expt. Sta. Rept.* 3, Madison, Wis., April, 1955.
32. Marschner, R. F., and J. P. Beverly: *J. Chem. Ed.*, **33**:604 (1956).
33. Martin, T. J., and Hou Yu-chun: *AIChE J.*, **1**:142 (1955).
34. Mayfield, F. D.: *Ind. Eng. Chem.*, **38**:843 (1942).
35. Meissner, H. P.: *Chem. Eng. Progr.*, **45**:149 (1949).
36. Meissner, H. P., and E. M. Redding: *Ind. Eng. Chem.*, **34**:521 (1942).
37. Miller, D. G.: *Ind. Eng. Chem. Fundamentals*, **2**:78 (1963).
38. Monsanto Chemical Company: Evaluation of High Temperature Hydrocarbon Fuels, *Quartermonthly Progr. Rept.* 8, Apr., 14, 1961, Research and Engineering Division, Everett, Mass.
39. Móritz, P.: *Acta Chim. Acad. Sci. Hung.*, **11**:271 (1957); *ibid.*, **32**:97 (1962); *Per. Polytech.*, **7**:27 (1963).
40. Nokay, R.: *Chem. Eng.*, **66**(4):147 (1959).
41. Ogata, Y., and M. Tsuchida: *Ind. Eng. Chem.*, **49**:415 (1957).
42. Pilcher, R. W., and J. M. Ward: *Chem. Eng. Data Ser.*, **3**:193 (1958).
43. Pitzer, K. S.: *J. Am. Chem. Soc.*, **77**:3427 (1955).
44. Pitzer, K. S., D. Z. Lippmann, R. F. Curl, C. M. Huggins, and D. E. Petersen: *J. Am. Chem. Soc.*, **77**:3433 (1955).
45. Plank, R., and L. Riedel: *Ing.-Arch.*, **16**:255 (1948).
46. Prud'homme, M.: *J. chim. phys.*, **18**:95, 270, 307 (1920).
47. Quayle, O. R.: *Chem. Revs.*, **53**:439 (1953).
48. Ramsay, W., and J. Shields: *Z. physik. Chem.*, **12**:433 (1893).
48a. Reed, T. M., III, and M. D. McKinley: *Chem. Eng. Data Ser.*, **9**:553 (1964).
49. Rice, O. K.: Critical Phenomena, sec. E, in F. D. Rossini (ed.), "Thermodynamics and Physics of Matter," Princeton University Press, Princeton, N.J., 1955.
50. Riedel, L.: *Z. Elektrochem.*, **53**:222 (1949).
51. Riedel, L.: *Chem.-Ing.-Tech.*, **24**:353 (1952).
52. Riedel, L.: *Chem.-Ing.-Tech.*, **26**:83 (1954).
53. Riedel, L.: *Chem.-Ing.-Tech.*, **27**:475 (1955).
54. Riedel, L.: *Chem.-Ing.-Tech.*, **28**:419 (1956).
55. Riedel, L.: *Chem.-Ing.-Tech.*, **35**:433 (1963).
56. Sato, K.: *Chem. Eng. (Japan)*, **15**:78 (1951).
57. Schuster, F.: *Z. Elektrochem.*, **32**:191 (1926).
58. Shemilt, L. W.: *Proc. Conf. on Thermodynamics and Transport Properties of Fluids*, London, 1957, p. 62.
59. Simkin, D. J.: Paper presented at the National Meeting of the American Institute of Chemical Engineers, Seattle, Wash., June, 1957.
60. Smith, W. T., S. Greenbaum, and G. P. Rutledge: *J. Phys. Chem.*, **58**:443 (1954).
61. Somayajulu, G. R., and S. R. Palit: *J. Chem. Soc.*, **1957**:2540.
62. Stiel, L. I., and G. Thodos: *Chem. Eng. Data Ser.*, **7**:234 (1962).
63. Stiel, L. I., and G. Thodos: *Can. J. Chem. Eng.*, **40**:253 (1962).
64. Stiel, L. I., and G. Thodos: *AIChE J.*, **8**:527 (1962).
65. Stiel, L. I., and G. Thodos: *AIChE J.*, **10**:266 (1964).
66. Svehla, R. A.: Estimated Viscosities and Thermal Conductivities at High Temperatures, *NASA Tech. Rept.* R-132, 1962.

67. Svehla, R. A.: Private communication, June, 1964.
68. Thodos, G.: *AIChE J.*, **1**:165 (1955).
69. Thodos, G.: *AIChE J.*, **2**:508 (1956).
70. Thodos, G.: *AIChE J.*, **3**:428 (1957).
71. Thomas, L. H.: *J. Chem. Soc.*, **1949**:3411, 3415.
72. Van der Waals, J. D.: *Z. physik. Chem.*, **13**:716 (1894).
73. Van Dranen, J.: *J. Chem. Phys.*, **21**:1404 (1953).
74. Van Hecke, F.: S.M. thesis in chemical engineering, Massachusetts Institute of Technology, 1954.
75. Vowles, C.: S.M. thesis in chemical engineering, Massachusetts Institute of Technology, 1951.
76. Wan, S. W.: *J. Phys. Chem.*, **45**:903 (1941).
77. Watson, K. M.: *Ind. Eng. Chem.*, **23**:360 (1931).

CHAPTER 3

PRESSURE-VOLUME-TEMPERATURE RELATIONSHIPS
OF PURE GASES AND LIQUIDS

3-1 Scope

The volumetric behavior of pure gases and liquids as functions of temperature and pressure is covered in this chapter; mixtures are treated in Chap. 7. Emphasis has been placed on those methods which are general in nature and applicable to more than a single material or a homologous series of compounds.

The basis for the correlations is the thermodynamic fact that for each substance there exists a unique relation among pressure, temperature, and specific volume for any single phase. This fact stems, not from the phase rule, but rather from the fundamental Gibbs equation relating energy, entropy, and volume. Callen (23) presents an excellent discussion of the properties and limitations of such *equations of state*.

3-2 Pure Gases—General Considerations

Methods of correlating the P-V-T behavior of pure gases can be conveniently, but somewhat arbitrarily, divided into three general groups. First there are the methods which are classified under the general term *corresponding states* and are based on dimensional-similitude considerations. The well-known compressibility factor-reduced property correlation is a good example of this treatment. Second there is the more theoretical approach employing a virial expansion of P-V-T equations, with the constants directly related to the intermolecular potential-energy–distance relationship applicable to the substance in question. Third, and finally, many analytical equations of state have been proposed. In the last class, only those equations which allow a prediction of all parameters from some other known or predictable pure-component constants (Chap. 2) will be discussed.

The corresponding-state methods yield good results and are most convenient for obtaining spot values of V at some P and T (or other combination) and usually involve use of a table or graph. The virial-expansion equation is generally not so accurate or convenient, but it possesses the most rigorous theoretical basis; the results will be found to be useful in studying the properties of mixtures.

The generalized equation of state is capable of yielding the most accurate, but most complex, correlations between P, V, and T. Many of the more complex techniques, however, are conveniently programmed for machine computation. The mathematical formulations are often convenient in the mathematical operations required to determine other thermodynamic functions, such as $(\partial H/\partial P)_T$, as discussed in Chaps. 6 and 7.

3-3   Ideal-gas Law and the Compressibility Factor

The limiting case wherein the gas molecules are assumed to have no volume and not to interact in any way leads immediately to the ideal-gas law*

$$PV = RT \tag{3-1}$$

Defining a compressibility factor Z,

$$Z = PV/RT \tag{3-2}$$

then Z is unity for an ideal gas. Z approaches unity at low pressures for all gases and may be greater or less than unity at higher pressures. If the temperature is above the so-called Boyle temperature, Z will always be greater than unity, but if the temperature is below the Boyle temperature, Z is less than unity at low pressures and greater than unity at high pressures. The reasons why Z deviates from unity are discussed in detail below. It may be noted, however, that Eq. (3-1) is still a very useful approximation, even at quite high pressures if the temperature is two or three times the critical value. In many cases, it is a poor approximation.

3-4   Nonideality of Gases

It is important to consider the principal reasons why Eq. (3-1) is not applicable for real gases (12, 32, 72).

Shape Factors and Intermolecular Forces. Molecules are not point masses and may have many diverse shapes. Even simple spherical atoms such as argon attract or repel other argon atoms, depending upon the separation distance; in addition, at high pressures, the volume fraction occupied by the atoms themselves may be significant. Molecules

---

* It should be noted that Eq. (3-1) is a necessary, but not sufficient, criterion to define an "ideal gas." In addition, some other condition such as $(\partial E/\partial V)_T = 0$ is needed to complete the definition (72, 81).

behave in a similar way. The fact that real molecules have interacting forces and finite molecular volumes is usually the most important reason why Eq. (3-1) is not obeyed.

Electrical Forces. Electrical forces of a permanent kind are usually important only in so-called "polar" molecules. Nonpermanent electrical forces, such as electric moments arising from the short-lived perturbation of the electron positions during a collision or near collision, are included above and are present in all real systems. These forces are included in the potential-energy relationships between molecules.

Electrical forces, excluding hydrogen bonding, depend upon the molecular dipole moment, the quadrupole and higher multipole moments, and the polarizability. An excellent summary of the physical significance of these quantities is given by Bird and Brock (12). They will be referred to later in several of the proposed correlations.

Hydrogen Bonding. Hydrogen bonding between molecules usually occurs in systems of a polar nature. Such forces are often considered in the same category as electrical forces.

Quantum Effects. Quantum effects are important only in those molecules where the translational-energy modes must be quantized; such molecules as H_2, He, and Ne at low temperatures are the only ones which have significant quantum effects.

These four effects must be considered when methods are proposed to describe the variation of the P-V-T behavior of a real gas from that of an ideal gas.

3-5 Corresponding-state Correlations

The basis of the corresponding-state correlations is the observation that graphs of P versus V, with isotherms, are qualitatively similar for all gases. Such graphs for several substances can be made quantitatively similar by superposing the critical points and properly modifying the P and V scales of ordinate and abscissa.

The variation in the compressibility factor Z, as defined in Eq. (3-2), is small compared with possible variations in P, V, or T. Values range from 0.2 to a little over unity even up to ten times the critical pressure or temperature. To show the P-V-T behavior of a particular gas, Z is often plotted against pressure, with curves representing isotherms and isometrics. To show the behavior of the compressibility factor in a general way, i.e., for many different gases, recourse is usually had to the principle of corresponding states. This principle has been stated in many ways, but it is perhaps most easily visualized by applying dimensional analysis to the important system parameters. The set of dimensionless groups which are obtained may then be utilized to define the system.

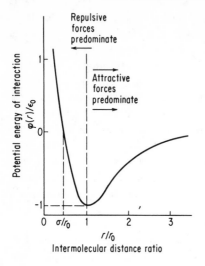

FIG. 3-1. Schematic representation of inter-molecular energies.

The properties P, V, and T are necessary system parameters. Characterizing parameters in the appropriate intermolecular potential function are also necessary; it will be shown later that for nonpolar molecules these parameters are usually chosen so as to represent in an approximate manner the collision diameter σ and the minimum potential energy ϵ_0. For polar molecules, in addition to σ and ϵ_0, the dipole moment μ, the quadrupole moment Q, and the polarizability α are convenient choices. Finally, some variable characteristic of the shape (or nonsphericity) is probably required; following the suggestion of Bird and Brock (12), the elliptic eccentricity β is chosen.* Finally, the molecular mass m, Planck's constant h, and Boltzmann's constant k complete the list. That is,

$$\phi_1(P,V,T,\sigma,\epsilon_0,\mu,Q,\alpha,\beta,m,h,k) = 0 \qquad (3\text{-}3)$$

Bird and Brock (12) suggest a convenient arrangement in terms of dimensionless groups,

$$\phi_2\left[\frac{PV}{kT}, \frac{V}{\sigma^3}, \frac{kT}{\epsilon_0}, \frac{\mu^2}{\epsilon_0\sigma^3}, \frac{Q^2}{\epsilon_0\sigma}, \frac{\alpha}{\sigma^3}, \frac{h}{\sigma(m\epsilon_0)^{\frac{1}{2}}}, \beta\right] = 0 \qquad (3\text{-}4)$$

This equation is much too complicated to be of any practical use at the present time. The group $h/\sigma\sqrt{m\epsilon_0}$ appears to be important only to account for quantum effects at very low temperature. In general, though not always (116), it is neglected. The parameters ϵ_0 and σ are often related to critical temperature and volume, respectively.

---

* Other choices may be made. For example, Pitzer (94, 97) uses the ratio of the core dimension of the molecule to the intermolecular distance at ϵ_0.

Intermolecular potentials are discussed more in detail later when virial equations are considered. However, to give a physical meaning of ϵ_0 and σ, a brief introductory treatment is presented here. Nonpolar molecules usually have an interacting potential energy relation similar to that shown in Fig. 3-1. At large intermolecular distances, $r/r_0 \gg 1$, the energy of interaction is negligible. At shorter distances, the molecules attract one another, and the potential energy of the system decreases. At some distance r_0, the repulsive forces equal the attractive forces, and if r decreases further, the potential energy increases rapidly. The value of σ is usually defined as that point on the repulsion curve at $\varphi(r) = 0$. The exact shape of the curve depends, of course, on the particular formulation of the potential. "Simple" molecules, for example, A, Kr, Xe, are defined as having a spherical shape and an inverse-sixth-power attractive potential. The exact shape of the repulsive potential is not known; a convenient choice, and one often made, is that this may be adequately represented by an inverse-twelfth-power law. Such fluids are then said to be represented by a Lennard-Jones 6-12 potential,

$$\varphi(r)/\epsilon_0 = (r_0/r)^{12} - 2(r_0/r)^6 \tag{3-5}$$

Differentiating Eq. (3-5) with respect to r and setting the result equal to zero yields $\varphi(r) = -\epsilon_0$ and $r = r_0$; thus the depth of the well is the negative of the parameter ϵ_0, and the intermolecular distance at this minimum energy is, of course, r_0. Further, if $\varphi(r) = 0$ in Eq. (3-5), it is easy to show that the intermolecular distance for this energy (called σ) is given as

$$\sigma = (2^{-\frac{1}{6}})r_0 \tag{3-6}$$

There are many suggested potential-energy–distance functions. The Lennard-Jones 6-12 potential is the most commonly used potential for nonpolar materials. It is characterized by only two constants, ϵ_0 or ϵ_0/k and σ, and as such is compatible with the dimensionless equation (3-4). It is also just about the only potential function for which any attempt has been made to tabulate and correlate the constants for various materials. Section 2-10 discusses estimation methods for obtaining the ϵ_0/k and other values for this potential. As shown in this section $\epsilon_0/k = f(T_c, Z_c)$ and $\sigma = f(V_c, Z_c)$ for many materials. Upon using these simplifications and neglecting the quantum group, Eq. (3-7) is obtained,

$$\phi_3[PV/kT,\ V/V_c,\ T/T_c,\ \mu^2/V_c k T_c,\ Q^2/V_c^5 k T_c,\ \alpha/V_c,\ \beta] = 0 \tag{3-7}$$

Equations (3-4) and (3-7) are the basic relations for all the corresponding-state correlations.

3-6 Nonpolar Molecules

If one considers only nonpolar molecules, for which μ, Q, and α are small, and if V/V_c is eliminated from Eq. (3-7) by

$$V_r = V/V_c = (Z/Z_c)(T_r/P_r) \qquad (3\text{-}8)$$

then, with Eq. (3-2),

$$\phi_4(Z,P_r,T_r,Z_c,\beta) = 0 \qquad (3\text{-}9)$$

Equation (3-9) indicates that the compressibility factor is a function of reduced pressure and temperature, and of Z_c and β as well. No simple correlations have yet been advanced to account for all four independent variables P_r, T_r, Z_c, and β, although several generalized equations of state to be discussed later may utilize all of them.

For simple fluids, the assumption is made and experimentally justified that Z is primarily a function only of T_r and P_r. Until recently, the same correlation was also assumed for other types of fluids. At least 20 different charts have been published which show this generalized relationship (36). The best charts are due to Nelson and Obert (88) and Viswanath (123). The former are shown in Figs. 3-2 to 3-4. To

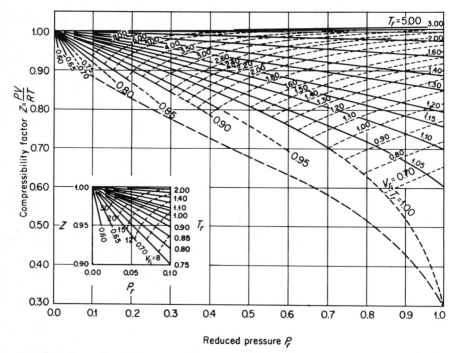

FIG. 3-2. Generalized compressibility chart. [*Reproduced from the charts of L. C. Nelson and E. F. Obert, Northwestern University, Evanston, Ill.; Trans. ASME,* **76**:1057 (1954).]

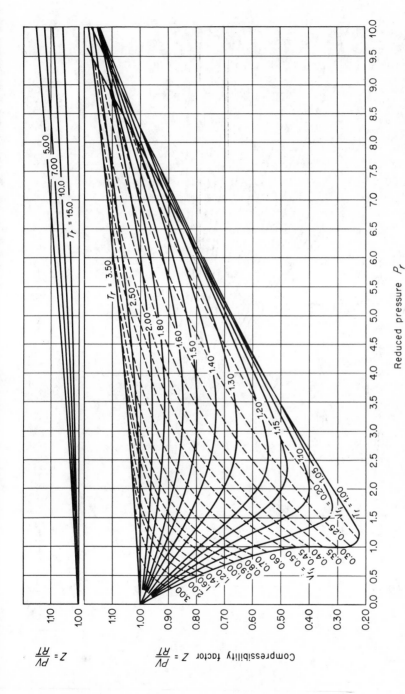

Reduced pressure P_r

Compressibility factor $Z = \dfrac{PV}{RT}$

$Z = \dfrac{PV}{RT}$

$T_r = 15.0$

5.00
7.00
10.0

$T_r = 3.50$

2.50
2.00
1.80
1.60
1.50
1.40
1.30
1.20
1.15
1.10
1.05
1.00

0.20
0.25
0.30
0.35
0.40
0.45
0.50
0.60
0.70
0.80
0.90
1.00
1.20
1.40
1.60
2.00
3.00

Fig. 3-3. Generalized compressibility plot. [*Reproduced from the charts of L. C. Nelson and E. F. Obert, Northwestern University, Evanston, Ill.; Trans. ASME,* **76:**1057 (1954).]

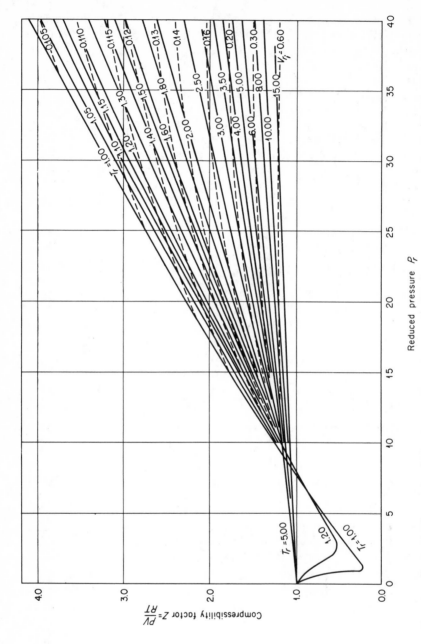

FIG. 3-4. Generalized compressibility plot. [*Reproduced from the charts of L. C. Nelson and E. F. Obert, Northwestern University, Evanston, Ill.; Trans. ASME,* **76**:1057 (1954).]

use Figs. 3-2 to 3-4, critical temperatures and pressures are required. Experimental values (from Appendix A) may be used or estimated values obtained by techniques described in Secs. 2-3 and 2-4. Su's ideal-volume concept (121) is used in Figs. 3-2 to 3-4 to obviate the necessity of knowing the critical volume. This ideal-reduced-volume V_{r_i} is defined as

$$V_{r_i} = V/V_{c_i} = V/(RT_c/P_c) = ZT_r/P_r \qquad (3\text{-}10)$$

Figure 3-2, representing the low-pressure region (P_r from 0 to 1), is based on experimental data for 30 gases. The maximum deviation for 26 of these gases is 1 per cent. Hydrogen and helium (both with uncorrected critical constants; see below) and ammonia and water vapor show a maximum deviation of 3 to 4 per cent. Figure 3-3 is drawn for the intermediate-pressure region (P_r from 1 to 10) and is also based on data for 30 gases. The maximum deviation in this case is 2.5 per cent, except for hydrogen, helium, ammonia, and fluoromethane. These materials deviate in different regions; e.g., ammonia cannot be correlated satisfactorily above $P_r = 1$, and fluoromethane deviates as much as 7 per cent at the lower temperatures.

Figure 3-4 correlates Z in the high-pressure region (P_r from 10 to 40). Only limited experimental data were available to construct this graph, but those available are represented within 5 per cent in the range T_r from 1 to 3.5 and P_r from 10 to 20. Above a T_r of 5 the data available for hydrogen and helium were used to construct the plots; in this case Newton's pseudocritical* constants were employed. These constants stem from the suggestion (89) that, to calculate Z for hydrogen, helium, and neon, more reliable results are to be obtained, with reduced properties calculated as follows:

$$T_r = T/(T_c + 8) \qquad P_r = P/(P_c + 8) \qquad (3\text{-}11)$$

where temperatures are expressed in degrees Kelvin and pressures in atmospheres.

This type of correction has been criticized by Morgan and Childs (85), who state that such pseudocritical constants do not remain constant except over limited ranges of temperature and pressure. If P-V-T properties of hydrogen, helium, neon, or argon are to be determined, it is recommended that the special compressibility chart presented by Maslan and Littman (75) be employed. The deviation of these gases from the generalized compressibility correlation rule raises the question of how adequately generalized compressibility correlations may be extrapolated to regions of very high values of P_r if such an extrapolation is based on hydrogen and helium. Nelson and Obert (88) noted,

---

* The term *pseudocritical* has an entirely different meaning here from that in Chap. 7, where pseudocritical mixture constants are discussed.

however, that P-V-T data on air, carbon dioxide, and nitrogen correlated reasonably well with helium and hydrogen data where pseudocritical constants were employed for the latter two materials.

Example 3-1.   The critical temperature of ethyl alcohol is 243.2°C, and the critical pressure is 63.0 atm (Appendix A).

(a) Estimate the molal volume of ethyl alcohol vapor at 154°C and 6.8 atm, and compare this value with the experimental value of 4,780 cm³/g mole.

(b) A reactor has a volume of 1,213 liters.   It must hold 45,400 g of alcohol vapor at 227°C.   What will be the pressure inside the reactor?

Solution

(a) $T_r = (154 + 273)/(243 + 273) = {}^{427}\!/_{516} = 0.827$ $P_r = 6.8/63.0 = 0.108$

From Fig. 3-2

$$Z = 0.920$$
$$V = ZRT/P = (0.920)(82.07)(427)/6.8 = 4,740 \text{ cm}^3/\text{g mole}$$

(b)
$$V = (1,213)(1,000)(46.1)/45,400 = 12,400 \text{ cm}^3/\text{g mole}$$
$$T_r = (227 + 273)/(243 + 273) = {}^{500}\!/_{516} = 0.969$$
$$V_{r_i} = V/(RT_c/P_c) = (12,400)(63.0)/(82.06)(516) = 1.85$$

From Fig. 3-2

$$Z = 0.820 \qquad P_r = 0.430$$
$$\therefore P = (0.430)(63.0) = (0.82)(82.06)(500)/12,400 = 27.1 \text{ atm}$$

The experimental value is 27.2 atm.

3-7   Three-parameter Correlations

Several suggested techniques employ a third parameter to improve the accuracy of the two-parameter correlation of Z as illustrated in Figs. 3-2 to 3-4.   One might state that Eq. (3-9) is used with the Z_c and β factors combined into a single term.

Critical Compressibility-factor Correlation.   Meissner and Sefarian (80) first suggested the correlation based on

$$Z = f(T_r, P_r, Z_c) \tag{3-12}$$

and Lydersen, Greenkorn, and Hougen (70) have developed this in considerable detail.   A complete tabulation of Z as a function of P_r and T_r for values of Z_c between 0.23 and 0.29 is given in Appendix B.   This range of Z_c encompasses most compounds of interest.   Both the liquid and gas ranges are covered.   If values of Z_c are not known, they may be calculated from critical properties or estimated by methods discussed in Sec. 2-5.

Hamrin and Thodos (46) have shown that for He, Ne, A, Kr, and Xe the reduced density is a single-valued function of T_r and P_r, if comparisons are made for those materials having the same Z_c.   Also, Hobson and Weber (54) have correlated Z for saturated vapors by $Z = f(P_{vp_r}, Z_c)$ with good results.

Acentric-factor Correlation. Pitzer (94, 96, 97) chose a third parameter, which is believed to be a measure of the deviation of the intermolecular potential from that of a simple fluid (i.e., a molecule with a spherical shape and a sixth-power attractive force relation). For nonspherical molecules the attractive (or repulsive) forces between various portions of molecule pairs cannot be represented by a single attractive force between molecular centers. To account for these noncentralized forces, the term *acentric factor* was coined. The convenient, but empirical, method chosen to distinguish quantitatively between simple and non-simple molecules was a comparison of reduced vapor pressures at a common reduced temperature. For *simple* fluids, represented by A, Kr, Xe, and CH_4, the value of P_{vp_r} at $T_r = 0.7$ is almost exactly 0.1. Thus the simple fluid deviation is measured by ω, where,

$$\omega \equiv -1.000 - \log P_{vp_r} \qquad \text{at } T_r = 0.7 \qquad (3\text{-}13)$$

Thus $\omega \cong 0$ for simple fluids, and for all other nonpolar substances

$$Z = f(T_r, P_r, \omega) \qquad (3\text{-}14)$$

A convenient way to express Eq. (3-14) is

$$Z = Z^0 + \omega Z^1 \qquad (3\text{-}15)$$

where Z^0, Z^1 are now functions only of T_r and P_r; Z^0 is then the compressibility factor for a simple fluid. Pitzer and Curl's (96) and Edmister's (30) graphs are reproduced as Figs. 3-5 and 3-6. Satter and Campbell (116) have extended these plots to somewhat higher pressures.

Values of ω may be estimated as described in Sec. 2-7 or calculated from vapor-pressure data with the defining equation (3-13). A similar method using the Riedel factor (Sec. 2-8) has been suggested (102, 103).

Discussion. Hooper and Joffe (56) calculated compressibilities using the critical compressibility and acentric-factor correlations and compared the results with experimental data. Neither method is consistently better except for polar compounds, for which the acentric-factor method yielded less accurate results. Hooper and Joffe state that the acentric-factor method yields somewhat more accurate results for nonpolar materials if the grand average of all deviations is considered. However, examination of their tables shows so many exceptions that it may be concluded that both predict compressibility factors of the same order of accuracy, i.e., within 2 to 3 per cent.

Other Corresponding-state Correlations. Rowlinson (111), Havliček (49), Bloomer and Peck (14), and Su (120) have also proposed correlations based upon the corresponding-state concept. Rowlinson's method

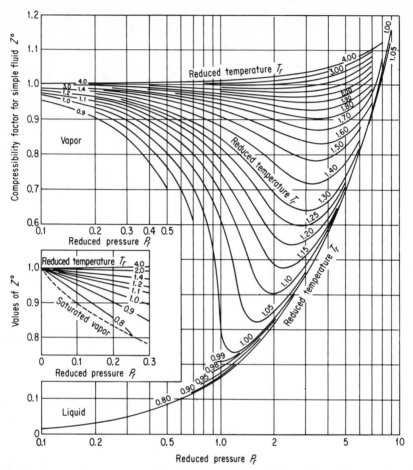

FIG. 3-5. Generalized compressibility factor for simple fluid. [*W. C. Edmister, Petrol. Refiner*, **37**(4):173 (1958).]

is similar to the acentric-factor method; Bloomer and Peck propose a three-parameter correlation in which the third parameter is the slope of an isometric taken at a specially defined critical volume, $(RT_c)(0.29)/P_c$. This parameter is, however, related to Z_c, and the method becomes a variation of the other three-parameter methods discussed earlier. Boas (15) combined the corresponding-state concept with a truncated form of the virial equation [Eq. (3-22)] and calculated Z values referenced to some material whose P-V-T properties were well known. Good accuracy was claimed.

Example 3-2. Estimate the specific volume of 1-butene at 480°F and 600 psia. Compare with the experimental value of 13.8 ft³/lb mole (125). The critical properties are $T_c = 419.6°K$, $P_c = 39.7$ atm (Appendix A).

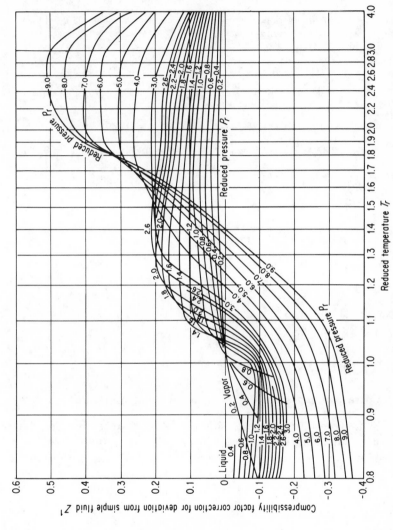

Fig. 3-6. Generalized compressibility-factor correction for deviation from simple fluid. [W. C. Edmister, Petrol. Refiner, **37**(4):173 (1958).]

Solution. The reduced conditions are

$$T = (480 + 460)/1.8 = 522.1°K$$
$$T_r = 522.1/419.6 = 1.24$$
$$P_r = (600)/(14.7)(39.7) = 1.03$$

For the sake of illustration, assume that no values are available to obtain Z_c or ω directly; they are then estimated as shown in Secs. 2-5 and 2-9, respectively. Z_c from Eq. (2-24) and Table 2-6

$$Z_c = 0.293 - (CH_3{-}) - 2({-}CH_2{-}) - ({-}\overset{|}{\underset{|}{C}}H) - (C{=}C)$$

$$= 0.293 - 0.0046 - 2(0.0046) - (-0.0035) - (0.0133)$$
$$= 0.269 \text{ (exp. value} = 0.277)$$

From Eq. (2-28), with $T_b = 267°K$, $\theta = 267/419.6 = 0.636$,

$$\omega = \tfrac{3}{7}[0.636/(1 - 0.636)] \log_{10} 39.7 - 1.00 = 0.196 \text{ (exp. value} = 0.203)$$

Critical Compressibility-factor Method. From Appendix B, at $T_r = 1.24$, $P_r = 1.03$, $Z_c = 0.269$,

$$Z = 0.815$$

Thus

$$V = (0.815)(480 + 460)(10.71)/600 = 13.7 \text{ ft}^3/\text{lb mole}$$
$$\text{Error} = [(13.7 - 13.8)/13.8] \times 100 = -0.7\%$$

Acentric-factor Method. From Figs. 3-5 and 3-6, at $T_r = 1.24$, $P_r = 1.03$,

$$Z^0 = 0.805 \quad \text{and} \quad Z^1 = 0.07$$

∴ from Eq. (3-15),

$$Z = 0.805 + (0.196)(0.07) = 0.819$$
$$V = (0.819)(480 + 460)(10.71)/600 = 13.8 \text{ ft}^3/\text{lb mole}$$
$$\text{Error} = [(13.8 - 13.8)/13.8] \times 100 = 0\%$$

3-8 Corresponding-state Correlations for Polar Molecules

Since there are insufficient data to delineate directly the effect of quadrupole moments and polarizability, and since those molecules exhibiting quantum corrections are nonpolar, Eqs. (3-4) and (3-7) reduce to (32, 44, 87)

$$\phi_2(Z, V/\sigma^3, kT/\epsilon_0, \mu^2/\epsilon_0\sigma^3, \beta) = 0 \tag{3-16}$$

and

$$\phi_3(Z, P_r, Z_c, T_r, \mu^2/kT_cV_c, \beta) = 0 \tag{3-17}$$

To write such functional equations in a usable form, they may be expanded as

$$Z = f_1(T_r, P_r) + K_2 f_2(T_r, P_r) + K_3 f_3(T_r, P_r) \tag{3-18}$$

Here $f_1(\ )$ is the corresponding-state function for simple fluids and may be considered to be the Z^0 function plotted in Fig. 3-5. K_2 depends upon shape and K_3 on polarity. $f_2(\ )$ and $f_3(\ )$ are functions only of reduced temperature and pressure.   Eubank and Smith (32) took K_2 to be the acentric factor ω and $f_2(\ )$ to be Z^1 in Fig. 3-6.   On this basis, Eq. (3-18) reduces to the acentric-factor correlation for nonpolar molecules ($K_3 = 0$).   Hall and Ibele (44) have grouped K_2 and K_3 into a single function but retain $f_1(\ )$ as about equal to Z^0.   Eubank and Smith's correlation appears to be the more accurate, and further discussion will be limited to this case.

Rewriting Eq. (3-18),

$$Z = Z^0 + \omega Z^1 + \eta Z^{11} \qquad (3\text{-}19)$$

where Z^0 and Z^1 are compressibility factors for the *hydrocarbon homomorph** *at the reduced temperature and pressure of the homomorph.* ω is the acentric factor of the homomorph. Z^{11} is the polar correction to Z and is evaluated from Fig. 3-7 at the reduced conditions for the polar compound.

The factor η might be expected to be related to the dimensionless dipole moment μ_r ($\mu^2/\epsilon_0\sigma^3$ or μ^2/kT_cV_c), but molecules with the same T_r, P_r, ω, and μ_r still show deviations in Z.   Apparently the position of the dipole is also important, and if buried in the molecule, it has a different effect from that if terminal.   The data are not sufficient to delineate precisely this "buriedness" effect but, approximately,

$$\eta = c(\mu_r)^{5/6} \qquad (3\text{-}20)$$

where $c = 1.0$ for alcohols (only normal alcohols tested)

~ 0.1 for methyl fluorides and ammonia

~ 0.7 for ketones and 0.3 for ethers

For compounds other than normal alcohols, ketones, ethers, and methyl fluorides, the correct choice of c is presently uncertain and the correlation should not be used.

The calculation of the value of μ_r is not easy.   Eubank and Smith

---

* When the polar compound is an alcohol, ketone, or ether, the hydrocarbon homomorph has the same structure except that the oxygen is replaced by a CH_3 or CH_2. The homomorph of ethanol is propane.   Difficulties in choosing homomorphs for most inorganic materials exclude inorganic compounds from this correlation.

FIG. 3-7. The compressibility-factor polar correction function $Z^{11}(P_r,T_r)$. [*P. T. Eubank and J. M. Smith, AIChE J.,* **8**:117 (1962).]

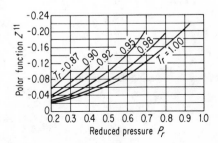

used $\mu_r = \mu^2/\epsilon_0\sigma^3$, where ϵ_0 and σ^3 must be considered as force constants for a Stockmayer (see Sec. 3-13) and not a Lennard-Jones potential, as discussed earlier. Hirschfelder, Curtiss, and Bird (53) clearly illustrate how ϵ_0 and σ are determined if the second virial coefficient B is known.* If a value of B is not available, Eubank and Smith suggest that it be estimated from the Berthelot virial equation [Eq. (3-21)] if the temperature exceeds 420°K.

$$B(T) = \tfrac{9}{128}(RT_c/P_c)(1 - 6/T_r^2) \qquad (3\text{-}21)$$

Values of some Stockmayer potentials are given in Table 3-1. η is positive and ranges from about 0.2 for ethers to around 2 for some alcohols; Z^{11} is negative and may range as low as -0.25 near the critical point, but in most cases it is between 0 and -0.1. The polar correction decreases the calculated compressibility and improves the correlation for polar gases. It is, however, somewhat difficult to use, and for rough approximations or for only slightly polar molecules, it may be neglected.

Example 3-3. Estimate the compressibility factor for methyl alcohol at 214°C and 39.25 atm. Use the Stockmayer potentials of $\epsilon_0/k = 630°K$, $\sigma = 2.40$ A as determined from second virial coefficient data. The dipole moment is 1.70 debyes. Compare with the experimental compressibility factor of 0.725.

    Solution. $\mu = 1.70$ debyes $= 1.70 \times 10^{-18}$ (dyne-cm⁴)$^{\frac{1}{2}}$. $\epsilon_0 = 630k = (630)(1.38 \times 10^{-16})$ dyne-cm.†

Thus $\mu_r = \mu^2/\epsilon_0\sigma^3 = (1.70 \times 10^{-18})^2/[(417)(1.38 \times 10^{-16})(3.69)^3(10^{-8})^3]$
                      $= 1.00$

For methyl alcohol, $T_c = 513.2°K$, $P_c = 78.5$ atm, so

$$T_r = (214 + 273)/513.2 = 0.949$$
$$P_r = 39.25/78.5 = 0.50$$

From Fig. 3-7 $Z^{11} = -0.10$
Also $\eta = c(\mu_r)^{\frac{5}{6}} = (1.0)(2.40)^{\frac{5}{6}} = 2.09$

    To obtain Z^0 and Z^1, the hydrocarbon homomorph must be used. In this case ethane is the homomorph.
    For ethane, $T_c = 305.4°K$, $P_c = 48.2$ atm, $\omega = 0.105$, $T_r = (214 + 273)/305.4 = 1.59$, $P_r = 39.25/48.2 = 0.814$.
    From Figs. 3-5 and 3-6, $Z^0 = 0.941$, $Z^1 = 0.075$.
    From Eq. (3-19)

$$Z = 0.941 + (0.105)(0.075) + (1.00)(-0.10)$$
$$Z = (0.941) + (0.105)(0.075) + (2.09)(-0.10) = 0.740$$
$$\text{Error} = [(0.740 - 0.725)/0.725] \times 100 = +2.1\%$$

    It is interesting to note that the Nelson-Obert chart (Fig. 3-3) gives $Z = 0.76$.

---

* The second virial coefficient B is discussed in Sec. 3-10.
† k = Boltzmann's constant = 1.38×10^{-16} erg/°K = 1.38×10^{-16} dyne-cm/°K.

3-9   Recommendations for Estimating Compressibility Factors by Corresponding-state Methods

Nonpolar Gases. Good results may be obtained by the use of Figs. 3-2 to 3-4; more accurate results are possible with either the critical compressibility or acentric-factor correlation, i.e., Appendix B, or by Eq. (3-15) with Figs. 3-5 and 3-6, respectively. The latter two methods usually give results within 3 per cent of experimental values. For the light gases, H_2, He, Ne, the reduced parameters are to be determined from Eq. (3-11).

Polar Gases. Either Figs. 3-2 to 3-4 or Appendix B are often satisfactory. The best results, albeit the most difficult to calculate, are obtained from Eq. (3-19) with Fig. 3-7. Errors for polar gases are difficult to predict; usually less than 5 to 10 per cent are to be expected.

3-10   Virial Equations of State

An expansion of the compressibility factor in inverse powers of specific volume is called a *virial equation of state,*

$$Z = 1 + B(T)/V + C(T)/V^2 + D(T)/V^3 + \cdots \qquad (3\text{-}22)$$

The virial coefficients, of which B is the second, C the third, and so on, are functions only of temperature for a pure material. In addition, these virial coefficients are calculable from first principles after establishing an intermolecular energy-distance relation. The actual calculation of the coefficients is discussed in Secs. 3-11 and 3-12 for nonpolar molecules and in Sec. 3-13 for polar molecules.

It is instructive to inquire about the relative magnitude of each of the terms in the virial expansion. For example, at a given temperature, $B, C, \ldots$ are fixed, and if the system pressure is lowered so as to increase V, then, of course, $Z \to 1$ as $V \to \infty$ or $P \to 0$. It is obvious that the B term is larger than the C term at low pressures, the C term is important at somewhat higher pressures, etc. Often this allows a truncation of the series after the B term or, at somewhat higher pressures, after the C term. Hirschfelder, Curtiss, and Bird (53) present a simple table to illustrate the relative magnitude of the terms for nitrogen at 0°C. In this case, the third virial term does not become important except at very high pressures.

Pressure, atm	B/V	C/V^2
1	−0.0005	+0.000003
10	−0.005	+0.0003
100	−0.05	+0.03

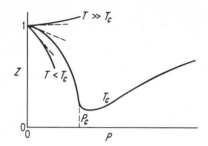

FIG. 3-8. Geometrical interpretation of the second virial coefficient B. Tangents have slopes $= B/RT$ as $P \to 0$.

Another way to visualize Eq. (3-22) is to modify it by the use of Eq. (3-2) to eliminate V; that is,

$$Z = 1 + (BP/RT)(1/Z) + [CP^2/(RT)^2](1/Z)^2$$
$$+ [DP^3/(RT)^3](1/Z)^3 + \cdots \quad (3\text{-}23)$$

From Eq. (3-22),

$$1/Z = 1 - B/V + (B^2 - C)/V^2 - (B^3 - 2BC + D)/V^3 + \cdots \quad (3\text{-}24)$$

Substituting Eq. (3-24) into (3-23) and retaining terms no higher than V^{-3},

$$Z = 1 + BP/RT + (C - B^2)P^2/(RT)^2$$
$$+ (D - 3BC + 2B^3)P^3/(RT)^3 + \cdots \quad (3\text{-}25)$$

At low pressures where the P^2, P^3, . . . terms are small compared with BP/RT, it is easy to see from Fig. 3-8 that the slope of an isotherm on the graph of Z versus P approaches B/RT. Except at very high temperatures the slope of the isotherm is negative at low pressures, and B is a negative quantity. At any temperature exceeding the so-called "Boyle temperature," slopes are positive. At the Boyle temperature where $(dZ/dP)_{p \to 0} = 0$, then $B = 0$. The relationship between B and T is considered later when specific potential functions are introduced.

A geometrical interpretation of the third virial coefficient is not so obvious. If, however, the term $Z_p \equiv Z - P(\partial Z/\partial P)_T$ is evaluated,*

$$Z_p = Z - P(\partial Z/\partial P)_T = 1 - (C - B^2)[P^2/(RT)^2] \quad (3\text{-}26)$$

higher terms being neglected. If a tangent line to an isotherm on a Z-P plot is extrapolated to the $P = 0$ axis, the ordinate is Z_p. If Z_p is less than unity, i.e., if the tangent intersects below $Z = 1.0$, then $C - B^2 > 0$, or $C > 0$. This is shown in Fig. 3-9 for isotherm T_a at point a. The difference $1 - A'$ is $(C - B^2)P^2/(RT)^2$, and the magnitude is indicative of the relative importance of C and B^2. Similar reasoning may be

---

* The function Z_p is discussed in detail in Sec. 6-9.

applied for isotherm T_b at point b. In this case $1 - B'$ is negative and $C - B^2 < 0$. Thus $C < B^2$; if the tangent yields a value of $Z_p = 1.0$, then $C = B^2$ and Eq. (3-25) may be satisfactorily truncated after the first-power P term. Still, even in this latter case $C > 0$. If C were zero then,

$$Z_p = 1 + P^2B^2/(RT)^2 = 1 + (Z - 1)^2 \qquad C(T) = 0$$

or $Z_p - 1 > 0$. Thus the temperature must be such as to have the tangent line intersect at $Z > 1.0$ (for example, point C' in Fig. 3-9). Finally, it can be noted in this simple analysis that for any isotherm C, B, and T are constants so that $1 - Z_p = C'P^2$, where

$$C' = (C - B^2)/(RT)^2 = \text{const.}$$

If $C' > 0$, then $1 - Z_p$ will always be positive and the tangent to the Z-P isotherm intersects at some point such as A' in Fig. 3-9. Likewise, if $C' < 0$, $1 - Z_p$ is negative and intersections such as B' or C' in Fig. 3-9 are found. Note that for a given temperature the $1 - Z_p$ values cannot be positive at one pressure and negative at another. Reference to Fig. 3-3 shows, however, that this rule is not obeyed in all cases. For example, at $T_r = 1.05$, $1 - Z_p*$ is negative at low pressures (that is, $C' < 0$) and positive at high pressures (that is, $C' > 0$). The reason for this phenomenon is that higher terms in the virial expansion were not considered. Thus, still examining the $T_r = 1.05$ isotherm in Fig. 3-3, the curve is essentially a straight line at low pressure and the second virial coefficient (B/RT) yields the slope of the line; at somewhat higher pressures the third virial term begins to be important, and the isotherm begins to curve downward. At still higher pressures there begins a pronounced change in curvature as higher virial terms become important.

Usually Eq. (3-25) may be truncated after the second virial term for

---

* Here Z_p may be expressed as $Z - P_r(\partial Z/\partial P_r)_{T_r}$, which is identical to the definition given before.

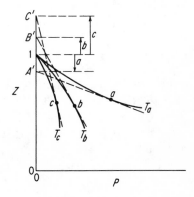

FIG. 3-9. Generalized interpretation of the third virial coefficient C. The arrows are the values of $(P/RT)^2(C - B^2)$ for the points a, b, c.

pressures less than half the critical; if the third virial term is employed, but no higher terms, then the equation is satisfactory up in the region of the critical pressure if $T > T_c$. For higher pressures, the fourth and higher virial terms are necessary. These conclusions are important, for, as shown in Secs. 3-11 and 3-12, only the second virial coefficient can be estimated with any accuracy. If the virial expression, truncated after the third virial term, were applicable at the critical point, then it may be shown (106) that, with Eqs. (2-1),

$$Z_c = \tfrac{1}{3}$$
$$B(T_c) = V_c \qquad\qquad (3\text{-}27)$$
$$C(T_c) = \tfrac{1}{3}(V_c)^2$$

While not exact, these simple relations are not unreasonable.

3-11 Potential Functions for Nonpolar Molecules

Nonpolar molecules, or, as they are sometimes called, *angle-independent molecules*, do not possess any permanent charge distributions. To calculate virial coefficients for such molecules, it is first necessary to choose a suitable potential function, since it is from this function that the coefficients are calculated. Many potential functions are described in the literature. The excellent reference text of Hirschfelder, Curtiss, and Bird (53) covers the development of the more common ones, and a succinct summary and discussion are given by Rowlinson (107). In the latter reference it is pointed out that all potential functions must take into account the fact that molecules are attracted to one another at large separations but repel at small separations. It is usual, therefore, to make the attractive and repulsive force (or energy) terms additive to yield an equilibrium distance where both forces are essentially balanced and the system energy is minimized. It is also assumed that the potential energy of a large group of molecules is additive for all possible pairs. Repulsive forces result from overlapping electron clouds of the molecular pair, and though theoretically the quantitative expression is exponential, mathematical expediency has led to a general acceptance of the potential being represented as Ar^{-n}.

The predominant attractive force results from the oscillatory nature of the orbital electrons in that they may induce transient dipoles and lead to what is generally termed *London dispersion forces*. The result of such forces is to cause the molecules to attract in proportion to the inverse sixth power of the distance of separation (higher terms being neglected). These forces are present even in those cases where the molecules are spherically symmetrical and where classical electrostatics would predict no interaction.

Of all the potential functions suggested, the simplest and most widely used is of the bireciprocal form

$$\varphi(r) = Ar^{-n} - Br^{-m} \tag{3-28}$$

The first term accounts for the repulsive potential energy and the second for the attractive contribution. The equation has two constants and has spherical symmetry. If the choice of n and m is 12 and 6, one obtains the 12-6 Lennard-Jones potential given as Eq. (3-5) or with Eq. (3-6),

$$\varphi(r) = 4\epsilon_0[(\sigma/r)^{12} - (\sigma/r)^6] \tag{3-29}$$

This is a reasonable approximation for the inert gases and simple non-polar molecules, but it is often used also for other molecular types. The greatest motivation for using the Lennard-Jones potential is that the parameters ϵ_0 and σ are known or can be estimated for many molecules. Other, perhaps more suitable potentials such as those mentioned below still contain two (or more) constants similar to the ϵ_0, σ constants in Eq. (3-29); to get these, good P-V-T data or gas-transport properties must be available. The requirement of data defeats the value of the potential as an estimating relation, but these studies do provide an insight into the behavior and properties of molecules.

Since the publication of the reference text of Hirschfelder, Curtiss, and Bird (53), in which, as noted above, most other useful potential functions are summarized, attention has been given primarily to the Morse exponential function (63) or to a modified form of Eq. (3-29), in which the repulsive-term exponent is 28 and the attractive-term exponent 7 (45). The 28-7 potential was found to be superior to the 12-6 form, especially for quasi-spherical molecules such as CCl_4, SF_6, P_4, etc. However, no general way has been suggested to predict a priori the values of ϵ_0 and σ for this potential. Recently, Sherwood and Prausnitz (118a) have compared the Kihara, exponential-6, and square-well potentials to determine the third virial coefficient.

3-12   Virial Coefficients from the Lennard-Jones 12-6 Potential

Virial coefficients in Eq. (3-22) may be calculated once the potential function is chosen. For a Lennard-Jones potential as in Eq. (3-29), it may be shown, for example, that the second virial $B(T)$ is (53)

$$B(T) = 2\pi N_0 \int_0^\infty (1 - e^{-\phi(r)/kT})r^2 \, dr$$

$$= \tfrac{2}{3}\pi N_0 \sigma^3 \sum_{j=0}^\infty b^{(j)}(T^*)^{-(2j+1)/4} \tag{3-30}$$

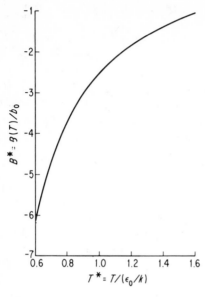

FIG. 3-10. Lennard-Jones second virial coefficient, low-temperature range.

where T^* is a dimensionless temperature and is defined as

$$T^* = T/(\epsilon_0/k) = kT/\epsilon_0 \tag{3-31}$$

and $b^{(j)}$ is given as

$$b^{(j)} = -(2^{(j+\frac{1}{2})}/4j!)\ \Gamma(2j - 1)/4 \tag{3-32}$$

Defining the "hard-sphere" volume as

$$b_0 = \tfrac{2}{3}\pi N_0 \sigma^3 \tag{3-33}$$

then
$$B(T) = f(T^*, b_0) \tag{3-34}$$

or
$$B^*(T) = B(T)/b_0 = f(T^*). \tag{3-35}$$

Equation (3-35) is shown plotted in Figs. 3-10 and 3-11. Hirschfelder, Curtiss, and Bird (53) have also calculated third virial coefficients by a difficult numerical-integration technique. These are shown in Fig. 3-12, where

$$C^* = C/b_0^2 = f(T^*) = f[T/(\epsilon_0/k)] \tag{3-36}$$

Others have expressed the third virial in explicit forms (11, 60, 112), and Rowlinson has examined the limits at very high and low temperatures (108). Few experimental data are available to compare theory with experiment, and in the few comparisons made, good agreement is often not obtained (see Example 3-4).

When higher virials are considered, the mathematical difficulty has prevented any exact solutions except for extremely simple potentials such as for rigid spheres (109) where $D^* = D(T)/b_0^3$ (rigid sphere) $= 0.287$. However, Boys and Shavitt (19) have obtained approximate solutions

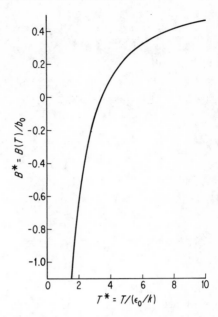

FIG. 3-11. Lennard-Jones second virial coefficient, high-temperature range.

for the Lennard-Jones potential, and Rowlinson has studied the high and low temperature limits (109). These results are shown in Fig. 3-13 but are to be treated only as approximate values.

In summary, therefore, the Lennard-Jones potential leads to values of B^*, C^*, and D^* as shown in Figs. 3-10 to 3-13. At values of T^* of

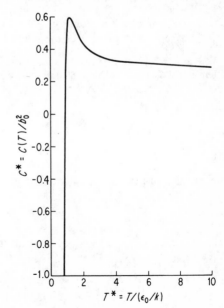

FIG. 3-12. Lennard-Jones third virial coefficient.

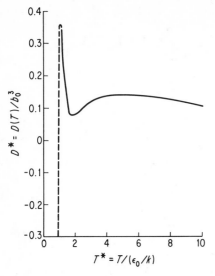

FIG. 3-13. Lennard-Jones fourth virial coefficient.

about 2 or less (note that, since ϵ_0/k is about $0.75T_c$, then $T^* \sim 1.33$ is about equivalent to the critical temperature) the virial coefficients become very sensitive to T^*. The value of $B^* = f(T^*)$ in Figs. 3-10 and 3-11 is relatively insensitive to the choice of potential, but C^* and especially D^* are very sensitive (53). Example 3-4 illustrates how virial coefficients and compressibility factors may be calculated from this potential. The results using a virial approach are less accurate than those obtained from the corresponding-state methods but because of their theoretical basis hold exciting promise for further development.

Values of ϵ_0/k and σ may be estimated by methods described in Sec. 2-10; Appendix G summarizes the best available values from the literature.

Example 3-4. Estimate the virial coefficients and compressibility factors for carbon tetrafluoride at 0°C and 50 and 100 atm. Compare with the experimental values of Douslin (28, 29) as follows:

$$T = 0°C \qquad\qquad B = -111.00 \text{ cm}^3/\text{(g mole)}$$
$$C = 7,100 \text{ cm}^6/\text{(g mole)}^2$$
$$D = 5,000 \text{ cm}^9/\text{(g mole)}^3$$
$$Z = 0.725 \quad \text{at 50 atm}$$
$$= 0.563 \quad \text{at 100 atm}$$

The Lennard-Jones parameters tabulated in Appendix G are $\epsilon_0/k = 134.0°$K, $\sigma = 4.662$ A, $b_0 = 127.9$ cm^3/g mole.
Solution. At 0°C, $T^* = 273.2/134.0 = 2.04$. From Fig. 3-11,

$$B^* = -0.60$$
$$B = B^*b_0 = (-0.60)(127.9) = -76.7 \text{ cm}^3/\text{g mole}$$

From Fig. 3-12,

$$C^* = 0.43$$
$$C = C^*b_0{}^2 = (0.43)(127.9)^2 = 7,030 \text{ cm}^6/\text{(g mole)}^2$$

From Fig. 3-13,

$$D^* = 0.080$$
$$D = D^*b_0{}^3 = (0.080)(127.9)^3 = 167,000 \ cm^9/(g \ mole)^3$$

To determine Z, use Eq. (3-25). At 50 atm and 0°C, $P/RT = 50/(82.06)(273.2) = 2.23 \times 10^{-3}$ g mole/cm^3, whence

$$Z = 1 + (2.23)(10^{-3})(-76.7) + [7,030 - (-76.7)^2][(2.23)(10^{-3})]^2$$
$$+ [167,000 - 3(-76.7)(7,030) + 2(-76.7)^3][(2.23)(10^{-3})]^3$$
$$= 1 - 0.171 + 0.006 - 0.037 = 0.80$$

At 100 atm, the P/RT is twice as large,

$$Z = 1 - 2(0.171) + 4(0.006) - 8(0.037) = 0.36$$

The calculated and experimental values of B and C are in fair agreement; the estimation of D is very poor, but this does not affect the estimation of Z appreciably. The calculated value of Z at 50 atm is in reasonable agreement with the experimental value; the value at 100 atm is in poor agreement. Higher terms are required to raise the calculated value of Z, since at this pressure and temperature the Z-P curve is at a minimum (28). For comparison, the Z values from Fig. 3-3 are 0.76 and 0.55. In this case, the value at 100 atm is estimated more accurately than at 50 atm.

3-13 Polar Molecules and the Stockmayer Potential

Forces between polar molecules, as between nonpolar molecules, consist of electron-cloud repulsion and London dispersion forces of attraction. In addition, polarity is manifested by a permanent unsymmetrical charge distribution which gives rise to an electrostatic contribution to the potential energy. The mathematics to describe such interactions is complex (53, 107). Usually the potential-energy contribution is expressed as an infinite series in inverse powers of the separation distance between two points, one in each molecule. Such a series is termed a *multipole expansion*. The coefficients of the various inverse distance terms are products of two functions; one describes the relative orientation of the molecules, and the other describes the charge distribution (107). The description of the charge distribution is given in terms called *multipoles* and may involve many or few terms to convey more or less information about the charge distribution. A simple description results in specifying only the net charge; a more complete description would involve a vector sum of each charge multiplied by a moment arm from some arbitrary center, i.e., a dipole moment. Other terms are higher-ordered tensors and are called *quadrapole, octapole,* . . . interactions. Thus the formal problem of setting up potential-energy terms describing permanent charge distributions for polar molecular pairs is extremely complex, and simplifications are necessary to obtain practical results.

The most commonly used polar potential is the Stockmayer potential. This assumes that the only significant charge distribution results from

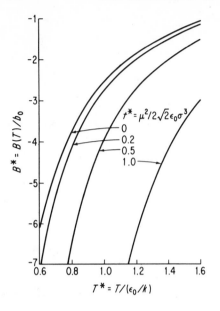

FIG. 3-14. Stockmayer second virial coefficient, low-temperature range.

dipole-dipole interactions and that it may be expressed in a convenient manner by

$$\varphi(r) = 4\epsilon_0[(\sigma/r)^{12} - (\sigma/r)^6 - (\mu^2/r^3)g(\Theta)] \qquad (3\text{-}37)$$

Here ϵ_0 and σ are the Stockmayer-potential parameters and are not numerically equal to the Lennard-Jones potentials. The first bracketed term is similar in form to the Lennard-Jones 12-6 potential in that it accounts for repulsive and dispersive attraction energies; the third term involves the molecular dipole moment and a function of the angles between molecules. Hirschfelder, Curtiss, and Bird (53) and Rowlinson (105) describe how this potential function may be used to obtain the second and third virial coefficients from the Stockmayer potential,

$$B^* = B(T)/b_0 = f_1(T^*,t^*) \qquad (3\text{-}38)$$
$$C^* = C(T)/b_0^2 = f_2(T^*,t^*) \qquad (3\text{-}39)$$

Here $T^* = T/(\epsilon_0/k)$, $b_0 = \tfrac{2}{3}\pi N_0\sigma^3$, and $t^* = \mu^2/2\sqrt{2}\,\epsilon_0\sigma^3$, where ϵ_0 and σ are Stockmayer-potential parameters and μ the dipole moment. Equations (3-38) and (3-39) are plotted in Figs. 3-14 to 3-16. The curves at $t^* = 0$ correspond to the usual Lennard-Jones curves (Figs. 3-10 to 3-12). The B^* curves are displaced downward for polar materials; so the second virial is more negative, and lower compressibility factors result. The greater ease of compressing polar molecules comes from the multipole attraction described earlier. The C^* curves are displaced above those for nonpolar molecules except, perhaps, at T^* less than unity (105). Estimation of second and third virial coefficients from Figs. 3-14 and 3-15

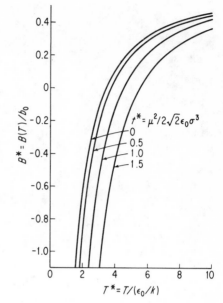

Fig. 3-15. Stockmayer second virial coefficient, high-temperature range.

is illustrated in Example 3-5. Limited comparison of experimental values of B and C for moderately polar gases with calculated values indicates that Eq. (3-37) is a good approximation. Water is an exception at pressures sufficiently high so that the third virial is important; there is poor agreement between calculated and experimental values of C for water vapor. This disagreement is believed to result from the fact that higher multipole terms, e.g., the dipole-quadrapole contribution, were not considered.

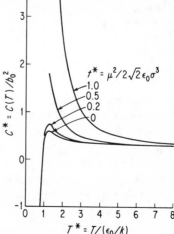

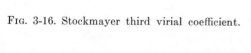

Fig. 3-16. Stockmayer third virial coefficient.

TABLE 3-1. STOCKMAYER-POTENTIAL PARAMETERS*

	Dipole moment μ, debyes	σ, A	ϵ_0/k, °K	b_0, cm^3/g mole	t^*	δ_{max}
H_2O	1.85	2.52	775	20.2	0.7	1.0
NH_3	1.47	3.15	358	39.5	0.5	0.7
HCl	1.08	3.36	328	47.8	0.24	0.34
HBr	0.80	3.41	417	50.0	0.10	0.14
HI	0.42	4.13	313	88.9	0.20	0.029
SO_2	1.63	4.04	347	83.2	0.30	0.42
H_2S	0.92	3.49	343	53.6	0.15	0.21
$NOCl$	1.83	3.53	690	55.5	0.3	0.4
$CHCl_3$	1.013	5.31	355	189	0.05	0.07
CH_2Cl_2	1.57	4.52	483	117	0.14	0.2
CH_3Cl	1.87	3.94	414	77.2	0.35	0.5
CH_3Br	1.80	4.25	382	96.9	0.3	0.4
C_2H_5Cl	2.03	4.45	423	111	0.3	0.4
CH_3OH	1.70	3.69	417	63.4	0.35	0.5
C_2H_5OH	1.69	4.31	431	101	0.2	0.3
$n\text{-}C_3H_7OH$	1.69	4.71	495	132	0.14	0.2
$i\text{-}C_3H_7OH$	1.69	4.64	518	126	0.14	0.2
$(CH_3)_2O$	1.30	4.21	432	94.2	0.13	0.19
$(C_2H_5)_2O$	1.15	5.49	362	209	0.06	0.08
$(CH_3)_2CO$†	1.20	3.82	428	70.1	0.9	1.3
CH_3COOCH_3	1.72	5.04	418	162	0.14	0.2
$CH_3COOC_2H_5$	1.78	5.24	499	182	0.11	0.16
CH_3NO_2†	2.15	4.16	290	90.8	1.6	2.3

NOTES

$b_0 = \frac{2}{3}\pi N_0\sigma^3 = 1.2615\sigma^3$

$t^* = \mu^2/2\sqrt{2}\,\epsilon_0\sigma^3$

δ_{max} (required in Chap. 9) = $2^{1/2}t^*$

* L. Monchick and E. A. Mason, *J. Chem. Phys.*, **35**:1676 (1961).

† From Ref. 18a; Monchick and Mason show that $\sigma = 4.50$ A, $\epsilon_0/k = 549$°K, $t^* = 0.08$ for acetone.

Stockmayer-potential parameters are not known for most polar molecules. Tabulations of those available often differ considerably (18a, 53, 82, 110), and it is difficult to make a priori any best selection. For consistency in this book, the most extensive and recent tabulation given by Monchick and Mason (82) has been selected and reproduced as Table 3-1. These values were determined primarily from an analysis of viscosity data for polar materials, but it was shown that these values are applicable for determining second virial coefficients within the accuracy expected from this theory at the present time.

An approximate estimation technique to determine Stockmayer-potential parameters for nonhydrogen-bonded polar molecules is given as $(119a)$

$$\sigma = 0.785 V_c^{1/3} \qquad (3\text{-}40)$$
$$\epsilon_0/k = 0.897 T_c \qquad (3\text{-}41)$$

Errors of 5 to 20 per cent in the estimation of σ and ϵ_0/k may result, but this technique is the best available. For hydrogen-bonded materials, a rough approximate rule is $(119a)$

$$\sigma = 36.9 V_c^{1/3} Z_c^{2.75} \qquad (3\text{-}42)$$
$$\epsilon_0/k = 0.00331 T_c/Z_c^4 \qquad (3\text{-}43)$$

Other polar potential functions similar in form to Eq. (3-37) have been suggested; for example, Suh and Storvick (122a) have used the Kihara-core model, and Saxena and Joshi (117) suggest an 18-6-3 potential and furnish new ϵ_0/k and σ values as well as tables giving B^* as a function of T^* and t^*.

Example 3-5. Repeat Example 3-3, but use the Stockmayer potential to determine the virial coefficients.

Solution. From Table 3-1, $\epsilon_0/k = 417°K$, $\sigma = 3.69$ A, $b_0 = 63.4$ cm³/g mole. Thus,

$$T^* = (214 + 273)/417 = 1.17$$
$$\mu_r = 1.0$$

(as by the calculation procedure given in Example 3-3) and

$$t^* = \mu_r/2\sqrt{2} = \mu^2/2\sqrt{2}\,\epsilon_0\sigma^3 = 0.35$$

From Fig. 3-14,

$$B^* = -2.5 \qquad B = B^* b_0 = (-2.5)(63.4) = -159 \text{ cm}^3/\text{g mole}$$

From Fig. 3-16,

$$C^* = 1.2 \qquad C = C^* b_0^2 = (1.2)(63.4)^2 = 4{,}800 \text{ (cm}^3/\text{g mole)}^2$$

Thus, from Eq. (3-25),

$$Z = 1 + [(-159)(39.25)/(82.06)(487)]$$
$$+ \{[4{,}800 - (159)^2](39.25)^2/(82.06)^2(487)^2\}$$
$$= 1 - 0.16 - 0.02 = 0.82 \qquad Z_{exp} = 0.69$$
Error $= [(0.82 - 0.69)/0.69] \times 100 = +19\%$

3-14 General Comments on the Virial-equation Technique

Reference to Eq. (3-4) and the preceding sections will show that an effort has been made in the virial approach to account for all dimensionless groups except β, α/σ^3, and the quantum group $h/\sigma(m\epsilon_0)^{1/2}$, though no real correlations exist for higher multipole terms such as $Q^2/\epsilon_0\sigma^3$. The β, or shape, term, which accounts for nonsphericity, has been introduced into several potential functions (53), but the resulting forms are rather complex. Prausnitz has used the Kihara potential (61) in low-temperature fugacity studies (98) with good results. The polarizability group (α/σ^3), which takes into account an interaction between a permanent dipole and an induced dipole, was introduced by Buckingham and Pople (22) and discussed by Saxena and Joshi (117). The general form which results is $B^* = B(T)/b_0 = f(T^*,t^*,q^*)$, where

$$q^* \equiv \alpha/\sigma^3 \tag{3-44}$$

but no complete tables of the effect of q^* on B^* have been developed.

Other interesting papers dealing with the virial equation include the work of Epstein (31), who truncated Eq. (3-22) after the third virial and added a residual term which he expressed as a function of T and the critical constants. Gyorog and Obert (41a) generalized the virial coefficients for spherically symmetrical molecules, and David and Hamann (26) and Black (13) tabulate second virial coefficients as a function of temperature for various materials. Pitzer and Curl (95) represent the second virial coefficient in an expansion involving the acentric factor which is quite useful for nonpolar or slightly polar materials, i.e.,

$$B(T) = B^0 + \omega B^1 \tag{3-45}$$

where

$$B^0 P_c/RT_c = f^0(T_r) = 0.1445 - 0.330/T_r - 0.1385/T_r^2 - 0.0121/T_r^3 \tag{3-46}$$

$$B^1 P_c/RT_c = f^1(T_r) = 0.073 + 0.46/T_r - 0.50/T_r^2 - 0.097/T_r^3 \\ - 0.0073/T_r^8 \tag{3-47}$$

3-15 Recommendations for Use of the Virial Equation

For nonpolar molecules, use the Lennard-Jones potential, and determine B, C, and D from Figs. 3-10 to 3-13. Potential parameters ϵ_0/k and σ may be determined as described in Sec. 2-10. Alternatively, B may be determined directly with Eqs. (3-45) to (3-47) from the acentric factor and critical properties. Second virial coefficients may be estimated within ± 10 per cent in most cases, but large errors are to be expected in the determination of higher terms.

For polar molecules, the only well-developed potential is the Stockmayer potential. Obtain Stockmayer potentials from Table 3-1, and use Figs. 3-14 to 3-16. Errors will, in general, exceed those obtained for nonpolar materials.

For rapid estimation of P-V-T properties, the methods recommended in Sec. 3-9 are more accurate and convenient. In future work, however, the greatest advances will probably come in refining the theory of molecular interactions, with the result that virial coefficients may be predicted with considerable accuracy from the fundamental properties of the molecules involved. Even now the calculation of P-V-T properties of very-high-temperature gases is best handled by estimating virial coefficients from theory (2, 3, 68, 76, 77, 128). Compressibility-factor charts are available with ϵ_0/k and σ^3 replacing T_c and V_c (88), and properties of air have been calculated for extreme ranges of temperature and pressure from the virial equations (43, 50).

3-16 Equations of State

Equations of state are analytical formulations of the relationships among P, V, and T. The virial equation [(Eq. 3-22)] is, for example, an open-ended type of equation of state. Well over one hundred equations of state have been proposed, but only a few seem to be sufficiently accurate to be useful. A comprehensive bibliography of suggested equations is available (21), and a critical review of many of these was made by Joffe (58).

For engineering estimations of P-V-T properties, the generalized correlations based on the corresponding-state concept appear to be preferable. However, equations of state are convenient for storage of experimental P-V-T data, as interpolation formulae, and in describing P-V-T data when subsequent mathematical operations must be performed, especially for the calculation of fugacity, since the measurement of this property is almost never made but instead is calculated.

It is convenient to classify the more common equations by the number of arbitrary constants. However, this classification scheme is meaningless for reduced equations of state if all the constants are expressed in terms of critical properties, since if only T_c and P_c are used, then all are essentially two-constant equations. In some cases, however, a third, even a fourth, parameter is used to determine the constants. All reasonable equations of state must be cubic in volume to represent the P-V curves adequately in the critical region.

Two-constant Equations of State. There are four two-constant equations which have been widely used,

van der Waals:	$(P + a/V^2)(V - b) = RT$	(3-48)
Berthelot:	$(P + a/TV^2)(V - b) = RT$	(3-49)
Dieterici:	$(Pe^{a/VRT})(V - b) = RT$	(3-50)
Redlich-Kwong:	$\left[P + \dfrac{a}{T^{0.5}V(V + b)}\right](V - b) = RT$	(3-51)

The first three are discussed by Hirschfelder, Curtiss, and Bird (53), and the last is considered to be the best of the four by Gambill (36). Due to the fact that the first and second isothermal derivatives of pressure with respect to volume are zero at the critical point [Eq. (2-1)], it is

TABLE 3-2. RELATIONSHIP OF EQUATION-OF-STATE CONSTANTS TO
CRITICAL CONSTANTS

	van der Waals	Berthelot	Dieterici	Redlich and Kwong
P_c	$\dfrac{a}{27b^2}$	$\left(\dfrac{aR}{216b^3}\right)^{\frac{1}{2}}$	$\dfrac{a}{4e^2b^2}$	$\left[\left(\dfrac{0.0867}{b}\right)^5\left(\dfrac{a}{0.4278}\right)^2 R\right]^{\frac{1}{3}}$
T_c	$\dfrac{8a}{27bR}$	$\left(\dfrac{8a}{27bR}\right)^{\frac{1}{2}}$	$\dfrac{a}{4bR}$	$\left(\dfrac{a}{b}\dfrac{0.0867}{0.4278}\dfrac{1}{R}\right)^{\frac{2}{3}}$
V_c	$3b$	$3b$	$2b$	$3.847b$
Z_c	0.375	0.375	0.270	0.333
$B(T)$	$b - \dfrac{a}{RT}$	$b - \dfrac{a}{RT^2}$	$b - \dfrac{a}{RT}$	$b - \dfrac{a}{RT^{\frac{3}{2}}}$
$C(T)$	b^2	b^2	$b^2 - \dfrac{ab}{RT} + \dfrac{a^2}{2R^2T^2}$	$b^2 + \dfrac{ab}{RT^{\frac{3}{2}}}$

possible to relate the critical properties to the constants as in Table 3-2. Only Dieterici's equation gives a reasonable value of Z_c, and none predicts the second virial-coefficient curvature as would be obtained from theory by using the Lennard-Jones potential. Of the four relations, van der Waals' is probably the easiest to manipulate mathematically, but the Dieterici and Redlich and Kwong equations are more accurate. The latter is the best at high pressures, and its use is illustrated in Example 3-6.

Example 3-6. Estimate the specific volume of 1-butene at 480°F and 600 psia, using the Redlich-Kwong equation. Compare with the experimental value of 13.8 ft^3/lb mole (125).

Solution. The critical properties of 1-butene are $T_c = 419.6°K$, $P_c = 39.7$ atm (Appendix A). Upon converting the temperature and pressure of this example to comparable units, $T = 522.1°K$, $P = 40.8$ atm.

Redlich and Kwong (101) suggest, for the determination of compressibility factors, that Eq. (3-51) be arranged as

$$Z = 1/(1 - h) - (a^{*2}/b^*)h/(1 + h)$$
$$h = b^*P/Z$$
$$a^{*2} = a/R^2T^{2.5} = 0.4278T_c^{2.5}/P_cT^{2.5} \qquad \text{atm}^{-1}$$
$$b^* = b/RT = 0.0867T_c/P_cT \qquad \text{atm}^{-1}$$

Thus

$$a^{*2} = (0.4278)(419.6)^{2.5}/(39.7)(522.1)^{2.5} = 6.294 \times 10^{-3} \text{ atm}^{-1}$$
$$b^* = (0.0867)(419.6)/(39.7)(522.1) = 1.761 \times 10^{-3} \text{ atm}^{-1}$$
$$h = (1.761)(10^{-3})(40.8)/Z = 0.07185/Z$$
$$Z = Z/(Z - 0.07185) - [(6.294)(10^{-3})/(1.761)(10^{-3})](0.07185)/(Z + 0.07185)$$
$$\text{or} \qquad Z^3 = Z^2 - 0.1802Z + 0.0185$$
$$Z = 0.806$$
$$V = ZRT/P = (0.806)(10.71)(480 + 460)/600 = 13.51 \text{ ft}^3/\text{lb mole}$$
$$\text{Error} = [(13.51 - 13.8)/13.8] \times 100 = -2.1\%$$

To improve Eq. (3-51), Redlich and Dunlop (100) and Ackerman (1) have introduced additional terms and used the acentric factor as a third correlating parameter. As proposed by Ackerman, if Z_{RK} is the uncorrected compressibility factor calculated from the Redlich-Kwong equation,

$$Z = Z_{RK} + Z^* + \omega Z^{**} \qquad (3\text{-}52)$$

where

$$Z^* = -A_1 P_r{}^3 / \{1.0 + A_2(T_r - 1.0)^2 + A_3[P_r - A_4 - A_5(T_r - 1.0)]^4\}$$
$$+ \frac{B_1 P_r(T_r - B_2 - B_3 P_r + B_4 P_r T_r{}^2)(1.0 - B_5 P_r + B_6 T_r P_r)}{1.0 + B_7(T_r - B_8 - B_9 P_r - B_{10} P_r T_r)^4}$$
$$+ B_{11} T_r{}^3 P_r{}^3 / (T_r{}^4 + B_{12} P_r{}^4) \qquad (3\text{-}53)$$
$$Z^{**} = \frac{T_r P_r(T_r - 1.0 - 0.049 P_r)(C_1 + C_2 P_r - C_3 T_r P_r + C_4 T_r)}{T_r{}^4 + C_5(T_r - C_6 - C_7 P_r + C_8 T_r P_r)^4} \qquad (3\text{-}54)$$

The constants are shown in Table 3-3.

Use of Eq. (3-52) requires machine-computation assistance, but it is claimed that the results agree closely with Pitzer's compressibility tables, i.e., as represented by Figs. 3-5 and 3-6.

TABLE 3-3. ACKERMAN'S CONSTANTS FOR EQS. (3-53) AND (3-54)*

A_1	0.035
A_2	14,137.6
A_3	1,397.124
A_4	1.030
A_5	13.440
B_1	0.00260913
B_2	3.19325
B_3	1.77486
B_4	0.434418
B_5	0.144392
B_6	0.00704658
B_7	616.830
B_8	1.00122
B_9	0.0112141
B_{10}	0.0495574
B_{11}	0.000442593
B_{12}	0.0602768
C_1	0.825714
C_2	0.00736587
C_3	0.00255204
C_4	0.00115729
C_5	0.101212
C_6	2.46596
C_7	0.220411
C_8	0.0161963

* F. J. Ackerman, M.S. thesis, University of California, Berkeley, Calif., February, 1963.

Three-constant Equations of State. Gambill (36) discusses the generalized Wohl equation

$$[P + a_1/V(V - b) - a_2/V^3](V - b) = RT \qquad (3\text{-}55)$$

where
$$a_1 = 6P_cV_c^2$$
$$a_2 = 4P_cV_c^3$$
$$b = V_c/4$$

Equation (3-55) is not much, if any, more accurate than any of the two-constant equations and is restricted to regions not near the saturation curve; nor should it be considered valid at reduced densities greater than unity. Su and Chang (121) have generalized the Lorentz equation, but it does not appear to have any real advantage over the Wohl equation. Black (13) has also presented a three-constant generalized equation of state which requires critical temperatures and pressures with at least one vapor-pressure point.

Four-constant Equations of State. The most useful four-constant equation of state is the McLeod equation,

$$(P + a/V^2)(V - b') = RT \qquad (3\text{-}56)$$

where
$$b' = A - B\pi + C\pi^2$$
$$\pi = P + a/V^2$$

The relationship of the four constants a, A, B, C to critical properties has been studied by Rush and Gamson (113) and by Kobe and Murti (62). In both cases better correlation was noted if the Su ideal critical volume [Eq. (3-10)] were utilized rather than the actual critical volume. With this modification, the constants are

$$a = 0.472P_cV_{c_i}^2 = 0.472(R^2T_c^2/P_c)$$
$$A = 0.146V_{c_i} = 0.146(RT_c/P_c)$$
$$B \times 10^6 = 1.124(V_{c_i}/P_c)(10^3) + 39 \qquad \text{if } (V_{c_i}/P_c)(10^3) \geq 60$$
$$B \times 10^6 = 1.124(V_{c_i}/P_c)(10^3) + 39 - 36.3[1 - (V_{c_i}/P_c)(1,000/60)]1.786$$
$$\text{if } (V_{c_i}/P_c)(10^3) \leq 60$$
$$C \times 10^{10} = 5.280 + 19.01(V_{c_i}/P_c^2)(10^7/1,600)$$
$$- 1.158(V_{c_i}/P_c^2)^2(10^7/1,600)^2 - 1.149(V_{c_i}/P_c^2)^3(10^7/1,600)^3$$

Five-constant Equations of State. By far the best-known and most accurate of the five-constant equations is the Beattie-Bridgman (6). In the generalized form suggested by Su and Chang (122),

$$P_r = (T_r/V_{r_i}^2)(1 - 0.050/T_r^2V_{r_i})\{V_{r_i} + 0.1867[(1 - 0.03833)/V_{r_i}]\}$$
$$- (0.4758/V_{r_i}^2)[(1 - 0.1127)/V_{r_i}] \qquad (3\text{-}57)$$

The equation is reliable at high pressures, but not when the critical density is exceeded.

Multiconstant Equations of State. A number of very complex but highly accurate equations of state have been proposed. The eight-constant Benedict-Webb-Rubin equation (8, 9) is accurate for light hydrocarbons. Constants are available (24, 25, 40, 41, 58, 90, 120, 123) for many molecules and the equations with the values of the constants are summarized in Appendix E. Pings and Sage (93) have developed an open-ended orthogonal polynomial equation of state.

There are two quite accurate but somewhat cumbersome generalized equations of state which have been widely used when machine computation was possible. They are described briefly below.

Hirschfelder, Buehler, McGee, and Sutton Equation of State (51, 52). The correlation relates the quantities P_r, T_r, ρ_r, Z_c, and α_c. Thus the parameters employed that are characteristic of a given material are T_c, P_c, Z_c (or V_c), and α_c. The input is temperature and specific volume or density, and the output is pressure. If volume is desired from a pressure and temperature, then the equations must be iterated by a trial-and-error procedure. The method is applicable to liquids as well as gases, but only the gas is discussed here, as easier and more accurate liquid P-V-T estimation methods are available; these are discussed in Sec. 3-19.

There are two gas regions, which are designated as follows:
Region I, all T, $\rho_r \leq 1$
Region II, $T_r > 1$, $\rho_r \geq 1$

Region I:
$$(P_r/T_r)_\mathrm{I} = -W_1(T_r)\rho_r{}^2 - W_2(T_r)\rho_r{}^3 + g(\rho_r) \qquad (3\text{-}58)$$
where
$$W_1(T_r) = k_0/T_r + (\beta - k_0)/T_r{}^2 \qquad (3\text{-}59)$$
$$W_2(T_r) = \tfrac{1}{2}(1 - k_0 - \alpha_c + 2\beta)(1 - 1/T_r{}^2) \qquad (3\text{-}60)$$
$$g(\rho_r) = \frac{(1 + \beta)^3 \rho_r}{\beta(3\beta - 1) - (3\beta^2 - 6\beta - 1)\rho_r + \beta(\beta - 3)\rho_r{}^2} \qquad (3\text{-}61)$$
$$k_0 = 5.5$$
$$\beta = f(Z_c), \text{ that is, } Z_c = \beta(3\beta - 1)(1 + \beta)^{-3} \qquad (3\text{-}62)$$
$$\alpha_c = \text{Riedel factor (see Sec. 2-8)}$$

Region II:
$$(P_r/T_r)_\mathrm{II} = -W_1(T_r)\rho_r{}^2 - W_2(T_r)\rho_r{}^3 + 1$$
$$+ \beta\rho_r{}^2 + s(\rho_r - 1)^5/\rho_r + D(\rho_r,T_r) \qquad (3\text{-}63)$$

where W_1, W_2, β are defined above, and

$$s = -8.44 + 4.50\beta - 0.363\beta^2 \qquad (3\text{-}64)$$
$$D(\rho_r,T_r) = (\rho_r - 1)^3(T_r - 1)\left[\frac{1}{\rho_r}\left(\frac{h_0}{T_r} + h_1\right) + \frac{h_2}{T_r} + h_3\right] \qquad (3\text{-}65)$$
$$h_0 = 88.5 - 3.12\beta$$
$$h_1 = -44.4 + 5.22\beta$$
$$h_2 = -47.8 + 4.06\beta$$
$$h_3 = 23.7 - 3.26\beta$$

Martin and Hou Equation of State (73, 74). In an extraordinarily careful study of the properties of real gases, Martin and Hou proposed an equation of state for gases which involves the critical properties and a single vapor-pressure–temperature datum point. In general form it may be solved explicitly for pressure as

$$P = \sum_{i=1}^{5} f_i (V - b)^{-i} \tag{3-66}$$

where the f's are temperature-dependent,

$$f_i = A_i + B_i T + C_i e^{(k'T/T_c)} \tag{3-67}$$

A similar, but less complex, equation was suggested by Hansen (47).

To obtain the constants for use in the equations, the procedure given below is recommended:

1. Determine Z_c from Eq. (3-2) at the critical point, or use the Z_c estimation methods given in Sec. 2-5.

2. Calculate the Boyle temperature T_{B_0} as

$$T_{B_0} = 30 + 2.42T_c - 5.67 \times 10^{-4}T_c^2 \qquad T_c, T_{B_0} \text{ in } °K \tag{3-68}$$

3. Calculate parameters T' and β as

$$T' = T_c(0.9869 - 0.6751Z_c) \tag{3-69}$$
$$\beta = 20.533Z_c - 31.883Z_c^2 \tag{3-70}$$

4. Determine the parameter $-M$ from one vapor-pressure datum point and Fig. 3-17. M is defined as $d(\ln P_r)/d(1/T_r)$. At the critical point, $T_r = P_r = 1$; M is thus equal to $-(dP_r/dT_r)$ and as such is equal to the negative of the Riedel factor, α_c (Secs. 2-8 and 4-8). From Riedel's vapor-pressure equation [Eq. (4-14)] one can plot curves similar to those shown in Fig. 3-17. Instead of superimposing with $\alpha_c = -M$, there is a rather constant displacement, and it appears that $(-M) - 0.25 \sim \alpha_c$. As Fig. 3-17 however, was developed for this P-V-T correlation, it should be used rather than calculated from α_c by the approximation given above. From $-M$, the parameter m is found,

$$m = (\partial P/\partial T)_{V=V_c} = (-M)(P_c/T_c) \tag{3-71}$$

5. Determine the parameter b as

$$b = V_c - \beta V_c/15Z_c = (RT_c/P_c)(Z_c - \beta/15) \tag{3-72}$$

6. Determine the remaining parameters as indicated below:

$A_1 = 0$
$B_1 = R$
$C_1 = 0$
$Y_2 = 9P_c(V_c - b)^2 - 3.8RT_c(V_c - b)$

$$Y_3 = 5.4RT_c(V_c - b)^2 - 17P_c(V_c - b)^3$$

$$Y_4 = 12P_c(V_c - b)^4 - 3.4RT_c(V_c - b)^3$$

$$Y_5 = 0.8RT_c(V_c - b)^4 - 3P_c(V_c - b)^5$$

$$C_2 = \frac{\{Y_2 + bRT' + [(RT')^2/P_c](1 - Z_c)\}(T_{B_0} - T_c) + [(Y_2 + bRT_{B_0})(T_c - T')]}{(T_{B_0} - T_c)(e^{k'} - e^{k'T'/T_c}) - (T_c - T')(e^{k'T_{B_0}/T_c} - e^{k'})}$$

$$B_2 = \frac{-Y_2 - bRT_{B_0} - C_2(e^{k'T_{B_0}/T_c} - e^{k'})}{T_{B_0} - T_c}$$

$$A_2 = Y_2 - B_2T_c - C_2e^{k'}$$

$$C_3 = C_2 \frac{(V_c - b)^3 - [(V_c/n) - b]^3}{[(V_c/n) - b]^2 - (V_c - b)^2}$$

$$B_3 = \frac{m(V_c - b)^5 - my[(V_c/n) - b]^5}{(V_c - b)^2 - [(V_c/n) - b]^2} - B_2 \frac{(V_c - b)^3 + [(V_c/n) - b]^3}{(V_c - b)^2 - [(V_c/n) - b]^2} - R\{(V_c - b)^2 + [(V_c/n) - b]^2\}$$

$$A_3 = Y_3 - B_3T_c - C_3e^{k'}$$

$$A_4 = Y_4$$

$$B_4 = 0$$

$$C_4 = 0$$

$$C_5 = -C_2(V_c - b)^3 - C_3(V_c - b)^2$$

$$B_5 = m(V_c - b)^5 - R(V_c - b)^4 - B_2(V_c - b)^3 - B_3(V_c - b)^2$$

$$A_5 = Y_5 - B_5T_c - C_5e^{k'}$$

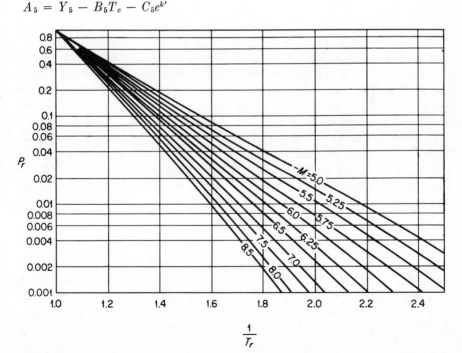

FIG. 3-17. Reduced $P_{vp} - T$ plot. [*J. J. Martin and Yu-Chun Hou, AIChE J.*, 1:142 (1955).]

In determining the set of constants A_i, B_i, C_i, there are three parameters yet unspecified, that is, n, y, k'. If experimental data were available, it would be preferable to choose these parameters to give the best fit to the data. If none are available, then the following rules may be used (71):

1. k' is chosen as -5.0.

2. n is determined such that $(\partial^2 P / \partial T^2)_V = 0$ at $V = V_c/n$. n is about equal to 1.8.

3. y is the ratio of the slope of the isometric at $V = V_c/n$ to that of the critical isometric $(\partial P / \partial T)_{V_c}$; y is about 3.0.

Discussion of the Complex Equations of State. For values of $V_r = 1/\rho_r > 1$, the Martin-Hou equation appears somewhat more accurate, and errors in estimating the pressure should not exceed 1 per cent.

For values of $V_r < 1$, the Hirschfelder et al. equations were considerably more accurate than the original Martin-Hou equation (73), but the modified form (74) as presented here is of comparable accuracy, as tested with carbon dioxide. Both equations are superior to any of the other generalized equations of state, but their complexity obviously discourages their use with hand-calculation techniques.

For light hydrocarbons, use the Benedict, Webb, and Rubin equation summarized in Appendix E.

3-17 Pure Liquids—General Considerations

Liquid specific volumes are easier to measure experimentally than gas volumes, and, for most known materials, at least one measurement is available. The usual handbooks such as the "Handbook of Chemistry and Physics" (55) have excellent tabulations. There are many recent papers which extend the availability of experimental results. Francis (34) has published constants for empirical equations to allow one to determine saturated-liquid densities and the variation of density with pressure for 130 diverse pure liquids over large temperature ranges. The same worker has also made available the necessary constants to determine saturated-liquid densities of some 44 pure hydrocarbons as a function of temperature (35). A similar treatment, but with a different correlating equation, has covered a number of compounds in the n-alkyl series (66). Either equation will permit quite accurate calculation of liquid-hydrocarbon densities. Other density data, specific to C_3 and C_4 alkenes (84) and normal and isoparaffins (27, 86), are available. Ritter, Lenoir, and Schweppe (104) have published convenient nomographs to estimate the saturated-liquid-density–temperature relationship for some 90 liquids, covering primarily hydrocarbons and hydrocarbon derivatives. For rapid estimations within 0.5 to 2 per cent, these charts are very convenient; they are reproduced as Figs. 3-18 to 3-20. If at all possible, experimental data should be used in preference to the correlating equations discussed later.

There is no convenient law for a "perfect liquid" upon which to base P-V-T estimations, such as the perfect-gas law for gas systems. All the reliable liquid P-V-T estimation techniques require at least one experimental datum point or an accurate value of the critical volume. As noted above, in most cases at least one such point would be available; however, in some cases an initial estimation of a liquid volume may be necessary. The only convenient reference point (besides the critical)

Example—at 0°F. Ⓐ liquid methyl chloride Ⓑ has a specific gravity of 0.993 Ⓒ

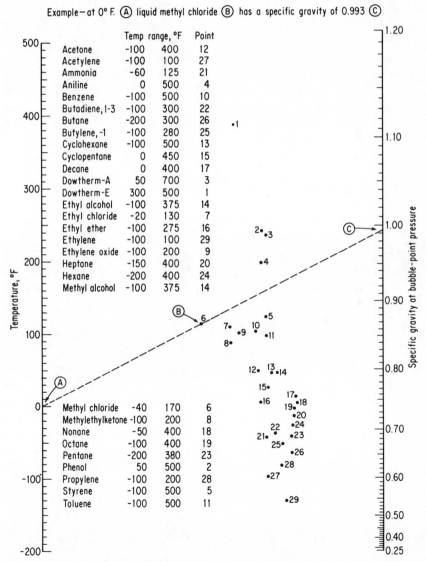

FIG. 3-18. Specific gravity of light liquids. [R. B. Ritter, J. M. Lenoir, and J. L. Schweppe, Petrol. Refiner, **37**(11):225 (1958).]

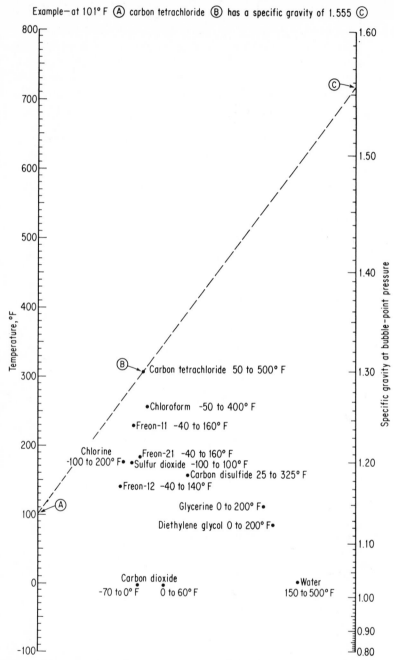

Example—at 101° F Ⓐ carbon tetrachloride Ⓑ has a specific gravity of 1.555 Ⓒ

Fig. 3-19. Specific gravity of heavy liquids. [*R. B. Ritter, J. M. Lenoir, and J. L. Schweppe, Petrol. Refiner*, **37**(11):225 (1958).]

Example—paraffinic mixture at 218° F Ⓐ with molecular weight of 82.3 Ⓑ has a specific gravity of 0.564 Ⓒ

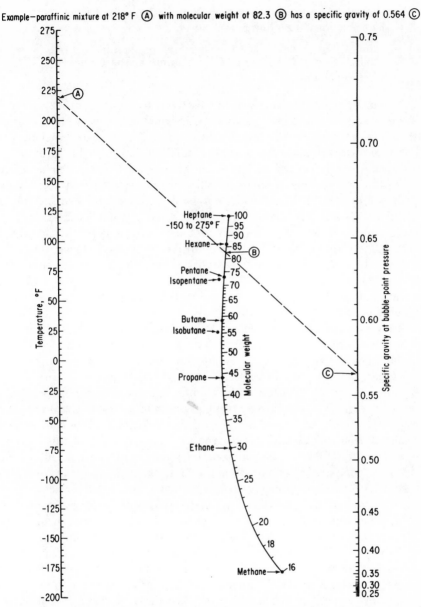

FIG. 3-20. Specific gravity of paraffinic hydrocarbons. [*R. B. Ritter, J. M. Lenoir, and J. L. Schweppe, Petrol. Refiner,* **37**(11):225 (1958).]

where liquid-volume estimation techniques have been specifically studied is that at the normal boiling point.

3-18 Estimation of the Liquid Molal Volume at the Normal Boiling Point

A number of additive methods are discussed by Partington (92). Each element and certain bond linkages are assigned numerical values so that the molal volume at the normal boiling point may be calculated by the addition of these values in a manner similar to that described in Chap. 2 for estimating the critical volume. In contrast to the success achieved in estimating the critical volume by this technique, the additive method does not appear to be particularly reliable for the estimation of liquid molal volumes at the boiling point, as this point is not a corresponding-state point. It has also been postulated that association in the liquid state affects the accuracy of such additive methods at lower temperatures, but this factor appears to have little effect on the additive character of atomic volumes at the critical point (5, 67). A very rough rule of thumb is that the ratio of the volume at the boiling point to the critical volume is 3:8.

Additive Methods. Schroeder (92) has suggested a very novel and extremely simple additive method for estimating molal volumes at the boiling point. His rule is to count the number of atoms of carbon, hydrogen, oxygen, and nitrogen, add one for each double bond, and multiply the sum by 7. This gives the volume in cubic centimeters per gram mole. This rule is surprisingly good, giving results within 3 to 4 per cent except for highly associated liquids. Table 3-4 indicates the value to be assigned each atom or functional group.* The accuracy of this method is shown in Table 3-5, in which molal volumes at the normal boiling point are compared with experimental volumes for a wide range of materials. The average error for the compounds tested is 2.8 per cent.

Additive volumes published by Le Bas (65) represent a refinement of Schroeder's rule. Volume increments from Le Bas are shown in Table 3-4, and calculated values of V_b are compared with experimental values in Table 3-5. The average error for the compounds tested is 4.7 per cent. Although the average error in this case is greater than the average error found by using Schroeder's increments, the method appears to be somewhat more general and as accurate as Schroeder's method for most of the compounds tested; i.e., the average error is not representative.

Other additive methods are primarily for hydrocarbons (7, 39).

Benson's Method. Benson (10) found that the reduced density at the normal boiling point is a linear function of the logarithm of the

---

* Schroeder's original rule has been expanded to include halogens, sulfur, triple bonds, etc.

TABLE 3-4. ADDITIVE-VOLUME INCREMENTS* FOR THE CALCULATION OF
MOLAL VOLUMES V_b

	Increment, cm^3/g mole	
	Schroeder	Le Bas
Carbon...........................	7	14.8
Hydrogen..........................	7	3.7
Oxygen (except as noted below)..........	7	7.4
In methyl esters and ethers...........	.....	9.1
In ethyl esters and ethers............	.....	9.9
In higher esters and ethers...........	.....	11.0
In acids...........................	.....	12.0
Joined to S, P, N....................	.....	8.3
Nitrogen...........................	7	
Doubly bonded......................	.....	15.6
In primary amines...................	.....	10.5
In secondary amines.................	.....	12.0
Bromine...........................	31.5	27
Chlorine...........................	24.5	24.6
Fluorine...........................	10.5	8.7
Iodine.............................	38.5	37
Sulfur..............................	21	25.6
Ring, three-membered.................	−7	−6.0
Four-membered.....................	−7	−8.5
Five-membered......................	−7	−11.5
Six-membered......................	−7	−15.0
Napthalene........................	−7	−30.0
Anthracene........................	−7	−47.5
Double bond between carbon atoms......	7	
Triple bond between carbon atoms.......	14	

* The additive-volume procedure should not be used for simple molecules. The following approximate values are employed in estimating diffusion coefficients by the methods of Chap. 11: H_2, 14.3; O_2, 25.6; N_2, 31.2; air, 29.9; CO, 30.7; CO_2, 34.0; SO_2, 44.8; NO, 23.6; N_2O, 36.4; NH_3, 25.8; H_2O, 18.9; H_2S, 32.9; COS, 51.5; Cl_2, 48.4; Br_2, 53.2; I_2, 715.

critical pressure,

$$V_c/V_b = \rho_b/\rho_c = 0.422 \log P_c + 1.981 \qquad (3\text{-}73)$$

Here P_c is the critical pressure in atmospheres, ρ_b is the density at the boiling point, and ρ_c is the critical density. This simple relationship is accurate to within 3 per cent for most organic and some inorganic liquids. The materials which were found to deviate by more than 3 per cent were helium, neon, and phosphine, the measured reduced densities of which are less than calculated, and hydrogen sulfide, carbon disulfide, hydrocyanic acid, and various nitriles, whose measured reduced densities are larger than calculated.

TABLE 3-5. COMPARISON OF CALCULATED AND EXPERIMENTAL LIQUID
MOLAL VOLUMES AT THE NORMAL BOILING POINT
Molal volume, cm^3/g mole

Compound	Exp. V_b	Ref.	Calculated by method of					
			Benson		Schroeder		Le Bas	
			V_b	% Error*	V_b	% Error	V_b	% Error
Methane............	37.7	57	37.1	− 1.6	35	− 7.2	30	−20
Propane.............	74.5	115	75.3	+ 1.1	77	+ 3.3	74	− 0.7
Heptane.............	162	57	165	+ 1.8	161	− 0.6	163	− 0.6
Cyclohexane........	117	57	120	+ 2.7	119	+ 1.7	118	− 0.9
Ethylene............	49.4	57	45.9	− 7.2	49	− 0.8	44	−11
Acetylene...........	42.0	57	41.3	− 1.7	42	0.0	37	−12
Benzene.............	96.5	57	97.0	+ 0.5	98	+ 1.6	96	− 0.5
Fluorobenzene.......	102	57	101	− 1.0	102	0.0	101	− 1.0
Bromobenzene.......	120	57	115	− 4.2	122	+ 1.6	118	− 1.6
Chlorobenzene.......	115	57	115	0.0	115	0.0	114	− 0.9
Iodobenzene........	130	57	131	+ 0.7	129	− 0.7		
Methanol...........	42.5	57	42.4	− 0.2	42	− 1.2	42	− 1.2
n-Propyl alcohol......	81.8	57	81.5	− 0.4	84	+ 2.7	86	+ 5.1
Dimethyl ether.......	63.8	57	62.7	− 1.7	63	− 1.3	62	− 2.8
Ethylpropyl ether....	129	57	131	+ 1.5	126	− 2.3	129	0.0
Acetone.............	77.5	57	81.0	+ 3.2	77	− 0.6	74	− 4.5
Acetic acid..........	64.1	57	62.9	− 2.2	63	− 1.7	64	0.0
Isobutyric acid.......	109	57	109	0.0	105	− 3.7	108	− 1.0
Methyl formate......	62.8	57	63.0	+ 0.3	63	+ 0.3	61	− 2.9
Ethyl acetate........	106	57	108	+ 1.8	105	− 0.9	106	0.0
Diethylamine........	109	57	113	+ 3.7	112	+ 2.8	112	+ 2.7
Acetonitrile.........	57.4	57	63.6	+12.5	56	− 2.4		
Methyl chloride......	50.6	57	49.8	− 1.6	52.5	+ 3.7	48	− 5.1
Carbon tetrachloride..	102	57	103	+ 1.0	105	+ 2.8	101	− 1.0
Dichlorodifluoro- methane...........	80.7	55	82.3	+ 1.9	77	− 4.6	75	− 7.0
Ethyl mercaptan.....	75.5	57	76.0	+ 0.6	77	+ 2.0	77	+ 2.0
Diethyl sulfide.......	118	57	122	+ 3.4	119	+ 0.9	122	+ 3.4
Phosgene...........	69.5	57	70.2	+ 1.0	70	+ 0.7	65	− 6.5
Ammonia...........	25.0	57	25.5	+ 2.0	28	+11		
Chlorine............	45.5	57	44.6	− 1.8	49	+ 7.7		
Water..............	18.7	59	19.0	+ 1.6	21	+11		
Hydrochloric acid....	30.6	57	31.2	+ 1.9	31.5	+ 2.9	25.3	−17
Hydriodic acid.......	45.6	57	45.9	+ 0.7	45.5	− 0.2		
Sulfur dioxide........	43.8	114	44.3	+ 1.1	49	−12	40	− 8.6
Average error........				2.0		2.8		4.7

* % Error = [(calculated − experimental)/(experimental)] × 100.

Table 3-5 compares the values of V_b, the molal volume at the boiling point, calculated by Eq. (3-73), with experimental values of V_c and P_c. An average error of 2.0 per cent was found.

Example 3-7. Estimate the molal volume of liquid chlorobenzene at its normal boiling point. The critical pressure is 44.6 atm and the critical volume is 308 cm³/g mole. The experimental value of V_b is 115 cm³/g mole (57).
Solution. *Schroeder's Increments.* From Table 3-4, C = 7, H = 7, Cl = 24.5, the ring = -7, and each double bond = 7. Therefore for C_6H_5Cl,

$$V_b = (6)(7) + (5)(7) + 24.5 - 7 + (3)(7) = 115 \text{ cm}^3/\text{g mole}$$
$$\text{Error} = [(115 - 115)/115] \times 100 = 0\%$$

Le Bas Increments. From Table 3-4, C = 14.8, H = 3.7, Cl = 21.6, the ring = -15.0. Therefore,

$$V_b = 6(14.8) + 5(3.7) + 21.6 - 15.0 = 114 \text{ cm}^3/\text{g mole}$$
$$\text{Error} = [(114 - 115)/115] \times 100 = -0.9\%$$

Benson's Method

$$\rho_b/\rho_c = V_c/V_b = 0.422 \text{ (log } 44.6) + 1.981 = 2.68$$
$$V_b = 308/2.68 = 115 \text{ cm}^3/\text{g mole}$$
$$\text{Error} = [(115 - 115)/115] \times 100 = 0\%$$

Recommendations. To estimate the molal volume of a liquid at the normal boiling point:

1. If the critical volume and pressure are known (or if they can be estimated with reasonable accuracy) and if the compound is not a low-boiling "permanent" gas or nitrile, use Eq. (3-73); otherwise

2. Use the additive procedure, with volume increments from either Schroeder or Le Bas, as given in Table 3-4.

3-19 Estimation of Liquid Densities

Corresponding-state Methods. There is no reason why many of the corresponding-state methods to estimate gas P-V-T data should not be applied to liquids. Figures 3-5 and 3-6 and Eq. (3-15), which correlate the compressibility factor with reduced pressure and temperature and acentric factor, include a liquid range as low as $T_r = 0.8$. These charts however, are not particularly accurate below $T_r = 1$.

The best corresponding-state correlation for liquids is presented by Lydersen, Greenkorn, and Hougen (70) and is based on the critical compressibility factor as a third correlating parameter. This method is a refinement of the original expansion-factor method first introduced by Watson (124). The form of the correlation is the identity

$$V_1\rho_{r_1} = V_2\rho_{r_2} \tag{3-74}$$

Here ρ_r is the reduced density $\rho/\rho_c = f(T_r, P_r, Z_c)$ as tabulated in Table 3-6. Four different Z_c values are used for these tables, and interpolation

THE PROPERTIES OF GASES AND LIQUIDS

TABLE 3-6. REDUCED DENSITY OF LIQUIDS*

T_r	Saturated liquid				$P_r = 1.0$				$P_r = 2.0$		
	W $Z_c = 0.23$	I $Z_c = 0.25$	II $Z_c = 0.27$	III $Z_c = 0.29$	W $Z_c = 0.23$	I $Z_c = 0.25$	II $Z_c = 0.27$	III $Z_c = 0.29$	I $Z_c = 0.25$	II $Z_c = 0.27$	III $Z_c = 0.29$
0.30	......	3.487	3.287	3.081	.....	3.490	3.290	3.084	3.494	3.294	3.088
0.32	......	3.450	3.253	3.049	.....	3.454	3.256	3.052	3.458	3.260	3.056
0.34	......	3.419	3.223	3.021	.....	3.423	3.227	3.025	3.427	3.231	3.029
0.36	......	3.383	3.189	2.989	.....	3.387	3.193	2.993	3.392	3.198	2.998
0.38	......	3.348	3.156	2.959	.....	3.354	3.162	2.964	3.358	3.170	2.970
0.40	......	3.306	3.118	2.922	.....	3.313	3.123	2.928	3.322	3.132	2.936
0.42	3.140	3.271	3.084	2.891	3.181	3.278	3.090	2.897	3.287	3.099	2.905
0.44	3.138	3.234	3.049	2.858	3.174	3.239	3.054	2.863	3.251	3.065	2.873
0.46	3.130	3.195	3.012	2.824	3.164	3.203	3.020	2.831	3.215	3.031	2.841
0.48	3.118	3.156	2.975	2.789	3.149	3.165	2.984	2.797	3.177	2.995	2.808
0.50	3.101	3.115	2.937	2.753	3.132	3.126	2.947	2.763	3.136	2.957	2.772
0.52	3.082	3.076	2.900	2.719	3.115	3.088	2.911	2.729	3.099	2.922	2.739
0.54	3.060	3.036	2.862	2.683	3.099	3.050	2.875	2.696	3.063	2.888	2.707
0.56	3.032	2.996	2.825	2.648	3.071	3.012	2.840	2.662	3.028	2.855	2.676
0.58	3.005	2.956	2.787	2.613	3.040	2.974	2.800	2.630	2.990	2.823	2.646
0.60	2.973	2.913	2.746	2.574	3.007	2.932	2.764	2.591	2.952	2.783	2.609
0.61	2.957	2.893	2.727	2.556	2.989	2.913	2.746	2.574	2.936	2.768	2.595
0.62	2.940	2.868	2.704	2.535	2.965	2.888	2.723	2.553	2.916	2.749	2.577
0.63	2.923	2.849	2.686	2.518	2.954	2.868	2.704	2.535	2.897	2.731	2.560
0.64	2.904	2.825	2.663	2.496	2.938	2.845	2.682	2.514	2.877	2.712	2.542
0.65	2.889	2.800	2.640	2.475	2.919	2.824	2.660	2.494	2.852	2.689	2.521
0.66	2.868	2.781	2.622	2.458	2.900	2.800	2.640	2.475	2.836	2.674	2.507
0.67	2.848	2.757	2.599	2.436	2.882	2.784	2.625	2.461	2.816	2.655	2.489
0.68	2.827	2.733	2.577	2.416	2.864	2.761	2.603	2.440	2.797	2.637	2.472
0.69	2.810	2.709	2.554	2.394	2.846	2.737	2.580	2.419	2.777	2.618	2.454
0.70	2.785	2.686	2.532	2.374	2.828	2.718	2.562	2.402	2.757	2.599	2.436
0.71	2.768	2.661	2.509	2.352	2.805	2.693	2.539	2.380	2.733	2.577	2.416
0.72	2.741	2.637	2.486	2.330	2.782	2.673	2.520	2.362	2.711	2.555	2.395
0.73	2.717	2.614	2.460	2.310	2.759	2.650	2.498	2.342	2.687	2.533	2.376
0.74	2.693	2.586	2.438	2.285	2.736	2.621	2.471	2.316	2.662	2.512	2.351
0.75	2.667	2.557	2.411	2.260	2.714	2.598	2.449	2.296	2.640	2.490	2.333
0.76	2.643	2.534	2.389	2.240	2.690	2.573	2.426	2.274	2.620	2.473	2.317
0.77	2.617	2.505	2.363	2.215	2.668	2.546	2.400	2.250	2.594	2.445	2.292
0.78	2.593	2.478	2.336	2.190	2.644	2.522	2.378	2.229	2.571	2.423	2.271
0.79	2.566	2.450	2.310	2.168	2.621	2.494	2.351	2.204	2.546	2.400	2.250
0.80	2.535	2.420	2.284	2.145	2.597	2.470	2.329	2.183	2.524	2.377	2.230
0.81	2.502	2.390	2.257	2.121	2.577	2.446	2.306	2.160	2.500	2.354	2.206
0.82	2.478	2.359	2.231	2.096	2.553	2.418	2.280	2.137	2.472	2.330	2.183
0.83	2.442	2.327	2.201	2.070	2.526	2.387	2.250	2.109	2.447	2.306	2.161
0.84	2.407	2.295	2.171	2.044	2.498	2.359	2.224	2.085	2.420	2.281	2.137
0.85	2.370	2.263	2.141	2.014	2.468	2.327	2.194	2.057	2.394	2.256	2.114
0.86	2.340	2.227	2.107	1.984	2.436	2.290	2.161	2.038	2.358	2.231	2.098
0.87	2.297	2.191	2.077	1.957	2.402	2.253	2.131	2.002	2.330	2.204	2.070
0.88	2.256	2.155	2.043	1.925	2.364	2.217	2.098	1.972	2.302	2.177	2.049
0.89	2.216	2.116	2.006	1.891	2.324	2.179	2.063	1.941	2.274	2.150	2.022
0.90	2.191	2.076	1.969	1.859	2.285	2.140	2.027	1.911	2.243	2.122	1.998
0.91	2.131	2.032	1.932	1.824	2.232	2.094	1.990	1.877	2.211	2.092	1.970
0.92	2.077	1.989	1.890	1.789	2.174	2.051	1.948	1.843	2.180	2.064	1.943
0.93	2.020	1.940	1.846	1.747	2.113	2.000	1.904	1.802	2.145	2.033	1.913
0.94	1.965	1.888	1.797	1.707	2.057	1.948	1.855	1.762	2.104	2.001	1.887
0.95	1.898	1.829	1.745	1.657	1.994	1.889	1.803	1.713	2.063	1.965	1.856
0.96	1.784	1.765	1.685	1.605	1.920	1.824	1.743	1.661	2.028	1.931	1.825
0.97	1.729	1.689	1.617	1.545	1.850	1.740	1.667	1.594	1.988	1.892	1.790
0.98	1.628	1.508	1.535	1.469	1.748	1.644	1.580	1.513	1.946	1.852	1.755
0.99	1.475	1.470	1.420	1.368	1.624	1.450	1.450	1.397	1.902	1.810	1.719
1.00	1.000	1.000	1.000	1.000	1.000	1.000	1.000	1.000	1.854	1.764	1.676

*A. L. Lydersen, R. A. Greenkorn, and O. A. Hougen, Generalized Thermodynamic Properties of Pure Fluids, *Coll. Eng., Univ. Wisconsin, Eng. Expt. Sta. Rept.* 4, Madison, Wis., October, 1955.

Just recently Yen and Wood (127) have developed an equation-set to express reduced liquid density as a function of reduced temperature and pressure and Z_c.

TABLE 3-6. REDUCED DENSITY OF LIQUIDS (*Continued*)

T_r	$P_r = 4.0$ I $Z_c = 0.25$	II $Z_c = 0.27$	III $Z_c = 0.29$	$P_r = 6.0$ I $Z_c = 0.25$	II $Z_c = 0.27$	III $Z_c = 0.29$	$P_r = 10$ I $Z_c = 0.25$	II $Z_c = 0.27$	III $Z_c = 0.29$	$P_r = 15$ I $Z_c = 0.25$	II $Z_c = 0.27$	III $Z_c = 0.29$
0.30	3.500	3.300	3.094	3.506	3.305	3.098	3.512	3.320	3.112	3.527	3.325	3.116
0.32	3.465	3.267	3.063	3.471	3.272	3.067	3.484	3.285	3.079	3.495	3.295	3.088
0.34	3.437	3.240	3.037	3.442	3.245	3.041	3.453	3.255	3.051	3.463	3.265	3.060
0.36	3.402	3.207	3.006	3.407	3.212	3.011	3.421	3.225	3.028	3.431	3.235	3.032
0.38	3.373	3.180	2.981	3.378	3.185	2.986	3.389	3.195	2.995	3.401	3.206	3.005
0.40	3.334	3.143	2.946	3.339	3.148	2.951	3.357	3.165	2.967	3.370	3.177	2.978
0.42	3.301	3.112	2.917	3.306	3.117	2.922	3.325	3.135	2.938	3.340	3.147	2.950
0.44	3.267	3.080	2.887	3.273	3.086	2.894	3.292	3.104	2.909	3.307	3.118	2.923
0.46	3.232	3.047	2.856	3.239	3.054	2.863	3.262	3.075	2.882	3.278	3.090	2.896
0.48	3.195	3.012	2.824	3.208	3.024	2.835	3.230	3.045	2.854	3.242	3.068	2.876
0.50	3.156	2.975	2.789	3.171	2.990	2.803	3.198	3.015	2.826	3.214	3.030	2.840
0.52	3.120	2.941	2.757	3.140	2.960	2.775	3.166	2.985	2.798	3.182	3.000	2.812
0.54	3.088	2.911	2.729	3.104	2.926	2.743	3.134	2.955	2.770	3.153	2.973	2.787
0.56	3.056	2.881	2.701	3.072	2.896	2.715	3.103	2.925	2.742	3.120	2.949	2.764
0.58	3.020	2.847	2.669	3.040	2.870	2.691	3.072	2.896	2.714	3.093	2.916	2.733
0.60	2.984	2.813	2.637	3.008	2.836	2.659	3.044	2.870	2.690	3.063	2.888	2.707
0.61	2.964	2.794	2.619	2.996	2.825	2.649	3.028	2.855	2.676	3.050	2.875	2.695
0.62	2.945	2.776	2.602	2.980	2.809	2.634	3.013	2.841	2.663	3.036	2.862	2.683
0.63	2.929	2.761	2.588	2.964	2.794	2.620	2.998	2.828	2.651	3.022	2.849	2.670
0.64	2.913	2.746	2.574	2.948	2.779	2.606	2.985	2.814	2.638	3.008	2.836	2.660
0.65	2.893	2.727	2.556	2.932	2.764	2.591	2.970	2.800	2.624	2.995	2.824	2.647
0.66	2.877	2.712	2.542	2.916	2.749	2.577	2.951	2.782	2.602	2.982	2.811	2.635
0.67	2.856	2.693	2.524	2.900	2.734	2.563	2.940	2.772	2.598	2.968	2.798	2.623
0.68	2.836	2.676	2.507	2.881	2.716	2.546	2.918	2.751	2.579	2.954	2.785	2.610
0.69	2.820	2.660	2.494	2.865	2.701	2.532	2.910	2.743	2.571	2.940	2.776	2.602
0.70	2.802	2.642	2.477	2.849	2.686	2.518	2.890	2.730	2.560	2.928	2.760	2.589
0.71	2.784	2.625	2.461	2.833	2.671	2.500	2.872	2.716	2.547	2.915	2.748	2.577
0.72	2.765	2.607	2.444	2.816	2.655	2.489	2.860	2.701	2.533	2.901	2.735	2.565
0.73	2.747	2.590	2.428	2.799	2.639	2.474	2.851	2.688	2.521	2.894	2.720	2.559
0.74	2.729	2.573	2.412	2.781	2.622	2.458	2.837	2.675	2.509	2.874	2.710	2.542
0.75	2.709	2.554	2.394	2.761	2.603	2.441	2.812	2.661	2.495	2.861	2.697	2.530
0.76	2.689	2.535	2.376	2.745	2.588	2.426	2.800	2.646	2.480	2.848	2.685	2.518
0.77	2.672	2.518	2.360	2.729	2.573	2.412	2.784	2.631	2.468	2.833	2.671	2.505
0.78	2.652	2.500	2.344	2.709	2.554	2.394	2.770	2.617	2.454	2.820	2.659	2.494
0.79	2.631	2.480	2.325	2.693	2.539	2.380	2.750	2.602	2.440	2.807	2.646	2.482
0.80	2.609	2.460	2.306	2.673	2.520	2.362	2.735	2.587	2.432	2.790	2.634	2.476
0.81	2.588	2.440	2.287	2.656	2.504	2.347	2.719	2.572	2.418	2.778	2.621	2.464
0.82	2.567	2.420	2.269	2.638	2.487	2.331	2.704	2.558	2.405	2.762	2.609	2.452
0.83	2.546	2.400	2.250	2.619	2.470	2.315	2.687	2.542	2.389	2.750	2.595	2.439
0.84	2.524	2.380	2.232	2.660	2.449	2.295	2.671	2.527	2.375	2.740	2.583	2.428
0.85	2.503	2.360	2.214	2.580	2.433	2.281	2.655	2.512	2.361	2.720	2.571	2.417
0.86	2.482	2.340	2.195	2.562	2.416	2.265	2.639	2.496	2.346	2.708	2.559	2.405
0.87	2.461	2.320	2.176	2.543	2.398	2.248	2.621	2.479	2.330	2.698	2.545	2.392
0.88	2.438	2.299	2.156	2.524	2.380	2.232	2.606	2.465	2.317	2.682	2.532	2.380
0.89	2.415	2.277	2.136	2.505	2.362	2.216	2.590	2.450	2.303	2.670	2.519	2.368
0.90	2.390	2.257	2.119	2.486	2.344	2.200	2.572	2.434	2.282	2.658	2.506	2.349
0.91	2.365	2.235	2.100	2.466	2.325	2.182	2.560	2.418	2.267	2.644	2.493	2.340
0.92	2.342	2.214	2.080	2.440	2.307	2.165	2.540	2.402	2.252	2.632	2.481	2.330
0.93	2.316	2.191	2.060	2.420	2.288	2.147	2.532	2.387	2.238	2.620	2.470	2.316
0.94	2.292	2.168	2.039	2.400	2.268	2.129	2.514	2.370	2.222	2.606	2.457	2.303
0.95	2.267	2.145	2.018	2.378	2.249	2.113	2.498	2.355	2.208	2.593	2.445	2.292
0.96	2.240	2.120	1.995	2.356	2.229	2.096	2.480	2.338	2.192	2.581	2.433	2.281
0.97	2.211	2.095	1.973	2.334	2.208	2.077	2.463	2.322	2.177	2.567	2.420	2.269
0.98	2.184	2.072	1.950	2.313	2.188	2.059	2.446	2.306	2.162	2.555	2.409	2.258
0.99	2.155	2.043	1.925	2.289	2.165	2.038	2.429	2.290	2.147	2.541	2.396	2.246
1.00	2.127	2.016	1.900	2.266	2.143	2.018	2.412	2.274	2.132	2.532	2.383	2.234

THE PROPERTIES OF GASES AND LIQUIDS

TABLE 3-6. REDUCED DENSITY OF LIQUIDS (*Continued*)

T_r	$P_r = 20$			$P_r = 25$			$P_r = 30$		
	I $Z_c = 0.25$	II $Z_c = 0.27$	III $Z_c = 0.29$	I $Z_c = 0.25$	II $Z_c = 0.27$	III $Z_c = 0.29$	I $Z_c = 0.25$	II $Z_c = 0.27$	III $Z_c = 0.29$
0.30	3.535	3.333	3.124	3.540	3.337	3.128	3.546	3.343	3.133
0.32	3.506	3.305	3.098	3.511	3.310	3.102	3.517	3.316	3.108
0.34	3.474	3.275	3.070	3.481	3.282	3.076	3.489	3.289	3.083
0.36	3.442	3.245	3.042	3.453	3.255	3.051	3.459	3.261	3.057
0.38	3.410	3.215	3.013	3.421	3.225	3.023	3.430	3.233	3.030
0.40	3.378	3.185	2.985	3.390	3.196	2.996	3.400	3.205	3.004
0.42	3.350	3.158	2.960	3.360	3.168	2.969	3.370	3.177	2.978
0.44	3.319	3.129	2.933	3.306	3.140	2.943	3.341	3.150	2.952
0.46	3.288	3.100	2.906	3.302	3.113	2.918	3.310	3.121	2.925
0.48	3.257	3.071	2.878	3.274	3.085	2.892	3.282	3.094	2.900
0.50	3.226	3.041	2.850	3.245	3.059	2.867	3.252	3.066	2.874
0.52	3.197	3.014	2.825	3.214	3.030	2.840	3.225	3.040	2.849
0.54	3.167	2.986	2.799	3.186	3.004	2.816	3.198	3.015	2.826
0.56	3.139	2.959	2.773	3.157	2.976	2.789	3.170	2.989	2.802
0.58	3.109	2.931	2.750	3.130	2.951	2.766	3.145	2.965	2.779
0.60	3.081	2.905	2.723	3.103	2.925	2.742	3.120	2.941	2.757
0.61	3.070	2.894	2.713	3.090	2.913	2.730	3.108	2.930	2.746
0.62	3.056	2.881	2.700	3.076	2.900	2.718	3.096	2.919	2.736
0.63	3.044	2.870	2.690	3.064	2.889	2.708	3.082	2.906	2.724
0.64	3.031	2.858	2.679	3.052	2.877	2.697	3.065	2.890	2.709
0.65	3.018	2.845	2.667	3.040	2.866	2.686	3.060	2.885	2.704
0.66	3.005	2.833	2.655	3.028	2.855	2.676	3.050	2.875	2.695
0.67	2.991	2.820	2.643	3.016	2.843	2.665	3.038	2.864	2.684
0.68	2.980	2.809	2.633	3.004	2.832	2.654	3.027	2.854	2.675
0.69	2.967	2.797	2.622	2.912	2.820	2.643	3.016	2.843	2.665
0.70	2.955	2.786	2.613	2.981	2.810	2.635	3.005	2.833	2.657
0.71	2.943	2.775	2.600	2.969	2.799	2.625	2.994	2.823	2.648
0.72	2.931	2.763	2.591	2.956	2.787	2.614	2.985	2.814	2.639
0.73	2.917	2.750	2.579	2.945	2.776	2.604	2.974	2.804	2.630
0.74	2.906	2.740	2.570	2.933	2.765	2.593	2.964	2.794	2.620
0.75	2.896	2.730	2.560	2.921	2.754	2.583	2.953	2.784	2.610
0.76	2.886	2.721	2.552	2.911	2.744	2.574	2.942	2.774	2.602
0.77	2.870	2.706	2.538	2.899	2.733	2.563	2.932	2.764	2.592
0.78	2.859	2.695	2.528	2.887	2.722	2.553	2.920	2.753	2.582
0.79	2.847	2.684	2.517	2.877	2.712	2.544	2.910	2.743	2.578
0.80	2.830	2.673	2.513	2.864	2.702	2.540	2.900	2.734	2.570
0.81	2.820	2.661	2.501	2.852	2.693	2.531	2.890	2.725	2.561
0.82	2.810	2.650	2.490	2.844	2.683	2.522	2.880	2.715	2.552
0.83	2.798	2.639	2.481	2.832	2.673	2.513	2.870	2.706	2.544
0.84	2.784	2.628	2.470	2.820	2.664	2.504	2.860	2.698	2.536
0.85	2.772	2.616	2.459	2.810	2.655	2.496	2.852	2.689	2.528
0.86	2.762	2.605	2.449	2.800	2.645	2.486	2.840	2.680	2.519
0.87	2.752	2.595	2.439	2.792	2.635	2.477	2.829	2.672	2.512
0.88	2.740	2.585	2.430	2.780	2.626	2.468	2.821	2.669	2.509
0.89	2.730	2.574	2.420	2.770	2.616	2.459	2.816	2.655	2.496
0.90	2.719	2.563	2.403	2.760	2.608	2.445	2.808	2.647	2.482
0.91	2.707	2.552	2.392	2.756	2.598	2.435	2.798	2.638	2.473
0.92	2.695	2.541	2.382	2.745	2.588	2.426	2.790	2.630	2.466
0.93	2.685	2.531	2.373	2.736	2.579	2.418	2.781	2.622	2.458
0.94	2.674	2.521	2.363	2.726	2.570	2.409	2.773	2.614	2.451
0.95	2.663	2.511	2.354	2.717	2.561	2.400	2.763	2.605	2.442
0.96	2.652	2.500	2.344	2.706	2.551	2.391	2.753	2.596	2.434
0.97	2.640	2.489	2.333	2.696	2.542	2.383	2.745	2.588	2.426
0.98	2.628	2.480	2.323	2.686	2.532	2.373	2.736	2.580	2.419
0.99	2.617	2.467	2.313	2.676	2.523	2.365	2.727	2.571	2.410
1.00	2.606	2.457	2.303	2.667	2.514	2.357	2.720	2.563	2.403

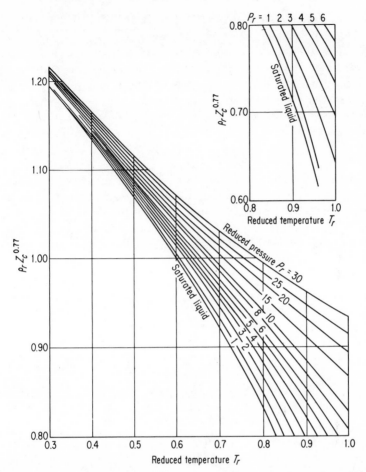

FIG. 3-21. $\rho_r Z_c^{0.77}$ as a function of T_r and P_r.   [*B. C. Y. Lu, Chem. Eng.*, **66**(9):137 (1959).]

may be employed for values other than those shown. Z_c may be determined from experimental T_c, P_c, V_c data and Eq. (3-2), or it may be estimated as shown in Sec. 2-5.   It is preferable to have a single reliable experimental value of V (say, V_1 at T_{r_1}, P_{r_1}) to calculate V_2 at T_{r_2}, P_{r_2}, but for saturated liquids it is possible to use V_c as a reference value, in which case Eq. (3-74) becomes

$$V_1 = V_c/\rho_{r_1} \qquad\qquad (3\text{-}75)$$

since at $V_2 = V_c$, $T_2 = T_c$, $P_2 = P_c$, $\rho_{r_2} = 1.0$.   Table 3-8 shows experimental values of saturated liquid molal volumes at several temperatures and also those calculated by Eqs. (3-74) and (3-75).   For Eq. (3-74) experimental values of the molal volume at the normal boiling point were used as the reference volume V_2.   For Eq. (3-74) an average error of 1.2

per cent was found (except for V_c, where the error was 2.5 per cent); for Eq. (3-75) the average error was 2.8 per cent.

Hooper and Joffe (56) compared the results from Eq. (3-74) with those obtained with the acentric-factor method described above and concluded the former was more applicable and accurate for liquids. Lu (69) has approximated the Lydersen et al. tables by Fig. 3-21, and Wicks (126) has expressed the saturated-liquid region for Z_c from 0.25 to 0.29, up to $T_r = 0.99$, as

$$\rho_r = 1.20 + (5.563 - 11.03Z_c)(1 - T_r)^{0.800Z_c+0.310} \qquad (3\text{-}76)$$

In other corresponding-state methods Osburn (91) plots a nomograph relating ρ to T_c and T which requires one known value of liquid density. This plot is said to be accurate in most cases to 5 per cent. Brebach and Thodos (20) and Hanson (48) present plots similar to Fig. 3-21, and Meissner and Paddison (79) suggest that the liquid-compressibility factor be correlated by using only T_r and P_r.

Example 3-8. Estimate the molal volume of saturated-liquid isobutyric acid at 220°C. The "Handbook of Chemistry and Physics" (55) lists a density of 0.949 at 20°C. Appendix A lists $T_c = 609.5°K$, $P_c = 40$ atm, $V_c = 292$ cm³/g mole, and $Z_c = 0.234$. The experimental value is 122 cm³/g mole (57).

Solution. *Lydersen Method* [Eq. (3-74)].

$$V_2 = (1/0.949)(88.10) = 92.8 \text{ cm}^3/\text{g mole}$$
$$T_{r_2} = (20 + 273)/609.5 = 0.481$$

From Table 3-6, with the liquid assumed saturated, $Z_c = 0.23$, $\rho_{r_2} = 3.117$. At 220°C,

$$T_{r_1} = (220 + 273)/609.5 = 0.809$$

From Table 3-6, as above, $\rho_{r_1} = 2.505$. Then

$$V_1 = (92.8)(3.117)/2.505 = 115 \text{ cm}^3/\text{g mole}$$
$$\text{Error} = [(115 - 122)/122] \times 100 = -5.7\%$$

If the experimental value of V_b, 109 cm³/g mole at the normal boiling point of 154°C, is used (57) the method just illustrated yields $V_1 = 121$ cm³/g mole. In Table 3-8, all values calculated were based on the normal-boiling-point volume rather than low-temperature liquid densities.

Lydersen Method [Eq. (3-75)]. Using the numbers generated above and $V_c = 292$ cm³/g mole,

$$V_1 = 292/2.505 = 116 \text{ cm}^3/\text{g mole}$$
$$\text{Error} = [(116 - 122)/122] = 100 = -4.9\%$$

A very interesting paper based upon a modified law of corresponding states was presented by Bondi and Simkin (16). The writers wished to establish parameters other than critical properties for high-molecular-weight substances because such compounds decompose before the critical state may be attained. A new reduced density was defined as

$$\rho_r^* = V^*/V \qquad (3\text{-}77)$$

where V^* is calculated from bond distances and the van der Waals radii of atoms.   Table 3-7 presents group contributions to determine V^*.   A reduced temperature is defined as

$$T_r^* = T/T^* \tag{3-78}$$

where $\qquad\qquad\qquad T^* = E^0/5cR$

and E^0 is the internal energy of vaporization at $V_r^* = 1.70$.   The quantity $3c$ is the external degrees of freedom per molecule. E^0 can also be estimated approximately by a group contribution method (16).   Although the method has a theoretical basis, it is most useful for the determination of high-molecular-weight liquid densities as a function of temperature, given one experimental point.   For example, suppose that one had available the liquid density at one temperature.   From the molecular structure, V^* could be determined from Table 3-7 and ρ_r^* determined by Eq. (3-77).   The correlation between ρ_r^* and T_r^* is

$$\rho_r^* = 0.726 - 0.249T_r^* - 0.019T_r^{*2} \tag{3-79}$$

with ρ_r^* known, T_r^* is determined and T^* found from Eq. (3-78).   This value of T^* is then used to determine a new T_r^*, and ρ_r^* is given as a function of T_r^* by Eq. (3-79).   This method is illustrated in Example 3-9.

Example 3-9.   Estimate the density of 1,1-biscyclohexylethane at 300°F.   The density at 100°F is reported as 0.88 g/cm³.   Compare with the experimental value of about 0.82 g/cm³ (82).

Solution.   In this case no critical temperature is known.   The material boils around 523°F, and rapid decomposition begins around 690°F, well below any anticipated critical temperature.   The method of Bondi and Simkin will be used.   From Table 3-7,

$$V^* = \Sigma V^* = 10(\overset{|}{-}CH_2) + 3(\overset{|}{-}CH) + 1(-CH_3)$$

$$= (10)(10.23) + (3)(6.78) + 13.67 = 136.3 \text{ cm}^3/\text{g mole}$$

At 100°F, $\rho_r^* = 136.3/194/0.88 = 0.62$ $M = 194$

With this value of ρ_r^* and Eq. (3-79), T_r^* at 100°F = 0.41.   Thus

$$T^* = T/T_r^* = (460 + 100)/0.41 = 1370°\text{R}$$

At 300°F, $\qquad T_r^* = (300 + 460)/1{,}370 = 0.554$

and from Eq. (3-79),

$$\rho_r^* = 0.726 - 0.249(0.554) - 0.019(0.554)^2 = 0.582$$
$$V = V^*/\rho_r^* = 136.3/0.582 = 234 \text{ cm}^3/\text{g mole}$$
$$\rho = M/V = {}^{194}\!/_{234} = 0.83 \text{ g/cm}^3$$
$$\text{Error} = [(0.83 - 0.82)/0.82] \times 100 = +1.2\%$$

Liquid-Gas Density Relations.   There are three empirical rules relating liquid and gas densities with temperature which are often useful.

Benson Method.   By the empirical rule of Cailletet and Mathias, saturated-liquid densities are related as follows:

$$\rho_L + \rho_v = a + bT + cT^2 + \cdots \tag{3-80}$$

TABLE 3-7. GROUP CONTRIBUTIONS TO DETERMINE V^*†

Contribution, V^*,
cm^3/g mole

—$\overset{|}{\underset{|}{C}}$—.. 3.33

—$\overset{|}{CH}$.. 6.78

—$\overset{|}{CH_2}$.. 10.23

—CH_3.. 13.67

CH_4.. 17.12

Aromatic groups:

$\diagdown$CH.. 8.06

$\diagdown$C—... 5.54

$\diagdown$C— (condensation)... 4.74

Olefinic groups:

=C$\diagup$.. 5.01

=C—H... 8.47

=CH_2.. 11.94

=C—... 6.87

≡C—H.. 10.42

≡C— (in diacetylene).. 6.65

Ether oxygen (attached to carbon atoms)... 5.20

Hydroxyl group (attached to carbon atoms)....................................... 8.04‡

Keto group ($\overset{|}{C}$=O) (attached to carbon atoms)...................... 11.70

Primary aliphatic —NH_2 (attached to carbon atoms)............................ 10.54

Secondary aliphatic $\diagup^{\diagdown}$NH (attached to carbon atoms)........... 8.08

Tertiary aliphatic —$\overset{|}{N}$ (attached to carbon atoms)................. 4.33

Cyano group (attached to carbon atoms).. 14.70

Nitro group (attached to carbon atoms).. 16.8

Thioether sulfur (attached to carbon atoms)..................................... 10.8

Thiol group (attached to carbon atoms).. 14.8

Fluorine (attached to alkane, primary).. 5.72

Fluorine (attached to alkane, secondary, tertiary)............................. 6.20

Fluorine (in perfluoro alkane).. 6.00

Fluorine (attached to phenyl ring).. 5.80

Chlorine (attached to alkane, primary).. 11.62

Chlorine (attached to alkane, secondary, tertiary or
polychloroalkane)... 12.24

† A. Bondi and D. J. Simkin, *AIChE J.*, **6**:191 (1960).

‡ For typical hydrogen-bonded system O · · · H = 2.78 A, deduct 1.05 cm^3/g mole per hydrogen bond.

TABLE 3-7. GROUP CONTRIBUTIONS TO DETERMINE V^* (Continued)

Contribution, V^*, cm^3/g mole

Chlorine (attached to vinyl group)................................ 11.65
Chlorine (attached to phenyl ring)................................ 12.0
Bromine (attached to alkane, primary)............................. 14.40
Bromine (attached to alkane, secondary, tertiary, or polybromide)..... 14.60
Bromine (attached to phenyl ring)................................. 15.12
Iodine (attached to alkane, primary).............................. 19.18
Iodine (attached to alkane, tertiary, or polyiodo alkane).............. 20.35
Iodine (attached to phenyl ring).................................. 19.64

Furan ring... 37.50
Pyridine ring.. 46.18
Pyrrole ring... 39.76
Carbazole ring... 93.10

It is often a good approximation (even near the critical point) to assume the coefficients $c, d, \ldots$ to be zero. Benson (10) made this approximation and derived an equation for the variation of the saturated-liquid specific volume as a function of temperature, saturated-vapor density, critical constants, and one known liquid density. By writing the equality,

$$\rho_L = \rho_v = \rho_c \qquad \text{at the critical point}$$

then
$$2\rho_c = a + bT_c$$

whence
$$\rho_L + \rho_v = 2\rho_c - bT_c + bT = 2\rho_c + b(T - T_c) \qquad (3\text{-}81)$$

At the normal boiling point, usually

$$\rho_{L_b} \gg \rho_{v_b} \qquad \therefore \rho_{L_b} = 2\rho_c + b(T_b - T_c) \qquad (3\text{-}82)$$

Combining Eqs. (3-80), (3-81), and (3-82),

$$\rho_L = 2\rho_c + [(T_c - T)/(T_c - T_b)](\rho_{L_b} - 2\rho_c) - \rho_v \qquad (3\text{-}83)$$

ρ_v may be approximated by the gas-compressibility charts. ρ_c is preferably obtained from experimental data, but if these are lacking, it may be estimated by the methods given in Sec. 2-6. If the density at the boiling point is not known but a density determination at another temperature is available, then ρ_{L_b} may be replaced by the liquid density at this temperature. T_b is then replaced by this new temperature in Eq. (3-83); this new reference temperature must be far enough from the critical temperature so that $\rho_L \gg \rho_v$.

Equation (3-83) was tested on 32 different liquids at various temperatures ranging from a T_r of about 0.6 to very near the critical point. Experimental critical and normal-boiling-point volumes were employed. Table 3-8 shows a comparison between calculated and experimental values; the average error found was 1.1 per cent. In general, if reliable values of ρ_{L_b} (or other low-temperature density) and ρ_c are available, the method will yield calculated volumes with an accuracy within 2 per cent. The

TABLE 3-8. COMPARISON OF CALCULATED AND EXPERIMENTAL SATURATED-LIQUID VOLUMES

Compound	T, °C	T_r	V_{exp}	Ref.	Lydersen et al.[b] V	% Error[c]	Lydersen et al.[d] V	% Error[c]	Benson V	% Error[c]	Goldhammer V	% Error[c]	Mathias V	% Error[c]
Methane	−161.5[a]	0.58	37.7	57	....	....	38.2	+1.3						
	−150	0.64	39.2		39.6	+1.0	40.1	+2.2	39.3	+0.3	38.9	−0.8	39.2	+0.8
	−130	0.75	42.8		43.5	+1.6	44.0	+4.1	42.1	−1.6	42.2	−1.4	42.8	+2.6
	−110	0.85	48.2		49.3	+2.3	50.0	+3.6	48.5	+0.6	46.1	−4.4	48.2	+5.2
	−90	0.96	60.0		61.2	+2.0	62.0	+3.2	60.6	+1.0	56.5	−5.8	60.0	+8.2
	−82.2[f]	1.0	99.5	4	98.2	−1.3								
Propane	20.6	0.79	87.5	115	87.3	−0.2	87.3	−0.2	87.7	+0.2	88.5	+1.1	87.5	+1.1
	59.0	0.90	101		102	+1.0	102	+1.0	102	+1.0	104	+3.0	101	+3.0
	85.5	0.97	121		124	+2.4	124	+2.4	127	+5	113	−6.6	121	+9.1
	97.0[f]	1.0	201		201	0.0								
n-Heptane	99[a]	0.69	162	57	....	....	157	−3.1						
	140	0.76	175		175	0.0	169	−3.4	175	0.0	173	−1.1	175	0.0
	180	0.84	191		191	0.0	185	−3.1	191	0.0	188	−1.6	191	0.0
	220	0.91	216		217	+0.5	210	−2.8	216	0.0	211	−2.3	216	0.0
	260	0.99	289		287	−0.7	278	−3.8	289	0.0	268	−7.3	289	−0.3
	267[f]	1.0	426		440	+3.2								
Cyclohexane	80.8[a]	0.64	117	57	....	....	123	+5.1						
	120	0.71	124		124	0.0	131	+5.6	123	−0.8	122	−1.6	123	−0.8
	160	0.78	133		134	+0.8	141	+6.0	131	−1.5	131	−1.5	133	0.0
	200	0.86	145		146	+0.7	154	+6.2	144	−0.7	141	−2.8	146	+0.7
	240	0.93	166		166	0.0	174	+4.8	165	−0.6	158	−4.8	169	+1.8
	279.8[f]	1.0	307		292	−9.1								

Ethylene													
−103.8ᵃ	0.60	49.4	57	...	...	45.1	−9.5	52.0	−0.9	52.4	−0.2	52.9	+0.8
−80	0.68	52.5	...	52.9	+0.8	48.2	−8.9	58.6	−3.5	59.5	−2.0	62.1	+2.3
−40	0.83	60.7	...	61.3	+1.0	55.9	−8.6	75.1	−7.5	76.9	−5.3	84.0	+3.4
0	0.97	81.2	...	82.2	+1.2	74.9	−7.7						
9.2ᶠ	1.0	124	...	136	+9.6								
Acetylene													
−84ᵉ	0.61	42.0	57	...	...	41.5	−1.2	47.4	+0.6	46.7	−0.8	47.8	+1.5
−40	0.75	47.1	...	47.7	+1.3	47.3	+0.4	56.1	0.0	54.1	−3.6	57.1	+1.8
0	0.88	56.1	...	56.2	+0.2	55.7	−0.7	75.2	−0.1	68.0	−9.7	78.1	+3.7
30	0.98	75.3	...	74.2	−1.8	73.6	−2.3						
36ᶠ	1.0	113	...	114	+0.9								
Benzene													
100	0.66	98.4	57	99.7	+1.3	99.7	+1.3	99.2	+0.8	98.0	−0.4	100	+1.6
150	0.75	107	...	109	+1.9	109	+1.9	108	+0.9	106	−0.9	108	+0.9
210	0.86	121	...	123	+1.7	123	+1.7	123	+1.6	119	−1.7	123	+1.7
270	0.97	156	...	158	+1.3	158	+1.3	160	+2.5	146	−6.4	162	+3.8
289.4ᶠ	1.0	261	...	261	0.0								
Fluorobenzene													
85ᵃ	0.64	102	57	...	...	102	0.0	108	+0.9	107	0.0	108	+0.9
120	0.70	107	...	107	0.0	107	0.0	120	0.0	120	0.0	121	+0.8
180	0.81	120	...	120	0.0	120	0.0	141	−0.8	141	−0.7	144	+1.4
240	0.92	142	...	142	0.0	142	0.0						
286.5ᶠ	1.0	271	...	271	0.0								
Bromobenzene													
156ᵃ	0.64	120	57	...	...	121	+0.8	125	0.0	123	−1.6	126	+0.7
190	0.69	125	...	125	0.0	127	+1.6	135	+0.8	134	0.0	135	+0.7
240	0.77	134	...	135	+0.7	136	+1.5	142	−0.7	141	−1.4	142	−0.7
270	0.81	143	...	142	−0.7	143	0.0						
397ᶠ	1.0	323	...	320	−0.9								

TABLE 3-8. COMPARISON OF CALCULATED AND EXPERIMENTAL SATURATED-LIQUID VOLUMES (Continued)

Compound	T, °C	T_r	V_{exp}	Ref.	Lydersen et al.[b] V	Lydersen et al.[b] % Error[c]	Lydersen et al.[d] V	Lydersen et al.[d] % Error[c]	Benson V	Benson % Error[c]	Goldhammer V	Goldhammer % Error[c]	Mathias V	Mathias % Error[c]
Chlorobenzene.........	132[a]	0.64	115	57	.....	.....	116	+0.9						
	170	0.70	120	...	121	+0.8	122	+1.7	121	+0.8	121	+0.8	121	+0.8
	210	0.76	128	...	128	0.0	129	+0.8	129	+0.8	128	0.0	129	+0.8
	270	0.86	144	...	145	+0.7	146	+1.4	145	+0.7	144	0.0	146	+1.4
	359.2[f]	1.0	308	...	306	-0.7								
Iodobenzene.........	190[a]	0.64	130	57	.....	.....	132	+1.5						
	210	0.67	133	...	133	0.0	135	+1.5	133	0.0	132	-0.8	133	0.0
	240	0.71	138	...	138	0.0	140	+1.4	139	+0.7	137	-0.7	139	+0.7
	270	0.75	144	...	144	0.0	146	+1.4	144	0.0	143	-0.7	144	0.0
	448[f]	1.0	351	...	346	-1.4								
Methanol...........	64.7[a]	0.66	42.5	57	.....	.....	41.0	-3.5						
	110	0.75	45.6	...	45.5	-0.2	44.0	-3.5	46.0	+0.9	45.2	-0.9	45.7	+0.2
	170	0.86	51.9	...	52.4	+1.0	50.7	-2.3	53.1	+2.3	51.3	-1.2	52.1	+0.4
	240[f]	1.0	118	...	122	+3.4								
n-Propyl alcohol......	97.4[a]	0.69	81.8	57	.....	.....	81.2	-0.7						
	150	0.79	89.3	...	90.3	+1.1	89.5	+0.2	90.5	+1.3	88.5	-0.9	89.3	0.0
	210	0.90	105	...	107	+1.9	106	+0.9	107	+1.9	100	-4.8	104	-1.0
	260	0.99	154	...	167	+8.5	166	+7.8	154	0.0	135	-12.3	149	-3.2
	263.8[f]	1.0	220	...	222	+0.9								
Dimethyl ether.......	-23.7[a]	0.62	63.8	57	.....	.....	63.0	-1.3						
	20	0.73	69.6	...	68.0	-2.3	69.3	-0.4	69.8	+0.1	72.5	+3.5	73.5	+5.6
	80	0.88	83.4	...	82.1	-1.6	83.6	+0.2	83.8	+0.5	84.7	+0.4	90.1	+7.4
	120	0.98	114	...	111	-2.6	113	-0.9	115	+0.9	107	-6.1	127	+11.4
	126.9[f]	1.0	170	...	167	-1.8								

Substance	t		obs.		calc.	Δ	calc.	Δ	calc.	Δ	calc.	Δ	calc.	Δ
Ethylpropyl ether	61.4ᵃ	0.67	129	57			131	+1.5						
	100	0.75	139		139	0.0	141	+1.4	141	+1.4	136	−2.2	141	+1.4
	160	0.89	161		161	0.0	163	+1.2	163	+1.2	155	−3.7	163	+1.2
	220	0.99	229		227	−0.9	231	+0.9	231	+0.9	207	−9.6	233	+1.7
	227.4ᶠ	1.0	341		336	−1.5								
Acetone	56.1ᵃ	0.65	77.5	57			77.3	−0.3						
	100	0.73	84.0		83.6	−0.5	83.3	−0.8	84.2	+0.2	84.0	0.0	83.3	−0.8
	160	0.85	96.8		96.5	−0.3	96.0	−0.8	96.6	−0.2	97.1	+0.3	95.2	−1.7
	230	0.99	148		147	−0.7	146	−1.4	149	+0.7	143	−3.4	142	−4.1
	235.5ᶠ	1.0	217		218	+0.5								
Acetic acid	118.5ᵃ	0.66	64.1	57			59.5	−7.2						
	160	0.73	68.1		67.5	−0.9	62.8	−7.8	68.3	+0.3	68.0	−0.1	67.6	−0.7
	220	0.83	75.8		75.2	−0.8	69.9	−7.8	76.1	+0.4	76.3	+0.7	75.8	0.0
	280	0.93	90.8		91.0	+0.2	84.6	−6.8	90.6	+0.2	90.9	+0.1	90.9	+0.1
	320	0.99	130						130	0.0	134	+3.1	130	0.0
	321.6ᶠ	1.0	171		184	+4.1								
Isobutyric acid	154ᵃ	0.70	109	57			104	−4.6						
	170	0.73	111		111	0.0	107	−3.6	112	+0.9	111	0.0	112	+0.9
	220	0.81	122		121	−0.8	116	−4.9	123	+0.8	122	0.0	122	0.0
	280	0.91	143		141	−1.4	135	−5.6	144	+0.7	143	0.0	141	−1.4
	300	0.94	155		155	0.0	148	−4.5	155	0.0	155	0.0	152	−1.9
	336ᶠ	1.0	290		303	+4.5								
Methyl formate	31.9ᵃ	0.63	62.8	57			60.2	−4.1						
	80	0.72	68.3		68.1	−0.3	65.5	−4.1	68.4	0.0	68.0	−0.6	68.5	+0.1
	110	0.79	72.6		72.7	+0.1	69.8	−3.9	72.9	+0.4	72.5	−0.1	73.0	+0.6
	150	0.87	81.3		81.4	+0.1	78.2	−3.8	81.6	+0.4	80.6	−0.9	82.0	+0.9
	210	0.99	124		126	+1.6	121	−2.5	124	0.0	117	−5.6	125	+0.8
	214ᶠ	1.0	172		179	+3.9								

TABLE 3-8. COMPARISON OF CALCULATED AND EXPERIMENTAL SATURATED-LIQUID VOLUMES (*Continued*)

Compound	T, °C	T_r	V_{exp}	Ref.	Lydersen et al.[b] V	Lydersen et al.[b] % Error[c]	Lydersen et al.[d] V	Lydersen et al.[d] % Error[c]	Benson V	Benson % Error[c]	Goldhammer V	Goldhammer % Error[c]	Mathias V	Mathias % Error[c]
Ethyl acetate..........	77.2[a]	0.67	106	57	.....	.....	104	−1.9						
	120	0.75	115		115	0.0	112	−2.6	115	0.0	114	−0.9	114	−0.9
	180	0.87	133		133	0.0	130	−2.3	132	−0.8	132	−0.8	132	−0.8
	240	0.98	184		183	−0.5	180	−2.2	184	0.0	178	−3.3	182	−1.1
	250.1[f]	1.0	286		293	+2.5								
Diethylamine.........	55.4[a]	0.66	109	57	.....	.....	113	+3.7						
	100	0.75	118		118	0.0	123	+4.2	119	+0.9	118	0.0	117	−0.8
	160	0.87	138		138	0.0	143	+3.6	140	+1.4	136	−1.1	136	−1.4
	210	0.97	183		180	−1.6	188	+2.7	181	−1.1	180	−1.6	175	−4.3
	222.8[f]	1.0	297		285	−4.0								
Acetonitrile.........	82[a]	0.65	57.4	57	.....	.....	59.1	+3.0						
	110	0.70	60.0		59.6	−0.7	61.4	+2.3	60.5	+0.8	59.9	−0.2	59.9	−0.2
	160	0.79	66.2		64.7	−2.2	66.7	+0.8	67.5	+2.0	66.2	0.0	66.4	+0.3
	210	0.88	76.5		74.1	−3.1	76.3	−0.3	77.3	+1.0	76.3	−0.3	73.0	−4.6
	260	0.97	103		98.8	−4.1	102	−1.0	101	−1.9	99.0	−3.9	90.9	−12
	274.7[f]	1.0	171		166	−2.9								
Methyl chloride......	−24[a]	0.60	50.6	57	.....	.....	52.0	+2.8						
	10	0.68	54.0		53.8	−0.4	55.4	+2.6	54.3	+0.5	53.8	−0.4	54.3	+0.6
	80	0.85	64.5		64.5	0.0	66.4	+2.9	65.6	+1.7	64.1	−0.6	65.4	+0.2
	130	0.97	85.3		84.5	−0.9	86.9	+1.5	87.5	+2.5	81.3	−4.9	87.0	+2.0
	143.1[f]	1.0	143		139	+1.8								

Carbon tetrachloride.													
77[a]	0.63	102	57			103	+1.0						
100	0.67	106		105	−1.0	106	0.0	106	0.0	105	−0.9	107	+0.9
150	0.76	115		115	0.0	115	0.0	115	0.0	117	+1.7	117	+1.7
220	0.89	135		135	0.0	136	+0.7	134	−0.8	134	−0.7	139	+3.0
270	0.98	175		175	0.0	176	+0.6	177	+1.1	169	−3.4	182	+4.0
283.2[f]	1.0	276		274	−0.7								
Dichlorodifluoro-methane													
−29[a]	0.63	80.7	57			81.5	+1.0						
−6.7	0.69	84.8		84.8	0.0	85.6	+0.9	85.1	+0.4	84.7	−0.1	84.7	−0.1
21	0.76	90.5		90.7	+0.2	91.5	+1.1	91.2	+0.8	90.1	−0.4	91.7	+1.3
49	0.84	98.3		99.3	+1.0	100	+1.7	99.5	+1.2	98.0	−0.3	101	+2.7
Ethyl mercaptan													
34.4[a]	0.62	75.5	57			75.8	+0.4						
80	0.71	81.5		81.4	−0.1	81.8	+0.4	81.0	−0.6	81.3	−0.2	81.3	−0.2
150	0.85	95.0		95.3	+0.3	95.8	+0.8	93.9	−1.2	95.2	+0.2	96.2	+1.3
210	0.97	124		126	+1.6	126	+1.6	121	−2.5	125	+0.8	125	+0.8
225.8[f]	1.0	206		205	−0.5								
Diethyl sulfide													
90.3[a]	0.65	118	57			122	+3.4						
130	0.72	125		126	+0.8	131	+4.6	126	+0.8	126	+0.8	126	+0.8
200	0.85	144		145	+0.7	151	+4.6	145	+0.7	146	+1.4	144	0.0
270	0.98	197		197	0.0	205	+4.1	200	+1.5	197	0.0	196	−0.5
283.8[f]	1.0	323		311	−3.7								
Phosgene													
8.3[a]	0.62	69.5	57			75.1	+7.5						
50	0.71	75.1		75.2	+0.1	81.2	+7.5	75.4	+0.4	75.2	+0.1	75.8	+0.9
120	0.86	89.1		89.7	+0.7	96.8	+8.6	89.6	+0.6	91.7	+2.9	90.1	+1.1
170	0.97	119		116	−2.5	125	+5.1	120	+0.8	120	+0.8	120	+0.8
182[f]	1.0	191		177	−7.4								

TABLE 3-8. COMPARISON OF CALCULATED AND EXPERIMENTAL SATURATED-LIQUID VOLUMES (Continued)

Compound	T, °C	T_r	V_{exp}	Ref.	Lydersen et al.[b] V	% Error[c]	Lydersen et al.[d] V	% Error[c]	Benson V	% Error[c]	Goldhammer V	% Error[c]	Mathias V	% Error[c]
Ammonia	−33[a]	0.59	25.0	57	...	...	24.5	−2.0						
	0	0.67	26.6	...	26.8	+0.8	26.3	−1.1	27.1	+1.9	26.6	0.0	26.7	+0.4
	60	0.82	31.2	...	31.2	0.0	30.7	−1.6	31.6	+1.3	31.2	0.0	31.0	−0.6
	120	0.97	44.0	...	43.3	−1.6	42.5	−3.4	43.7	−0.7	44.0	0.0	42.2	−4.1
	132.4[f]	1.0	72.4	...	73.8	+1.9								
Chlorine	−34.6[a]	0.57	45.5	57	...	...	43.9	−3.5						
	−20	0.61	46.5	...	46.8	+0.6	45.3	−2.6						
	40	0.75	52.8	...	53.1	+0.6	51.4	−2.6						
	110	0.92	67.0	...	67.5	+0.7	65.4	−2.4						
	144[f]	1.0	124	...	128	+3.2								
Water	100[a]	0.58	18.7	59	...	...	18.7	0.0						
	160	0.67	19.7	...	19.8	+0.5	19.7	0.0	20.3	+3.1	19.8	+0.5	20.2	+2.5
	240	0.79	22.0	...	22.1	+0.5	22.1	+0.5	23.1	+5.1	21.9	−0.5	22.7	+3.2
	330	0.93	28.1	...	28.3	+0.7	28.2	+0.4	29.2	+4.0	26.4	−6.0	27.9	−0.4
	370	0.99	39.2	...			....	....	39.4	+0.5	34.5	−12.0	36.8	−6.1
	374[f]	1.0	56.4	...	56.5	+0.2	....	....						
Hydrochloric acid	−85[a]	0.58	30.6	57	...	...	31.2	+2.0						
	−40	0.72	34.4	...	34.2	−0.6	34.9	+1.4	36.4	+5.9	34.4	0.0	34.5	+0.3
	10	0.87	41.5	...	41.1	−0.9	41.9	+0.9	41.8	+0.7	41.5	0.0	41.8	+0.7
	40	0.96	52.4	...	51.4	−1.9	52.5	+0.2	53.0	+1.1	51.8	−1.1	52.9	+1.0
	51.4[f]	1.0	87.0	...	85.3	−1.9								

TABLE 3-8. COMPARISON OF CALCULATED AND EXPERIMENTAL SATURATED-LIQUID VOLUMES (*Continued*)

Compound	T, °C	T_r	V_{exp}	Ref.	Lydersen et al.[b]		Lydersen et al.[a]		Benson		Goldhammer		Mathias	
					V	% Error[c]	V	% Error[c]	V	% Error[c]	V	% Error[c]	V	% Error[c]
Sulfur dioxide.......	− 56.7	0.50	40.6	114	40.6	0.0	42.0	+ 3.5	40.5	− 0.2	40.3	− 0.7	40.7	+ 0.2
	− 28.8	0.57	42.5	...	42.2	− 0.7	47.2	+ 4.0	42.5	0.0	42.4	− 0.2	42.6	+ 0.2
	− 10.0[a]	0.61	43.8	...	.....	.....	45.1	+ 2.9						
	65.5	0.79	51.4	...	51.2	− 3.9	53.0	+ 3.1	51.7	+ 0.6	52.1	+ 1.4	51.5	+ 0.2
	149	0.98	80.1	...	77.5	− 3.2	80.2	+ 0.1	80.6	+ 0.6	79.3	− 1.0	80.0	− 0.1
	157.2[f]	1.0	123	...	119	− 3.3	.....		.....		.....		.....	
Average error.......	.....	.....	.....	.....	.....	1.3	.....	2.6	.....	1.1	.....	1.9	.....	1.7

[a] Normal boiling point.
[b] Method based on V_b.
[c] Per cent error = [(calculated − experimental)(experimental)] × 100.
[d] Method based on V_c.
[e] Sublimation temperature.
[f] Critical point.

105

method was proposed for saturated liquids, but since the effect of pressure on specific liquid volumes is small (except near the critical point), the method may be used for slightly subcooled liquids.

The law of Cailletet and Mathias may also be used in a more straightforward manner if two or more saturated-liquid densities are known at different temperatures. Constants $a, b, c, \ldots$ may then be determined in Eq. (3-80) and the resulting expression used to calculate other saturated liquid densities.

Goldhammer Method. Gambill (37) discusses the Goldhammer correlation (38)

$$\rho_L - \rho_v = a(1 - T_r)^n \tag{3-84}$$

The constant a appears to be proportional to the critical density. Bowden and Costello (18) indicate that a is about $3.5\rho_c$ and for polar molecules may be estimated as a complex function of ρ_c (17).

The most useful form of the correlation results from eliminating the parameter a with one known density-temperature datum point to give

$$\Delta\rho = \rho_L - \rho_v = (\Delta\rho)_1 \left(\frac{T_c - T}{T_c - T_1} \right)^n \tag{3-85}$$

The constant n varies from compound to compound and ranges from 0.24 to 0.34; Fishtine (33) suggests the following values:

$$n$$

Alcohols and water	0.25
Hydrocarbons and ethers	0.29
All other organic compounds	0.31
All inorganic compounds except water	0.33

However, he cautions that Eq. (3-85) is not valid above $T_r = 0.85$, since n is temperature-sensitive above this level. Also, Eq. (3-85) is not applicable if the vapor-phase molecular weight is temperature-sensitive. The method is illustrated in Example 3-10, and calculated and experimental liquid values are compared for some 32 compounds in Table 3-8. The accuracy is within 1 per cent in most cases below $T_r = 0.85$. Even above this temperature, in most cases, the errors do not exceed 2 to 5 per cent. No critical density value is required.

Mathias Method. Mathias (78) suggested an extraordinarily simple relation requiring no exponential constants or critical densities,

$$\rho_L + \rho_v = \rho_{L_b}(2 - T_r)/(2 - T_{b_r}) \tag{3-86}$$

The value 2 is an empirical value, and perhaps other values would be better; a test of Eq. (3-86) is shown in Table 3-8. Except very near the critical point this simple equation yields errors of only a few per cent. The average error for all 32 compounds is 1.7 per cent. Only the critical temperature, normal boiling point, liquid volume, and an approximate value of the saturated vapor density are required. The method is illustrated in Example 3-10.

Example 3-10. Estimate the saturated liquid volume of bromobenzene at 220°C. From Appendix A the critical properties are $T_c = 670.2°K$, $P_c = 44.6$ atm, and $V_c = 324$ cm³/g mole. At 15°C the density is 1.499 g/cm³ (55). The experimental value at 220°C is 130 cm³/g mole (57).

Solution. *Benson Method.* In Eq. (3-83), the variables ρ_{L_b} and T_b are replaced by ρ_L at 15°C and $T = 15°C$ inasmuch as these are the reference values. Also $\rho_c = \frac{1}{324} = 0.00309$ g mole/cm³. Thus

$$\rho_L = (2)(0.00309)$$
$$+ [(670.2 - 493.2)/(670.2 - 288.2)][1.499/157 - (2)(0.00309)] - \rho_v$$
$$= 0.00618 + \frac{177}{382}(0.00955 - 0.00618) - \rho_v$$
$$= 0.00618 + 0.00156 - \rho_v = 0.00774 - \rho_v$$

ρ_v may be estimated from gas compressibilities and vapor pressures (Chap. 4) as 0.00011 g mole/cm³.

$$\rho_L = 0.00774 - 0.00011 = 0.00763$$
$$V = 1/0.00763 = 131 \text{ cm}^3/\text{g mole}$$
$$\text{Error} = [(131 - 130)/130] \times 100 = +0.8\%$$

A value of 131 cm³/g mole is also obtained if V_b (Table 3-5) is used as a reference. *Goldhammer Method.* By using the same data as above in Eq. (3-85) with $n = 0.31$ and $\Delta\rho_1 = (\Delta\rho)_{15°C} \cong \rho_{L_{15°C}}$, then

$$\rho_L \text{ (at 220°C)} = 0.00011 + (1.499/157)[(670.2 - 493.2)/(670.2 - 288.2)]^{0.31}$$
$$= 0.00011 + 0.00955(0.463)^{0.31} = 0.00763$$
$$V = 1/0.00763 = 131 \text{ cm}^3/\text{g mole}$$
$$\text{Error} = [(131 - 130)/130] \times 100 = +0.8\%$$

Mathias Method. From the data given above and the experimental value of $V_{L_b} = 120$ cm³/g mole at $T_b = 156°C$, $T_{b_r} = 0.641$, Eq. (3-86) gives

$$\rho_L = -0.00011 + \frac{1}{120}[2 - (493.2/670.2)/(2 - 0.641)]$$
$$= -0.00011 + 0.00775 = 0.00764 \text{ g mole/cm}^3 \qquad V = 131 \text{ cm}^3/\text{g mole}$$
$$\text{Error} = [(131 - 130)/130] \times 100 = +0.8\%$$

Recommendations. There are many liquid P-V-T correlations which have not been presented in detail. Scott and Dillon correlate liquid volumes with the triple-point temperature (118). Kurtz and Sankin (64) and Hadden and Simha (42, 119) have presented equations to allow calculation for medium- and high-molecular-weight liquid hydrocarbons. For the general case, however, the following recommendations are listed:
Experimental data are preferred to any correlation.

If an accurate volume measurement is available at any single temperature and if critical constants are known or can be estimated with reasonable accuracy, use Benson's method [Eq. (3-83)], Goldhammer's method [Eq. (3-85)], or Lydersen, Greenkorn, and Hougen's method [Eq. (3-75)] and Table 3-6. Benson's method requires a knowledge of the critical volume, and both it and Goldhammer's method are limited to orthobaric or slightly subcooled liquids. Lydersen, Greenkorn, and Hougen's method may be used at any pressure.   Except near the critical point, errors should be less than 2 per cent.   If the density at the normal boiling point is known, Mathias's method [Eq. (3-86)] is often convenient.

If no experimental volume data are available but the critical constants are known or can be estimated, the volume at any temperature may be estimated in either of two ways: (1) obtain V_b from methods described in Sec. 3-18, and use this volume in Benson's method [Eq. (3-82)], Goldhammer's method [Eq. (3-85)], or Lydersen, Greenkorn, and Hougen's method [Eq. (3-74)], or (2) use Lydersen, Greenkorn, and Hougen's method based on V_c [Eq. (3-75)] to calculate the volume directly.   Both (1) and (2) yield about the same error, i.e., about 2 to 5 per cent depending upon the compound and the accuracy of the critical constants.   Method 2 is preferable at pressures above the saturation pressure.

For hydrocarbons of high molecular weight whose critical constants are unknown, the method of Bondi and Simkin [Eq. (3-79)] should be used to estimate specific volumes; one experimental datum point is necessary.

NOMENCLATURE FOR CHAPTER 3

a = constant in Eqs. (3-48) to (3-51), (3-56), (3-80), and (3-84)

a^* = parameter in Example 3-6

a_1, a_2 = parameters in Eq. (3-55)

A = constant in Eqs. (3-28), (3-56)

$A_1, A_2, \ldots, A_5$ = constants in Eq. (3-68)

A' = intercept in Fig. 3-9

b = constant in Eqs. (3-48) to (3-51), (3-55), (3-66), (3-72), and (3-80)

$b^{(j)}$ = constant in Eq. (3-32)

b_0 = hard-sphere volume, $\frac{2}{3}\pi N_0\sigma^3$

b^* = parameter in Example 3-6

b' = parameter in Eq. (3-56)

B = second virial coefficient, cm^3/g mole; also constant in Eqs. (3-28), (3-56)

B' = intercept in Fig. 3-9

$B^* = B/b_0$

B^0, B^1 = second virial expansion terms in Eq. (3-45)

$B_1 \cdots B_5$ = constants in Eq. (3-67)

c = constant in Eqs. (3-20) and (3-80), or the external degrees of freedom in a molecule

C = third virial coefficient and constant in Eq. (3-56)

C' = intercept in Fig. 3-9

$C^* = c/b_0^2$

$C_1 \cdots C_5$ = constants in Eq. (3-67)

D = fourth virial coefficient

$D^* = D/b_0^3$

E^0 = internal energy of vaporization, cal/g mole at $V_r^* = 1.70$

$f(\ )$ = function of

$g(\ )$ = parameter in Eq. (3-61)

h = Planck's constant or b^*P/Z in Example 3-6

$h_0 \cdots h_3$ = parameters in Eq. (3-65)

k = Boltzmann's constant

k_0 = parameter in Eqs. (3-59) and (3-60)

k' = parameter in Eq. (3-67)

K_2 = shape factor in Eq. (3-18)

K_3 = polarity factor in Eq. (3-18)

m = mass, constant in Eq. (3-28), or $-MP_c/T_c$ in Eq. (3-71)

M = $d(\ln P_{vp_r})/d(1/T_r)$, or molecular weight

n = constant in Eqs. (3-28), (3-84), or as described in Eq. (3-66)

N_0 = Avogadro's number

P = pressure, atm

P_c = critical pressure, atm

P_{vp} = vapor pressure, atm

q^* = α/σ^3 in Eq. (3-44)

Q = quadrupole moment

r = intermolecular distance

r_0 = equilibrium intermolecular distance

R = gas constant, 82.06 cm³-atm/(g mole)(°K)

s = parameter in Eq. (3-64)

t^* = $\mu^2/2\sqrt{2}\,\epsilon_0\sigma^3$

T = temperature

T_b = normal boiling temperature, °K

T_c = critical temperature, °K

T^* = $T/(\epsilon_0/k)$ or $E^0/5cR$; T_r^* = T/T^*

T_{B_0} = Boyle temperature in Eq. (3-68)

T' = parameter in Eq. (3-69)

V = volume, cm³/g mole

V_c = critical volume, cm³/g mole

V_{c_i} = RT_c/P_c; V_{r_i} = V/V_{c_i}

V^* = van der Waals' volume (see Table 3-7); V_r^* = V/V^*

W_1, W_2 = parameters in Eqs. (3-59), (3-60)

y = parameter described by Eq. (3-66)

Y = parameter in Eq. (3-66)

Z = compressibility factor, PV/RT

Z_c = P_cV_c/RT_c

Z_p = $Z - P(\partial Z/\partial P)_T = Z - P_r(\partial Z/\partial P_r)_{T_r}$

Z^0, Z^1 = compressibility factors in the expansion of Eq. (3-15)

Z^{11} = polar correction to compressibility factor in Eq. (3-19)

Z^* = parameter in Eq. (3-53)

Z^{**} = parameter in Eq. (3-54)

Greek

α = polarizability

α_c = Riedel factor (Sec. 2-8)

β = shape factor [Eq. (3-7)]; parameter in Eq. (3-62)

$\varphi(r)$ = interaction energy

ϵ_0 = interaction-energy correlating parameter

η = polarity factor in Eq. (3-20)

θ = T_b/T_c

Θ = term representative of angles between polar groups and some fixed molecular axis

μ = dipole moment

π = 3.1416, or parameter in Eq. (3-56)

ρ = density, g moles/cm^3
ρ_c = critical density
ρ_b = density at the normal boiling point
$\rho_r^* = V^*/V$
σ = interaction-molecular-distance correlating parameter
ω = acentric factor [Eq. (3-13)]

Subscripts Other than Those Noted

r = ratio of property to the same property at critical point
v = reference to vapor state
L = reference to liquid state

REFERENCES FOR CHAPTER 3

1. Ackerman, F. J.: M.S. thesis, UCRL-10650, University of California, Berkeley, Calif., February, 1963.
2. Amdur, I., and E. A. Mason: *Phys. Fluids*, **1**:370 (1958).
3. Amdur, I., and J. Ross: *Combustion and Flame*, **2**:412 (1958).
4. American Petroleum Institute: "Selected Values of Physical and Thermodynamic Properties of Hydrocarbons and Related Compounds," Project 44, Carnegie Press, Pittsburgh, Pa., 1953.
5. Baschinski, A.: *Z. physik. Chem.*, **40**:629 (1902).
6. Beattie, J. A., and O. C. Bridgman, *Proc. Am. Acad. Arts Sci.*, **63**:229 (1928).
7. Beck, C. W., and L. Y. Beck: *Ind. Eng. Chem.*, **50**:1301 (1958).
8. Benedict, M., G. B. Webb, and L. C. Rubin, *J. Chem. Phys.*, **8**:334 (1940).
9. Benedict, M., G. B. Webb, L. C. Rubin, and L. Friend: *Chem. Eng. Progr.*, **47**:419, 449, 571, 609 (1951).
10. Benson, S. W., *J. Phys. & Colloid Chem.*, **52**:1060 (1948).
11. Bergeon, R.: *Compt. rend.*, **234**:1039 (1952).
12. Bird, R. B., and J. R. Brock: *AIChE J.*, **5**:436 (1959).
13. Black, C.: *Ind. Eng. Chem.*, **50**:391 (1958).
14. Bloomer, O. T., and R. G. Peck: *AIChE J.*, **6**:240 (1960).
15. Boas, A. H.: Ph.D. thesis, Polytechnic Institute of Brooklyn, 1962.
16. Bondi, A., and D. J. Simkin: *AIChE J.*, **6**:191 (1960).
17. Bowden, S. T., and J. M. Costello: *Chem. Ind. (London)*, **1957**:268.
18. Bowden, S. T., and J. M. Costello: *Rec. trav. chim.*, **77**:28 (1958).
18a. Bottomley, G. A., and T. H. Spurling, *Australian J. Chem.*, **16**:1 (1963).
19. Boys, S. F., and I. Shavitt: *Proc Roy. Soc. (London)*, **A254**:487 (1960).
20. Brebach, W. J., and G. Thodos: *Chem. Eng. Data Ser.* **3**:338 (1958).
21. Brush, S. G., R. Kraft, and J. Senkin: High-pressure Equation of State Bibliography and Index, *Lawrence Rad. Lab.*, UCRL-7160, Livermore, Calif., Jan. 22, 1963.
22. Buckingham, A. D., and J. A. Pople: *Trans. Faraday Soc.*, **51**:1173 (1955).
23. Callen, H. B.: "Thermodynamics," John Wiley & Sons, Inc., New York, 1960.
24. Canjar, L. N., R. F. Smith, E. Volianitis, J. F. Galluzzo, and M. Cabarcos: *Ind. Eng. Chem.*, **47**:1028 (1955).
25. Darin, S. R., E. B. Stuart, and J. Coull: *Oil Gas J.*, **56**(24):105 (1958).
26. David, H. G., and S. D. Hamann: *Conf. on Thermodynamic and Transport Properties of Fluids*, London, 1957, p. 74, 1958, Institution of Mechanical Engineering.
27. Doolittle, A. K.: *AIChE J.*, **6**:150, 153, 157 (1960).
28. Douslin, D. R.: 1962 *Symposium on Thermophys. Properties*, Princeton University, Jan. 24–26, 1962.

29. Douslin, D. R., R. H. Harrison, R. T. Moore, and J. P. McCullough: *J. Chem. Phys.*, **35**:1357 (1961).
30. Edmister, W. C.: *Petrol. Refiner*, **37**(4):173 (1958).
31. Epstein, L. F.: *Ind. Eng. Chem. Fundamentals*, **1**:123 (1962).
32. Eubank, P. T., and J. M. Smith: *AIChE J.*, **8**:117 (1962).
33. Fishtine, S. H.: *Ind. Eng. Chem. Fundamentals*, **2**:149 (1963).
34. Francis, A. W.: *Chem. Eng. Sci.*, **10**:37 (1959).
35. Francis, A. W.: *Ind. Eng. Chem.*, **49**:1779 (1957).
36. Gambill, W. R.: *Chem. Eng.*, **66**(21):195 (1959).
37. Gambill, W. R.: *Chem. Eng.*, **66**(23):193 (1959).
38. Goldhammer, D. A.: *Z. physik. Chem.*, **71**:577 (1910).
39. Greenshields, J. B., and F. D. Rossini: *J. Phys. Chem.*, **62**:271 (1958).
40. Griskey, R. G., and H. H. Beyer: *AIChE J.*, **9**:507 (1963).
41. Griskey, R. G., and L. N. Canjar: *AIChE J.*, **9**:182 (1963).
41a. Gyorog, D. A., and E. F. Obert: *AIChE J.*, **10**:625 (1964).
42. Hadden, S. T., and R. Simha: *J. Chem. Eng. Data*, **7**:444 (1962).
43. Hall, N. A., and W. E. Ibele: *Trans. ASME*, **76**:1039 (1954).
44. Hall, N. A., and W. E. Ibele: *Trans. ASME*, **77**:1003 (1955).
45. Hamann, S. D., and J. A. Lambert: *Australian J. Chem.*, **7**:1, 18 (1954).
46. Hamrin, C. E., Jr., and G. Thodos: *AIChE J.*, **4**:480 (1958).
47. Hansen, R. E.: *Chem. Eng. Progr.*, **60**(4):49 (1964).
48. Hanson, E. S.: *Ind. Eng. Chem.*, **41**:96 (1949).
49. Havliček, V.: *Strojirenstvi*, **8**:903 (1958).
50. Hilsenrath, J., et al.: *Natl. Bur. Standards (U.S.) Circ.* 564, 1955.
51. Hirschfelder, J. O., R. J. Buehler, H. A. McGee, Jr., and J. R. Sutton: *Ind. Eng. Chem.*, **50**:375 (1958); WIS-OOR-15, Oct. 5, 1956.
52. Hirschfelder, J. O., R. J. Buehler, H. A. McGee, Jr., and J. R. Sutton: *Ind. Eng. Chem. Fundamentals*, **1**:224 (1962).
53. Hirschfelder, J. O., C. F. Curtiss, and R. B. Bird: "Molecular Theory of Gases and Liquids," John Wiley & Sons, Inc., New York, 1954.
54. Hobson, M., and J. H. Weber: *AIChE J.*, **2**:354 (1956).
55. Hodgman, C. D. (ed.): "Handbook of Chemistry and Physics," 30th ed., Chemical Rubber Publishing Co., Cleveland, Ohio, 1948.
56. Hooper, E. D., and J. Joffe: *Chem. Eng. Data Ser.*, **5**:155 (1960).
57. "International Critical Tables," McGraw-Hill Book Company, New York, 1926–1930.
58. Joffe, J.: *Chem. Eng. Prog.*, **45**:160 (1949).
59. Keenan, J. H., and F. G. Keyes: "Thermodynamic Properties of Steam," John Wiley & Sons, Inc., New York, 1936.
60. Kihara, T.: *J. phys. Soc. Japan*, **3**:265 (1948); *ibid.*, **6**:184 (1951).
61. Kihara, T.: *Revs. Modern Phys.*, **25**:831 (1953).
62. Kobe, K. A., and P. S. Murti: *Ind. Eng. Chem.*, **51**:332 (1959).
63. Konowalow, D. D., and J. O. Hirschfelder: Intermolecular Potential Functions for Non-polar Molecules, *ARL Tech. Note* 60-158, December, 1960; *Phys. Fluids*, **4**:622, 629, 637 (1961); *ibid.*, **5**:126 (1962).
64. Kurtz, S. S., and A. Sankin: *Ind. Eng. Chem.*, **46**:2186 (1954).
65. Le Bas, G.: "The Molecular Volumes of Liquid Chemical Compounds," Longmans, Green & Co., Inc., New York, 1915.
66. Li, K., R. L. Arnett, M. B. Epstein, R. B. Ries, L. P. Butler, J. M. Lynch, and F. D. Rossini: *J. Phys. Chem.*, **60**:1400 (1956).
67. Lihatecheva, A. I., and G. P. Loutchinski: *J. chim. phys.*, **33**:488 (1936).
68. Longwell, P. A., J. B. Olin, and B. H. Sage: *Chem. Eng. Data Ser.*, **3**:175 (1958).

69. Lu, B. C. Y.: *Chem. Eng.*, **66**(9):137 (1959).
70. Lydersen, A. L., R. A. Greenkorn, and O. A. Hougen: Generalized Thermo-dynamic Properties of Pure Fluids, *Coll. Eng., Univ. Wisconsin, Eng. Expt. Sta. Rept.* 4, Madison, Wis., October, 1955.
71. Martin, J. J.: University of Michigan, personal communications, August, 1962, November, 1963.
72. Martin, J. J.: *Chem. Eng. Progr. Symposium Ser.*, **59**(44):120 (1963).
73. Martin, J. J., and Yu-Chun Hou: *AIChE J.*, **1**:142 (1955).
74. Martin, J. J., R. M. Kapoor, and N. De Nebers: *AIChE J.*, **5**:159 (1959).
75. Maslan, F. D., and T. M. Littman: *Ind. Eng. Chem.*, **45**:1566 (1953).
76. Mason, E. A.: Calculation of Second Virial and Joule-Thompson Coefficients of Gases at Very High Temperature, IMP-OSR-3, Institute of Molecular Physics, University of Maryland, Feb. 18, 1957.
77. Mason, E. A., and J. T. Vanderslice: *Ind. Eng. Chem.*, **50**:1033 (1958).
78. Mathias: *Ann. Fac. Sci. Toulouse*, **6**:M1 (1893); quoted in personal communica-tion, D. G. Miller, December, 1963.
79. Meissner, H. P., and O. H. Paddison: *Ind. Eng. Chem.*, **33**:1189 (1941).
80. Meissner, H. P., and R. Seferian: *Chem. Eng. Progr.*, **47**:579 (1951).
81. Miller, D. G., and W. H. Dennis: *Am. J. Phys.*, **28**:796 (1960).
82. Monchick, L., and E. A. Mason: *J. Chem. Phys.*, **35**:1676 (1961).
83. Monsanto Chemical Co.: S.P.D. Project 2004, Everett, Mass., Dec. 15, 1960.
84. Morecroft, D. W.: *J. Inst. Petrol.*, **44**:433 (1958).
85. Morgan, R. A., and J. A. Childs: *Ind. Eng. Chem.*, **37**:667 (1945).
86. Nakanishi, K., M. Kurata, and M. Tamura: *Chem. Eng. Data Ser.*, **5**:210 (1960).
87. Nelson, L., and E. F. Obert: *AIChE J.*, **1**:74 (1955).
88. Nelson, L. C., and E. F. Obert: *Trans. ASME*, **76**:1057 (1954).
89. Newton, R. H.: *Ind. Eng. Chem.*, **27**:302 (1935).
90. Opfell, J. P., B. H. Sage, and K. S. Pitzer: *Ind. Eng. Chem.*, **48**:2069 (1956).
91. Osburn, J. O.: *Chem. Eng.*, **63**(3):196 (1956).
92. Partington, J.: "An Advanced Treatise on Physical Chemistry," vol. 1, Funda-mental Principles—The Properties of Gases, Longmans, Green & Co., Inc., New York, 1949.
93. Pings, C. J., Jr., and B. H. Sage: *Ind. Eng. Chem.*, **49**:1315, 1321 (1957).
94. Pitzer, K. S.: *J. Am. Chem. Soc.*, **77**:3427 (1955).
95. Pitzer, K. S., and R. F. Curl: *J. Am. Chem. Soc.*, **79**:2369 (1957).
96. Pitzer, K. S., and R. F. Curl: The Thermodynamic Properties of Normal Fluids, *Conf. on Thermodynamics and Transport Properties of Fluids*, London, July, 1957, Institution of Mechanical Engineering.
97. Pitzer, K. S., D. Z. Lippmann, R. F. Curl, C. M. Huggins, and D. E. Petersen: *J. Am. Chem. Soc.*, **77**:3433 (1955).
98. Prausnitz, J. M., and A. L. Myers: *AIChE J.*, **9**:5 (1963).
99. Ramsay, W., and S. Young: *Trans. Roy. Soc. (London)*, **A178**:314 (1887).
100. Redlich, O., and A. K. Dunlop: *Chem. Eng. Symposium Ser.*, **59**:95 (1963).
101. Redlich, O., and J. N. S. Kwong: *Chem. Rev.*, **44**:233 (1949).
102. Riedel, L.: *Chem.-Ing.-Tech.*, **26**:83, 259, 679 (1954); see also *ibid.* **27**:209, 475 (1955); *ibid.*, **28**:557 (1956).
103. Riedel, L.: *Kaltetech.*, **9**:127 (1957).
104. Ritter, R. B., J. M. Lenoir, and J. L. Schweppe: *Petrol. Refiner*, **37**(11):225 (1958).
105. Rowlinson, J. S.: *J. Chem. Phys.*, **19**:827 (1951).
106. Rowlinson, J. S.: *J. Chem. Phys.*, **19**:831 (1951).
107. Rowlinson, J. S.: "Liquids and Liquid Mixtures," chap. 7, Butterworth & Co. (Publishers), Ltd., London, 1959.

108. Rowlinson, J. S.: *Mol. Phys.*, **6**:75 (1963).
109. Rowlinson, J. S.: *Mol. Phys.*, **6**:429 (1963).
110. Rowlinson, J. S.: *Trans. Faraday Soc.*, **45**:974 (1949).
111. Rowlinson, J. S.: *Trans. Faraday Soc.*, **50**:647 (1954); see also *ibid.*, **51**:1317 (1955); *Proc. Roy. Soc. (London)*, **A219**:405 (1953).
112. Rowlinson, J. S., F. H. Summer, and J. R. Sutton: *Trans. Faraday Soc.*, **50**:1 (1954).
113. Rush, W. F., and B. W. Gamson: *Ind. Eng. Chem.*, **41**:78 (1949).
114. Rynning, D. F., and C. O. Hurd: *Trans. AIChE*, **41**:265 (1945).
115. Sage, B. H., W. W. Lacey, and J. G. Schaafsma: *Ind. Eng. Chem.*, **26**:1218 (1934).
116. Satter, Abdus, and J. M. Campbell: *Soc. Petrol. Eng. J.*, December, 1963, p. 333.
117. Saxena, S. C., and K. M. Joshi: *Phys. Fluids*, **5**:1217 (1962).
118. Scott, A. F., and R. Dillon: *J. Chem. Phys.*, **17**:1179 (1949).
118a. Sherwood, A. E., and J. M. Prausnitz: *J. Chem. Phys.*, **41**:413, 429 (1964).
119. Simha, R., and S. T. Hadden: *J. Chem. Phys.*, **25**:702 (1956); *ibid.*, **26**:425 (1957).
119a. Stiel, L. I., and G. Thodos: *AIChE J.*, **10**:266 (1964).
120. Su, G.-J.: "Generalized Thermodynamic Properties of Real Gases as Functions of Reduced Pressure and Reduced Temperature—A Theoretical and Experimental Investigation," University of Rochester, February, 1960.
121. Su, G.-J., and C.-H. Chang: *Ind. Eng. Chem.*, **38**:800, 801, 802 (1946).
122. Su, G.-J., and C.-H. Chang: *J. Am. Chem. Soc.*, **68**:1080 (1946).
122a. Suh, K. W., and T. S. Storvick: Paper submitted to *J. Chem. Phys.*
123. Viswanath, D. S.: Ph.D. thesis, University of Rochester, 1962.
124. Watson, K. M.: *Ind. Eng. Chem.*, **35**:398 (1943).
125. Weber, J. H.: *AIChE J.*, **1**:210 (1955).
126. Wicks, Moye, III: *Petrol. Refiner*, **40**(3):196 (1961).
127. Yen, L. C., and S. S. Woods: *AIChE J.*, **12**:95 (1966).
128. Zwanzig, R. W.: *J. Chem. Phys.*, **23**:1915 (1955).

CHAPTER 4

VAPOR PRESSURES AND LATENT HEATS OF VAPORIZATION OF PURE COMPOUNDS

4-1 Scope

Vapor pressures and enthalpies of vaporization and sublimation are discussed in this chapter. Techniques are presented to predict vapor pressures with various types of input data. Latent-heat correlations are discussed in detail.

4-2 Vapor Pressure—General Considerations

The phase rule states that the vapor pressure of a pure liquid is a single-valued function of the saturation temperature. Almost all vapor-pressure data are thus expressed in a form

$$P_{vp} = f(T)$$

P_{vp} could be related to any other intensive property of the saturated liquid (or vapor), but the saturation temperature is most convenient.

All vapor-pressure equations may be traced back to the Clapeyron equation,

$$dP_{vp}/dT = \Delta H_v/T\,\Delta V_v = \Delta H_v/(RT^2/P_{vp})\,\Delta Z_v$$

or
$$d(\ln P_{vp})/d(1/T) = -\Delta H_v/R\,\Delta Z_v \qquad (4\text{-}1)$$

Equation (4-1) is easily derived from thermodynamics by using the phase equilibrium criteria, that fugacities (or chemical potentials), temperatures, and pressures are equal in both phases.* The key to the integration of Eq. (4-1) is the evaluation of the ratio $\Delta H_v/\Delta Z_v$. As a first approximation it is often assumed constant; Eq. (4-1) is then written as

$$\ln P_{vp} = A + B/T \qquad (4\text{-}2)$$

* For example, $f^v = f^L$ or $d(\ln f^v) = d(\ln f^L)$; the total differential is then expanded in terms of pressures and temperatures. Equation (4-1) results when the dP and dT terms are collected.

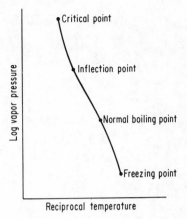

FIG. 4-1. Schematic vapor-pressure plot.

A graph of the logarithm of the vapor pressure against the reciprocal of the absolute temperature is a straight line if this applies. Often Eq. (4-2) is not a bad approximation (99), but, in general, actual $\ln P_{vp}$-$1/T$ curves have some curvature, as illustrated (and exaggerated) in Fig. 4-1. Thodos (108) and Waring (119) studied this curvature for many materials and found that the point of inflection occurred near a value of $T_r = 0.8$ to 0.85.* The curvature is caused by variations in the ratio $\Delta H_v/\Delta Z_v$ with temperature. Figure 4-2 shows this ratio plotted against reduced temperature for several compounds. Except for ethanol, the ratio is relatively insensitive to temperature from near the normal boiling point to the critical point; i.e., the decrease in the latent heat of vaporization with temperature is somewhat balanced by the decrease in ΔZ_v. The limit of $\Delta H_v/\Delta Z_v$ as T approaches T_c is about $7RT_c$ (119). Below the normal boiling point (T_r of 0.6 to 0.7), ΔZ_v is very close to unity and the variation in the ratio $\Delta H_v/\Delta Z_v$ is due almost entirely to ΔH_v variations with temperature. This suggests that Eq. (4-2) is not applicable at temperatures below the normal boiling point.

Any vapor-pressure correlation which is to represent real materials must take into account this S curvature indicated on Fig. 4-1. Thus most acceptable correlations are rather complex algebraically. Miller (65), in an excellent study of the available correlations, suggests a convenient way to compare the various methods. Two divisions are made. First, depending upon the available input data, different methods may be selected. Second, some methods are better below the normal boiling point and some above; so a separation in temperature range of applicability is also indicated.

* The value is lower for low-boiling or for very nonpolar compounds, for example, 0.7 for CH_4, and higher for high-boiling or polar compounds, that is, 1.0 for ethanol (66).

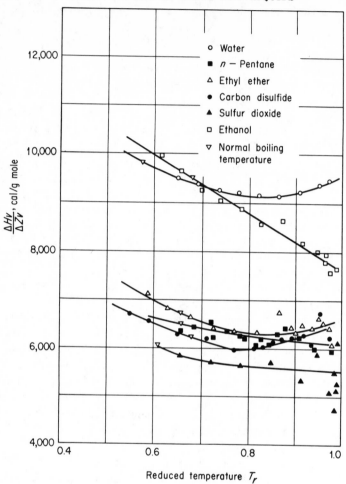

Fig. 4-2. Effect of temperature on $\Delta H_v/\Delta Z_v$.

Recommendations for choosing the most accurate estimating relations are given in Sec. 4-12. Those which will be selected are discussed individually below. Many other relationships which yield less accurate predictions are not covered.

4-3 Reduced Kirchhoff Vapor-pressure Equation

Although not applicable to temperatures below the normal boiling point, Eq. (4-2) yields reasonable results for temperatures between T_b and T_c. Section 4-11 presents a statistical evaluation of the errors expected in this latter region. The reduced form of Eq. (4-2) is obtained by assuming $B = $ const. Applying Eq. (4-2) to the critical point and subtracting the result from Eq. (4-2),

$$\log P_{vp_r} = (B/T_c)[(1/T_r) - 1] \qquad (4\text{-}3)^*$$

The generalized constant $B/T_c \equiv -h$ is determined by using Eq. (4-3) at the normal boiling point where $\log P_{vp_{br}} = -\log P_c$, $T_r = T_{b_r}$, and thus,

$$h = T_{b_r} [\log P_c/(1 - T_{b_r})] \qquad (4\text{-}4)\dagger$$

Equation (4-3) becomes

$$\log P_{vp_r} = h(1 - 1/T_r) \qquad (4\text{-}5)$$

To use Eq. (4-5), the normal boiling point and the critical constants T_c and P_c must be known. The equation may be considered as an interpolation formula between T_b and T_c. Example 4-1 illustrates its use.

Example 4-1. Estimate the vapor pressure of isopropyl ether at 205°C, using the reduced Kirchhoff equation. The normal boiling point is 341.3°K, and the critical properties are $T_c = 500.1°K$, $P_c = 28.4$ atm. Compare with the experimental value of 20.2 atm (50).

Solution

$$T_b = 341.3°K \qquad T_{b_r} = 341.3/500.1 = 0.682$$

From Eq. (4-4),

$$h = (0.682)(\log 28.4)/(1 - 0.682) = 3.12$$

From Eq. (4-5), at $T_r = (205 + 273)/500.1 = 0.956$,

$$\log (P_{vp}/28.4) = 3.12(1 - 1/0.956) = -0.144$$
$$P_{vp} = 20.4 \text{ atm}$$
$$\text{Error} = [(20.4 - 20.2)/20.2] \times 100 = +1.0\%$$

4-4 Cox-Antoine Vapor-pressure Correlation

Cox (18) suggested a graphical correlation in which the ordinate, representing P_{vp}, is laid off as a log scale and a straight line (with a positive slope) is drawn on the graph. The sloping line is taken to represent the vapor pressure of water (or some other reference substance). Since

---

* All final vapor-pressure relations are expressed as log (vapor pressure), where log is $\log_{10}$; ln indicates $\log_e$.

† It should be noted here and in many of the equations to follow that the normal boiling point is the favorite reference point, for two reasons: (1) T_b is more often known than any other boiling point and (2) the value of $\log P_{vp_b}$ is zero when vapor pressures are expressed in atmospheres. This latter point allows some simplification in the final form. However, if desirable, all the equations given in this chapter can be adapted for other reference boiling points. Also, for those compounds such as acetylene and carbon dioxide which sublime at 1 atm pressure and thus have no normal boiling point, the sublimation temperature may be substituted for T_b in all equations here and in those which follow.

the vapor pressure of water is accurately known as a function of temperature, the abscissa scale can be marked off in temperature units. When the vapor-pressure and temperature scales prepared in this way are used, vapor pressures for other compounds are found to plot as quite straight lines. Such graphs are somewhat inconvenient, since interpolation on the temperature scale is awkward.

Calingaert and Davis (12) have shown that the temperature scale obtained in such a manner is nearly equivalent to the function $1/(T - C)$, where C is suggested as being approximately 43°K for many materials boiling between 0 and 100°C. These same authors plotted a variety of vapor-pressure data in this manner and obtained almost straight lines. Their equation

$$\log P_{vp} = A - B/(T - C) \tag{4-6}$$

is similar to the one proposed by Antoine (1), in which C was taken as 13°K. Equation (4-6) is often called the *Antoine equation*, but a graph representing the relation is commonly referred to as a *Cox chart*.

The constant C varies from compound to compound. Simple rules for estimating C have been given by Thompson (112) and Fishtine (27); both give very similar results for materials boiling over 125°K. Thompson's rules are given below:

For monatomic elements and all substances with $T_b < 125°K$
$C = -0.3 + 0.034T_b \quad °K$
For all other substances
$C = -18 + 0.19T_b \quad °K$

$$\tag{4-7}$$

Upon applying Eq. (4-6) to the normal boiling point and to the critical point in a manner similar to that used to obtain Eq. (4-5), a reduced equation results (93),

$$\log P_{vp_r} = [(T_b - C)/(T_c - T_b)][(T - T_c)/(T - C)] \log P_c \tag{4-8}$$

Unfortunately Eq. (4-8) appears to be less accurate than the simpler Eq. (4-3) in the region from T_b to T_c, and although more accurate in the region below T_b, even here it is quite undependable. An example illustrating the use of Eq. (4-8) is given below.

Example 4-2. Repeat Example 3-1, using the Antoine equation (4-8).
Solution. The constant C is estimated from Eq. (4-7) as

$$C = -18 + 0.19(341.3) = 47°K$$

From Eq. (4-8),

$$\log P_{vp_r} = [(341.3 - 47)/(500.1 - 341.3)][(478 - 500.1)/(478 - 47)] \log 28.4$$
$$= -0.138$$

$P_{vp} = 20.7$ atm
Error $= [(20.7 - 20.2)/20.2] \times 100 = +2.5\%$

Another, more useful form of the Cox-Antoine correlation results when Eq. (4-6) is differentiated with respect to $1/T$ and equated to Eq. (4-1). At the normal boiling point the constants A and B may be expressed as

$$A = B/(T_b - C)$$
$$B = (1/\Delta Z_{v_b})[(T_b - C)^2 \, \Delta H_{v_b}/2.303RT_b{}^2] \qquad (4\text{-}9)$$

and
$$\log P_{vp} \text{ (in atm)} = A - B/(T - C)$$

Equation (4-9) is not a reduced equation and requires only ΔH_{v_b} and T_b as input data. Miller (65) suggests that $1/\Delta Z_{v_b}$ is about 1.05 for most materials at low pressures, but it may be obtained directly from Fig. 4-5a and b if the normal boiling point and the acentric factor are known or can be estimated.

Until recently the Antoine equation was considered to be one of the best vapor-pressure estimating correlations (15, 21, 111); although still useful, other, more accurate correlations are now available. The nonreduced form [Eq. (4-9)] is illustrated in Example 4-3.

Example 4-3. From the nonreduced form of the Antoine equation (4-9), estimate the vapor pressure of thiophene at 500°K. The normal boiling point is 84.2°C (357.3°K), and the experimental vapor pressure at 500°K is 20.1 atm (50). The latent heat of vaporization at the normal boiling point is 7520 cal/g mole (117).

Solution. $1/\Delta Z_{v_b}$ is chosen as about 1.05. From the definition of C in Eq. (4-7),

$$C = -18 + 0.19(357.3) = 50°K$$

Then B from Eq. (4-9) is determined as

$$B = (1.05)[(357.3 - 50)^2(7,520)/(2.303)(1.987)(357.3)^2] = 1280°K$$
$$A = B/(357.3 - 50) = 1,280/307.3 = 4.16$$

Thus, from Eq. (4-9),

$$\log P_{vp} \text{ (in atm)} = A - B/(500 - 50)$$
$$= 4.16 - 1,280/450 = 4.16 - 2.84 = 1.32$$
$$P_{vp} = 20.9 \text{ atm}$$
$$\text{Error} = [(20.9 - 20.1)/20.1] \times 100 = +4.0\%$$

Section 4-11 discusses the accuracy of all the correlations and recommendations given in Sec. 4-12. Various authors have suggested methods to fit the best values of A, B, and C to experimental data if the generalized equations presented above are not to be used (45, 55, 63, 86, 111).

For a homologous series of compounds an interesting and useful phenomenon is often noted in Cox charts. The straight lines for all materials of such a series often nearly converge to a point, when extrapolated. This "infinite point," when determined for a homologous series, provides one known point for obtaining vapor-pressure correlations for a new

member of the series.   Dreisbach (20) gives a tabulation of these infinite
points and a number of examples of their use.

4-5   Riedel Vapor-pressure Correlation

It was shown in Chap. 3 that reduced P-V-T properties of gases and
liquids could be rather accurately described by correlations involving a
third correlating parameter, in addition to reduced temperature and
pressure.   The parameters which were found to be most useful were the
Pitzer acentric factor ω [Eq. (2-27)], the Riedel factor α_c [Eq. (2-31)],
the factor h [Eq. (4-4)(65)], and the critical compressibility factor Z_c.
As both the acentric factor and the Riedel factor are defined in terms
of vapor pressures, they are obvious choices to be used in generalized
correlations of the form

$$P_{vp_r} = f(T_r, \omega \text{ or } \alpha_c)$$

In other words, compounds with the same value of ω or α_c would be
expected to show similar reduced-vapor-pressure–reduced-temperature
behavior.   A similar assumption has been made regarding Z_c (56).   The
Riedel correlation is the best of these correlations.

Riedel (90) proposed a reduced-vapor-pressure equation based on the
following relation (84):

$$\log P_{vp_r} = A - B/T_r + C \ln T_r + DT_r^6 \qquad (4\text{-}10)$$

By defining

$$\alpha = d(\ln P_r)/d(\ln T_r) \qquad (4\text{-}11)$$

Plank and Riedel (84, 85) found that from experimental vapor-pressure–
temperature data

$$d\alpha/dT_r = 0 \qquad \text{when } T_r = 1 \qquad (4\text{-}12)$$

and

$$D = k_1(\alpha_c - k_2) \qquad (4\text{-}13)$$

where $\alpha_c = \alpha$ at $T_r = 1$ and both k_1 and k_2 are universal constants.

By using Eqs. (4-12) and (4-13) and imposing the condition that
$P_{vp_r} = 1$ when $T_r = 1$, then a single-constant reduced-vapor-pressure
equation is obtained,

$$\log P_{vp_r} = -\phi(T_r) - (\alpha_c - 7)\psi(T_r) \qquad (4\text{-}14)$$

where $\phi(T_r) = 0.118\varphi(T_r) - 7 \log T_r$
$\psi(T_r) = 0.0364\varphi(T_r) - \log T_r$
$\varphi(T_r) = 36/T_r + 42 \ln T_r - 35 - T_r^6$

The Riedel factor is discussed in Sec. 2-8, and the functions $\phi(T_r)$ and
$\psi(T_r)$ are tabulated in Tables 4-1 and 4-2 as functions of reduced temperature.   The accuracy of the Riedel correlation is discussed in Sec.
4-11; Example 4-4 illustrates the application.

TABLE 4-1. $\phi(T_r)$ AS A FUNCTION OF T_r FOR USE IN EQ. (4-14)*

T_r	0	1	2	3	4	5	6	7	8	9	10
0.35	6.003	5.974	5.944	5.916	5.887	5.859	5.830	5.802	5.774	5.747	5.719
0.36	5.719	5.692	5.664	5.637	5.610	5.583	5.557	5.530	5.504	5.478	5.452
0.37	5.452	5.426	5.400	5.375	5.350	5.324	5.299	5.274	5.250	5.225	5.200
0.38	5.200	5.176	5.152	5.128	5.104	5.080	5.056	5.033	5.010	4.986	4.963
0.39	4.963	4.940	4.917	4.895	4.872	4.849	4.827	4.805	4.783	4.761	4.739
0.40	4.739	4.717	4.696	4.674	4.653	4.632	4.610	4.589	4.568	4.548	4.527
0.41	4.527	4.506	4.486	4.465	4.445	4.425	4.405	4.385	4.365	4.345	4.326
0.42	4.326	4.306	4.287	4.268	4.248	4.229	4.210	4.191	4.173	4.154	4.135
0.43	4.135	4.117	4.098	4.080	4.062	4.044	4.026	4.008	3.990	3.972	3.955
0.44	3.955	3.937	3.919	3.902	3.885	3.868	3.850	3.833	3.816	3.799	3.783
0.45	3.783	3.766	3.749	3.733	3.716	3.700	3.683	3.667	3.651	3.635	3.619
0.46	3.619	3.603	3.587	3.572	3.556	3.540	3.525	3.509	3.494	3.479	3.463
0.47	3.463	3.448	3.433	3.418	3.403	3.388	3.374	3.359	3.344	3.330	3.315
0.48	3.315	3.301	3.286	3.272	3.258	3.243	3.229	3.215	3.201	3.187	3.174
0.49	3.174	3.160	3.146	3.132	3.119	3.105	3.092	3.078	3.065	3.052	3.039
0.50	3.039	3.025	3.012	2.999	2.986	2.973	2.960	2.948	2.935	2.922	2.909
0.51	2.909	2.897	2.884	2.872	2.860	2.847	2.835	2.823	2.810	2.798	2.786
0.52	2.786	2.774	2.762	2.750	2.738	2.726	2.715	2.703	2.691	2.680	2.668
0.53	2.668	2.656	2.645	2.634	2.622	2.611	2.600	2.588	2.577	2.566	2.555
0.54	2.555	2.544	2.533	2.522	2.511	2.500	2.489	2.479	2.468	2.457	2.447
0.55	2.447	2.436	2.425	2.415	2.404	2.394	2.384	2.373	2.363	2.353	2.343
0.56	2.343	2.333	2.322	2.312	2.302	2.292	2.282	2.273	2.263	2.253	2.243
0.57	2.243	2.233	2.224	2.214	2.204	2.195	2.185	2.176	2.166	2.157	2.147
0.58	2.147	2.138	2.129	2.119	2.110	2.101	2.092	2.082	2.073	2.064	2.055
0.59	2.055	2.046	2.037	2.028	2.019	2.011	2.002	1.993	1.984	1.976	1.967
0.60	1.967	1.958	1.950	1.941	1.932	1.924	1.915	1.907	1.899	1.890	1.882
0.61	1.882	1.874	1.865	1.857	1.849	1.841	1.832	1.824	1.816	1.808	1.800
0.62	1.800	1.792	1.784	1.776	1.768	1.760	1.752	1.744	1.737	1.729	1.721
0.63	1.721	1.713	1.706	1.698	1.690	1.683	1.675	1.668	1.660	1.653	1.645
0.64	1.645	1.638	1.630	1.623	1.615	1.608	1.601	1.594	1.586	1.579	1.572
0.65	1.572	1.565	1.558	1.550	1.543	1.536	1.529	1.522	1.515	1.508	1.501
0.66	1.501	1.494	1.487	1.480	1.474	1.467	1.460	1.453	1.446	1.440	1.433
0.67	1.433	1.426	1.420	1.413	1.406	1.400	1.393	1.387	1.380	1.374	1.367
0.68	1.367	1.361	1.354	1.348	1.341	1.335	1.328	1.322	1.316	1.310	1.303
0.69	1.303	1.297	1.291	1.285	1.278	1.272	1.266	1.260	1.254	1.248	1.242
0.70	1.242	1.236	1.230	1.224	1.218	1.212	1.206	1.200	1.194	1.188	1.182
0.71	1.182	1.176	1.170	1.165	1.159	1.153	1.147	1.142	1.136	1.130	1.125
0.72	1.125	1.119	1.113	1.108	1.102	1.096	1.091	1.085	1.080	1.074	1.069
0.73	1.069	1.063	1.058	1.052	1.047	1.041	1.036	1.031	1.025	1.020	1.015
0.74	1.015	1.009	1.004	0.999	0.993	0.988	0.983	0.978	0.973	0.967	0.962
0.75	0.962	0.957	0.952	0.947	0.942	0.936	0.931	0.926	0.921	0.916	0.911
0.76	0.911	0.906	0.901	0.896	0.891	0.886	0.881	0.876	0.872	0.867	0.862
0.77	0.862	0.857	0.852	0.847	0.842	0.838	0.833	0.828	0.823	0.818	0.814
0.78	0.814	0.809	0.804	0.800	0.795	0.790	0.786	0.781	0.776	0.772	0.767
0.79	0.767	0.762	0.758	0.753	0.749	0.744	0.740	0.735	0.731	0.726	0.722
0.80	0.722	0.717	0.713	0.708	0.704	0.699	0.695	0.691	0.686	0.682	0.677
0.81	0.677	0.673	0.669	0.664	0.660	0.656	0.652	0.647	0.643	0.639	0.635
0.82	0.635	0.630	0.626	0.622	0.618	0.613	0.609	0.605	0.601	0.597	0.593
0.83	0.593	0.588	0.584	0.580	0.576	0.572	0.568	0.564	0.560	0.556	0.552
0.84	0.552	0.548	0.544	0.540	0.536	0.532	0.528	0.524	0.520	0.516	0.512
0.85	0.512	0.508	0.504	0.500	0.496	0.492	0.488	0.484	0.481	0.477	0.473
0.86	0.473	0.469	0.465	0.461	0.457	0.454	0.450	0.446	0.442	0.438	0.435
0.87	0.435	0.431	0.427	0.423	0.420	0.416	0.412	0.409	0.405	0.401	0.398
0.88	0.398	0.394	0.390	0.387	0.383	0.379	0.376	0.372	0.368	0.365	0.361
0.89	0.361	0.358	0.354	0.350	0.347	0.343	0.340	0.336	0.333	0.329	0.325
0.90	0.325	0.322	0.318	0.315	0.311	0.308	0.304	0.301	0.297	0.294	0.290
0.91	0.290	0.287	0.284	0.280	0.277	0.273	0.270	0.266	0.263	0.259	0.256
0.92	0.256	0.253	0.249	0.246	0.242	0.239	0.236	0.232	0.229	0.226	0.222
0.93	0.222	0.219	0.216	0.212	0.209	0.206	0.202	0.199	0.196	0.193	0.189
0.94	0.189	0.186	0.183	0.179	0.176	0.173	0.170	0.166	0.163	0.160	0.157
0.95	0.157	0.153	0.150	0.147	0.144	0.140	0.137	0.134	0.131	0.128	0.124
0.96	0.124	0.121	0.118	0.115	0.112	0.109	0.105	0.102	0.099	0.096	0.093
0.97	0.093	0.090	0.086	0.083	0.080	0.077	0.074	0.071	0.068	0.065	0.061
0.98	0.061	0.058	0.055	0.052	0.049	0.046	0.043	0.040	0.037	0.034	0.031
0.99	0.031	0.027	0.024	0.021	0.018	0.015	0.012	0.009	0.006	0.003	0.000

* L. Riedel, *Chem.-Ing.-Tech.*, **26**:83 (1954).

THE PROPERTIES OF GASES AND LIQUIDS

TABLE 4-2. $\psi(T_r)$ AS A FUNCTION OF T_r FOR USE IN EQ. (4-14)*

T_r	0	1	2	3	4	5	6	7	8	9	10
0.35	1.321	1.313	1.306	1.298	1.291	1.284	1.276	1.269	1.262	1.255	1.248
0.36	1.248	1.241	1.234	1.227	1.220	1.213	1.206	1.199	1.193	1.186	1.179
0.37	1.179	1.173	1.166	1.160	1.153	1.147	1.140	1.134	1.128	1.122	1.115
0.38	1.115	1.109	1.103	1.097	1.091	1.085	1.079	1.073	1.067	1.061	1.055
0.39	1.055	1.050	1.044	1.038	1.032	1.027	1.021	1.016	1.010	1.005	0.999
0.40	0.999	0.994	0.988	0.983	0.978	0.972	0.967	0.962	0.956	0.951	0.946
0.41	0.946	0.941	0.936	0.930	0.926	0.921	0.916	0.911	0.906	0.901	0.896
0.42	0.896	0.892	0.887	0.882	0.877	0.873	0.868	0.863	0.859	0.854	0.850
0.43	0.850	0.845	0.840	0.836	0.832	0.827	0.823	0.818	0.814	0.810	0.805
0.44	0.805	0.801	0.797	0.793	0.788	0.784	0.780	0.776	0.772	0.768	0.764
0.45	0.764	0.760	0.756	0.752	0.748	0.744	0.740	0.736	0.732	0.728	0.724
0.46	0.724	0.721	0.717	0.713	0.709	0.706	0.702	0.698	0.695	0.691	0.687
0.47	0.687	0.684	0.680	0.677	0.673	0.670	0.666	0.663	0.659	0.656	0.652
0.48	0.652	0.649	0.645	0.642	0.639	0.635	0.632	0.629	0.626	0.622	0.619
0.49	0.619	0.616	0.613	0.609	0.606	0.603	0.600	0.597	0.594	0.591	0.588
0.50	0.588	0.585	0.582	0.579	0.576	0.573	0.570	0.567	0.564	0.561	0.558
0.51	0.558	0.555	0.552	0.549	0.546	0.544	0.541	0.538	0.535	0.532	0.530
0.52	0.530	0.527	0.524	0.521	0.519	0.516	0.513	0.511	0.508	0.505	0.503
0.53	0.503	0.500	0.498	0.495	0.492	0.490	0.487	0.485	0.482	0.480	0.477
0.54	0.477	0.475	0.472	0.470	0.468	0.465	0.463	0.460	0.458	0.456	0.453
0.55	0.453	0.451	0.449	0.446	0.444	0.442	0.439	0.437	0.435	0.433	0.430
0.56	0.430	0.428	0.426	0.424	0.422	0.419	0.417	0.415	0.413	0.411	0.409
0.57	0.409	0.406	0.404	0.402	0.400	0.398	0.396	0.394	0.392	0.390	0.388
0.58	0.388	0.386	0.384	0.382	0.380	0.378	0.376	0.374	0.372	0.370	0.368
0.59	0.368	0.366	0.364	0.362	0.360	0.359	0.357	0.355	0.353	0.351	0.349
0.60	0.349	0.347	0.346	0.344	0.342	0.340	0.338	0.337	0.335	0.333	0.331
0.61	0.331	0.330	0.328	0.326	0.324	0.323	0.321	0.319	0.318	0.316	0.314
0.62	0.314	0.313	0.311	0.309	0.308	0.306	0.304	0.303	0.301	0.300	0.298
0.63	0.298	0.296	0.295	0.293	0.292	0.290	0.289	0.287	0.286	0.284	0.283
0.64	0.283	0.281	0.280	0.278	0.277	0.275	0.274	0.272	0.271	0.269	0.268
0.65	0.268	0.266	0.265	0.264	0.262	0.261	0.259	0.258	0.257	0.255	0.254
0.66	0.254	0.252	0.251	0.250	0.248	0.247	0.246	0.244	0.243	0.242	0.240
0.67	0.240	0.239	0.238	0.236	0.235	0.234	0.232	0.231	0.230	0.229	0.227
0.68	0.227	0.226	0.225	0.224	0.222	0.221	0.220	0.219	0.218	0.216	0.215
0.69	0.215	0.214	0.213	0.212	0.210	0.209	0.208	0.207	0.206	0.204	0.203
0.70	0.203	0.202	0.201	0.200	0.199	0.198	0.197	0.195	0.194	0.193	0.192
0.71	0.192	0.191	0.190	0.189	0.188	0.187	0.186	0.185	0.184	0.183	0.181
0.72	0.181	0.180	0.179	0.178	0.177	0.176	0.175	0.174	0.173	0.172	0.171
0.73	0.171	0.170	0.169	0.168	0.167	0.166	0.165	0.164	0.163	0.162	0.161
0.74	0.161	0.160	0.159	0.158	0.158	0.157	0.156	0.155	0.154	0.153	0.152
0.75	0.152	0.151	0.150	0.149	0.148	0.147	0.146	0.146	0.145	0.144	0.143
0.76	0.143	0.142	0.141	0.140	0.139	0.138	0.138	0.137	0.136	0.135	0.134
0.77	0.134	0.133	0.133	0.132	0.131	0.130	0.129	0.128	0.128	0.127	0.126
0.78	0.126	0.125	0.124	0.124	0.123	0.122	0.121	0.120	0.120	0.119	0.118
0.79	0.118	0.117	0.116	0.116	0.115	0.114	0.113	0.113	0.112	0.111	0.110
0.80	0.110	0.110	0.109	0.108	0.107	0.107	0.106	0.105	0.104	0.104	0.103
0.81	0.103	0.102	0.101	0.101	0.100	0.100	0.099	0.098	0.097	0.097	0.096
0.82	0.096	0.095	0.094	0.094	0.093	0.092	0.092	0.091	0.090	0.090	0.089
0.83	0.089	0.088	0.088	0.087	0.086	0.086	0.085	0.084	0.084	0.083	0.082
0.84	0.082	0.082	0.081	0.081	0.080	0.079	0.079	0.078	0.077	0.077	0.076
0.85	0.076	0.075	0.075	0.074	0.074	0.073	0.072	0.072	0.071	0.071	0.070
0.86	0.070	0.069	0.069	0.068	0.068	0.067	0.066	0.066	0.065	0.065	0.064
0.87	0.064	0.063	0.063	0.062	0.062	0.061	0.061	0.060	0.059	0.059	0.058
0.88	0.058	0.058	0.057	0.057	0.056	0.056	0.055	0.054	0.054	0.053	0.053
0.89	0.053	0.052	0.052	0.051	0.051	0.050	0.049	0.049	0.048	0.048	0.047
0.90	0.047	0.047	0.046	0.046	0.045	0.045	0.044	0.044	0.043	0.043	0.042
0.91	0.042	0.042	0.041	0.041	0.040	0.040	0.039	0.039	0.038	0.038	0.037
0.92	0.037	0.037	0.036	0.036	0.035	0.035	0.034	0.034	0.033	0.033	0.032
0.93	0.032	0.032	0.031	0.031	0.030	0.030	0.029	0.029	0.028	0.028	0.027
0.94	0.027	0.027	0.026	0.026	0.025	0.025	0.024	0.024	0.023	0.023	0.023
0.95	0.023	0.022	0.022	0.021	0.021	0.020	0.020	0.019	0.019	0.018	0.018
0.96	0.018	0.017	0.017	0.016	0.016	0.016	0.015	0.015	0.014	0.014	0.013
0.97	0.013	0.013	0.012	0.012	0.012	0.011	0.011	0.010	0.010	0.009	0.009
0.98	0.009	0.008	0.008	0.008	0.007	0.007	0.006	0.006	0.005	0.005	0.004
0.99	0.004	0.004	0.004	0.004	0.003	0.003	0.002	0.002	0.001	0.001	0.000

* L. Riedel, *Chem.-Ing.-Tech.*, **26**:83 (1954).

Example 4-4. Repeat Example 4-3, using the Riedel correlation [Eq. (4-14)] and Tables 4-1 and 4-2. The critical temperature and pressure of thiophene are $T_c = 580°K$, $P_c = 56.2$ atm (50).

Solution. A value of α_c must first be estimated. From Eq. (4-14) at the normal boiling point, ($T_{b_r} = 357.3/580 = 0.615$)

$$\begin{aligned}
\alpha_c &= [\log P_c - \phi(T_{b_r})]/\psi(T_{b_r}) + 7.00 \\
&= [\log 56.2 - \phi(0.615)]/0.615 + 7.00 \\
&= (1.750 - 1.841)/0.323 + 7.00 \\
&= 6.72
\end{aligned}$$

Then with Eq. (4-14) at $T = 500°K$, $T_r = 0.863$

$$\begin{aligned}
\log P_{vp_r} &= -\phi(0.863) - (6.72 - 7.00)\psi(0.863) \\
&= -0.461 + 0.019 = -0.442 \\
P_{vp} &= (0.362)(56.2) = 20.3 \text{ atm} \\
\text{Error} &= [(20.3 - 20.1)/20.1] \times 100 = +1.0\%
\end{aligned}$$

In general the correlations based on α_c, ω, or Z_c are more accurate at high reduced temperatures. Hooper and Joffe (43) have compared the ω and Z_c third-parameter correlations and conclude that the former is somewhat preferable, though the Riedel correlation is more accurate than either.

4-6 Frost-Kalkwarf-Thodos Vapor-pressure Correlation

Many published integrations of Eq. (4-1) are based on various empirical rules for the variation of ΔH_v and ΔZ_v with temperature. The most common relation was advanced by Frost and Kalkwarf (28), who assumed that (1) the heat of vaporization is a linear function of temperature,

$$\Delta H_v = \Delta H_{v_0} + \Delta C_s T \tag{4-15}$$

(2) van der Waals' equation satisfactorily represents the volumetric behavior of the gas [Eq. (3-48)], and (3) the molal volume of the liquid is approximated by the van der Waals' constant b. The general form of the equation derived is

$$\log P_{vp} = A + B/T + C \log T + DP_{vp}/T^2 \tag{4-16}$$

D is related in the derivation to the van der Waals' constant a as

$$D = a/2.303R^2 \tag{4-17}$$

and, from Table 3-2, $a = {}^{27}\!/_{64}R^2T_c{}^2/P_c$; thus

$$D = [27/(64)(2.303)]T_c{}^2/P_c = 0.1832T_c{}^2/P_c \tag{4-18}$$

Thodos et al. (7, 36, 77, 88, 89, 100, 102) have examined the Frost-Kalkwarf equation in great detail. They proposed that the constants B

and C be related by,

$$C = 1.80(B/T_c) + 2.67 \qquad (4\text{-}19)$$

so that, with Eqs. (4-16), (4-18), and (4-19), a reduced-vapor-pressure equation is easily written,

$$\log P_{vp_r} = (B/T_c)(1/T_r - 1) + (1.80B/T_c + 2.67) \log T_r$$
$$+ 0.1832(P_{vp_r}/T_r^2 - 1) \qquad (4\text{-}20)$$

The constant B may be obtained from one other boiling point, for example, the normal boiling point, although Bondi and McConaughy (9) and Thodos and his associates also present additive-group methods to obtain B for hydrocarbons. Since it is unlikely that the critical constants would be available but no other boiling points, this additive-group technique is not often necessary and will not be covered here. The paper by Bondi and McConaughy is of considerable interest, however, since a physical concept is attached to each of the constants in Eq. (4-16). This logical procedure is necessary if values of the constants are to be developed from theory; however, the assumptions which went into the original derivation are rather approximate, and caution must be exercised in attaching too much physical significance to the constants (9). In fact, it is surprising that Eq. (4-20) is so accurate (see Sec. 4-11).

The general form [Eq. (4-16)] may be used with very high accuracy if the constants are fitted to experimental data. To accomplish this, Eq. (4-16) is written for some reference temperature T', P'_{vp} and subtracted from the general equation at T and P_{vp}. There results an equation of the form,

$$Y = BX + C \qquad (4\text{-}21)$$

where $Y = [\log (P_{vp}/P'_{vp}) - D(P_{vp}/T^2 - P'_{vp}/T'^2)]/\log (T/T')$
$X = [(1/T) - (1/T')]/\log (T/T')$

The constant D, obtained from Eq. (4-18), is considered a variable parameter and adjusted to give the best straight line when Y is plotted against X; the slope and intercept are the constants B and C (28).

Many modifications of the reduced equation (4-20) have been proposed; for example, Miller (64) differentiated it with respect to temperature and used the definition of α_c from Riedel's correlation [Eq. (4-14)] to obtain a slightly different relation between B and C. That is,

$$C = 2.303(B/T_c) + 0.578\alpha_c + 0.844 \qquad (4\text{-}22)$$

Equation (4-20) with (4-22) instead of (4-19), however, is slightly less accurate (65).

The Frost-Kalkwarf-Thodos correlation is not well suited for hand calculations, as it cannot be solved explicitly for pressure, but is easily handled by the use of a high-speed computer. The accuracy of the reduced correlation [Eq. (4-20)] is discussed in Sec. 4-11; Example 4-5 illustrates the method.

Example 4-5. Repeat Example 4-3, using the Frost-Kalkwarf-Thodos correlation [Eq. (4-20)].

Solution. In Eq. (4-20), the constant B must first be obtained; at the normal boiling point $T_{b_r} = 0.615$,

$$-\log P_c = -\log 56.2 = (B/580)(1/0.615 - 1) + (1.80B/580 + 2.67) \log 0.615$$
$$+ 0.1832[1/(56.2)(0.615)^2 - 1]$$
$$B = -2380°K$$

At $500°K$, $T_r = 0.863$,

$$\log P_{vp_r} = (-2380/580)(1/0.862 - 1) + [(1.80)(-2{,}380)/580 + 2.67] \log 0.862$$
$$+ 0.1832[P_{vp_r}/(0.862)^2 - 1]$$
$$= -0.660 + 0.304 + (0.1832)(P_{vp_r}/0.743 - 1)$$
$$P_{vp_r} = 0.358 \text{ (by iteration)}$$
$$P_{vp} = (0.358)(56.2) = 20.2 \text{ atm}$$
$$\text{Error} = [(20.2 - 20.1)/20.1] \times 100 = +0.5\%$$

4-7 Riedel-Plank-Miller Vapor-pressure Correlation

Miller (66), in a search for accurate vapor-pressure correlations more suitable to hand computation, chose an equation explicit in pressure as

$$\log P_{vp} = A' + B'/T + C'T + D'T^2 \tag{4-23}$$

Equation (4-23) written for the critical point and subtracted from Eq. (4-23) yields the reduced correlation

$$\log P_{vp_r} = (B'/T_c)(1/T_r - 1) + C'T_c(T_r - 1) + (D'T_c^2)(T_r^2 - 1)$$
$$= B(1/T_r - 1) + C(T_r - 1) + D(T_r^2 - 1) \tag{4-24}$$

where $B \equiv B'/T_c$
$C \equiv C'T_c$
$D \equiv D'T_c^2$

To eliminate two of the three constants, the definition of the Riedel factor [Eq. (4-11)] and critical restriction [Eq. (4-12)] are used to give

$$\log P_{vp_r} = -(G/T_r)[1 - T_r^2 + g(1 - T_r)^3] \tag{4-25}$$

G and g are parameters and functions* of α_c and D, B and C having been eliminated. However, in testing Eq. (4-25) Miller found more convenient and accurate ways to express G and g. In essence, he used a

* $G = \alpha_c/(2)(2.303)$, $g = (2)(2.303)(D)/\alpha_c$.

slight modification of Eq. (2-34) to express α_c, and thus G, and found g by application of Eq. (4-25) at the normal boiling point. The final recommended values for G and g are

$$G = 0.2471 + 0.4525h \qquad 10 < P_{vp} < 1{,}500 \text{ mm Hg} \qquad (4\text{-}26)$$
$$= 0.2271 + 0.4525h \qquad P_{vp} > 1{,}500 \text{ mm Hg} \qquad (4\text{-}27)$$

where h is given by Eq. (4-4) and

$$g = [h/G - (1 + T_{b_r})]/(1 - T_{b_r})^2 \qquad (4\text{-}28)$$

Equation (4-25) requires as input data T_b, T_c, and P_c. The accuracy is discussed in Sec. 4-11. It is more convenient than either the Riedel or the Frost-Kalkwarf-Thodos reduced equation for hand computation once the constants G and g are determined, and usually more accurate. Example 4-6 illustrates the method.*

Example 4-6. Repeat Example 4-1, using the Riedel-Plank-Miller correlation [Eq. (4-25)].

Solution. In Example 4-1, h was calculated as 3.12. From Eq. (4-27), $G = 0.2271 + 0.4525h = 1.64$. Then from Eq. (4-28), with $T_{b_r} = 0.682$,

$$g = [3.12/1.64 - (1 + 0.682)]/(1 - 0.682)^2 = 2.18$$

Thus, from Eq. (4-25), at $T_r = 0.956$,

$$\log P_{vp_r} = (-G/T_r)[1 - T_r^2 + g(1 - T_r)^3] = -0.148$$

$$P_{vp} = (0.712)(28.4) = 20.2 \text{ atm}$$

$$\text{Error} = [(20.2 - 20.2)/20.2] \times 100 = 0\%$$

4-8 Miller Semireduced Vapor-pressure Correlation

It often happens that reliable values of critical temperature but not of critical pressure are available. If the latent heat of vaporization is available, a good low-pressure vapor-pressure correlation can be obtained. The best of many equations seems to be that proposed by Miller (66). In this development, Eq. (4-1) is integrated by using the Watson correlation [Eq. (4-67)] to express the variation of ΔH_v with temperature. The integration is carried out numerically, with the normal boiling point

* Recently, Miller (67a) modified Eq. (4-25) to

$$\log P_{vp_r} = -(G'/T_r)[1 - T_r^2 + g'(3 + T_r)(1 - T_r)^3]$$

where $G' = 0.210 + 0.4605h$
$\qquad g' = g/(3 + T_{b_r})$

This equation fits vapor pressure data from 10 mm Hg to the critical point with almost the same accuracy as equation set (4-25) to (4-28).

used as a reference or base point. The numerical solutions may be approximated analytically, and the final result is given as

$$\log P_{vp} \text{ (in atm)} = (k/T_r)[T_r^2(0.607T_r - 1.448) - I_bT_r - 0.980] \quad (4\text{-}29)$$
$$I_b = -1.448(T_{b_r}^2 - 1)/T_{b_r} + 0.607(T_{b_r}^3 - 4)/T_{b_r} \quad (4\text{-}30)$$
$$k = \Delta H_v \text{ (at } T')/2.303RT_c(1 - T_r')^{0.38} \quad (4\text{-}31)$$

where T' is any temperature where a reliable heat of vaporization is available. Equation (4-29) is not a reduced equation (inasmuch as the critical pressure is not required); thus the result is given directly in terms of P_{vp} in atmospheres. The accuracy of the method is discussed in Sec. 4-11; Example 4-7 illustrates the method.

Example 4-7. From the Miller semireduced-vapor-pressure correlation, estimate the vapor pressure of aniline at 102.6°C. The normal boiling point is 457.3°K and the critical temperature 698.8°K (Appendix A). The heat of vaporization at the normal boiling point is 10,360 cal/g mole. The experimental value of the vapor pressure is 51.1 mm Hg (58).
Solution. From Eq. (4-31), with $T_{b_r} = 457.3/698.8 = 0.655$,

$$k = 10,360/(2.303)(1.987)(698.8)(1 - 0.655)^{0.38} = 4.86$$

From Eq. (4-30),

$$I_b = (-1.448)[(0.655)^2 - 1]/0.655 + 0.607[(0.655)^3 - 4]/0.655$$
$$= -2.18$$

Then from Eq. (4-29), at $T_r = (102.6 + 273.2)/698.8 = 0.538$,

$$\log P_{vp} \text{ (in atm)} = (4.86/0.538)\{(0.538)^2[(0.607)(0.538) - 1.448]$$
$$+ (2.18)(0.538) - 0.980\} = -1.19$$
$$P_{vp} = 0.0646 \text{ atm} = 49.1 \text{ mm Hg}$$
$$\text{Error} = [(49.1 - 51.1)/51.1] \times 100 = -3.9\%$$

The analytical forms of Eqs. (4-29) and (4-30) were obtained on the assumption that the value of h in Eq. (4-27) was a general constant for all materials and equal to 2.98. While this assumption appears to yield good predictions of vapor pressure at low temperatures, empirical corrections were found necessary at higher temperatures. Thus, for predicting vapor pressures greater than 1,500 mm, Miller (65, 66) recommends an alternative form of Eq. (4-29). The modification is given below; as with Eq. (4-29) only the normal boiling point, the critical temperature, and the latent heat of vaporization at the normal boiling point are necessary as input data.

$$\log P_{vp} \text{ (in atm)} = k[N(T_r - T_{b_r}) + Q(T_r^2 - T_{b_r}^2)$$
$$+ M(1/T_r - 1/T_{b_r})] \quad (4\text{-}32)$$

where k is defined in Eq. (4-31) and

$$M = f(h^*) = -0.80344 - 0.04772h^* + 0.00346h^{*2} \qquad (4\text{-}33)$$
$$N = f(h^*) = -0.82365 - 0.22436h^* + 0.02181h^{*2} \qquad (4\text{-}34)$$
$$Q = f(h^*) = 1.34422 - 0.13486h^* + 0.00270h^{*2} \qquad (4\text{-}35)$$
$$h^* = 0.50 + h' \qquad (4\text{-}36)$$
$$h' = \Delta H_{v_b}/RT_c = 2.303h \qquad (4\text{-}37)$$

The accuracy of Eq. (4-32) is discussed in Sec. 4-11, and Example 4-8 shows the method of application.

Example 4-8. Repeat Example 4-3, but use the high-pressure form of the Miller semireduced-vapor-pressure correlation [Eq. (4-32)]. The critical temperature of thiophene is 580°K, and the enthalpy of vaporization at the normal boiling point is 7520 cal/g mole.

Solution. At 500°K, $T_r = 0.863$, and $T_{b_r} = 357.3/580 = 0.615$. From Eq. (4-31)

$$k = 7,520/(2.303)(1.987)(580)[1 - 357.3/580]^{0.38} = 4.07$$

From Eqs. (4-36) and (4-37)

$$h^* = 0.50 + 7,520/(1.987)(580) = 7.05$$

Then, from Eqs. (4-33) to (4-35)

$$M = -0.80344 - 0.04772(7.05) + 0.00346(7.05)^2 = -0.968$$
$$N = -0.82365 - 0.22436(7.05) + 0.02181(7.05)^2 = -1.321$$
$$Q = 1.34422 - 0.13486(7.05) + 0.00270(7.05)^2 = 0.528$$

Using Eq. (4-32),

$$\log P_{vp} \text{ (in atm)} = 4.07\{(-1.321)(0.863 - 0.615) + 0.528[(0.863)^2 - (0.615)^2]$$
$$- 0.968(1/0.863 - 1/0.615)\} = 1.295$$
$$P_{vp} = 19.7 \text{ atm}$$
$$\text{Error} = [(19.7 - 20.1)/20.1] \times 100 = -2.0\%$$

4-9 Erpenbeck-Miller Nonreduced Correlation

Starting with a semireduced low-pressure-range vapor-pressure equation proposed by Erpenbeck and Miller (25), Miller modified it to avoid the necessity of knowing any critical properties. The result is given as

$$\log P_{vp} \text{ (in atm)} = [B(T - T_b)/T] + \log \{[1 - C(T/T_b)]/(1 - C)\} \qquad (4\text{-}38)$$
$$B = 0.4343[1.03 \, \Delta H_{v_b}/RT_b + C/(1 - C)] \qquad (4\text{-}39)$$
$$C = 0.512 + 4.13 \times 10^{-4}T_b \text{ (in °K)}$$
$$\text{organic compounds}$$
$$= 0.59 \qquad \text{inorganic compounds} \qquad (4\text{-}40)$$

Only the boiling point and heat of vaporization at the normal boiling point are necessary as data.   The accuracy is discussed in Sec. 4-11, and Example 4-9 illustrates the method.

Example 4-9.   Repeat Example 4-7, using the Erpenbeck-Miller nonreduced correlation [Eq. (4-38)].
Solution.   From Eq. (4-40), with $T_b = 457.3°K$,

$$C = 0.512 + 4.13 \times 10^{-4}(457.3) = 0.700$$

From Eq. (4-39),

$$B = (0.4343)[(10{,}360)(1.03)/(1.987)(457.3) + 0.700/(1 - 0.700)] = 6.10$$

From Eq. (4-38) at $T = 102.6°C = 375.8°K$,

$$\log P_{vp} \text{ (in atm)} = 6.10[(375.8 - 457.3)/375.8]$$
$$+ \log \{[1 - 0.700(375.8)/457.3]/(1 - 0.700)\}$$
$$= -1.17$$
$$P_{vp} = 0.0676 \text{ atm} = 51.4 \text{ mm Hg}$$
$$\text{Error} = [(51.4 - 51.1)/51.1] \times 100 = +0.6\%$$

4-10   Comparative Vapor-pressure Correlations

Comparison at Equal Temperatures.   If Eq. (4-1) is written for two different compounds *and compared at the same temperature*, the equations may be divided into each other so that $d(1/T)$ cancels,

$$d(\ln P_{vp}) = (\Delta H_v/\Delta H_v')(\Delta Z_v'/\Delta Z_v)\, d(\ln P_{vp}') \qquad (4\text{-}41)^*$$

whence

$$\ln P_{vp} = m \ln P_{vp}' + C \qquad (4\text{-}42)$$

$\ln P_{vp}$ plotted against $\ln P_{vp}'$ produces a line which is very nearly straight if the unknown and reference compounds are not too different in chemical type.   Variations in ΔH_v or ΔZ_v in one compound tend to offset similar variations in ΔH_v and ΔZ_v in the other.   Since the ratio $\Delta Z_v'/\Delta Z_v$ often is close to 1, the slope of the line on logarithmic coordinates is close to the ratio of the heats of vaporization of the two materials.   Othmer (73) first suggested such a plot (often now called an *Othmer plot*) and has published numerous papers covering its use.   As was noted in the Cox-Antoine correlation, infinite points of convergence for homologous series are also found for certain series on Othmer plots.

To evaluate m and C in Eq. (4-42), at least two vapor pressures of a compound or one vapor pressure and the heat of vaporization must be known, in addition to the properties of the reference substance.   If, however, only a single vapor pressure were known (or ΔH_v were known

---

* The primes refer to a reference substance for which accurate vapor-pressure-temperature data are available.

at a single temperature), and if the critical constants of the unknown compound were known, then the following reduced-comparative equations might be useful (74). If comparisons are made at equal reduced temperatures, $T_r = T_r'$, then

$$\ln P_{vp_r} = (\Delta H_v/\Delta H_v')(\Delta Z_v'/\Delta Z_v)(T_c'/T_c) \ln P_{vp_r}' \qquad (4\text{-}43)$$

Othmer and his coworkers have published a nomograph of Eq. (4-42) to determine P_{vp} at various temperatures. The reference substance chosen was water. However, instead of using a water vapor-pressure scale, these vapor pressures are plotted as the corresponding saturation temperatures. This makes the nomograph very quick and easy to use (75). The constants m and C may be found either from experimental data or from the convenient tabulations of m and C for 500 compounds given in Appendix C. The nomograph is shown in Fig. 4-3. In Fig. 4-3 the "hydrocarbon" line refers to the locus of the m-C values of most straight-chain, branched, or cyclic hydrocarbons. Thus only a single vapor-pressure point of a new hydrocarbon is necessary to locate both m and C. The line noted as "hydrocarbon mixtures" approximates the m-C locus of petroleum mixtures. A similar type of nomograph has been developed by Nakanishi (71).

Comparison at Equal Pressures. In a similar manner, by canceling the $d(\ln P_{vp})$ terms and comparing at the same vapor pressure, the following expression may be derived.

$$d(1/T) = (\Delta H_v'/\Delta H_v)(\Delta Z_v/\Delta Z_v') \, d(1/T')$$

This may be integrated as before by assuming the ratio $(\Delta H_v'/\Delta Z_v')/(\Delta H_v/\Delta Z_v)$ constant,

$$1/T = (\Delta H_v'/\Delta H_v)(\Delta Z_v/\Delta Z_v')(1/T') + C \qquad (4\text{-}44)$$

Equation (4-44) states that a straight line should be obtained by plotting the reciprocal of the absolute saturation temperature of an unknown substance against a similar quantity for a reference substance* both at the same vapor pressure. Seglin (96) has proposed such a plot and has found that a straight line fits experimental vapor-pressure data quite well. Equation (4-44) may also be written as a reduced equation, if comparison is made at equal reduced pressures,

$$1/T_r - 1 = (\Delta H_v'/\Delta H_v)(\Delta Z_v/\Delta Z_v')(T_c/T_c')(1/T_r' - 1) \qquad (4\text{-}45)$$

Equation (4-45) is comparable with Eq. (4-43) in that, besides the critical constants of the unknown, only a single vapor pressure or heat of vapori-

---

* If possible, a reference substance with a similar value of Z_c or ω should be chosen.

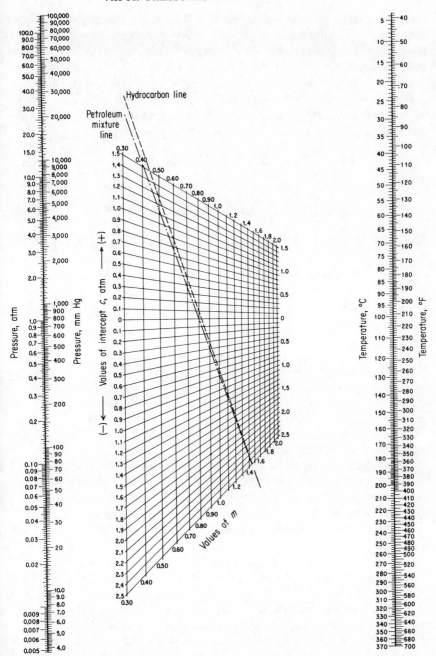

FIG. 4-3. Nomogram for vapor pressures (m and C are listed in Appendix C).   [*From D. F. Othmer et al., Ind. Eng. Chem.,* **49**:125 (1957).]

zation is needed to establish completely the vapor-pressure–temperature curve of the unknown.   Seglin found that this equation will represent the experimental data for such diverse compounds as propane, methyl chloride, ammonia, and carbon dioxide, with errors in the vapor pressures of about 4 per cent and in the saturation temperatures of 1 per cent.

Equation (4-44) may be arranged in still another form if it is written for two temperatures T_1 and T_2, where, at each temperature, the vapor pressures of the known and reference substance are equal,

$$1/T_1 - 1/T_2 = (\Delta H'_v/\Delta H_v)(\Delta Z_v/\Delta Z'_v)(1/T'_1 - 1/T'_2) \qquad (4\text{-}46)$$

whence

$$(T_1 - T_2)/(T'_1 - T'_2) = (\Delta H'_v/\Delta H_v)(\Delta Z_v/\Delta Z'_v)(T_1 T_2/T'_1 T'_2) \qquad (4\text{-}47)$$

Since $\Delta H'_v/\Delta H_v$ and $\Delta Z_v/\Delta Z'_v$ are almost constant and since $T_1 T_2/T'_1 T'_2$ has been found to be nearly constant, Eq. (4-47) reduces to a linear correlation of saturation temperatures between any two substances at equal vapor pressures (121), a correlation first noted by Dühring (22) and discussed by Perry and Smith (80).

$$T = C_1 T' + C_2 \qquad (4\text{-}48)$$

or. at equal reduced vapor pressures,

$$T_r - 1 = C_3(T'_r - 1) \qquad (4\text{-}49)$$

Equations (4-48) and (4-49) are very easy to plot and often give results well within engineering accuracy.

Comparisons at equal pressures may be represented graphically, as shown by Myers and Fenske (69, 70).   Figure 4-4 is a reproduction of a vapor-pressure chart of this kind, as given by Myers for low-boiling hydrocarbons.   Only the abscissa scale is used, with pressure as a parameter.   As an example, suppose that a compound is known to have a normal boiling point of 300°F.   Upon proceeding vertically at 300°F to the line for 760 mm Hg, horizontally to 10 mm Hg, and down vertically to the abscissa scale, it is estimated that the compound will boil at 100°F at 10. mm Hg pressure.   This chart is remarkable in that it represents several classes of compounds (paraffins, olefins, diolefins, acetylenes, aromatics, and naphthenes) with an accuracy of about 5°F or better, without recourse to identification of "families" of compounds, as is common in the construction of Cox charts.

Myers and Fenske do not indicate any theoretical basis for this type of graph.   It may be shown, however, that its form must apply to compounds giving straight lines on a Dühring graph, as represented by Eq.

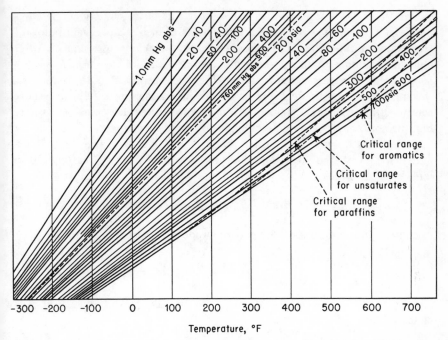

Temperature, °F

FIG. 4-4. Hydrocarbon vapor-pressure low-boiling range. (*Industrial and Engineering Chemistry, 47, pages 1652–1660, August 1955. Measurement and Correlation of Vapor Pressure Data for High Boiling Hydrocarbons, by H. S. Myers and M. R. Fenske. Vapor Pressure Chart for All Types of Low Boiling Hydrocarbons, by H. S. Myers. Chart reprinted from Braun Engineering Data-Book, August 1955. Copyright 1955 by C. F. Braun & Co.*)

(4-48), whether or not they are parallel or have a common intersection. It is better described as a form of the Dühring graph than as a variation of the Cox chart.

4-11 Discussion of Vapor-pressure Correlations

A thorough error analysis has been made by Miller (66) of the vapor-pressure correlation methods discussed in Secs. 4-3 to 4-10.*

In the low-temperature low-pressure range, 10 mm to 1500 mm, 71 test compounds were selected and calculated vapor pressures compared with experimental values.   In this testing scheme there were 18 inorganic and 53 organic materials; the latter included 34 hydrocarbons, 7 halogenated hydrocarbons, 4 alcohols, 1 carboxylic acid, 1 ketone, 4 sulfur compounds, and 2 amines. H_2, He, and compounds that showed substantial

* Actually many other techniques have also been evaluated.   Only the best are presented in this chapter.

association in the vapor phase were tested but not included in the comparisons. In the pressure range from 1,500 mm to the critical point 24 inorganic compounds and methane were tested. Considerable effort was made to evaluate reported experimental data (2, 3, 6, 17, 24, 27, 58, 60, 105, 114). For this reason, in the high-pressure range, the emphasis was placed on inorganic compounds inasmuch as it was felt that there was no uniform critical presentation of vapor pressures of a variety of organic compounds available at high pressures.

To express deviations quantitatively, the value ΔP_{vp} was first determined for each point tested (1,000 points in low-pressure region, 250 in high-pressure region).

$$\Delta P_{vp} = (P_{exp} - P_{calc})/P_{exp} \qquad (4\text{-}50)$$

A mean-squared deviation for each compound tested was found as

$$s = \left[\sum_n (\Delta P_{vp})^2\right]/[\text{number of points } (n) \text{ tested}] \qquad (4\text{-}51)$$

Finally, for a group of compounds the total squared deviation was calculated as

$$S = \Sigma s \qquad (4\text{-}52)$$

(the sum being over all compounds). This method of determining errors thus gives a comparison between different methods; the method with the smallest value of S is the best. An approximate estimation of an average error may be obtained as follows: For example, consider the Riedel-Plank-Miller correlation in Table 4-3. For 71 compounds $S = 0.0707$ or s (average) $= 0.0010$. If each point has the same error, $\Delta P_{vp} = (0.0010)^{1/2} = 0.032$ or the error is 3.2 per cent.

Tables 4-3 and 4-4 list the S values for both pressure ranges as obtained from values of P_{calc} for the various algebraic methods discussed in Secs. 4-3 to 4-10. Also listed is the average of the maximum per cent error found for each compound.* Various divisions are presented to illustrate the fit of the individual equations to different types of materials. As the absolute values of S tabulated are not of much significance except to provide a statistical comparison of the accuracy of the methods, the average of the maximum errors is perhaps a more valid criterion for selection. The inorganic compounds in the high-pressure range yielded small errors. Organic compounds would probably have shown more error, but it is hoped that the relative ranking of the methods presented here (and of the large number of other correlations tested by Miller which were less accurate for inorganics) would not change.

---

* The average error for a compound was about one-half the maximum error.

TABLE 4-3. COMPARISON BETWEEN CALCULATED AND EXPERIMENTAL VAPOR PRESSURES, VAPOR-PRESSURE RANGE 10 TO 1,500 MM HG*

All deviations except per cent error given as $10^3 S$

Estimation method	Equation numbers	34 hydro-carbons	45 nonpolar organics	8 polar organics	All 53 organics	All 18 in-organics	All 71 com-pounds	66 com-pounds not in-cluding acids or alcohols	Average maxi-mum % error
Reduced Equations—Requires T_c, P_c, T_b									
Riedel-Plank-Miller	(4-4), (4-25), (4-26), (4-28)	7.7	20.6	37.3	58.0	12.7	70.7	40.7	5.2
Frost-Kalkwarf-Thodos	(4-20)	6.5	17.4	37.0	54.4	20.1	74.5	43.2	5.1
Riedel	(4-14)	9.3	20.5	35.8	56.3	17.1	73.4	43.4	5.3
Semireduced Equations—Requires T_c, T_b, ΔH_v at T									
Miller—semireduced	(4-29), (4-30), (4-31)	7.2	9.6	7.1	16.6	5.5	22.1	16.5	2.9
Nonreduced Equations—Requires T_b, ΔH_{v_b}									
Erpenbeck-Miller	(4-38), (4-39), (4-40)	20.3	23.8	9.3	33.1	8.1	41.2	33.0	4.5
Antoine	(4-7), (4-9)	24.6	30.4	5.3	35.7	23.8	59.5	56.1	5.0

* D. G. Miller, *Ind. Eng. Chem.*, **56**(3):46 (1964).

TABLE 4-4. COMPARISON BETWEEN CALCULATED AND EXPERIMENTAL VAPOR PRESSURES, VAPOR-PRESSURE RANGE GREATER THAN 1,500 MM HG*
All deviations except per cent error given as $10^3 S$

Estimation method	Equation No.	All 24 compounds	All compounds except NO	Average max. % error
Reduced Equations—Requires T_c, P_c, T_b				
Riedel-Plank-Miller........	(4-25), (4-4), (4-27), (4-28)	2.6	1.9	1.5
Frost-Kalkwarf-Thodos....	(4-20)	2.9	2.1	1.5
Riedel..................	(4-14)	3.7	2.6	1.7
Reduced Kirchhoff........	(4-4), (4-5)	10.8	9.7	3.2
Semireduced Equations—Requires T_c, T_b, ΔH_v at T				
Miller semireduced........	(4-32), (4-33), (4-34), (4-35), (4-36), (4-37)	85.4	73.0	7.3
Nonreduced Equations—Requires T_b and ΔH_{v_b}				
Antoine.................	(4-7), (4-9)	234.7	76.9	9.4

* D. G. Miller, *Ind. Eng. Chem.*, **56**(3):46 (1964).

4-12 Recommended Methods to Estimate Vapor Pressures

In recommending methods for use, accuracy has been given first priority, although in many cases convenience or the fact that a particular equation is better suited for a certain class of compounds may dictate the choice of another correlation. The recommended methods are listed in Table 4-5. As noted before, the recommendations are broken down into separate methods requiring different input data and which are applicable in the low- or high-pressure ranges. It is easy to see that the reduced equations are in essence interpolation equations between T_b and T_c, whereas the semi- and nonreduced equations are more or less extrapolation formulas around T_b.

Besides the methods listed in Table 4-5, which are all algebraic in structure, the graphical methods described in Sec. 4-10 are often useful. For quick approximate estimations, the nomograph Fig. 4-3 with the tables in Appendix C are often of sufficient accuracy for most engineering use.

It must be emphasized again that the methods presented here represent the best available estimation techniques for certain types of input

TABLE 4-5. RECOMMENDED VAPOR-PRESSURE ESTIMATION METHODS

Estimation method	Equation No.	Average max. % error	Comments
Reduced Equations—Requires T_c, P_c, T_b			
Low-pressure Range: 10 to 1,500 Mm Hg			
Frost-Kalkwarf-Thodos..	(4-20)	5.1	Best for organic compounds. Iteration type of calculation
Riedel-Plank-Miller......	(4-25), (4-26), (4-4), (4-28)	5.2	Best for inorganic compounds. Easiest to use
Riedel.................	(4-14), Tables 4-1, 4-2	5.3	May be used either algebraically or with Tables 4-1, 4-2
High-pressure Range: 1,500 Mm Hg to Critical Pressure			
Riedel-Plank-Miller......	(4-25), (4-4), (4-27), (4-28)	1.5	Good. Relatively easy to use
Frost-Kalkwarf-Thodos ..	(4-20)	1.5	Good. Requires iteration calculation
Riedel.................	(4-14), Tables 4-1, 4-2	1.7	Good. Easy to use with Tables 4-1, 4-2
Reduced Kirchhoff.......	(4-4), (4-5)	3.2	Not as accurate but very easy to use
Semireduced Equations—Requires T_c, T_b, ΔH_v at T			
Low-pressure Range: 10 to 1,500 Mm Hg			
Miller semireduced.......	(4-29), (4-30), (4-31)	2.9	Accurate. Preferable to reduced equation if ΔH_v data available
High-pressure Range: 1,500 Mm Hg to Critical Pressure			
Miller semireduced.......	(4-32), (4-33), (4-34), (4-35), (4-36), (4-37)	7.3	Only fair if ΔH_{v_b} used. None better
Nonreduced Equations—Requires T_b, ΔH_{v_b}			
Low-pressure Range: 10 to 1,500 Mm Hg			
Erpenbeck-Miller........	(4-38), (4-39), (4-40)	4.5	Good. Better than reduced methods. Not as good for polar organics
Antoine.................	(4-7), (4-9)	5.0	Good. Recommended for polar organics
High-pressure Range: 1,500 Mm Hg to Critical Pressure			
Antoine.................	(4-7), (4-9)	9.4	Poor. Equation (4-1) with $\Delta Z_v = 1$, $\Delta H_v = \Delta H_{v_b}$ almost as good

information. There are many other less accurate estimation methods which are not discussed. Also, if one has some reliable vapor pressures and desires to fit them to an analytical equation, there are many suggested techniques (25, 28, 29, 81, 92, 118). Probably the Frost-Kalkwarf-Thodos method is as good as any, with the constants determined as indicated in Sec. 4-6 and Eq. (4-21).

4-13 Latent Heat of Vaporization of Pure Compounds

The enthalpy of vaporization ΔH_v is commonly referred to as the *latent heat of vaporization*. It is the difference between the enthalpies of the saturated vapor and liquid.

Because of the forces of attraction between the molecules of the liquid, the molecules escaping are those of higher than average velocity and energy. The average energy of the remaining molecules in the liquid is reduced, and energy must be supplied to maintain the temperature constant. This is the *internal energy of vaporization* ΔE_v. Work is done on the vapor phase as vaporization proceeds, since the vapor volume must increase if the pressure is maintained constant at P_{vp}. This work is $P_{vp}(V_g - V_L)$. Thus

$$\Delta H_v = \Delta E_v + P_{vp}(V_g - V_L) = \Delta E_v + RT(Z_g - Z_L)$$
$$= \Delta E_v + RT\,\Delta Z_v \quad (4\text{-}53)$$

Since the nature of the intermolecular forces in liquids is but poorly understood, there are at present no useful theoretical relations connecting ΔE_v or ΔH_v with molecular properties. Some theoretical insight into the classification of the internal order of liquids has been obtained, however, from recent studies (see Sec. 4-20). The forces which a molecule must overcome in escaping from a liquid have been related to the Lennard-Jones and other intermolecular potentials (see Sec. 3-11), which might properly be expected to form the basis of any theoretical or empirical latent-heat correlations. However, no such correlations are available at present.

Equation (4-1) states that ΔH_v is directly related to the slope of the vapor-pressure–temperature curve. As discussed earlier in this chapter, the vapor-pressure–temperature relation may often be estimated with some accuracy. Thus the most common type of correlation of heats of vaporization may be traced to Eq. (4-1). A number of such correlation methods for ΔH_v are discussed in Secs. 4-14 to 4-20; they are reviewed and recommendations presented in Sec. 4-21. In reviewing ΔH_v correlation methods, many recent articles were rejected as being too specialized or inaccurate (30, 51, 94, 97, 98, 116).

4-14 **Estimation of ΔH_v from the Clapeyron Equation and Experimental Vapor Pressures**

Equation (4-1) may be employed to obtain ΔH_v directly from vapor-pressure data, by using any one of various methods to obtain the slope dP_{vp}/dT. For example, the Douglass-Avakian method of differentiation is convenient where P_{vp} is tabulated over equal temperature intervals. As applied to the Clapeyron equation, this gives

$$\Delta H_v = T \, \Delta V_v (397\Sigma n P/1{,}512\delta_T - 7\Sigma n^3 P/216\delta_T) \qquad (4\text{-}54)$$

where δ_T is the temperature interval and n is the number of the point in question, varying from -3 to $+3$. ΔH_v is obtained at the midpoint of the seven temperatures $(n = 0)$. To use Eq. (4-54), a value of ΔV_v or ΔZ_v is necessary. Approximations to ΔZ_v may be made by a number of rough rules shown later in specific estimation techniques [e.g., Eq. (4-60)], or, alternatively, the compressibilities of the saturated vapor and liquid may be estimated separately and ΔZ_v determined by the difference. Edmister (23) has used Pitzer's correlation [Eq. (3-15)] to draw Fig. 4-5 relating saturated vapor and liquid compressibilities as functions of T_r (or P_r) and ω.

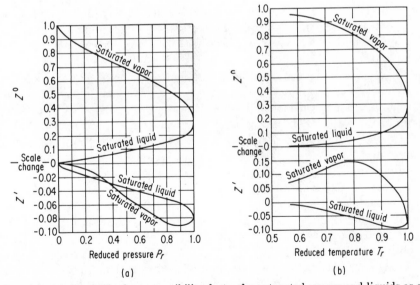

FIG. 4-5. (a) Generalized compressibility factor for saturated vapors and liquids as a function of reduced pressure. (b) Generalized compressibility factor for saturated vapors and liquids as a function of the reduced temperature. (*W. C. Edmister, Petrol. Refiner, April,* 1958, *p.* 173.)

Example 4-10. The vapor pressures of water at 15, 20, 25, 30, 35, 40, and 45°C are 12.79, 17.54, 23.76, 31.82, 42.18, 55.32, and 71.88 mm Hg. Evaluate ΔH_v at 30°C.

Solution. Following the indicated procedure for numerical differentiation, $n = -3$ at $T = 15$, -2 at 20, . . . , $+3$ at 45°. ΣnP is 271.27, and Σn^3P is 1,916.22. The product $T \Delta V_v$ is $\Delta Z_v RT^2/P$. As an approximation, take $\Delta Z_v = 1.0$. Then

$$\Delta H_v = (RT^2/P)[(397 \times 271.27)/(1,512 \times 5) - (7 \times 1,916.22)/(216 \times 5)]$$
$$= [(1.985 \times 303^2)/31.82](14.244 - 12.420) = 10,445 \text{ cal/g mole}$$

The value given in the Steam Tables (46) is 10,452 cal/g mole. At 30°C (86°F) water vapor follows the gas laws closely, with $\Delta Z_v = 1.0014$.

4-15   Estimation of ΔH_v Using the Law of Corresponding States

Equation (4-1), in reduced form, becomes,

$$d(\ln P_{vp_r}) = (-\Delta H_v/RT_c \Delta Z_v) d(1/T_r) \tag{4-55}$$

It is seen that $-\Delta H_v/RT_c$ is a function of $d(\ln P_{vp_r})/d(1/T_r)$ and ΔZ_v; both these parameters are commonly assumed to be functions of T_r and P_{vp_r} and some third correlating factor such as α_c, ω, Z_c, or h. A number of correlations based on this approach have been suggested.

Riedel Factor Correlation (91). Riedel tabulated $\Delta H_v/T_c$ as functions of T_r and α_c. α_c is the Riedel factor discussed in Sec. 2-8 and used in Eq. (4-14) for vapor pressures. These tables provide reliable estimates. For example, when they were tested with 33 hydrocarbons at over 478 temperatures, the average error in estimating ΔH_v was only about 1.8 per cent (113). However, Pitzer's method described below is slightly more convenient and generally more accurate. The parameter M introduced in the Martin-Hou equation of state (Sec. 3-16) has also been proposed as a third correlating parameter for the $\Delta H_v - T_r$ relation (61). M is formally defined in a similar manner as α_c [Eq. (4-11)], but Martin's values of M are obtained from Fig. 3-17 and differ slightly from α_c values obtained from Eq. (4-14) and tabulated in Appendix A.

Lydersen, Greenkorn, and Hougen Correlation (56). Appendix B lists enthalpies of saturated vapor and liquid for various reduced temperatures and values of Z_c. From these values, ΔH_v can be obtained, but the accuracy is poor (113). A similar technique was suggested by Hobson and Weber (41).

Pitzer Acentric-factor Correlation (83). Pitzer has suggested that ΔH_v be obtained by an equation similar to Eq. (3-15) for the compressibility factor,

$$\frac{\Delta H_v}{T} = \Delta S_v^0 + \omega \Delta S_v^1 \tag{4-56}$$

TABLE 4-6. PITZER VALUES OF $\Delta S_v{}^0$ AND $\Delta S_v{}^1$*

T_r	$\Delta S_v{}^0$, entropy units	$\Delta S_v{}^1$, entropy units
1.00	0.00	0.00
0.99	2.57	2.83
0.98	3.38	3.91
0.97	4.00	4.72
0.96	4.52	5.39
0.95	5.00	5.96
0.94	5.44	6.51
0.92	6.23	7.54
0.90	6.95	8.53
0.88	7.58	9.39
0.86	8.19	10.3
0.84	8.79	11.2
0.82	9.37	12.1
0.80	9.97	13.0
0.78	10.57	13.9
0.76	11.20	14.9
0.74	11.84	16.0
0.72	12.49	17.0
0.70	13.19	18.1
0.68	13.89	19.3
0.66	14.62	20.5
0.64	15.36	21.8
0.62	16.12	23.2
0.60	16.92	24.6
0.58	17.74	26.2
0.56	18.64	27.8

* K. S. Pitzer, D. Z. Lippman, R. F. Curl, C. M. Huggins, and D. E. Petersen, *J. Am. Chem. Soc.*, **77**:3433 (1955).

where $\Delta S_v{}^0$ and $\Delta S_v{}^1$ are expressed in entropy units and are functions only of reduced temperature as given in Table 4-6. In the original form, Eq. (4-56) had an additional term, $\omega^2 \Delta S_v{}^{11}$, but this term is negligibly small. Equation (4-56), in general, is easy to use and yields good results. It is somewhat sensitive to the values of ω chosen, since $\Delta S_v{}^1$ is larger than $\Delta S_v{}^0$ and small changes in ω can affect the final result significantly. The method is illustrated in Example 4-11.

Example 4-11. Estimate the latent heat of vaporization of ethyl alcohol at 100°C with Eq. (4-56). Repeat for *n*-octane at 171°C. Compare with experimental values of 8,760 and 7,254 cal/g mole, respectively (59, 87).

Solution. *Critical Data (Appendix A)*

$$T_c(\text{ethyl alcohol}) = 516°\text{K}$$
$$T_c(n\text{-octane}) = 568.6°\text{K}$$

142   THE PROPERTIES OF GASES AND LIQUIDS

Acentric Factors (Appendix A)

$$\omega(\text{ethyl alcohol}) = 0.650$$
$$\omega(n\text{-octane}) = 0.394$$

Reduced Temperatures

$$T_r(\text{ethyl alcohol}) = (100 + 273)/516 = 0.723$$
$$T_r(n\text{-octane}) = (171 + 273)/568.6 = 0.780$$

Entropy Functions (Table 4-6)

	Ethyl alcohol	n-octane
$\Delta S_v{}^0$	12.39	10.57
$\Delta S_v{}^1$	16.85	13.9

Thus from Eq. (4-56)

$$\Delta H_v(\text{ethyl alcohol}) = 373[12.39 + (0.650)(16.85)]$$
$$= 8710 \text{ cal/g mole}$$
$$\text{Error} = [(8,710 - 8,760)/8,760] \times 100 = -0.6\%$$
$$\Delta H_v(n\text{-octane}) = 444[10.57 + (0.394)(13.9)]$$
$$= 7130 \text{ cal/g mole}$$
$$\text{Error} = [(7,130 - 7,254)/7,254] \times 100 = -1.7\%$$

Chen Modification to Pitzer Acentric-factor Correlation. Chen (13) has used Eq. (4-56) and a similar equation proposed by Pitzer to correlate vapor pressures* to eliminate the acentric factor. He obtained a generalized correlation relating reduced vapor pressure and temperature to the enthalpy of vaporization as follows:

$$\Delta H_v = T(7.90T_r - 7.82 - 7.11 \log P_{vp_r})/(1.07 - T_r) \quad (4\text{-}57)$$

Chen tested Eq. (4-57) with 12 diverse compounds at various temperatures and found an average error of 2.55 per cent. A more detailed test was made for ΔH_{v_b}, where $T_r = T_{b_r}$, $\log P_r = -\log P_c$; with 169 different materials, the average error between calculated and experimental values of ΔH_{v_b} was 2.1 per cent. Table 4-8 shows another set of experimental and calculated values of ΔH_{v_b} for 94 compounds; in this test the error in Chen's method was 1.7 per cent.

The Chen modification of the Pitzer correlation appears to be accurate. Instead of ω values, the reduced vapor pressure must be known. Both methods require the critical temperature to determine T_r.

Example 4-12. Estimate the heat of vaporization of phenol at the normal boiling point of 454.9°K. Use Chen's equation (4-57). The experimental value from Table 4-8 is 10,760 cal/g mole.

* This equation was not discussed earlier in this chapter, as there are better vapor-pressure correlations available.

Solution. From Appendix A, $T_c = 694.3°K$. Thus $T_r = 454.9/694.3 = 0.655$.
$P_c = 60.5$ atm. Thus, from Eq. (4-57),

$$\Delta H_{v_b} = (454.9)\{[(7.90)(0.655) - 7.82 + 7.11 \log 60.5]/(1.07 - 0.655)\}$$
$$= 10,990 \text{ cal/g mole}$$

Error $= [(10,990 - 10,760)/10,760] \times 100. = +2.2\%$

4-16   Estimation of ΔH_v from Vapor-pressure Equations

The various vapor-pressure equations presented in Secs. 4-3 to 4-9 may
be used with Eq. (4-1) to yield heat-of-vaporization estimation methods.
The Riedel equation (4-14), though quite reliable in estimating vapor
pressure, does not yield an accurate ΔH_v relation when differentiated
as shown in Eq. (4-1). This conclusion is confirmed by an independent
study by St. Pierre and Tien (104). Two other vapor-pressure equations
are discussed below; the reduced Kirchhoff equation leads to the well-
known Giacalone type of equations for ΔH_{v_b}, and the Riedel-Plank-Miller
equation yields the most accurate correlation for ΔH_{v_b}.

Reduced Kirchhoff Equation. The reduced Kirchhoff vapor-pressure
equation (4-5) employs the generalized constant h as defined in Eq. (4-4).
In the derivation, from Eq. (4-1), as $\Delta H_v/\Delta Z_v$ is assumed constant, h is
related to ΔH_{v_b} as

$$h = \Delta H_{v_b}/(2.303 \, \Delta Z_v \, RT_c) = (T_{b_r} \log P_c)/(1 - T_{b_r}) \qquad (4\text{-}58)$$

Equation (4-58) may be written for temperatures other than the
normal boiling point, but in most instances it is best known as a ΔH_{v_b}-
estimating rule. The success attained in estimating ΔH_{v_b} apparently
results because the average value of $\Delta H_v/\Delta Z_v$ from T_b to T_c is found to
be approximately ΔH_{v_b}. Below T_b, application of Eq. (4-58) may lead
to large errors (27). Many writers have proposed slight modifications
to the basic equation (16, 32, 42, 49, 53, 62, 91, 95, 120). Two are discussed below.

Giacalone Modification (32). In this case, the simple assumption is
made that ΔZ_v is unity. Then Eq. (4-58) becomes

$$\Delta H_{v_b} = (2.303RT_bT_c \log P_c)/(T_c - T_b) \qquad (4\text{-}59)$$

This equation is the simplest of the ΔH_{v_b}-correlating equations; when it
was tested with 94 compounds in Table 4-8, an average error of 2.8 per
cent was found. This error is larger than obtained with the other ΔH_{v_b}
correlations, but the simplicity of the method has made it a popular one.

Klein-Fishtine Modification (27, 49). In this case, ΔZ_v is retained but
approximated by the Haggenmacher correction (35),

$$\Delta Z_v = (1 - 1/P_cT_{b_r}^3)^{1/2} \qquad (4\text{-}60)$$

Equation (4-58) becomes

$$\Delta H_{v_b} = [(2.303RT_bT_cK_v \log P_c)/(T_c - T_b)](1 - 1/P_cT_{b_r}^3)^{1/2} \quad (4\text{-}61)$$

where K_v is an empirical constant given as

$$K_v = \begin{cases} 1.02 & T_b < 200°\mathrm{K} \\ 1.04 & 200 \le T_b \le 300°\mathrm{K} \\ 1.045 & T_b > 300°\mathrm{K} \end{cases} \quad (4\text{-}62)$$

In Table 4-8, the average error for 94 compounds was found to be 1.9 per cent; Miller (67), in a similar test, found an average error of 1.7 per cent for 76 different compounds. Even for inorganic compounds errors of only 2 to 4 per cent may be expected. Example 4-13 illustrates the method.

Example 4-13. Estimate the latent heat of vaporization of triethylamine at the normal boiling point, using both the Giacalone and the Klein-Fishtine methods. The experimental value given in Table 4-8 is 7675 cal/g mole.

Solution. From Appendix A, $T_c = 535.4°\mathrm{K}$, $T_b = 362.7°\mathrm{K}$, $P_c = 30.0$ atm, $T_{b_r} = 362.7/535.4 = 0.6774$.
Giacalone Method [Eq. (4-59)]

$\Delta H_{v_b} = [(2.303)(1.987)(362.7)(535.4) \log 30.0]/(535.4 - 362.7) = 7600$ cal/g mole
  Error $= [(7,600 - 7,675)/7,675] \times 100 = -1.0\%$

Klein-Fishtine Method [Eq. (4-60)]. From Eq. (4-60),

$$\Delta Z_v = [1 - 1/(30)(0.6774)^3]^{1/2} = 0.945$$
From Eq. (4-62), $K_v = 1.045$
  $\Delta H_{v_b} = (7,600)(0.945)(1.045) = 7500$ cal/g mole
  Error $= [(7,500 - 7,675)/7,675] \times 100 = -2.2\%$

Riedel-Plank-Miller Equation. Miller (67), after a comprehensive study of the best methods to estimate ΔH_{v_b} from vapor-pressure equations, recommends the Riedel-Plank-Miller equation discussed in Sec. 4-7. The final form is given as

$$\Delta H_{v_b} = 2.303GRT_c \Delta Z_{v_b}[1 + T_{b_r}^2 + k'(1 + 2T_{b_r})] \quad (4\text{-}63)$$

where G is given by Eqs. (4-26) and (4-4), i.e.,

$$G = 0.2471 + 0.1965a$$

where ΔZ_{v_b} is approximated as $1 - 0.97/P_cT_{b_r}$ and where

$$k' = [a/2.303G - (1 + T_{b_r})]$$
$$a = (T_{b_r} \ln P_c)/(1 - T_{b_r})$$

Equation (4-63) is somewhat complex to use, but in Table 4-8 it yielded the smallest error of any method for ΔH_{v_b}, that is, 1.7 per cent for 94 compounds.   In a comparable test, Miller indicated an error of 1.52 per cent for 76 organic compounds and 1.19 per cent for 24 inorganic compounds. The use of the method is shown in Example 4-14.

Example 4-14.   Repeat Example 4-13, using Eq. (4-63).
Solution.   Using the same critical constants as in the previous example,

$$a = (0.6774 \ln 30.0)/(1 - 0.6774) = 7.143$$
$$G = 0.2471 + 0.1965(7.143) = 1.651$$
$$k' = [7.143/(2.303)(1.651) - (1 + 0.6774)] = 0.201$$
$$\Delta Z_{v_b} = 1 - 0.97/(30)(0.6774) = 0.952$$

Then, from Eq. (4-63),

$$\Delta H_{v_b} = (2.303)(1.651)(1.987)(535.4)(0.952)$$
$$\{1 + (0.6774)^2 + 0.201[1 + (2)(0.6774)]\} = 7427 \text{ cal/g mole}$$

Error $= [(7,427 - 7,675)/7,675] \times 100 = -3.2\%$

4-17   Comparative Correlations for Latent Heats of Vaporization

As in the case of vapor pressures, enthalpies of vaporization for different compounds vary similarly with temperature. ΔH_v for one compound can be related to $\Delta H_v'$ for a reference compound, either through temperature or through vapor pressure.

From Eq. (4-41), an Othmer plot of log P_{vp} versus log P'_{vp}, both at the same temperature, gives very nearly a straight line having a slope $m = (\Delta H_v/\Delta H_v')(\Delta Z_v'/\Delta Z_v)$.   This slope, neglecting the ratio $\Delta Z_v'/\Delta Z_v$, has also been correlated with the acentric factor (55a).

Equation (4-43) may be used in a similar way; i.e., a graph of log P_{vp_r} versus the logarithm of the reduced vapor pressure for water (both evaluated at the same reduced temperature) gives an almost straight line passing through the point $P_{vp_r} = 1.0$, $P'_{vp_r} = 1.0$, and with the slope $(T_c'/T_c)(\Delta H_v/\Delta H_v')(\Delta Z_v'/\Delta Z_v)$ (109).   This slope, with the ratio $\Delta Z_v'/\Delta Z_v$ neglected, has also been correlated with the acentric factor (55a).

Seglin's modification of the Othmer approach (81) is given as Eq. (4-44).   This suggests a graph T_c/T versus T_c'/T' (for water or other reference substance) at the same reduced pressure, and ΔH_v determined from the slope.

For both these techniques it is necessary to have some vapor-pressure data on both substances and detailed values giving the variation of $\Delta H_v'$ with temperature for the reference substance.   The vapor-pressure data do not need to be so complete, however, as for the numerical calculation of ΔH_v as described in Sec. 4-14.

Othmer and Zudkevitch (76) have applied Eq. (4-42) to some 500 common organic compounds, using water as the reference substance and the Lydersen et al. (56) values of ΔZ_v as a function of P_r and have published values of m to be used for each substance.   These tables are given

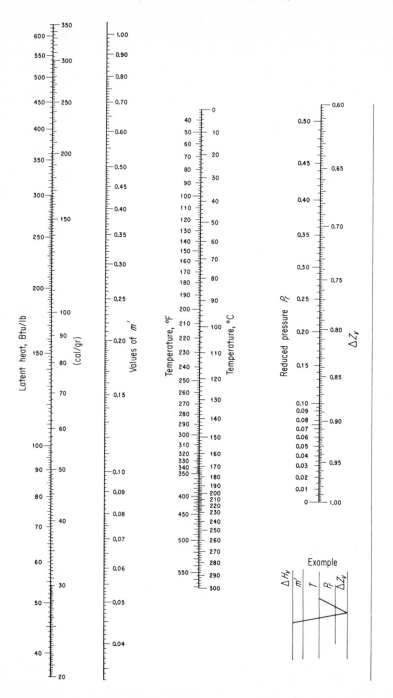

Fig. 4-6. Nomogram for latent heats.　(Values of m' and C are given in Appendix C.) [*D. F. Othmer and D. Zudkevitch, Ind. Eng. Chem.,* **51**:791 (1959).]

in Appendix C. For convenience in use, their nomograph is shown in Fig. 4-6. In this figure the correlating parameter is m' ($m' = 18m/M$) to allow ΔH_v to be determined per unit mass. Values of m' are also given in Appendix C. ΔH_v may be determined for any compound up to $P_r = 0.5$ if the temperature and reduced pressure are known.* For example, ΔH_v for ethanol ($m' = 0.3832$), at 100°C, [$P_{vp} = 32.6$ psia, $P_c = 63.0$ atm, $P_r = 32.6/(63.0)(14.7) = 0.035$] as read from Fig. 4-6 gives 200 cal/g or $(200)(46) = 9200$ cal/g mole, a value 5 per cent higher than experimentally measured.

4-18   Miscellaneous Methods to Estimate Latent Heats of Vaporization

Estimation from Structure.   A few attempts have been made to relate ΔH_v directly to molecular structure. Chu et al. (15) were able to correlate latent heats for 73 paraffin hydrocarbons within 2 per cent, using an equation relating ΔH_v to the parachor and polarity number, terms which may be determined from additive group techniques. Similarly Bowden and Jones (11), Wright (122), and Patton (78) tabulate additive bond values to determine a structural parameter called the *normal lyoparachor*. ΔH_v has been empirically correlated with this parameter and the specific volumes of the saturated vapor and liquid.

Both structural methods appear to be best suited for nonpolar or slightly polar compounds in the vicinity of T_b. Critical constants are not required, but the Chu method is limited to hydrocarbons, and the lyoparachor technique requires accurate volumetric data. It appears that, generally, the methods described in Secs. 4-14 to 4-16 are preferable even if T_c and P_c have to be estimated by empirical correlations such as those shown in Chap. 2.

Bondi and Simkin Method for Hydrogen-bonded Substances.   Only a few papers have dealt with hydrogen-bonded substances (10, 57). In the more general study, Bondi and Simkin (10) proposed a method to relate ΔH_v to the enthalpy of vaporization of the hydrocarbon homomorph.†

$$\Delta H_v = \Delta H_{vHM} + \text{(correction terms)} \qquad (4\text{-}64)$$

Tables are given in the original reference to allow an approximation of the correction terms in Eq. (4-64). Though this correlation makes a start toward the solution of the difficult problem of correlating properties of hydrogen-bonded materials, better results are still obtained from other methods such as those summarized in Secs. 4-14 to 4-17; errors in the

---

* Othmer and Zudkevitch suggest $\Delta Z_v = 1\,003 - 0.66P_r^{0.74}$ for values of P_r between 0.1 and 0.5.

† A homomorph is the hydrocarbon of similar geometry, with a CH_3 replacing the polar group; e.g., toluene is the hydrocarbon homomorph of phenol.

estimation of ΔH_{v_b} for several hydrogen-bonded materials by these latter methods may be judged from an examination of Table 4-8.

Riedel Empirical Method (91). Riedel proposed an empirical, accurate method to estimate ΔH_{v_b} from critical constants.

$$\Delta H_{v_b} = T_b(5 \log P_c - 2.17)/(0.930 - T_{b_r}) \qquad (4\text{-}65)$$

In testing with 94 compounds as shown in Table 4-8, an average error of 1.8 per cent was found. This equation is certainly simple, and the accuracy is rather surprising. Example 4-15 illustrates the method.

Example 4-15. Repeat Example 4-13, using the Riedel method.
Solution. Using the critical constants listed in Example 4-13,

$$\Delta H_{v_b} = (362.7)(5 \log 30.0 - 2.17)/(0.930 - 0.677) = 7490 \text{ cal/g mole}$$
$$\text{Error} = [(7,490 - 7,675)/7,675] \times 100 = -2.4\%$$

4-19 Variation of Enthalpy of Vaporization with Temperature

Many of the methods discussed in previous sections allow one to estimate heats of vaporization at any desired temperature. Occasionally, however, one has available a single experimental or estimated value of ΔH_v and desires to determine other values at different temperatures. While many estimation techniques have been suggested (30, 54, 106) to accomplish this task, the simple empirical Theisen correlation

$$\Delta H_v = k(T_c - T)^n \qquad (4\text{-}66)$$

where k and n are constants, has proved to be the most useful. By writing Eq. (4-66) at two different temperatures and dividing one into the other,

$$\Delta H_{v_2} = \Delta H_{v_1}[(1 - T_{r_2})/(1 - T_{r_1})]^n \qquad (4\text{-}67)$$

Gambill (30) gives references to many writers who proposed various values for the exponent n. Values range from $\frac{1}{3}$ to $\frac{2}{5}$, but, in general, the best results are obtained with $n = 0.38$. With this choice, Eq. (4-63) is often called the Watson correlation (120). Fishtine (27) has recently suggested that the exponent n be given as

$$n = \begin{cases} 0.740T_{b_r} - 0.116 & 0.57 < T_{b_r} < 0.71 \\ 0.30 & T_{b_r} < 0.57 \\ 0.41 & T_{b_r} > 0.71 \end{cases} \qquad (4\text{-}68)$$

and Narsimhan (72) has justified that n should be $\frac{3}{8}$ if the Eötvös equation is valid. Figure 4-7 shows a nomograph of Eq. (4-66) with $n = 0.38$ (47).

The Watson correlation is simple and appears to be reliable; e.g., Fig. 4-8 shows calculated and experimental values of ΔH_v as a function

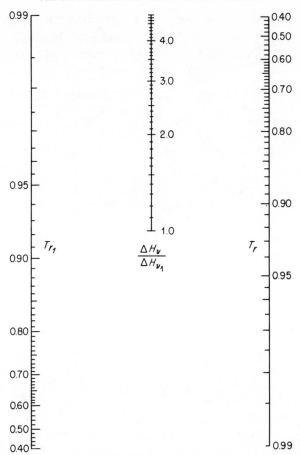

F_{IG}. 4-7. Nomogram for Watson's correlation of enthalpies of vaporization as a function of temperature. [*O. P. Kharbanda, Indian Chemist,* **31**:124 (1955).]

of temperature for six selected compounds, based on experimental rather than predicted values of ΔH_v at T_b. The average error is 1.8 per cent for the 76 points plotted for temperatures more than 10°C below the critical. Within 10°C of the critical the prediction is considerably less reliable. In a very detailed study on 33 hydrocarbons, Thompson and Braun (113) found the Watson correlation [Eq. (4-67)] to be quite reliable if experimental values of ΔH_{v_1} at T_1 were used to determine other ΔH_v values. The average error found was about 1.2 per cent.

4-20 Entropy-of-vaporization Rules

No discussion of the heat-of-vaporization estimation methods would be complete without mention of the widely quoted rules used to approximate entropies of vaporization ($\Delta S_v = \Delta H_v/T$).

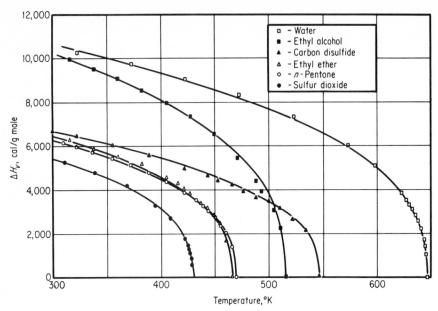

FIG. 4-8. Comparison between experimental and calculated heats of vaporization.

Trouton (115) in 1884 suggested that, as an approximation, the entropy of vaporization of all "normal" materials at their normal boiling point is approximately equal to 21 cal/(g mole)(°K). Hildebrand (38) in 1915 observed that the accuracy of Trouton's rule could be improved if the entropies were evaluated, not at the normal boiling point, but at temperatures at which the saturated-vapor concentrations were equal. The ideal-gas law being assumed, this meant that ΔS_v is a constant at some arbitrarily chosen value of RT/P_{vp}. The argument for such a choice was that it seemed more reasonable to compare vaporization entropies when their molecules were separated by equal distances in the vapor phase. By choosing the saturated-vapor volume as $RT/P_{vp} = 49.5$ liters/g mole, Hildebrand and Scott (39) calculated ΔS_v for many compounds. For simple, symmetrical molecules ΔS_v is about 20.1 cal/(g mole)(°K), but variations of 0.2 to over 6 cal/(g mole)(°K) occur for more complex structures. ΔS_v values were later found to vary much less if the gas phase was not assumed to be ideal (37); e.g., normal paraffins from C_1 to C_{20}, many branched hydrocarbons, some naphthenes, and aromatics showed deviations usually less than 0.3 cal/(g mole)(°K). Following these "rules" were many others, of which the better known are:

Pitzer (82): $\Delta S_v = $ const, when materials are compared under conditions such that $v_{sat\ vap}/$ $v_{sat\ liq}$ are equal

Guggenheim (34): ΔS_v = const at equal reduced pressures

Barclay and Butler (4): ΔS_v^* = const

$$= A + B\,\Delta H_v^*; \quad A \text{ and } B \text{ are universal}$$

constants and ΔS_v^* and ΔH_v^* are entropies and enthalpies of vaporization at some chosen standard-state pressure (not necessarily 1 atm)

Everett (26): ΔS_v^{**} = const

$$= \Delta H_{v_b}/T_b + [R \ln (v^{**}/v_{sat\ vap} \text{ at } T_b)]$$

In the last method, v^{**} is an arbitrarily chosen volume. If the gases are ideal and on the assumption that v^{**} is 22.4 liters, $v_{sat\ vap}$ at $T_b = RT_b$, and ΔS^{**} = 19.16 cal/(g mole)(°K) for "spherical" hydrocarbons, then

$$\Delta S^{**} = \Delta S_{v_b} + R \ln (273.2/T_b) = 19.16$$

or $\quad\quad\quad \Delta S_{v_b} = 8.00 + R \ln T_b \quad\quad\quad\quad\quad\quad\quad (4\text{-}69)$

Interestingly enough, as Everett himself notes, Eq. (4-69) is similar to that proposed by Kistiakowsky (48) except that the constant 8.75 was used rather than 8.0. Equation (4-69) has also been used by Griswold and May (33), by Chu et al. (15) for estimating ΔS_v for organic compounds, and by Chipman (14) to determine ΔS_v for elements boiling from 5 to 7000°K and for various classes of organic materials.

None of these or other, related techniques (109, 110) are sufficiently accurate to be of real value to the engineer charged with the estimation of latent heats. This was not the main purpose of these investigators. The deviations of entropies of vaporization from some standard reference equation, e.g., Eq. (4-69), were used in an attempt to deduce the degree of internal order existing in the liquid and/or the extent to which molecular rotation was restricted. This type of study is well exemplified by the review article by Stavely and Tupman (103), who discuss in some detail the relationship of ΔS_v to the chemical structure and degree of internal order existing in the liquid phase.

The one exception to the general statement made above results from Fishtine's modification of the Kistiakowsky equation to estimate latent heats at the normal boiling point (27), using only the normal boiling temperature. Such a relation would be valuable for those cases where critical constants or vapor pressures were unavailable or unreliable. The technique used was to express Eq. (4-69) as

$$\Delta H_{v_b}/T_b = \Delta S_{v_b} = K_F(8.75 + R \ln T_b) \quad\quad\quad (4\text{-}70)$$

Recommended values of the correction factor K_F are shown in Table 4-7 for many types of organic structures. Substituted aromatic compounds are not included (though K_F for nonsubstituted simple aromatic com-

THE PROPERTIES OF GASES AND LIQUIDS

TABLE 4-7. K_F FACTORS FOR ALIPHATIC AND ALICYLIC ORGANIC COMPOUNDS*

Compound type	n, number of carbon atoms in compound, including carbon atoms of functional group											
	1	2	3	4	5	6	7	8	9	10	11	12–20
Hydrocarbons:												
n-Alkanes	0.97	1.00	1.00	1.00	1.00	1.00	1.00	1.00	1.00	1.00	1.00	1.00
Alkane isomers			0.99	0.99	0.99	0.99	0.99	0.99	0.99	0.99	0.99	0.99
Mono- and diolefins and isomers		1.01	1.01	1.01	1.01	1.01	1.01	1.01	1.01	1.01	1.01	1.00
Cyclic saturated hydrocarbons			1.00	1.00	1.00	1.00	1.00	1.00	1.00	1.00	1.00	1.00
Alkyl derivatives of cyclic saturated hydrocarbons				0.99	0.99	0.99	0.99	0.99	0.99	0.99	0.99	0.99
Halides (saturated or unsaturated):												
Monochlorides	1.05	1.04	1.03	1.03	1.03	1.03	1.03	1.03	1.02	1.02	1.02	1.01
Monobromides	1.04	1.03	1.03	1.03	1.03	1.03	1.02	1.02	1.02	1.01	1.01	1.01
Monoiodides	1.03	1.02	1.02	1.02	1.02	1.02	1.01	1.01	1.01	1.01	1.01	1.01
Polyhalides (not entirely halogenated)	1.05	1.05	1.05	1.04	1.04	1.04	1.03	1.03	1.03	1.02	1.02	1.01
Mixed halides (completely halogenated)	1.01	1.01	1.01	1.01	1.01	1.01	1.01	1.01	1.01	1.01	1.01	1.01
Perfluorocarbons	1.00	1.00	1.00	1.00	1.00	1.00	1.00	1.00	1.00	1.00	1.00	1.00
Compounds containing the keto group:												
Esters		1.14	1.09	1.08	1.07	1.06	1.05	1.04	1.04	1.03	1.02	1.01
Ketones			1.08	1.07	1.06	1.06	1.05	1.04	1.04	1.03	1.02	1.01
Aldehydes		1.09	1.08	1.08	1.07	1.06	1.05	1.04	1.04	1.03	1.02	1.01
Nitrogen compounds:												
Primary amines	1.16	1.13	1.12	1.11	1.10	1.10	1.09	1.09	1.08	1.07	1.06	1.05†
Secondary amines		1.09	1.08	1.08	1.07	1.07	1.06	1.05	1.05	1.04	1.04	1.03†
Tertiary amines			1.01	1.01	1.01	1.01	1.01	1.01	1.01	1.01	1.01	1.01
Nitriles		1.05	1.07	1.06	1.06	1.05	1.05	1.04	1.04	1.03	1.02	1.01
Nitro compounds	1.07	1.07	1.07	1.06	1.06	1.05	1.05	1.04	1.04	1.03	1.02	1.01
Sulfur compounds:												
Mercaptans	1.05	1.03	1.02	1.01	1.01	1.01	1.01	1.01	1.01	1.01	1.01	1.01
Sulfides		1.03	1.02	1.01	1.01	1.01	1.01	1.01	1.01	1.01	1.01	1.01
Alcohols:												
Alcohols (single-OH group)	1.22	1.31	1.31	1.31	1.31	1.30	1.29	1.28	1.27	1.26	1.25	1.24†
Diols (glycols or condensed glycols)		1.33	1.33	1.33	1.33	1.33	1.33	1.33				
Triols (glycerol, etc.)			1.38	1.38	1.38							
Cyclohexanol, cyclohexyl methyl alcohol, etc.							1.20	1.20	1.21	1.24	1.26	
Miscellaneous compounds:												
Ethers (aliphatic only)		1.03	1.03	1.02	1.02	1.01	1.01	1.01	1.01	1.01	1.01	1.01
Oxides (cyclic ethers)		1.08	1.07	1.06	1.05	1.05	1.04	1.03	1.02	1.01	1.01	1.01

NOTES:

1. Alicyclic compounds are carbocyclic or heterocyclic compounds having aliphatic properties.

2. Consider any phenyl group as a single carbon atom.

3. K_F factors are the same for all aliphatic isomers of a given compound. For example, $K_F = 1.31$ for n-butyl alcohol, i-butyl alcohol, t-butyl alcohol, and s-butyl alcohol.

4. In organometallic compounds, consider any metallic atom as a carbon atom.

* S. H. Fishtine, *Ind. Eng. Chem.*, **55**(6):47 (1963).

† For $n = 12$ only; no prediction is made for K_F where $n > 12$.

pounds is near unity), and the original article should be consulted for methods to determine K_F in these cases. The method for such aromatics involves an estimation of the dipole moment (or finding an experimental value) and calculating K_F as

$$K_F(\text{substituted aromatics}) = 1 + 2\mu/100 \qquad (4\text{-}71)$$

where μ is in debyes.

The K_F values in Table 4-7 are usually very close to unity, although they are larger for polar molecules and those exhibiting hydrogen bonding. With all polar compounds disregarded for which no specific K_F values are tabulated, e.g., carboxylic acids, and with no inorganic materials included, a test of Eq. (4-70) with 52 compounds, covering both hydrocarbons and nonhydrocarbons, showed that the experimental and calculated values of ΔH_{v_b} differed by an average of 1.3 per cent. Several multifunctional group materials were tested and following Fishtine's suggestion, the single-functional group analogue with the highest K_F value was chosen. For example, in chloroacetone, $K_F = 1.03$ for propyl chloride and 1.08 for acetone; thus the higher value, 1.08, would be chosen. The method is illustrated in Example 4-16.

Example 4-16. Estimate the value of ΔH_{v_b} for ethylcyclopentane with Fishtine's modification of the Kistiakowsky equation [Eq. (4-70)]. Compare with the experimental value of 7715 cal/g mole (2).

Solution. In ethylcyclopentane, there are seven carbon atoms, and, from Table 4-10, $K_F = 0.99$. The normal boiling point is 103.5°C or 376.7°K. Thus, from Eq. (4-70),

$$\Delta H_{v_b} = (376.7)(0.99)[8.75 + 1.987(\ln 376.7)]$$
$$= 7660 \text{ cal/g mole}$$
$$\text{Error} = [(7{,}660 - 7{,}715)/7{,}715] \times 100 = -0.7\%$$

4-21 Recommendations for Estimating Latent Heats of Vaporization

If there are sufficient accurate vapor-pressure data available in the temperature region of interest, use a numerical differentiation technique such as the one shown in Eq. (4-54). The accuracy of the result is limited only by that of the vapor-pressure data.

To estimate the latent heat of vaporization at the normal boiling point, there are several methods of comparable accuracy. Calculated values of ΔH_{v_b} are compared with experimental values for all the better methods except the Kistiakowsky-Fishtine method in Table 4-8. The most accurate, but the most complicated, is the Riedel-Plank-Miller equation (4-63); for rapid estimations, the Chen equation (4-57), the Klein-Fishtine equations (4-61) and (4-62), and the Riedel equation (4-65) are almost as accurate and much easier to use. All the methods listed in Table 4-8 require critical constants; if these are unavailable and their estimation judged unreliable, the Kistiakowsky-Fishtine method [Eq.

TABLE 4-8. COMPARISON BETWEEN EXPERIMENTAL AND CALCULATED LATENT HEATS OF VAPORIZATION AT THE NORMAL BOILING POINT*

Values in cal/g mole

Compound	Exp. ΔH_{vb}	Calculated by method of									
		Riedel		Giacalone		Riedel-Plank-Miller		Klein-Fishtine		Pitzer-Chen	
		ΔH_{vb}	% Error†	ΔH_{vb}	% Error†	ΔH_{vb}	% Error†	ΔH_{vb}	% Error†	ΔH_{vb}	% Error†
Paraffins:											
Methane	1,955	1,990	+ 1.8	2,049	+ 4.8	1,975	+ 1.0	1,973	+ 0.9	1,987	+ 1.6
Ethane	3,517	3,541	+ 0.7	3,594	+ 2.2	3,521	+ 0.1	3,489	− 0.8	3,538	+ 0.6
Propane	4,487	4,502	+ 0.3	4,574	+ 1.9	4,482	− 0.1	4,519	+ 0.7	4,493	+ 0.1
n-Butane	5,352	5,385	+ 0.6	5,476	+ 2.3	5,363	+ 0.2	5,400	+ 0.9	5,368	+ 0.3
Isobutane	5,089	5,073	− 0.3	5,184	+ 1.9	5,054	− 0.7	5,099	+ 0.2	5,061	− 0.6
n-Pentane	6,160	6,206	+ 0.7	6,315	+ 2.5	6,180	+ 0.3	6,243	+ 1.3	6,174	+ 0.2
2-Methylbutane	5,901	5,902	0	6,035	+ 2.3	5,880	− 0.4	5,954	+ 0.9	5,881	− 0.3
Neopentane	5,438	5,412	− 0.5	5,569	+ 2.4	5,395	− 0.8	5,450	+ 0.2	5,400	− 0.7
n-Hexane	6,896	6,955	+ 0.9	7,081	+ 2.7	6,919	+ 0.3	6,984	+ 1.3	6,903	+ 0.1
2,3-Dimethylbutane	6,519	6,538	+ 0.3	6,691	+ 2.6	6,512	− 0.1	6,592	+ 1.1	6,509	− 0.2
n-Heptane	7,575	7,650	+ 1.0	7,795	+ 2.9	7,599	+ 0.3	7,668	+ 1.2	7,573	0
3-Methylhexane	7,358	7,451	+ 1.3	7,596	+ 3.2	7,408	+ 0.7	7,478	+ 1.6	7,388	+ 0.4
3-Ethylpentane	7,398	7,440	+ 0.6	7,590	+ 2.6	7,401	0	7,474	+ 1.0	7,383	− 0.2
2,3-Dimethylpentane	7,262	7,340	+ 1.1	7,488	+ 3.1	7,303	+ 0.6	7,376	+ 1.6	7,288	+ 0.4
2,4-Dimethylpentane	7,050	7,095	+ 0.6	7,267	+ 3.1	7,059	+ 0.1	7,139	+ 1.3	7,046	− 0.1
2,2,3-Trimethylbutane	6,918	6,982	+ 0.9	7,156	+ 3.4	6,954	+ 0.5	7,041	+ 1.8	6,950	+ 0.5
n-Octane	8,224	8,354	+ 1.6	8,506	+ 3.4	8,280	+ 0.7	8,349	+ 1.5	8,241	+ 0.2
2-Methylheptane	8,080	8,102	+ 0.3	8,266	+ 2.3	8,037	− 0.5	8,111	+ 0.4	8,004	− 0.9
3-Ethyl-2-methylpentane	7,878	7,948	+ 0.9	8,107	+ 2.9	7,900	+ 0.3	7,975	+ 1.2	7,877	0
2,2,4-Trimethylpentane	7,410	7,380	− 0.4	7,601	+ 2.6	7,344	− 0.9	7,441	+ 0.4	7,333	− 1.0
n-Nonane	8,822	8,974	+ 1.7	9,143	+ 3.6	8,874	+ 0.6	8,950	+ 1.5	8,823	0
n-Decane	9,390	9,610	+ 2.3	9,783	+ 4.2	9,474	+ 0.9	9,554	+ 1.7	9,409	+ 0.2

154

Olefins and acetylenes:										
Ethylene	3,237	3,247 +0.3	3,292 +1.7	3,227 −0.3	3,199 −1.2	3,244 +0.2				
Propene	4,402	4,415 +0.3	4,471 +1.6	4,393 −0.2	4,427 +0.6	4,407 +0.1				
1-Butene	5,237	5,289 +1.0	5,365 +2.4	5,266 +0.6	5,296 +1.1	5,273 +0.7				
trans-2-Butene	5,438	5,586 +2.7	5,630 +3.5	5,560 +2.2	5,581 +2.6	5,563 +2.3				
Isobutylene	5,286	5,287 0	5,363 +1.5	5,265 −0.4	5,298 +0.2	5,271 +0.3				
1-Pentene	6,022	6,371 +5.8	6,388 +6.1	6,336 +5.2	6,367 +5.7	6,327 +5.1				
1,3-Butadiene	5,367	5,404 +0.7	5,456 +1.7	5,372 +0.1	5,405 +0.7	5,387 +0.4				
Propyne	5,248	5,254 +0.1	5,233 −0.3	5,224 −0.5	5,225 −0.4	5,236 −0.2				
Cycloparaffins:										
Cyclopentane	6,524	6,529 +0.1	6,575 +0.8	6,497 −0.4	6,555 +0.5	6,508 −0.2				
Methylcyclopentane	7,002	6,958 −0.6	7,047 +0.6	6,927 −1.1	6,992 −0.1	6,926 −1.1				
Ethylcyclopentane	7,715	7,652 −0.8	7,764 +0.6	7,616 −1.3	7,684 −0.4	7,605 −1.4				
Cyclohexane	7,190	7,121 −1.0	7,201 +0.2	7,089 −1.4	7,157 −0.5	7,094 −1.3				
Methylcyclohexane	7,580	7,461 −1.6	7,593 +0.2	7,430 −2.0	7,510 −0.9	7,428 −2.0				
Aromatics:										
Benzene	7,353	7,340 −0.2	7,340 −0.2	7,301 −0.7	7,346 −0.1	7,312 −0.6				
Toluene	7,933	8,073 +1.8	8,085 +1.9	8,029 +1.2	8,068 +1.7	8,021 +1.1				
o-Xylene	8,801	8,689 −1.3	8,756 −0.5	8,642 −1.8	8,695 −1.2	8,624 −2.0				
m-Xylene	8,700	8,720 +0.2	8,765 +0.7	8,665 −0.4	8,706 +0.1	8,638 −0.7				
Ethylbenzene	8,599	8,700 +1.2	8,721 +1.4	8,646 +0.5	8,680 +0.9	8,622 +0.3				
1,3,5-Trimethylbenzene	9,330	9,655 +3.5	9,639 +3.3	9,564 +2.5	9,575 +2.6	9,504 +1.9				
Naphthalene	10,240	10,533 +2.9	10,513 +2.7	10,468 +2.2	10,496 +2.5	10,444 +2.0				
Alcohols:										
Methyl alcohol	8,430	9,079 +7.7	8,569 +1.6	8,942 +6.1	8,752 +3.8	8,903 +5.6				
Ethyl alcohol	9,220	9,650 +4.7	9,083 −1.5	9,465 +2.7	9,250 +0.3	9,366 +1.6				
n-Propyl alcohol	9,852	9,833 −0.2	9,340 −5.2	9,646 −2.1	9,465 −3.9	9,530 −3.3				
Isopropyl alcohol	9,729	9,548 −1.9	9,052 −7.0	9,342 −4.0	9,161 −5.8	9,207 −5.4				

TABLE 4-8. COMPARISON BETWEEN EXPERIMENTAL AND CALCULATED LATENT HEATS OF VAPORIZATION AT THE BOILING POINT* (Continued)

Values in cal/g mole

Compound	Exp. ΔH_{vb}	Calculated by method of									
		Riedel		Giacalone		Riedel-Plank-Miller		Klein-Fishtine		Pitzer-Chen	
		ΔH_{vb}	% Error†	ΔH_{vb}	% Error†	ΔH_{vb}	% Error†	ΔH_{vb}	% Error†	ΔH_{vb}	% Error†
Alcohols (Cont.)											
n-Butyl alcohol	10,470	9,987	− 4.6	9,585	− 8.5	9,809	− 6.3	9,667	− 7.7	9,691	− 7.4
Phenol	10,760	11,155	+ 3.7	10,756	0	11,034	+ 2.5	10,905	+ 1.3	10,993	+ 2.2
p-Cresol	11,250	11,815	+ 5.0	11,385	+ 1.2	11,658	+ 3.6	11,509	+ 2.3	11,568	+ 2.8
Ethers:											
Dimethyl ether	5,141	5,240	+ 1.9	5,220	+ 1.5	5,210	+ 1.3	5,212	+ 1.4	5,222	+ 1.6
Ketones:											
Acetone	6,952	7,228	+ 4.0	7,158	+ 3.0	7,180	+ 3.3	7,181	+ 3.3	7,169	+ 3.1
Organic acids and esters:											
Acetic acid‡	9,526	9,492	− 0.4	9,179	− 3.6	9,392	− 1.4	9,292	− 2.5	9,353	− 1.8
Isobutyric acid	10,620	10,808	+ 1.8	10,404	− 2.0	10,608	− 0.1	10,468	− 1.4	10,472	− 1.4
Methyl formate	6,708	6,694	− 0.2	6,597	− 1.7	6,650	− 0.9	6,652	− 0.8	6,663	− 0.7
Ethyl acetate	7,744	7,685	− 0.8	7,648	− 1.2	7,627	− 1.5	7,632	− 1.4	7,594	− 1.9
Organic nitrogen compounds:											
Methylamine	6,170	6,150	− 0.3	5,985	− 3.0	6,101	− 1.1	6,043	− 2.1	6,121	− 0.8
Ethylamine	6,700	6,432	− 4.0	6,334	− 5.5	6,388	− 4.7	6,351	− 5.2	6,391	− 4.6
Diethylamine	6,975	6,920	− 0.8	6,952	− 0.3	6,880	− 1.4	6,914	− 0.9	6,863	− 1.6
Triethylamine	7,675	7,490	− 2.4	7,600	− 1.0	7,445	− 3.0	7,504	− 2.2	7,423	− 3.3
Acetonitrile	7,500	7,813	+ 4.2	7,729	+ 3.1	7,761	+ 3.5	7,759	+ 3.5	7,749	+ 3.3
Aniline	10,360	10,657	+ 2.9	10,405	+ 0.4	10,562	+ 1.9	10,496	+ 1.3	10,528	+ 1.6

Sulfur compounds:

Dimethyl sulfide	6,453	6,467	+ 0.2	6,447	− 0.1	6,430	− 0.4	6,469	+ 0.2	6,450	0
Ethyl mercaptan	6,400	6,413	+ 0.2	6,395	− 0.1	6,376	− 0.4	6,416	+ 0.3	6,396	− 0.1
Diethyl sulfide	7,591	7,716	+ 1.6	7,733	+ 1.9	7,672	+ 1.1	7,706	+ 1.5	7,657	+ 0.9
Thiophene	7,522	7,487	− 0.5	7,450	− 1.0	7,442	− 1.1	7,483	− 0.5	7,467	− 0.7

Organic halides:

Methyl chloride	5,150	5,195	+ 0.9	5,157	+ 0.1	5,159	+ 0.2	5,170	+ 0.4	5,191	+ 0.8
Methylene chloride	6,690	6,645	− 0.7	6,587	− 1.5	6,603	− 1.3	6,630	− 0.9	6,628	+ 0.9
Chloroform	6,841	7,108	+ 3.9	7,062	+ 3.2	7,066	+ 3.3	7,093	+ 3.7	7,081	+ 3.5
Carbon tetrachloride	7,154	7,071	− 1.2	7,121	− 0.5	6,818	− 4.7	7,101	− 0.7	7,049	− 1.5
Ethyl chloride	5,900	5,905	+ 0.1	5,901	0	5,872	− 0.5	5,884	− 0.3	5,902	0
Ethyl bromide	6,349	6,767	+ 6.6	6,678	+ 4.9	6,723	+ 5.9	6,734	+ 6.1	6,744	+ 6.2
Fluorobenzene	7,534	7,500	− 0.5	7,505	− 0.4	7,460	− 1.0	7,499	− 0.5	7,461	− 1.0
Chlorobenzene	8,423	8,492	+ 0.8	8,494	+ 0.8	8,446	+ 0.3	8,489	+ 0.8	8,446	+ 0.3
Bromobenzene	8,966	9,006	+ 0.4	9,007	+ 0.5	8,957	− 0.1	9,002	+ 0.4	8,958	− 0.1
Iodobenzene	9,548	9,673	+ 1.3	9,677	+ 1.4	9,621	+ 0.8	9,671	+ 1.3	9,622	+ 0.8

Inert elementary gases:

Helium△	20	−14	……	37	+ 85.0	13	− 35.0	16	− 20.0	18	− 10.0
Hydrogen	216	216	0	267	+ 24.0	213	− 1.4	221	+ 2.3	218	+ 0.9
Oxygen	1,630	1,634	+ 0.2	1,672	+ 2.6	1,620	− 0.6	1,617	− 0.8	1,632	+ 0.1
Nitrogen	1,333	1,328	− 0.4	1,392	+ 4.4	1,322	− 0.8	1,324	− 0.7	1,328	− 0.4
Fluorine	1,561	1,699	+ 8.8	1,710	+ 9.5	1,688	+ 8.1	1,669	+ 6.9	1,698	+ 8.8
Chlorine	4,878	4,826	− 1.1	4,801	− 1.6	4,781	− 2.0	4,815	− 1.3	4,830	− 1.0

Inorganic, nitrogen, and sulfur compounds:

Ammonia	5,581	5,710	+ 2.3	5,495	− 1.5	5,654	+ 1.3	5,590	+ 0.2	5,713	+ 2.4
Hydrazine	9,700	9,853	+ 1.6	9,350	− 3.6	9,740	+ 0.4	9,606	− 1.0	9,863	+ 1.7
Carbon disulfides	6,295	6,627	+ 5.3	6,562	+ 4.2	6,569	+ 4.4	6,627	+ 5.3	6,633	+ 5.4
Hydrogen sulfide	4,463	4,397	− 1.5	4,342	− 2.7	4,352	− 2.5	4,373	− 2.0	4,406	− 1.3

TABLE 4-8. COMPARISON BETWEEN EXPERIMENTAL AND CALCULATED LATENT HEATS OF VAPORIZATION AT THE NORMAL BOILING POINT* (*Continued*)

Values in cal/g mole

Compound	Exp. ΔH_{vb}	Calculated by method of									
		Riedel		Giacalone		Riedel-Plank-Miller		Klein-Fishtine		Pitzer-Chen	
		ΔH_{vb}	% Error†	ΔH_{vb}	% Error†	ΔH_{vb}	% Error†	ΔH_{vb}	% Error†	ΔH_{vb}	% Error†
Inorganic halides:											
Hydrogen chloride..........	3,860	3,969	+ 2.8	3,917	+ 1.5	3,934	+ 1.9	3,867	+ 0.2	3,973	+ 2.9
Hydrogen bromide..........	4,210	4,252	+ 1.0	4,210	0	4,210	0	4,234	+ 0.6	4,258	+ 1.1
Hydrogen iodide..........	4,724	4,758	+ 0.7	4,734	+ 0.2	4,706	− 0.4	4,750	+ 0.6	4,764	+ 0.8
Phosgene..........	5,831	5,891	+ 1.0	5,861	+ 0.5	5,856	+ 0.4	5,859	− 0.5	5,875	+ 0.8
Oxides:											
Nitrous oxide..........	3,956	3,876	− 2.0	3,833	− 3.1	3,847	− 2.8	3,777	− 4.5	3,875	− 2.0
Nitric oxide..........	3,293	3,259	− 1.0	3,082	− 6.4	3,204	− 2.7	3,063	− 7.0	3,176	− 3.6
Nitrogen dioxide..........	9,110	9,347	+ 2.6	8,510	− 6.6	9,087	− 0.3	8,711	− 4.4	8,985	− 1.4
Sulfur dioxide..........	5,955	6,010	+ 0.9	5,854	− 1.7	5,962	+ 0.1	5,914	− 0.7	5,993	+ 0.6
Sulfur trioxide..........	9,990	8,371	−16.2	7,931	−20.6	8,261	−17.3	8,103	−18.9	8,247	−17.4
Water..........	9,717.1	10,065	+ 3.6	9,438	− 2.9	9,926	+ 2.1	9,744	+ 0.3	10,115	+ 4.1
Average error..........	....	....	1.8	....	2.8	....	1.7	....	1.9	....	1.7

* D. G. Miller, *Ind. Eng. Chem.*, **56**:46 (1964); J. H. Perry (ed.), "Chemical Engineers' Handbook," McGraw-Hill Book Company, New York, 1950.

† % Error = [(calculated−experimental)/experimental] × 100.

‡ Based on the assumed molecular weight of 100 for acetic acid vapor.

Δ Helium—calculated values not included in % error.

(4-70)] with Table 4-7 is convenient, as only a boiling point is necessary, although, of course, the value of K_F must be obtainable from Table 4-7. In all cases average errors between 1 and 3 per cent can be expected.

To estimate the latent heat of vaporization at any temperature, two methods are recommended:

1. Obtain one value of ΔH_{v_1} at temperature T_1 (for example, at T_b determine ΔH_{v_b} as noted above), and use the Watson correlation [Eq. (4-67)] to determine ΔH_v at any other temperature.

2. Use the Pitzer correlation [Eq. (4-56)] with Table 4-6 or, alternatively, the Chen modification [Eq. (4-57)]. In the first case, an accurate value of the acentric factor must be available either from methods described in Sec. 2-7 or from Appendix A; in the second case, no acentric factor is required, but the critical pressure and the vapor pressure at the temperature in question must be known. Both methods require knowledge of the critical temperature.

Both methods 1 and 2 have been tested rather thoroughly, and both appear to be equally applicable and reliable, at least at temperatures not far below T_b or very near T_c. Errors of only 2 to 4 per cent are usually encountered if the required input data are accurate.

The estimation methods are summarized in Table 4-9.

TABLE 4-9. SUMMARY OF CORRELATIONS OF LATENT HEAT OF VAPORIZATION

Method	Equations, tables, and figures required	Input data required	Output	% accuracy (approx.)	Comments
Numerical differentiation	Eq. (4-54), for example	$P_{vp}, \Delta Z_v$	ΔH_v at T	Varies with data	Best method if input data are closely spaced and reliable
Pitzer	Eq. (4-56), Table 4-6	T, T_c, ω	ΔH_v at T	2–5	Accurate values of acentric factor required. Interpolation in tables necessary
Pitzer-Chen	Eq. (4-57)	T, T_c, P_{vp}, P_c	ΔH_v at T	2–5	Reasonably accurate value of P_{vp} and P_c necessary
Giacalone	Eq. (4-59)	T_b, P_c, T_c	ΔH_{v_b}	3–7	Very simple and easy to use
Klein-Fishtine	Eqs. (4-61), (4-62)	T_b, P_c, T_c	ΔH_{v_b}	1–4	Accurate and simple
Riedel-Plank-Miller	Eq. (4-63)	T_b, P_c, T_c	ΔH_{v_b}	1–3	Most accurate of ΔH_{v_b} equations; somewhat complex to use
Othmer-Zudkevitch	Fig. 4-5; Appendix C	P_{vp}, P_c, m'	ΔH_v at T	5–10	Quick. Need m' value from Appendix C. Good only below $P_r = 0.5$
Riedel	Eq. (4-65)	T_b, P_c, T_c	ΔH_{v_b}	2–5	Very simple and easy to use
Watson	Eq. (4-67)	ΔH_{v_1} at T_1, T_c	ΔH_v at T	2–5	Reliable if good value of ΔH_{v_1} available. Use $n = 0.38$
Kistiakowsky-Fishtine	Eq. (4-70), Table 4-7	T_b	ΔH_{v_b}	2–5	Simple. K_F value must be obtained from Table 4-7

4-22   Latent Heat of Fusion

The enthalpy change on fusion or melting is commonly referred to as the *latent heat of fusion*. It depends in part on the crystal form of the solid phase, and attempts to obtain general correlations have been quite unsuccessful (31). The Clapeyron equation is applicable, but its use to calculate ΔH_m requires data on the variation of melting point with pressure—information which is seldom available.

Sutra (107) and Mukherjee (68) have indicated how the prediction of ΔH_m might be approached on the basis of the modern hole theory of liquids, but their calculated values compare poorly with experimental values. Kuczinski (52) presents a theory relating ΔH_m and the modulus of rigidity of the solid. Good agreement between theoretical and experimental values is shown for eight metallic elements. For monatomic substances, ΔS_m is about equal to the gas constant R (40).

The difficulty in obtaining a general correlation of ΔH_m in terms of other physical properties is suggested by the selected values tabulated for some hydrocarbons in Table 4-10. It is evident that the simple introduction of a methyl group often has a marked effect, either increasing or decreasing ΔH_m. Optical and stereo isomers differ markedly. The variation of ΔH_m and of the entropy of fusion $\Delta H_m/T_m$ is as great as that of the melting points, which have never been correlated with other properties. It appears that there is no simple correlation between ΔH_m and melting point. From theoretical considerations it would appear that ΔH_m might be related to the surface tension of the liquid, but no correlation between ΔH_m and either surface tension or parachor has been found. Table 4-10 also shows, for comparison, the relative constancy of the latent heat of vaporization at the normal boiling point. The ratio of $\Delta H_m/\Delta H_{v_b}$ varies greatly; i.e., in the table values are found between 0.02 and 1.12. Since the heat of vaporization increases with decreasing temperature, the ratio of heat effects between melting and vaporization at the melting point probably varies from about 0.1 to about 0.9.

4-23   Latent Heat of Sublimation

Solids vaporize without melting (*sublime*) at pressures below the vapor pressure corresponding to the triple point temperature. Sublimation at constant pressure involves an enthalpy increase, or *latent heat of sublimation*. This may be considered to be the sum of a latent heat of fusion and a latent heat of vaporization, even though liquid cannot exist at the pressure and temperature in question.

The latent heat of sublimation ΔH_s is best obtained from solid vapor-pressure data where such exist (44). For this purpose, the Clapeyron equation [Eq. (4-1)] is applicable. In the correlations of latent heat of

TABLE 4-10. SAMPLE TABULATION OF SOME ENTHALPIES AND ENTROPIES
OF FUSION FOR SIMPLE HYDROCARBONS*

Compound	T_m, °C	T_m, °K	M	ΔH_m, cal/g	ΔH_m, cal/g mole	$\Delta S_m =$ $\Delta H_m/T$, cal/(g mole)(°K)	ΔH_{v_b}, cal/g	$\Delta H_m/$ ΔH_{v_b}
Methane	−182.5	90.7	16.04	14.03	225	2.48	122	0.12
Ethane	−183.3	89.9	30.07	22.73	683	7.60	117	0.19
Propane	−187.7	85.5	44.09	19.10	842	9.85	102	0.19
n-Butane	−138.4	134.8	58.12	19.17	1,114	8.26	92.1	0.21
Isobutane	−159.6	113.6	58.12	18.67	1,085	9.55	87.6	0.21
n-Pentane	−129.7	143.5	72.15	27.81	2,006	13.98	85.4	0.33
Isopentane	−159.9	113.3	72.15	17.06	1,231	10.86	81.0	0.21
Neopentane	− 16.6	256.6	72.15	10.79	779	3.03	75.4	0.14
n-Hexane	− 95.4	177.8	86.17	36.14	3,114	17.51	80.0	0.45
2-Methylpentane	−153.7	119.5	86.17	17.41	1,500	12.55	77.1	0.23
2,2-Dimethylbutane	− 99.9	173.3	86.17	1.61	139	0.80	73.0	0.02
2,3-Dimethylbutane	−128.5	144.7	86.17	2.25	194	1.34	75.7	0.03
n-Heptane	− 90.6	182.6	100.2	33.47	3,350	18.37	75.6	0.44
2-Methylhexane	−118.3	155.0	100.2	21.91	2,195	14.16	73.1	0.30
3-Ethylpentane	−118.6	154.6	100.2	22.78	2,283	14.77	73.8	0.31
2,2-Dimethylpentane	−123.8	149.4	100.2	13.89	1,392	9.33	69.6	0.20
2,4-Dimethylpentane	−119.2	154.0	100.2	16.32	1,635	10.62	70.4	0.23
3,3-Dimethylpentane	−134.5	138.7	100.2	16.86	1,689	12.18	70.7	0.24
2,2,3-Trimethylbutane	− 24.9	248.3	100.2	5.39	540	2.18	69.0	0.08
n-Octane	− 56.8	216.4	114.2	43.40	4,956	22.90	71.9	0.60
3-Methylheptane	−120.5	152.7	114.2	23.81	2,719	17.81	71.3	0.33
4-Methylheptane	−12υ.9	152.3	114.2	22.68	2,590	17.01	70.9	0.32
n-Nonane	− 53.5	219.7	128.2	28.83	3,696	16.82	68.4	0.42
n-Decane	− 29.6	243.6	142.3	48.24	6,865	28.18	66.0	0.73
n-Dodecane	9.6	263.6	170.3	51.69	8,803	33.40	61.3	0.84
n-Octadecane	28.2	301.4	254.4	57.65	14,660	48.66	51.5	1.12
n-Nonadecane	32.1	305.3	268.5	40.78	10,950	35.88	50.3	0.81
n-Eicosane	36.8	310.0	282.5	59.11	16,700	53.87	48.8	1.21
Benzene	5.5	278.7	78.1	30.09	2,350	8.43	94.1	0.32
Toluene	− 94.9	178.3	92.1	17.1	1,575	8.83	86.8	0.20
Ethylbenzene	− 94.9	178.3	106.1	20.63	2,188	12.27	81.0	0.25
o-Xylene	− 25.1	248.1	106.1	30.61	3,250	13.10	82.9	0.37
m-Xylene	− 47.9	225.3	106.1	26.04	2,760	12.25	82.0	0.32
p-Xylene	13.3	286.5	106.1	38.5	4,080	14.24	81.2	0.47
n-Propyl benzene	− 99.5	173.7	120.1	16.97	2,040	11.74	76.0	0.22
Isopropyl benzene	− 96.0	177.2	120.1	14.15	1,700	9.59	74.6	0.19
1,2,3-Trimethylbenzene	− 25.4	247.8	120.1	16.6	1,990	8.03	79.6	0.21
1,2,4-Trimethylbenzene	− 43.8	229.4	120.1	25.54	3,070	13.4	78.0	0.33
1,3,5-Trimethylbenzene	− 44.7	228.5	120.1	19.14	2,300	10.1	77.6	0.25
Cyclohexane	6.5	279.7	84.1	7.57	637	2.28	85.4	0.09
Methylcyclohexane	−126.5	146.7	98.1	16.4	1,610	10.97	77.2	0.21
Ethylcyclohexane	−111.3	160.9	112.2	17.73	1,930	12.00	73.9	0.24
1,1-Dimethylcyclohexane	− 33.5	239.7	112.2	1.32	148	0.62	70.2	0.02
1,cis-2-Dimethylcyclohexane	− 50.0	223.2	112.2	3.50	393	1.76	72.9	0.05
1,trans-2-Dimethylcyclohexane	− 88.1	185.1	112.2	22.34	2,507	13.54	71.1	0.31

* Data taken primarily from R. R. Dreisbach, Physical Properties of Chemical Compounds, *Advances in Chem. Ser., ACS Monographs* 15 and 22, 1955, 1959.

vaporization there were usually two convenient reference points T_b, T_c from which to interpolate between T_b and T_c or extrapolate below T_b. Even in the nonreduced cases T_b and ΔH_{v_b} were required as input. Contrast this situation with what data are usually available to estimate heats of sublimation.

In only a very few cases is even the sublimation pressure at the melting point known with any accuracy. It may be calculated from a liquid-vapor–pressure correlation, with input such as T_b and T_c, by extrapolating to the melting point. Such a method is not recommended generally, as none of the vapor-pressure correlations are accurate in the very-low-pressure range. Even if P_{vp} at T_m were known, at least one other value of the vapor pressure of the solid is still necessary to calculate ΔH_s from the integrated form of the Clapeyron equation. Thus, there appear to be no useful vapor-pressure–heat-of-sublimation generalized correlations available.

Another difficulty is the fact that, whereas the freezing point is a first-order transition* between vapor and solid, the solid may have some liquidlike characteristics. In many cases, at temperatures somewhat below the melting point there is another first-order solid-solid transition between the crystallinelike solid and the more mobile liquidlike solid. The heat of fusion and heat of sublimation are different for these different solid phases. Ordinarily the literature values for ΔH_m and ΔH_s refer to the liquidlike solid phase. Bondi (8) suggests that ΔH_m or ΔH_s correlations would be much better if the crystalline solid phase were considered; i.e., the correlations would be based on the lowest first-order transition temperature, where there is some definite semblance of order in the solid structure.

In some cases it is possible to obtain ΔH_s from thermochemical data and the standard techniques of calculation, by using known values of the heats of formation of solid and vapor. This is hardly a basis of estimation of an unknown ΔH_s, however, since the heats of formation tabulated in the standard references are often based in part on measured values of ΔH_s. If the heats of dissociation of both solid and gas phases are known, it is possible to describe a cycle involving the sublimation of the solid, the dissociation of the vapor, and the recombination of the elements to form the solid compound. Sodha and Varshni (101) describe this method as applied to the calculation of ΔH_s for 15 inorganic compounds, based on heats of dissociation obtained from spectroscopic data.

---

* In a first-order phase transition, there is a discontinuity in volume, enthalpy, and entropy between the phases in equilibrium. Vaporization and melting are first-order transitions. Second-order transitions are relatively rare and are characterized by the fact that the volume, enthalpy, and entropy are continuous between the phases, but there is a discontinuity in the heat capacity and compressibilities between the phases. Expressions analogous to Eq. (4-1) may be derived.

Bondi [8] has suggested an additive group technique to estimate ΔH_s at the lowest first-order transition temperature for molecular crystals of organic substances and of inorganic hydrides, perhalides, and percarbonyls. Usually the lowest first-order transition temperature is not greatly less than the melting point; e.g., for paraffins the two are almost identical.* For some molecules, however, there is a considerable difference. Cyclohexane melts at 6.5°C, but the lowest first-order transition temperature is −87°C. There appear to be no general rules to predict any of the first-order transition temperatures. Bondi's method, however, is only approximate, and great care must be taken in deciding what contributions are necessary in many cases.

Finally, as a very rough engineering rule, one might estimate ΔH_v and ΔH_m separately and obtain ΔH_s as the sum. The latent heat of fusion is usually less than one-quarter of the sum; so the estimate may be fair even though that for ΔH_m is very crude.

Example 4-17. Estimate the latent heat of sublimation of benzene at 0°C.
Solution. Substituting $T_c = 562.1°K$ and $P_c = 48.6$ atm (Appendix A) in Eq. (4-59), with $T_b = 353.3°K$,

$$\Delta H_{v_b} = [(2.303)(1.987)(562.1)(353.3)(\log 48.6)]/(562.1 - 353.3) = 7315 \text{ cal/g mole}$$

Correcting this to 0°C by Eq. (4-67),

$$\Delta H_v \text{ at } 0°C = 7{,}315[(1 - 273/562.1)/(1 - 353.3/562.1)]^{0.38} = 8290 \text{ cal/g mole}$$
$$\Delta H_v/T \text{ at } 0°C = 8{,}290/273 = 30.3 \text{ cal/(g mole)(°C)}$$

Making a guess as to ΔH_m by reference to Table 4-10 (without reference to the listed value for benzene), take $\Delta H_m/T$ as 10 cal/(g mole)(°C). Then,

$$\Delta H_s = 273(30.3 + 10) = 11{,}000 \text{ cal/g mole}$$

This may be compared with the value 10,600 given by the International Critical Tables.

The large error introduced by guessing $\Delta H_m/T$ to be 10 is of secondary concern, since ΔH_v, which is the larger part of ΔH_s, is estimated with reasonable reliability by Eq. (4-59).

NOMENCLATURE FOR CHAPTER 4

A = constant in Eqs. (4-2), (4-6), (4-10), (4-16)
A' = constant in Eq. (4-23)
B = constant in Eqs. (4-2), (4-6), (4-10), (4-16), (4-24); parameter in Eq. (4-38) and defined in Eq. (4-39)
B' = constant in Eq. (4-23)
C = parameter in Eq. (4-6) and defined in Eq. (4-7); parameter in Eq. (4-16)

---

* The exception appears to be n-butane; the usually quoted freezing point is 135°K, whereas API-44, table 23-2 (1.101)-m, p. 1, states that the lowest first-order transition temperature is 107°K.

and defined in Eq. (4-19) or (4-22); constant in Eqs. (4-10), (4-24), (4-42), (4-44); parameter in Eq. (4-38) and defined in Eq. (4-40)

C' = constant in Eq. (4-23)

$C_{1,2,3}$ = constant in Eqs. (4-48), (4-49)

ΔC_s = difference between heat capacities of saturated vapor and liquid

D = parameter in Eq. (4-16) and defined in Eq. (4-17); constant in Eqs. (4-10), (4-24)

D' = constant in Eq. (4-23)

ΔE_v = internal energy of vaporization, cal/g mole

f^v, f^L = fugacities of saturated vapor and liquid, atm

g = parameter in Eq. (4-25) and defined in Eq. (4-48)

G = parameter in Eq. (4-25) and defined in Eqs. (4-26) and (4-27)

h = parameter defined in Eq. (4-4); parameter in Eqs. (4-26) and (4-27)

h^* = parameter in Eqs. (4-33), (4-34), and (4-35) and defined in Eq. (4-36)

h' = parameter in Eq. (4-36) and defined in Eq. (4-37)

ΔH_m = enthalpy of melting, cal/g mole

ΔH_v = enthalpy of vaporization, cal/g mole; ΔH_{v_b}, at T_b; ΔH_{v_0} a constant in Eq. (4-15); $\Delta H_{v_{HM}}$, for the hydrocarbon homomorph; ΔH_v^*, a constant in Barclay and Butler correlation

ΔH_s = enthalpy of sublimation, cal/g mole

I_b = parameter in Eq. (4-29) and defined in Eq. (4-30)

k = parameter in Eqs. (4-29) and (4-32) and defined in Eq. (4-31)

k_1, k_2 = constants in Eq. (4-13)

K_F = parameter in Eq. (4-70)

K_v = parameter in Eq. (4-62)

m = parameter in Eq. (4-42)

m' = $18m/M$

M = molecular weight; parameter in Eq. (4-32) and defined in Eq. (4-33)

n = exponent in Eq. (4-67), 0.38, or defined in Eq. (4-68)

N = parameter in Eq. (4-32) and defined in Eq. (4-34)

P = pressure, atm

P_c = critical pressure, atm

P_{vp} = vapor pressure, atm; $P_{vp_r} = P_{vp}/P_c$; P'_{vp} refers to some reference point

Q = parameter in Eq. (4-32) and defined in Eq. (4-35)

R = gas constant

s = parameter in Eq. (4-51)

S = parameter in Eq. (4-52)

ΔS_v = entropy change in vaporization, cal/(g mole)(°K); ΔS_v^0 and ΔS_v^1, Pitzer parameters in Eq. (4-56), Table 4-6; ΔS_v^* and S_v^{**}, empirical constants in Barclay and Butler and Everett correlations

T = temperature, °K; $T_r = T/T_c$; T_b, normal boiling point; T' refers to some reference point; T_m, melting point

T_c = critical temperature, °K

v^{**} = empirical factor

V = volume, cm³/g mole; V_g, saturated vapor; v_L, saturated liquid

V_c = critical volume, cm³/g mole

ΔV_v = volume change in vaporization, cm³/g mole

X = parameter defined in Eq. (4-21)

Y = parameter defined in Eq. (4-21)

Z = compressibility factor, PV/RT; Z_g, saturated vapor; Z_L, saturated liquid; Z_c, at the critical point; Z^0, Z^1, parameters in Eq. (3-15), Fig. 4-5a, b

ΔZ_v = $Z_g - Z_L$; ΔZ_{v_b}, at normal boiling point

Greek

α = parameter in Eq. (4-11)
α_c = Riedel factor, Eq. (2-31)
μ = dipole moment
ρ = density, g moles/cm^3
ω = acentric factor [Eq. (2-27)]

REFERENCES FOR CHAPTER 4

1. Antoine, C.: *Compt. rend.*, **107**:681, 836 (1888).
2. American Petroleum Institute: "Selected Values of Physical and Thermodynamic Properties of Hydrocarbons and Related Compounds," Project 44, Carnegie Press, Pittsburgh, Pa., 1953, plus supplements.
3. Banks, W. H.: *J. Chem. Soc.*, **1939**:292.
4. Barclay, I. M., and J. A. V. Butler, *Trans. Faraday Soc.*, **34**:1445 (1938).
5. Bennewitz, K., and W. Rossner: *Z. physik. Chem.*, **39B**:126 (1938).
6. Benson, S. W.: *J. Phys. and Colloid Chem.*, **52**:1060 (1948).
7. Bond, D. L., and G. Thodos: *J. Chem. Eng. Data*, **5**:289 (1960).
8. Bondi, A.: *J. Chem. Eng. Data*, **8**:371 (1963).
9. Bondi, A., and R. B. McConaughy: Estimation of Vapor Pressures for Pure Hydrocarbons with 5 to 30 Carbon Atoms, paper presented at the Twenty-seventh midyear meeting of the American Petroleum Institute, San Francisco, Calif., May, 1962.
10. Bondi, A., and D. J. Simkin: *AIChE J.*, **3**:473 (1957); *ibid.*, **4**:498 (1958).
11. Bowden, S. T., and W. J. Jones: *Phil. Mag.*, **39**:155 (1948).
12. Calingaert, G., and D. S. Davis: *Ind. Eng. Chem.*, **17**:1287 (1925).
13. Chen, N. H.: *J. Chem. Eng. Data*, **10**:207 (1965).
14. Chipman, J.: *J. Phys. Chem.*, **32**:1528 (1928); *ibid.*, **33**:131 (1929).
15. Chu, J. C., M. Dmytryszyn, J. J. Modern, and R. L. Overbeck: *Ind. Eng. Chem.*, **41**:131 (1949).
16. Chu, P. L., and S. S. Chin: *Zhur. Fiz. Khim.*, **25**:102 (1951).
17. Cornelessen, J., and H. I. Waterman: *Chem. Eng. Sci.*, **5**:141 (1956).
18. Cox, E. R.: *Ind. Eng. Chem.*, **15**:592 (1923).
19. Dreisbach, R. R.: Physical Properties of Chemical Compounds, *Advances in Chem. Ser., ACS Monographs* 15 and 22, 1955 and 1959.
20. Dreisbach, R. R.: "Pressure-Volume-Temperature Relationships of Organic Compounds," 3d ed., McGraw-Hill Book Company, New York, 1952.
21. Dreisbach, R. R., and R. S. Spencer: *Ind. Eng. Chem.*, **41**:176 (1949).
22. Dühring, E.: "Neue Grundgesetze zur rationelle Physik und Chemie," Leipzig, 1878.
23. Edmister, W. C.: *Petrol. Refiner*, **37**(4):173 (1958).
24. Edwards, D. G.: The Vapor Pressures of 30 Inorganic Liquids between One Atmosphere and the Critical Point, *Univ. Calif. Radiation Lab.*, UCRL 7167, Livermore, Calif., June 13, 1963.
25. Erpenbeck, J. J., and D. G. Miller: *Ind. Eng. Chem.*, **51**:329 (1959).
26. Everett, D. H.: *J. Chem. Soc.*, **1960**:2566.
27. Fishtine, S. H.: *Ind. Eng. Chem.*, **55**(4):20; *ibid.*, **55**(5):49; *ibid.*, **55**(6):47 (1963); *Hydrocarbon Process. Petrol. Refiner*, **42**(10):143 (1963).
28. Frost, A. A., and D. R. Kalkwarf: *J. Chem. Phys.*, **21**:264 (1953).
29. Frost, A. A., D. R. Kalkwarf, and G. Thodos: Paper presented at the One

166   THE PROPERTIES OF GASES AND LIQUIDS

Hundred and Nineteenth meeting, American Chemical Society, Cleveland, Ohio, April, 1951.
30. Gambill, W. R.: *Chem. Eng.*, **64**(12):261 (1957); *ibid.*, **65**(1):159 (1958).
31. Gambill, W. R.: *Chem. Eng.*, **65**(3):147 (1958).
32. Giacalone, A.: *Gazz. chim. ital.*, **81**:180 (1951).
33. Griswold, J., and J. A. May: *Petrol. Refiner*, **26**:107 (1957).
34. Guggenheim, E. A.: *J. Chem. Phys.*, **13**:253 (1945).
35. Haggenmacher, J. E.: *J. Am. Chem. Soc.*, **68**:1633 (1946).
36. Hamrin, C. E., Jr., and G. Thodos: *J. Chem. Phys.*, **35**:899 (1961).
37. Hermsen, R. W., and J. M. Prausnitz: *J. Chem. Phys.*, **34**:1081 (1961).
38. Hildebrand, J. H.: *J. Am. Chem. Soc.*, **37**:970 (1915).
39. Hildebrand, J. H., and R. L. Scott: Solubility of Non-electrolytes, *ACS Monograph Ser.* 17, p. 79, Reinhold Publishing Co., New York, 1950.
40. Hirschfelder, J. O., C. F. Curtiss, and R. B. Bird: "Molecular Theory of Gases and Liquids," John Wiley & Sons, Inc., New York, 1954.
41. Hobson, M., and J. H. Weber: *AIChE J.*, **2**:354 (1956).
42. Hobson, M., and J. H. Weber: *Petrol. Processing*, **12**(8): 43 (1957).
43. Hooper, E. D., and J. Joffe: *Chem. Eng. Data Ser.*, **5**:155 (1960).
44. Jones, A. H.: *J. Chem. Eng. Data*, **5**:196 (1960).
45. Karapet'yants, M. Kh., and K. Ch'ung: *Ssu Ch'uan Ta Hsüeh Hsüeh Pao-Tzu Jan K'o Hsüeh*, **1958**:91; *Chem. Abstr.*, **53**:17613 (1959).
46. Keenan, J. H., and F. G. Keyes: "Thermodynamic Properties of Steam," John Wiley & Sons, Inc., New York, 1936.
47. Kharbanda, O. P.: *Indian Chemist*, **31**:124 (1955).
48. Kistiakowsky, W.: *Z. physik. Chem.*, **107**:65 (1923).
49. Klein, V. A.: *Chem. Eng. Progr.*, **45**:675 (1949).
50. Kobe, K. A., A. E. Ravicz, and S. P. Vohra: *Chem. Eng. Data Ser.*, **1**:50 (1956).
51. Kordes, E.: *Z. Electrochem.*, **58**:424 (1954).
52. Kuczinski, G. C.: *J. Appl. Phys.*, **24**:1250 (1953).
53. Kunte, M. V., and L. K. Doraiswamy: *Chem. Eng. Sci.*, **12**:1 (1960).
54. Li, C., and L. N. Canjar: *Petrol. Refiner*, **38**(1):233 (1959).
55. Lu, B. C. Y.: *Can. J. Chem. Eng.*, **38**:33 (1960).
55a. Lu, B. C. Y.: *Can. J. Chem. Eng.*, **42**:123 (1964).
56. Lydersen, A. L., R. A. Greenkorn, and O. A. Hougen: Generalized Thermodynamic Properties of Pure Fluids, *Coll. Eng., Univ., Wisconsin, Eng. Expt. Sta. Rept.* 4, Madison, Wis., October, 1955.
57. McCurdy, K. G., and K. J. Laidler: *Can. J. Chem.*, **41**:1867 (1963).
58. McDonald, R. A., S. A. Shrader, and D. R. Stull: *Chem. Eng. Data Ser.*, **4**:311 (1959).
59. McKay, R. A., and B. H. Sage: *J. Chem. Eng. Data*, **5**:21 (1960).
60. Manufacturing Chemists Association: Manufacturing Chemists Association Research Project, "Selected Values of Properties of Chemical Compounds," Carnegie Institute of Technology, Pittsburgh, Pa., various dates.
61. Martin, J. J., and J. B. Edwards: Private communication, 1964.
62. Meissner, H. P.: *Ind. Eng. Chem.*, **33**:1440 (1941).
63. Miller, D. G.: *Ind. Eng. Chem. Fundamentals*, **2**:68 (1963).
64. Miller, D. G. (also discussion by G. Thodos): *Ind. Eng. Chem. Fundamentals*, **2**:78, 80 (1963).
65. Miller, D. G.: *Ind. Eng. Chem.*, **56**(3):46 (1964).
66. Miller, D. G.: *J. Phys. Chem.*, **68**:1399 (1964).
67. Miller, D. G.: Personal communication, April, 1964.

67a. Miller, D. G.: *Univ. Calif. Radiation Lab. Rept.* 14115-T, April 21, 1965.
68. Mukherjee, N. R.: *J. Chem. Phys.*, **19**:502, 1431 (1951).
69. Myers, H. S.: *Ind. Eng. Chem.*, **47**:1659 (1955).
70. Myers, H. S., and M. R. Fenske: *Ind. Eng. Chem.*, **47**:1652 (1955).
71. Nakanishi, K.: *J. Chem. Eng. Data*, **8**:355 (1963); *ibid.*, **9**:155 (1964).
72. Narsimhan, G.: *J. Phys. Chem.*, **67**:2238 (1963).
73. Othmer, D. F.: *Ind. Eng. Chem.*, **32**:841 (1940).
74. Othmer, D. F.: *Ind. Eng. Chem.*, **34**:1072 (1942).
75. Othmer, D. F., P. W. Maurer, C. J. Molinary, and R. C. Kowalski: *Ind. Eng. Chem.*, **49**:125 (1957).
76. Othmer, D. F., and D. Zudkevitch: *Ind. Eng. Chem.*, **51**:791 (1959).
77. Pasek, G., and G. Thodos: *J. Chem. Eng. Data*, **7**:21 (1962).
78. Patton, H. W.: Ph.D. thesis, Vanderbilt University, 1952.
79. Perry, J. H. (ed.), "Chemical Engineers' Handbook," 3d ed., McGraw-Hill Book Company, New York, 1950.
80. Perry, J. H., and E. R. Smith: *Ind. Eng. Chem.*, **25**:195 (1933).
81. Perry, R. E., and G. Thodos: *Ind. Eng. Chem.*, **44**:1649 (1952).
82. Pitzer, K. S.: *J. Chem. Phys.*, **7**:583 (1939).
83. Pitzer, K. S., D. Z. Lippmann, R. F. Curl, C. M. Huggins, and D. E. Petersen, *J. Am. Chem. Soc.*, **77**:3433 (1955).
84. Plank, R., and L. Riedel: *Ing.-Arch.*, **16**:255 (1948).
85. Plank, R., and L. Riedel: *Texas J. Sci.*, **1**:86 (1949).
86. Rehberg, C. E.: *Ind. Eng. Chem.*, **42**:829 (1950).
87. Reid, R. C., and J. M. Smith: *Chem. Eng. Progr.*, **47**:415 (1951).
88. Reynes, E. G., and G. Thodos: *AIChE J.*, **8**:357 (1962).
89. Reynes, E. G., and G. Thodos: *Ind. Eng. Chem. Fundamentals*, **1**:127 (1962).
90. Riedel, L.: *Chem.-Ing.-Tech.*, **26**:83 (1954).
91. Riedel, L.: *Chem.-Ing.-Tech.*, **26**:679 (1954).
92. Rose, A., and V. N. Schrodt: *Chem. Eng. Data Ser.*, **8**:9 (1963).
93. Rudkin, J.: *Chem. Eng.*, **68**(4):202 (1961).
94. Rykov, V. I.: *Zhur. Fiz. Khim.*, **34**:2013 (1960).
95. Sama, D. A.: S. M. thesis in chemical engineering, Massachusetts Institute of Technology, 1955.
96. Seglin, L.: *Ind. Eng. Chem.*, **38**:402 (1946).
97. Selitskiï, I. A.: *Zhur. Fiz. Khim.*, **31**:513 (1957).
98. Shimanskiï, Yu. I.: *Zhur. Fiz. Khim.*, **32**:1893 (1958).
99. Smialek, R. J., and G. Thodos: *J. Chem. Eng. Data*, **9**:52 (1964).
100. Smith, C. H., and G. Thodos: *AIChE J.*, **6**:569 (1960).
101. Sodha, M. S., and Y. P. Varshni: *Indian J. Phys.*, **27**:520 (1953).
102. Sondak, N. E., and G. Thodos: *AIChE J.*, **2**:347 (1956).
103. Staveley, L. A. K., and W. I. Tupman: *J. Chem. Soc.*, **1950**:3597.
104. St. Pierre, C., and C. Tien: *Can. J. Chem. Eng.*, **39**(4):170 (1961).
105. Stull, D. R.: *Ind. Eng. Chem.*, **39**:517 (1947).
106. Su, G.-J.: *Ind. Eng. Chem.*, **38**:923 (1946).
107. Sutra, G.: *Compt. rend.*, **233**:1027, 1186 (1951).
108. Thodos, G.: *Ind. Eng. Chem.*, **42**:1514 (1950).
109. Thomas, L. H.: *J. Chem. Soc.*, **1949**:3411, 3415.
110. Thomas, L. H.: *J. Chem. Soc.*, **1959**:2132.
111. Thomson, G. W.: *Chem. Revs.*, **38**:1 (1946).
112. Thomson, G. W.: "Techniques of Organic Chemistry," A. Weissberger, 3d ed., vol. I, pt. I, p. 473, Interscience Publishers, Inc., New York, 1959.
113. Thompson, W. H., and W. G. Brown: *Preprint* 06-64, paper for presentation at

the Twenty-ninth midyear meeting of the American Petroleum Institute, Division of Refining, St. Louis, Mo., May 11, 1964.

114. Timmermans, J.: "Physico-chemical Constants of Pure Organic Compounds," Elsevier Publishing Company, Amsterdam, 1950.
115. Trouton, F.: *Phil. Mag.*, **18**(5):54 (1884).
116. Voronel, A. V.: *Zhur. Tekh. Fiz.*, **29**:304 (1959).
117. Waddington, G., J. W. Knowlton, D. W. Scott, G. D. Oliver, S. S. Todd, W. N. Hubbard, J. C. Smith, and H. M. Huffman: *J. Am. Chem. Soc.*, **71**:797 (1949).
118. Wall, F. T.: *J. Chem. Phys.*, **16**:508 (1948).
119. Waring, W.: *Ind. Eng. Chem.*, **46**:762 (1954).
120. Watson, K. M.: *Ind. Eng. Chem.*, **35**:398 (1943).
121. White, A. M.: *Ind. Eng. Chem.*, **22**:230 (1930).
122. Wright, F. J.: *Rec. trav. chim.*, **79**:784 (1960).

CHAPTER 5

IDEAL - GAS HEAT CAPACITIES; HEATS AND
FREE ENERGIES OF FORMATION

5-1 Scope

In this chapter techniques are presented for the estimation of ideal-gas heat capacities, heats and free energies of formation, and absolute entropies of organic and simple inorganic compounds. Both theoretical and empirical methods are considered. Pressure effects on thermodynamic properties of real gases are discussed in Chap. 6.

5-2 The Ideal-gas State

Heat capacities and other properties considered in this chapter are ideal-gas values. For enthalpy or energy functions $(C_p, \Delta H_f)$ this state may be an actual pressure low enough so that the gas closely approaches the ideal-gas state. Often the term *zero pressure* is used to denote such a state. For entropy or free-energy functions, the low-pressure state is not convenient, as the former becomes positive infinite and the latter negative infinite as pressure decreases to zero. For these two functions, the reference state is some arbitrarily chosen pressure. The reason why the enthalpy functions are treated differently from the entropy or free-energy functions is simply that, for an ideal gas enthalpy is not a function of pressure and, once a sufficiently low pressure is chosen where the gas approaches ideal behavior, then enthalpy (or C_p) values are unaffected even if one goes to the limit of zero pressure. However, even for an ideal gas, entropy and free energies depend on pressure; so a standard, or reference, pressure must be chosen for these materials.

Pressure effects are treated in detail in Chap. 6. In the present chapter only temperature effects are considered. For all the methods it is necessary to keep in mind only that all the values estimated apply to the ideal-gas state at some reference pressure P_s. The value of P_s is not important if only temperature variations are considered, as $(\partial S/\partial T)_p$, $(\partial H/\partial T)_p$, etc., for an ideal gas are independent of pressure. The value of P_s becomes important only when the ideal-gas values must be corrected to the real-gas region. This type of correction is discussed fully in Chap. 6.

169

5-3 Theory of Ideal-gas Heat Capacities

Molecular energy is conveniently subdivided into several types so that the total is the sum of the various subtypes. Heat capacity is the derivative of energy with respect to temperature, $(dE/dT)_v = C_v$, so that, by expressing the total energy as an algebraic sum, it is then possible to calculate heat capacities.* The total energy which is temperature-dependent (see footnote) is divided into translational, rotational (external and internal), vibrational, electronic, and nuclear. Thus, if some energy is added, for example in the form of heat, this energy increment is distributed over the several subtypes. From classical theory, the principle of equipartition of energy postulates that each type of energy which can be expressed as a *squared term* kx^2, where x is a coordinate of momentum, contributes an amount of energy equal to $\frac{1}{2}kT$ per molecule. k is the Boltzmann constant and is equal to R/N_0, where N_0 is Avogadro's number.

Translational energy is expressed in terms of three coordinate axes x, y, and z, so $E_t = \frac{1}{2}M(v_x^2 + v_y^2 + v_z^2)$, where M equals the mass and v the velocity. Since there are three squared terms, the translational-energy contribution to the total energy equals $(3)(\frac{1}{2})kT = \frac{3}{2}kT$ per molecule. *Rotational* energy is proportional to the square of the angular momentum; so rotation about any axis contributes $\frac{1}{2}kT$ to the total energy of the molecule. A molecule may rotate as an entity, in which case the energy is referred to as *external* rotational energy, or groups of atoms within the molecule may rotate with respect to each other, this type being referred to as *internal* rotational energy. A nonlinear molecule rotates externally with respect to the three coordinate axes and contributes $\frac{3}{2}kT$, whereas, for a linear molecule, the moment of inertia with respect to the axis joining the atoms is negligibly small and so a contribution of only kT is to be expected. Calculations of rotational energy contributions are usually based on rigid rotators, i.e., molecules whose dimensions are assumed to be constant. *Vibrational*-energy contributions are divided into two square terms per vibration, one representing the kinetic energy of vibration and the other representing the potential energy of separation of the bonding molecules. Each contributes $\frac{1}{2}kT$ so that each vibrational degree of freedom contributes kT per molecule. No interactions are assumed to occur between rotation and vibration modes. *Electronic-* and *nuclear*-energy contributions are

---

* By the same reasoning, absolute ideal-gas entropies may be calculated from $S^0 = \int (C_p^0/T)\, dT$, assuming that the entropy is zero at absolute zero. However, absolute energies, per se, cannot be calculated, since there is an unknown, constant energy affiliated with molecules even at absolute zero. This constant term disappears when energy is differentiated with respect to temperature, i.e., when heat capacities are determined.

not considered here; they do not vary appreciably with temperature (except at very high temperatures) and thus add only a constant value to the total energy of a molecule.

From classical theory, therefore, the total energy of a molecule may be expressed as a sum of constants and terms of the form akT, where $a = \frac{1}{2}, \frac{2}{2}, \frac{3}{2}$, etc. The heat capacity $(dE/dT)_v$ should then be constant, independent of temperature. This conclusion is, of course, not usually true. Equipartition of energy into the various subtypes may not occur. Quantum mechanics indicates that the energies of molecules are not continuous but rather that there are discrete levels and the molecular energies increase or decrease by finite steps rather than in a continuous fashion. The farther apart the steps are, the poorer the approximation mentioned above that each storage mode contributes $\frac{1}{2}kT$ to the molecular energy.

Actually it is the ratio of this difference between energy levels to the quantity kT which is important. If the ratio is small, then equipartition is a valid approximation. For translational-energy levels in almost all molecules even at low temperatures, the ratio is very small, and energy absorption is essentially continuous. Each translational-energy mode then amounts to $\frac{1}{2}kT$, or $\frac{3}{2}kT$ per molecule.

For external rotational energy, the energy levels are farther apart. In most molecules, however, the spacing is still small. For hydrogen the full value of $\frac{1}{2}kT$ per mode of rotation is not applicable except near room temperature, whereas, for almost all other molecules, the rotational-energy levels are essentially continuous at temperatures greater than a few degrees absolute. Thus, except for hydrogen and perhaps other very-low-boiling diatomic gases, all important industrial gases may be considered to have continuous rotational-energy levels, and the contribution of $\frac{1}{2}kT$ per rotational mode is applicable.

Vibrational levels may have large energy differences. A convenient criterion of the applicability of equipartition is the ratio $h\nu/kT$, ν being the frequency [see Eq. (5-2) for numerical values of h and k]. For small values of this ratio, e.g., at high temperatures, the vibrational-energy spacing is small, the equipartition limit is valid, and for each mode of vibration there is an energy increment kT.

It is not easy to calculate the heat capacity of a molecule. Quantum and statistical mechanics allow a mathematical formulation of the problem, but detailed knowledge of the structure and spectra is necessary to obtain numerical values. Usually the molecule is assumed to be a rigid rotator and the vibration to be simple harmonic; i.e., the atoms displaced from equilibrium are acted upon by restoring forces proportional to the displacement. It is also assumed that the various energies are noninteracting. Even with these simplifications, when care is taken to obtain a complete picture of the vibrational characteristics, calculated heat capacities agree very closely with experimental values.   For engineering work, it is usually impossible to obtain readily all the desired information such as the bond vibration frequencies from spectra, the molecular moments of inertia, and the steric blocking effects to internal rotation.   Furthermore, few engineers are trained in the necessary detailed calculational procedure.   Consequently, averaging techniques have been adopted and empirical structural correlations suggested.   These approximate methods are described below.   However, the engineer who desires a clearer insight into the theoretical basis would enjoy the treatment given by Slater (86). Other well-presented discussions are found in books by Janz (44), Denbigh (19), Wenner (106), and Glasstone (31).

5-4   Heat Capacities from the Method of Bennewitz, Rossner, and Dobratz

In 1938, Bennewitz and Rossner (8) suggested that for most gases translational and rotational energies could be expressed by classical theory but that vibrational energies should be expressed as a function of temperature, with *average* characteristic bond vibrational frequencies used.   A molecule having n atoms has $3n$ degrees of freedom.   Three may be chosen to represent translational modes and three to represent external rotational modes (for linear molecules there are only two). Thus $3n$-6 represents the number of vibrational modes for nonlinear molecules.   Vibrational modes are divided into stretching types, i.e., vibrations acting in line with the vibrating bodies, and bending, or deformation, types, i.e., vibrations acting perpendicular to the line between the bodies.   Each bond possesses characteristic frequencies.   If a molecule has n atoms, there will usually be $n - 1$ stretching vibrational modes and the remainder would be bending vibrations.

The energy contribution for a vibrational mode may be expressed in terms of the dimensionless group $h\nu/kT$, which was mentioned above as a criterion of how well equipartition would apply to the vibrational energy states.   In terms of heat capacities, for each vibrational mode, the heat capacity per molecule is given (86) as

$$C_{vib} = k(h\nu/kT) \exp (h\nu/kT)[\exp (h\nu/kT) - 1]^{-2} \qquad (5\text{-}1)$$

For low values of ν or large T, it can be shown by L'Hôpital's rule that C_{vib} approaches k per molecule or R per mole; i.e., equipartition is applicable.

There must also be some allowance for internal rotation.   The restricting potential to internal rotation of most C—C bonds is so low that it may be assumed that essentially unrestricted rotation occurs above 250°K.   The heat-capacity contribution of completely free rotation for each such bond is $\frac{1}{2}R$ per mole.   Internal rotation of a bond removes one mode of vibration. Dobratz (20) suggested that internal rotation be included by subtracting the number of free rotations from the vibrational degrees of freedom and adding the term $(m/2)R$, where m equals the number of bonds which can freely rotate. The only common bond types which may be assumed to rotate freely are, however, C—C or the C—O in esters or ethers.

The final equation proposed by Dobratz is

$$C_p{}^0 = 4R + (m/2)R + \Sigma q_i C_{\nu_i} + [(3n - 6 - m - \Sigma q_i)/\Sigma q_i]\Sigma q_i C_{\delta_i} \quad (5\text{-}2)$$

where $C_p{}^0$ = ideal-gas heat capacity at constant pressure
$\qquad = C_v{}^0 + R$, cal/(g mole)(°K)
$\quad 4R$ = $\frac{3}{2}R$ (for translation) + $\frac{3}{2}R$ (for external rotation) + R
$\quad n$ = number of atoms in the molecule
$\quad m$ = number of freely rotating internal bonds
$\quad q_i$ = number of bonds of the ith type
$\quad C_{\nu_i}, C_{\delta_i}$ = Einstein function, i.e., $R(X^2)(e^X)/(e^X - 1)^2$
$\quad X$ = $h\nu/kT$ or $h\delta/kT$
$\quad h$ = Planck's constant, 1.58×10^{-34} cal-sec/molecule
$\quad \nu$ = characteristic frequency for stretching vibrations, sec^{-1}
$\quad \delta$ = characteristic frequency for bending vibrations, sec^{-1}
$\quad k$ = Boltzmann's constant, 3.29×10^{-24} cal/(molecule)(°K)
$\quad T$ = temperature, °K

The multiplier of the δ, or bending, vibrational contribution, $(3n - 6 - m - \Sigma q_i)/\Sigma q_i$, represents the ratio of bending vibrational modes to stretching vibrational modes and thus becomes analogous to a weighting factor.

To use this equation, experimentally determined vibrational frequencies of the various bonds may be inserted, but since all stretching and bending frequencies of a molecule are usually not known, use of characteristic or average bond frequencies may be necessary. These average bond frequencies are assigned two to each bond type, one for stretching and one for bending. Such assignment is an approximation since by so doing one neglects any effects of neighboring atoms. For example, the average stretching vibration (expressed as a wave number) assigned to the C—H bond by Bennewitz and Rossner is 2,920 cm^{-1}. In the case of ethylene, Herzberg (40) gives the following experimental vibrational wave numbers for the four C—H bonds: 2,989.5, 3,019.3, 3,105.5, and 3,272.3 cm^{-1}. In other molecules containing C—H groups, the C—H wave numbers may be different; the average of all types would, however, be near 2,920 cm^{-1}.

Table 5-1 lists Dobratz's values for the average bond stretching and bending vibrational wave numbers. The wave number is the usual way to describe the vibrational characteristics of a bond. The frequency ν

is related to the wavelength λ and wave number ω as

$$\nu = c/\lambda = \omega c \qquad (5\text{-}3)$$

where c is the velocity of light. Thus the parameter $h\nu/kT$ is often written as

$$X = h\nu/kT = hc/\lambda kT = h\omega c/kT \qquad (5\text{-}4)$$

In fact, since the terms h, c, and k are constants in Eq. (5-6), then X may be expressed as

$$X = 1.4385\omega/T \qquad (5\text{-}5)$$

where ω is expressed in cm^{-1} and T in degrees Kelvin. The group 1.4385ω is also called the *characteristic vibrational temperature* and should be small compared with the absolute temperature if equipartition is to be a valid approximation. From Table 5-1, it can be seen that, since most wave numbers are between 500 and 3,000 cm^{-1}, then most characteristic vibrational temperatures are in the range of 700 to 4000°K. Even with the lower value of the characteristic temperature and a gas temperature as high as 700°K, X is still about unity and C_{vib} is only 1.8 cal/(g mole)(°K) instead of the value of 1.987 if equipartition were applicable. Ordinarily, then, the vibrational modes must be assumed to contribute appreciably less than R per mole to the heat capacity.

One may employ the tabulated values of bond vibration wave numbers for all the various bonds of the molecule, calculate $X(h\nu/kT)$, C_ν, and C_δ, and then use Eq. (5-2) directly to determine C_p^0. However, from these average vibrational bond wave numbers, Dobratz has also listed

TABLE 5-1. BOND FREQUENCIES AND CONSTANTS*

Bond	ω_ν wave number, cm^{-1}	Stretching			ω_δ wave number, cm^{-1}	Bending		
		A	$B \times 10^3$	$C \times 10^6$		A	$B \times 10^3$	$C \times 10^6$
C—I, S—S	500	0.181	4.664	-3.338	260	1.461	1.730	-1.272
C—Br	560	-0.073	5.158	-3.591	280	1.242	2.046	-1.501
C—Cl, C—S	650	-0.562	6.385	-4.495	330	1.023	2.590	-1.874
C—C, C—N, N—N	990	-1.090	6.000	-3.441	390	0.730	3.414	-2.577
C—O, N—O	1,030	-1.173	6.132	-3.555	205	1.461	1.633	-1.414
C—F, C=S	1,050	-1.128	5.845	-3.253	530	0.011	5.119	-3.699
C=C, C=N	1,620	-0.432	1.233	0.935	845	-1.140	7.254	-4.936
C=O, N=O	1,700	-0.324	0.724	1.308	390	0.730	3.414	-2.577
S—H	2,570	0.129	-1.333	2.263	1,050	-1.128	5.845	-3.253
C—H, N—H	2,920	0.229	-1.224	1.658	1,320	-0.938	3.900	-1.342
O—H	3,420	0.150	-0.810	1.055	1,150	-1.135	5.363	-2.740

* C. J. Dobratz, *Ind. Eng. Chem.*, **33**:759 (1941).

values of the constants A, B, and C for a series expansion of $C^0_{p\,vib}$,

$$C_\nu \text{ or } C_\delta = A + BT + CT^2 \qquad (5\text{-}6)$$

These constants are also listed in Table 5-1.*

To use Eq. (5-6), terms accounting for translational energy, external and internal rotation, and the conversion of C_v^0 to C_p^0 must be included, i.e., the C_ν and C_δ values in Eq. (5-6) allow one to determine these vibrational heat-capacity contributions as a function of temperature for use in Eq. (5-2).

Heat capacities calculated from Eq. (5-2) with C_ν and C_δ determined from Eq. (5-6) and Table 5-1 are compared with experimental or accurate theoretical values in Table 5-8. The errors found are discussed in Sec. 5-8. It will be noted that at low temperatures (around 298°K) the calculated value of C_p^0 is usually lower than the experimental value; i.e., the per cent error is negative. As the temperature increases, the error decreases. At high temperatures the calculated values are often larger than the experimental values, and the error is positive. Compounds with triple bonds cannot be treated by this method. Convenient nomographs which simplify the use of Eq. (5-2) have been presented by McKelvey (66).

The method is illustrated in Example 5-1.

Example 5-1. Calculate the heat capacity of propane at 700°K in the ideal-gas state by Eqs. (5-2) and (5-6) with Table 5-1.

Solution. Propane has eight C—H bonds and two C—C bonds. Both C—C bonds are assumed to exhibit free rotation. Thus, $n = 11$, $m = 2$, $\Sigma q_i = 10$. For the stretching vibrations, in Table 5-1,

$$\Sigma q_i C_{v_i} = 8(0.229 - 1.224 \times 10^{-3}T + 1.658 \times 10^{-6}T^2)$$
$$+ 2(-1.090 + 6.00 \times 10^{-3}T - 3.441 \times 10^{-6}T^2)$$
$$= -0.348 + 2.208 \times 10^{-3}T + 6.382 \times 10^{-6}T^2$$

Since there are 10 valence bonds,

$$(3n - 6 - m - \Sigma q_i)/\Sigma q_i = (33 - 6 - 2 - 10)/10 = 1.5$$

Therefore, employing the bending-vibration contributions in Table 5-1,

$$[(3n - 6 - m - \Sigma q_i)/\Sigma q_i](\Sigma q_i C_{\delta_i}) = 1.5[(8)(-0.938 + 3.900 \times 10^{-3}T$$
$$- 1.342 \times 10^{-6}T^2) + (2)(0.730 + 3.414 \times 10^{-3}T - 2.577 \times 10^{-6}T^2)]$$
$$C_p^0 = (4)(1.987) + [(2)(1.987)/2] - 9.414 + 59.250 \times 10^{-3}T - 17.453 \times 10^{-6}T^2$$
$$= 0.521 + 59.250 \times 10^{-3}T - 17.453 \times 10^{-6}T^2$$

* Heat capacities are normally expressed as a polynomial in temperature, but other techniques are also used in some cases, e.g., Kothari and Doraiswamy (54) suggest that C_p^0 is a linear function of T_r.

At 700°K

$$C_p{}^0 = 0.521 + (59.250 \times 10^{-3})(700) - (17.453 \times 10^{-6})(700)^2$$
$$= 33.44 \text{ cal}/(\text{g mole})(°K)$$

The experimental value is 34.20 cal/(g mole)(°K) (2).

$$\text{Error} = [(33.44 - 34.20)/34.20] \times 100 = -2.2\%$$

5-5   Modifications of the Bennewitz, Rossner, and Dobratz Method

A number of papers have appeared which present modifications of Eq. (5-2). Stull and Mayfield (95) have tabulated values of C_v or C_δ as a function of temperature for various types of hydrocarbon bonds. The average characteristic bond vibrational wave numbers were, however, chosen to be slightly different from those in Table 5-1. This paper also presents a complete tabulation of C_{vib} [Eq. (5-1)] as a function of $X(h\nu/kT)$ for values of X from 0 to 15 at 0.01 intervals. While Stull and Mayfield's calculated values of $C_p{}^0$ for hydrocarbons are significantly better than those calculated by Dobratz's values (from Table 5-1), the method is not discussed in detail here, as there are more accurate ways to determine $C_p{}^0$ for hydrocarbons (see Sec. 5-6).

Gambill (28) and Meghreblian (67) have also tabulated recommended values of average vibrational bond wave numbers. These, as well as those suggested by Dobratz and by Stull and Mayfield, are summarized in Table 5-2. There are many large differences, especially for the bending or deformation wave numbers. Gambill's values are in most cases identical to Stull and Mayfield's for hydrocarbons and to Dobratz's for nonhydrocarbons. As Meghreblian's values were often considerably different from the others, they were used to calculate Einstein functions, which were then fitted to a quadratic expansion similar to Eq. (5-6), the technique presented by Crawford and Parr (18) being used. The values of the constants A, B, and C so determined are tabulated in Table 5-3. The method of application to determine $C_p{}^0$ is identical to that illustrated in Example 5-1. Heat capacities calculated by this method, referred to as the *Meghreblian, Crawford, and Parr method*, are compared with experimental values in Table 5-8 and the accuracy discussed in Sec. 5-8.

Since these and other methods (27) are based on Eq. (5-2), it is advisable to emphasize some of the limitations of this type of correlation (14):

1. The *lower* temperature limit that is advisable for use is about 200 to 300°K. The *upper* temperature limit that is recommended for use is about 1000°K. At the low temperatures the rotational-energy states may not be fully occupied and will contribute less than $\frac{1}{2}k$ per mode;

also, the assumption of free rotation breaks down at the low temperatures. At high temperatures, electronic contributions influence heat capacities, and these are not considered in this method.

2. Heat capacities of compounds with *strained structures* (e.g., cyclopropane) cannot be calculated accurately, nor can structural or optical isomers be distinguished. Dobratz's method allows one to calculate heat capacities for most compounds containing C, H, N, O, and S but is not applicable for acetylenic compounds. Stull and Mayfield's method

TABLE 5-2. AVERAGE CHARACTERISTIC VIBRATIONAL-BOND WAVE NUMBERS
In cm^{-1}

Bond	Dobratz (20)		Stull and Mayfield (95)		Gambill (28)		Meghreblian (67)	
	ω_ν	ω_δ	ω_ν	ω_δ	ω_ν	ω_δ	ω_ν	ω_δ
C—H (aliphatic)	2,920	1,320	2,914	1,247	2,914	1,247	3,000	1,050
C—H (aromatic)	2,920	1,320	3,045	1,318	3,045	1,318	3,000	1,050
C—C (aliphatic)	990	390	989	390	989	390	910	650
C—C (aromatic and conjugated double bonds	990	390	989	390	989	390	1,500	600
C=C (aliphatic, symmetric)	1,620	845	1,618	599	1,618	599	1,200	910
C=C (aliphatic, unsymmetric)	1,620	845	1,664	421	1,664	421	1,200	910
C=C (aromatic)	1,620	845	1,618	844	1,618	844	1,500	600
C≡C	.....	.....	.....	.....	2,215	333	2,080	375
C—O	1,030	205	.....	.....	1,030	205	1,030	1,120
C=O	1,700	390	.....	.....	1,700	390	1,740	780
C—N	990	390	.....	.....	990	390	1,000	450
C≡N	.....	.....	.....	.....	.....	.....	2,220	240
C—F	1,050	530	.....	.....	1,050	530	1,050	1,200
C—Cl	650	330	.....	.....	650	330	650	260
C—Br	560	280	.....	.....	560	280	610	950
C—I	500	260	.....	.....	500	260	530	880
C—S	650	330	.....	.....	650	330	690	280
O—H	3,420	1,150	.....	.....	3,420	1,150	3,500	1,350
S—H	2,570	1,050	.....	.....	2,570	1,050	2,570	860
S=O	.....	.....	.....	.....	.....	.....	1,250	520
N—N (not for N_2O or N_2O_4)	990	390	.....	.....	990	390	1,000	900
N—H	2,920	1,320	.....	.....	2,920	1,320	3,300	1,200
N—O	1,030	205	.....	.....	1,030	205	1,270	660
N=O	1,700	390	.....	.....	1,700	390	1,470	650
C=S	1,050	530	.....	.....	1,050	530		
S—S	500	260	.....	.....	500	260		

TABLE 5-3. BOND FREQUENCIES AND HEAT-CAPACITY CONSTANTS*

Bond	ω_ν, wave number, cm⁻¹	Stretching			ω_δ, wave number, cm⁻¹	Bending		
		A	$B \times 10^3$	$C \times 10^6$		A	$B \times 10^3$	$C \times 10^6$
C—C†	910	−0.339	3.564	−1.449	650	0.343	2.707	−1.150
C—C‡	1,500	−0.836	3.288	−1.087	600	0.503	2.472	−1.058
C=C	1,200	−0.740	3.730	−1.404	910	−0.339	3.564	−1.449
C≡C	2,080	−0.606	1.861	−0.306	375	1.268	1.244	−0.544
C—H	3,000	−0.139	0.168	0.447	1,050	−0.579	3.741	−1.471
C—O	1,030	−0.458	3.722	−1.471	1,120	−0.665	3.757	−1.449
C=O	1,740	−0.778	2.721	−0.759	780	−0.034	3.220	−1.341
C—N	1,000	−0.501	3.695	−1.471	450	1.016	1.663	−0.723
C≡N	2,220	−0.525	1.528	−0.141	240	1.665	0.566	−0.249
C—Cl	650	0.343	2.707	−1.150	260	1.613	0.656	−0.289
C—F	1,050	−0.579	3.471	−1.471	1,200	−0.740	3.730	−1.404
C—Br	610	0.471	2.519	−1.076	950	−0.415	3.630	−1.462
C—I	530	0.740	2.106	−0.908	880	−0.275	3.498	−1.431
O—H	3,500	0.000	−0.240	0.560	1,350	−0.819	3.563	−1.267
S—H	2,570	−0.331	0.805	0.192	860	−0.230	3.450	−1.416
S=O	1,250	−0.772	3.685	−1.363	520	0.774	2.051	−0.886
C—S	690	0.219	2.884	−1.218	280	1.558	0.750	−0.330
N—N§	1,000	−0.501	3.695	−1.471	900	−0.320	3.547	−1.445
N—H	3,300	−0.04	−0.12	0.53	1,200	−0.740	3.730	−1.404
N—O	1,270	−0.785	3.668	−1.347	660	0.311	2.754	−1.168
N=O	1,470	−0.835	3.347	−1.125	650	0.343	2.707	−1.150

* B. L. Crawford and R. G. Parr, *J. Chem. Phys.*, **16**:233 (1948); R. V. Meghreblian, *J. Am. Rocket Soc.*, September, 1951, p. 128.
† Aliphatic.
‡ Aromatic and conjugated double bonds.
§ Not for N_2O or N_2O_4.

is applicable only to hydrocarbons. Meghreblian, Crawford, and Parr's method has almost no limitations as to the type of compound treated.

5-6 Heat Capacities from the Method of Souders, Matthews, and Hurd

This group-contribution method (87) is limited to the estimation of ideal-gas hydrocarbon heat capacities. Translational contributions are taken as $\frac{3}{2}R$ and external rotational contributions as $\frac{3}{2}R$ for nonlinear and as R for linear molecules. Vibrational contributions are given for various hydrocarbon groups at a number of temperatures in Table 5-4. Internal rotational and resonance contributions are tabulated for various bonds in Table 5-5.   The eight types of bonds upon which Table 5-5 was based are

Type	Bond	Compound upon which type was based
I	—CH₂—CH₂—	n-Butane
II	CH₃—CH₂—	Propane
III	R—C—H	Isobutane
IV	R—C—	Neopentane
V(a)	R—CH=	Propylene
V(b)	R—CH=	cis-2-Butene
VI	=CH—CH=	1,3-Butadiene
VII	≡C—C≡	Diacetylene
VIII	R—C=	Isobutylene

In using Table 5-5 to determine the internal rotational contributions, the type of bond chosen should be as similar as possible to the bond in the compound upon which the value was based.   Example 5-2 illustrates the method, and in Table 5-8 calculated heat capacities are compared with experimental or theoretically determined values.   The errors are discussed in Sec. 5-8.

Example 5-2. Estimate the heat capacity at zero pressure and 298°K of 1,3-butadiene by the method of Souders, Matthews, and Hurd.

Solution

Translational contribution................................. $\frac{3}{2}R = 2.98$
Rotational contribution................................. $\frac{3}{2}R = 2.98$
$C_p - C_v$.. $R = 1.99$

From Table 5-4:

Vibrational contribution $= 2(=\overset{|}{\text{CH}}) + 2(=CH_2)$
$= 2(2.84) + 2(1.22)$
$= 8.12$............................. 8.12

From Table 5-5:

Internal rotation and conjugation contributions Type VI........ $\underline{3.02}$
19.09

Thus the calculated heat capacity is 19.09 cal/(g mole)(°K) at 298°K, and the experimental value is 19.01 (2).

Error $= [(19.09 - 19.01)/19.01] \times 100 = +0.4\%$

TABLE 5-4. VIBRATIONAL GROUP CONTRIBUTIONS TO DETERMINE C_p^0*

Values in cal/(g mole)(°K)

T, °K	Paraffinic				Cycloparaffinic		Aromatic		Acetylenic		Olefinic			
	CH_3-	$-CH_2-$	$-CH-$	$-C-$	$-CH_2-$†	$-CH_2-$‡	$HC=$	$-C=$	$HC\equiv$	$-C\equiv$	$H_2C=$	$HC=$	$-C=$	$=C=$
200	0.29	1.35	2.97	5.58	1.00	1.40	....	....	0.76	2.58	0.27	1.50	3.94	2.58
298	1.29	2.83	4.86	8.09	2.36	2.90	1.93	4.79	1.79	3.44	1.22	2.84	5.55	3.67
400	2.85	4.50	6.56	9.72	4.04	4.67	3.14	5.72	2.53	3.97	2.46	4.11	6.47	4.28
500	4.45	6.07	7.93	10.80	5.57	6.26	4.16	6.40	3.06	4.32	3.60	5.15	7.15	4.63
600	5.79	7.34	9.05	11.54	6.87	7.60	4.98	6.96	3.46	4.56	4.55	6.00	7.68	4.87
700	7.06	8.47	9.93	12.08	7.97	8.70	5.64	7.36	3.79	4.77	5.41	6.71	8.09	5.04
800	8.18	9.40	10.63	12.46	8.90	9.64	6.20	7.68	4.08	4.92	6.12	7.27	8.40	5.18
900	9.14	10.18	11.22	12.73	9.68	10.43	6.66	7.91	4.34	5.04	6.76	7.73	8.64	5.30
1000	10.02	10.86	11.71	12.96	10.36	11.08	7.04	8.10	4.57	5.14	7.29	8.15	8.82	5.41

* M. Souders, C. S. Matthews, and C. O. Hurd, *Ind. Eng. Chem.*, **41**:1037 (1949).
† Five-membered ring.
‡ Six-membered ring.

TABLE 5-5. CHARACTERISTIC INTERNAL-ROTATIONAL CONTRIBUTIONS TO DETERMINE C_p^0*

Values in cal/(g mole)(°K)

T, °K	Type								
	I	II	III	IV	V(a)	V(b)	VI	VII	VIII
	—CH₂—CH₂—	CH₃—CH₂—	R—C—H	R—C—	R—CH=	R—CH=	=CH—CH=	≡C—C≡	R—C=
200	2.64	1.74	1.76	1.60	2.02	1.48	2.09	0.81	1.91
298	3.18	2.10	2.12	1.99	2.02	1.26	3.02	0.92	2.15
400	2.74	2.17	2.19	2.18	1.82	1.16	3.25	0.76	2.10
500	2.39	2.09	2.12	2.23	1.65	1.11	2.96	0.60	1.95
600	2.12	1.96	2.00	2.18	1.50	1.07	2.67	0.48	1.79
700	1.90	1.82	1.85	2.08	1.40	1.05	2.44	0.39	1.65
800	1.73	1.69	1.71	1.96	1.32	1.04	2.24	0.35	1.54
900	1.60	1.59	1.62	1.85	1.26	1.03	2.09	0.32	1.46
1000	1.51	1.51	1.55	1.76	1.21	1.02	1.96	0.31	1.38

* M. Souders, C. S. Matthews, and C. O. Hurd, *Ind. Eng. Chem.*, **41**:1037 (1949).

5-7   Group-contribution Techniques to Estimate Ideal-gas Heat Capacities

Various additive-group techniques have been suggested to estimate ideal-gas heat capacities without recourse to any of the theory which led to the development of Eq. (5-2) (32, 81). Anderson, Beyer, and Watson (4, 41, 54) suggest an additive-group method similar in nature to the ones discussed later to estimate heats of formation and absolute entropies (Secs. 5-13 and 5-19). The two most accurate methods appear, however, to be due to Johnson and Huang (48) and to Rihani and Doraiswamy (78). Both methods present contributions for certain atomic groups (for example, $-CH_3$, $-CH_2-$) to be used in a series expansion of heat capacity,

$$C_p{}^0 = a + bT + cT^2 + dT^3 \qquad (5\text{-}7)$$

Johnson and Huang's group contributions are tabulated in Table 5-6 Only hydrocarbons can be treated, and even in this class, methane benzene, and multisubstituted aromatics cannot be treated. There is even a question whether or not the method is applicable to substituted naphthenes, but Example 5-3 indicates that in some cases the use of

the linear $-\overset{|}{C}H-$ increment may be employed as a group in a naphthene ring.

TABLE 5-6. JOHNSON AND HUANG'S GROUP CONTRIBUTIONS TO IDEAL-GAS HEAT CAPACITIES*

Group	a	$b \times 10^2$	$c \times 10^4$	$d \times 10^6$
$-CH_2-$	-0.186	2.243	-0.1263	0.00274
$-CH_3$	0.427	2.183	-0.0863	0.00111
$=CH_2$	0.662	1.770	-0.0874	0.00167
$=CH-$	-0.239	1.663	-0.1056	0.00260
⬡—	-7.576	11.007	-0.729	0.01801
$\equiv CH$	2.017	1.400	-0.1157	0.00352
$-C\equiv$	-5.252	3.887	-0.4400	0.01521
$-\overset{\|}{C}H$	-1.942	2.832	-0.2281	0.00661
$-CH_2-$ (6-ring)	-2.137	2.473	-0.1195	0.00198
$-CH_2-$ (5-ring)	-2.318	2.471	-0.1294	0.00257
$-\overset{\|}{\underset{\|}{C}}-$	-4.655	3.682	-0.3551	0.00982
$\diagdown C=$	-0.0535	1.342	-0.1019	0.00273

* A. I. Johnson, and C.-J. Huang, *Can. J. Tech.*, **34**:405 (1957).

Rihani and Doraiswamy's contributions are listed in Table 5-7.   Most types of materials can be treated, although there are exceptions, e.g., substituted acetylenes.   Calculated values are compared with experimental values in Table 5-8 and the errors discussed in Section 5-8.

Example 5-3.   Estimate the ideal-gas heat capacity of 1,2-dimethylcyclopentane at 300 and 1000°K, using Johnson and Huang's group contributions in Table 5-6. Compare with the API values of 32.34 and 85.57 cal/(g mole)(°K) (2).

Solution.   From Table 5-6,

	a	$b \times 10^2$	$c \times 10^4$	$d \times 10^6$
3($-CH_2-$)(ring)	(3)(-2.318)	(3)(2.471)	(3)(-0.1294)	(3)(0.00257)
2($-\overset{|}{C}H$)	(2)(-1.942)	(2)(2.832)	(2)(-0.2281)	(2)(0.00661)
2($-CH_3$)	(2)(0.427)	(2)(2.183)	(2)(-0.0863)	(2)(0.00111)
	-9.984	17.443	-1.017	0.02315

$$C_p^0 = -9.984 + (17.443)(10^{-2})T - (1.017)(10^{-4})T^2 + (0.02315)(10^{-6})T^3$$
$$= 33.82 \text{ cal/(g mole)(°K)} \quad \text{at } 300°K$$
$$\text{Error} = [(33.82 - 32.34)/32.34] \times 100 = +4.6\%$$
$$C_p^0 = 85.89 \text{ cal/(g mole)(°K)} \quad \text{at } 1000°K$$
$$\text{Error} = [(85.89 - 85.57)/85.57] \times 100 = +0.4\%$$

Example 5-4.   Repeat Example 5-3, using the group contributions of Rihani and Doraiswamy in Table 5-7.

Solution

	a	$b \times 10^2$	$c \times 10^4$	$d \times 10^6$
3($-\overset{|}{C}H_2$)	(3)(0.3945)	(3)(2.1363)	(3)(-0.1197)	(3)(0.002596)
2($-\overset{|}{C}H$)	(2)(-3.5232)	(2)(3.4158)	(2)(-0.2816)	(2)(0.008015)
2($-CH_3$)	(2)(0.6087)	(2)(2.1433)	(2)(-0.0852)	(2)(0.001135)
5-membered ring	-12.2850	1.8609	-0.1037	0.002145
	-16.930	19.388	-1.196	0.0283

Thus,

$$C_p^0 = -16.930 + (19.388)(10^{-2})T - (1.196)(10^{-4})T^2 + (0.0283)(10^{-6})T^3$$
$$= 31.23 \text{ cal/(g mole)(°K)} \quad \text{at } 300°K$$
$$\text{Error} = [(31.23 - 32.34)/32.34] \times 100 = -3.4\%$$

Similarly,

$$C_p^0 = 85.65 \text{ cal/(g mole)(°K)} \quad \text{at } 100°K$$
$$\text{Error} = [(85.65 - 85.57)/85.57] \times 100 = +0.1\%$$

TABLE 5-7. RIHANI AND DORAISWAMY'S GROUP CONTRIBUTIONS TO IDEAL-GAS HEAT CAPACITIES*

Group	a	$b \times 10^2$	$c \times 10^4$	$d \times 10^6$
Aliphatic Hydrocarbon Groups				
—CH$_3$	0.6087	2.1433	−0.0852	0.001135
—CH$_2$	0.3945	2.1363	−0.1197	0.002596
=CH$_2$	0.5266	1.8357	−0.0954	0.001950
—C—H	−3.5232	3.4158	−0.2816	0.008015
—C—	−5.8307	4.4541	−0.4208	0.012630
H C=CH$_2$	0.2773	3.4580	−0.1918	0.004130
C=CH$_2$	−0.4173	3.8857	−0.2783	0.007364
H—C=C—H	−3.1210	3.8060	−0.2359	0.005504
H—C=C—H	0.9377	2.9904	−0.1749	0.003918
H—C=C	−1.4714	3.3842	−0.2371	0.006063
C=C	0.4736	3.5183	−0.3150	0.009205
H—C=C=CH$_2$	2.2400	4.2896	−0.2566	0.005908
C=C=CH$_2$	2.6308	4.1658	−0.2845	0.007277
H—C=C=C—H	−3.1249	6.6843	−0.5766	0.017430
≡CH	2.8443	1.0172	−0.0690	0.001866
Aromatic Hydrocarbon Groups				
HC	−1.4572	1.9147	−0.1233	0.002985

TABLE 5-7. RIHANI AND DORAISWAMY'S GROUP CONTRIBUTIONS TO
IDEAL-GAS HEAT CAPACITIES (*Continued*)

Group	a	$b \times 10^2$	$c \times 10^4$	$d \times 10^6$
—C⟨	-1.3883	1.5159	-0.1069	0.002659
↔C⟨	0.1219	1.2170	-0.0855	0.002122

Contributions Due to Ring Formation

3-membered ring	-3.5320	-0.0300	0.0747	-0.005514
4-membered ring	-8.6550	1.0780	0.0425	-0.000250
5-membered ring:				
Pentane	-12.2850	1.8609	-0.1037	0.002145
Pentene	-6.8813	0.7818	-0.0345	0.000591
6-membered ring:				
Hexane	-13.3923	2.1392	-0.0429	-0.001865
Hexene	-8.0238	2.2239	-0.1915	0.005473

Oxygen-containing Groups

Group	a	$b \times 10^2$	$c \times 10^4$	$d \times 10^6$
—OH	6.5128	-0.1347	0.0414	-0.001623
—O—	2.8461	-0.0100	0.0454	-0.002728
H | —C=O	3.5184	0.9437	0.0614	-0.006978
⟩C=O	1.0016	2.0763	-0.1636	0.004494
O ‖ —C—O—H	1.4055	3.4632	-0.2557	0.006886
O ∥ —C⟨ O—	2.7350	1.0751	0.0667	-0.009230
O⟨	-3.7344	1.3727	-0.1265	0.003789

Nitrogen-containing Groups

Group	a	$b \times 10^2$	$c \times 10^4$	$d \times 10^6$
—C≡N	4.5104	0.5461	0.0269	-0.003790
—N≡C	5.0860	0.3492	0.0259	-0.002436
—NH₂	4.1783	0.7378	0.0679	-0.007310
⟩NH	-1.2530	2.1932	-0.1604	0.004237
⟩N—	-3.4677	2.9433	-0.2673	0.007828
N⟨	2.4458	0.3436	0.0171	-0.002719
—NO₂	1.0898	2.6401	-0.1871	0.004750

TABLE 5-7. RIHANI AND DORAISWAMY'S GROUP CONTRIBUTIONS TO
IDEAL-GAS HEAT CAPACITIES (Continued)

Group	a	$b \times 10^2$	$c \times 10^4$	$d \times 10^6$
Sulfur-containing Groups				
—SH	2.5597	1.3347	−0.1189	0.003820
—S—	4.2256	0.1127	−0.0026	−0.000072
S⤵	4.0824	−0.0301	0.0731	−0.006081
—SO₃H	6.9218	2.4735	0.1776	−0.022445
Halogen-containing Groups				
—F	1.4382	0.3452	−0.0106	−0.000034
—Cl	3.0660	0.2122	−0.0128	0.000276
—Br	2.7605	0.4731	−0.0455	0.001420
—I	3.2651	0.4901	−0.0539	0.001782

* D. N. Rihani and L. K. Doraiswamy, *Ind. Eng. Chem. Fundamentals*, **4**:17 (1965).

5-8   Discussion of Ideal-gas Heat-capacity Estimation Techniques

Two types of ideal-gas heat-capacity correlations have been presented. Those based on Eq. (5-2) have employed theoretical concepts to obtain contributions for translational and rotational energy. For vibrational energy, the contribution C_{vib} for each vibrational mode is given by Eq. (5-1). The various methods differ, however, as to the recommended average vibrational bond frequencies (or wave numbers). The second type of correlation is empirical and assumes that each atomic group contributes to the overall heat capacity in an additive fashion. This type of additivity concept is very useful and is certainly a familiar one in many types of correlations. A particularly interesting study of its applicability to heat capacity is given by Benson and Buss (9); the conclusion reached is that, by assigning contributions to atomic groups rather than to single atoms, one may tolerate a reasonable degree of interaction without additivity becoming a poor assumption.

For the methods tested, calculated values of C_p^0 are compared with experimental or reliable theoretical values in Table 5-8. From the results in this table the following recommendations may be formulated.

1. For hydrocarbons, the method of Matthews, Souders, and Hurd (Sec. 5-6, Tables 5-4 and 5-5) is the most accurate. In testing with 17 hydrocarbons and with 68 data points, the average error was about 0.9 per cent. The most serious disadvantage is the difficulty of interpolating in Tables 5-4 and 5-5 if the desired temperature is not tabulated. It is often convenient to have an analytical expression for heat capacity

as a function of temperature, and in this case the method of Rihani and Doraiswamy (Sec. 5-7, Table 5-7) is quite satisfactory. In testing with the same 16 hydrocarbons noted above (the method is not applicable for methylacetylene) and with 64 data points between 298 and 1000°K, an average error of 1.2 per cent was noted. For comparison, the other methods described earlier gave the following errors for the same hydrocarbons:

Dobratz (20)	6.9%
Stull and Mayfield (95)	4.1%
Meghreblian, Crawford, and Parr (18, 67)	5.0%
Anderson, Beyer, and Watson (4, 41)	3.1%
Johnson and Huang (48)	1.4%

2. For organic compounds, but not hydrocarbons, the method of Rihani and Doraiswamy (Sec. 5-7, Table 5-7) is recommended. In testing with 18 nonhydrocarbons and with 54 data points, the average error was 4.0 per cent. The method is easy to use, general in nature, and yields directly a polynomial expansion of C_p^0 in temperature. The method is least accurate at low temperatures, near 300°K, and usually is considerably more accurate at high temperatures. The range stated by Rihani and Doraiswamy is 300 to 1500°K, but at the latter temperature many organic materials are not stable, and so the indicated range is misleading. For the other methods tested, the following average errors were found for the nonhydrocarbon series:

Dobratz (20)	4.7%
Meghreblian, Crawford, and Parr (18, 67)	6.9%
Anderson, Beyer, and Watson (4, 41)	5.8%

3. For simple inorganic molecules of a very diverse sort (as seen in Table 5-8), only the methods utilizing Eq. (5-2) were applicable. Dobratz's vibrational contributions (Table 5-1) lead to an average error of 6.6 per cent for five compounds and 17 data points, while the Meghreblian, Crawford, and Parr contributions (Table 5-3) yield an average error of 7.8 per cent for six compounds and 20 data points. There is little to choose between the two methods; the average error is very misleading, as there are wide fluctuations for individual compounds. For example, if hydrazine were rejected from Meghreblian, Crawford, and Parr's evaluation, the average error would almost be halved and the same could be said for carbon dioxide if Dobratz's method were used.

4. In this discussion of recommended C_p^0 estimation techniques, it should be emphasized again that, whenever possible, recourse should be made to experimental data. For hydrocarbons, the API references (e.g., Ref. 2) should be consulted. Many articles treating miscellaneous gases have been published. Some of the more recent are Refs. 36, 61, 77,

TABLE 5-8. COMPARISON BETWEEN CALCULATED AND EXPERIMENTAL IDEAL-GAS HEAT CAPACITIES

Values in cal/(g mole)(°K)

Compound	T, °K	Experimental		Calculated by method of									
		$C_p{}^0$	Ref.	Dobratz		Johnson and Huang		Meghreblian, Crawford, and Parr		Souders, Matthews, and Hurd		Rihani and Doraiswamy	
				$C_p{}^0$	% Error[a]	$C_p{}^0$	% Error	$C_p{}^0$	% Error	$C_p{}^0$	% Error	$C_p{}^0$	% Error
Methane..............	298	8.54	2	8.52	−0.2	.....	.....	9.77	+14				
	500	11.13	2	11.46	+3.0	.....	.....	12.97	+15				
	700	13.88	2	14.36	+3.5	.....	.....	15.33	+10				
	1000	17.21	2	18.70	+8.6	.....	.....	18.30	+6.3				
Propane.............	298	17.57	2	16.59	−5.6	17.84	+1.5	18.73	+6.6	17.56	−0.6	18.21	+3.6
	500	27.02	2	25.77	−4.6	26.86	−0.6	27.86	+3.1	27.10	+0.3	27.08	+0.2
	700	34.20	2	33.44	−2.2	33.99	−0.6	35.21	+2.9	34.18	−0.1	33.55	−1.9
	1000	41.83	2	42.37	+1.3	41.83	0	43.29	+3.5	41.87	+0.1	41.70	−0.3
n-Heptane...........	298	39.67	2	33.55	−15	39.64	−0.1	36.99	−6.8	41.60	+4.9	41.37	+4.3
	500	60.07	2	54.97	−8.5	59.72	−0.6	58.25	−3.0	60.94	+1.4	60.72	+1.1
	700	75.38	2	71.94	−4.5	75.05	−0.4	75.30	−0.1	75.66	+0.4	75.53	+0.2
	1000	91.2	2	89.47	−1.8	91.2	0	93.35	+2.4	91.35	+0.2	91.2	0
2,2,3-Trimethylbutane...	298	39.33	2	33.53[b]	−15	39.05	−0.7	36.99[b]	−5.9	40.74	+3.6	39.75	+1.1
	500	61.04	2	54.97	−9.9	60.06	−1.6	58.25	−4.5	62.25	+2.0	61.70	+1.0
	700	76.74	2	71.94	−6.2	75.36	−1.8	75.30	−1.9	77.10	+0.5	77.53	+0.7
	1000	92.32	2	89.47	−3.1	90.34	−2.2	93.35	+1.1	92.61	+0.3		

Compound	T												
Cyclopentane	298	19.82	2	25.90	+31	19.82	0	27.13	+37	19.75	− 0.3	21.23	+ 7.1
	500	35.86	2	38.38	+ 7.0	35.62	− 0.7	39.48	+10	35.80	− 0.2	36.74	+ 2.5
	700	47.81	2	48.01	+ 0.4	47.60	− 0.4	49.39	+ 3.3	47.80	0	48.26	+ 0.9
	1000	59.75	2	57.36	− 4.0	60.11	+ 0.6	59.96	+ 0.4	59.75	0	60.02	+ 0.5
Cyclohexane	298	25.40	2	30.22	+19	25.34	− 0.2	31.71	+25	25.35	− 0.2	27.15	+ 6.8
	500	45.47	2	45.76	+ 0.6	44.93	− 1.2	47.08	+ 3.5	45.51	− 0.1	46.44	+ 2.2
	700	60.87	2	57.72	− 5.2	59.99	− 1.4	59.41	− 2.4	60.15	− 1.2	61.08	+ 0.4
	1000	75.80	2	69.24	− 8.6	75.74	− 0.1	72.48	− 4.3	74.43	− 1.8	76.13	+ 0.4
Methyl cyclopentane	298	26.24	2	30.22[c]	+15	26.70	+ 1.6	31.71[c]	+21	25.66	− 2.2	26.09	− 0.6
	500	44.94	2	45.76	+ 1.8	45.16	+ 0.5	47.08	+ 4.8	44.73	− 0.5	45.16	+ 0.5
	700	58.68	2	57.72	− 1.6	58.91	+ 0.4	59.41	+ 1.2	58.67	0	59.02	+ 0.6
	1000	72.44	2	69.24	− 4.4	73.00	+ 0.8	72.48	+ 0.1	72.67	+ 0.3	72.71	+ 0.4
Ethylene	298	10.41	2	9.41	− 9.6	10.41	0	11.10	+ 6.6	10.39	− 0.2	10.40	− 0.1
	500	15.16	2	14.03	− 7.4	15.07	− 0.6	15.64	+ 3.2	15.15	0	15.13	− 0.3
	700	18.76	2	18.04	− 3.8	18.68	− 0.4	19.34	+ 3.1	18.77	0	18.74	− 0.1
	1000	22.57	2	23.04	+ 2.1	22.58	+ 0.1	23.40	+ 3.7	22.53	− 0.2	22.59	+ 0.1
1-Butene	298	20.47	2	16.89	−17	20.70	+ 1.1	20.17	− 1.5	19.49	− 4.8	21.03	+ 2.7
	500	30.93	2	27.16	−12	30.83	− 0.3	30.82	− 0.4	30.42	− 1.6	31.04	+ 1.6
	700	38.71	2	35.33	− 8.7	38.59	− 0.3	39.37	+ 1.7	38.47	− 0.6	38.70	0
	1000	46.82	2	43.87	− 6.3	46.81	− 0.1	48.50	+ 3.6	46.80	0	46.85	+ 0.1
2-Butene(cis)	298	18.86	2	16.89[d]	−10	20.09	+ 6.6	20.17[d]	+ 7.0	18.73	− 0.7	18.81	− 0.3
	500	29.39	2	27.16	− 7.6	30.17	+ 2.6	30.82	+ 4.9	29.37	− 0.1	29.37	− 0.1
	700	37.60	2	35.33	− 6.0	37.96	+ 1.0	29.37	+ 4.7	37.59	0	37.50	− 0.3
	1000	46.15	2	43.87	− 4.9	46.34	+ 0.4	48.50	+ 5.1	46.33	+ 0.4	46.17	+ 0.1

189

TABLE 5-8. COMPARISON BETWEEN CALCULATED AND EXPERIMENTAL IDEAL-GAS HEAT CAPACITIES (*Continued*)

Compound	T, °K	Experimental C_p^0	Ref.	Dobratz C_p^0	% Error[a]	Johnson and Huang C_p^0	% Error	Meghreblian, Crawford, and Parr C_p^0	% Error	Souders, Matthews, and Hurd C_p^0	% Error	Rihani and Doraiswamy C_p^0	% Error
2-Butene(trans)[e]	298	20.99	2	16.89	− 20	20.09	− 4.3	20.17	− 3.9	18.73	−10	20.94	− 0.2
	500	30.68	2	27.16	− 11	30.17	− 1.7	30.82	+ 0.5	29.37	− 4.3	30.68	0
	700	38.38	2	35.33	− 7.9	37.96	− 1.1	29.37	+ 2.6	37.59	− 2.1	38.30	− 0.2
	1000	46.58	2	43.87	− 5.8	46.34	− 0.5	48.50	+ 0.4	46.33	− 0.5	46.58	0
1,3-Butadiene	298	19.01	2	14.58	− 23	18.10	− 4.8	16.58	−13	19.09	+ 0.4	17.98	− 5.4
	500	28.52	2	23.98	− 16	26.59	− 6.8	25.60	−10	28.41	− 0.3	26.58	− 6.8
	700	34.55	2	31.41	− 9.1	32.92	− 4.7	32.84	− 4.9	34.63	+ 0.2	33.00	− 4.5
	1000	40.52	2	39.03	− 3.7	39.45	− 2.6	40.54	0	40.79	+ 0.7	39.61	− 2.2
Acetylene	298	10.50	2	......		10.51	+ 0.1	9.96	− 5.1	10.53	− 0.1	10.62	+ 1.1
	500	12.97	2	......		13.13	+ 1.3	12.10	− 6.7	13.07	+ 0.5	12.88	− 0.8
	700	14.34	2	......		14.71	+ 2.6	13.89	− 3.1	14.53	+ 1.3	14.45	+ 0.8
	1000	15.92	2	......		15.93	+ 0.1	15.96	+ 0.3	16.09	+ 1.1	15.97	+ 0.3
Methylacetylene	298	14.50	2	......		14.28	− 1.5	14.92	+ 2.9	14.47	− 0.2		
	500	19.74	2	......		20.97	+ 6.2	19.61	− 0.7	19.78	+ 0.2		
	700	23.58	2	......		24.82	+ 5.2	23.45	− 0.6	23.57	0		
	1000	27.71	2	......		27.53	− 0.7	27.69	− 0.1	27.68	− 0.1		

Calculated by method of

190

Benzene	298	19.52	2	20.04	+ 2.7	.....	.....	20.02	+ 2.6	19.53	+ 0.1	19.40	− 0.6
	500	32.80	2	32.74	− 0.2	.....	.....	32.04	− 2.4	32.91	+ 0.3	32.45	− 1.1
	700	41.75	2	41.80	+ 0.1	.....	.....	41.58	− 0.4	41.79	+ 0.1	41.58	− 0.4
	1000	50.16	2	48.88	− 2.5	.....	.....	51.50	+ 2.7	50.19	+ 0.1	50.10	− 0.1
Ethylbenzene	298	30.69	2	28.41	− 7.4	30.87	+0.6	28.39	− 7.5	30.76	+ 0.2	30.45	− 0.8
	500	49.35	2	47.06	− 4.6	49.02	−0.7	46.36	− 6.0	49.71	+ 0.7	48.70	− 1.3
	700	62.28	2	60.74	− 2.5	62.06	−0.4	60.69	− 2.5	62.51	+ 0.4	61.75	− 0.9
	1000	74.77	2	71.99	− 3.7	74.70	−0.1	75.73	+ 1.3	75.02	+ 0.3	74.54	− 0.3
o-Xylene	298	31.89	2	28.41[f]	−11	.....	.....	28.39[f]	−11	29.82	− 6.5	29.97	− 6.0
	500	49.13	2	47.06	− 4.2	.....	.....	46.36	− 5.6	48.28	− 1.7	48.00	− 2.3
	700	61.77	2	60.74	− 1.7	.....	.....	60.69	− 1.7	61.34	− 0.7	61.17	− 1.0
	1000	74.35	2	71.99	− 3.2	.....	.....	75.73	+ 1.8	74.34	0	74.20	− 0.2
m-Xylene	298	30.44	2	28.41[f]	− 6.7	.....	.....	28.39[f]	− 6.7	29.82[g]	− 2.0	29.97	− 1.5
	500	48.44	2	47.06	− 2.8	.....	.....	46.36	− 4.3	48.28	− 0.3	48.00	− 0.9
	700	61.44	2	60.74	− 1.1	.....	.....	60.69	− 1.2	61.34	− 0.1	61.17	− 0.4
	1000	74.25	2	71.99	− 3.0	.....	.....	75.73	+ 2.0	74.34	+ 0.1	74.20	− 0.1
Fluorobenzene	370	28.6	56	26.8	− 4.9	.....	.....	25.0	− 9.7	.....	.....	25.91	− 9.4
	390	29.9	56	28.2	− 4.4	.....	.....	26.2	− 9.5	.....	.....	27.24	− 9.0
	410	31.2	56	29.4	− 4.4	.....	.....	27.4	− 9.2	.....	.....	28.52	− 8.6
Methanol	298	10.76	37	10.93	+ 1.6	.....	.....	10.63	− 1.4	.....	.....	12.70	+18
	500	14.72	45	15.11	+ 2.6	.....	.....	15.14	+ 2.9	.....	.....	16.01	+ 8.7
	700	17.79	53	18.51	+ 4.0	.....	.....	18.84	+ 5.9	.....	.....	18.87	+ 6.1
	1000	21.57	...	22.28	+ 3.3	.....	.....	22.95	+ 6.4	.....	.....	22.33	+ 3.5
n-Propyl alcohol	410	24.9	45	26.1	+ 4.8	.....	.....	25.7	+ 3.2	.....	.....	29.23	+17
Isopropyl alcohol	410	26.6	45	26.1[h]	− 1.9	.....	.....	25.7	− 3.4	.....	.....	28.93	+ 8.7

TABLE 5-8. COMPARISON BETWEEN CALCULATED AND EXPERIMENTAL IDEAL-GAS HEAT CAPACITIES (*Continued*)

| Compound | T, °K | Experimental | | Calculated by method of | | | | | | | | |
| | | $C_p^{\,0}$ | Ref. | Dobratz | | Johnson and Huang | | Meghreblian, Crawford, and Parr | | Souders, Matthews, and Hurd | | Rihani and Doraiswamy | |
				$C_p^{\,0}$	% Error[a]	$C_p^{\,0}$	% Error	$C_p^{\,0}$	% Error	$C_p^{\,0}$	% Error	$C_p^{\,0}$	% Error
Dimethyl ether	298	15.2	45	16.5	+ 8.5	...	...	14.9	− 2.0	...	...	15.69	+ 3.2
	370	16.8	45	18.9	+12	...	...	17.7	+ 5.4	...	...	18.15	+ 8.0
Acetone	340	20.4	16	20.0	− 2.0	...	...	20.3	− 0.5	...	...	20.3	− 0.5
	380	22.2	45	21.7	− 2.3	...	...	22.0	− 0.9	...	...	22.0	− 0.9
	420	24.0		23.2	− 3.3	...	...	23.6	− 1.7	...	...	23.6	− 1.7
Acetaldehyde	298	13.1	15	13.7	+ 4.6	...	...	13.9	+ 6.1	...	...	13.0	− 0.8
	500	18.3	53	18.6	+ 1.6	...	...	19.1	+ 4.4	...	...	18.3	0
	700	22.5	76	22.7	+ 0.9	...	...	23.2	+ 3.0	...	...	22.6	+ 0.5
	1000	27.0		27.3	+ 1.1	...	...	27.8	+ 2.9	...	...	26.8	− 0.7
Ethyl acetate	346	29.7	45	29.6	− 0.3	...	...	26.8	− 9.8	...	...	27.4	− 7.8
	385	32.7	45	31.9	− 2.5	...	...	29.3	−10	...	...	29.6	−10
	440	35.3	45	34.9	− 1.1	...	...	32.7	− 7.4	...	...	32.6	− 7.6
Acetonitrile	298	12.4		...	...	...	...	14.0	+13	...	...	12.5	+ 0.8
	500	16.7		...	...	...	...	17.3	+ 3.6	...	...	16.8	+ 0.6
	700	20.0	35	...	...	...	...	20.0	0	...	...	20.2	+ 1.0
	1000	23.6	98	...	...	...	...	23.0	− 2.6	...	...	23.5	− 0.5

	Temp								
	500	15.6	98			14.6	− 6.4	14.9	− 4.5
	700	16.9	98			15.9	− 5.9	16.7	− 1.2
	1000	18.3	98			17.3	− 5.4	17.8	− 2.7
Methyl chloride	293	11.5	109	11.3	− 1.7	12.5	+ 8.7	9.8	−15
Methylene chloride	370	13.8	46	15.4	+12	16.3	+18	14.2	+ 2.9
	407	15.1	46	16.0	+ 6.0	16.8	+11	14.8	− 2.0
Chloroform	298	15.6	46	18.0	+15	18.2	+17	15.1	− 3.2
	500	19.3	60	21.3	+10	20.4	+ 5.7	19.1	− 1.0
	700	21.2		22.9	+ 8.0	22.1	+ 4.3	21.4	+ 0.9
	1000	22.8		22.2	− 2.6	23.7	+ 4.0	23.1	+ 1.3
Carbon tetrachloride	298	19.9	46	19.9	0	21.1	+ 6.0	18.4	− 7.5
	500	23.1	60	23.2	+ 0.4	22.9	− 0.9	22.9	− 0.9
	700	24.3		24.4	+ 0.4	24.3	0	25.1	+ 3.3
	1000	25.0		22.0	−12	25.5	+ 2.0	26.0	+ 4.0
Dichlorodifluoromethane	298	17.4	61	17.6	+ 1.1	15.9	− 8.6	16.0	− 8.0
	500	21.5	61	21.7	+ 0.9	19.2	− 9.8	21.0	− 2.3
	700	23.4	61	23.4	0	21.7	− 7.3	23.8	+ 1.7
	1000	24.8	61	21.5	−13	24.1	− 2.8	25.2	+ 1.6
Ethyl mercaptan	298	17.6	6	16.3	− 7.4	18.4	+ 4.5	17.6	0
	500	24.8	6	23.7	− 4.4	25.3	+ 2.0	24.5	− 1.2
	700	30.0	6	29.5	− 1.7	30.9	+ 3.0	29.6	− 1.3
	1000	35.2	6	35.4	+ 0.6	36.9	+ 4.8	34.9	− 0.9
Thiophene	298	17.3	104	18.8	+ 8.7	19.2	+ 1.1	17.4	+ 0.6
	500	27.1	104	27.2	+ 0.4	27.7	+ 2.2	26.6	− 1.8
	1000	38.6	104	36.7	− 4.9	36.3	− 6.0	38.4	− 0.5

Table 5-8. Comparison between Calculated and Experimental Ideal-gas Heat Capacities (*Continued*)

Compound	T, °K	Experimental		Calculated by method of									
		$C_p°$	Ref.	Dobratz		Johnson and Huang		Meghreblian, Crawford, and Parr		Souders, Matthews, and Hurd		Rihani and Doraiswamy	
				$C_p°$	% Error[a]	$C_p°$	% Error	$C_p°$	% Error	$C_p°$	% Error	$C_p°$	% Error
Ammonia	298	8.49	39	8.13	− 4.2	.....	.....	8.61	+ 1.4				
	500	10.1	98	9.60	− 5.0	.....	.....	10.4	+ 3.0				
	700	11.4	....	11.0	− 3.5	.....	.....	11.9	+ 4.4				
	1000	13.3	....	12.9	− 3.0	.....	.....	13.8	+ 3.7				
Carbon dioxide	273	8.67	58	9.83	+11	.....	.....	8.27	− 4.6				
	373	9.06	58	10.5	+16	.....	.....	9.19	+ 1.4				
	673	10.5	58	12.2	+16	.....	.....	11.5	+ 9.5				
	1273	12.1	58	14.2	+17	.....	.....	13.7	+13				
Carbon disulfide	370	11.2	47	10.9	− 2.7	.....	.....						
Hydrazine	298	12.6	83	11.7	− 7.1	.....	.....	9.23	−27				
	500	16.9	83	15.5	− 8.3	.....	.....	13.1	−22				
	700	19.5	83	18.8	− 3.6	.....	.....	16.3	−16				
	1000	22.3	83	22.7	+ 1.8	.....	.....	19.9	−11				
Hydrogen sulfide	298	8.17	6	8.14	− 0.4			8.48	+ 3.8			13.58	+ 7.9
	500	8.87	23	9.00	+ 1.5			9.33	+ 5.2			17.30	+ 2.4
	700	9.62	109	9.94	+ 3.3			10.1	+ 5.0			20.33	+ 4.1
	1000	10.7	....	11.6	+ 8.6			11.1	+ 3.8			22.07	− 1.0

194

Sulfur dioxide	298	9.52	6	......	......	9.98	+ 4.8	15.8	0
	500	11.10	23	......	......	11.57	+ 4.2	16.5	− 0.6
	700	12.14	109	......	......	12.78	+ 5.2	17.7	− 5.4
	1000	12.96	...	......	......	13.93	+ 7.5		
Dimethyl amine	283	15.8	5	17.8	+13	21.5	+36	15.8	
	298	16.6	5	18.7	+13	22.4	+35	16.5	
	323	18.7	5	20.2	+ 8.0	23.7	+27	17.7	
Average error		...	...	6.0	6.0	1.4	6.1	0.9	2.5

[a] % error = [(calculated−experimental)/experimental] × 100.
[b] Same as n-heptane.
[c] Same as cyclohexane.
[d] Same as 1-butene.
[e] No method, except Rihani and Doraiswamy's, distinguishes between cis and trans isomers.
[f] Same as ethylbenzene.
[g] Same as o-xylene.
[h] Same as n-propyl alcohol.

and 80, and discussions of the temperature dependence of $C_p{}^0$ are given in Refs. 51, 63, and 89 to 92. Hougen, Watson, and Ragatz (42) have tabulated literature $C_p{}^0$ values for a large number of organic compounds in a form identical to Eq. (5-7). Finally, mention is again made of the book by Janz (44), which discusses in greater detail than here many of the theoretical and empirical ideal-gas heat-capacity correlations.

5-9 Standard Heat of Formation $\Delta H_f{}^0$

The standard heat of formation $\Delta H_f{}^0$ is defined as the heat absorbed in the reaction where 1 mole is formed from its elements at a given temperature and given pressure. In this book, the reference state is understood to correspond to unit fugacity and the material to be an ideal gas (or zero pressure, since the enthalpy of an ideal gas does not depend on pressure). The *elements* making up the compound are considered to be in the usually specified standard states, e.g., carbon as a solid in the form of graphite.

Heats of formation may be measured directly in some instances—i.e., for water, the heat of formation is directly equivalent to the heat of combustion of hydrogen—or they may be determined indirectly by experimentally obtaining heats of combustion or hydrogenation and using these enthalpies of reaction in conjunction with the known heats of formation of all other reactants and products (except the unknown) to calculate a specific $\Delta H_f{}^0$. This heat of formation may then be corrected to the appropriate standard-state condition.

Estimation techniques for the heat of formation can be broken down into three general types, correlations involving bond energies, additive atomic-group methods, and, indirectly, by estimation of the heat of combustion with an oxygen-requirement balance. All three types are discussed below, and all appear to have some advantages and disadvantages which specify their use in certain situations and not in others. The accuracy of the methods is discussed and specific recommendations are given in Sec. 5-15.

5-10 Heats of Formation Estimated from Bond Energies

As noted in the previous section, $\Delta H_f{}^0$ is an enthalpy change when the compound is formed from the elements. It then seems probable that the numerical value of $\Delta H_f{}^0$ would be reflected by the type and number of valence bonds formed or broken in the synthesis. For example in the molecule CH_4, the heat of formation at 298.2°K is -17.889 kcal/g mole (3). An interpretation of this value would be that if 1 g atom of carbon as graphite and 2 g moles of hydrogen gas were to react, then the heat evolved would amount to 17.889 kcal. The enthalpies of carbon as graphite and hydrogen as a diatomic molecule are chosen as zero at

298.2°K. For the synthesis of methane as an ideal gas by adding bond energies, the carbon must be present as a gas and the hydrogen as gaseous atoms.

To obtain the enthalpy of carbon gas, the heat of sublimation of carbon at 298.2°K must be added. Upon assuming for the moment that $\Delta H_{s\,carbon}$ is 171.7 kcal/g atom (see below for a discussion of this value) and noting that to dissociate 1 g mole of H_2 to 2H requires about 104.2 kcal, then the following reactions are written:

$$C(\text{graphite}) \qquad\qquad \rightarrow C(g) \qquad \Delta H = +171.7 \text{ kcal}$$
$$2H_2(g) \qquad\qquad\qquad \rightarrow 4H(g) \qquad \Delta H = +208.4 \text{ kcal}$$
$$C(\text{graphite}) + 2H_2(g) \rightarrow CH_4(g) \qquad \Delta H = -17.889 \text{ kcal}$$

Then the value of ΔH for the reaction

$$C(g) + 4H(g) \rightarrow CH_4(g)$$

is $\qquad -17.889 - 208.4 - 171.7 = -398.0 \text{ kcal}$

This 398 kcal represents the energy liberated when 4(C—H) bonds are formed. If each bond were equal, then the C—H bond energy would be about 100 kcal. By proceeding in a similar manner from known values of ΔH_f^0 of various compounds, a tabulation of bond energies can be made. Such tabulations are readily available (10, 22, 44, 68, 69, 72, 73, 84, 96, 97), and the one due to Penner (73) is shown in Table 5-9. Bond energies from the various tabulations are often quite different, especially the energies of those bonds containing a carbon atom. These differences reflect the choice of the enthalpy of sublimation of carbon. Offtermatt (69) in his thesis preferred the value of 135.8 kcal, although he also tabulated bond energies based on the value of 171.7 kcal. Pauling (72) chose 124.1, Droward et al. (21) 169.6, Syrkin and Dyatkina (97) 124.1, Janz (44) and Gaydon (29) 170.4, and Laidler (55, 59) 171.7 kcal. It is obvious that one should not mix bond energies from different tables. In Table 5-9, the value, $\Delta H_{s\,carbon} = 171.7$ was chosen.

Another confusing point about such bond-energy tabulations is that the temperature level is often not specified. Usually, however, the values are applicable either to 298.2 or to 0°K. The supposed advantage of the 0°K value is that the thermal-energy contributions have been removed and the use of an "average" bond energy appears more reasonable (see below for discussion of this averaging concept). At zero temperature it is even possible to deduct the so-called "zero-point" vibrational-energy contribution to yield the bond energy of molecules in a completely quiescent state; this residual energy is called the *binding energy*. However, no real advantage has been shown for tabulating absolute-zero bond energies, and the usefulness of such energies in a practical sense is greatly decreased. Table 5-9 is applicable at 298.2°K.

The example shown above to estimate the average C—H bond energy in methane gave a value of about 100 kcal; however, in Table 5-9 the average bond energy of C—H is tabulated as 98.1 kcal. This suggests an inconsistency. The latter value is the "average" of a large number of C—H bond energies in various molecules; i.e., the C—H bond energy is not the same in different molecules. In fact, as Penner (73) points out, values of the terminal C—H bond energy in molecules such as CH_2=CH—CH_2--H are around 77 kcal. Other types of bonds show similar variation. This inconsistency is one of the very serious difficulties encountered in using this additive scheme to determine heats of formation. It is surprising that calculated values are as close as they are to experimental values as shown in Table 5-17.

To improve the estimations of $\Delta H_f{}^0$ from Table 5-9, certain resonance contributions have been empirically formulated; these, too, are shown in the table. They must be considered as *additional* increments in excess of the usual bond-energy terms. Rossini (79) and Swarc (96) have critically discussed additive bond-energy schemes and point out that certain other energy terms have been neglected. Primarily the next-neighbor interaction terms need inclusion, and steric effects must be taken into account in certain molecules such as gauche n-butane where fifth-neighbor hydrogens may interact.

Some improvement in estimating $\Delta H_f{}^0$ from bond energies was made by Laidler (55) and Lovering and Laidler (59), who tabulated primary, secondary, and tertiary C—H bond energies for nonaromatic hydrocarbons and singly bonded sulfur and oxygen compounds. However, a significant increase in accuracy resulted from the work of Allen (1), which was later extended by McCullough and Good (65) and Skinner (85). After a careful examination of $\Delta H_f{}^0$ for saturated hydrocarbons and naphthenes, Allen concluded that consistent and accurate predictions of $\Delta H_f{}^0$ could be made by using "average" bond energies if allowance were made for next-neighbor interactions and, though less important, trigonal and gauche n-butane interactions. All these interaction effects were assumed to be due to the shape of the carbon skeleton; i.e., the next-neighbor types like HCC, HCH were neglected.

To illustrate these interaction corrections for hydrocarbons and naphthenes, the ΔH for the reaction

$$mC(g) + nH(g) \rightarrow C_mH_n$$

may be written

$$-\Delta H_{298} = N_{CH}(C—H) + N_{CC}(C—C) + X\alpha_{CCC} - Y\beta_{CCC} - Z\gamma_{H_sH} \quad (5\text{-}8)$$

where N_{CH} and N_{CC} are the number of C—H and C—C bonds and C—H and C—C are the bond energies; Allen choose C—H = 99.825 kcal and

TABLE 5-9. TABLE OF BOND ENERGIES*
In kcal/g mole at 298.2°K

Bond	Energy		Resonance contributions	
			Group	Energy
C—C	85.5		Benzene	48.9
C—H	98.1		Naphthalene	88.0
C=C	143.0		Aniline	69.6
C≡C	194.3		Dialkylcarbonate	32.7
			Furfural	30.1
C—F	101.7		Phenyl acetylene	55.5
C—Cl	78.3		Phenyl cyanide	57.0
C—Br	66.8		Acetophenone	49
C—I	64.2			
C—N	81.0			
C≡N	210.6			
C—S	63.7			
C—O	85.8			
C =O	167	(formaldehyde)		
	172	(other aldehydes)		
	183	(ketones)		
N—N	60			
N≡N	225.5			
N—H	88.0			
S—H	81.1			
S—S	50.3			
O—O	33.1			
O—H	110.6			

NOTES:

$$H_2(g) \rightarrow 2H(g) \qquad \Delta H = 104.2 \text{ kcal}$$
$$C(\text{graphite}) \rightarrow C(\text{gas}) \qquad \Delta H = 171.7 \text{ kcal}$$
$$O_2(g) \rightarrow 2O(g) \qquad \Delta H = 118.3 \text{ kcal}$$
$$F_2(g) \rightarrow 2F(g) \qquad \Delta H = 36.4 \text{ kcal}$$
$$Cl_2(g) \rightarrow 2Cl(g) \qquad \Delta H = 58.0 \text{ kcal}$$
$$Br_2(g) \rightarrow 2Br(g) \qquad \Delta H = 46.4 \text{ kcal}$$
$$I_2(c) \rightarrow I_2(g) \qquad \Delta H = 14.9 \text{ kcal}$$
$$I_2(g) \rightarrow 2I(g) \qquad \Delta H = 36.5 \text{ kcal}$$
$$S(c) \rightarrow S(g) \qquad \Delta H = 53.3 \text{ kcal}$$
$$N_2(g) \rightarrow 2N(g) \qquad \Delta H = 225.6 \text{ kcal}$$

Acids and esters cannot be treated.   Bond values for such groups are listed by Syrkin and Dyatkina (97).

* S. S. Penner, "Chemistry Problems in Jet Propulsion," Pergamon Press, New York, 1957.

C—C = 78.85 kcal.* X is the number of pairs of carbon atoms which are the next nearest neighbors, and α_{CCC} was found to have an average value of 2.3 kcal. To obtain X for a molecule such as 2,2,3-trimethylbutane,

$$
\begin{array}{cc}
\overset{5}{C} & \overset{6}{C} \\
| & | \\
C\!-\!\underset{1}{\overset{|2}{C}}\!-\!\underset{3}{C}\!-\!\underset{4}{C} \\
| \\
\underset{7}{C}
\end{array}
$$

the pairs of next nearest neighbors are 1-3, 1-5, 1-7, 2-4, 2-6, 3-5, 3-7, 4-6, and 5-7, where $X = 9$. Y is the number of trigonal interactions, and β_{CCC} is about 0.6 kcal. Trigonal interactions in the carbon skeleton correspond to interactions of carbon atoms over tetrahedral faces; for example, for isobutane $Y = 1$ and, for neopentane $Y = 4$. Finally, the term $Z\gamma_{H_5H}$ accounts for fifth-neighbor interactions between hydrogens occurring in such molecules as gauche n-butane. Z is the number of such interactions,† and γ_{H_5H} is about 0.5 kcal.

For naphthenes, except cyclohexanes, ring-strain energies must also be included: e.g., for cyclopentanes this amounts to about 6.1 kcal per ring. Larger corrections would be expected for cyclobutane, cyclopropane, etc.

Similar corrections are available for organic sulfur compounds (1, 65) and for some olefins, alkyl alcohols, and bromides and amines (85). Use of the method requires a clear picture of the three-dimensional molecules and is limited, at present, to only a very few families of materials, in fact to those families where there are sufficient experimental data to delineate the correction terms. However, in such cases no estimation method really needs to be used, and experimental values are definitely preferable.

In summary, for rapid estimation but with the expectation of obtaining only approximate results, ΔH_f^0 can be obtained with the bond energies in Table 5-9. Example 5-5 illustrates the method. For aliphatic hydrocarbons, sulfur compounds, and a few other types of materials, the Allen scheme [e.g., Eq. (5-8)] can be used to obtain values of ΔH_f^0 which are, in many cases, almost within the range of experimental accuracy. Example 5-6 indicates how Eq. (5-8) can be applied.

Example 5-5. The standard heat of formation of acetone as an ideal gas at 298°K has been given as -51.79 kcal/g mole (74). Compare this with the heat of formation as estimated by the bond-energy scheme and Table 5-9.

* Note that these values differ from comparable values in Table 5-9.

† For example, $Z = 0$ for n-paraffins, isobutane, neopentane, cyclohexane, methylcyclohexane, cyclopentane, methylcyclopentane, etc.; $Z = 1$ for isopentane, isohexane, isoheptane, etc.; $Z = 2$ for 3-methylpentane, 3-methylhexane, 2,3-dimethylbutane, 2,4-dimethylpentane, 2,2-dimethylpentane, 2,2-dimethylbutane; $Z = 3$ for 2,3-dimethylpentane, etc.; $Z = 4$ for 3-ethylpentane, 3,3-dimethylpentane, 2,2,4-trimethylbutane, etc. (1).

Solution.   The reaction

$$3C(\text{graphite}) + 3H_2(g) + \tfrac{1}{2}O_2(g) \rightarrow CH_3\text{—}CO\text{—}CH_3(g) \qquad (1)$$

involves the following stepwise reactions:

$$3C(\text{graphite}) \rightarrow 3C(g) \qquad (2)$$
$$3H_2(g) \rightarrow 6H(g) \qquad (3)$$
$$\tfrac{1}{2}O_2(g) \rightarrow O(g) \qquad (4)$$
$$3C(g) + 6H(g) + O(g) \rightarrow CH_3\text{—}CO\text{—}CH_3(g) \qquad (5)$$

From the footnotes in Table 5-9,

$$\Delta H_2 = 3(171.7) \qquad \Delta H_3 = 3(104.2) \qquad \Delta H_4 = (\tfrac{1}{2})(118.3)$$

ΔH_5 involves an exothermic reaction in which six C—H, one C=O, and two C—C bonds are formed.   The bond-energy values are given in Table 5-9.

$$
\begin{array}{lll}
6 \text{ C—H} & = (6)(98.1) & = 589 \\
1 \text{ C}{=}\text{O} & & = 183 \\
2 \text{ C—C} & = (2)(85.5) & = \underline{171} \\
& & 943
\end{array}
$$

Thus,

$$\Delta H_f{}^0 \text{ for acetone is } (-943) + 3(171.7) + 3(104.2) + (\tfrac{1}{2})(118.3) = -56 \text{ kcal}$$

(as against -51.79 kcal).

Example 5-6.   Estimate the heat of formation of 2,2,3-trimethylbutane at 298°K, using Allen's modification of the bond-energy technique.   The experimental value is -48.96 kcal/g mole (2).

Solution

$$7C(g) + 16H(g) = 2,2,3\text{-trimethylbutane}$$

From Eq. (5-8)

$$-\Delta H = N_{CH}(C\text{—}H) + N_{CC}(C\text{—}C) + X\alpha_{CCC} - Y\beta_{CCC} - Z\gamma_{H_3H}$$

where $N_{CH} = 16$, $N_{CC} = 6$, C—H $= 99.825$, C—C $= 78.85$, $X = 9$, $\alpha_{CCC} = 2.3$, $Y = 1$, $\beta_{CCC} = 0.6$, $Z = 4$, $\gamma_{H_3H} = 0.5$.   [These terms are explained and illustrated under Eq. (5-8).]   Thus,

$$
\begin{aligned}
-\Delta H &= 16(99.825) + 6(78.85) + 9(2.3) - 0.6 - 4(0.5) \\
&= 1,597 + 473 + 21 - 0.6 - 2 \\
&= 2088 \text{ kcal}
\end{aligned}
$$

To obtain $\Delta H_f{}^0$, the enthalpy effects from the reactions 7C(graphite) $\rightarrow$ 7C(g) and $8H_2 = 16H$ must be included as shown in Example 5-5.

$$\therefore \Delta H_f{}^0 = -2,088 + 7(171.7) + 8(104.2) = -52.5 \text{ kcal}$$

As illustrated by Example 5-6, the $Y\beta$ and $Z\gamma$ terms are usually small. It is also interesting to note that, if Table 5-9 is used in this case with no correction factors, $\Delta H_f{}^0 = -47$ kcal.   It is apparent that the subtraction process with such large numbers robs both techniques of close accuracy.

Values of $\Delta H_{f_{298}}^0$ calculated with bond energies from Table 5-9 are compared with experimental values in Table 5-17 and recommendations presented in Sec. 5-16.

5-11 Heats of Formation from the Methods of Franklin and Verma and Doraiswamy

To account for next-neighbor interactions, atomic groups rather than individual bonds are often chosen. A common tenet is that the heat of formation at absolute zero temperature $\Delta H_{f_0}^0$ is an additive function of the various atomic groups comprising the molecule. Janz (44) and Cottrell (17) discuss the contributions to $\Delta H_{f_0}^0$ from the zero-point energy and chemical binding energy. Upon assuming such additivity, the heat of formation at temperatures greater than zero may then be determined as shown in Eq. (5-9),

$$\Delta H_f^0 = \Delta H_{f_0}^0 + (H^0 - H_0^0)_{\text{compound}} - \sum (H^0 - H_0^0)_{\text{elements}}$$

$$= \Delta H_{f_0}^0 + \int_0^T (C_p^0)_{\text{compound}} \, dT - \sum \int_0^T (C_p^0)_{\text{elements}} \, dT \quad (5\text{-}9)$$

where, as discussed earlier in the chapter, C_p^0 may be approximated by summing temperature-dependent atomic-group contributions for the various portions of the molecule. Pitzer has stated this same conclusion, but in a slightly different way (75). The significance of Eq. (5-9) is that the heat of formation of a compound at any temperature may be expressed approximately by the sum of temperature-dependent group contributions. Franklin has developed a consistent set of such group contributions (25, 26), and these are given in Table 5-10. In most cases the temperature dependence is shown from 0 to 1500°K. It is even possible to determine the values of ΔH_f^0 (298°K) for simple free radicals and carbonium ions (except when there is pi-electron resonance). Halogenated structures, however, cannot be treated.

In a similar study Verma and Doraiswamy (101a) suggest that the group increments for ΔH_f^0 be expressed as

$$\Delta H_f^0 = A + BT \quad (5\text{-}10)$$

where group contributions for A and B are tabulated in Table 5-11. Two temperature ranges are given, as the simple linear form of Eq. (5-10) does not apply over the temperature span 300 to 1500°K. Esters, anhydrides, and conjugated compounds cannot be treated, and only halogenated derivatives containing chlorine are considered.

Experimental and calculated values of ΔH_f^0 at 298°K are compared in Table 5-17 and the errors discussed in Sec. 5-15. In general the values of ΔH_f^0 estimated by the methods of Franklin or Verma and Doraiswamy agree with experimental values within ± 5 kcal/g mole.

Example 5-7. Using both the methods of Franklin and Verma and Doraiswamy, calculate the standard heat of formation of ethylbenzene as an ideal gas at 298°K. Compare with the experimental value of 7.12 kcal/g mole (2).

Solution. *Method of Franklin.* From Table 5-10, the group contributions would be as follows:

5 $\quad$ CH $\quad$ (5)(3.30) $=\quad$ 16.50

1 $\quad$ C— $\qquad = \quad$ 5.57

1 $\quad$ CH$_2$ $\qquad = -\ $ 4.93
1 $\quad$ CH$_3$ $\qquad = -10.12$
$\qquad\qquad\qquad\qquad\qquad$ 7.02 kcal/g mole

Difference $= |7.02| - |7.12| = -0.10$ kcal/g mole

Method of Verma and Doraiswamy. From Table 5-11, the group contributions are:

$$A \qquad\qquad\qquad B \times 10^2$$

5 $\quad$ CH $\quad$ (5)(3.768) $=$ 18.840 $\qquad$ (5)(-0.167) $= -0.835$

1 $\quad$ C— $\qquad\qquad = \quad$ 5.437 $\qquad\qquad\qquad = \quad$ 0.037

1 $\quad$ CH$_2$ $\qquad\qquad = -4.240$ $\qquad\qquad\quad = -0.235$
1 $\quad$ CH$_3$ $\qquad\qquad = -8.948$ $\qquad\qquad\quad = -0.436$
$\qquad\qquad\qquad\qquad\qquad$ 11.089 $\qquad\qquad\qquad\qquad -1.469$

That is,

$$\Delta H_f{}^0 = 11.089 - 1.469 \times 10^{-2}T. \quad \text{At } 298°K, \ \Delta H_f{}^0 = 6.71 \text{ kcal/g mole}$$
$$\text{Difference} = |6.71| - |7.12| = -0.41 \text{ kcal/g mole}$$

Example 5-8. Estimate the bond strength of the C—C bonds in cyclopropane at 298°K.

Solution. For the reaction

$$\text{Cyclopropane} \rightarrow \ ·CH_2CH_2CH_2·$$

the bond strength of the ring C—C may be expressed as

$$\text{C—C} = \Delta H_f{}^0(\text{cyclopropane}) - 2\,\Delta H_f{}^0(CH_2·) - \Delta H_f{}^0(—CH_2—)$$

From Table 5-10, for cyclopropane, $\Delta H_f{}^0 = 3CH_2 +$ ring contribution, that is, $\Delta H_{f_{298}}^0 = (3)(-4.926) + 28 = +13.2$ kcal/g mole. Thus,

$$\text{C—C} = +13.2 - 2(34) - (-4.93) = -50 \text{ kcal/bond}$$

Thus the estimated bond strength is 50 kcal. Similar ring bond strengths as tabulated by Franklin (26) are

Bond strength, kcal/mole

$\square \qquad\qquad \rightarrow \dot{C}CC\dot{C} \qquad\qquad 60$

$\rightarrow \dot{C}CCC\dot{C} \qquad\qquad 72$

$\rightarrow \dot{C}CCCC\dot{C} \qquad\qquad 78$

$\rightarrow \dot{C}C\dot{S} \qquad\qquad 52$
$\rightarrow \dot{C}S\dot{C} \qquad\qquad 59$

$\rightarrow \dot{C}C\dot{O} \qquad\qquad 49$
$\rightarrow CO\dot{C} \qquad\qquad 53$

TABLE 5-10. $\Delta H_f{}^\circ$ GROUP CONTRIBUTIONS*

In kcal/g mole

Group	Temperature, °K								
	0	298	400	500	600	800	1000	1200	1500
CH₃	-8.26	-10.12	-10.71	-11.22	-11.64	-12.27	-12.64	-12.82	-12.87
CH₂	-3.673	-4.926	-5.223	-5.465	-5.648	-5.871	-5.941	-5.886	-5.692
CH	0.18	-1.09	-1.17	-1.12	-1.05	-0.80	-0.50	-0.12	0.33
C	1.74	0.80	1.07	1.45	1.89	2.77	3.60	4.38	5.34
H₂C=	7.26	6.25	5.88	5.57	5.30	4.88	4.60	4.44	4.31
H\C=CH₂ / H	16.73	15.00	14.47	14.01	13.62	13.03	12.67	12.50	12.39
\C=C/ ...H (trans)	19.03	17.83	17.57	17.37	17.17	16.92	16.82	16.83	16.92
\C=C/ ...H (cis)	20.31	18.88	18.42	18.07	17.77	17.37	17.14	17.09	17.12
\C=CH₂	18.20	16.89	16.68	16.53	16.40	16.23	16.16	16.24	16.39
\C=C/ ...H	21.10	20.19	20.10	20.08	20.07	20.13	20.24	20.44	20.75
\C=C/ ...H	25.08	24.57	24.74	24.88	25.06	25.38	25.76	(26.2)	(26.9)
=C=	33.0‡	33.42	33.59	33.71	33.82	33.95	34.03	34.06	34.06
HC≡	27.16	27.10	27.07	27.02	26.97	26.81	26.65	26.50	26.27
—C≡	27.12	27.34	27.42	27.48	27.50	27.53	27.49	27.51	27.46

204

CH†	4.00	3.30	3.09	2.92	2.79	2.59	2.47	2.42	2.40
⟩C⟨	5.76	5.57	5.59	5.63	5.62	5.72	5.85	5.99	6.14
⟩C↔‡	5.29	4.28	4.33	4.28	4.27	4.56	4.16	3.51	
↔CH₂ / H	11.3‡	10.08	9.81	9.64	9.48	9.25	9.12	9.06	9.05
↔C⟨	12.65	12.04	12.11	12.16	12.17	12.27	12.43	12.59	12.66
C₆ cycloparaffin ring	1.10	− 0.45	− 1.13	− 1.67	− 1.96	− 2.12	− 1.86	− 1.41	− 0.52
C₅ cycloparaffin ring	6.72	5.68	4.94	4.28	3.74	3.00	2.57	2.22	1.96
C₄ cycloparaffin ring‡		18							
C₃ cycloparaffin ring‡		28							

Correction factors for paraffin chains

Ethyl side chain	1.5	0.8	0.8	0.8	0.8	0.8	0.8	0.8	0.8
Three adjacent CH groups	1.6	2.3	2.3	2.3	2.3	2.3	2.3	2.3	2.3
Adjacent C and CH groups	2.5	2.5	2.5	2.5	2.5	2.5	2.5	2.5	2.5
Adjacent quaternary C's	5.0	5.4	5.4	5.4	5.4	5.4	5.4	5.4	5.4
Quaternary C not adjacent to terminal methyl	2.1	1.7	1.7	1.7	1.7	1.7	1.7	1.7	1.7

Correction factors for substituents on aromatic nucleus

1,2-Dimethyl or 1,3-methylethyl	0.1	0.6	0.6	0.6	0.6	0.6	0.6	0.6	0.6
1,2-Methylethyl or 1,2,3-trimethyl	0.9	1.4	1.4	1.4	1.4	1.4	1.4	1.4	1.4

TABLE 5-10. ΔH_f^0 GROUP CONTRIBUTIONS* (*Continued*)

Nonhydrocarbon groups

Group	0°K	298°K	600°K	1000°K
—OH (primary)	−40.1	−41.9	−42.2	−40.6
—OH (sec)	−43.1	−44.9	−44.6	−41.4
—OH (tert)	−46.9	−49.2	−48.9	−44.4
—OH (phenol)	−44.0	−46.9	−45.6	−39.9
H—C=O	−32.7	−33.9	−34.0	−33.9
C=O	−30.6	−31.6	−31.2	−30.5
O—C—O	−93.1	−94.6	−93.0	−90.4
—O—C—OH (ester)	......	−79.8		
—O—C—O— (ether)	......	−27.2		
—O—C—O—, =O	......	−102.6		

Free radicals and carbonium ions

Group	298°K
—CH₃·	34
·CH	34
·C	33
·O	7.5
—O—O·	7.5
—S·	43
⁺CH₂	212
⁺CH	209
⁺C	195
⁺C=CH₂	240
H—C⁺=CH	245
—S⁺	232

TABLE 5-10. ΔH_f° GROUP CONTRIBUTIONS* (*Continued*)

	Nonhydrogen groups				Free radicals and carbonium ions	
Group	0°K	298°K	600°K	1000°K	Group	298°K
—NH₂	.....	2.8				
—NH—	.....	12.0				
—N—	.....	−19.2				
↔NH₂	.....	− 0.8				
—NO₂	.....	− 8.5				
—ONO	.....	−10.9				
—ONO₂	.....	−18.4				
—C≡N	.....	29.5				
—N=C	.....	44.4				
—SH	.....	5.7				
—S—	.....	11.6				
↔S↔	.....	11.3				

* J. L. Franklin, *Ind. Eng. Chem.*, **41**:1070 (1949); *J. Chem. Phys.*, **21**:2029(1953).

† CH indicates a resonating structure, e.g., one of the CH groups in benzene.

‡ Estimated as in footnote of Ref. 26.

TABLE 5-11. VERMA AND DORAISWAMY GROUP CONTRIBUTIONS TO
CALCULATE ΔH_f^{0*}

Aliphatic Hydrocarbon Groups

Group	300–850°K		850–1500°K		Highest temp., °K
	A	$B \times 10^2$	A	$B \times 10^2$	
—CH$_3$	− 8.948	−0.436	−12.800	0.0000	1500
—CH$_2$	− 4.240	−0.235	− 6.720	0.090	1500
—CH	− 1.570	0.095	− 2.200	0.172	1500
—C— †	− 0.650	0.425	0.211	0.347	1500
=CH$_2$	7.070	−0.295	4.599	−0.0114	1500
—C≡	27.276	0.036	27.600	−0.010	1500
≡CH‡	27.242	−0.046	27.426	−0.077	1500
=C=	33.920	−0.563	33.920	−0.563	1500
H$\backslash$C=CH$_2$ /	16.323	−0.437	12.369	0.128	1500
$\backslash$C=CH$_2$ /	16.725	−0.150	15.837	0.038	1500
$\backslash$C=C$\diagup$ / $\diagdown$	29.225	0.415	30.129	0.299	1500
$\backslash$C=C$\diagup$^H / $\diagdown$^H	20.800	−0.100	19.360	0.080	1500
$\backslash$C=C$\diagup$ / $\diagdown$^H	20.100	0.000	19.212	0.102	1500
H$\backslash$C=C$\diagup$^H / $\diagdown$ (cis)	19.088	−0.378	17.100	0.000	1500
$\backslash$C=C$\diagup$^H / $\diagdown$ H (trans)	18.463	−0.211	16.850	0.000	1500
$\backslash$C=C=CH$_2$ /	51.450	−0.050	50.200	0.100	1500
$\backslash$C=C=CH$_2$ / H	50.163	−0.233	48.000	0.000	1500
$\backslash$C=C=C$\diagup$ / $\diagdown$ H H	54.964	0.027	53.967	0.133	1500

† The temperature ranges in this case are 300 to 1100°K and 1100 to 1500°K
‡ The temperature ranges in this case are 300 to 600°K and 600 to 1500°K.

TABLE 5-11. VERMA AND DORAISWAMY GROUP CONTRIBUTIONS TO
CALCULATE ΔH_f^0* (*Continued*)

Aromatic Hydrocarbon Groups

Group	300–750°K		750–1500°K		Highest temp., °K
	A	$B \times 10^2$	A	$B \times 10^2$	
HC	3.768	−0.167	2.616	−0.016	1500
—C	5.437	0.037	5.279	0.058	1500
↔C	4.208	0.092	4.050	0.100	1500

Branching in Paraffin Chains

Group	300–750°K		750–1500°K		Highest temp., °K
	A	$B \times 10^2$	A	$B \times 10^2$	
Side chain with 2 or more C— atoms	0.800	0.000	0.800	0.000	1500
3 adjacent —CH groups	−1.200	0.000	.....	.....	1500
Adjacent —CH and —C—	0.600	0.000	0.600	0.000	1500

Branching in Cycloparaffins

Group	300–850°K		850–1000°K		Highest temp., °K
	A	$B \times 10^2$	A	$B \times 10^2$	

Branching in Six-membered Rings

Single branching	0.00	0.00	2.85	−0.40	1000
Double branching:					
1,1 Position	1.10	0.45	−0.40	0.00	1000
cis 1,2 Position	3.05	−1.09	1.46	−0.13	1000
trans 1,2 Position	−0.90	−0.60	−1.50	0.00	1000
cis 1,3	0.00	−1.00	−2.60	0.00	1000
trans 1,3	0.00	−0.16	2.80	−0.32	1000
cis 1,4	0.00	−0.16	2.80	−0.32	1000
trans 1,4	0.00	−1.00	−2.60	0.00	1000

TABLE 5-11. VERMA AND DORAISWAMY GROUP CONTRIBUTIONS TO
CALCULATE $\Delta H_f{}^0$* (*Continued*)

Group	300–850°K		850–1000°K		Highest temp., °K
	A	$B \times 10^2$	A	$B \times 10^2$	
Branching in Five-membered Rings					
Single branching	0.00	0.00	1.40	−0.20	1000
Double branching:					
1,1 Position	0.30	0.00	1.90	−0.25	1000
cis 1,2	0.70	0.00	0.00	0.00	1000
trans 1,2	−1.10	0.00	−1.60	0.00	1000
cis 1,3	−0.30	0.00	0.15	0.00	1000
trans 1,3	−0.90	0.00	−1.40	0.00	1000

Group	300–850°K		850–1500°K		Highest temp., °K
	A	$B \times 10^2$	A	$B \times 10^2$	
Branching in Aromatics					
Double branching:					
1,2 Position	0.85	0.03	0.85	0.03	1500
1,3 Position	0.56	−0.06	0.56	−0.06	1500
1,4 Position	1.00	−0.14	1.40	−0.12	1500
Triple branching:					
1,2,3 Position	2.01	−0.07	1.50	0.00	1500
1,2,4 Position	1.18	−0.25	1.50	−0.10	1500
1,3,5 Position	1.18	−0.25	1.80	−0.08	1500

Group	300–750°K		750–1500°K		Highest temp., °K
	A	$B \times 10^2$	A	$B \times 10^2$	
Ring Correction					
C_3, cycloparaffin ring	24.850	−0.240	24.255	−0.174	1500
C_4, cycloparaffin ring	19.760	−0.440	17.950	−0.231	1500
C_5, cycloparaffin ring	7.084	−0.552	4.020	−0.140	1500
C_6, cycloparaffin ring	0.378	−0.382	−4.120	0.240	1500

Group	300–850°K		850–1500°K		Highest temp., °K
	A	$B \times 10^2$	A	$B \times 10^2$	
Oxygen-containing Groups					
$\diagdown$C=O	−31.505	0.007	−32.113	0.073	1500
—O—	−24.200	0.000	−24.200	0.000	1000
O	−21.705	0.030	−21.600	0.020	1500

TABLE 5-11. VERMA AND DORAISWAMY GROUP CONTRIBUTIONS TO CALCULATE ΔH_f^0* (*Continued*)

Group	300–850°K		850–1500°K		Highest temp., °K
	A	$B \times 10^2$	A	$B \times 10^2$	
—CHO†	−29.167	−0.183	−30.500	0.000	1000
$-C\overset{O\dagger}{\underset{OH}{\diagup}}$	−94.488	−0.063	−94.880	0.000	1500

† The temperature ranges in this case are 300 to 750°K and 750 to 1500°K.

Contribution of —OH Group

Group	300–600°K		600–1000°K		Highest temp., °K
	A	$B \times 10^2$	A	$B \times 10^2$	
HO—CH₃	−37.207	−0.259	−37.993	−0.136	1000
HO—CH₂—	−40.415	−0.267	−41.265	−0.116	1000
HO—CH	−43.200	−0.200	−43.330	−0.143	1000
HO—C—	−46.850	−0.250	−47.440	−0.146	1000
HO—C	−44.725	−0.125	−45.220	−0.021	1000

Nitrogen- and Sulfur-containing Groups

Group	300–750°K		750–1500°K		Highest temp., °K
	A	$B \times 10^2$	A	$B \times 10^2$	
—NO₂ (aliphatic)	− 7.813	−0.043	− 9.250	0.143	1500
—C≡N	36.580	0.080	37.170	0.000	1000
—NH₂ ⎫	3.832	−0.208	2.125	0.002	1500
=NH ⎬ aliphatic	13.666	−0.067	12.267	0.133	1500
≡N ⎭	18.050	0.300	18.050	0.300	1500
—NH₂ ⎫	− 0.713	−0.188	− 1.725	0.000	1000
>NH ⎬	9.240	−0.250	8.460	−0.140	1000
N ⎭ aromatic†	18.890	0.110	16.200	0.250	1000
SH ‡	4.84	−0.080	....	.....	1000
—S— ‡	10.695	0.160	....	.....	1000

† The temperature ranges in these cases are 300 to 600°K and 600 to 1000°K.
‡ The temperature range in these cases is 300 to 1000°K. Standard state of sulfur is rhombic crystal.

TABLE 5-11. VERMA AND DORAISWAMY GROUP CONTRIBUTIONS TO
CALCULATE ΔH_f^0* *(Continued)*

Halogen-containing Groups

Group	300–750°K		750–1500°K		Highest temp., °K
	A	$B \times 10^2$	A	$B \times 10^2$	
H | H—C···Cl | H	− 9.322	−0.045	− 9.475	−0.025	1000
H | H₃C—C···Cl | H	−10.007	−0.033	−10.438	0.029	1000
Cl | H₃C—C—H | Cl	−14.780	−0.040	−14.780	−0.040	1500
H | H—C···Cl | Cl	−13.222	−0.029	−13.222	−0.029	1500
Cl | H—C···Cl | Cl	− 6.684	−0.033	− 6.684	−0.033	1500
Cl···C···Cl | Cl	− 6.400	−0.050	− 6.400	−0.050	1500
H Cl \ / C=C / \ H H	− 7.622	0.029	− 7.390	0.000	1500
H Cl \ / C=C / \ H Cl	− 6.171	−0.029	− 6.171	−0.029	1500
H Cl \ / C=C / \ Cl Cl (cis 1,2)	− 5.916	0.071	− 5.386	−0.007	1500
Cl H \ / C=C / \ H Cl (trans 1,2)	− 6.532	0.233	− 5.480	0.106	1500
Cl Cl \ / C=C / \ Cl Cl	− 6.047	0.236	− 6.047	0.236	1500

* K. K. Verma and L. K. Doraiswamy, *Ind. Eng. Chem. Fundamentals,* **4**:389 (1965).

This table is of some interest, as it indicates that the unstrained cyclohexane ring has a C—C bond energy close to an aliphatic type (see Table 5-9), whereas strained-structure C—C bond strengths are less. In fact, as Franklin points out, the value of the C—C bond energy for cyclobutane is about 60 kcal, which is close to the activation energy in the decomposition of cyclobutane (30), suggesting that such decomposition is initiated by ring rupture.

5-12 Heats of Formation from the Method of Souders, Matthews, and Hurd

An additive-group estimation technique for ΔH_f^0 has been developed for hydrocarbons by Souders, Matthews, and Hurd (88). It is very similar to their technique for obtaining C_p^0, as discussed in Sec. 5-6. Table 5-12 lists the group contributions to determine ΔH_f^0 at 298°K. To improve the accuracy, certain conjugation and adjacency corrections are also listed. Calculated values of $\Delta H_{f_{298}}^0$ are compared with experimental values in Table 5-17. In general, agreement is excellent, and discrepancies rarely exceed a few tenths of a kilocalorie.

To obtain ΔH_f^0 values at temperatures different from 298°K, Eq. (5-9) could be used. However, Souders, Matthews, and Hurd have already carried out the necessary integrations, which, for hydrocarbons, may be expressed as

$$\Delta H_{fT}^0 = \Delta H_{f_{298}}^0 + \left[\int_{298}^{T} \sum C_{p_{\text{vibrational}}}^0 \, dT - (n/2) \int_{298}^{T} C_{p_{H_2}}^0 \, dT \right.$$
$$\left. - m \int_{298}^{T} C_{p_{\text{carbon}}} \, dT \right]_{\text{I}} + \left(\int_{298}^{T} \sum C_{p_{\text{internal rotation}}}^0 \, dT \right)_{\text{II}} + 4R(T - 298)$$
$$(5\text{-}11)$$

where $C_{p_{H_2}}^0$ = heat capacity of hydrogen at zero pressure (standard state)

$C_{p_{\text{carbon}}}$ = heat capacity of solid graphite (standard state)

m, n = number of atoms of carbon and hydrogen in the molecule

$\Sigma C_{p_{\text{vibrational}}}^0$ = vibrational contribution to heat capacity as determined from Table 5-4

$\Sigma C_{p_{\text{internal rotation}}}^0$ = internal rotational contribution to heat capacity as determined from Table 5-5

Integrals I and II have been evaluated for various atomic groups and bond linkages found in hydrocarbons and are tabulated in Tables 5-13a and 5-13b. The term $4R(T - 298)$ represents the change in enthalpy with temperature, resulting from translational and external rotational contributions (for nonlinear molecules) and for the quantity $C_p - C_v = R$. Example 5-9 illustrates the method and calculated values of $\Delta H_{f_{298}}^0$ are compared with experimental values in Table 5-17. The method is compared with others in Sec. 5-16. Differences less than 1.0 kcal/g mole are to be expected in the use of this method.

TABLE 5-12. ΔH_{f298}^0 GROUP CONTRIBUTIONS*

Group	Primary contributions, kcal/g mole			
	Aliphatic hydro-carbon	Six-carbon naph-thenic ring	Five-carbon naph-thenic ring	Aromatic ring
—CH₃	−10.05			
—CH₂—	− 4.95	−4.91	−3.68	
—CH (2d carbon)†	− 1.57	−1.53	−1.63	
(3d or higher)†	− 0.88			
—C— (2d carbon)†	0.85	(0.85)	(0.85)	
(3d or higher)†	2.45			
H₂C=	5.80			
HC=‡	9.28	9.20	9.57	3.33
HC = (trans)	8.70			
—C=	10.84	(10.75)	(11.10)	5.48
=C=	34.09			
HC≡	27.04			
—C≡	27.65			
	Conjugation and adjacency contributions§			
=C—C= (aliphatics) (H H)	−3.28			
=C—C= (aliphatics) (H)	−4.45			
=C—C= (aliphatics)	−2.10			
=C—C= (5-member naphthenic ring) (H H)	−2.88			
=C—C= (6-member naphthenic ring) (H H)	−1.76			
(ring)—C=CH (H R)	−2.01			
Each pair ortho groups in aromatics	0.69			
Ethyl side chain (aliphatics)	0.88			
—C—C— (H H)	0.75			
—C—C— (H |)	2.39			
—C—C—C— (H H H)	2.30			

TABLE 5-12. ΔH^0_{f298} GROUP CONTRIBUTIONS* (Continued)

Group	Conjugation and adjacency contributions §
$-\overset{\mid}{\underset{\mid}{C}}-\overset{\mid}{\underset{\mid}{C}}-$	4.61
$-\overset{\mid}{C}=\overset{\mid}{C}-$	2.61

* M. Souders, C. S. Matthews, and C. O. Hurd, *Ind. Eng. Chem.*, **41**:1037 (1949).
† Indicates position of group in the longest chain of an aliphatic hydrocarbon (measured from shortest end).
‡ To be used when groups are in the adjacent (cis) position or when there is no cis-trans effect.
§ To be added to the group contributions whenever these molecular groups appear. The symbol — indicates a C—C bond; R indicates either H or C.

Example 5-9. Estimate the standard heat of formation of trans-2-butene at 800°K by the method of Souders, Matthews, and Hurd.
Solution. At 298°K, from Table 5-12,

$$2(-CH_3) \quad (2)(-10.05) = -20.10$$
$$2(H\overset{\mid}{C}\!\!=\!)_{trans} \; (2)(8.70) \quad = \quad \underline{17.40}$$
$$\Delta H_f{}^0 = -\;2.70 \text{ kcal/g mole}$$

Integral I in Eq. (5-11) is read from Table 5-13a and includes the following group values:

$$2(-CH_3) = -\;9.19$$
$$2(\overset{\mid}{=}CH) = -\;\underline{1.71}$$
$$-10.90$$

Integral II in Eq. (5-11) is read from Table 5-13b and includes the contribution of two type $V(b)$ bonds,

$$2V(b) = 1.11$$

As the value of $\Delta H^0_{f298} = -2.70$ kcal/g mole and $4R(800 - 298) = 3.99$, then

$$\Delta H^0_{f800} = -2.70 - 10.90 + 1.11 + 3.99$$
$$= -8.50 \text{ kcal/g mole}$$

The experimental value is -7.89 kcal/g mole (2).

5-13   Heats of Formation from the Method of Anderson, Beyer, and Watson

The standard heat of formation at 298°K, $\Delta H_f{}^0$, may be estimated by a group contribution method proposed by Anderson, Beyer, and Watson (4, 42). Each compound is considered to be composed of a basic group which has been modified by the addition of other groups. The base

TABLE 5-13a. VIBRATIONAL GROUP CONTRIBUTIONS TO HEAT OF FORMATION*

Values in kcal/g mole

Temp., °K	Paraffinic				Cycloparaffinic		Aromatic		Acetylenic		Olefinic			
	—CH₃	—CH₂—	—CH	—C—	—CH₂—†	—CH₂—‡	HC=	—C=	HC≡	—C≡	H₂C=	HC=	—C=	=C=
300	−0.016	−0.008	+0.001	+0.012	−0.008	−0.008	−0.004	+0.007	−0.004	+0.004	−0.011	−0.003	+0.007	+0.003
400	−1.099	−0.582	−0.017	0.664	−0.627	−0.570	−0.343	0.287	−0.379	0.129	−0.767	−0.245	0.363	0.156
500	−2.101	−1.066	+0.043	1.377	−1.160	−1.036	−0.643	0.577	−0.764	0.227	−1.478	−0.447	0.727	0.285
600	−3.008	−1.463	+0.174	2.126	−1.607	−1.412	−0.905	0.873	−1.154	0.300	−2.139	−0.608	1.098	0.389
700	−3.839	−1.793	+0.353	2.888	−1.985	−1.719	−1.146	1.169	−1.563	0.346	−2.762	−0.742	1.468	0.465
800	−4.594	−2.060	+0.572	3.657	−2.304	−1.965	−1.364	1.463	−1.980	0.373	−3.348	−0.853	1.835	0.517
900	−5.278	−2.276	+0.825	4.432	−2.570	−2.156	−1.561	1.758	−2.399	0.387	−3.898	−0.944	2.202	0.557
1000	−5.905	−2.448	+1.107	5.210	−2.791	−2.303	−1.740	2.052	−2.819	0.392	−4.419	−1.014	2.569	0.587
1100	−6.480	−2.580	+1.412	5.991	−2.974	−2.413	−1.904	2.345	−3.234	0.390	−4.911	−1.067	2.939	0.610
1200	−7.010	−2.682	+1.736	6.774	−3.123	−2.491	−2.054	2.637	−3.646	0.384	−5.380	−1.105	3.311	0.629
1300	−7.505	−2.756	+2.075	7.557	−3.245	−2.544	−2.194	2.926	−4.054	0.376	−5.830	−1.132	3.685	0.643
1400	−7.973	−2.821	+2.425	8.339	−3.348	−2.580	−2.325	3.212	−4.460	0.364	−6.265	−1.152	4.058	0.652
1500	−8.419	−2.864	+2.782	9.119	−3.435	−2.603	−2.451	3.494	−4.866	0.347	−6.689	−1.167	4.428	0.655
2000	−10.527	−2.963	+4.623	12.978	−3.735	−2.622	−3.054	4.870	−6.905	0.207	−8.725	−1.221	6.236	0.607

* M. Souders, C. S. Matthews, and C. O. Hurd, *Ind. Eng. Chem.*, **41**:1048 (1949).
† Five-membered ring.
‡ Six-membered ring.

216

TABLE 5-13b. INTERNAL-ROTATIONAL CONTRIBUTIONS TO HEAT OF FORMATION*

Values in kcal/g mole

Temp. °K	I —CH₂—CH₂—	II CH₃—CH₂—	III R—CH—	IV R—C—	V(a) R—CH=	V(b) R—CH=	VI =CH—CH=	VII ≡C—C≡	VIII R—C≡	4R (T − 298)
300	0.005	0.004	0.003	0.004	0.003	0.002	0.005	0.001	0.003	0.015
400	0.304	0.218	0.221	0.214	0.196	0.123	0.325	0.086	0.218	0.809
500	0.560	0.432	0.437	0.435	0.370	0.235	0.637	0.154	0.421	1.604
600	0.785	0.634	0.642	0.655	0.527	0.343	0.918	0.207	0.608	2.398
700	0.986	0.822	0.834	0.868	0.673	0.449	1.173	0.250	0.779	3.193
800	1.168	0.997	1.013	1.070	0.809	0.554	1.408	0.286	0.939	3.988
900	1.335	1.161	1.181	1.261	0.938	0.656	1.625	0.321	1.089	4.782
1000	1.488	1.319	1.339	1.441	1.061	0.760	1.828	0.353	1.230	5.577
1100	1.636	1.465	1.488	1.613	1.181	0.862	2.019	0.382	1.366	6.371
1200	1.775	1.606	1.631	1.776	1.297	0.963	2.201	0.409	1.496	7.166
1300	1.908	1.742	1.769	1.932	1.410	1.064	2.375	0.434	1.623	7.961
1400	2.036	1.873	1.902	2.082	1.522	1.165	2.542	0.458	1.746	8.755
1500	2.159	2.001	2.032	2.227	1.632	1.266	2.702	0.480	1.865	9.550
2000	2.739	2.599	2.638	2.894	2.171	1.769	3.424	0.579	2.435	13.523

* M. Souders, C. S. Matthews, and C. O. Hurd, *Ind. Eng. Chem.*, **41**:1048 (1949).

217

groups are listed in Table 5-14 and comprise methane, cyclopentane, benzene, naphthalene, methylamine, dimethylamine, trimethylamine, dimethyl ether, and formamide.   For example, ethane may be considered to be a modification of methane, i.e., methane with a methyl substitution for one of the hydrogens.   The first substitution of a methyl group for a hydrogen on the base group is called a *primary methyl substitution,* and this adds a particular increment to the base-group value; these primary-methyl-substitution values are also tabulated in Table 5-14.   Any further substitution by CH_3, either for a hydrogen on the basic group or for a hydrogen on the primary substitution group, is termed a *secondary methyl substitution.*   The increment to be added here depends both upon the type of carbon atom upon which the substitution is made and upon the types of atoms adjacent to the substituted atom.   Anderson, Beyer, and Watson designate by the letter A the carbon atom upon which the substitution is made and by the letter B the highest type number (see below) of a carbon atom adjacent to A.   The type numbers are as follows:

Type	
1	CH_3
2	CH_2
3	CH
4	C
5	C (in benzene or naphthalene ring)

Thus a substitution of a hydrogen in ethane by CH_3 (to form propane) would be a secondary methyl substitution and would be denoted as a 1,1 type of substitution since $A = 1$, $B = 1$.   A secondary methyl substitution of a hydrogen in toluene to form ethylbenzene would be a type $A = 1$, $B = 5$, or 1,5.

Two special secondary substitutions are defined in Table 5-14; one is used in forming a methyl ester from a carboxylic acid and the other in forming an ethyl ester or ether from a methyl ester or ether.   Contributions for multiple bonds and for nonhydrocarbon groups are also included in Table 5-14.   The latter group contributions when added are substituted for a methyl group, *not* a hydrogen atom.

Example 5-10 indicates how the method may be applied, and a comparison between calculated and experimental values of ΔH_f^0 at 298°K is given in Table 5-17.*   Calculated values of ΔH_f^0 generally agree with experimental values within 5 kcal/g mole, although in most cases the agreement is much closer; the method is compared with others in Sec. 5-16.   Values for almost all types of compounds may be calculated by this method.

* When it is possible to use two different methods to build up the desired molecular configuration, an average of both calculated values should be used.

Example 5-10. Estimate, by the method of Anderson, Beyer, and Watson, the standard heat of formation of n-propyl alcohol as an ideal gas at 298°K.

Solution. From Table 5-14,

		Contribution
Base group..........................	CH_4	-17.9
Primary methyl substitution............	CH_3	-2.2
Secondary methyl substitution of type		
$A = 1, B = 1$......................	CH_3	-4.5
Secondary methyl substitution of type		
$A = 1, B = 2$......................	CH_3	-5.2
Substitution of —OH for —CH_3........	OH	-32.7
		-62.5 kcal/g mole

The experimental value is -61.2 kcal/g mole (74).

TABLE 5-14. ΔH^0_{f298} GROUP CONTRIBUTIONS*

Group	Base-group contributions, kcal/g mole
Methane......................................	-17.9
Cyclopentane.................................	-21.4
Benzene......................................	18.1
Naphthalene..................................	35.4
Methylamine..................................	-7.1
Dimethylamine...............................	-7.8
Trimethylamine...............................	-10.9
Dimethyl ether...............................	-46.0
Formamide...................................	-49.5

	Contributions of primary CH_3 substitution groups
1. Methane...................................	-2.2
2. Cyclopentane	
a. First-substitution outside ring..............	-5.2
b. Second substitution:	
Ortho................................	-12.2
Meta.................................	-8.4
Para.................................	-7.1
c. Third substitution.......................	-7.0
d. Enlargement of ring.....................	-9.3
3. Benzene and naphthalene	
a. First-substitution outside ring..............	-4.5
b. Second substitution:	
Ortho................................	-6.3
Meta.................................	-6.5
Para.................................	-8.0
4. Methylamine...............................	-5.7
5. Dimethylamine.............................	-6.3
6. Trimethylamine............................	-4.1
7. Formamide	
Substitution on C atom.....................	-9.0

* J. W. Anderson, G. H. Beyer, and K. M. Watson, *Natl. Petrol. News, Tech. Sec.*, **36**:R476 (July 5, 1944).

TABLE 5-14. ΔH^0_{f298} GROUP CONTRIBUTIONS* (Continued)

A	B	Secondary methyl substitutions
1	1	−4.5
1	2	−5.2
1	3	−5.5
1	4	−5.0
1	5	−6.1
2	1	−6.6
2	2	−6.8
2	3	−6.8
2	4	−5.1
2	5	−5.8
3	1	−8.1
3	2	−8.0
3	3	−6.9
3	4	−5.7
3	5	−9.2
1	—O— in ester or ether	−7.0
Substitution of H in OH group to form ester		+9.5

A	Type of bond	B	Multiple-bond contributions
1	=	1	32.8
1	=	2	30.0
1	=	3	28.2
2	=	2	28.0
2	=(cis)	2	28.4
2	=(trans)	2	27.5
2	=	3	26.7
3	=	3	25.5
Correction for each pair of conjugated double bonds			−3.8
1	≡	1	74.4
1	≡	2	69.1
2	≡	2	65.1
Correction for double bond adjacent to aromatic ring			−5.1

TABLE 5-14. ΔH^0_{f298} GROUP CONTRIBUTIONS* (Continued)

	Substitution of CH_3 by nonhydrocarbon group
—OH (aliphatic, meta, para)	−32.7
—OH (ortho)	−47.7
—NO₂	1.2
—CN	39.0
—Cl	0 for first Cl on a carbon; 4.5 for each additional
—Br	10.0
—F	−35.0
—I	24.8
=O (aldehyde)	−12.9
=O (ketone)	−13.2
—COOH	−87.0
—SH	15.8
—C₆H₅	32.3
—NH₂	12.3

5-14   Heats of Formation and Combustion from the Method of Handrick

None of the methods of estimating heats of formation described previously is expected to be very reliable for complex organic compounds. Handrick (38) carefully reviewed all available methods and suggested that for such materials a real improvement in estimating techniques was needed. He proposed a rather novel and simple procedure to estimate heats of combustion for many types of organic compounds. The heat of combustion was defined for the reaction

$$C_mH_nN_pO_qX_rS_t + \left[\frac{2(m + t) - q + (n - r)/2}{2}\right]O_2 \rightarrow$$
$$mCO_2 + [(n - r)/2]H_2O(l) + (p/2)N_2 + rHX + tSO_2 \quad (5\text{-}12)$$

The number of oxygen atoms required

$$x \equiv 2(m + t) - q + (n - r)/2 \quad (5\text{-}13)$$

is called the *molar oxygen balance*. The basic tenet of the method is that the heat of combustion is a linear function of x, that is,

$$-\Delta H_c = \Sigma a' + x\Sigma b' \quad (5\text{-}14)$$

where a' and b' are tabulated for a large number of structural groups in Table 5-15. The value of ΔH_c obtained may be considered to be the value at 298°K, though Handrick does not discuss any temperature dependence. The state for which the value is applicable is the normal, stable state at 1 atm, unless the contributions allow a choice of phase (see rule 5 below).

The ("higher") heat of combustion was chosen, rather than the heat of formation, as most of the data used to devise the correlation were obtained from experimental heats of combustion. To obtain a heat of formation from a heat of combustion such as written for Eq. (5-12),

$$\Delta H_f = -\Delta H_c - m \, \Delta H_{f_{CO_2}} - [(n - r)/2] \, \Delta H_{f_{H_2O(l)}}$$
$$- (r/2) \, \Delta H_{f_{HX}} - t \, \Delta H_{f_{SO_2}} \qquad (5\text{-}15)$$

where $\Delta H_{f_{CO_2, H_2O(l)}, \text{etc.}}$ are heats of formation of the various products in the states shown below,

	$\Delta H_{f_{298}}$, kcal/g mole
$CO_2(g)$	-94.05
$H_2O(l)$	-68.30
$HF(g)$	-64.20
$HCl(g)$	-22.10
$HBr(g)$	$- 8.70$
$HI(g)$	$+ 6.20$
$SO_2(g)$	-71.00

The value of ΔH_f so obtained applies to the state of aggregation for which ΔH_c was determined. For all product species, the ΔH_f values apply to 298°K and about 1 atm; in all cases, except liquid water, these are very close to the ideal-gas $\Delta H_f{}^0$ values.

To use Handrick's method, the following rules should be observed:

1. In *all* cases there is a base contribution of $a' = 5.7$, $b' = 52.08$ (compound is in the liquid or solid state) or $a' = 5.5$, $b' = 52.48$ (if in the gas state). For normal, straight-chain hydrocarbons this is the only contribution; e.g., for propane, $m = 3$, $n = 8$, $x = 10$, $-\Delta H_c$ is 530.3 kcal/g mole. From Eq. (5-15),

$$\Delta H_f = 530.3 - 3(94.05) - 4(68.3) = -25.1 \text{ kcal/g mole}$$

whereas from Table 5-17 the experimental value in the ideal-gas state is -24.8.

2. Use the paraffin branching increment in Table 5-15 for branching on straight chains or for *more* than a single alkyl substitution on a ring. Never use more than one such increment per molecule. Thus toluene would not require a branching increment, while xylene, hexamethylbenzene, and triethylpentane would have only one.

3. If more than one functional group of the same type is present, the a' contribution is multiplied by the number of such groups. The b' contribution is the same as though only a single group were present. In cases of conflict between rules 2 and 3, rule 2 takes precedence.

4. If there is difficulty in choosing a particular functional group from a larger grouping embodying characteristics of several, choose the most "complicated" grouping or the one which appears farther from the top of Table 5-15. Exceptions are molecules containing urea or biuret groups; these are treated as diamides.

TABLE 5-15. COEFFICIENTS OF EQUATIONS FOR HEAT OF
COMBUSTION $(-\Delta H_c)^a$

Base values $a' = 5.7$, $b' = 52.08$ (gas); $a' = 5.5$, $b' = 52.48$ (liquid)

Functional type	a'	b'	No. of compounds used for equations	Structural formula (R = aliphatic chain or hydrogen)
Paraffin branched (liq.)..	$-\ 3.7$	$+0.09$	28	
Cyclopropane (liq.)......	$+\ 16.2$	-0.13	9	R_2C——CR_2 / C / R_2
Cyclobutane (liq.).......	$+\ 10$	$+0.11$	5	R_2C——CR_2 / R_2C——CR_2
Cyclopentane (liq.)......	$-\ 1.7$	0.00	16	R_2C——CR_2 / CR_2 / R_2C——CR_2
Cyclohexane (liq.).......	$-\ 7.4$	0.00	15	$R_2\ \ R_2$ / C——C / R_2C CR_2 / C——C / $R_2\ \ R_2$
Cycloheptane (liq.)......	$+\ 17$	-0.99	8	$R_2\ \ R_2$ / C——C / R_2C CR_2 CR_2 / C——C / $R_2\ \ R_2$
Bicyclohexyl[b] (liq.)......	$-\ 12.0$	-0.01	...	(bicyclohexyl structure)
Tercyclohexyl[b] (liq.)....	$-\ 27.6$	0.11	...	(tercyclohexyl structure)
Decalin[b] (liq.)..........	$-\ 13.9$	0.0	...	(decalin structure)
Hydrindan[b] (liq.)........	$-\ 21.2$	0.25	...	(hydrindan structure)
Olefin: Normal (liq.).........	$+\ 14.2$	-0.01	18	$R_2C{=}CR_2$
Normal (gas).........	$+\ 14.2^e$	0.00^e	18	

TABLE 5-15. COEFFICIENTS OF EQUATIONS FOR HEAT OF
COMBUSTION $(-\Delta H_c)^a$ *(Continued)*

Functional type	a'	b'	No. of compounds used for equations	Structural formula (R = aliphatic chain or hydrogen)
Acetylene, normal (liq.)..	+ 37.3	0.00	18	$RC\equiv CR$
Benzene:				
Liq.................	− 10.1	+0.07	16	
Gas.................	− 7.0^c	+0.00^c	12	
Solid................	− 16.5^d	+0.45^d	10	
Biphenyl (liq.)..........	− 31	+0.37	6	
Naphthalene (solid).....	− 6.1	−0.59	22	
Alcohol:				
Primary (liq.).........	+ 9.2	−0.05	10	RCH_2OH
Primary (gas).........	+ 18.3^c	−0.24	10	
Secondary (liq.)......	+ 4.5	−0.44	10	$(R_2C)_2CHOH$
Tertiary (liq.)........	+ 8.6	−0.95	18	$(R_3C)_3COH$
Mixed (liq.)..........	+ 10.3	−0.63	7	
Mixed (solid).........	+ 3.8	+1.27	6	
Aromatic hydroxyl (solid)..............	+ 7.0	−0.29	22	
Ether:				
Liq.................	+ 15.5	+0.02	16	R_3COCR_3
Gas.................	+ 28^c	−0.05^c	6	
Oxirane (ethylene oxide) (liq.)	+ 41	−1.05	4	
Furan (liq.)...........	+ 35	−1.17	4	
Peroxide (liq. or solid)...	+ 66	+0.09	8	$R-O-O-R$
Aldehyde:				
Liq.................	+ 11.5	−0.09	10	$RC(=O)H$
Gas.................	+ 21^c	−0.68^c	4	
Ketone (liq.)..........	+ 5.5	−0.19	8	$RC(=O)R$
Acid:				
Liq.................	− 4.7	+0.07	12	$RCOOH$
Solid^g..............	− 3.8	−0.01	55	

TABLE 5-15. COEFFICIENTS OF EQUATIONS FOR HEAT OF
COMBUSTION $(-\Delta H_c)^a$ *(Continued)*

Functional type	a'	b'	No. of compounds used for equations	Structural formula (R = aliphatic chain or hydrogen)
Acid anhydride:				RC$=$O
Liq^f	$+$ 9	-0.03	3	
Solid	$+$ 2.4	-0.01	15	\O
				RC$=$O
Ester:				RC($=$O)OR
Liq	$+$ 16.1	-0.42	39	
Solid^g	$+$ 16	-0.62	5	
Nitrile:				RC$\equiv$N
Liq	$+$ 9.3	-0.01	13	
Solid^g	$+$ 9	$+0.29$	6	
Carbylamine (isonitrile) (liq.)	$+$ 26.6	$+0.57$	9	RNC
Imino (liq. + solid)^i	$+$ 11.8	-0.02	10	R$_2$C$=$N—
Amine				R$_3$CNH$_2$
Primary (liq.)	$+$ 17.7	-0.81	18	
Primary (gas)	$+$ 18.0^c	-0.49^c	4	
Primary (solid)	$+$ 4^h	-0.08^h	12	
Secondary (liq.)	$+$ 18.3	-0.12	7	(R$_3$C)$_2$NH
Secondary (solid)	$+$ 0	$+0.54$	5	
Tertiary (liq.)	$+$ 20	$+0.08$	6	(R$_3$C)$_3$N
Azide (liq. + solid)	$+$ 89	-1.14	9	R—N$_3$
Hydrazine (solid)^i	$+$ 32.5	-0.10	19	—N—N— | |
Azo (solid)^i	$+$ 35.4	$+0.11$	13	—N$=$N—
Azoxy (solid)^i	$+$ 32	$+1.44$	5	—N$=$N— ↓ O
Amide:				RC($=$O)N— |
Liq^j	$-$ 6	$+0.57$	6	
Solid^j	$-$ 6.0	$+0.16$	41	
Imide (solid)^i	$-$ 6	$+0.45$	8	(RC)$_2$N— ‖ O
Hydrazide (solid)^i	$+$ 30	-0.15	7	RC($=$O)N—N— | |
Isocyanate (liq. + solid) .	$+$ 26	-0.38	3	R—NCO
Oxime (solid)	$+$ 45.3	-0.12	13	R$_2$C$=$NOH
Guanidine (solid)^i	$+$ 0.7	-0.46	22	—N—C($=$NH)N— | |
Nitro:				R$_3$CNO$_2$
Aliphatic (liq.)	$+$ 88.4	-0.38	20	
Aliphatic (solid)	$+$ 92.8	-0.68	24	
Aromatic (liq.)	$+$ 97.9	-0.39	10	
Aromatic (solid)	$+$ 92.2	-0.40	113	
gem-Trinitro:				RC(NO$_2$)$_3$
Liq	$+292.2$	$+0.34$	16	
Solid	$+287.5$	-0.59	21	
Nitrate:				R$_3$CONO$_2$
Liq	$+129.0$	$+0.17$	33	
Solid	$+128.1$	$+0.28$	31	
Nitramine (solid)^i	$+$ 94	$+0.86$	34	—NNO$_2$ |

TABLE 5-15. COEFFICIENTS OF EQUATIONS FOR HEAT OF COMBUSTION $(-\Delta H_c)^a$ *(Continued)*

Functional type	a'	b'	No. of compounds used for equations	Structural formula (R = aliphatic chain or hydrogen)
Nitramide (solid)[i]	+101	+0.55	16	RC(=O)NNO$_2$
Nitrosamine (liq. + solid)[i]	+ 56	+1.05	9	—NNO
Nitroso (solid)	+ 21	+1.9	4	R$_3$CNO
Fluorine: Liq	+ 10.9	+0.61	24	R$_3$CF
Solid	+ 14.2	+0.19	14	
gem-Trifluoro (liq.)	+ 36.1	−0.44	5	RCF$_3$
Chlorine: Liq[k]	− 0.3	−0.32	73	R$_3$CCl
Solid[k]	− 11.4	+0.14	25	
Gas[k]	− 1.3[c]	+0.21[c]	12	
Bromine (gas)[l]	− 8[c]	+0.21[c]	5	R$_3$CBr
Thiol (liq.)[i]	− 32	−0.44	3	R$_3$CSH
Sulfide (liq.)[i]	− 35	+0.22	5	R—S—R
Thiol acid (liq. + solid)[i]	− 25	0.23	4	RC(=O)SH
Thiophene (liq. + solid)[i]	− 56	+0.98	6	
Pyrrole (liq. + solid)[i]	+ 1.3	−0.03	42	
1,2,3-Triazole: Liq	+ 45	−0.43	3	
Solid	+ 43	−1.42	6	
1,2,4-Triazole (solid)[i]	+ 15	−1.56	13	
Tetrazole (solid)[i]	+ 49	+0.32	17	
Pyridine (liq. + solid)	+ 14	−0.77	7	

TABLE 5-15. COEFFICIENTS OF EQUATIONS FOR HEAT OF
COMBUSTION $(-\Delta H_c)^a$ (Continued)

Functional type	a'	b'	No. of compounds used for equations	Structural formula (R = aliphatic chain or hydrogen)
Furazan (solid).........	+ 85.6	+0.02	9	RC——CR / N / N / O
Furoxan (solid).........	+126.3	−0.06	7	RC——CR / N / N / O / O
1,2,4-Oxdiazole (solid)...	+ 44	+0.42	5	RC——N / N / CR / O
Salt formation..........	− 16.1	....	52	
Hydrate formation......	+ 4.5	....	20	

a G. R. Handrick, *Ind. Eng. Chem.*, **48**:1366 (1956).
b Values based on Ref. 7.
c Based on normal paraffin (gas) value.
d For hydrocarbons only.
e From dibasic acids.
f Based on small number of data and not so reliable as value for solid.
g Based on limited number of data and less reliable than value for liquid.
h From aromatic amines only.
i For calculations to SO_2.
j For substituents on the nitrogen atom(s), add appropriate bond-group values. Add primary amine values for one substituent on nitrogen, secondary amine values for two substituents on the same nitrogen.
k For calculations to HX.
l For calculations to X_2.

5. Where a group in Table 5-15 has a choice of physical states, choose the one applicable to the compound being studied unless otherwise noted in the table. If liquid values are used, by necessity, to obtain ΔH_c for a solid, then the value of $-\Delta H_c(s)$ could be obtained by subtracting the molar heat of fusion from the calculated liquid value.

6. If salts of organic bases and inorganic acids, or hydrates, are studied, the ΔH_c of the inorganic acid must be obtained from other sources and added separately. There is, in addition, a salt-link and hydrate correction as shown at the bottom of Table 5-15 (see Example 5-11). A similar procedure is necessary for organic acids–inorganic base salts. For organic base–organic acid salts, a salt correction is still required [see Example 5-11 (b) and (c)].

7. There are special rules for certain nitrogen compounds. As Handrick states:

Additional contributions are necessary for amine or hydrazine when a carbon-nitrogen or nitrogen-nitrogen bond has been formed by substitution. Such is the case for amide, hydrazine, hydrazide, azo, azoxy, guanidine, tetrazole, nitramine, nitramide, nitrosamine, nitrosamide, and the like. Thus a primary nitramine is considered to have both a nitramine and a primary amine contribution . . . [Example 5-11(c)], and an N-substituted nitramide also has a primary amine contribution. To calculate an organic azo compound of the type Ar—N=N—Ar, two primary amine contributions besides the azo, aromatic, and paraffin features must be included.

To apply the method to very complex molecules requires a rather careful study of the molecular structure, particularly if salts or nitrogen linkages are present. To illustrate the method, six examples are given (38), and these also illustrate the rules given above. For simple molecules, other methods are preferable (see Sec. 5-16 for a discussion of all methods), but, for complex structures, this method appears to be the most general and usually predicts $-\Delta H_c$ values to within 2 per cent. According to Handrick, only 40 of some 1,500 compounds tested deviated by more than 4 per cent; greater deviations were usually noted in the first member of a series, and particularly poor results were obtained if the series were very polar in nature.

Example 5-11. The following examples illustrate the use of Eq. (5-14) and Table (5-15) for estimating heats of combustion.

(a) 3,5-Dicarbethoxy-2-(α-hydroxypropyl)-4-methylpyrrole

$$H_5C_2OOC—C \overset{NH}{\diagup} \overset{OH}{\underset{\diagdown}{C—CHCH_2CH_3}}$$

$$CH_3—C \underline{\hspace{1cm}} C—COOC_2H_5$$

$C_{14}H_{21}NO_5(s) + 16.75O_2 \rightarrow 14CO_2 + 10.5H_2O + 0.5N_2 \qquad x = 33.5$

	a'	b'	Rule
1 paraffin (liq.)	+ 5.7	52.08	1
1 branch paraffin (liq.)	− 3.7	+0.09	2
1 alcohol, sec (liq.)	+ 4.5	−0.44	5
2 ester (liq.)	+32.2	−0.42	3, 5
1 pyrrole (solid)	+ 1.3	−0.03	Fundamental
	40.0	51.28	

$-\Delta H_c = 40 + (51.28)(33.5) = 1758$ kcal/mole (calc.), 1779 kcal/mole (obs.)

(b) Diaminoguanidine nitrate

$$NH_2NHCNHNH_2 \cdot HNO_3$$
$$\overset{\|}{NH}$$

$CH_3N_6O_3$ (solid) $+ 1.5 O_2 \rightarrow CO_2 + 4H_2O + 3N_2$
$x = 5.5$ (for diaminoguanidine)   Rule 6

	a'	b'	Rule
1 normal paraffin (liq.)	5.7	52.08	1
1 guanidine (solid)	0.7	−0.46	7
2 hydrazine (solid)	65.0	−0.10	7
	71.4	51.52	

$$-\Delta H_c = 71.4 + (51.52)(5.5) = 354.8 \text{ kcal/mole}$$

1 salt link	−16.1	......	6
1 HNO₃ (liq.)	− 7.2	......	6

$-\Delta H_c$ (diaminoguanidine nitrate) = 332 kcal/mole (calc.), 329.8 kcal/mole (obs.)

(c) 5-Nitraminotetrazole monoguanidine salt

$$\begin{array}{c} N-N \\ \| \quad \diagdown \\ \| \quad \quad CNHNO_2.NH_2CNH_2 \\ N-NH \quad \quad \quad NH \end{array}$$

$$C_2H_7N_9O_2 + 2.75O_2 \rightarrow 2CO_2 + 3.5H_2O + 4.5N_2 \qquad x = 5.5$$

	a'	b'	Rule
1 paraffin (liq.)	+ 5.7	52.08	1
1 amine, primary (liq.)	+17.7	−0.81	5, 7
1 guanidine (solid)	+ 0.7	−0.46	4
1 tetrazole (solid)	+48.7	+0.32	Fundamental
1 nitramine (solid)	+94	+0.86	Fundamental
1 salt link	−16.1	......	6
	150.7	51.99	

$$-\Delta H_c = 150.7 + (51.99)(5.5) = 437 \text{ kcal/mole (calc.)}, 453.8 \text{ kcal/mole (obs.)}$$

(d) 5-Hydrazinotetrazole benzalhydrazone

$$\begin{array}{c} N-N \\ \| \quad \diagdown \\ \| \quad \quad CNHN=CHC_6H_5 \\ N-NH \end{array}$$

$$C_8H_8N_6(s) + 10O_2 \rightarrow 8CO_2 + 4H_2O + 3N_2 \qquad x = 20.0$$

	a'	b'	Rule
1 normal paraffin (liq.)	+ 5.7	+52.08	1
1 benzene (liq.)	−10.1	+ 0.07	Fundamental
1 amine, primary (liq.)	+17.7	− 0.81	7
1 imino (liq. + solid)	+11.8	− 0.02	Fundamental
1 hydrazine (solid)	+32.5	− 0.10	7
1 tetrazole (solid)	+48.7	+ 0.32	Fundamental
	106.3	51.54	

$$-\Delta H_c = 106.3 + (51.54)(20) = 1137 \text{ kcal/mole (calc.)}, 1135 \text{ kcal/mole (obs.)}$$

(e) Vitamin A (carotene)

$$C_{20}H_{30}O(s) + 27O_2 \rightarrow 20CO_2 + 15H_2O \qquad x = 54$$

	a'	b'	Rule
1 normal paraffin (liq.)...................	5.7	52.08	1
1 branched paraffin (liq.).................	− 3.7	+0.09	2
1 cyclohexane (liq.)......................	− 7.4	0.00	Fundamental
5 normal olefin (liq.)	+71.0	−0.01	3
1 primary alcohol (liq.)..................	+ 9.2	−0.05	5
	74.8	52.11	

$$-\Delta H_c = 74.8 + (52.11)(54) = 2889 \text{ kcal/mole}$$

(f) Phenolphthalein

$$C_{20}H_{14}O_4(s) + 21.5O_2 \rightarrow 20CO_2 + 7H_2O \qquad x = 43$$

	a'	b'	Rule
1 normal paraffin (liq.)...................	5.7	52.08	1
1 branched paraffin (liq.).................	− 3.7	+0.09	2
3 benzene (liq.).........................	−30.3	+0.07	3, 5
2 aromatic hydroxyl (solid)...............	+14.0	−0.29	3
1 ester (liq.)............................	+16.1	−0.42	5
	1.8	51.53	

$$-\Delta H_c = +1.8 + (51.53)(43) = 2218 \text{ kcal/mole}$$

5-15 Variation of Heats of Formation with Temperature

Values of $\Delta H_f{}^0$ values are usually tabulated at 298°K. Values at other temperatures are often desired. The methods of Franklin (Sec.

5-11) and Souders, Matthews, and Hurd (Sec. 5-12) allow an estimation at higher temperatures, but interpolation is required if the desired temperature does not coincide with the tabulated values; however, the method of Verma and Doraiswamy (Sec. 5-11) allows $\Delta H_f{}^0$ to be determined at any temperature.

Since enthalpy is a point function, an enthalpy cycle for a compound

TABLE 5-16. VARIATION OF $C_p{}^0$ WITH TEMPERATURE FOR VARIOUS ELEMENTS IN THEIR STANDARD STATES*

$$C_p{}^0 = a + bT + cT^2 + dT^3$$
$$C_p{}^0 \text{ in cal/(g mole)(}^\circ\text{K), } T \text{ in } ^\circ\text{K}$$

Element	Standard state	Stoichio-metric multiplier	a	b $\times 10^2$	c $\times 10^4$	d $\times 10^9$
C	Graphite	n	-0.8666	1.217	-0.07942	1.812
H	$H_2(g)$	$n/2$	6.853	0.016	0.0006	0.149
N	$N_2(g)$	$p/2$	7.051	-0.115	0.0306	-1.153
O	$O_2(g)$	$q/2$	6.191	0.292	-0.0071	-0.080
$X(F)$	$F_2(g)$	$r/2$	6.115	0.586	-0.0419	0.978
$X(Cl)$	$Cl_2(g)$	$r/2$	6.821	0.571	-0.0511	1.547
$X(Br)$	$Br_2(g)$	$r/2$	8.051	0.246	-0.0213	0.641
$X(I)$†	I_2(crystal)	$r/2$				
	$I_2(g)$	$r/2$	8.504	0.131	-0.0107	0.313
S‡	Crystal-rhombic	t				
	$S_2(g)$	$t/2$	6.499	0.530	-0.0389	0.952

* D. J. Patterson and G. J. Van Wyler, *J. Heat Transfer*, **85**:281 (1963); M. Souders, C. S. Matthews, and C. O. Hurd, *Ind. Eng. Chem.*, **41**:1037 (1949).

† Usual standard state at 298°K is a solid crystal. At 298°K, the ΔH change from crystal to the ideal-gas state is 14.88 kcal/g mole I_2 (74).

‡ The standard state usually (but not always) assumed for sulfur at 298°K is rhombic crystalline sulfur. At higher temperatures, the standard state changes; i.e., the monoclinic form becomes the standard state at 368.6°K, the liquid the standard state above 392°K, and the vapor the standard state above 717.8°K. Even in the vapor, the composition varies with the equilibrium $S_8 \rightleftharpoons S_6 \rightleftharpoons S_2$ so that determination of the enthalpy of sulfur above 298°K requires a detailed calculation. Stull (94) discusses this question in some detail. A convenient tabulation of sulfur enthalpies is given in the same article.

Reference temperature $T = 298.2°K$, $H = 0$, rhombic crystal.

Change as rhombic crystal, 298.2–368.6°K............... $\Delta H = 395.2$ cal/g atom
Transition of rhombic to monoclinic form at 368.6°K..... $\Delta H = 86.0$ cal/g atom
Change as monoclinic crystal, 368.6–392°K............... $\Delta H = 145.1$ cal/g atom
Transition of monoclinic crystal to liquid at 392°K....... $\Delta H = 295.0$ cal/g atom
Change as liquid sulfur, 392–717.8°K.................... $\Delta H = 2790.0$ cal/g atom
Transition of liquid to vapor at 717.8°K................ $\Delta H = 2228.0$ cal/g atom

As a vapor with equilibrium $S_8 \rightleftharpoons S_6 \rightleftharpoons S_2$, the heat capacity varies greatly with temperature owing to dissociation. See the plot in Ref. 94.

$C_mH_nN_pO_qX_rS_t$ may be formulated between 298°K and any other temperature T. (The base temperature may obviously be any temperature for which a value of $\Delta H_f{}^0$ is known.)

$$\Delta H_{f_T}^0 = \Delta H_{f_{298}}^0 + \int_{298}^{T} C_{p_{\text{compound}}}^0 \, dT - \sum \int_{298}^{T} C_{p_{\text{elements}}}^0 \, dT \qquad (5\text{-}16)$$

The value of $C_{p_{\text{compound}}}^0$ may be estimated by the methods described earlier; e.g., Rihani and Doraiswamy's method (Sec. 5-7) gives $C_p{}^0$ as a polynomial in T. The second integral yields the enthalpy change to heat the elements (corrected for stoichiometry; see below) from 298 to T°K. For convenience, Table 5-16 shows $C_p{}^0$ for most of the common elements in their standard states; the analytical form is similar to Eq. (5-7), and the column marked "Stoichiometric multiplier" accounts for the number of atoms in the molecule with the general formula $C_mH_nN_pO_qX_rS_t$.

Use of Eq. (5-16) is straightforward except in the case of elements which undergo a phase transition as temperatures are raised. For example, the usual standard states for iodine and sulfur are solid at 298°K. However, at high temperatures, these elemental standard states are $I_2(g)$ and $S_2(g)$. At some intermediate temperature, there is a phase change (usually associated with the normal-boiling-point temperature of the element). Thus $\Delta H_f{}^0$ for iodine and sulfur compounds may have different element standard states at different temperatures. As a footnote in Table 5-16, the heats of sublimation of I_2 and S_2 at 298°K are given to allow one to use $\Delta H_{f_{298}}^0$ values as a reference to calculate higher-temperature $\Delta H_f{}^0$ values where $I_2(g)$ and $S_2(g)$ are the reference element standard states. These complications enter into consideration only to obtain $\Delta H_f{}^0$. If a heat of reaction is desired at some high temperature, the actual reference state of each element is immaterial (as long as, for each $\Delta H_f{}^0$, the *same* element standard state is chosen), since in calculating heats of reaction, the subtraction operation between $\Delta H_f{}^0$ of the products and the reactants cancels out the enthalpy of the individual elements in the standard states.

5-16   Recommendations to Estimate the Heat of Formation

Six methods were presented in Secs. 5-10 to 5-14 to estimate heats of formation. Calculated values of $\Delta H_{f_{298}}^0$ by five of the methods are compared with experimental values in Table 5-17. Based on these results and the discussion presented with each method, the following recommendations for the estimation of $\Delta H_{f_{298}}^0$ are presented:

1. For hydrocarbons, use the method of Souders, Matthews, and Hurd (Sec. 5-12). Errors will probably not be in excess of 0.5 kcal/g mole. Almost all types of hydrocarbons may be treated. Of course, as con-

tinually emphasized, wherever possible use the experimental values (2, 34) in preference to this or any estimation technique.

2. For simple nonhydrocarbons, the best general method is that of Verma and Doraiswamy (Sec. 5-11, Table 5-11). In a few cases, as seen in Table 5-17, the methods of Franklin (Sec. 5-11) and Anderson, Beyer, and Watson (Sec. 5-13) are, however, more accurate. Errors, in general, do not exceed a few kilocalories per gram mole except for acetic anhydride, cyanogen, hydrazine, and the like. Franklin's method is applicable to simple free radicals.

3. For rapid, approximate estimates of ΔH_f^0, the simple bond-energy technique (Sec. 5-10) may be used. However, whenever possible use the estimation techniques discussed above. The bond-energy technique is probably the most convenient for quick estimations and with the Allen modifications is capable of high accuracy for certain hydrocarbons and sulfur compounds.

4. For very complex organic compounds, the heat-of-combustion estimation technique of Handrick (Sec. 5-14) is recommended. Heats of formation may then be obtained with Eq. (5-15). Heats of combustion may usually be estimated within 2 per cent. This leaves an uncertainty of $0.02 \Delta H_c$ in the heat of formation. In a typical ΔH_c of about $-1,000$ kcal/g mole, the uncertainty in ΔH_f^0 would be about 20 kcal/g mole. This method has almost no limitation as to molecular type and can be applied to extremely complex materials, as indicated in Example 5-11.

5. Though this book is limited to gases and liquids, it is worthwhile to note that considerable efforts have also been expended to develop methods to estimate ΔH_f^0 for inorganic salts. The best method available was developed by Wilcox and Bromley (3, 107, 108). Metallic halides, carbonates, sulfates, etc., may be treated. The method is essentially an additive technique with contributions for various types of bonds. Average errors less than 10 kcal/g mole may usually be expected.

5-17 Free Energies of Formation ΔF_f^0

As used here, the standard free energy of formation ΔF_f^0 may be defined as the free-energy change resulting from a chemical reaction in which the desired compound is formed in the ideal-gas state at 1 atm (unit fugacity) from its elements, which are initially in their standard states. Since elements in their standard states are assigned the value 0, this free energy of reaction becomes numerically equal to the standard free energy of formation. The free-energy change of a chemical reaction is equal to the sum of the free energies of formation of the products, less the sum of the free energies of formation of the reactants. All values are multiplied by their stoichiometric multipliers. The equilibrium constant of a chemical reaction is a function of the standard free-energy

TABLE 5-17. COMPARISON BETWEEN CALCULATED AND EXPERIMENTAL HEATS OF FORMATION

Values in kcal/g mole for the ideal-gas state at 1 atm and 298°K

| Compound | Experimental | | Calculated by method of | | | | | | | | | |
| | ΔH_f° | Ref. | Bond energies | | Franklin | | Anderson, Beyer, and Watson | | Souders, Matthews, and Hurd | | Verma and Doraiswamy | |
			ΔH_f°	Diff.*	ΔH_f°	Diff.	ΔH_f°	Diff.	ΔH_f°	Diff.	ΔH_f°	Diff.
Propane	−24.82	2	−23.9	−0.9	−25.17	+0.35	−24.6	−0.22	−25.05	+0.23	−25.43	+0.61
n-Heptane	−44.89	2	−47.1	+2.2	−44.87	−0.02	−45.4	+0.51	−44.85	−0.04	−45.19	+0.30
3-Methylhexane	−45.96	2	−47.1	+1.1	−46.23	+0.27	−47.0	+1.04	−45.88	−0.08	−46.85	+0.89
2,4-Dimethylpentane	−48.30	2	−47.1	−1.2	−47.59	−0.71	−48.6	+0.30	−48.29	−0.01	−48.50	+0.20
2,2,3-Trimethylbutane	−48.96	2	−47.1	−1.9	−48.39	−0.57	−50.3	+1.34	−48.58	−0.38	−51.91	+2.95
Cyclopentane	−18.46	2	−29.0	+10.5	−18.97	+0.51	−21.4	+2.94	−18.4	−0.06	−19.26	+0.80
Cyclohexane	−29.43	2	−34.8	+5.4	−30.01	+0.58	−30.7	+1.27	−29.46	+0.03	−30.40	+0.97
Methylcyclopentane	−25.50	2	−34.8	+9.3	−25.23	−0.27	−26.6	+1.10	−26.40	+0.90	−25.86	+0.36
Ethylene	12.50	2	16.20	+3.7	12.50	0.00	12.7	+0.20	11.6	−0.90	12.38	−0.12
1-Butene	0.03	2	4.8	+4.8	0.05	+0.02	0.2	+0.17	0.08	+0.05	0.17	+0.14
2-Butene (cis)	−1.67	2	4.8	+6.5	−1.36	−0.31	−1.4	−0.27	−1.54	−0.13	−2.53	+0.86
2-Butene (trans)	−2.67	2	4.8	+7.5	−2.41	−0.26	−2.3	−0.33	−2.70	+0.03	−2.66	−0.01
1,3-Butadiene	26.33	2	39.30	+13.0	......	...	26.4	+0.07	26.78	+0.45	30.04	+3.71
Acetylene	54.19	2	57.1	+2.9	54.20	+0.01	54.3	+0.11	54.08	−0.09	54.21	+0.02
Methylacetylene	44.32	2	51.3	+7.0	44.32	0.00	44.5	+0.18	44.64	+0.32	44.24	−0.08
Benzene	19.82	2	19.8	0	19.80	−0.02	18.1	−1.71	19.98	+0.16	19.62	−0.20
Ethylbenzene	7.12	2	8.2	+1.1	7.02	−0.10	8.6	+1.48	7.13	+0.01	6.71	−0.41
o-Xylene	4.54	2	8.2	+3.7	4.20	−0.34	7.3	+2.76	4.18	−0.36	4.62	+0.08
m-Xylene	4.12	2	8.2	+4.1	4.10	−0.02	7.1	+2.98	4.18	+0.06	4.06	−0.06

Substance											
Hydrazine	22.25	43	22.00	− 0.3	5.6	−16.65	4.5	−17.75	....	− 10.6	+1.2
Ethyl mercaptan	− 9.4	70	−11.5	+ 2.1	− 9.35	− 0.05	8.8	− 0.60	....	− 19.2	+0.7
Diethyl sulfide	− 18.5	70	−18.3	− 0.2	−18.5	0.00	....	....	....		
Thiophene	− 27.82	104	....	....	−24.5	− 3.32	....	....	....		
Acetonitrile	19.81	74	22.1	+ 2.3	19.4	− 0.41	....	....	....	26.57	+6.76
Aniline	19.7	102	5.1	−14.6	21.3	+ 1.6	25.9	+ 6.2	....	20.62	+0.9
Cyanogen	73.84	50	62.3	−11.5	59.0	−14.84	57.9	−15.9	....	73.64	−0.20
Ethylamine	− 12.24	74	−12.6	− 0.2	−12.3	+ 0.06	−12.8	− 0.56	....	− 11.98	−0.26
Dimethylether	− 46.4	11	−44.5	− 1.9	−47.4	+ 1.0	−46.0	− 0.40	....	− 44.69	−1.7
Acetaldehyde	− 39.76	53	−39.0	− 0.8	−44.0	+ 4.24	−44.1	+ 4.34	....	− 39.96	+0.20
Acetone	− 51.79	74	−55.8	+ 4.0	−51.8	+ 0.01	−52.5	+ 0.71	....	− 51.98	+0.19
Acetic acid	−104.72	74	....	....	−104.7	− 0.02	−107.1	+ 2.38	....	−104.92	+0.20
Acetic anhydride	−148.82	74	....	....	−122.8	−26.02	....	....	....		
Methyl formate	− 84.69	74	....	....	−83.9	− 0.79	95.4	+10.71	....		
Ethyl acetate	−103.4	103	....	....	−104.0	+ 0.6	−104.6	+ 1.2	....		
Methanol	− 48.1	53	−51.5	+ 3.4	−52.0	+ 3.9	−52.8	+ 4.7	....	− 48.23	+0.1
n-Propyl alcohol	− 61.17	74	−63.1	+ 1.9	−61.87	+ 0.70	−62.5	+ 1.33	....	− 61.34	+0.17
Isopropyl alcohol	− 62.41	74	−63.1	+ 0.7	−66.2	+ 3.8	−63.9	+ 1.49	....	− 65.58	+3.17
Phenol	− 21.71	74	−19.4	− 2.3	−24.8	+ 3.09	−19.71	+ 2.00	....	− 23.20	+1.5
Phosgene	− 53.3	11, 105	−50.8	− 2.5	....	....	−48.0	− 5.3	....		
Methyl chloride	− 19.58	52	−15.6	− 4.0	....	....	−20.1	− 0.52	....	− 19.70	+0.12
Chloroform	− 21.4	52	−22.2	+ 0.8	....	....	−22.2	+ 0.8	....	− 21.63	+0.2
Carbon tetrachloride	− 25.5	52	−25.5	0	....	....	−25.8	+ 0.3	....	− 25.58	+0.1
Ethyl bromide	− 15.3	57	−15.7	+ 0.4	....	....	−14.6	+ 0.7	....		
Average difference	....	....	....	3.9	....	2.3	....	2.7	0.23	....	3.84

* Difference = |calculated ΔH_f^0| − |experimental ΔH_f^0| except when the terms have an opposite sign.

change of the reaction, i.e.,

$$\Delta F^0_{\text{reaction}} = -RT \ln K \qquad (5\text{-}17)$$

where K is the equilibrium constant for the reaction and

$$\Delta F^0_{\text{reaction}} = \Sigma \, \Delta F^0_{f \, prod} - \Sigma \, \Delta F^0_{f \, reactants} \qquad (5\text{-}18)$$

Unless very accurate values of $\Delta F^0_{\text{reaction}}$ can be obtained, estimated values of K are, at best, approximate. The exponential character of the $K - \Delta F^0_{\text{reaction}}$ equality shows that K is very sensitive to small variations in $\Delta F^0_{\text{reaction}}$. Except in fortuitous situations, methods for estimating ΔF^0 are not of sufficient accuracy to give more than a rough indication of K.

Values of ΔF_f^0 may be estimated directly as shown in the van Krevelin method (Sec. 5-20) or as obtained from standard enthalpies and entropies of formation, as

$$\Delta F_f^0 = \Delta H_f^0 - T \, \Delta S_f^0 \qquad (5\text{-}19)$$

ΔH_f^0 estimation techniques are discussed earlier in this chapter, and ΔS_f^0 may be determined by either of two additive-group techniques discussed below. All estimation techniques are compared in Sec. 5-21, and recommendations are presented to aid in the selection of a particular method depending upon the class of compounds being studied.

5-18 Free Energies and Entropies of Formation from the Method of Souders, Matthews, and Hurd

This additive-group method (88) is similar to the one described in Sec. 5-12 for ΔH_f^0, but in this case the standard entropies of formation at 298°K are estimated. Free energies of formation may then be determined by Eq. (5-19). Group contributions are listed in Table 5-18.

Symmetry and Optical Isomer Corrections. In addition to summing the atomic-group increments in Table 5-18, two additional corrections are required. Calculations of absolute entropies from statistical mechanics have shown that, in the determination of the energy-storage modes due to rotation, molecular symmetry will decrease the possible number of distinguishable molecular configurations by the factor $1/n$, where n is the number of planes of symmetry. Further, in the mathematics used to obtain entropies from molecular-partition functions, this symmetry-correction term for entropy turns out to be $-R \ln \sigma$, where σ is defined as the number of identical spatial orientations that a molecule may assume by rotation of the rigid molecule about any axis or by rotation about any axis in the molecular structure. For diatomic molecules it is

TABLE 5-18. GROUP CONTRIBUTIONS FOR ENTROPY OF FORMATION AT 298°K*
Values in cal/(g mole)(°K)
Primary

Group	Aliphatic hydrocarbon	Six-carbon naphthenic ring	Five-carbon naphthenic ring	Aromatic ring
—CH₃	−19.66			
—CH₂—	−23.37	−20.09	−17.68	
—CH (2d carbon)†	−30.19	−26.08	−24.71	
—CH (3d or higher)†	−30.19			
—C— (2d carbon)†	−37.17	(−32.82)	(−30.80)	
—C— (3d or higher)†	−37.17			
H₂C=	− 5.05			
HC=‡	− 8.61	− 3.93	(− 1.80)	−5.43
HC=(trans)	− 9.28			
—C=	−14.55	(− 9.00)	(− 6.50)	−9.49
=C=	4.51			
HC≡	7.64			
—C≡	4.68			

Conjugation and Adjacency Contributions
ΔS_f^0

R H
=C—C=   −3.73
≡C—C≡   −8.83

⬡ H R
    C=CH   −2.05

Each pair ortho groups in aromatics   −0.8

* M. Souders, C. S. Matthews, and C. O. Hurd, *Ind. Eng. Chem.*, **41**:1048 (1949).
† Indicates position of group in the longest chain of an aliphatic hydrocarbon (measured from shortest end).
‡ To be used when groups are in the adjacent (cis) position or when there is no cis-trans effect.

obvious that $\sigma = 1$ for heteronuclear and $\sigma = 2$ for homonuclear molecules, for example, HCl and Cl_2. For organic molecules, evaluation of σ is more difficult. A few examples are listed below; in case of doubt, construction of a three-dimensional model is suggested, but, even with such visual aids, it is sometimes difficult to determine σ readily for complex but symmetrical molecules.

Methane has a tetrahedral structure, and rigid rotation produces 12 identical configurations. Ethane with two end-to-end tetrahedrons and with rotation of the methyl groups as well as 180° rotation about a plane bisecting the C—C axis gives $\sigma = 18$. Other paraffins also have $\sigma = 18$. Values of σ rise rapidly with some isomers with a high degree of symmetry; that is, $\sigma = 81$ for 2-methyl propane. To simplify the symmetry-factor correction, all estimation methods discussed in this book have included as a part of each group contribution all symmetry resulting from rotations of methyl groups. The net "effective" symmetry correction is then due only to the number of identical orientations when the entire molecule is considered rigid and rotated about an axis of symmetry. For methane σ is still 12; for ethane and the normal paraffins σ is decreased to 2; for 2-methyl propane $\sigma = 3$; for 2,2-dimethyl propane $\sigma = 12$; for 1,3-butadiene $\sigma = 2$; for 1-pentyne $\sigma = 1$; for anthracene $\sigma = 4$; for cyclohexane $\sigma = 6$; for methylcyclohexane $\sigma = 1$; for trans-1,4-dimethylcyclohexane $\sigma = 2$; for tertiary butyl alcohol $\sigma = 1$; for quinoline $\sigma = 1$; for mesitylene $\sigma = 6$; for 2,2,3,3-tetramethylbutane $\sigma = 6$.

In addition to molecular-symmetry corrections, if the molecule has optical isomers, i.e., contains one or more completely asymmetric carbon atoms (such as 3-methylhexane), then the number of possible spatial orientations is increased and a correction of $+R \ln \eta$ must be added to the calculated absolute entropy, η being the number of such isomers. In theory the number of possible optical isomers is 2^m, where m is the number of asymmetric carbons (the so-called "van't Hoff rule"). However, in many molecules with more than one asymmetric carbon atom, there exist planes of symmetry which negate the optical activity of some arrangements, e.g., the meso form of tartaric acid. Again, a molecular three-dimensional model is invaluable in deciding upon the correct value of η.

The corrections noted above are applicable to absolute entropy calculations; for free energy, the correction terms are still additive but are multiplied by temperature and are opposite in sign [as illustrated in Eq. (5-19)]. Entropy corrections are illustrated in Example 5-12 and free energy corrections in the van Krevelin method discussed in Sec. 5-20.

Entropy of Formation at Temperatures Other than 298°K. The values for ΔS_f^0 determined from Table 5-18 are applicable only at 298°K. For other temperatures, since

$$(\partial S^0 / \partial T)_P = C_p^0 / T \qquad (5\text{-}20)$$

an integration may be carried out whereby the temperature variation of the entropy variations of compound and elements are taken into account. Rather than use Eq. (5-20) directly, Souders, Matthews, and Hurd have already performed the integrations for hydrocarbons in a manner similar

TABLE 5-19. VIBRATIONAL GROUP CONTRIBUTIONS TO ENTROPY OF FORMATION (INTEGRAL III)*

Values in cal/(g mole)(°K)

Temp., °K	Paraffinic				Cycloparaffinic		Aromatic		Acetylenic		Olefinic			
	—CH₃	—CH₂—	—CH	—C—	—CH₂— (5)	—CH₂— (6)	HC=	—C=	HC≡	—C≡	H₂C=	HC=	—C=	=C=
300	− 0.068	− 0.040	− 0.004	+ 0.037	− 0.041	− 0.037	− 0.022	+ 0.017	− 0.023	+ 0.008	− 0.047	− 0.016	+ 0.021	+ 0.010
400	− 3.185	− 1.693	− 0.062	1.905	− 1.826	− 1.657	− 0.998	0.823	− 1.101	0.372	− 2.225	− 0.717	1.046	0.447
500	− 5.425	− 2.778	+ 0.070	3.493	− 3.020	− 2.704	− 1.670	1.466	− 1.960	0.593	− 3.815	− 1.169	1.859	0.733
600	− 7.087	− 3.507	0.301	4.851	− 3.841	− 3.395	− 2.154	2.003	− 2.684	0.724	− 5.026	− 1.469	2.530	0.919
700	− 8.365	− 4.017	0.576	6.026	− 4.427	− 3.869	− 2.525	2.459	− 3.314	0.795	− 5.986	− 1.676	3.097	1.035
800	− 9.370	− 4.373	0.868	7.054	− 4.852	− 4.197	− 2.815	2.852	− 3.870	0.857	− 6.768	− 1.822	3.588	1.106
900	−10.177	− 4.628	1.165	7.966	− 5.167	− 4.425	− 3.047	3.199	− 4.364	0.874	− 7.418	− 1.928	4.020	1.152
1000	−10.837	− 4.809	1.460	8.784	− 5.400	− 4.582	− 3.236	3.508	− 4.805	0.878	− 7.966	− 2.003	4.406	1.183
1100	−11.381	− 4.934	1.752	9.527	− 5.572	− 4.684	− 3.391	3.787	− 5.200	0.876	− 8.433	− 2.052	4.753	1.205
1200	−11.842	− 5.022	2.034	10.207	− 5.702	− 4.752	− 3.522	4.041	− 5.558	0.871	− 8.841	− 2.086	5.076	1.221
1300	−12.240	− 5.083	2.303	10.833	− 5.803	− 4.798	− 3.635	4.272	− 5.886	0.862	− 9.203	− 2.109	5.373	1.232
1400	−12.585	− 5.122	2.562	11.412	− 5.878	− 4.825	− 3.733	4.484	− 6.187	0.852	− 9.525	− 2.124	5.650	1.239
1500	−12.891	− 5.149	2.809	11.948	− 5.939	− 4.841	− 3.820	4.678	− 6.467	0.839	− 9.817	− 2.135	5.906	1.240
2000	−14.069	− 5.210	3.869	14.166	− 6.120	− 4.861	− 4.172	5.468	− 7.645	0.758	−10.992	− 2.173	6.948	1.206

* M. Souders, C. S. Matthews, and C. O. Hurd, Ind. Eng. Chem., 41:1048 (1949).

TABLE 5-20. INTERNAL-ROTATIONAL CONTRIBUTIONS TO ENTROPY OF FORMATION (INTEGRAL IV)*

Values in cal/(g mole)(°K)

Temp.	I —CH₂—CH₂—	II CH₃—CH₂—	III R—CH—	IV R—C—	V(a) R—CH=	V(b) R—CH=	VI =CH—CH=	VII ≡C—C≡	VIII R—C≡	$4R \ln$ $(T/298.16)$
300	0.020	0.013	0.013	0.012	0.013	0.008	0.018	0.006	0.013	0.049
400	0.885	0.631	0.635	0.614	0.572	0.355	0.936	0.252	0.631	2.335
500	1.459	1.107	1.118	1.107	0.960	0.606	1.635	0.402	1.085	4.108
600	1.869	1.475	1.519	1.509	1.247	0.804	2.148	0.499	1.425	5.557
700	2.179	1.765	1.815	1.837	1.470	0.967	2.542	0.566	1.691	6.781
800	2.422	1.999	2.052	2.108	1.650	1.106	2.854	0.614	1.904	7.842
900	2.617	2.192	2.248	2.333	1.802	1.228	3.110	0.653	2.080	8.778
1000	2.781	2.355	2.415	2.525	1.932	1.335	3.324	0.686	2.229	9.615
1100	2.921	2.495	2.558	2.688	2.046	1.432	3.506	0.713	2.358	10.373
1200	3.042	2.617	2.683	2.830	2.147	1.520	3.665	0.737	2.471	11.064
1300	3.148	2.725	2.793	2.955	2.238	1.600	3.804	0.757	2.572	11.700
1400	3.242	2.822	2.892	3.066	2.321	1.675	3.927	0.774	2.663	12.289
1500	3.327	2.909	2.981	3.161	2.397	1.744	4.037	0.790	2.746	12.837
2000	3.659	3.255	3.331	3.523	2.705	2.031	4.455	0.846	3.076	15.123

* M. Souders, C. S. Matthews, C. O. Hurd, *Ind. Eng. Chem.*, **41**:1048 (1949).

to Eq. (5-11). The final result is

$$\Delta S^0_{f_T} = \Delta S^0_{f_{298}} + \left[\int_{298}^{T} \sum (C^0_{p_{\text{vibrational}}}/T)\ dT - (n/2) \int_{298}^{T} (C^0_{p_{H_2}}/T)\ dT \right.$$
$$\left. - m \int_{298}^{T} (C^0_{p_{\text{carbon}}}/T)\ dT \right]_{\text{III}} + \left[\int_{298}^{T} \sum (C^0_{p_{\text{internal rotation}}}/T)\ dT \right]_{\text{IV}}$$
$$+ 4R \ln (T/298) \quad (5\text{-}21)$$

where the terms have the same meaning as in Eq. (5-11).

Group contributions for integral III are given in Table 5-19 and for integral IV in Table 5-20.

Values of $\Delta F^0_{f_{298}}$ calculated by this method are compared with some experimental values in Table 5-24, and the method is compared with others in Sec. 5-21. In general, $\Delta F_f{}^0$ values for hydrocarbons are estimated within 0.5 kcal.

Example 5-12. Estimate the standard entropy and free energy of formation of trans-2-butene at 800°K, using the method of Souders, Matthews, and Hurd. Experimental values are $\Delta S^0_{f_{800}} = -70.4$ cal/(g mole)(°K), $\Delta F^0_{f_{800}} = 48.44$ kcal/g mole (2).

Solution. At 298°K, from Table 5-18, with $\sigma = 2$, $\eta = 1$,

$$
\begin{array}{llr}
2 & CH_3- & (2)(-19.66) = -39.32 \\
2 & HC{=}(\text{trans}) & (2)(-9.28) = -18.56 \\
& & -R \ln \sigma = -\ 1.38 \\
& & \Delta S^0_{f_{298}} = \overline{-59.26} \text{ cal/(g mole)(°K)}
\end{array}
$$

To obtain $\Delta S^0_{f_{800}}$, from Eq. (5-21) and integral III, Table 5-19,

$$
\begin{array}{llr}
2 & CH_3- & (2)(-9.370) = -18.740 \\
2 & HC{=} & (2)(-1.822) = -\ 3.644 \\
& & \overline{-22.384}
\end{array}
$$

From integral IV, Table 5-20, with two type V(b) bonds,

$$
\begin{array}{lll}
2 & R{-}CH{=} & (2)(1.106) = 2.212
\end{array}
$$
$$4R \ln (T/298) \text{ at } 800°K \text{ from Table 5-20} = 7.842$$

Thus

$$\Delta S^0_{f_{800}} = -59.26 - 22.38 + 2.21 + 7.84 = -71.59 \text{ cal/(g mole)(°K)}$$

From Example 5-9,

$$\Delta H^0_{f_{800}} = -8.50 \text{ kcal/g mole (calc.)}$$

Thus

$$\Delta F_f{}^0 = \Delta H_f{}^0 - T\ \Delta S_f{}^0 = -8.50 - (800)(-71.59)/1,000 = 48.77 \text{ kcal/g mole}$$

TABLE 5-21. ABSOLUTE ENTROPIES AT 298°K*

Element	Standard state	Entropy, cal/(g mole)(°K)
Carbon.............	Graphite	1.361
Bromine...........	Ideal gas, 1 atm	58.639
Chlorine...........	Ideal gas, 1 atm	53.286
Fluorine...........	Ideal gas, 1 atm	48.600
Hydrogen..........	Ideal gas, 1 atm	31.211
Iodine.............	Crystal	27.900
	Ideal gas, 1 atm	62.280
Nitrogen...........	Ideal gas, 1 atm	45.767
Oxygen............	Ideal gas, 1 atm	49.003
Phosphorus........	(As P_2) Ideal gas, 1 atm	52.130
Sulfur.............	Rhombic, crystal	7.620
	(As S) Ideal gas, 1 atm	40.085
	(As S_2) Ideal gas, 1 atm	54.410

* O. A. Hougen, K. M. Watson, and R. A. Ragatz, "Chemical Process Principles," 2d ed., pt. II, Thermodynamics, John Wiley & Sons, Inc., New York, 1959.

5-19 Absolute Entropies, Entropies and Free Energies of Formation from the Method of Anderson, Beyer, and Watson

Anderson, Beyer, and Watson (4, 42) proposed an additive-group method to calculate the absolute entropy of a compound at 298°K, ideal gas at 1 atm, i.e., unit fugacity. For a hypothetical compound $C_mH_nN_pO_qX_rS_t$, the standard entropy of formation is then calculated as

$$\Delta S^0_{f_{298}} = S^0_{298(\text{compound})} - mS^0_C - (n/2)S^0_{H_2} - (p/2)S^0_{N_2} - (q/2)S^0_{O_2} \\ - (r/2)S^0_X - tS^0_{S(c)} \quad (5\text{-}22)$$

where S_C, $S^0_{H_2}$, etc., are absolute entropies of the elements—carbon as graphite, hydrogen as an ideal gas at 1 atm, etc. For convenience, the absolute-entropy values of the elements in their standard states are tabulated in Table 5-21 (42).

The additive-group method for S^0_{298} is identical to that for ΔH_f^0 described in Sec. 5-13, and group-contribution values are tabulated in Table 5-22. After $\Delta S^0_{f_{298}}$ is determined from S^0_{298}, Tables 5-21 and 5-22, with Eq. (5-22); then $\Delta F^0_{f_{298}}$ may be determined from Eq. (5-19). *No symmetry or optical isomer corrections are required.* Either a calculated or an experimental value of ΔH_f^0 may be used. Example 5-13 illustrates the procedure to be followed, and Table 5-24 compares some experimental values of $\Delta F^0_{f_{298}}$ with calculated values. For hydrocarbons, the difference between calculated and experimental values is usually less than 2 kcal/g mole; for nonhydrocarbons, larger discrepancies appear, but these are usually

TABLE 5-22. S°_{298} GROUP CONTRIBUTIONS*

Group	cal/(g mole)(°K)
Base-group Contributions	
Methane..	44.5
Cyclopentane..	70.7
Benzene...	64.4
Naphthalene...	80.7
Methylamine...	57.7
Dimethylamine..	65.2
Dimethyl ether..	63.7
Contributions of Primary CH₃ Substitution Groups	
1. Methane...	10.4
2. Cyclopentane:	
a. First-substitution outside ring.........................	11.5
b. Enlargement of ring...............................	0.7
3. Benzene and naphthalene:	
a. First-substitution outside ring.........................	12.0
b. Second substitution:	
Ortho...	8.1
Meta..	9.2
Para..	7.8
c. Third substitution (sym)............................	8.0

Secondary Methyl Substitutions

A	B	
1	1	9.8
1	2	9.2
1	3	9.5
1	4	11.0
1	5	10.0
2	1	5.8
2	2	7.0
2	3	6.3
2	4	6.0
2	5	2.7
3	1	2.7
3	2	4.8
3	3	5.8
3	4	1.7
3	5	1.3
1	—O— in ester or ether	14.4
Substitution of H of OH group to form ester.................		16.7

* J. W. Anderson, G. H. Beyer, and K. M. Watson, *Natl. Petrol. News, Tech. Sec.*, **36**:R476 (July 5, 1944).

TABLE 5-22. S_{298}° GROUP CONTRIBUTIONS* *(Continued)*

Multiple-bond Contributions

A	Type of bond	B	
1	=	1	− 2.1
1	=	2	0.8
1	=	3	2.2
2	=	2	− 0.9
2	=(cis)	2	− 0.6
2	=(trans)	2	− 1.2
2	=	3	1.6
Correction for each pair of conjugated double bonds			−10.4
1	≡	1	− 6.8
1	≡	2	− 7.8
2	≡	2	− 6.3
Correction for double bond adjacent to aromatic ring			− 4.3

Substitution of CH_3 by Nonhydrocarbon Groups

—OH (aliphatic, meta, para).	2.6
—NO₂.	2.0
—CN.	13.1
—Cl.	0†
—Br.	3.0†
—F.	− 1.0†
—I.	5.0†
=O (aldehyde).	−12.3
=O (ketone).	− 2.4
—COOH.	15.4
—SH.	5.2
—C₆H₅.	21.7
—NH₂.	− 4.8

† Add 1.0 to the calculated entropy contributions of halides for methyl derivatives, e.g., methyl chloride = 44.4 (base) + 10.4 (primary CH_3) − 0.0 (Cl substitution) + 1.0.

less than 5 kcal/g mole. The method is compared with others in Sec. 5-21.

Example 5-13. Estimate the standard free energy of formation of phenol as an ideal gas at 298°K and at 1 atm, using the method of Anderson, Beyer, and Watson.

Solution. The entropy of phenol at 298°K and unit fugacity may be calculated from the group contributions given in Table 5-22.

$$\Delta S_{298}^{0},$$
$$cal/(g\ mole)(°K)$$

Base group—benzene.	64.4
Primary methyl substitution.	12.0
Substitution of —OH for —CH₃.	2.6
	79.0

The entropy values for the elements are obtained from Table 5-21.

$$C(graphite) \dots\dots\dots\dots\dots\dots\dots 1.36$$
$$H_2(g) \dots\dots\dots\dots\dots\dots\dots\dots 31.21$$
$$O_2(g) \dots\dots\dots\dots\dots\dots\dots\dots 49.00$$

Therefore the entropy of formation $\Delta S_f{}^0$ may be calculated as

$$\Delta S_f{}^0 = S^0 - \Sigma S^0_{elements}$$
$$= 79.0 - (6)(1.36) - (3)(31.21) - (0.5)(49.00)$$
$$= -47.2 \ cal/(g \ mole)(°K)$$

The value of $\Delta H_f{}^0$ as calculated by Anderson, Beyer, and Watson's method (Sec. 5-13, Table 5-14) $= 19.1$ kcal/g mole.

$$\Delta F_f{}^0 = \Delta H_f{}^0 - T \ \Delta S_f{}^0$$
$$\Delta F_f{}^0 = -19.1 - (298)(-47.2)/1,000 = 19.1 + 14.1$$
$$= -5.0 \ kcal/g \ mole$$

The experimental value of $\Delta F_f{}^0$ is -6.26 kcal/g mole.

5-20 Free Energies of Formation from the Method of van Krevelen

Van Krevelen (100, 101) suggested that $\Delta F_f{}^0$ might be correlated as a linear function of temperature and that the constants were additive functions of the atomic groups comprising the molecule.

$$\Delta F_f{}^0 = A + BT \tag{5-23}$$

Group contributions for A and B are given in Table 5-23; two broad temperature bands are specified in the table as a single linear equation which is not applicable over the entire temperature range of 300 to 1500°K. In light of Eq. (5-19), the constant A in Eq. (5-23) can be interpreted as $\Delta H_f{}^0$ and B as $-\Delta S_f{}^0$, but it is not recommended that Eq. (5-23) be used as an estimation method for either $\Delta H_f{}^0$ or $\Delta S_f{}^0$ individually.

A comparison between calculated and experimental values of $\Delta F^0_{f_{298}}$ is given in Table 5-24. As discussed in Sec. 5-18, symmetry and optical isomer corrections, $R \ln \sigma$ and $-R \ln \eta$, must be added to the calculated value of B. Example 5-14 illustrates the use of the method. Several of van Krevelen's contributions were based on experimental values of $\Delta F_f{}^0$ different from those used in other estimations, e.g., ethyl mercaptan, acetone, and chloroform. Ordinarily those used by van Krevelen are from more recent work and should perhaps be preferred to the older values. For the sake of comparison, Table 5-24 lists both values of $\Delta F_f{}^0$ and illustrates the agreement between different methods which are based on different experimental values.

In general, van Krevelen's values differ by 5 kcal/g mole from experimental values, although in many cases the discrepancy is less and in a few much greater. The method is compared with others in Sec. 5-21.

Example 5-14. Calculate the standard free energy of formation of acetaldehyde at 298°K in the ideal-gas state at 1 atm.

Solution. From Table 5-23 with $\sigma = 1$, $\eta = 1$,

	A	B
—CH₃	−10.94	2.215
—CHO	−29.28	0.77
$R \ln \sigma$	....	0
	−40.22	2.99

$$\therefore \Delta F_f{}^0 = -40.22 + 2.99 \times 10^{-2}T = -31.31 \text{ kcal/g mole} \quad \text{at } 298°K$$

The experimental value is -31.96 kcal/g mole (53).

5-21 Recommendations to Estimate Free Energies of Formation

Many other free-energy-of-formation estimation techniques were evaluated but rejected as being too limited in scope or less accurate than the three methods presented for $\Delta F_f{}^0$ (12, 13, 24, 25). Many tabulations of experimental values of $\Delta S_f{}^0$ and $\Delta F_f{}^0$ (usually at 298°K) should be chosen as preferable to any estimation technique; see, for example, Refs. 2, 34, 42, 70, and 74. However, based on a test of the methods, a few results of which are shown in Table 5-24, it may be recommended that:

1. For hydrocarbons, the method of Souders, Matthews, and Hurd (Sec. 5-18) is to be preferred. In almost all tests, estimated values of $\Delta F_{f_{298}}^0$ differed not more than 0.5 kcal/g mole from experimental results. Values at temperatures other than 298°K may be obtained with Eqs. (5-11), (5-19), and (5-21), although interpolation is required for temperatures other than shown in Tables 5-13a, 5-13b, 5-19, and 5-20.

2. For nonhydrocarbons, both the methods of van Krevelen (Sec. 5-20) and Anderson, Beyer, and Watson (Sec. 5-19) are satisfactory. Differences between calculated and experimental values vary widely but are usually less than a few kilocalories per gram mole. (See below for a discussion of the effect of such errors on the equilibrium constant.) The method of Anderson, Beyer, and Watson does not determine $\Delta F_f{}^0$ directly; rather, $S_f{}^0$ and an auxiliary value $\Delta H_f{}^0$ and entropies of formation of the elements are also necessary. However, no symmetry or optical isomer correction is necessary, as required for van Krevelen's method.

Van Krevelen's method yields directly an equation relating $\Delta F_f{}^0$ to temperature, whereas the Anderson, Beyer, and Watson method is applicable only at 298°K. To use the latter method at other temperatures, an integration of Eq. (5-20) is required. The technique is similar

TABLE 5-23. TABULATION OF GROUP CONTRIBUTIONS FOR ΔF_f^0*

Group	300–600°K		600–1500°K	
	A	$B \times 10^2$	A	$B \times 10^2$
Alkane groups:				
CH_4	−18.948	2.225	−21.250	2.596
—CH_3	−10.943	2.215	−12.310	2.436
—CH_2—	− 5.193	2.430	− 5.830	2.544
—$\overset{\vert}{\underset{\vert}{C}}H$	− 0.705	2.910	− 0.705	2.910
—$\overset{\vert}{\underset{\vert}{C}}$—	+ 1.958	3.735	+4.385	3.350
Alkene groups:				
$H_2C{=}CH_2$	+11.552	1.545	9.450	1.888
$H_2C{=}C\overset{H}{\diagdown}$	13.737	1.655	12.465	1.762
$H_2C{=}C\diagdown$	16.467	1.915	16.255	1.966
$\overset{H}{\diagup}C{=}C\overset{H}{\diagup}$	17.663	1.965	16.180	2.116
$\overset{H}{\diagup}C{=}C\underset{H}{\diagup}$	17.187	1.915	15.815	2.062
$\overset{H}{\diagup}C{=}C\diagup$	20.217	2.295	19.584	2.354
$\diagdown C{=}C\diagdown$	25.135	2.573	25.135	2.573
$H_2C{=}C{=}CH_2$	45.250	1.027	43.634	1.311
$H_2C{=}C{=}C\overset{H}{\diagdown}$	49.377	1.035	48.170	1.208
$H_2C{=}C{=}C\diagup$	51.084	1.474	51.084	1.474
$\overset{H}{\diagup}C{=}C{=}C\overset{H}{\diagdown}$	52.460	1.483	52.460	1.483
Conjugated alkene groups:				
$H_2C{\leftrightarrow}$	5.437	0.675	4.500	0.832
$\overset{H}{\diagup}C{\leftrightarrow}$	7.407	1.035	6.980	1.088
$\diagdown\!\diagup C{\leftrightarrow}$	9.152	1.505	10.370	1.308
Alkyne groups:				
$HC{\equiv}$	27.048	−0.765	26.700	−0.704
—$C{\equiv}$	26.938	−0.525	26.555	−0.550

TABLE 5-23. TABULATION OF GROUP CONTRIBUTIONS FOR $\Delta F_f{}^0{}^*$ *(Continued)*

Group	300–600°K		600–1500°K	
	A	$B \times 10^2$	A	$B \times 10^2$
Aromatic groups:				
HC⟨	3.047	0.615	2.505	0.706
—C⟨	4.675	1.150	5.010	0.988
↔C⟨	3.513	0.568	3.998	0.485
Ring formation:				
3 ring	23.458	−3.045	22.915	−2.966
4 ring	10.73	−2.65	10.60	−2.50
5 ring	4.275	−2.350	2.665	−2.182
6 ring	− 1.128	−1.635	− 1.930	−1.504
Pentene ring	− 3.657	−2.395	− 3.915	−2.250
Hexene ring	− 9.102	−2.045	− 8.810	−2.071
Branching in paraffin chains:				
Side chain with 2 or more C atoms	1.31	0	1.31	0
Three adjacent—CH groups	2.12	0	2.12	0
Adjacent —CH—C— groups	1.80	0	1.80	0
Two adjacent —C— groups	2.58	0	2.58	0
Branching in cycloparaffins:				
Branching in 5-membered ring:				
Single branching	− 1.04	0	− 1.69	0
Double branching:				
1,1 position	− 1.85	0	− 1.190	−0.160
cis 1,2 position	− 0.38	0	− 0.38	0
trans 1,2 position	− 2.55	0	− 0.945	−0.266
cis 1,3 position	− 1.20	0	− 0.370	−0.166
trans 1,3 position	− 2.35	0	− 0.800	−0.264
Branching in 6-membered ring:				
Single branching:	− 0.93	0	0.230	−0.192
Double branching				
1,1 position	0.835	−0.367	1.745	−0.556
cis 1,2 position	− 0.19	0	1.470	−0.276
trans 1,2 position	− 2.41	0	0.045	−0.398
cis 1,3 position	− 2.70	0	− 1.647	−0.185
trans 1,3 position	− 1.60	0	0.260	−0.290
cis 1,4 position	− 1.11	0	− 1.11	0
trans 1,4 position	− 2.80	0	− 0.995	−0.245
Branching in aromatics:				
Double branching:				
1,2 position	1.02	0	1.02	0
1,3 position	− 0.31	0	− 0.31	0
1,4 position	0.93	0	0.93	0
Triple branching:				
1,2,3 position	1.91	0	2.10	0
1,2,4 position	1.10	0	1.10	0
1,3,5 position	0	0	0	0

TABLE 5-23. TABULATION OF GROUP CONTRIBUTIONS FOR ΔF_f^{0*} *(Continued)*

Group	300–600°K		600–1500°K	
	A	$B \times 10^2$	A	$B \times 10^2$
Oxygen-containing groups:				
H_2O	−58.076	1.154	−59.138	1.316
—OH	−41.56	1.28	−41.56	1.28
—O—	−15.79	−0.85		
O (↗ ↖)	−18.37	0.80	−16.07	0.40
H_2CO	−29.118	0.653	−30.327	0.854
—C=O (H)	−29.28	0.77	−30.15	0.83
C=O	−28.08	0.91	−28.08	0.91
HC—OH (O)	−87.660	2.473	−90.569	2.958
—C—OH (O)	−98.39	2.86	−98.83	2.93
—C—OH (O)	−92.62	2.61	−92.62	2.61
H_2C=C=O	−14.515	0.295	−14.515	0.295
HC=C=O	−12.86	0.46	−12.86	0.46
C=C=O	− 9.62	0.72	− 9.38	0.73
Nitrogen-containing groups:				
HCN	31.179	−0.826	30.874	−0.775
—C≡N	30.75	−0.72	30.75	−0.72
—N=C	46.32	−0.89	46.32	−0.89
NH_3	−11.606	2.556	−12.972	2.784
—NH_2	2.82	2.71	− 6.78	3.98
NH	12.93	3.16	12.93	3.16
N—	19.46	3.82	19.46	3.82
N (↗ ↖)	11.32	1.11	12.26	0.96
—NO_2	− 9.0	3.70	−14.19	4.38
Sulfur-containing groups:				
H_2S	−20.552	1.026	−21.366	1.167
—SH	−10.68	1.07	−10.68	1.07
—S—	− 3.32	1.42	− 3.32	1.44
S (↗ ↖)	− 0.97	0.51	− 0.65	0.44
SO	−30.19	3.39	−30.19	3.39

TABLE 5-23. TABULATION OF GROUP CONTRIBUTIONS FOR ΔF_f^0* (*Continued*)

Group	300–600°K		600–1500°K	
	A	$B \times 10^2$	A	$B \times 10^2$
Sulfur-containing groups: (*cont.*)				
$\diagdown$SO$_2$ $\diagup$	-82.58	5.58	-80.69	5.26
Halogen-containing groups:				
HF............................	-64.476	-0.145	-64.884	-0.081
—F............................	-45.10	-0.20		
HCl...........................	-22.100	-0.215	-22.460	-0.156
—Cl...........................	-8.25	0	-8.25	0
HBr..........................	-12.553	-0.234	-13.010	-0.158
—Br..........................	-1.62	-0.26	-1.62	-0.26
HI............................	-1.330	-0.225	-1.718	-0.176
—I............................	$+7.80$	0	$+7.80$	0
Ring formation: (three-membered ring with O)	12.86	-0.63	12.86	-0.63
(five-membered ring with O)	-5.82	0.25	-3.53	-0.16

* From D. W. van Krevelen and H. A. G. Chermin, *Chem. Eng. Sci.*, **1**(2):66 (1951); **1**(5):238 (1952).

to that illustrated for ΔH_f^0 in Eqs. (5-16) and (5-10), i.e.,

$$\Delta S_f^0 = \Delta S_{f_{298}}^0 + \int_{298}^{T} (C_p^0/T)_{\text{compound}}\, dT - \sum \int_{298}^{T} (C_p^0/T)_{\text{elements}}\, dT \quad (5\text{-}24)$$

where C_p^0 values may be obtained from the methods discussed in Sec. 5-8 and Table 5-16. The same problems of changing element standard states as discussed in Sec. 5-15 are encountered.

Importance of Errors. It must be recognized that the equilibrium constant K_f is very sensitive to errors in ΔF_f^0. Thus an error of 1.00 kcal/g mole in ΔF_f^0 causes the true K_f to be multiplied by $e^{500/T}$. The resulting error in K_f is much less at high than at low temperatures: the factor $e^{500/T}$ is 7.4 at 298°, 1.95 at 1000°, and 1.394 at 1500°K. It is evident from the size of the errors in ΔF_f^0 indicated by Table 5-24 that values of K_f estimated by any of the several methods may frequently differ substantially from the true values. The error involved in predicting the conversion of a chemical reactant depends not only on the error

TABLE 5-24. COMPARISON BETWEEN CALCULATED AND EXPERIMENTAL
FREE ENERGIES OF FORMATION
Values in kcal/g mole for the ideal gas state at 1 atm and 298°K

Compound	Experimental		Anderson, Beyer, and Watson		Van Krevelen		Souders, Matthews, and Hurd	
	ΔF_f^0	Ref.	ΔF_f^0	Diff.*	ΔF_f^0	Diff.	ΔF_f^0	Diff.
Propane	− 5.61	2	− 5.44	− 0.17	− 6.18	+ 0.57	− 5.96	+0.35
n-Heptane	1.94	2	1.64	− 0.30	1.87	− 0.07	2.10	+0.16
3-Methylhexane	1.10	2	0.70	− 0.40	1.08	− 0.02	1.07	−0.03
2,4-Dimethylpentane	0.72	2	− 0.25	− 0.97	1.06	+ 0.34	0.51	−0.21
2,2,3-Trimethylbutane	1.02	2	− 0.92	− 1.94	1.56	+ 0.54	1.44	+0.42
Cyclopentane	9.23	2	6.09	− 3.14	8.86	− 0.37	9.31	+0.08
Cyclohexane	7.59	2	6.29	− 1.30	7.16	− 0.43	7.93	+0.34
Methylcyclopentane	8.55	2	7.18	− 1.37	8.05	− 0.50	7.90	−0.65
Ethylene	16.28	2	16.39	+ 0.11	16.97	+ 0.69	15.4	−0.88
1-Butene	17.09	2	16.79	− 0.30	16.37	− 0.72	16.97	−0.12
2-Butene (cis)	15.74	2	15.60	− 0.14	15.24	− 0.50	15.31	−0.43
2-Butene (trans)	15.05	2	14.88	− 0.17	15.09	+ 0.04	14.96	−0.09
1,3-Butadiene	36.01	2	36.54	+ 0.53	36.30	+ 0.29	35.33	−0.68
Acetylene	50.00	2	50.08	+ 0.08	52.23	+ 2.23	49.94	−0.06
Methylacetylene	46.31	2	47.37	+ 1.06	48.50	+ 2.19	46.42	+0.11
Benzene	31.05	2, 62	29.26	− 1.79	30.73	− 0.32	31.16	+0.11
Ethylbenzene	31.10	2, 62	32.33	+ 1.23	30.62	− 0.48	31.28	+0.18
o-Xylene	29.18	2	31.89	+ 2.71	28.47	− 0.71	28.68	−0.50
m-Xylene	28.41	2	31.37	+ 2.96	27.14	− 1.27	28.44	+0.03
Ethyl mercaptan	1 ± 4	70	1.37	+ 0.4				
	− 9.5	6			− 9.7	+ 0.2		
Diethylsulfide	6.8 ± 8	70			− 3.3	−10.1		
Thiophene	20.6	100, 5			20.5	− 0.1		
		104						
Aniline	39.4	102	46.39	+ 7.0	43.9	+ 4.5		
Ethylamine	10.01	74			9.28	− 0.73		
Pyridine	39.6	49, 100			39.6	0.0		
		101						
Dimethylether	− 26.2	70, 74	− 28.9	+ 2.7	−25.9	− 0.3		
Acetaldehyde	− 31.96	53	−34.7	+ 2.74	−31.31	− 0.55		
Acetone	− 36.45	74	−37.16	+ 0.71				
	− 33.4	33, 82, 100			−33.5	+ 0.1		
Acetic acid	− 93.7	100, 110	−94.02	+ 0.37	−94.1	+ 0.4		
Acetic anhydride	−101.7	70						
	−119.3	74						
Methyl formate	− 71.4	74	−84.21	+12.8	−89.17	+17.8		
Ethyl acetate	− 76.9	103	−81.37	+ 4.5	−91.4	+14.5		
Methanol	− 38.7	53	−43.21	+ 4.5				
n-Propyl alcohol	− 39.9	100	−39.55	− 0.3	−38.0	− 1.9		
Isopropyl alcohol	− 38.2	74	−39.9	+ 1.7	−38.3	+ 0.1		
Phenol	− 6.26	74	− 5.0	− 1.26	− 5.2	− 1.06		

TABLE 5-24. COMPARISON BETWEEN CALCULATED AND EXPERIMENTAL
FREE ENERGIES OF FORMATION (*Continued*)

Compound	Experimental		Calculated method of					
			Anderson, Beyer, and Watson		Von Krevelen		Souders, Matthews, and Hurd	
	ΔF_f^0	Ref.	ΔF_f^0	Diff.*	ΔF_f^0	Diff.	ΔF_f^0	Diff.
Phosgene..................	− 50.3	105	−45.8	− 4.5	−41.9	− 8.4		
Methyl chloride............	− 13.96	52	−14.45	+ 0.49	−11.9	− 2.1		
Methylene chloride.........	− 25.16	52	−14.08	−11.1	−15.34	− 9.8		
Chloroform................	− 13.66	52	−14.6	+ 0.9				
	− 15.1	93, 100			−16.1	+ 1.0		
Carbon tetrachloride........	− 15.35	52	−15.73	+ 0.38	−22.3	+ 8.9		
Ethyl bromide.............	− 5.90	70	− 1.96	− 3.94	− 4.67	− 1.23		
Dichlorodifluoromethane.....	− 94.3	84, 100	−95.5	+ 1.2	−95.2	+ 0.9		
Fluorobenzene.............	− 12.7	100	− 8.5	− 4.2	−11.7	− 1.0		
Chlorobenzene.............	23.8	100	26.9	+ 3.1	24.7	+ 0.9		
Average difference........	....	...	....	2.2	....	2.3	....	0.03

* Difference = |calculated ΔF_f^0| − |experimental ΔF_f^0| (except when calculated and experimental values have opposite signs).

in the estimated value of ΔF^0 but on the relation of K to the stoichiometry of the reaction and on the level of conversion of interest.

The estimation of the temperature corresponding to a specified value of K_f will have a fractional error equal to the fractional error in ΔF_f^0. Thus an error of 1.00 kcal/g mole introduces an error of uncertainty of ± 61 for propane at 500°K, and an error of only ± 9.6 for cyclohexane at 1000°K. Perhaps the greatest practical value of estimates of ΔF^0 is in providing a basis for useful predictions of the temperature necessary to attain a specified equilibrium conversion for a reaction of interest.

NOMENCLATURE FOR CHAPTER 5

a = constant in Eq. (5-7)
a' = intercept parameter in Eq. (5-14)
A = constant in Eq. (5-6)
b = constant in Eq. (5-7)
b' = slope parameter in Eq. (5-14)
B = constant in Eq. (5-6)
c = constant in Eq. (5-7), velocity of light
C = constant in Eq. (5-6)
C_p^0 = heat capacity at zero pressure, usually cal/(g mole)(°K)
C_ν, C_δ = heat-capacity contribution due to in-line and bending vibrations
d = constant in Eq. (5-7)
ΔF_f^0 = standard free energy of formation, usually kcal/g mole

h = Planck's constant

H^0 = enthalpy at zero pressure; $H_0{}^0$, enthalpy at both zero pressure and zero temperature, usually cal/g mole

ΔH_c = heat of combustion, usually kcal/g mole

$\Delta H_f{}^0$ = standard heat of formation, $\Delta H_{0_f}^0$ at absolute zero, usually kcal/g mole

ΔH_s = heat of sublimation, usually cal/g mole

k = Boltzmann's constant

K, K_f = equilibrium constant

m = number of carbon atoms in molecule; number of freely rotating C—C or C—O bonds

n = number of hydrogen atoms in molecule; number of atoms in a molecule

N_{CC} = number of carbon-carbon bonds in molecule

N_{CH} = number of carbon-hydrogen bonds in the molecule

p = number of nitrogen atoms in molecule

P = pressure; P_s, standard-state pressure

q = number of oxygen atoms in molecule

q_i = bond of the ith type

r = number of halogen atoms in molecule

R = gas constant

S^0 = absolute entropy at unit fugacity, usually cal/(g mole)(°K)

$\Delta S_f{}^0$ = standard entropy of formation, usually cal/(g mole)(°K)

t = number of atoms of sulfur in molecule

T = absolute temperature, usually °K

x = oxygen-balance parameter in Eq. (5-13)

X = $h\nu/kT$; pairs of carbon atoms [Eq. (5-8)]; halogen atom

Y = number of trigonal interactions [Eq. (5-8)]

Z = fifth-neighbor hydrogen interactions [Eq. (5-8)]

Greek

α_{CCC} = parameter in Eq. (5-8)

β_{CCC} = parameter in Eq. (5-8)

γ_{H_5H} = parameter in Eq. (5-8)

δ = designation for a bending or deformation vibration

η = number of optical isomers

λ = wavelength

ν = frequency; designation for stretching or in-line vibrations

σ = symmetry number

ω = wave number

REFERENCES FOR CHAPTER 5

1. Allen, T. L.: *J. Chem. Phys.*, **31**:1039 (1959).
2. American Petroleum Institute: "Selected Values of Physical and Thermodynamic Properties of Hydrocarbons and Related Compounds," Project 44, Carnegie Press, Pittsburgh, Pa., 1953, and supplements.
3. Anderson, H. W.: M.S. thesis, UCRL-8152, University of California, Berkeley, Calif., January, 1958.
4. Anderson, J. W., G. H. Beyer, and K. M. Watson: *Natl. Petrol. News, Tech. Sec.*, **36**:R476 (July 5, 1944).
5. Aston, J. G., M. L. Edinoff, and W. S. Forster: *J. Am. Chem. Soc.*, **61**:1539 (1939).
6. Barrow, K. M., and K. S. Pitzer: *Ind. Eng. Chem.*, **41**:2737 (1949).

254   THE PROPERTIES OF GASES AND LIQUIDS

7. Belenyessy, L. I., B. J. Gudzinowicz, R. C. Reid, and J. O. Smith: *J. Chem. Eng. Data*, **1**:66 (1962).
8. Bennewitz, K., and W. Rossner: *Z. physik. Chem.*, **39B**:126 (1938).
9. Benson, S. W., and J. H. Buss: *J. Chem. Phys.*, **29**:546 (1958).
10. Bernstein, H. J.: *Trans. Faraday Soc.*, **58**:2285 (1962).
11. Bichowsky, F. R., and F. D. Rossini: "Thermochemistry of Chemical Substances," Reinhold Publishing Corporation, New York, 1936.
12. Bremner, J. G. M., and G. D. Thomas: *Trans. Faraday Soc.*, **44**:230 (1948).
13. Bruins, P. F., and J. D. Czarnecki: *Ind. Eng. Chem.*, **33**:201 (1941).
14. Clack, B. W.: *Proc. Phys. Soc. (London)*, **36**:313 (1924).
15. Coleman, C. F., and T. De Vries: *J. Am. Chem. Soc.*, **71**:2839 (1949).
16. Collins, B. T., C. F. Coleman, and T. De Vries: *J. Am. Chem. Soc.*, **71**:2929 (1949).
17. Cottrell, T. L.: *J. Chem. Soc.*, **1948**:1448.
18. Crawford, B. L., and R. G. Parr: *J. Chem. Phys.*, **16**:233 (1948).
19. Denbigh, K.: "The Principles of Chemical Equilibrium," Cambridge University Press, New York, 1957.
20. Dobratz, C. J.: *Ind. Eng. Chem.*, **33**:759 (1941).
21. Drowart, J., R. P. Burns, G. De Maria, and M. G. Inghram: *J. Chem. Phys.*, **31**:1131 (1959).
22. Earl, J. C.: *Tetrahedron*, **9**:65 (1960).
23. Evans, W. H., and D. D. Wagman: *J. Research Natl. Bur. Standards*, **49**:141 (1952).
24. Fal'kovskii, V. B.: *Zhur. Obshchei Khim.*, **18**:1639 (1948): *Chem. Abstr.*, **43**:3276.
25. Franklin, J. L.: *Ind. Eng. Chem.*, **41**:1070 (1949).
26. Franklin, J. L.: *J. Chem. Phys.*, **21**:2029 (1953).
27. Fugassi, P., and C. E. Rudy: *Ind. Eng. Chem.*, **30**:1029 (1938).
28. Gambill, W. R.: *Chem. Eng.*, **64**(9):267 (1957).
29. Gaydon, A. G.: "Dissociation Energies and Spectra of Diatomic Molecules," Chapman & Hall, Ltd., London, 1947.
30. Genaux, C. T., and W. D. Walters: *J. Am. Chem. Soc.*, **73**:4497 (1951).
31. Glasstone, S.: "Theoretical Chemistry," D. Van Nostrand Company, Inc., Princeton, N.J., 1944.
32. Glocker, G., and W. F. Edgell: *Ind. Eng. Chem.*, **34**:532 (1942).
33. Gootnev, I. N., A. Payokhina, and A. Sverdlin: *J. Phys. Chem. (U.S.S.R.)*, **14**:374 (1940).
34. Green, J. H. S.: *Quart. Rev.*, **15**:125 (1961).
35. Günthard, H. H., and E. Kováts: *Helv. Chim. Acta.*, **35**:1190 (1952).
36. Gupta, V. S.: *J. Chem. Phys.*, **25**:373 (1956).
37. Halford, J. O.: *J. Chem. Phys.*, **18**:1051 (1950).
38. Handrick, G. R.: *Ind. Eng. Chem.*, **48**:1366 (1956).
39. Haupt, R. F., and E. Teller: *J. Chem. Phys.*, **7**:925 (1939).
40. Herzberg, G.: "Infrared and Raman Spectra of Polyatomic Molecules," D. Van Nostrand Company, Inc., Princeton, N.J., 1945.
41. Hougen, O. A., and K. M. Watson: "Chemical Process Principles," John Wiley & Sons, Inc., New York, 1947.
42. Hougen, O. A., K. M. Watson, and R. A. Ragatz: "Chemical Process Principles," 2d ed., pt. II, Thermodynamics, John Wiley & Sons, Inc., New York, 1959.
43. Hughes, A. M., R. J. Corruccini, and E. C. Gilbert: *J. Am. Chem. Soc.*, **61**:2639 (1939).
44. Janz, G. J.: "Estimation of Thermodynamic Properties of Organic Compounds," Academic Press, Inc., New York, 1958.

45. Jatkar, S. K. K.: *J. Indian Inst. Sci.*, (II) **22A**:19 (1939).
46. Jatkar, S. K. K.: *J. Indian Inst. Sci.*, (II) **22A**:59 (1939).
47. Jatkar, S. K. K.: *J. Indian Inst. Sci.*, (II) **22A**:93 (1939).
48. Johnson, A. I., and C.-J. Huang: *Can. J. Tech.*, **34**:405 (1957).
49. Kline, C. H., and J. Turkevitch: *J. Chem. Phys.*, **12**:300 (1944).
50. Knowlton, J. W., and E. J. Prosen: *J. Research Natl. Bur. Standards*, **46**:489 (1951); *Chem. Abstr.*, **45**:7864.
51. Kobe, K. A., et al.: *Petrol. Refiner*, 19 parts, January, 1949–December, 1951.
52. Kobe, K. A., and E. G. Long: *Petrol. Refiner*, **29**(3):157 (1950).
53. Kobe, K. A., and R. E. Pennington: *Petrol. Refiner*, **29**(9):135 (1950).
54. Kothari, M. S., and L. K. Doraiswamy: *Hydrocarbon Proc. and Petrol. Refiner*, **43**(3):133 (1964).
55. Laidler, K. J.: *Can. J. Chem.*, **34**:626 (1956).
56. "Landolt-Börnstein Tables," vol. 4, pt. 1., Springer-Verlag OHG, Berlin, 1955.
57. Lane, M. R., J. W. Linnett, and H. G. Oswin: *Proc. Roy. Soc. (London)*, **A216**:361 (1953).
58. Lange, N. A.: "Handbook of Chemistry," 10th ed., McGraw-Hill Book Company, New York, 1961.
59. Lovering, E. G., and K. J. Laidler: *Can. J. Chem.*, **38**:2367 (1960).
60. Madigan, J. R., and F. F. Cleveland: *J. Chem. Phys.*, **19**:119 (1951).
61. Masi, J. F.: *J. Am. Chem. Soc.*, **74**:4738 (1952).
62. Maslov, P. G.: *J. Appl. Chem. (U.S.S.R.)*, **26**(5):501 (1953).
63. Maslov, P. G.: *Zhur. Priklad. Khim.*, **30**:736 (1957).
64. Maslov, P. G.: *J. Appl. Chem. (U.S.S.R.)*, **30**:777 (1957).
65. McCullough, J. P., and W. D. Good: *J. Phys. Chem.*, **65**:1430 (1960).
66. McKelvey, F. E.: *Hydrocarbon Proc. and Petrol. Refiner*, **43**(3):129 (1964).
67. Meghreblian, R. V.: *J. Am. Rocket Soc.*, September, 1951, p. 128.
68. Nutt, C. W.: *Trans. Faraday Soc.*, **53**:1538 (1957).
69. Offtermatt, W. F.: Tables of Bond and Resonance Energies for Estimating Standard Heats of Formation, thesis in aeronautical engineering, AD-24936 California Institute of Technology, Pasadena, Calif., 1953; see also S. S. Penner, "Chemistry Problems in Jet Propulsion," Pergamon Press, New York, 1957.
70. Parks, G. S., and H. M. Huffman: The Free Energies of Some Organic Compounds, *Am. Chem. Soc. ACS Monograph 60*, Reinhold Publishing Corporation, New York, 1932.
71. Patterson, D. J., and G. J. Van Wyler: *J. Heat Transfer*, **85**:281 (1963).
72. Pauling, L.: "The Nature of the Chemical Bond," Cornell University Press, Ithaca, N.Y., 1945.
73. Penner, S. S.: "Chemistry Problems in Jet Propulsion," Pergamon Press, New York, 1957.
74. Perry, J. H. (ed.): "Chemical Engineers' Handbook," 3d ed., McGraw-Hill Book Company, New York, 1950.
75. Pitzer, K. S.: *J. Chem. Phys.*, **8**:711 (1940).
76. Pitzer, K. S., and W. Weltner: *J. Am. Chem. Soc.*, **71**:2842 (1949).
77. Reid, R. C., and T. K. Sherwood, "The Properties of Gases and Liquids," 1st ed., McGraw-Hill Book Company, New York, 1958.
78. Rihani, D. N. and L. K. Doraiswamy: *Ind. Eng. Chem. Fundamentals*, **4**:17 (1965).
79. Rossini, F. D.: *Ind. Eng. Chem.*, **29**:1424 (1937).
80. Saltzman, B. E.: *Ind. Eng. Chem.*, **50**:1593 (1958).
81. Satoh, S.: *J. Sci. Research Inst. (Tokyo)*, **43**:79 (1948).
82. Schuman, S. C., and J. C. Aston: *J. Chem. Phys.*, **6**:485 (1938).

83. Scott, D. W., G. D. Oliver, M. E. Gross, W. N. Hubbard, and H. M. Huffman: *J. Am. Chem. Soc,,* **71**:2293 (1949).
84. Shingu, Haruo, and Takehiki Fujimoto: *J. Chem. Phys.,* **31**:556 (1959).
85. Skinner, H. A.: *J. Chem. Soc.,* **1962,** 4396.
86. Slater, J. C.: "Introduction to Chemical Physics," McGraw-Hill Book Company, New York, 1939.
87. Souders, M., C. S. Matthews, and C. O. Hurd: *Ind. Eng. Chem.,* **41**:1037 (1949).
88. Souders, M., C. S. Matthews, and C. O. Hurd: *Ind. Eng. Chem.,* **41**:1048 (1949).
89. Spencer, H. M.: *J. Am. Chem. Soc.,* **67**:1859 (1945).
90. Spencer, H. M.: *Ind. Eng. Chem.,* **40**:2152 (1948).
91. Spencer, H. M.: *J. Chem. Phys.,* **25**:357 (1956).
92. Spencer, H. M., and G. N. Flannagan: *J. Am. Chem. Soc.,* **64**:2511 (1942).
93. Stevenson, D. P., and J. V. Beach: *J. Chem. Phys.,* **6**:25 (1938).
94. Stull, D. R.: *Ind. Eng. Chem.,* **41**:1968 (1949).
95. Stull, D. R., and F. D. Mayfield: *Ind. Eng. Chem.,* **35**:639 (1943).
96. Swarc, M.: *Chem. Revs.,* **47**:75 (1950).
97. Syrkin, Y. K., and M. E. Dyatkina: "Structure of Molecules and the Chemical Bond," Interscience Publishers, Inc., New York, 1950; translated by M. A. Partridge and D. O. Jordan.
98. Thompson, W.: *Trans. Faraday Soc.,* **37**:344 (1941).
99. Thompson, W., and R. B. Temple: *J. Chem. Soc.,* **1948**:1428.
100. Van Krevelen, D. W., and H. A. G. Chermin: *Chem. Eng. Sci.,* **1**:66 (1951).
101. Van Krevelen, D. W., and H. A. G. Chermin: *Chem. Eng. Sci.,* **1**:238 (1952).
101a. Verma, K. K., and L. K. Doraiswamy: *Ind. Eng. Chem. Fundamentals,* **4**:389 (1965).
102. Vriens, G. N., and A. G. Hill: *Ind. Eng. Chem.,* **44**:2732 (1952).
103. Vvedensky, A. A., P. Ya. Ivannikov, and V. A. Nekrasova: *J. Gen. Chem. U.S.S.R.,* **19**:1094 (1949).
104. Waddington, G., J. W. Knowlton, D. W. Scott, G. A. Oliva, S. S. Todd, W. N. Hubbard, J. C. Smith, and H. A. Huffman: *J. Am. Chem. Soc.,* **71**:797 (1949).
105. Walker, C. A.: Thesis, Yale School of Engineering, 1948.
106. Wenner, R. R.: "Thermochemical Calculations," McGraw-Hill Book Company, New York, 1941.
107. Wilcox, D. E.: M.S. thesis, UCRL-10397, University of California, Berkeley, Calif., August, 1962.
108. Wilcox, D. E., and L. A. Bromley: *Ind. Eng. Chem.,* **55**:32 (1963).
109. Works Laboratory Tables of Physical Properties, Carbide and Carbon Chemicals Corp., South Charleston, W. Va., Feb. 1, 1945.
110. Zeise, H.: *Z. Elektrochem.,* **45**:456 (1939).

CHAPTER 6

THERMODYNAMIC PROPERTIES OF REAL FLUIDS

6-1 Scope

In this chapter equations are derived to express the isothermal variations of enthalpy, entropy, fugacity, internal energy, and heat capacity
with pressure in terms of P-V-T properties. These equations are then
used as a basis of a discussion of various graphical and analytical estimation techniques suggested in the literature. Three levels of estimation
techniques are discussed: a simple, rapid reduced-temperature–reduced-
pressure method; a more complex, three-parameter technique using T_r,
P_r and a third correlating parameter; and, finally, a method based upon
an analytical equation of state. The last method yields equations inconvenient for hand calculation but suitable for machine-computation
programs.

The latter portion of the chapter is devoted to a discussion of recommended methods to estimate liquid-phase heat capacities.

Only pure components are treated; mixtures are considered in Chap. 7.

6-2 Fundamental Thermodynamic Principles

Enthalpy, internal energy, entropy, fugacity, and heat capacity are
very important thermodynamic properties. In analyzing or designing
engineering systems involving momentum and/or heat transfer, the
variation in such properties can often be related to important operating
variables, e.g., the temperature rise of a fluid in a heat exchanger.* It
is important, therefore, to be able to estimate such property variations
as the temperature and pressure as other independent variables of a
system are changed.

A thermodynamic property has the very important distinction that
the *difference* between any two states is independent of the path chosen
to pass from one state to another. For example, if the difference in
enthalpy between states P_1, T_1 and P_2, T_2 is desired, there are an infinite
number of possible calculational paths all of which give the same numerical result. Two of the most obvious are illustrated in Eqs. (6-2) and

---

* Mass-transfer operations involve mixtures, and the thermodynamics of such
systems are treated in Chap. 7.

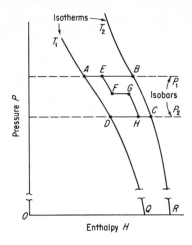

FIG. 6-1. Schematic diagram showing possible isotherms and isobars for changes in enthalpy.

(6-3).   That is,

$$H = f(P,T)$$
$$dH = (\partial H/\partial P)_T\, dP + (\partial H/\partial T)_P\, dT \tag{6-1}$$
$$H_2 - H_1 = \int_{P_1}^{P_2} (\partial H/\partial P)_{T_1}\, dP + \int_{T_1}^{T_2} (\partial H/\partial T)_{P_2}\, dT \tag{6-2}$$
$$H_2 - H_1 = \int_{P_1}^{P_2} (\partial H/\partial P)_{T_2}\, dP + \int_{T_1}^{T_2} (\partial H/\partial T)_{P_1}\, dT \tag{6-3}$$

In the first method, a stepwise process is visualized whereby the temperature is held constant at T_1 and the isothermal variation in H determined from P_1 to P_2; this change is then added to the isobaric variation in H with T from T_1 to T_2 at the pressure level P_2.   The second method is similar; but now the variation in H is first determined at P_1 from T_1 to T_2, and then the variation of H with P from P_1 to P_2 is determined at T_2.   These paths are shown schematically in Fig. 6-1, where Eq. (6-2) is illustrated by path A-D-C, whereas Eq. (6-3) refers to path A-B-C. The net $\Delta H = H_2 - H_1$ represents the change A-C.   Obviously any other convenient path is possible, for example, A-E-F-G-H-C, but to calculate ΔH by this path, values of $(\partial H/\partial P)_T$ and $(\partial H/\partial T)_P$ must be available for the various isotherms and isobars.

The partial derivatives of enthalpy (or other thermodynamic properties) referred to above can be visualized as slopes of the isotherms or isobars in Fig. 6-1.   To obtain numerical values of such derivatives, both a pressure and a temperature must be specified; i.e., values of these derivatives are also functions of two independent intensive variables in the same way that H, E, . . . are functions of two such variables.

In Chap. 5, the quantity $(\partial H/\partial T)_{P^0}$ was considered in some detail. This derivative is, of course, usually called the *constant-pressure* heat capacity $C_p{}^0$, and the superscript zero merely refers to the fact that in this particular instance the pressure level is zero absolute pressure; i.e., the material is an ideal gas. It is only in isolated circumstances that experimental or theoretical heat capacities are available at high pressures (although later in this chapter the estimation of $C_{p\ liq}$ is considered); so the required path to determine $H_2 - H_1$ in Fig. 6-1 with values of C_p^0 is A-Q-R-C, that is,

$$\Delta H = \int_{P_1}^{P_0} (\partial H/\partial P)_{T_1} dP + \int_{T_1}^{T_2} C_p^0 dT + \int_{P_0}^{P_2} (\partial H/\partial P)_{T_2} dP \quad (6\text{-}4)$$

To summarize these few introductory comments, the useful engineering thermodynamic properties are path-independent, and variations in temperature and pressure may be calculated in a stepwise manner. Usually one of the steps will involve the quantity C_p (or C_v), and, of necessity, one of the steps of the calculation involves the ideal-gas state, where C_p^0 values are available or can be estimated. Finally, it should be noted that all derivatives at constant temperature can be expressed conveniently in terms of P-V-T properties only, so that with C_p (or C_p^0) known as a function of temperature, and P-V-T data, it is possible to calculate variations in H, E, S, etc., with temperature and pressure.

6-3 Expression of Isothermal Derivatives in Terms of P-V-T Properties

It was stated in the previous section that isothermal variations in thermodynamic properties could be expressed in terms of P-V-T relations. This statement is proved below for fugacity, enthalpy, internal energy, entropy, and heat capacity. For those readers who are not interested in the derivations, the final results are tabulated in Table 6-1.

All derivations are based on the first and second laws of thermodynamics, which are conveniently expressed for a single-component constant-mass system as

$$dE = T\ dS - P\ dV \quad (6\text{-}5)$$

By defining three other properties,*

$$\begin{aligned} H &= E + PV \\ A &= E - TS \\ F &= H - TS \end{aligned} \quad (6\text{-}6)$$

By taking the total differential of Eqs. (6-6) and combining with Eq.

---

* These definitions are not arbitrary. Equation (6-5) states that $E = f(S,V)$, and if the variables S and V are not convenient, then it is possible to make a transformation of coordinates without loss in information value of the original equation. That is, if P, T were the desired system variables, then it can be shown by a simple form of mathematics called *Legendre transforms* that, for example, the thermodynamic variable which is a function of P, T is F. Callen (3) and Epstein (13) discuss such transforms in detail.

(6-5), one obtains,

$$dH = T\,dS + V\,dP \tag{6-7}$$
$$dA = -S\,dT - P\,dV \tag{6-8}$$
$$dF = -S\,dT + V\,dP \tag{6-9}$$

It is a fact that for any equation such as (6-5), (6-7), (6-8), or (6-9), written generally as

$$dZ = P\,dX + Q\,dY \tag{6-10}$$

where Z, X, Y are properties in the sense that they are path-independent, or $\partial^2 Z/\partial X\,\partial Y = \partial^2 Z/\partial Y\,\partial X$, then dZ is a total differential and

$$(\partial P/\partial Y)_X = (\partial Q/\partial X)_Y \tag{6-11}$$

Equation (6-11) is very important in that it allows one to express many partial derivatives which are difficult to evaluate directly in terms of other derivatives which may be calculated more conveniently. For example, from Eq. (6-9), using Eq. (6-11),

$$(\partial S/\partial P)_T = -(\partial V/\partial T)_P \tag{6-12}$$

and the entropy variation with pressure is shown to depend only on the isobaric variation of volume with temperature, a quantity which may be evaluated from an equation of state; for an ideal gas it is R/P.

In the various sections which follow the variations of some of the more important thermodynamic properties with pressure are shown. A tabulation of many other equations derived from Eq. (6-12) is given in the Bridgman table (Sec. 6-9, Table 6-2).

Enthalpy Variations with Pressure. By dividing Eq. (6-7) by dP, holding T constant, and using Eq. (6-12),

$$(\partial H/\partial P)_T = V - T(\partial V/\partial T)_P \tag{6-13}$$

By introducing the compressibility factor $Z = PV/RT$,

$$(\partial H/\partial P)_T = (-RT^2/P)(\partial Z/\partial T)_P \tag{6-14}$$

or $\qquad (H_2 - H_1)_T = -RT^2 \int_{P_1}^{P_2} (\partial Z/\partial T)_P \, d(\ln P) \tag{6-15}$

A convenient form of Eq. (6-15) is obtained by choosing the pressure P_1 to be P^0, or zero absolute pressure. This particular choice of one of the limits of integration does not cause the integral to diverge [as might be apparent from the variable $d(\ln P)$], since $(\partial Z/\partial T)_P \to 0$ as $P \to 0$ or, viewed in another way, from Eq. (6-13), as $P \to 0$, $V \to RT/P$ and $(\partial H/\partial P)_T \to 0$. Hence pressure variations at sufficiently low pressures do not change the value of enthalpy. Using this base pressure, and expressing all temperatures and pressures as reduced values,

$$(H - H^0)/RT_c = -T_r^2 \int_0^{P_r} (\partial Z/\partial T_r)_{P_r} \, d(\ln P_r) \tag{6-16}$$

The term $H - H^0$ is the enthalpy change from $P = 0$ to $P = P$ at constant temperature, and the right-hand side may be evaluated from any of the reduced equations of state described in Chap. 3. Integration of Eq. (6-16) will be considered in detail later.

Internal-energy Variations with Pressure. A treatment of internal energy E similar to that used for H is possible. However, from Eq. (6-6) it is easily seen that,

$$(E - E^0)/RT_c = (H - H^0)/RT_c - T_r(Z - 1) \qquad (6\text{-}17)$$

Entropy Variations with Pressure. From Eq. (6-12) and the definition of Z,

$$(\partial S/\partial P)_T = (-R/P)[Z + T(\partial Z/\partial T)_P] \qquad (6\text{-}18)$$

In the case of entropy, integration from a base state of zero pressure is not convenient, since $S \rightarrow \infty$ as $P \rightarrow 0$. It is convenient, therefore, to adopt the following artifice: Integrate as a real gas to some pressure near zero where all properties approximate those of an ideal gas. Then integrate up to some reference pressure P_s, assuming ideal-gas properties. By this means the low-pressure effects on entropy cancel out. Writing Eq. (6-18) for both steps and adding,

$$(S - S_s)/R = \int_0^P (1 - Z)\, d(\ln P) + \ln(P_s/P)$$
$$- T \int_0^P (\partial Z/\partial T)_P\, d(\ln P) \qquad (6\text{-}19)$$

or in reduced terms

$$(S - S_s)/R = \int_0^{P_r} (1 - Z)\, d(\ln P_r) + \ln(P_{r_s}/P_r)$$
$$- T_r \int_0^{P_r} (\partial Z/\partial T_r)_{P_r}\, d(\ln P_r) \qquad (6\text{-}20)$$

$S - S_s$ is the entropy change from T, P_s to T, P or from T_r, P_{r_s} to T_r, P_r. Two common reference states for P_s are 1 atm and the actual pressure P. The convenience of the latter state results from the elimination of the ln term in Eq. (6-20). Finally, it may be noted from Eq. (6-16) and Eq. (6-25) that

$$(S - S_s)/R = (H - H^0)/RT - \ln(f/P_s) \qquad P_s = P \qquad (6\text{-}21)$$

an equation which is often convenient if $H - H^0$ and fugacity values are available.

Fugacity Variations with Pressure. Fugacity is defined by

$$F = RT \ln f + \varphi(T) \qquad (6\text{-}22)$$

where $\varphi(T)$ is a function of temperature. From Eqs. (6-9) and (6-22),

$$(\partial F/\partial P)_T = V = RT[\partial(\ln f)/\partial P]_T \qquad (6\text{-}23)$$

Integrating, and choosing zero as a base pressure where, as part of the definition of fugacity, the fugacity equals the pressure,

$$RT \ln (f/f^0) = \int_0^P V \, dP \tag{6-24}$$

Both sides of Eq. (6-24) are positive infinite as written; by adding and subtracting $\int_0^P (RT/P) \, dP$ from the right-hand side of Eq. (6-24) and using $Z = PV/RT$,

$$\ln (f/P) = \int_0^P (Z - 1) \, d(\ln P) = \int_0^{P_r} (Z - 1) \, d(\ln P_r) \tag{6-25}$$

From Eq. (6-25) the fugacity ratio f/P is determined at any temperature by an integration of $Z - 1$ over an $\ln P_r$ range from 0 to P_r.

Heat-capacity Variations with Pressure. Variation of the heat capacity $C_p = (\partial H/\partial T)_P$, with pressure is obtained from Eq. (6-14), since

$$
\begin{aligned}
(\partial C_p/\partial P)_T &= \partial^2 H/\partial P \, \partial T = \partial^2 H/\partial T \, \partial P \\
&= (\partial/\partial T)[(-RT^2/P)(\partial Z/\partial T)_P]_P \tag{6-26}
\end{aligned}
$$

or $\qquad (\partial C_p/\partial P_r)_{T_r} = (\partial/\partial T_r)[(-RT_r^2/P_r)(\partial Z/\partial T_r)_{P_r}]_{P_r} \tag{6-27}$

As in the other cases, choosing a base pressure of zero absolute, and using Eq. (6-16),

$$(C_p - C_p^0)/R = - (\partial/\partial T_r)[\int_0^{P_r} T_r^2(\partial Z/\partial T_r)_{P_r} \, d(\ln P_r)]_{P_r} \tag{6-28}$$

$$(C_p - C_p^0)/R = (\partial/\partial T_r)[(H - H^0)/RT_c]_{P_r} \tag{6-29}$$

Whereas $H - H^0$, $E - E^0$, etc., involved only an integration step, $C_p - C_p^0$ involves first the determination of an integral and then this integral must be differentiated with respect to T_r at whatever values of P_r and T_r the ΔC_p difference is to be evaluated.

The isothermal variations derived above are summarized in Table 6-1.

TABLE 6-1. SUMMARY OF ISOTHERMAL VARIATIONS IN THE
THERMODYNAMIC PROPERTIES

Eq. no.

$$\frac{H - H^0}{RT_c} = - T_r^2 \int_0^{P_r} \left(\frac{\partial Z}{\partial T_r} \right)_{P_r} d(\ln P_r) \tag{6-16}$$

$$\frac{E - E^0}{RT_c} = \frac{H - H^0}{RT_c} - T_r(Z - 1) \tag{6-17}$$

$$\frac{S - S_s}{R} = \frac{1}{T_r} \left(\frac{H - H^0}{RT_c} \right) - \ln \frac{f}{P_s} \qquad P_s = P \tag{6-21}$$

$$\frac{S - S_s}{R} = \int_0^{P_r} (1 - Z) \, d(\ln P_r) + \ln \frac{P_{rs}}{P_r} - T_r \int_0^{P_r} \left(\frac{\partial Z}{\partial T_r} \right)_{P_r} d(\ln P_r) \tag{6-20}$$

$$\ln \frac{f}{P} = \int_0^{P_r} (Z - 1) \, d(\ln P_r) \tag{6-25}$$

$$\frac{C_p - C_p^0}{R} = \frac{\partial}{\partial T_r} \left(\frac{H - H^0}{RT_c} \right)_{P_r} \tag{6-29}$$

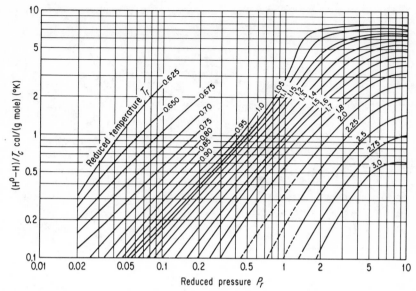

FIG. 6-2. Kordbachen-Tien enthalpy correction charts.   Reduced pressure $P_r = P/P_c$. Reduced temperature $T_r = T/T_c$.   [R. Kordbachen and Chi Tien, Can. J. Chem. Eng., **37**:162 (1959).]

6-4   Variation of Enthalpy with Pressure

The variation of enthalpy with pressure is given in reduced form by Eq. (6-16).   The integration requires the choice of a specific or generalized equation of state.   For an ideal gas it is easily shown that pressure variations have no effect on enthalpy; for real gases the most direct approach is to use the Nelson-Obert compressibility-factor charts as the source of compressibility-factor data.   Generalized graphs of $(H^0 - H)/T_c$ as a function of T_r and P_r, from such data, are shown in Figs. 6-2 and 6-3 (29).   Other, similar charts based on older compressibility data can be found in most standard chemical-engineering thermodynamics texts.   Edmister (9) presents a good review of such correlations and proposes a chart similar to Figs. 6-2 and 6-3, based primarily on hydrocarbon P-V-T data.   His chart, though not reproduced here, will be referred to later when the accuracy of all the enthalpy estimation methods is discussed.   Saltzman (44) treats the enthalpy deviations with pressure for simple di- and triatomic gases.

Three-parameter Correlations.   Rather than use the simple

$$Z = f(P_r, T_r)$$

correlations to evaluate Eq. (6-16), it is possible to use any of the three-parameter reduced equations of state discussed in Sec. 3-16.   Both the

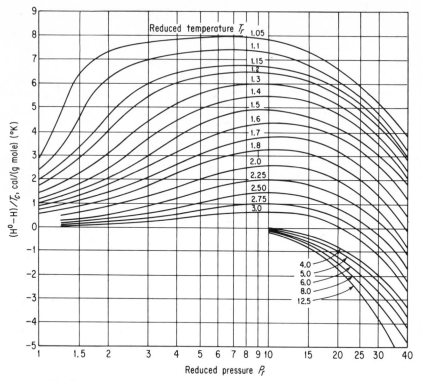

FIG. 6-3. Kordbachen-Tien enthalpy correction charts. [*R. Kordbachen and Chi Tien, Can. J. Chem. Eng.*, **37**:162 (1959).]

acentric-factor and critical compressibility-factor correlations have been integrated with Eq. (6-16) and $H - H^0$ values tabulated (26, 30, 39, 40). The values of $(H^0 - H)/T_c$ obtained by the critical compressibility-factor method are somewhat more extensive and are presented in Appendix B. Values of $(H - H^0)/T_c$ may be obtained* for materials with values of Z_c from 0.23 to 0.29 over a reduced pressure range from saturated vapor to a value of 30 with a T_r span from saturated vapor to 15. The tables in Appendix B (30) allow $(H - H^0)/T_c$ values also to be obtained in the liquid phase, by using the values for saturated vapor and a generalized correlation of latent heat of vaporization, expressed in the form

$$\Delta H_v = f_1(T_r, Z_c) \quad \text{or} \quad = f_2(P_r, Z_c) \quad (6\text{-}30)$$

As discussed in Chap. 4, more accurate correlations of ΔH_v are available so that the difference $H - H^0$ for liquid-phase enthalpies, by using Eq. (6-30), are less accurate than those in the vapor phase. However, if differences between liquid-phase enthalpies are desired, the tables in

---

* The tables list $(H^0 - H)/T_c$, which is usually positive.

Appendix B are quite good, as they are based on the reliable liquid-phase density correlation given in Sec. 3-19 and shown by Eq. (3-74). It is the ΔH_v contribution which is somewhat questionable. Yen and Alexander (50) have reevaluated the available experimental data and published new enthalpy deviation plots; they have also expressed their results in an analytical form. Erbor, Persyn, and Edmister (14) have formulated equations which approximate closely the Pitzer enthalpy-deviation tables.

In addition to the generalized correlations discussed above, Eubank and Smith (15) have developed a method of determining $(H - H^0)/RT_c$ for polar gases in a manner analogous to Eq. (3-19) for Z. Use of this specialized correlation will decrease the errors for highly polar materials, but the difficulty of obtaining reliable Stockmayer intermolecular potential parameters discourages general use.

Any of the analytical equations of state described in Chap. 3 may also be used with Eq. (6-16) to obtain enthalpy deviations with pressure. The simple two- or three-constant equations usually yield results less accurate than those obtained from the generalized methods such as are shown in Figs. 6-2 and 6-3 or in Appendix B, although Hou (27) has suggested the Berthelot equation [Eq. (3-49)] at low pressures. Viswanath (46) and Hobson and Weber (25) have utilized the Benedict-Webb-Rubin equation of state, Erbar et al. (14) employed the Redlich-Kwong equation of state, and Martin (32–34) has demonstrated the applicability of the Martin-Hou equation [Eq. (3-66)] (35, 36), but these and others, including the Hirschfelder et al. equations [Eqs. (3-58) and (3-63)] lead to results which, though accurate, are too complex except for machine-computation techniques. The Hirschfelder equations for $(H - H^0)/T$ are summarized in Appendix D (23, 24), and the Benedict-Webb-Rubin equations are given in Appendix E.

Discussion of Enthalpy-deviation Methods. It is extremely difficult to assess the accuracy of the proposed estimation techniques to determine pressure effects on enthalpy. Use of the Hirschfelder and Benedict-Webb-Rubin equations of state (Appendixes D, E) would be expected to be most accurate, as they are among the best of the generalized methods for computing gas-phase P-V-T properties. However, they are not easily used except with computer aid.

To evaluate the accuracy of the methods suitable for hand calculation, Garavito (16) compared experimental values of the pressure effect on enthalpy with values calculated from the methods of Pitzer (39, 40), Lydersen et al. (30), Edmister (9), and Kordbachen and Tien (29) (Figs. 6-2 and 6-3). The compounds tested were methyl, ethyl, and propyl alcohols, acetone, methylethyl ketone, ethyl ether, isopropyl ether, n-pentane, benzene, and carbon disulfide. Z_c values for this group ranged from 0.23 to 0.29. Plots similar to Fig. 6-4 were drawn for many

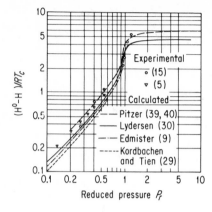

FIG. 6-4. Calculated and experimental enthalpy deviations for n-propyl alcohol at $T = T_c$.

reduced temperatures and pressures and included both the liquid and vapor regions.

The methods tested yielded different calculated results, varying largely with the temperature and pressure region investigated. However, no estimation method was clearly superior to the others when compared with experimental data. For each compound, conclusions could be drawn as to the most accurate estimating technique, but, with the compounds viewed as a group, definite recommendations were extremely difficult to make. It appears that, for materials with Z_c near to 0.27, any of the four methods tested could be used and Figs. 6-2 and 6-3 are as accurate as any. For temperature and pressure ranges near saturation, and for compounds with Z_c deviating greatly from 0.27, somewhat better results were obtained with either Lydersen's method (Appendix B) or Pitzer's method, although there were several exceptions to this general conclusion. Experimental values of T_c, P_c, Z_c, and ω were used in the study; so the discrepancies noted were due either to method errors or to experimental errors.

Recommendations. For superheated vapor, for materials with Z_c near 0.27, use any of the methods discussed; Figs. 6-2 and 6-3 are as good, in general, as any other and are very easy to use.

For materials near saturation or with a Z_c much greater or less than 0.27, use Lydersen's tables in Appendix B.

If a machine-computation program is to be used, then any of the complex equations of state may be employed with Eq. (6-16). For light hydrocarbons, the Benedict-Webb-Rubin equation is the best, and the final equations are summarized in Appendix E. For other materials, the Hirschfelder et al. enthalpy-deviation equations are given in Appendix D, or, equally good, the Martin-Hou equation of state may be used in the integration of Eq. (6-16).

Errors for the methods vary widely. Usually, less than 10 to 20 per cent variations are noted except at very low reduced pressures, where per cent errors are often much larger, but where the numerical value of $(H - H^0)/RT_c$ is quite small. Relatively large errors are permissible for many engineering calculations, since $H - H^0$ is a correction term (often small) to the enthalpy of the ideal gas.

Example 6-1. Estimate the value of $(H - H^0)/RT_c$ for n-propyl alcohol at 537°K and 27.2 atm.

Solution. The critical temperature, pressure, and compressibility factor of n-propyl alcohol are 537°K, 51 atm, and 0.25 (Appendix A). Thus $T_r = 1.0$, and $P_r = 27.2/51$ $= 0.533$.

From Fig. 6-2, $(H - H^0)/T_c = -1.34$ cal/(g mole)(°K), or $(H - H^0)/RT_c = -0.67$.

From Appendix B, with $Z_c = 0.25$, $(H - H^0)/T_c = -1.54$ cal/(g mole)(°K), or $(H - H^0)/RT_c = -0.77$.

Experimental values for these conditions have been reported as $(H - H^0)/RT_c = -1.09$ (15) and as -0.92 (5) (at $T_r = 0.992$). These calculated results and those of Edmister and Pitzer are shown in Fig. 6-4; Pitzer's method ($\omega = 0.60$) gives $(H - H^0)/RT_c = -0.95$, and Edmister's plots give -0.65. In this case the calculated and experimental values differ considerably.

6-5 The Fugacity-Pressure Ratio

The function $\ln (f/P)$ is determined by integration of Eq. (6-25) by using experimental or estimated values of Z. For an ideal gas, $f = P$, and for real gases, the shape of an $\ln (f/P)$ isotherm at various pressures resembles in many ways Z-P_r plots discussed in Chap. 3. However, when comparisons are made at equal P_r and T_r, $\ln (f/P)$-P_r correlations given in the literature often show considerably more disagreement than do the original Z-P_r correlations (10). This results from the integration of Eq. (6-25), in which discrepancies in Z are cumulative. The best simple f/P correlation appears to be that of Lydersen et al. (26, 30); Fig. 6-5 has been drawn from their correlation at a Z_c of 0.27. A complete tabulation of f/P values for various values of Z_c is given in Appendix B. Pitzer (39, 40) has presented a similar three-parameter correlation based on the acentric factor, and many thermodynamic textbooks present the now familiar f/P graph developed by Newton (38) in 1935 from early compressibility-factor charts for light hydrocarbons.

Integration of Eq. (6-25) with generalized equations of state has often been carried out. Maron and Turnbull (31) have used the Beattie-Bridgman equation; Viswanath (47) and others used the Benedict-Webb-Rubin equation (see Appendix E); and Hirschfelder et al. (23, 24) have used their equations of state [Eqs. (3-58) and (3-63)] discussed in Chap. 3. The last two equations lead to complex algebraic formulations suitable primarily for machine computation; and the necessary equations are summarized in Appendix D. Similar equations may be obtained from the Martin-Hou equation of state.

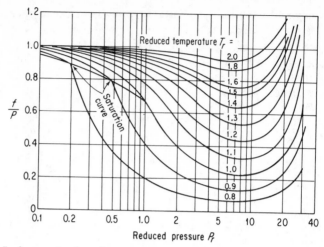

Fig. 6-5. Lydersen plot for f/P as a function of P_r, T_r. $Z_c = 0.27$. [*A. L. Lydersen, R. A. Greenkorn, and O. A. Hougen, Generalized Thermodynamic Properties of Pure Fluids, Coll. Eng., Univ. Wisconsin, Eng. Expt. Sta. Rept. 4, Madison, Wis., October, 1955.*]

Discussion. Very few experimental values of f/P are available as a basis for a direct comparison between calculated and experimental results. Presumably, the errors in f/P are a reflection of the errors of the original compressibility-factor correlation. That is, if such errors were random, the calculated values of f/P are in error by about the same amount as errors in Z. If, however, a bias is present such that there is a consistent positive or negative error in the estimation of Z, then calculated values of f/P can be considerably in error. Mehra and Thodos (37) compared experimental values* of f/P for n-butane from T_r of 1.2 to 1.4 and P_r from 0.3 to 5.0 with those determined from the correlation of Lydersen et al. (Appendix B or Fig. 6-5) and found good agreement; i.e., deviations ranged from 0.1 to 2 per cent.

Recommendations. Estimate f/P values from Fig. 6-5 if Z_c is about 0.27; for other Z_c values use the tables in Appendix B. Both liquid-and gas-phase fugacities may be determined. The fugacity-pressure ratio of the saturated vapor is equal to that of the saturated liquid, and integration into the liquid region is easily carried out.

For machine-computation programs, estimate f/P by means of the equations given in Appendix D or, for light hydrocarbons, from Appendix E.

Errors cannot be estimated; as a first approximation, the error will be comparable with or greater than the error in estimating Z by the method chosen, i.e., about 3 to 10 per cent for Lydersen's method and similar but

* Experimental values refer to f/P values determined from Eq. (6-25), where experimental values of Z were used.

possibly somewhat smaller errors for the analytical methods in Appendixes D and E.

Example 6-2. Estimate the value of f/P for n-butane at 555°K and 150 atm. The value determined by Mehra and Thodos was 0.602 (37).

Solution. For n-butane, $T_c = 425$°K, $P_c = 37.5$ atm, and $Z_c = 0.274$ (Appendix A). Thus,

$$T_r = {}^{555}\!/_{425} = 1.31$$
$$P_r = 150/37.5 = 4.0$$

and, from Fig. 6-5 (with $Z_c \sim 0.27$), $f/P = 0.61$.

6-6 Variation of Entropy with Pressure

Equation (6-20) may be solved by using an equation of state or generalized compressibility-factor correlation, but Eq. (6-21) is more convenient, and use may be made of the enthalpy and fugacity correlations discussed in Secs. 6-4 and 6-5. The ideal-gas standard state, denoted by the subscript s, represents some arbitrarily chosen pressure level so that the calculated value of $S - S_s$ then represents the isothermal entropy change from the real gas at pressure P to the ideal-gas state at P_s. The fugacity is, of course, evaluated at P, not P_s. Should one desire an isothermal entropy change of the real gas between pressures P_1 and P_2 (or P_{r_1} and P_{r_2}), it is usually convenient to choose the standard-state pressure to be the same for both states 1 and 2. By writing Eq. (6-21) for both states and noting that S_s is now the same, one obtains

$$(S_2 - S_1)/R = (1/T_r)\{[(H_2 - H^0)/RT_c]_{P_{r_2}} - [(H_1 - H^0)/RT_c]_{P_{r_1}}\}$$
$$- \ln (f_2/P_2) + \ln (f_1/P_1) - \ln (P_2/P_1) \quad (6\text{-}31)$$

The use of Eqs. (6-21) and (6-31) is illustrated in Example 6-3.

Recommendations. To determine isothermal entropy changes either between the real-gas and the ideal-gas states or between two pressures in the real-gas region, use Eq. (6-21) or (6-31). Evaluate the enthalpy and fugacity terms by the methods recommended in Secs. 6-4 and 6-5.

Example 6-3. Estimate the entropy changes for n-butane at 555°K for a pressure change from:

    (a) Gas at 150 atm to ideal-gas state at 150 atm
    (b) Gas at 150 atm to ideal-gas state at 1 atm
    (c) Gas at 150 atm to gas at 75 atm

Solution. As shown in Example 6-2, $Z_c = 0.274$; $T_r = 1.31$ and $P_r = 4.0$ at 555°K and 150 atm; and $(f/P)_{150\,atm} = 0.61$. From Appendix B, $(H - H^0)/T_c = -5.18$; at 75 atm $(P_r = 2)$, f/P is 0.77, and $(H - H^0)/T_c$ is -3.05. Substituting in Eq. (6-31),

  (a) $(S_{s_{150}} - S)/R = 2.59/1.31 + \ln 0.61$
                        $= 1.99 - 0.49 = +1.50$

  (b) $(S_{s_1} - S)/R = 1.99 + \ln 0.61 + \ln {}^{150}\!/_1$
                        $= +1.99 - 0.49 + 5.01 = +6.51$

  (c) $(S_{75} - S_{150})/R = {}^1\!/_{1.31}(-1.53 - 2.59) - \ln 0.77 + \ln 0.61 - \ln {}^{75}\!/_{150}$
                        $= +2.58$

6-7   Variation of Internal Energy with Pressure

Internal-energy variations with pressure are determined from Eq. (6-17), with the required enthalpy variations from Sec. 6-4 and the com pressibility factor determined by methods discussed in Chap. 3.

6-8   Heat-Capacity Variations with Pressure

The isothermal difference between the heat capacity in the real-gas state and that as an ideal gas (see Chap. 5) is evaluated by Eq. (6-29) The enthalpy-deviation term is to be differentiated with respect to T (or T). Since $(H - H^0)/RT_c$ is itself an integral involving the tempera ture derivative of the compressibility factor, the operation in essence involves both a second derivative and an integration. Values of Z are never exact, and after two differentiations and an integration, it is not surprising that generalized correlations of heat capacity with pressure are only approximate.

Several generalized plots of $C_p - C_p^0$ have, however, been published. Lydersen (30) differentiated the $(H - H^0)/T_c$ tables of Appendix B for $Z_c = 0.27$ to obtain a correlation of this heat-capacity difference with T_r and P_r. Weiss and Joffe (49) used the Benedict-Webb-Rubin equa tion of state for methane, ethane, ethylene, propane, and n-butane and obtained $C_p - C_p^0$ by analytical means. The results for the five sub stances were then averaged to yield a single plot of $C_p - C_p^0$ as a function of T_r and P_r. Edmister (7), using hydrocarbon compressibility data, and Sherwood (45), using Pitzer's P-V-T correlation, have also presented correlations of $C_p - C_p^0$ with P_r and T_r. Other, similar charts are found in several textbooks on thermodynamics.

Gambill (18) and Weiss and Joffe (49) discuss the various correlations. They found large differences among all the graphs, and even for an indi vidual method, agreement is sometimes poor for the very compounds upon which the correlation was based. The Weiss and Joffe review shows all the graphs superimposed, and the results are not encouraging. The graph with the widest range is that of Edmister, reproduced in Fig. 6-6. At low values of P_r, $C_p - C_p^0$ is small (for ideal gases the difference is, of course, zero). Near the critical point C_p approaches infinity; so in this region the correlation is necessarily poor. In most other regions the errors encountered may be as high as 50 to 100 per cent, although in most cases they are much less. Even these large errors are often not significant, since the value of C_p is the actual quantity desired; so it is really the uncertainty of $(C_p - C_p^0)/C_p$ that is of importance. Since C_p values are usually greater than 10 to 20 cal/(g mole)(°K) for all but the simple molecules, errors in $C_p - C_p^0$ of a few tenths of a calorie per gram mole per degree Kelvin are often insignificant.

Gambill (18) discusses the use of several of the simple equations of state to determine $C_p - C_p{}^0$.   An empirical modification of the results obtained with van der Waals' or Berthelot's equation is

$$(C_p - C_p{}^0)/R = 4.5P_r/T_r{}^6 \qquad T_r < 1.2 \Big\} \qquad (6\text{-}32)$$
$$\left.\begin{array}{l} (C_p - C_p{}^0)/R < 1 \end{array}\right.$$
$$(C_p - C_p{}^0)/R = 2.5/P_c \text{ (in atm)} T_r{}^3 \quad T_r > 1.2 \Big\} \qquad (6\text{-}33)$$

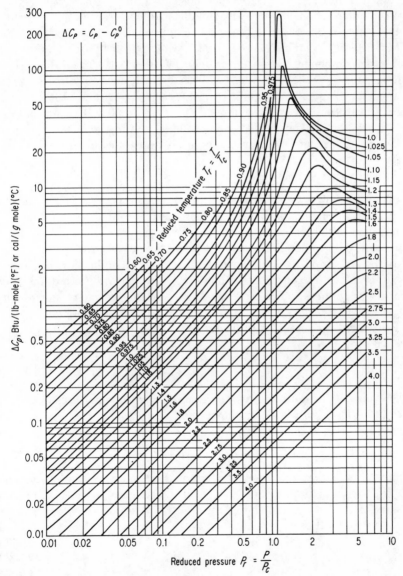

FIG. 6-6. Isothermal pressure correction to heat capacity of vapors. [*From W. C. Edmister, Petrol. Refiner,* **27**(11):609 (1948).]

For complex equations of state such as that of Hirschfelder et al. (23, 24) (see Appendix D), Eq. (6-29) can be solved analytically. This has not yet been carried out, but the group $(C_v - C_v^0)/R$ has been calculated instead. As in other cases where such complex equations of state were employed, the method is suitable only for machine computation. Appendix D summarizes the equations. $C_p - C_p^0$, may also be obtained from $C_v - C_v^0$ by the methods shown in this appendix.

Recommendations. Since all available methods are very approximate, it is recommended that, for the hand computation of $C_p - C_p^0$ for gases, Fig. 6-6 be used. This chart is based primarily on hydrocarbons, and, for polar compounds, large errors may be expected. If machine computation is possible, use the analytical equations for $(C_v - C_v^0)/R$ described in Appendix D, and then convert to $C_p - C_p^0$ by the methods there described. In the first method, errors up to 50 to 100 per cent are possible but not likely for nonpolar compounds; in the latter, errors of 10 to 30 per cent are most probable for all types of compounds.

6-9 Derivative Properties

There are many other real-gas equilibrium properties which may be estimated by generalized, reduced correlations. Most contain partial derivatives of the three properties P, V, T such as $(\partial V/\partial P)_T$ or $(\partial V/\partial T)_P$.* By establishing generalized, reduced means to evaluate these derivatives, it is then a simple task to express many useful equilibrium properties in terms of these generalized functions. Two very different methods are discussed here. The first makes use of the concept of *derivative compressibility factors*, while the second employs an equation of state.

Derivative Compressibility Factor. Two new properties of a real gas are defined,

$$Z_p \equiv Z - P_r(\partial Z/\partial P_r)_{T_r} \tag{6-34}$$
$$Z_T \equiv Z + T_r(\partial Z/\partial T_r)_{P_r} \tag{6-35}$$

These may be used to express, in general form, the quantities $(\partial V/\partial T)_P$ and $(\partial V/\partial P)_T$, for it is easily shown that

$$(\partial V/\partial T)_P = RZ_T/P \tag{6-36}$$
$$(\partial V/\partial P)_T = -RTZ_p/P^2 \tag{6-37}$$

Edmister was the first to suggest correlating functions such as Z_p and Z_T with reduced properties (8, 11), and a later correlation, (41) related Z_T and Z_p to T_r, P_r, and the Pitzer acentric factor ω. The dependence on ω is expressed as

$$Z_T = Z_T^0 + \omega Z_T^1 \tag{6-38}$$
$$Z_p = Z_p^0 + \omega Z_p^1 \tag{6-39}$$

---

* It can be shown that, by specifying these two derivatives, the third $(\partial P/\partial T)_V$ is determined, since $(\partial V/\partial P)_T(\partial P/\partial T)_V(\partial T/\partial V)_P = -1$.

The functions $Z_T{}^0$, $Z_T{}^1$, $Z_p{}^0$, and $Z_p{}^1$ depend only upon reduced temperature and pressure as shown in Table 6-3 or in Figs. 6-7 to 6-10 (12).   To
indicate the utility of the functions Z_p and Z_T, a Bridgman table is given
in Table 6-2 to aid in the evaluation of the desired partial derivatives.
For example, suppose that $(\partial H/\partial P)_T$ were desired.   To use Table 6-2,
$(\partial H)_T = (RT/P)(Z_T - Z)$ and $(\partial P)_T = -1$; thus

$$(\partial H/\partial P)_T = (RT/P)(Z - Z_T)$$

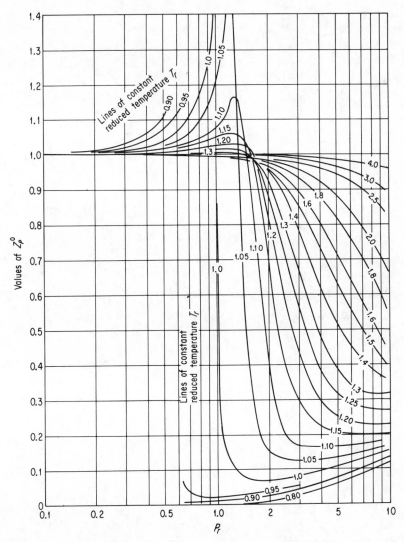

FIG. 6-7. $Z_p{}^0$ as a function of P_r and T_r.   [*Chart drawn by W. C. Edmister from data
in article by R. C. Reid and J. R. Valbert, Ind. Eng. Chem. Fundamentals,* **1**:292 (1962).]

TABLE 6-2. BRIDGMAN TABLE OF DIFFERENTIALS EXPRESSED IN TERMS OF Z_T AND Z_p

$$(\partial T)_P = -(\partial P)_T = 1$$

$$(\partial V)_P = -(\partial P)_V = \frac{RZ_T}{P}$$

$$(\partial S)_P = -(\partial P)_S = \frac{C_p}{T}$$

$$(\partial E)_P = -(\partial P)_E = C_p - RZ_T$$

$$(\partial H)_P = -(\partial P)_H = C_p$$

$$(\partial F)_P = -(\partial P)_F = -S$$

$$(\partial A)_P = -(\partial P)_A = -(S + RZ_T)$$

$$(\partial V)_T = -(\partial T)_V = \frac{Z_p RT}{P^2}$$

$$(\partial S)_T = -(\partial T)_S = \frac{RZ_T}{P}$$

$$(\partial E)_T = -(\partial T)_E = \frac{RZ_T T}{P} - \frac{RZ_p T}{P} = \frac{RT}{P}(Z_T - Z_p)$$

$$(\partial H)_T = -(\partial T)_H = -\frac{ZRT}{P} + \frac{Z_T RT}{P} = \frac{RT}{P}(Z_T - Z)$$

$$(\partial F)_T = -(\partial T)_F = -V = -\frac{ZRT}{P}$$

$$(\partial A)_T = -(\partial T)_A = -\frac{Z_p RT}{P}$$

$$(\partial S)_V = -(\partial V)_S = \frac{R}{P^2}(-C_p Z_p + RZ_T^2)$$

$$(\partial E)_V = -(\partial V)_E = -\frac{C_p Z_p RT}{P^2} + \frac{TR^2 Z_T^2}{P^2} = \frac{RT}{P^2}(-C_p Z_p + RZ_T^2)$$

$$(\partial H)_V = -(\partial V)_H = \frac{RT}{P^2}(-C_p Z_p + RZ_T^2 - RZZ_T)$$

$$(\partial F)_V = -(\partial V)_F = -\frac{RT}{P^2}(-SZ_p + RZZ_T)$$

$$(\partial A)_V = -(\partial V)_A = \frac{SZ_p RT}{P^2}$$

$$(\partial E)_S = -(\partial S)_E = \frac{R}{P}(-C_p Z_p + RZ_T^2)$$

$$(\partial H)_S = -(\partial S)_H = -\frac{ZRC_p}{P}$$

$$(\partial F)_S = -(\partial S)_F = \frac{R}{P}(SZ_T - C_p Z)$$

$$(\partial A)_S = -(\partial S)_A = \frac{R}{P}(-C_p Z_p + RZ_T^2 + SZ_T)$$

$$(\partial H)_E = -(\partial E_H) = \frac{RT}{P}(-ZC_P + RZZ_T + C_p Z_p - RZ_T^2)$$

$$(\partial F)_E = -(\partial E)_F = \frac{RT}{P}(RZZ_T - ZC_P + SZ_T - SZ_p)$$

$$(\partial A)_E = -(\partial E)_A = \frac{RT}{P}(-C_p Z_p + RZ_T^2)$$

$$(\partial F)_H = -(\partial H)_F = \frac{RT}{P}(SZ - C_p Z + SZ_T)$$

$$(\partial A)_H = -(\partial H)_A = \frac{RT}{P}(S + RZ_T)(Z_T - Z) - Z_p$$

$$(\partial A)_F = -(\partial F)_A = -\frac{RT}{P}(ZS - Z_p S + RZZ_T)$$

TABLE 6-3. DERIVATIVE COMPRESSIBILITY FACTORS*

$Z_p{}^0$ as a function of P_r and T_r

Reduced pressure P_r

T_r	0.2	0.4	0.6	0.8	1.0	1.2	1.4	1.6	1.8	2.0	2.2	2.4	2.6	2.8	3.0	3.2	3.4	3.6	3.8	4.0	5.0	6.0	7.0	8.0	9.0
0.80	0.006	0.000	0.000	0.005	0.010	0.010	0.010	0.013	0.013	0.021	0.024	0.030	0.036	0.042	0.038	0.034	0.030	0.028	0.028	0.025	0.050	0.066	0.082	0.099	0.117
0.85	0.003	0.000	0.005	0.010	0.010	0.010	0.010	0.014	0.019	0.021	0.026	0.028	0.033	0.038	0.039	0.042	0.049	0.050	0.051	0.053	0.067	0.083	0.008	0.113	0.125
0.90†	1.000	0.058	0.005	0.005	0.007	0.013	0.018	0.022	0.026	0.028	0.031	0.034	0.034	0.039	0.046	0.053	0.058	0.061	0.064	0.067	0.084	0.096	0.104	0.112	0.125
0.95†	1.006	1.042	1.120	0.171	0.02	0.029	0.032	0.034	0.037	0.040	0.043	0.045	0.047	0.049	0.055	0.060	0.068	0.073	0.075	0.080	0.098	0.110	0.110	0.117	0.114
1.00†	1.007	1.011	1.040	1.094	1.219	0.120	0.078	0.066	0.068	0.070	0.110	0.104	0.110	0.104	0.076	0.079	0.087	0.095	0.099	0.102	0.132	0.122	0.122	0.117	0.110
1.05†	1.003	1.009	1.026	1.053	1.073	1.59	0.680	0.310	0.175	0.150	0.137	0.120	0.180	0.170	0.166	0.114	0.124	0.126	0.128	0.130	0.165	0.138	0.140	0.140	0.141
1.10†	1.002	1.007	1.016	1.019	1.055	1.146	1.105	0.866	0.592	0.365	0.265	0.234	0.180	0.170	0.166	0.166	0.165	0.165	0.165	0.165	0.203	0.165	0.168	0.170	0.180
1.15†	1.005	1.005	1.010	1.006	1.052	1.063	1.063	1.986	0.874	0.667	0.496	0.435	0.365	0.316	0.284	0.268	0.257	0.244	0.231	0.217	0.203	0.200	0.200	0.200	0.200
1.20	1.003	1.003	1.006	1.000	1.026	1.030	1.028	1.015	0.913	0.803	0.668	0.604	0.538	0.484	0.442	0.406	0.373	0.340	0.305	0.280	0.260	0.236	0.234	0.226	0.224
1.25	1.003	1.002	1.003	0.999	1.016	1.016	1.012	0.990	0.943	0.870	0.794	0.722	0.663	0.610	0.560	0.517	0.476	0.434	0.394	0.360	0.330	0.286	0.276	0.268	0.265
1.30	1.011	1.001	1.000	0.997	1.008	1.005	1.003	0.989	0.966	0.915	0.860	0.796	0.741	0.696	0.657	0.615	0.572	0.532	0.496	0.460	0.394	0.333	0.319	0.318	0.318
1.40	1.001	1.000	1.000	0.998	0.998	0.995	0.991	0.983	0.973	0.937	0.928	0.920	0.861	0.820	0.780	0.731	0.687	0.648	0.608	0.570	0.525	0.448	0.410	0.383	0.352
1.50	1.001	1.000	0.998	0.997	0.996	0.994	0.989	0.981	0.970	0.957	0.941	0.894	0.861	0.852	0.852	0.827	0.799	0.762	0.731	0.697	0.638	0.560	0.506	0.457	0.399
1.60	1.000	0.999	0.998	0.998	0.996	0.993	0.988	0.983	0.975	0.966	0.956	0.923	0.923	0.907	0.917	0.878	0.860	0.837	0.816	0.798	0.712	0.638	0.578	0.524	0.464
1.70	1.000	0.999	0.999	0.998	0.996	0.992	0.991	0.984	0.979	0.973	0.973	0.951	0.942	0.934	0.933	0.900	0.880	0.867	0.854	0.842	0.770	0.705	0.645	0.584	0.515
1.80	1.000	0.999	0.999	0.998	0.996	0.993	0.993	0.986	0.982	0.982	0.976	0.960	0.960	0.945	0.945	0.920	0.911	0.901	0.888	0.876	0.816	0.757	0.702	0.647	0.583
1.90	1.001	0.999	0.999	0.999	0.995	0.994	0.992	0.989	0.988	0.984	0.982	0.972	0.965	0.960	0.954	0.934	0.920	0.938	0.932	0.885	0.849	0.800	0.752	0.702	0.644
2.00	1.001	1.000	1.000	0.999	0.999	0.998	0.997	0.989	0.987	0.991	0.991	0.982	0.980	0.980	0.979	0.978	0.943	0.938	0.932	0.925	0.877	0.833	0.792	0.747	0.696
2.5	1.001	1.000	1.000	0.999	0.999	0.998	0.997	0.993	0.992	0.991	0.990	0.985	0.983	0.986	0.988	0.988	0.975	0.967	0.960	0.955	0.944	0.924	0.902	0.876	0.847
3.0	1.001	1.001	1.000	1.000	0.999	0.998	0.999	0.996	0.994	0.992	0.993	0.991	0.991	0.991	0.991	0.991	0.988	0.991	0.989	0.979	0.968	0.952	0.938	0.922	0.905
3.5	1.001	1.001	1.000	1.000	1.000	0.999	0.999	0.999	0.998	0.997	0.997	0.996	0.995	0.993	0.993	0.993	0.991	0.993	0.993	0.987	0.980	0.973	0.963	0.955	6.945
4.0	1.001	1.001	1.000	1.000	1.001	1.001	1.001	1.001	1.001	1.000	0.998	0.995	0.993	0.993	0.993	0.993	0.993	0.993	0.993	0.991	0.986	0.979	0.972	0.969	0.963

Fine grid

T_r	0.4	0.5	0.6	0.7	0.8	0.9	1.0
0.90	1.058	1.125	0.005	0.005	0.005	0.006	0.007
0.91	1.068	1.103	0.153	0.008	0.008	0.008	0.008
0.92	1.050	1.091	1.140	0.012	0.012	0.012	0.013
0.93	1.047	1.085	1.130	0.01	0.02	0.02	0.02
0.94	1.043	1.076	1.120	1.301	0.02	0.02	0.02
0.95	1.042	1.068	1.108	1.244	0.40	0.02	0.02
0.96	1.035	1.060	1.104	1.219	1.30	0.04	0.03
0.97	1.030	1.052	1.097	1.169	1.217	1.712	0.08
0.98	1.026	1.048	1.089	1.136	1.171	1.325	0.138
0.99	1.023	1.045	1.070	1.115	1.148	1.239	1.875
1.00	1.020	1.039	1.064	1.103	1.140	1.196	1.535
1.01	1.018	1.032	1.057	1.096	1.115	1.157	1.355
1.02	1.016	1.031	1.051	1.090	1.101	1.130	1.263
1.03	1.014	1.029	1.046	1.079	1.094	1.130	1.219
1.04	1.012	1.027	1.046	1.071	1.101	1.157	1.263
1.05	1.011	1.024	1.040	1.060	1.094	1.130	1.219

T_r	1.0	1.1	1.2	1.3	1.4	1.5	1.6	1.7	1.8	1.9	2.0
0.98	0.08	0.073	0.063	0.057	0.056	0.056	0.054	0.046	0.051	0.053	0.055
0.99	0.138	0.123	0.085	0.074	0.072	0.065	0.058	0.052	0.056	0.057	0.059
1.00	1.875	0.182	0.120	0.094	0.078	0.073	0.066	0.067	0.068	0.069	0.070
1.01	1.535	1.307	0.322	0.128	0.096	0.092	0.089	0.086	0.084	0.081	0.073
1.02	1.355	2.249	0.656	0.225	0.150	0.130	0.125	0.120	0.105	0.095	0.080
1.03	1.263	1.666	1.56	0.54	0.281	0.173	0.155	0.141	0.128	0.109	0.101
1.04	1.219	1.511	1.67	0.86	0.475	0.302	0.200	0.170	0.152	0.141	0.127
1.05	1.178	1.338	1.59	1.086	0.680	0.477	0.310	0.215	0.175	0.162	0.150
1.06	1.135	1.249	1.530	1.331	0.848	0.598	0.340	0.298	0.222	0.182	0.168
1.07	1.110	1.201	1.319	1.396	0.997	0.745	0.430	0.397	0.278	0.226	0.192
1.08	1.095	1.165	1.244	1.284	1.072	0.875	0.575	0.489	0.394	0.298	0.226
1.09	1.080	1.141	1.190	1.226	1.105	0.953	0.708	0.599	0.493	0.383	0.285
1.10	1.066	1.113	1.146	1.162	1.090	0.995	0.808	0.716	0.592	0.458	0.365
1.11	1.054	1.091	1.116	1.126	1.071	1.014	0.866	0.803	0.669	0.537	0.438
1.13	1.055	1.069	1.085	1.080	1.080	1.026	0.907	0.892	0.792	0.669	0.556
1.15	1.055	1.053	1.062	1.053	1.050	1.024	0.986	0.937	0.874	0.780	0.667

275

TABLE 6-3. DERIVATIVE COMPRESSIBILITY FACTORS* (Continued)

Z_p^1 as a function of T_r and P_r

Reduced pressure P_r

T_r	0.2	0.4	0.6	0.8	1.0	1.2	1.4	1.6	1.8	2.0	2.2	2.4	2.6	2.8	3.0	4.0	5.0	6.0	7.0	8.0	9.0
0.8	.....	0.005	0.00	-0.005	-0.01	-0.01	-0.01	-0.015	-0.03	-0.03	-0.03	-0.03	-0.03	-0.03	-0.03	-0.08	-0.11	-0.11	-0.12	-0.15	-0.18
0.85	0.00	0.01	0.00	-0.01	-0.01	-0.02	-0.02	-0.025	-0.04	-0.04	-0.04	-0.04	-0.04	-0.06	-0.07	-0.08	-0.10	-0.10	-0.12	-0.14	-0.17
0.9†	0.00	0.03	-0.01	-0.02	-0.02	-0.02	-0.03	-0.04	-0.04	-0.04	-0.04	-0.06	-0.07	-0.08	-0.09	-0.10	-0.09	-0.10	-0.11	-0.12	-0.13
0.95†	0.00	0.02	-0.2	-0.01	-0.02	-0.03	-0.05	-0.05	-0.06	-0.06	-0.05	-0.06	-0.08	-0.08	-0.08	-0.09	-0.09	-0.08	-0.03	-0.07	-0.13
1.0†	-0.01	0.01	-0.01	0.3	....	-0.04	-0.04	-0.04	-0.05	-0.06	-0.07	-0.08	-0.08	-0.08	-0.07	-0.06	-0.02	0.02	0.02	-0.02	-0.07
1.05†	0.00	0.00	0.01	-0.01	-0.04	-0.10	0.17	0.23	0.07	0.04	0.03	0.01	-0.01	-0.02	-0.02	-0.02	0.12	0.12	0.11	0.02	-0.01
1.10†	0.00	0.00	-0.02	-0.05	-0.07	-0.09	0.11	0.39	0.47	0.26	0.11	0.08	0.06	0.04	0.02	0.03	0.17	0.16	0.12	0.05	0.03
1.15†	0.00	0.00	-0.03	-0.06	-0.06	-0.08	-0.07	0.07	0.32	0.45	0.40	0.34	0.27	0.24	0.20	0.24	0.30	0.20	0.16	0.12	0.02
1.20	0.00	0.00	0.02	-0.04	-0.08	-0.10	-0.08	0.00	0.13	0.22	0.33	0.40	0.41	0.39	0.36	0.29	0.33	0.25	0.18	0.13	0.12
1.25	0.00	0.00	-0.01	-0.03	-0.06	-0.08	-0.08	-0.03	0.04	0.14	0.24	0.33	0.40	0.44	0.40	0.39	0.33	0.28	0.19	0.14	0.13
1.30	0.00	0.00	0.00	-0.02	-0.04	-0.06	-0.06	-0.04	0.02	0.10	0.15	0.22	0.26	0.31	0.38	0.29	0.20	0.31	0.25	0.20	0.12
1.40	0.00	0.00	0.00	0.00	-0.02	-0.04	-0.04	-0.02	0.03	0.07	0.11	0.15	0.21	0.29	0.33	0.29	0.15	0.26	0.30	0.26	0.13
1.50	0.00	0.00	0.00	0.00	-0.01	-0.02	-0.02	-0.01	0.02	0.05	0.09	0.12	0.17	0.23	0.22	0.14	0.09	0.22	0.30	0.27	0.16
1.60	0.00	0.00	0.00	0.00	0.00	-0.01	-0.02	0.00	0.02	0.04	0.07	0.09	0.10	0.19	0.13	0.10	0.07	0.13	0.22	0.36	0.22
1.70	0.00	0.00	0.00	0.00	0.01	0.01	0.00	0.00	0.02	0.04	0.06	0.06	0.06	0.07	0.09	0.07	0.05	0.09	0.12	0.33	0.25
1.80	0.00	0.00	0.00	0.00	0.02	0.02	0.00	0.00	0.02	0.02	0.05	0.05	0.06	0.06	0.06	0.04	0.05	0.05	0.05	0.21	0.44
1.90	0.00	0.00	0.00	0.00	0.02	0.02	0.00	0.02	0.01	0.00	0.03	0.05	0.05	0.06	0.05	0.01	0.01	0.01	0.00	0.05	0.46
2.0	0.00	0.00	0.00	0.00	0.00	0.00	0.01	0.01	0.01	-0.01	-0.01	0.01	0.01	0.02	0.04	0.00	0.00	0.00	0.00	0.00	0.31
2.5	0.00	0.00	0.00	0.00	0.00	0.01	0.01	0.01	0.00	0.00	-0.01	-0.01	0.00	0.02	0.01	0.00	0.00	0.00	0.00	0.00	0.05
3.0	0.00	0.00	0.00	0.00	0.00	0.00	0.00	0.00	0.01	0.00	0.00	-0.01	-0.01	-0.01	0.00	0.00	0.00	0.00	0.00	0.00	0.02
3.5	0.00	0.00	0.00	0.00	0.00	0.00	0.01	0.01	0.00	0.00	0.00	0.00	0.00	0.00	0.00	0.00	0.00	0.00	0.00	0.00	0.00
4.0	0.00	0.00	0.00	0.00	0.00	0.00	0.01	0.00	0.00	0.00	0.00	0.00	0.00	0.00	0.00	0.00	0.00	0.00	0.00	0.00	0.00

Fine grid

P_r

T_r	0.4	0.6	0.8	1.0
0.90	0.03	-0.01	-0.02	-0.02
0.91	0.03	-0.02	-0.02	-0.015
0.92	0.03	0.7	-0.01	-0.015
0.93	0.02	0.4	-0.01	-0.02
0.94	0.01	0.3	-0.01	-0.02
0.95	0.00	0.2	-0.01	0.04
0.96	0.01	0.09	0.3	-0.05
0.97	0.01	0.07	0.3	-0.05
0.98	0.00	0.04	0.3	-0.06
0.99	0.00	0.02	0.00	....
1.00	0.00	0.01	0.00	0.2
1.01	0.00	0.00	0.00	0.2
1.02	-0.01	0.00	-0.01	0.1
1.03	0.00	-0.01	-0.01	0.04

P_r

T_r	1.0	1.2	1.4	1.6	1.8	2.0
0.98	-0.05	-0.05	-0.04	-0.05	-0.07	-0.08
0.99	-0.06	-0.05	-0.04	-0.04	-0.04	-0.05
1.00	....	-0.04	-0.04	-0.04	-0.05	-0.05
1.01	0.2	0.10	-0.02	-0.07	-0.10	-0.13
1.02	0.2	0.2	0.01	-0.06	-0.10	-0.14
1.03	0.1	0.11	0.04	-0.03	-0.06	-0.09
1.04	0.04	0.15	0.09	0.03	-0.01	-0.05
1.05	-0.14	0.10	0.17	0.23	0.07	-0.05
1.06	-0.20	-0.06	0.10	0.30	0.18	0.04
1.07	-0.14	-0.09	0.13	0.51	0.28	0.11
1.08	-0.08	-0.14	0.12	0.28	0.36	0.18
1.09	-0.08	-0.10	0.11	0.39	0.47	0.24
1.10	-0.06	-0.08	0.11	0.37	0.42	0.26
1.11	-0.06	-0.11	0.09	0.19	0.47	0.32
1.13		-0.11	0.01	-0.07	0.42	0.42
1.15		-0.08	0.08			0.45

TABLE 6-3. DERIVATIVE COMPRESSIBILITY FACTORS* *(Continued)*

$Z_r{}^0$ as a function of P_r and T_r

Reduced pressure P_r

T_r	0.2	0.4	0.6	0.8	1.0	1.2	1.4	1.6	1.8	2.0	2.2	2.4	2.6	2.8	3.0	3.2	3.4	3.6	3.8	4.0	4.5	5.0	6.0	7.0	8.0	9.0
0.80	1.452	0.082	0.116	0.148	0.180	0.210	0.233	0.258	0.271	0.282	0.296	0.332	0.368	0.385	0.413	0.425	0.440	0.452	0.460	0.472	0.464	0.474	0.484	0.508	0.52	0.54
0.85†	1.350	0.084	0.118	0.150	0.195	0.243	0.262	0.268	0.285	0.304	0.329	0.349	0.375	0.400	0.432	0.444	0.457	0.463	0.475	0.483	0.483	0.497	0.517	0.544	0.587	0.63
0.90†	1.234	1.735	0.31	0.21	0.238	0.263	0.302	0.322	0.334	0.351	0.357	0.373	0.402	0.430	0.442	0.464	0.477	0.482	0.508	0.509	0.519	0.529	0.550	0.596	0.660	0.70
0.95†	1.185	1.466	2.020	0.56	0.47	0.450	0.440	0.411	0.389	0.440	0.443	0.447	0.449	0.452	0.457	0.484	0.490	0.503	0.508	0.514	0.530	0.554	0.598	0.638	0.690	0.722
1.00†	1.157	1.386	1.776	2.505	∞	1.102	0.844	0.724	0.628	0.575	0.578	0.553	0.538	0.533	0.520	0.515	0.515	0.517	0.522	0.531	0.550	0.614	0.718	0.740	0.719	0.736
1.05†	1.133	1.302	1.556	2.010	2.807	4.803	3.531	1.797	1.226	1.065	0.865	0.780	0.738	0.723	0.713	0.698	0.681	0.668	0.644	0.626	0.660	0.681	0.772	0.768	0.745	0.752
1.10†	1.117	1.285	1.479	1.736	2.113	2.696	2.473	3.552	2.743	1.990	1.558	1.295	1.166	1.097	1.013	0.952	0.922	0.876	0.828	0.805	0.798	0.782	0.826	0.806	0.785	0.768
1.15†	1.102	1.233	1.391	1.538	1.740	2.040	2.150	2.725	2.741	2.423	2.395	2.047	1.773	1.504	1.333	1.218	1.121	1.051	0.988	0.935	0.887	0.862	0.899	0.862	0.791	0.785
1.20	1.080	1.179	1.340	1.443	1.629	1.832	1.902	2.068	2.463	2.310	2.215	2.118	1.930	1.748	1.616	1.465	1.341	1.282	1.186	1.148	1.010	0.991	0.964	0.899	0.831	0.791
1.25	1.069	1.156	1.268	1.366	1.536	1.693	1.738	1.855	2.178	2.164	2.095	2.038	1.892	1.832	1.670	1.594	1.537	1.430	1.370	1.285	1.134	1.170	1.038	1.015	0.910	0.799
1.30	1.061	1.136	1.216	1.316	1.404	1.579	1.561	1.607	1.940	2.014	1.941	1.953	1.861	1.809	1.717	1.676	1.604	1.542	1.519	1.446	1.269	1.347	1.263	1.175	0.971	0.804
1.4	1.051	1.097	1.181	1.264	1.309	1.388	1.341	1.355	1.716	1.777	1.809	1.617	1.636	1.762	1.665	1.732	1.692	1.678	1.609	1.506	1.402	1.402	1.329	1.338	1.063	0.899
1.5	1.044	1.072	1.148	1.198	1.256	1.317	1.304	1.272	1.451	1.512	1.572	1.406	1.489	1.502	1.514	1.517	1.521	1.630	1.541	1.536	1.453	1.459	1.369	1.369	1.127	1.025
1.6	1.038	1.063	1.122	1.158	1.213	1.254	1.254	1.243	1.387	1.443	1.461	1.389	1.422	1.439	1.444	1.455	1.467	1.526	1.496	1.538	1.468	1.436	1.373	1.346	1.193	1.111
1.7	1.035	1.054	1.110	1.141	1.178	1.213	1.210	1.207	1.344	1.344	1.389	1.367	1.393	1.402	1.410	1.429	1.442	1.458	1.465	1.461	1.471	1.400	1.343	1.321	1.277	1.177
1.8	1.034	1.063	1.096	1.129	1.141	1.179	1.189	1.176	1.257	1.305	1.329	1.314	1.264	1.343	1.355	1.359	1.366	1.377	1.384	1.390	1.394	1.366	1.373	1.265	1.283	1.200
1.9	1.032	1.054	1.077	1.093	1.136	1.154	1.156	1.091	1.225	1.260	1.278	1.242	1.264	1.302	1.311	1.316	1.321	1.326	1.328	1.330	1.331	1.343	1.343	1.321	1.254	1.260
2.0	1.029	1.046	1.067	1.076	1.116	1.128	1.084	1.068	1.202	1.231	1.242	1.314	1.147	1.147	1.150	1.154	1.167	1.213	1.217	1.228	1.238	1.250	1.261	1.165	1.277	1.260
2.5	1.010	1.021	1.039	1.060	1.060	1.050	1.060	1.046	1.101	1.106	1.126	1.141	1.093	1.102	1.106	1.110	1.115	1.127	1.137	1.141	1.144	1.147	1.151	1.110	1.254	1.251
3.0	1.007	1.018	1.031	1.041	1.041	1.038	1.042	1.026	1.072	1.074	1.076	1.076	1.058	1.065	1.071	1.073	1.075	1.078	1.081	1.086	1.092	1.092	1.102	1.080	1.184	1.183
3.5	1.007	1.012	1.027	1.034	1.035	1.021	1.023	1.046	1.049	1.051	1.053	1.055	1.047	1.048	1.049	1.050	1.052	1.055	1.057	1.065	1.070	1.074	1.076	1.080	1.117	1.117
4.0	1.003	1.008	1.016	1.030	1.020	1.021	1.023	1.026	1.032	1.036	1.043	1.046	1.047	1.048	1.049	1.050	1.052	1.055	1.057	1.065	1.070	1.074	1.076	1.080	1.088	1.097

Fine grid

P_r

T_r	0.4	0.5	0.6	0.7	0.8	0.9	1.0
0.90	1.735	2.050	0.31	0.25	0.21	0.222	0.238
0.91	1.660	1.926	0.38	0.30	0.244	0.285	0.241
0.92	1.600	1.862	2.277	0.34	0.288	0.353	0.283
0.93	1.538	1.814	2.178	0.42	0.380	0.396	0.396
0.94	1.494	1.764	2.092		0.45	0.418	0.404
0.95	1.466	1.729	2.020	2.872	0.56	0.490	0.470
0.96	1.445	1.710	1.966	2.566	0.71	0.628	0.580
0.97	1.433	1.679	1.915	2.378	3.72	0.762	0.700
0.98	1.410	1.628	1.853	2.248	3.248	0.97	0.91
0.99	1.395	1.587	1.824	2.168	2.780	5.074	1.24
1.00	1.386	1.534	1.776	2.093	2.505	3.862	∞
1.01	1.372	1.498	1.714	2.018	2.393	3.417	7.655
1.02	1.360	1.492	1.670	1.942	2.272	2.930	4.380
1.03	1.335	1.481	1.628	1.870	2.185	2.672	3.655
1.04	1.320	1.440	1.592	1.812	2.096	2.468	3.180
1.05	1.302	1.408	1.556	1.782	2.010	2.315	2.807

T_r	1.0	1.1	1.2	1.3	1.4	1.5	1.6	1.7	1.8	1.9	2.0
0.98	0.91	0.82	0.755	0.692	0.642	0.609	0.589	0.574	0.555	0.528	0.508
0.99	1.24	1.015	0.889	0.782	0.710	0.662	0.626	0.605	0.582	0.562	0.538
1.00	∞	2.34	1.102	0.950	0.844	0.775	0.724	0.667	0.628	0.602	0.575
1.01	7.655	13.78	4.290	1.292	1.075	0.945	0.848	0.765	0.692	0.645	0.617
1.02	4.380	9.15	9.38	2.162	1.395	1.155	1.005	0.885	0.725	0.712	0.678
1.03	3.655	5.477	4.803	4.30	2.066	1.456	1.175	1.045	0.940	0.865	0.796
1.04	3.180	3.826	4.486	5.080	3.179	1.940	1.420	1.190	1.075	0.985	0.921
1.05	2.807	3.321	3.576	4.016	4.327	2.620	1.797	1.425	1.226	1.118	1.065
1.06	2.622	2.970	3.321	3.577	4.258	3.385	2.973	1.769	1.473	1.278	1.194
1.07	2.432	2.668	2.970	3.321	3.721	3.704	3.367	2.350	1.797	1.453	1.325
1.08	2.307	2.502	2.668	3.030	3.531	3.628	3.482	2.876	2.152	1.699	1.510
1.09	2.225	2.365	2.494	2.696	3.184	3.455	3.552	3.229	2.496	2.045	1.831
1.10	2.113	2.260	2.250	2.509	2.770	2.963	3.152	3.080	2.836	2.312	1.990
1.11	2.042	2.058	2.040	2.265	2.473	2.629	2.725	2.790	2.741	2.619	2.121
1.12	1.875	1.870									2.356
1.13	1.740										2.423

TABLE 6-3. DERIVATIVE COMPRESSIBILITY FACTORS* (Continued)

Z^{r1} as a function of P_r and T_r

T_r	\multicolumn{21}{c}{Reduced pressure P_r}
	0.2	0.4	0.6	0.8	1.0	1.2	1.4	1.6	1.8	2.0	2.2	2.4	2.6	2.8	3.0	4.0	5.0	6.0	7.0	8.0	9.0
0.8	0.387	−0.088	−0.150	−0.176	−0.24	−0.22	−0.24	−0.25	−0.26	−0.32	−0.34	−0.36	−0.42	−0.34	−0.24	−0.13	−0.16	−0.17	−0.18	−0.20	−0.21
0.85	0.360	−0.099	−0.130	−0.163	−0.21	−0.25	−0.25	−0.25	−0.24	−0.25	−0.25	−0.26	−0.25	−0.21	−0.16	−0.05	−0.03	−0.08	−0.12	−0.15	−0.19
0.9†	0.334	0.872	−0.121	−0.151	−0.188	−0.22	−0.19	−0.12	−0.18	−0.10	−0.09	−0.09	−0.08	−0.07	−0.03	0.03	0.04	0.04	−0.04	−0.09	−0.17
0.95†	0.265	0.668	1.90	−0.072	−0.117	−0.08	−0.05	−0.02	0.06	0.16	0.18	0.15	0.15	0.14	0.12	0.11	0.11	0.10	0.04	−0.04	−0.15
1.0†	0.223	0.475	1.02	0.295	0.99	0.487	0.492	0.499	0.51	0.476	0.44	0.43	0.42	0.42	0.41	0.40	0.32	0.32	0.17	0.06	−0.08
1.05†	0.109	0.251	0.293	0.39	0.437	4.47	7.02	2.58	1.96	1.00	0.96	0.94	0.89	0.76	0.72	0.64	0.56	0.52	0.41	0.19	0.14
1.1†	0.084	0.135	0.195	0.314	0.227	0.350	0.49	2.12	2.25	1.92	1.63	1.40	1.25	1.08	1.00	0.94	0.88	0.68	0.63	0.58	0.50
1.15†	0.078	0.128	0.188	0.217	0.174	0.290	0.310	0.968	1.40	2.46	2.26	2.16	2.01	1.85	1.59	1.10	1.00	0.91	0.88	0.86	0.85
1.2	0.076	0.120	0.182	0.191	0.162	0.18	0.18	0.31	0.59	1.04	1.62	1.77	1.84	1.78	1.52	1.20	1.01	0.95	0.97	0.98	0.98
1.25	0.070	0.112	0.175	0.184	0.154	0.14	0.14	0.18	0.24	0.52	0.86	0.94	1.11	1.17	1.35	1.28	1.03	1.02	1.01	1.02	1.03
1.3	0.058	0.109	0.160	0.176	0.148	0.13	0.13	0.14	0.18	0.28	0.36	0.52	0.67	0.76	1.00	1.08	1.04	1.04	1.04	1.05	1.05
1.4	0.040	0.080	0.124	0.145	0.11	0.12	0.11	0.09	0.09	0.11	0.20	0.22	0.26	0.33	0.61	0.83	1.01	1.06	1.10	1.09	1.08
1.5	0.031	0.066	0.085	0.093	0.10	0.11	0.09	0.08	0.07	0.07	0.07	0.08	0.09	0.17	0.31	0.73	0.95	1.08	1.12	1.13	1.09
1.6	0.023	0.040	0.060	0.08	0.08	0.10	0.07	0.06	0.06	0.05	0.05	0.05	0.07	0.12	0.22	0.60	0.85	1.16	1.26	1.42	1.36
1.7	0.019	0.036	0.054	0.07	0.07	0.08	0.06	0.05	0.05	0.05	0.04	0.04	0.06	0.10	0.21	0.51	0.82	0.98	1.60	1.75	1.58
1.8	0.017	0.033	0.038	0.05	0.05	0.07	0.05	0.05	0.05	0.04	0.04	0.04	0.08	0.09	0.21	0.41	0.74	0.85	1.59	1.91	1.76
1.9	0.01	0.00	0.02	0.04	0.02	0.06	0.05	0.02	0.04	0.03	0.03	0.04	0.10	0.10	0.19	0.29	0.45	0.51	1.04	1.12	1.19
2.0	0.00	0.00	0.01	0.02	0.00	0.04	0.04	−0.01	0.02	0.01	0.01	0.02	0.00	0.05	0.12	0.25	0.35	0.34	0.72	0.78	0.88
2.5	0.00	0.00	0.00	−0.03	0.00	0.01	0.00	−0.03	−0.01	−0.01	−0.02	−0.02	−0.05	−0.05	0.04	0.18	0.28	0.28	0.42	0.50	0.57
3.0	0.00	0.00	0.00	−0.06	−0.02	−0.01	0.00	−0.06	−0.04	−0.02	−0.02	−0.02	−0.04	−0.06	−0.07	0.06	0.09	0.14	0.16	0.20	0.23
3.5	0.01	0.00	−0.03	−0.09	−0.04	−0.03	−0.03		−0.06						−0.08	−0.05	−0.04	−0.06	−0.07	−0.11	−0.12
4.0	0.02	0.01	−0.04													−0.10	−0.13	−0.16	−0.20	−0.22	−0.23

Fine grid

T_r	\multicolumn{4}{c}{P_r}
	0.4	0.6	0.8	1.0
0.90	0.872	−0.121	−0.151	−0.188
0.91	0.759	−0.119	−0.153	−0.188
0.92	0.501	3.14	−0.172	−0.186
0.93	0.567	2.38	−0.170	−0.180
0.94	0.650	2.07	−0.112	−0.151
0.95	0.668	1.90	−0.072	−0.117
0.96	0.690	1.56	−0.072	−0.091
0.97	0.698	1.49	2.77	−0.045
0.98	0.653	1.46	2.83	−0.136
0.99	0.505	1.42	2.89	0.328
1.00	0.475	1.02	2.95	
1.01	0.381	0.680	2.43	1.88
1.02	0.328	0.561	1.35	1.30
1.03	0.320	0.465	1.08	1.10
1.04	0.291	0.367	0.53	1.03
1.05	0.251	0.293	0.39	0.99

T_r	\multicolumn{6}{c}{P_r}
	1.0	1.2	1.4	1.6	1.8	2.0
0.98	0.136	0.216	0.177	0.249	0.277	0.342
0.99	0.328	0.343	0.352	0.365	0.380	0.394
1.00		0.487	0.492	0.499	0.515	0.476
1.01	1.88	1.21	0.698	0.588	0.66	0.573
1.02	1.30	1.65	1.113	0.767	0.87	0.68
1.03	1.10	1.86	1.61	1.121	1.17	0.76
1.04	1.03	2.77	2.26	1.560	1.53	0.86
1.05	0.99	4.47	7.02	2.58	1.96	1.00
1.06	0.97	1.68	3.98	3.66	2.12	1.13
1.07	0.901	0.89	1.41	2.58	2.38	1.26
1.08	0.600	0.55	1.04	2.98	2.76	1.44
1.09	0.479	0.38	0.75	2.83	2.35	1.65
1.10	0.437	0.350	0.49	2.62	2.25	1.92
1.11	0.377	0.341	0.45	2.12	2.17	2.16
1.13	0.265	0.329	0.35	1.73	1.89	2.43
1.15	0.227	0.290	0.310	1.23	1.402	2.46

* R. C. Reid and J. R. Valbert, *Ind. Eng. Chem. Fundamentals*, **1**:292 (1962).
† See fine grid.

Example 6-4. Estimate V, $(\partial V/\partial P)_T$ and $(\partial V/\partial T)_P$, for propane at 140°F and 1235 psia. Experimentally reported values are 0.0344 ft³/lb, -2.104×10^{-6} ft³/(lb)(psia), and 6.156×10^{-5} ft³/(lb)(°R) respectively (42).

Solution. The critical properties of propane are 369.9°K and 42.0 atm (Appendix A). Thus $T_r = (140 + 460)/(1.8 \times 369.9) = 0.90$, and $P_r = 1,235/(14.7)(42.0) = 2.0$.

For propane, $\omega = 0.152$ (39). From Eq. (3-15) and Figs. 3-5 and 3-6, $Z^0 = 0.316$, and $Z^1 = -0.14$.

$$Z = Z^0 + \omega Z^1 = 0.316 - (0.15)(0.14) = 0.298$$

From Table 6-3, $Z_p^0 = 0.028$, $Z_p^1 = -0.04$, $Z_T^0 = 0.351$, and $Z_T^1 = -0.010$; thus from Eqs. (6-38) and (6-39),

$$Z_p = 0.028 - (0.152)(0.04) = 0.022$$
$$Z_T = 0.351 - (0.152)(0.010) = 0.350$$

Then

$$V = ZRT/P = [(0.298)(10.73)(600)]/[(1,235)(44.07)] = 0.0352 \text{ ft}^3/\text{lb}$$
$$(\partial V/\partial P)_T = -RTZ_p/P^2 = -[(10.73)(600)(0.022)]/[(44.07)(1,235)^2]$$
$$= -2.1 \times 10^{-6} \text{ ft}^3/(\text{lb})(\text{psia})$$

$$(\partial V/\partial T)_P = RZ_T/P = [(10.73)(0.351)]/[(44.07)(1,235)] = 6.9 \times 10^{-5} \text{ ft}^3/(\text{lb})(°\text{R})$$

The errors in the three values are 3, 0, and 12 per cent respectively.

Many other thermodynamic relations may be expressed as simple partial derivatives and evaluated in terms of Z, Z_T, and Z_p. Two of the more common are the difference $C_p - C_v$ and the Joule-Thompson coefficient, i.e.,

$$C_p - C_v = T(\partial P/\partial T)_V(\partial V/\partial T)_P = -T(\partial P/\partial V)_T[\partial V/\partial T]_P^2$$
$$= RZ_T^2/Z_p \quad (6\text{-}40)$$

and $\quad \mu \equiv (\partial T/\partial P)_H = [T(\partial V/\partial T)_P - V]/C_p$

and

$$\mu C_p = (RT/P)(Z_T - Z) \quad (6\text{-}41)$$

Edmister (7, 8, 11) has shown plots of μC_p and $C_p - C_v$ as well as isentropic coefficients as functions of T_r and P_r without introducing a third parameter. His plots were derived from hydrocarbon P-V-T data, whereas the Z_p, Z_T plots were obtained from Pitzer's generalized correlation and as such should be applicable to most types of materials.

As a further illustration of the use of the derivative compressibility factors, the generalized sonic-velocity correlation of Sherwood (45) for compressed gases may be expressed as

$$V_s^2 = [aTZ^2(C_p^0 + \Delta C_p)]/[Z_p(C_p^0 + \Delta C_p) - RZ_T^2] \quad (6\text{-}42)$$

where V_s = velocity of sound, m/sec
$\quad a$ = dimensional constant = $(8,307/M)$, m²/(sec²)(°K)
$\Delta C_p = C_p - C_p^0$

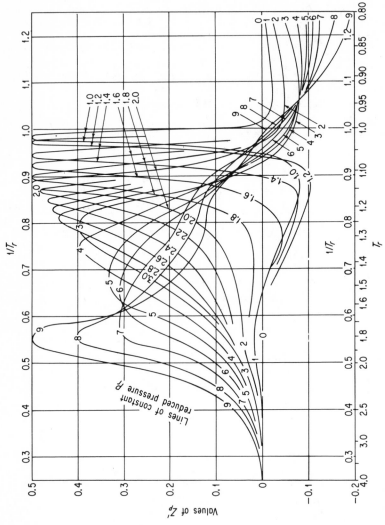

FIG. 6-8. Z_p^1 as a function of P_r and T_r. [Chart drawn by W. C. Edmister from data in article by R. C. Reid and J. R. Valbert, Ind. Eng. Chem. Fundamentals, **1**:292 (1962).]

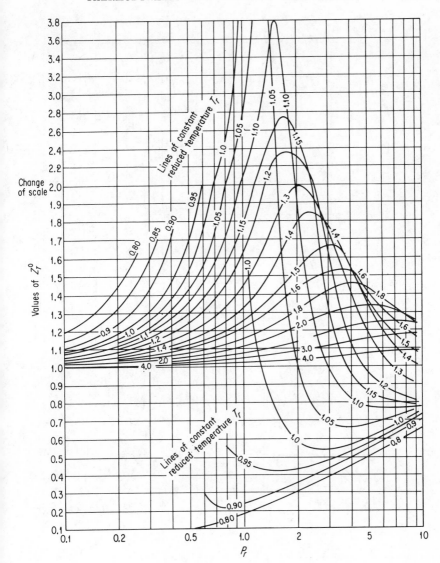

FIG. 6-9. $Z_T{}^0$ as a function of P_r and T_r.   [*Chart drawn by W. C. Edmister from data in article by R. C. Reid and J. R. Valbert, Ind. Eng. Chem. Fundamentals, **1**:292 (1962).*]

and the remainder of the terms have been defined previously.   This equation is illustrated in Example 6-5.

Example 6-5.   Estimate the velocity of sound in ethane gas at 305°K and 116 atm. The experimental value reported by Sherwood is 583 m/sec, and the heat capacity at zero pressure $C_p{}^0$ is 12.8 cal/(g mole)(°K).

Solution.   From Appendix A, $T_c = 305.4$°K, $P_c = 48.2$ atm, $\omega = 0.105$.   Thus $T_r = 305/305.4 = 1.0$; $P_r = 116/48.2 = 2.4$.   From Figs. 3-5, 3-6, and Table 6-3,

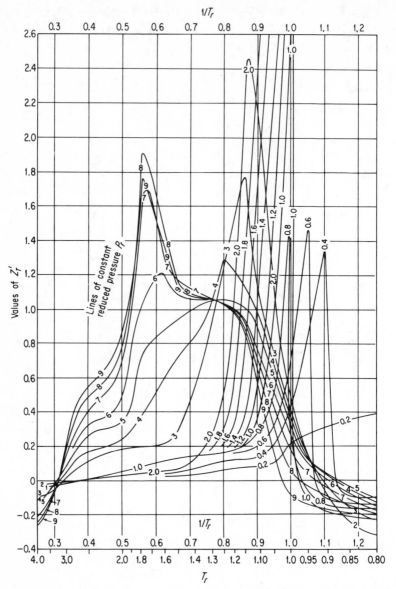

FIG. 6-10. $Z_T{}^1$ as a function of T_r and P_r. [*Chart drawn by W. C. Edmister from data in article by R. C. Reid and J. R. Valbert, Ind. Eng. Chem. Fundamentals,* **1**:292 (1962).]

$Z^0 = 0.384$, $Z^1 = -0.126$, $Z_p{}^0 = 0.072$, $Z_p{}^1 = -0.08$, $Z_T{}^0 = 0.553$, $Z_T{}^1 = 0.43$; thus

$$Z = Z^0 + \omega Z^1 = 0.384 + (0.105)(-0.126) = 0.371$$
$$Z_p = Z_p{}^0 + \omega Z_p{}^1 = 0.072 + (0.105)(-0.08) = 0.064$$
$$Z_T = Z_T{}^0 + \omega Z_T{}^1 = 0.553 + (0.105)(0.43) = 0.598$$

From Fig. 6-6, $C_p - C_p{}^0 = \Delta C_p = 32$ cal/(g mole)(°K) at $T_r = 1.0, P_r = 2.4$.   Thus, with $M = 30.07$,

$$V_s{}^2 = \frac{(8,307)(305)(0.371)^2(12.8 + 32)}{(30.07)[(0.064)(12.8 + 32) - (1.987)(0.598)^2]} = 243,000$$
$$V_s = 492 \text{ m/sec}$$
$$\text{Error} = [(492 - 583)/583] \times 100 = -15.0\%$$

Analytical Formulation of Derivative Functions.   Hirschfelder et al. (23, 24) have differentiated their equations of state [Eqs. (3-58) and (3-63)] to obtain values of the derivatives $(\partial P_r/\partial \rho_r)_T$ and $(\partial P_r/\partial T_r)_{\rho_r}$, in a generalized form.   These results are outlined in Appendix D and may be used to determine those thermodynamic relations requiring such derivatives.   This method is probably somewhat more accurate than that using the Z_p, Z_T functions, but it is more difficult to employ unless machine computation is possible.

6-10   Estimation of Liquid Heat Capacities

Liquid-phase heat capacities have been reviewed up to 1957 in a series of articles by Gambill (17), and only a few new correlations have since been published.   In general, as Gambill notes, most organic liquid heat capacities range between 0.4 and 0.5 cal/(g)(°K) and increase somewhat with temperature.   Pressure effects are small except in the critical region; for low-temperature liquids, the value of C_p decreases some 10 per cent for pressure increases to around 2,500 atm.   At even higher pressures, C_p decreases somewhat with pressure, though data are scarce.

Estimation techniques seem to fall into three categories; those based on empirical structural parameters; those based on a calculation of the energy-storage modes, as was described earlier for many ideal-gas heat-capacity correlations; and those based upon thermodynamics, i.e., a known ideal-gas heat capacity is corrected to the liquid region.   Each of these method types is discussed separately below; recommendations are presented in Sec. 6-14, where all methods are compared and discussed.

Liquid metals, salts, and complex organic coolants are not discussed, but several articles which specifically treat such liquids have been published (2, 6, 17).

6-11   Structural Liquid-heat-capacity Correlations

Johnson and Huang Method (28).   This is an additive group method to estimate C_p at 20°C.   The contributions to be used are listed in Table 6-4.   The method is appealingly simple, but for some types of compounds it is not applicable, and often the method is not particularly accurate, as shown in Table 6-5.   It is compared with other methods in Sec. 6-14.   Example 6-6 illustrates the method.

TABLE 6-4. ATOMIC-GROUP HEAT-CAPACITY CONTRIBUTIONS AT 20°C*

	Contribution $cal/(g\ mole)(°K)$
H— (formic acid and formates)	3.55
CH₃—	9.9
—CH₂—	6.3
—C̶—H	5.4
—COOH	19.1
—COO— (esters)	14.5
$\diagdown$C = 0	14.7
—CN	13.9
—OH	11.0
—NH₂	15.2
—Cl	8.6
—Br	3.7
—NO₂	15.3
—O— (ethers)	8.4
—S—	10.6
C₆H₅—	30.5

* A. I. Johnson and C. J. Huang, *Can. J. Technol.*, **33**:421 (1955).

Sakiadis and Coates Structural Method (43). Sakiadis and Coates proposed that liquid-hydrocarbon heat capacities below the normal boiling point could be correlated as a function of reduced temperature and structure. Paraffinic and olefinic hydrocarbons with five or more carbons and simple aromatics may be treated. If the compound is nonaromatic, the contribution due to the number of carbon atoms $(14 > N_c > 5)$ is read from Fig. 6-11. Any chain branching is considered next, and the corrections for the three most common branching types are shown in Fig. 6-12a. For all olefinic double bonds except the type

$$C$$
$$|$$
$$C—C=C$$

a negative contribution of $-0.020\ cal/(g)(°K)$ is required; for the special double bond above, no contribution is necessary.

For aromatic compounds, the benzene-ring contribution is read from Fig. 6-13, and each side chain CH₃— or —CH₂— group contributes an additional increment as given in Fig. 6-12b.

The method is illustrated in Example 6-6, and calculated values are compared with some experimental values in Table 6-5. The accuracy of the method is discussed in Sec. 6-14.

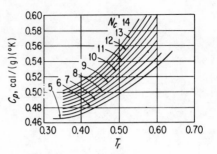

FIG. 6-11. Carbon-chain contributions to heat capacity. n-aliphatic hydrocarbons. NOTE: For isoparaffins add a branching contribution to these values (see Fig. 6-12a). [From B. C. Sakiadis and J. Coates, AIChE J., **2**:88 (1956).]

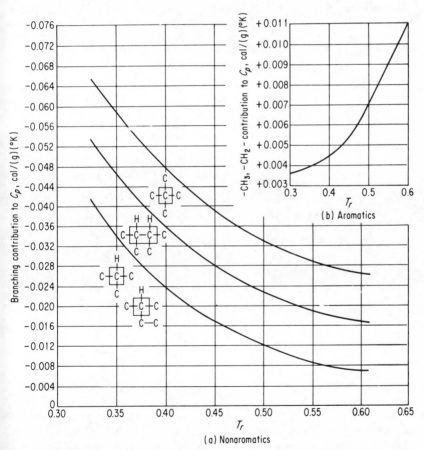

FIG. 6-12. Branching contributions to heat capacity. [From B. C. Sakiadis and J. Coates, AIChE J., **2**:88 (1956).]

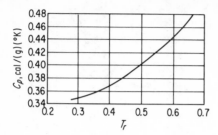

FIG. 6-13. Aromatic contributions to heat capacity. Values from chart may require a side-chain contribution (see Fig. 6-12b). [*From B. C. Sakiadis and J. Coates, AIChE J.*, **2**:88 (1956).]

Other group-contribution methods have been suggested but lack the generality and accuracy of the two noted above (4, 17).

Example 6-6. Estimate the liquid-heat capacity of 2-methylpentane at 20°C, using both the methods of Johnson and Huang and Sakiadis and Coates. The experimental value is 0.533 cal/(g)(°K) (43).

Solution. *Method of Johnson and Huang.* From Table 6-4.

$$3 \text{—CH}_3 = 3(9.9)$$
$$2 \text{—CH}_2 = 2(6.3)$$
$$1 \text{—CH} = \underline{\quad 5.4 \quad}$$
$$47.7 \text{ cal/(g mole)(°K)}$$
$$M = 86.17$$
$$C_p = 47.7/86.17 = 0.554 \text{ cal/(g)(°K)}$$
$$\text{Error} = [(0.554 - 0.533)/0.533] \times 100 = +4.0\%$$

Method of Sakiadis and Coates. The critical temperature is 496.5°K (Appendix A), so that $T_r = (273.2 + 20)/496.5 = 0.59$. From Fig. 6-11, the contribution due to the six carbons is 0.544 cal/(g)(°K).

The correction for branching of the type

$$
\begin{array}{c}
\text{H} \\
| \\
\text{C—C—C}
\end{array}
$$

in Fig. 6-12a is −0.007 cal/(g)(°K). Thus

$$C_p = 0.544 - 0.007 = 0.537 \text{ cal/(g)(°K)}$$
$$\text{Error} = [(0.537 - 0.533)/0.533] \times 100 = 0.8\%$$

6-12 Watson Method

As illustrated in Chap. 5, there are several reasonably reliable estimation techniques for ideal-gas heat capacities C_p^0; also, there are many instances in which accurate values of C_p^0 have been determined from theoretical considerations and spectroscopic data. One might then propose a liquid-heat-capacity correlation based upon C_p^0 but corrected for the real-gas nonidealities and condensation to the liquid phase. Since C_p is a temperature derivative of enthalpy, a point function, one could fashion a simple thermodynamic cycle as follows: (1) a saturated liquid at T_1 may be heated to T_2, saturated liquid; (2) liquid at T_2 is vaporized and expanded isothermally to a zero pressure, ideal-gas state; (3) as an ideal gas, the material is cooled from T_2 to T_1; (4) the material is compressed isothermally at T_1 to a saturated vapor and condensed. Since the cyclic change of enthalpy is zero, then, by writing the enthalpy changes for the steps 1 to 4 and equating to zero,

$$(H_{T_2} - H_{T_1})_{sL} = (\Delta H_v)_{T_1} - (\Delta H_v)_{T_2} + (H^0 - H_{sv})_{T_1}$$
$$- (H^0 - H_{sv})_{T_2} + C_p{}^0(T_2 - T_1) \quad (6\text{-}43)$$

Letting T_2 approach T_1,

$$(dH)_{sL} = -d\Delta H_v - d(H^0 - H_{sv}) + C_p{}^0 \, dT \quad (6\text{-}44)$$

Before proceeding farther, the definition of liquid-phase heat capacities must be considered. There are three in general use. C_{p_L}, C_{sL}, and $(dQ/dT)_{sL}$. The first represents the change in enthalpy with temperature at constant pressure; the second shows the change in the enthalpy of the saturated liquid with temperature, along the saturation curve, dH_{sL}/dT; and the third is the heat necessary to effect a temperature change if the liquid is held in a saturated-liquid state. It is the third form which is usually measured in the laboratory. They are related as

$$C_{sL} = dH_{sL}/dT = C_{p_L} + [V_{sL} - T(\partial V/\partial T)_P](dP/dT)_{sL} \quad (6\text{-}45)$$
$$C_{sL} = (dQ/dT)_{sL} + V_{sL}(dP/dT)_{sL} \quad (6\text{-}46)$$

Except near the critical point, all the forms are in close agreement numerically.* Choosing $(dQ/dT)_{sL}$ as the desired quantity, and then combining Eqs. (6-44) and (6-46),

$$(dQ/dT)_{sL} \equiv C'_{sL} = C_p{}^0 - d\Delta H_v/dT - (1/T_c)[(\partial/\partial T_r)(H^0 - H_{sv})]_{P_r}$$
$$- (1/T_c)[(\partial/\partial P_r)(H^0 - H_{sv})]_{T_r} - V_{sL}(dP/dT)_{sL} \quad (6\text{-}47)$$

Equation (6-47) written in reduced form has considered ΔH_v to be a function of T_r only and $H^0 - H_{sv}$ to be a function of T_r and P_r for any particular substance. Watson (48) first suggested such a form, although he solved for $(dH/dT)_{sL}$ rather than $(dQ/dT)_{sL}$.

Sobel (46) has evaluated the various terms in Eq. (6-47). The partial derivatives of $H^0 - H_{sv}$ were obtained by graphical differentiation of the tables of Lydersen, Greenkorn, and Hougen shown in Appendix B, wherein $(H^0 - H)/T_c$ are tabulated as functions of T_r, P_r, and Z_c. The

---

* Note that this statement is not valid for comparable expressions for the saturated vapor, as the volume of the vapor is a large value. In some cases, in fact, $(dQ/dT)_{sv}$ may even be negative.

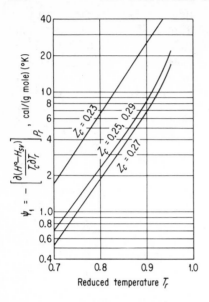

FIG. 6-14. Effect of T_r on ψ_1. [R. C. Reid and J. E. Sobel, Ind. Eng. Chem. Fundamentals, 4:328 (1965).]

slopes were obtained at the limit where the generalized reduced isobars or isotherms intersected the generalized saturation curve. The temperature derivative of the latent heat of vaporization was obtained from the Klein ΔH_v correlation [Eq. (4-61)] and Watson's temperature function [Eq. (4-67)]. The vapor-pressure derivative was determined from the Clapeyron equation (4-1), with ΔH_v determined as shown above and ΔV_v from $(RT/P) \Delta Z_v$. Finally, the value of ΔZ_v was correlated with the reduced vapor pressure as suggested by Lydersen (30).

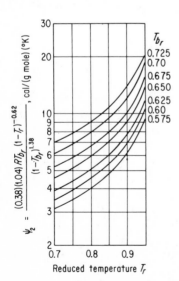

FIG. 6-15. The estimating-function ψ_2 variation with T_{b_r} and T_r. [R. C. Reid and J. E. Sobel, Ind. Eng. Chem. Fundamentals, 4:328 (1965).]

The final result is expressed as

$$(dQ/dT)_{sL} \equiv C'_{sL} = C_p^0 + \psi_0[(\psi_1/\psi_0) - \psi_2 + (\psi_4 P_{vp_r}/\Delta Z_v)(\psi_3 + RZ_c/\rho_{sL_r})] \quad (6\text{-}48)$$

The ψ functions are defined in the nomenclature, and all but ψ_0 are shown in Figs. 6-14 to 6-17. ΔZ_v may be determined from Figs. 4-5a and b, but for this correlation it may be rapidly approximated from Fig. 6-18. Finally, ρ_{sL_r} is shown in Fig. 6-19 as a function of T_r and Z_c.   Experimental values of C_p^0 may be used or estimations made as discussed in Sec. 5-8. The accuracy of the method is discussed in Sec. 6-14 and calculated values

FIG. 6-16. Effect of T_r on ψ_3. [R. C. Reid and J. E. Sobel, Ind. Eng. Chem. Fundamentals, **4**:328 (1965).]

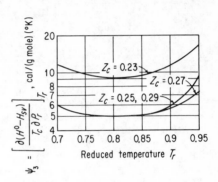

FIG. 6-17. The estimating-function Ψ_4 variation with T_{b_r} and T_r. [R. C. Reid and J. E. Sobel, Ind. Eng. Chem. Fundamentals, **4**:328 (1965).]

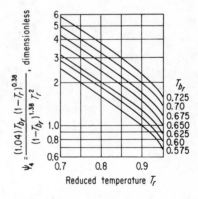

FIG. 6-18. $1/(Z_v - Z_L)$ as a function of P_{vp_r}. [R. C. Reid and J. E. Sobel, Ind. Eng. Chem. Fundamentals, **4**:328 (1965).]

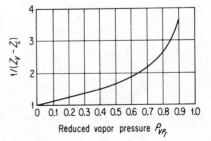

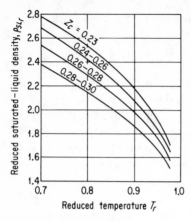

FIG. 6-19. Variation of ρ_{SL_r} with T_r. [R. C. Reid and J. E. Sobel, Ind. Eng. Chem. Fundamentals, **4**:328 (1965).]

compared with experimental values in Table 6-6. The method is illustrated in Example 6-7.

Example 6-7. Estimate the heat capacity of saturated-liquid isopropyl alcohol, expressed as $(dQ/dT)_{sL}$ at 204°C, using the Watson thermodynamic method. The experimental value is reported as 63.72 cal/(g mole)(°K) (19).

Solution. From Appendix A, $T_c = 508.2$°K, $P_c = 47.0$ atm, $V_c = 220.4$ cm³/g mole, $T_b = 355.5$°K, and $Z_c = 0.248$. At $T_r = (204 + 273.2)/508.2 = 0.939$, the reduced vapor pressure is 0.585 (21). T_{b_r} is $355.5/508.8 = 0.7$. The heat capacity at zero pressure $C_p{}^0$ is 31.1 cal/(g mole)(°K) at this temperature (1).

From Figs. 6-14 to 6-19,

$$\psi_1 = 17.1 \text{ at } T_r = 0.939$$
$$\psi_2 = 16.2 \text{ at } T_r = 0.939, \ T_{b_r} = 0.700$$
$$\psi_3 = 7.9 \text{ at } T_r = 0.939$$
$$\psi_4 = 1.5 \text{ at } T_r = 0.939, \ T_{b_r} = 0.700$$
$$1/\Delta Z_v = 1.82 \text{ at } P_{vp_r} = 0.585$$
$$\rho_{sL_r} = 1.89 \text{ at } T_r = 0.939$$

As defined in the nomenclature,

$$\psi_0 = \ln P_{b_r}(1 - P_{b_r}/T_{b_r}^3)^{1/2}$$
$$= \ln \tfrac{1}{47}[1 - \tfrac{1}{47}/(0.700)^3]^{1/2}$$
$$= -3.73$$

From Eq. (6-48),

$$C'_{sL} = 31.1 - 3.73\{17.1/(-3.73) - 16.2 + (1.5)(0.585)(1.82)$$
$$[7.9 + (1.987)(0.248)/1.89]\}$$
$$= 60.0 \text{ cal/(g mole)(°K)}$$
$$\text{Error} = [(60.0 - 63.7)/63.7] \times 100 = -5.8\%$$

To compare C'_{sL} with other liquid-heat capacities by using Eq. (6-46), an approximate value of $V_{sL}(dP/dT)_{sL}$ may be obtained from Eq. (4-1), with $\Delta H_v/\Delta Z_v$ (from Fig. 4-2) of about 9000 cal/g mole, i.e.,

$$V_{sL}(dP/dT)_{sL} = (V_{sL}P/RT^2)(\Delta H_v/\Delta Z_v)$$
$$\cong 9{,}000 Z_{sL}/T \qquad \text{cal/(g mole)(°K)}$$

Z_{sL} is usually ~ 0.1 except at high reduced T_r. From Fig. 4-5b, $Z_{sL} \sim 0.1$ at $T_r = 0.94$; thus

$$V_{sL}(dP/dT)_{sL} \text{ (at } 477°\text{K)} \sim (9,000 \times 0.1)/477 = 1.9 \text{ cal/(g mole)}(°\text{K)}$$

This value is small compared with $C'_{sL} = 63.7$ cal/(g mole)(°K) so that $dH_{sL}/dT \sim C'_{sL} = (dQ/dT)_{sL}$. At lower values of T_r the agreement would be closer.

6-13 Sakiadis and Coates Energy-mode Method

In a manner quite similar to the Bennewitz and Rossner ideal-gas heat-capacity correlation (Sec. 5-4), Sakiadis and Coates (43) proposed a method to estimate liquid-heat capacities. The various modes of energy storage were approximated and the temperature derivative equated to the constant-volume heat capacity (20).

Translational motion of the molecule as a rigid body, which contributes $\frac{3}{2}R$ per mole to the heat capacity of an ideal gas, is replaced by an oscillatory motion in the liquid. The oscillations have both a kinetic- and a potential-energy part, so that the comparable liquid-phase contribution is $2(\frac{3}{2})R = 3R$ per mole. As in the case of a gas, the frequency of oscillation is low enough so that the value of $h\nu/kT$ approaches zero and Eq. (5-1) indicates a full contribution of $R/2$ per mole per mode of energy storage.

External rotation in the ideal gas is replaced by a rigid-body torsional oscillation. As indicated in the preceding paragraph, each torsional mode consists of a kinetic and a potential term, and since there are three axes of torsion, the full contribution to heat capacity of liquids is again $3R$ per mole.*

Similar considerations apply to rotations within the molecule about a C—C or C—O bond; i.e., each such rotation contributes R to the liquid-phase heat capacity. Thus the so-called "external degrees of freedom" contribute $(3 + 3 + a)R$ to C_v; for an ideal gas such contributions were one-half this value. The difference results, as noted above, from the fact that in liquids the molecules are constrained and motions are oscillatory

---

* In other words, for in-line oscillations and torsional oscillations, classical theory appears to be applicable, and, as discussed in Secs. 5-3 and 5-4, each mode of energy storage then contributes $R/2$ to the molal heat capacity. Sakiadis and Coates suggest that a frequency of the in-line and torsional oscillations of the molecule (as a solid body) may be approximated by the ratio of the velocity of sound to the molecular-separation distance, since sound waves are presumably carried by molecular vibrations from torsional or in-line motion. Most velocity-of-sound measurements for liquids are in the range of 10^3 m/sec, and molecular spacings from X-ray diffraction are in the range of several angstroms; thus the frequencies referred to are near 10^{12} sec^{-1}, and $h\nu/kT$ at room temperature is then much less than unity.

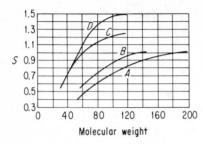

FIG. 6-20. S as a function of molecular weight. [*From B. C. Sakiadis and J. Coates, AIChE J.*, **2**:88 (1956).] *A*, aliphatic compounds, hydrocarbons, naphthenes, esters. *B*, aromatic compounds, hydrocarbons, halides, esters, ketones. *C*, aliphatic compounds, acids, alcohols, ethers. *D*, aromatic compounds, alcohols, amines, mercaptans.

in nature, each oscillation possessing two energy-storage modes, kinetic and potential, rather than only the kinetic mode as for an ideal gas.

Finally, for energy storage in in-line and deformation vibrations between atoms within the molecule, an analysis similar to that given in Sec. 5-4 for an ideal gas is possible. The "average" bond wave numbers recommended by Sakiadis and Coates differ somewhat from those given in Table 5-1. However, except for the C—H bending values, those given by Dobratz in Table 5-1 are usually sufficiently close to be applicable. For C—H bending, an average value of the wave number of about 1,225 cm^{-1} can be used. The polynomial values of A, B, C in Eq. (5-6) then become

C—H *bending*

$A = -0.758$

$B = 3.70 \times 10^{-3}$

$C = -1.38 \times 10^{-6}$

In addition, a temperature-independent correction factor S was found to be necessary; this S value occurs as a multiplier to the bending or deformation contribution and appears to be a function only of molecular weight and type of compound. Values are shown in Fig. 6-20.

In summary, the final form of the liquid-phase heat-capacity correlation is given as:

$$C_v(\text{liquid}) = (6 + a)R + \Sigma q_i C_{\nu_i} + [(3n - 6 - a - \Sigma q_i)/\Sigma q_i]S\Sigma q_i C_{\delta_i}$$

(6-49)

where C_v = heat capacity at constant volume, cal/(g mole)(°K)

a = number of freely rotating C—C, C—O (esters, ethers) bonds

q_i = number of valence bonds of ith type

n = number of atoms in molecule

S = correction factor given in Fig. 6-20

C_{ν_i}, C_{δ_i} = heat-capacity functions, given as polynomials in temperature in Table 5-1 except that for (C—H) bending the A, B, and C terms are -0.758, 3.70×10^{-3}, and -1.38×10^{-6}, respectively

The method is used in a manner similar to that illustrated in Example 5-1 and also as shown in Example 6-8 below.

Conversion of C_v to C_p. The method proposed in Eq. (6-49) yields C_v. However, values of C_p are of more use in engineering calculations. In ideal gases, $C_p{}^0 = C_v{}^0 + R$. For liquids, the difference between C_p and C_v is usually much larger than R. Sakiadis and Coates suggest that the conversion may be made if values of the velocity of sound and coefficient of thermal expansion are available. However, as such data are ordinarily not available, use may be made of Eq. (6-40), which, in reduced form, becomes

$$C_p - C_v = (RT_r Z_c / \rho_r{}^2)[\partial \rho_r / \partial T_r]_{P_r}^2 / (\partial \rho_r / \partial P_r)_{T_r} \qquad (6\text{-}50)$$

In Table 3-6, ρ_r is given as a generalized, tabular function of T_r, P_r, and Z_c, and, from this table, values of the necessary derivatives may be obtained by numerical differentiation. The technique is illustrated in Example 6-8.

Tables 6-5 and 6-6 show some values of C_p calculated for various liquids at several temperatures, and the method is compared with others in Section 6-14.

Example 6-8. Using the method of Sakiadis and Coates, estimate the liquid-heat capacity of ethyl-n-butyrate at both constant volume and pressure at 20°C. The experimental value of C_p quoted by Sakiadis and Coates is 53.2 cal/(g mole)(°K).

Solution. First estimate C_v from Eq. (6-49).

$$n = 20 \qquad a = 6 \qquad \Sigma q_i = 19 \qquad (3n - 6 - a - \Sigma q_i)/\Sigma q_i = 1.526$$

S (from Fig. 6-20) is 0.81 for $M = 116.1$, curve A. From Table 5-1,

$$\begin{aligned}
\Sigma q_i C_{v_i} &= 4(-1.090 + 6.00 \times 10^{-3}T - 3.441 \times 10^{-6}T^2) \\
&\quad + 12(0.229 - 1.224 \times 10^{-3}T + 1.658 \times 10^{-6}T^2) \\
&\quad + 2(-1.173 + 6.132 \times 10^{-3}T - 3.555 \times 10^{-6}T^2) \\
&\quad + (-0.324 + 0.724 \times 10^{-3}T + 1.308 \times 10^{-6}T^2) \\
&= -4.282 + 22.30 \times 10^{-3}T + 0.330 \times 10^{-6}T^2
\end{aligned}$$

At 20°C = 293°K

$$\Sigma q_i C_{v_i} = 2.28 \text{ cal/(g mole)(°K)}$$

From Table 5-1 except for (C—H) bending when A, B, and C values are given under Eq. (6-49),

$$\begin{aligned}
\Sigma q_i C_{\delta_i} &= 4(0.730 + 3.414 \times 10^{-3}T - 2.577 \times 10^{-6}T^2) \\
&\quad + 12(-0.758 + 3.700 \times 10^{-3}T - 1.38 \times 10^{-6}T^2) \\
&\quad + 2(1.461 + 1.633 \times 10^{-3}T - 1.414 \times 10^{-6}T^2) \\
&\quad + (0.730 + 3.414 \times 10^{-3}T - 2.577 \times 10^{-6}T^2) \\
&= -2.524 + 64.74 \times 10^{-3}T - 32.27 \times 10^{-6}T^2
\end{aligned}$$

At 20°C = 293°K

$$\Sigma q_i C_{\delta_i} = 13.68 \text{ cal/(g mole)(°K)}$$

Thus
$$\begin{aligned}
C_v &= (6 + 6)(1.987) + 2.28 + (1.526)(0.81)(13.68) \\
&= 43.03 \text{ cal/(g mole)(°K)}
\end{aligned}$$

To convert to a value of C_p by the use of Eq. (6-50), from Appendix A, $T_c = 566.2°K$, $P_c = 30.2$ atm, $Z_c = 0.273$. Using the values of $Z_c = 0.27$, from Table 3-6, with

$$T_r = 293/566.2 = 0.517 \qquad P_r \sim \text{low, near sat. liquid}$$

ρ_r VALUES

T_r	Sat. liq. $(P_r \sim 0)$	$P_r = 1$	$P_r = 2$
0.50	2.937	2.947	2.957
0.52	2.900	2.911	2.922
0.54	2.862	2.875	2.888

The differences are nearly linear; thus

$$(\Delta\rho_r/\Delta T_r)_{P_r} = 0.037/-0.02 = -1.85 \cong (\partial\rho_r/\partial T_r)_{P_r}$$
$$(\Delta\rho_r/\Delta P_r)_{T_r} = 0.011/1 = 0.011 \cong (\partial\rho_r/\partial P_r)_{T_r}$$
and
$$\rho_r = 2.906 \text{ at sat. liq.} \qquad T_r = 0.517$$

Thus, from Eq. (6-50),

$$C_p - C_v = [(1.987)(0.517)(0.273)/(2.906)^2](-1.85)^2/0.011$$
$$= 10.3 \text{ cal}/(\text{g mole})(°K)$$
and
$$C_p = 10.3 + 43.03 = 53.3 \text{ cal}/(\text{g mole})(°K)$$
$$\text{Error} = [(53.3 - 53.2)/53.2] \times 100 = +0.2\%$$

The major uncertainty in the $C_p - C_v$ calculation lies in the $(\partial\rho_r/\partial P_r)_{T_r}$ term. From Table 3-6, from differences, two-place accuracy is really all that is warranted, and as the value lies between 0.010 and 0.011, the uncertainty in the second figure introduces a large error in determining $C_p - C_v$.

6-14 Recommendations to Estimate Liquid Heat Capacity

Each of the four correlations proposed for liquid-heat capacity appears to have some merit. Tables 6-5 and 6-6 show a few calculated and experimental values to give some idea of the errors involved.

Rapid estimations of liquid-heat capacities at 20°C are best made with the Johnson-Huang method and by using Table 6-4. For temperatures slightly higher or lower than 20°C, the value of dC_{pL}/dT is about 0.001 to 0.002 cal/(g)(°K) so that reasonable estimations may then quickly be carried out in the room-temperature range (4, 22).

Although slightly more difficult to use, the corresponding-state method of Sakiadis and Coates for hydrocarbons (Figs. 6-11 to 6-13) yields good results. The method is not applicable for hydrocarbons with fewer than five carbon atoms, nor can it ordinarily be used for temperatures above the normal boiling point.

Above the normal boiling point, the modified Sakiadis and Coates method described in Sec. 6-13 may be used.   As seen in Table 6-6, the average error at $T > T_b$ is over 7 per cent, and for certain compounds, notably chlorinated materials, very poor results were obtained.   It is, however, about the only method applicable for liquids at temperatures slightly above the boiling point.

For reduced temperatures above T_r of 0.7, but below 0.95, the method of Watson as modified by Sobel (Sec. 6-12) appears preferable.   In this

TABLE 6-5. COMPARISON OF CALCULATED AND EXPERIMENTAL HEAT
CAPACITIES OF LIQUIDS AT 20°C
Values in cal/(g)(°K)

Compound	C_p exp.	Johnson and Huang, Table 6-4		Sakiadis and Coates structural method, Figs. 6-11 to 6-13		Sakiadis and Coates energy-mode method, Eqs. (6-49) and (6-50)	
		C_p	% Error	C_p	% Error	C_p	% Error
n-Butane..............	0.549	0.559	+ 1.8	.....	.....	0.567	+ 3.3
n-Pentane.............	0.558	0.538	− 3.6	0.545	−2.3	0.544	− 2.5
n-Hexane..............	0.534	0.522	− 2.3	0.533	−0.2	0.530	− 0.8
2-Methylpentane.......	0.533	0.554	+ 3.9	0.537	+0.8	0.548	+ 2.6
2,2,3-Trimethylbutane ..	0.497	0.548	+10	0.493	−0.8	0.490	− 1.4
Benzene...............	0.412	0.391	− 5.1	0.412	0	0.414	+ 0.5
p-Xylene..............	0.406	0.474	+17	0.405	−0.3	0.408	+ 0.5
Ethylbenzene..........	0.402	0.440	+ 9.5	0.405	+0.8	0.418	+ 4.0
1,2,4-Triethylbenzene...	0.420	0.501	+19	0.400	−4.8	0.415	− 1.2
Acetic acid	0.488	0.483	− 1.0	.....	.....	0.471	− 3.5
Propionic acid	0.473	0.477	+ 0.8	.....	.....	0.504	+ 6.6
n-Propyl alcohol	0.563	0.558	− 0.9	.....	.....	0.561	− 0.4
Isopropyl alcohol	0.602	0.602	0	.....	.....	0.603	+ 0.2
Ethyl acetate	0.457	0.461	+ 0.9	.....	.....	0.425	− 7.0
n-Propyl acetate	0.459	0.460	+ 0.2	.....	.....	0.447	− 2.6
Ethyl-n-butyrate.......	0.457	0.458	+ 0.2	.....	.....	0.459	+ 0.4
Acetone...............	0.517	0.594	+15	.....	.....	0.495	− 4.3
Aniline...............	0.496	0.491	− 1.0	.....	.....	0.483	− 2.6
Ethylamine............	0.691	0.696	+ 0.7	.....	.....	0.719	+ 4.1
Methyl chloride........	0.371	0.396	− 2.0	.....	.....	0.495	+33
n-Propyl chloride.......	0.404	0.347	+ 9.1	.....	.....	0.463	+14
Chlorobenzene.........	0.318	.....	.....	.....	.....	0.337	+ 6.0
Ethylcyclohexane.......	0.446	...		...		0.441	− 1.1
Phenetole.............	0.446	...		...		0.451	+ 1.1
Iodobenzene...........	0.186	...		...		0.190	+ 2.1
Average error, %.....	.....	5.0		1.1		.....	4.3

% error = [(calc.) − (exp.)/(exp.)] × 100

TABLE 6-6. COMPARISON OF CALCULATED AND EXPERIMENTAL LIQUID-HEAT
CAPACITIES AT TEMPERATURES ABOVE THE NORMAL BOILING POINTS
Comparison at $T_r \geq 0.7$, values in cal/(g mole)(°K)

Compound	T, °K	T_r	C_p exp.	(C'_{sL})*	% Error‡	C_p†	% Error‡
n-Butane.......	298	0.70	33.06	34.1	+3.1	33.9	+ 2.5
	340	0.80	38.28	37.6	−1.8	37.8	− 1.3
	383	0.90	44.66	48.4	+8.4	56.4	+26
n-Pentane......	329	0.70	42.88	42.9	0	41.0	− 4.4
	352	0.75	45.36	44.8	−1.2	43.2	− 4.8
	376	0.80	47.78	40.8	−2.1	46.3	− 3.1
n-Heptane......	378	0.70	63.09	62.2	−1.4	57.7	− 8.5
	432	0.80	68.71	68.7	0	64.8	− 5.7
	486	0.90	77.51	77.3	−0.3	85.1	+ 9.8
1-Pentene.......	325	0.70	38.64	40.2	+4.0	37.4	− 3.2
	349	0.75	39.55	42.2	+6.7	38.7	− 2.2
	372	0.80	41.02	44.0	+7.3	41.6	+ 1.4
Isopropyl alcohol	356	0.70	48.24	46.2	−4.2	38.7	−20
	407	0.80	55.44	50.5	−9.0	44.0	−21
	457	0.90	61.98	59.6	−3.8	62.5	+ 0.3
p-Xylene.......	433	0.70	55.36	55.3	−0.1	54.8	− 1.0
	495	0.80	61.49	61.5	0	62.3	+ 1.3
	557	0.90	70.73	68.5	−3.2	80.3	+14
Average error.	...	....	.....	....	3.1	....	7.3

* Watson method [Eq. (6-48)].
† Sakiadis and Coates energy-mode method [Eqs. (6-49) and (6-50)].
‡ Per cent error = [(calc. − exp.)/exp.] × 100.

case a separate value of C_p^0 must be found. Experimental vapor pressures are recommended, as the calculated results at high values of T_r are sensitive to the value of P_r chosen. Sobel tested this method with 15 different saturated liquids including water, ammonia, alcohols, hydrocarbons, and nitrogen and found an average deviation of about 2 per cent, with maximum deviations of 5.1 and 6.7 per cent for ammonia and nitrogen.

NOMENCLATURE FOR CHAPTER 6

a = number of C—C and C—O (ether and ester) bonds; dimensional constant in Eq. (6-42)

C_p = heat capacity at constant pressure, cal/(g mole)(°K); C_p^0, at zero pressure; C_{p_L}, of the liquid; C_{sL}, of the saturated liquid

C_v = heat capacity at constant volume, cal/(g mole)(°K); C_v^0, at zero pressure

C_{ν_i}, C_{δ_i} = heat-capacity contributions due to in-line and bending vibrations, cal/(g mole)(°K)

C'_{sL} = $(dQ/dT)_{sL}$, cal/(g mole)(°K)

E = internal energy, cal/g mole; E^0, at zero pressure

f = fugacity, atm; f_s, at pressure P_s; f^0, at zero pressure

F = free energy (Gibbs), cal/g mole

h = Planck's constant

H = enthalpy, cal/g mole; H^0, at zero pressure; H_{sL}, of the saturated liquid; H_{sv}, of the saturated vapor

ΔH_v = heat of vaporization, cal/g mole

k = Boltzmann's constant

M = molecular weight

n = number of atoms in molecule

N_c = number of carbon atoms in molecule

P = pressure, atm; P_c, critical pressure; P_s, in a standard state; P_r, reduced pressure P/P_c; P_{vp}, vapor pressure; P_{vp_r}, reduced vapor pressure P_{vp}/P_c; P_b, pressure at normal boiling point, 1 atm; P_{b_r}, reduced pressure at normal boiling point P_b/P_c

q_i = bond of the ith type

Q = heat, cal

R = gas constant

S = entropy, cal/(g mole)(°K); S_s, in standard state at pressure P_s; a correction factor from Fig. 6-20

T = temperature, °K; T_c, critical temperature; T_r, reduced temperature T/T_c; T_b, normal boiling temperature

V = volume, cm³/g mole; V_{sL}, of the saturated liquid; V_L, of the liquid

V_s = velocity of sound, m/sec

Z = compressibility factor, PV/RT; Z_p, Z_T, Z_p^0, Z_p^1, Z_T^0, Z_T^1, derivative compressibility factors [see Eqs. (6-34) and (6-35)]; Z_c, compressibility factor at the critical point; Z_{sL}, compressibility factor of the saturated liquid; ΔZ_v, difference between compressibility factors of saturated vapor and liquid

Greek

μ = Joule-Thompson coefficient $(\partial T/\partial P)_H$, °K/atm

ν = frequency of vibration, sec⁻¹

ρ = density, g moles/cm³; ρ_c, density of the critical point; ρ_r reduced density ρ/ρ_c; ρ_{sL}, density of the saturated liquid; ρ_{sL_r}, ρ_{sL}/ρ_c

ψ_0 = $\ln P_{b_r}(1 - P_{b_r}/T_{b_r}^3)^{1/2}$

ψ_1 = $-(1/T_c)[(\partial/\partial T_r)(H^0 - H_{sv})]_{P_r}$

ψ_2 = $[(0.38)(1.04)RT_{b_r}(1 - T_r)^{-0.62}]/(1 - T_{b_r})^{1.38}$

ψ_3 = $(1/T_c)[(\partial/\partial P_r)(H^0 - H_{sv})]_{T_r}$

ψ_4 = $[(1.04)T_{b_r}(1 - T_r)^{0.38}]/[(1 - T_{b_r})^{1.38}T_r^2]$

ω = Pitzer acentric factor (see Sec. 2-8)

REFERENCES FOR CHAPTER 6

1. American Petroleum Institute: "Selected Values of Physical and Thermodynamic Properties of Hydrocarbons and Related Compounds," Project 44, Carnegie Press, Pittsburgh, Pa., 1953, and supplements.
2. Brock, F. H.: *ARS J.*, **31**:265 (1961).
3. Callen, H. B.: "Thermodynamics," John Wiley & Sons, Inc., New York, 1960.
4. Chow, W. M., and J. A. Bright: *Chem. Eng. Progr.*, **49**:175 (1953).

5. Cosner, J. L., J. E. Gagliardo, and T. S. Storvick: *J. Chem. Eng. Data*, **6**:360 (1961).
6. Douglas, T. B.: *Trans. ASME*, **79**:23 (1957).
7. Edmister, W. C.: *Petrol. Refiner*, **27**(11):609 (1948).
8. Edmister, W. C.: *Petrol. Refiner*, **28**(1):128 (1949).
9. Edmister, W. C.: *Petrol. Refiner*, **28**(2):137 (1949).
10. Edmister, W. C.: *Petrol. Refiner*, **28**(5):149 (1949).
11. Edmister, W. C.: *Petrol. Refiner*, **37**(7):153 (1957).
12. Edmister, W. C.: Private communication, 1963.
13. Epstein, P. S.: "Textbook on Thermodynamics," John Wiley & Sons, Inc., New York, 1937.
14. Erbar, J. H., C. L. Persyn, and W. C. Edmister: Paper presented at the meeting of the National Gas Processors Association, New Orleans, March, 1964.
15. Eubank, P. T., and J. M. Smith: *AIChE J.*, **8**:117 (1962).
16. Garavito, L.: 10.90 Project, Department of Chemical Engineering, Massachusetts Institute of Technology, Cambridge, Mass., 1963.
17. Gambill, W. R.: *Chem. Eng.*, **64**(5):263; *ibid.*, (6):243; *ibid.* (7):263; *ibid.* (8):257 (1957).
18. Gambill, W. R.: *Chem. Eng.*, **64**(10):283 (1957).
19. Ginnings, D. C., and R. J. Corruccini: *Ind. Eng. Chem.*, **40**:1990 (1948).
20. Harrison, D., and E. A. Moelwyn-Hughes: *Proc. Roy. Soc. (London)*, **A239**:230 (1957).
21. Hatch, L. F.: "Isopropyl Alcohol," McGraw-Hill Book Company, New York, 1961.
22. Helfrey, P. F., D. A. Heiser, and B. H. Sage: *Ind. Eng. Chem.*, **47**:2385 (1955).
23. Hirschfelder, J. O., R. J. Buehler, H. A. McGee, Jr., and J. R. Sutton: *Ind. Eng. Chem.*, **50**:387 (1958).
24. Hirschfelder, J. O., R. J. Buehler, H. A. McGee, Jr., and J. R. Sutton: *Ind. Eng. Chem. Fundamentals*, **1**:224 (1962).
25. Hobson, M., and J. H. Weber: *Chem. Eng.*, **64**(11): 245 (1957).
26. Hougen, O. A., K. M. Watson, and R. A. Ragatz; "Chemical Process Principles," 2d ed., pt. II, Thermodynamics, John Wiley & Sons, Inc., New York, 1959.
27. Hsu, C. T.: *AIChE J.*, **9**:854 (1963).
28. Johnson, A. I., and C. J. Huang: *Can. J. Technol.*, **33**:421 (1955).
29. Kordbachen, R. and Chi Tien: *Can. J. Chem. Eng.*, **37**:162 (1959).
30. Lydersen, A. L. R. A. Greenkorn, and O. A. Hougen: Generalized Thermodynamic Properties of Pure Fluids, *Coll. Eng., Univ. Wisconsin, Eng. Expt. Sta. Rept.* 4, Madison, Wis., October, 1955.
31. Maron, S. H., and D. Turnbull: *Ind. Eng. Chem.*, **33**:246 (1941).
32. Martin, J. J.: *J. Chem. Eng. Data*, **8**:311 (1963).
33. Martin, J. J.: "Thermodynamic and Transport Properties of Gases, Liquids, and Solids," pp. 110–122, McGraw-Hill Book Company, New York, 1959.
34. Martin, J. J., J. A. Cambell, and E. M. Seidel: *J. Chem. Eng. Data*, **8**:560 (1963).
35. Martin, J. J., and Yu-Chun Hou: *AIChE J.*, **1**:142 (1955).
36. Martin, J. J., R. M. Kapoor, and N. De Nebers: *AIChE J.*, **5**:159 (1959).
37. Mehra, V. S., and G. Thodos: *J. Chem. Eng. Data*, **6**:366 (1961).
38. Newton, R. H.: *Ind. Eng. Chem.*, **27**:302 (1935).
39. Pitzer, K. S.: *J. Am. Chem. Soc.*, **77**:3427 (1955).
40. Pitzer, K. S., D. Z. Lippmann, R. F. Curl, C. M. Huggins, and D. E. Petersen: *J. Am. Chem. Soc.*, **77**:3433 (1955).
41. Reid, R. C., and J. R. Valbert: *Ind. Eng. Chem. Fundamentals*, **1**:292 (1962).
42. Sage, B. H., J. G. Schaafsma, and W. N. Lacey: *Ind. Eng. Chem.*, **26**:1218 (1934).
43. Sakiadis, B. C., and J. Coates, *AIChE J.*, **2**:88 (1956).

44. Saltzman, B. E.: *Ind. Eng. Chem.*, **50**:1593 (1958).
45. Sherwood, T. K.: *J. Chem. Eng. Data*, **7**:47 (1962).
46. Sobel, J. E. and R. C. Reid: *Ind. Eng. Chem. Fundamentals*, **4**:328 (1965).
47. Viswanath, D. S.: Ph.D. thesis, University of Rochester, 1962.
48. Watson, K. M.: *Ind. Eng. Chem.*, **35**:398 (1943).
49. Weiss, A. H., and J. Joffe: *Ind. Eng. Chem.*, **49**:120 (1957).
50. Yen, L. C., and R. E. Alexander: Paper 18c, Fifty-third National Meeting of the American Institute of Chemical Engineers, Pittsburgh, Pa., May, 1964.

CHAPTER 7

EQUILIBRIUM PROPERTIES OF MIXTURES

7-1 Scope

In Chaps. 2 to 6, techniques were presented for the estimation of various equilibrium properties of pure substances. In the present chapter, ways are considered to estimate most of these same properties for mixtures.

To avoid as much repetitious discussion as possible, reference will often be made to previous chapters; i.e., most mixture correlations are but modifications of techniques devised for pure components. The properties specifically covered in this chapter are, then, true mixture critical properties, P-V-T properties of mixtures, and the various thermodynamic properties of mixtures such as enthalpy, entropy, heat capacity, and fugacity. Usually the desired end point is the mixture property, but when it seems advisable, the partial molal property of a component will also be covered. This latter point is particularly important for such concepts as fugacity, where the mixture fugacity is of little value and it is the fugacity of a component in the mixture which is of real importance.

Finally it may be useful to indicate that, for gas mixtures, deviations in behavior from an ideal-gas mixture may be caused by either or both of two effects; i.e., the component behavior may be nonideal, and the interaction between components may contribute substantially to the nonideality. It is possible for a mixture to be nonideal even though the behavior of the individual pure components is ideal at the same temperature and pressure.

7-2 General Approach to Mixture Correlations

There are, in general, three ways to develop mixture-property estimation techniques.

First, there is the direct analogue of the concept of corresponding states. One may imagine that a mixture has the same properties as some hypothetical pure component. By specification of the pure-component constants for this hypothetical substance, it would then be possible to use the existing pure-component estimation techniques directly to determine mixture properties. The correct pure-component constants to use are usually called the *pseudo constants* of the mixture. Thus, for example, the pseudocritical temperature, pseudocritical pressure, etc., are desired. Estimation of such pseudo properties is taken up in detail in Sec. 7-9.

Second, one may utilize any pure-component correlation technique if all terms involved which are characteristic of the pure component are now changed to give a suitable average representation of the mixture. For example, all the P-V-T equations of state discussed in Chap. 3 contain certain constants which in the generalized form were related to properties such as T_c, P_c, Z_c, etc. By choosing these constants to correspond to the mixture, the same equations can be used for mixture calculations. This technique is utilized often in this chapter, though it may be noted that all such averaging schemes are empirical except the use of the virial P-V-T expansion [Eq. (3-22)]; in this case, the virial coefficients for the mixture may be expressed in terms of pure-component and interaction virials in an exact manner. As many mixture correlations stem from this theoretical base, the virial form of the P-V-T expansion for mixtures is discussed next in Sec. 7-3 to provide a base for further development.

The third and final mixture approach is to develop correlations for partial quantities and then determine the mixture property by a mole-fraction summation procedure. This is not a common approach, and it is usually easier to develop reliable techniques by the first and second methods. The estimation of partial enthalpies, etc., however, is often attempted, as these quantities are themselves valuable in that many partial derivatives of mixture properties depend upon them. This is particularly emphasized in the discussion of fugacity in Sec. 7-22.

7-3 The Virial Equation for Mixtures

Equation (3-22) expressed the compressibility factor in an inverse-power series in specific volume; this series is called a *virial equation of state*. The coefficients B, C, etc., are the second, third, etc., virial coefficients. They are functions only of temperature and may, in theory, be calculated if the intermolecular potential function can be clearly specified. Sections 3-10 to 3-15 describe in some detail the applicability of the equation. For mixtures, allowance must be made for unlike-molecular collisions as well as like-molecular collisions, and the result is that the virial coefficients are then functions of both temperature and composition (95) as

$$B_m = \sum_{i=1}^{n} \sum_{j=1}^{n} y_i y_j B_{ij} \qquad (7\text{-}1)$$

$$C_m = \sum_{i=1}^{n} \sum_{j=1}^{n} \sum_{k=1}^{n} y_i y_j y_k C_{ijk} \qquad (7\text{-}2)$$

For a binary mixture, these equations become

$$B_m = y_1{}^2 B_{11} + 2y_1 y_2 B_{12} + y_2{}^2 B_{22} \qquad (7\text{-}3)$$

$$C_m = y_1{}^3 C_{111} + 3y_1{}^2 y_2 C_{112} + 3y_1 y_2{}^2 C_{221} + y_2{}^3 C_{222} \qquad (7\text{-}4)$$

B_{11}, B_{22}, C_{111}, C_{222} are virial coefficients for pure components and can be estimated as described in Secs. 3-10 to 3-15.   Coefficients such as B_{12}, C_{112}, and C_{221} are interaction virial coefficients, or "cross" coefficients, and depend upon the forces of interaction between unlike molecules. Prausnitz and Gunn (118) show that, if ideal solutions are formed (i.e., if Amagat's law is valid; see Sec. 7-12), then

$$B_{12} = (B_{11} + B_{22})/2 \qquad (7\text{-}5)$$

$$C_{112} = (2C_{111} + C_{222})/3 - (B_{11} - B_{22})^2$$
$$C_{122} = (C_{111} + 2C_{222})/3 - (B_{11} - B_{22})^2 \qquad (7\text{-}6)$$

The mixture virial coefficients, in this special case, become

$$B_m = y_1 B_{11} + y_2 B_{22} \qquad (7\text{-}7)$$

$$C_m = y_1 C_{111} + y_2 C_{222} - 3y_1 y_2 (B_{11} - B_{22})^2 \qquad (7\text{-}8)$$

Unfortunately this ideal solution case is not generally valid, and the more general approach has been to attempt a formulation of an intermolecular potential function applicable to unlike molecules.   This will lead to potential parameters such as $\epsilon_{0_{12}}$, σ_{12}, and possibly μ_{12} as described in Secs. 3-11 for nonpolar molecules and 3-13 for polar molecules.   Estimation of these interaction parameters is discussed in Secs. 7-4 to 7-6 and recommendations presented in Sec. 7-7.   The actual calculation of mixture virial coefficients is described in Sec. 7-8 and the methods illustrated in Examples 7-1 and 7-2.

7-4   Interaction Parameters in Nonpolar Mixtures

Interaction Collision Diameters and Volumes.   The interaction collision diameter σ_{ij} is usually approximated as an arithmetic average of the pure component diameters, i.e.,

$$\sigma_{ij} = (\sigma_i + \sigma_j)/2 \qquad (7\text{-}9)$$

and for ternary-type collisions,

$$\sigma_{ijk} = (\sigma_i + \sigma_j + \sigma_k)/3 \qquad (7\text{-}10)$$

Thus far, σ_{ij} or σ_{ijk} has not been identified with any particular potential function; in fact, Eqs. (7-9) and (7-10) could be viewed as defining a collision diameter between hard spheres of respective diameters σ_i, σ_j, and σ_k. Most writers state flatly that they do not care particularly for Eq. (7-9) or (7-10), but as aptly stated by Hudson and McCoubrey (68), "It is extremely difficult to find a better approximation which can be readily used for calculational purposes."

It is often convenient to deal not with the interaction collision diameter but rather with an interaction critical volume, and it is often assumed to be a good approximation to assume a proportionality between σ^3 and V_c (see, for example, Sec. 2-10, for such an association for the Lennard-Jones potential).   Thus Eq. (7-9) becomes

$$V_{c_{ij}} = [(V_{c_i}^{1/3} + V_{c_j}^{1/3})/2]^3 \qquad (7\text{-}11)$$

where $V_{c_{ij}}$ is the critical volume associated with a hypothetical substance whose properties are determined solely by i-j collisions.   Equation (7-11) is often called a *Lorenz type* of expression.   Stewart, Burkhardt, and Voo (141) suggest a convenient mathematical simplification of Eq. (7-11) by noting that the approximation

$$[(V_{c_i}^{1/3} + V_{c_j}^{1/3})/2]^3 \cong [(V_{c_i} + V_{c_j})/2 + 2\sqrt{V_{c_i} V_{c_j}}]/3 \qquad (7\text{-}12)$$

holds within 0.3 per cent for $1/8 < V_{c_i}/V_{c_j} < 8$. In fact, many writers proceed one step further by approximating the right-hand side of Eq. (7-12) as

$$V_{c_{ij}} = [(V_{c_i}^{1/3} + V_{c_j}^{1/3})/2]^3 \cong (V_{c_i} + V_{c_j})/2 \qquad (7\text{-}13)$$

The fractional error introduced by this last simplification is about equal to

$$\tfrac{2}{3}(V_{c_i}^{1/2} - V_{c_j}^{1/2})^2/(V_{c_i} + V_{c_j}) \qquad (7\text{-}14)$$

and is small except when the critical volumes of i and j differ greatly.

Thus the best methods available to calculate the interaction collision diameter σ_{ij} and critical volume $V_{c_{ij}}$ are given by Eqs. (7-9) and (7-11), though $V_{c_{ij}}$ is often approximated by Eq. (7-13).   These interaction volume parameters will be referred to many times later in this chapter.

Interaction Collision Energy Parameter. In the discussion of the Lennard-Jones and other intermolecular potentials in Chap. 3, the characterizing energy parameter ϵ_0 (for example, the depth of the energy well in the Lennard-Jones potential) was used to denote the maximum potential energy of attraction between like molecules.   A similar parameter $\epsilon_{0_{ij}}$ is important for unlike molecular collisions.   A correspondence is often assumed between ϵ_0 and T_c; so for unlike molecules a parameter $T_{c_{ij}}$ is introduced, a critical temperature for the unlike-molecular system.

Although there is almost complete agreement on defining σ_{ij} by Eq. (7-9), there have been various suggestions advanced to determine $\epsilon_{0_{ij}}$ and $T_{c_{ij}}$. The most common technique is to base the derivations upon London's theory of dispersion energy (88), i.e., the theory used to explain the relatively weak attraction forces between nonpolar, nonreacting molecules. When comparing this dispersion energy with the attractive portion of the Lennard-Jones potential [the r^{-6} term in Eq. (3-29)], Eq. (7-15) is obtained.

$$\epsilon_{0_{ij}} = [2\sqrt{I_iI_j}/(I_i + I_j)](\sigma_i^3\sigma_j^3/\sigma_{ij}^6)(\epsilon_{0_i}\epsilon_{0_j})^{\frac{1}{2}} \qquad (7\text{-}15)$$

I_i, I_j are ionization potentials which, though often not known, are approximately proportional to σ_i^{-3} or σ_j^{-3} (126). In any case, the square bracket term, containing I, is usually near unity even though $I_i \neq I_j$ (69). The more important term is $\sigma_i^3\sigma_j^3/\sigma_{ij}^6$. This correction term has been studied by many workers (15, 69, 118, 139), though it is expressed in different ways. By associating σ^3 with V_c it can be shown that,* with Eq. (7-11), the σ term is almost unity except when the critical-volume ratio V_{c_i}/V_{c_j} is large. For example, if $V_{c_i}/V_{c_j} = 2$, then the term is about 0.96; for $V_{c_i}/V_{c_j} = 6$, it decreases only to 0.77. As the critical-volume ratio of most binary systems is less than 2, the term is often neglected and Eq. (7-15) simplifies to

$$\epsilon_{0_{ij}} = \sqrt{\epsilon_{0_i}\epsilon_{0_j}} \qquad (7\text{-}16)$$

Although the presentation of Eqs. (7-15) and (7-16) is logical, it is also misleading. Often neither equation fits experimental data well (114). Certainly, if one of the components is polar, the approximate equations are poor (see Sec. 7-5 for a discussion of such systems). Huff and Reed (69) have studied many binary systems and found that, in some (usually hydrocarbons), Eq. (7-16) is preferable. However, for systems containing N_2 or CO with a hydrocarbon, Eq. (7-15) is preferable. In some cases, neither was found suitable. For nonpolar systems with components differing greatly in size, even if the components are almost spherically symmetric (such as neopentane and methane) (59), Eq. (7-16) is a poor approximation and (7-15) is preferable. The general question of estimating $\epsilon_{0_{ij}}$ is in a state of uncertainty, and many studies have been made (2, 44, 49, 58, 60, 61, 68, 77, 93, 98) without significant improvement. A simplification of Kirkwood's (77) and Miller's (98) approaches, using magnetic susceptibilities rather than ionization potentials, leads to

$$\epsilon_{0_{ij}} \sim 2\epsilon_{0_i}\epsilon_{0_j}/(\epsilon_{0_i} + \epsilon_{0_j}) \qquad (7\text{-}17)$$

This relation is preferred by Fender and Halsey (42) for rare-gas binaries. However, except where ϵ_{0_i} and ϵ_{0_j} are greatly different, Eq. (7-17) gives results similar to Eq. (7-16). Also, in a study of the association of σ^3 to V_c and ϵ_0 to T_c, Gilbert (49) proposed that a combining rule which often

---

* This association may sometimes not be valid, and it can make considerable difference whether σ^3 or V_c is used. The experimental data for interaction virial coefficients seem to show better agreement with calculated values if V_c is used. This dilemma is illustrated in Example 7-1.

gives good results is

$$\epsilon_{0_{ij}} = (\sqrt{\sigma_i{}^3\sigma_j{}^3}/\sigma_{ij}^3) \sqrt{\epsilon_{0_i}\epsilon_{0_j}} \qquad (7\text{-}18)$$

Equation (7-18) is quite similar to Eq. (7-15) and has been used in the development of the Leland and Mueller pseudocritical rules discussed in Sec. 7-9. Special treatments applicable to low-temperature systems exhibiting quantum effects are also available (2, 82, 120).

7-5 Interaction Parameters in Polar Mixtures

For mixtures of polar substances, few virial coefficients have been measured. One would suppose that these coefficients would be best estimated from an intermolecular potential function applicable for polar molecules, such as the Stockmayer potential discussed in Sec. 3-13. Usually the Stockmayer interaction potential parameters σ_{ij} and $\epsilon_{0_{ij}}$ (see Table 3-1 for such pure-component parameters) are estimated from equations such as (7-9) and (7-16). By analogy, the parameter $t^* = \mu^2/2\sqrt{2}\,\epsilon_0\sigma^3$ may be estimated as

$$t_{ij}^* = \mu_i\mu_j/[2\sqrt{2}\,\epsilon_{0_{ij}}\sigma_{ij}^3] \qquad (7\text{-}19)$$

However, Blanks and Prausnitz (10) found that such combining rules were not satisfactory in predicting B_{ij} for polar-gas mixtures. They suggested that considerable improvement results by modifying Eq. (7-19), i.e., by noting that t^* is a measure of the dipole attraction relative to the dispersion forces discussed above, and by recognizing that dipole forces are sensitive to the distance between molecules undergoing collisions. They propose that

$$t_{ij}^* = \mu_i\mu_j/[2\sqrt{2}\,\epsilon_{0_{ij}}(\sigma_{ij} - \Delta_{ij})^3] \qquad (7\text{-}20)$$

The parameter Δ_{ij} is assumed to be independent of temperature but characteristic of a given polar type of bonding. It has been used particularly for hydrogen bonding between polar molecules. In fact, if both i and j (as pure materials) exhibit about the same degree of hydrogen bonding as does the interacting pair, then Δ_{ij} is close to zero. In systems where hydrogen bonding is weak in the pure gases but stronger in the i-j interaction, then Δ_{ij} is positive and increases with the i-j hydrogen-bond strength. Approximately, Δ_{ij} increases with the heat of solvation, and, for a few of the common types of hydrogen bonding, values of Δ_{ij} are shown in Table 7-1 (10).

In summary, for polar-polar interactions, Stockmayer potentials should be used with the interaction parameters estimated from Eqs. (7-9), (7-16), and (7-20), with Δ_{ij} approximated from Table 7-1.

TABLE 7-1. ESTIMATION OF Δ_{ij} FOR VARIOUS GROUPS*

Interacting groups		Δ_{ij}/σ_{ij}
Nitroketone	NO_2——O=	0.04
Hydrocarbon-nitrile	CH——N≡	0.08
Hydrocarbon-ester	CH——O—	0.16
Hydrocarbon-ether	CH——$O\diagup$	0.23
Hydrocarbon-amine	CH—$N\diagup$	0.27
Hydrocarbon-alcohol	CH——O—	0.19†
Hydrocarbon-aldehyde	CH——O=	0.11†

* R. F. Blanks and J. M. Prausnitz, *AIChE J.*, **8**:86 (1962).
† These values are of doubtful validity.

7-6 Interaction Parameters in Polar-Nonpolar Mixtures

These systems are characterized by the fact that the polar molecule polarizes the nonpolar component. In such systems interaction parameters are estimated from modified Lennard-Jones parameters as (64)

$$\sigma'_{ij} = \tfrac{1}{2}(\sigma_i + \sigma_j^*)\xi_{ij}^{-\frac{1}{6}} \tag{7-21}$$

$$\epsilon'_{0ij} = \sqrt{\epsilon_{0i}\epsilon_{0j}^*}\ \xi_{ij}^2 \tag{7-22}$$

$$\xi_{ij} = 1 + K_j\alpha_i\mu_j^2/4[(\sigma_i + \sigma_j^*)/2]^6 \sqrt{\epsilon_{0i}\epsilon_{0j}^*} \tag{7-23}$$

where i is the nonpolar component and j the polar component. The constant K_j is often assumed to be unity, but this can be a *very* poor assumption (10). The polarizability α_i may be estimated from bond polarizabilities (25); such estimations are discussed in detail in sec. 13-2 of Ref. 64. Equations (7-21) and (7-22) yield σ'_{ij} and ϵ'_{0ij}, which may be used to determine interaction virials B_{ij} from figures such as Figs. 3-10 to 3-13.

The parameters σ_i and ϵ_{0i}, referring to the nonpolar component, are Lennard-Jones parameters which may be estimated as discussed in Sec. 2-10. A convenient definition of the polar-component parameters σ_j^* and ϵ_{0j}^* is more difficult to find. Blanks and Prausnitz discuss this problem in some detail (10). When used to calculate B_j (or higher virial pure-component coefficients), they should be considered Stockmayer potentials. For calculation of B_{ij}, Figs. 3-10 to 3-13 and Eqs. (7-21) to (7-23) being used, the parameters are hybrids in that they apply to polar molecules but emphasize many of the nonpolar characteristics of the material. In a semitheoretical treatment, Blanks and Prausnitz prefer to define ϵ_{0j}^* and σ_j^* of the polar component in Eqs. (7-21) to (7-23) as

$$\sigma_j^* = 0.84 V_{cj}^{\frac{1}{3}} \tag{7-24}$$

$$\epsilon_{0j}^*/k = f(\Delta E_v^*) \qquad \text{Fig. 7-1} \tag{7-25}$$

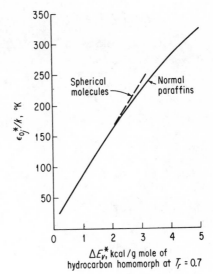

FIG. 7-1. Hybrid nonpolar-Stockmayer potential parameter as a function of the hydrocarbon homomorph energy of vaporization. [*From R. F. Blanks and J. M. Prausnitz, AIChE J.*, **8**:86 (1962).]

Here ΔE_v^* is the energy of vaporization of the *hydrocarbon homomorph* at a reduced temperature of 0.7. The hydrocarbon homomorph is the non-polar analogue of the polar material in which polar groups are replaced by —CH_3 groups. By combining Eqs. (2-28), (2-29), (4-53), and (4-60), it is easily shown that

$$\Delta E_v^* \cong RT_c\, \Delta Z_v\, \{[T_b/(T_c - T_b)]\ln P_c - 0.7\} \qquad (7\text{-}26)$$

Finally, the factor ξ is defined as in Eq. (7-23), but unfortunately K_j cannot be estimated with any accuracy at the present time. K_j reflects the displacement of the polar dipole from the center of the molecule. Values were determined (10) for some polar-hydrocarbon mixtures, and sometimes very large values (up to 100) were found.

It is obvious that the problem of determining reliable values of the interaction parameters for polar-nonpolar systems is very complex; only a start has been made in unraveling the effects of dipole position, correct pure-component potential parameters, etc. Proposed methods are based on limited experimental data and are only temporary devices to be used until further data becomes available and until current theories of inter-molecular forces more nearly reflect actual physical situations.

7-7   Summary of Recommended Methods to Determine Potential Parameters for Use in Mixture Virial Equations

The recommended methods to determine pure-component and inter-action potential parameters are summarized in Table 7-2. These are based on very limited data, and major improvements are to be expected.

TABLE 7-2. SUMMARY OF RECOMMENDED METHODS TO DETERMINE
POTENTIAL PARAMETERS IN MIXTURES

Classification of component in mixture		Parameters for pure components				Interaction parameters		Remarks
		σ		ϵ_0		σ_{ij}	$\epsilon_{0_{ij}}$	
i	j	i	j	i	j			
NP	NP	LJ	LJ	LJ	LJ	Eq. (7-9)	....	$V_{c_{ij}}$ from Eq. (7-11) or (7-12) or by (7-13) if $V_{c_i} \sim V_{c_j}$
							Eq. (7-16)	$0.5 < V_{c_i}/V_{c_j} < 2$
							Eq. (7-15) or Eq. (7-18)	$0.5 > V_{c_i}/V_{c_j} > 2$; neglect term in Eq. (7-15) involving I
P	P	S	S	S	S	Eq. (7-9)	Eq. (7-16)	Determine t^* by Eq. (7-20), with Δ_{ij} determined when possible from Table 7-1.
NP	P	LJ	S	LJ	S	Eq. (7-21)	Eq. (7-22)	Obtain, ξ_{ij} from Eq. (7-23); σ'_{ij} and $\epsilon'_{0_{ij}}$ from Eqs. (7-21), (7-22); σ_j^*, $\epsilon_{0_j}^*$ from Eqs. (7-24), (7-25), (7-26) and Fig. 7-1. K_j may be near unity or may be a very large number (10)

NP, nonpolar.

P, polar.

LJ, Lennard-Jones parameter (Sec. 2-10).

S, Stockmayer parameter (Table 3-1).

The nonpolar mixture has received the most attention, but, even here, there is often a large difference between experimentally measured* values of $\epsilon_{0_{ij}}$ and σ_{ij} and those calculated from the recommended equations.

No mention has been made of determining interaction parameters for ternary collisions except to indicate that, from the lack of any sound basis of choice, one is left with the arithmetic average rule for σ_{ijk} in Eq. (7-10), and perhaps the simple model for ϵ_{0ijk},

$$\epsilon_{0_{ijk}} = \sqrt[3]{\epsilon_{0_i}\epsilon_{0_j}\epsilon_{0_k}} \tag{7-27}$$

Neither equation should be construed as more than a gross approximation. In fact, at the present time, the virial equation for mixtures is not recommended for pressure ranges where use of the third virial coefficient term

* The phrase *experimentally measured values* refers to a back calculation of the best values of ϵ_0 and σ from measured virial coefficients and an assumed intermolecular potential function such as the Lennard-Jones.

is necessary (see Chap. 3 for a discussion of the pressure range where third virial coefficients are important).

7-8 Estimation of Virial Coefficients for Mixtures

The second and third mixture virial coefficients are calculated from Eqs. (7-1) and (7-2). Pure-component virials are determined by the methods described in Secs. 3-10 to 3-15. For nonpolar components, the Lennard-Jones parameters are either determined from Appendix G or estimated by use of equations in Sec. 2-10. These parameters are used to find T^*. Then B^* and higher reduced virials are read from Figs. 3-10 to 3-13. The virial coefficients are found by means of equations such as Eq. (3-35), using b_0 calculated as $\frac{2}{3}\pi N_0 \sigma^3$. Example 3-4 illustrates the technique. This procedure may be varied when other intermolecular potential functions are employed, e.g., with the use of the more accurate Kihara potential as described by Prausnitz and Myers (120).

For polar components, Stockmayer potential parameters are to be employed and a reduced dipole moment t^* determined as described in Sec. 3-13. Estimation of such parameters is discussed in Sec. 3-13, and Table 3-1 lists most known values; Figs. 3-14 to 3-16 show the reduced virial coefficients as functions of T^* and t^*, and an illustrative calculation is given in Example 3-5.

For interaction virial coefficients, the recommended equations to determine the potential parameters are summarized in Table 7-2 for various types of mixtures. For *nonpolar* mixtures and those mixtures where B_{ij} refers to an interaction between a *polar* and *nonpolar* component, the calculated interaction parameters are then used as Lennard-Jones parameters and B_{ij} determined in a manner similar to that outlined above for pure nonpolar components. For *polar* mixtures the interaction parameters determined are to be used as Stockmayer parameters similar to the procedure shown above for polar components. Examples 7-1 and 7-2 illustrate the technique for these three types of mixtures.

An alternative technique to determine the second virial cross coefficient of mixtures is to use the analytical form as shown in Eqs. (3-45) to (3-47) (13). It has been modified by Prausnitz and Gunn (118) to use $(Z_c/V_c)_{ij}$ rather than the group $(P_c/RT_c)_{ij}$, since $V_{c_{ij}}$ can be estimated from Eq. (7-11) or (7-13) and $Z_{c_{ij}}$ is well approximated by a mole-fraction average. However, Huff and Reed (69) used Eqs. (3-45) to (3-47) without modification and calculated B_{ij} from $T_{c_{ij}}$ by Eq. (7-15), with ϵ_0 proportional to T_c, ω_{ij} as a mole-fraction average, and

$$P_{c_{ij}} = [2\sqrt{I_i I_j}/(I_i + I_j)](\sigma_i^3 \sigma_j^3/\sigma_{ij}^6)^{3/2}\sqrt{P_{c_i}P_{c_j}} \qquad (7\text{-}28)$$

or by an association of σ^3 to V_c, and Eq. (7-9) to determine σ_{ij}; then

$$P_{c_{ij}} = [2\sqrt{I_i I_i}/(I_i + I_j)][V_{c_i}V_{c_j}/(V_{c_i}^{1/3} + V_{c_j}^{1/3})^6]^{3/2}\sqrt{P_{c_i}P_{c_j}} \qquad (7\text{-}29)$$

Comparison of experimental B_{ij} virial coefficients with values calculated by the methods outlined above shows occasional excellent agreement, but often serious differences are noted, especially in the few systems studied with polar components (10, 11, 44, 58–61, 68, 69, 93). Usually the use of Eqs. (3-45) to (3-47) as described above yields results as good as, if not better than, Figs. 3-10 to 3-13 in that the errors found probably lie in the actual form of the combining rules. For example, it was noted in numerous cases that better results for hydrocarbon mixtures were obtained with the simple geometric mean ϵ_0 [Eq. (7-16)] rather than the more complex equation (7-15), which presumably accounts for molecular-volume differences (69). This result, though not always found, did occur sufficiently often to cause real doubt whether or not accurate values of B_{ij} can be found for most mixtures even though the components be small in size, nonpolar, and spherically symmetric. However, at the present time, the recommendations for calculating B_i, B_j, B_{ij}, and B_m, given above, are believed to represent the best methods.

Example 7-1. Estimate the pure-component, cross, and mixture second virial coefficients for a mixture of methane and neopentane at 90°C. The mole-fraction neopentane is 0.608. Hamann, Lambert, and Thomas (59) report the B_m to be -265 cm^3/g mole and B_{ij} to be -106 cm^3/g mole. Huff and Reed (69) have tabulated the pure-component values as $B_{CH_4} = -24.2$ and $B_{neopentane} = -566$ cm^3/g mole at 90°C.

Solution. The properties of the pure components are as shown in the tabulation (Appendix A and Ref. 69). The Lennard-Jones parameters were estimated from Eqs. (2-42), (2-43), and (2-45).

	Methane	Neopentane
T_c, °K	190.7	433.8
P_c, atm	45.8	31.6
V_c, cm^3/g mole	99.5	303
ω (acentric factor)	0.013	0.195
Ionization potential, ev	13.16	10.55
Z_c	0.290	0.269
ϵ_0/k, °K	144.5	250.8
σ, A	3.83	6.72
b_0, cm^3/g mole	70.9	383

At 90°C,

$$T^* = \begin{cases} T/(\epsilon_0/k) & \\ 363.2/144.5 = 2.51 & \text{for methane} \\ 363.2/250.8 = 1.45 & \text{for neopentane} \end{cases}$$

From Figs. 3-10 and 3-11,

$$B^* = \begin{cases} -0.31 & \text{for methane} \\ -1.36 & \text{for neopentane} \end{cases}$$

Thus

$$B = \begin{cases} B^*b_0 \\ (-0.31)(70.9) = -22 \text{ cm}^3/\text{g mole} & \text{for methane} \\ (-1.36)(383) = -520 \text{ cm}^3/\text{g mole} & \text{for neopentane} \end{cases}$$

The error in the estimation of the pure-component second virials is

$$[(-22 - (-24.2))/-24.2] \times 100 = -9.1\% \qquad \text{for methane}$$
$$[(-520 - (-566))/-566] \times 100 = -8.2\% \qquad \text{for neopentane}$$

Huff and Reed used Eqs. (3-45) to (3-47) and obtained B(methane) $= -23.2$ cm³/ g mole and B(neopentane) $= -591$ cm³/g mole (69).

To determine the cross virial coefficients,

$$\sigma_{ij} = (\sigma_i + \sigma_j)/2 = (3.83 + 6.72)/2 = 5.28 \text{ A}$$

From Eq. (7-15)

$$\epsilon_{0_{ij}}/k = [2\sqrt{(13.16)(10.55)}/(13.16 + 10.55)][(3.83)^3(6.72)^3/(5.28)^6]\sqrt{(144.5)(250.8)}$$
$$= 149°\text{K}$$

The first bracket involves the ionization potentials, and though they differ considerably for methane and neopentane, the entire expression is very close to unity; this is so often the case that this particular term is usually taken as equal to unity. On the other hand, the second bracket is far from unity. In fact, this term, which was estimated by $\sigma_i^3\sigma_j^3/[(\sigma_i + \sigma_j)/2]^6$ as indicated in Eq. (7-15), is often calculated by using critical volumes rather than collision diameters; that is, σ^3 is assumed to be proportional to V_c, and so the term may be written as

$$V_{c_i}V_{c_j}/[(V_{c_i}^{1/3} + V_{c_j}^{1/3})/2]^6$$

However, substitution of critical-volume data into the expression above yields a value of 0.898 rather than 0.787, as found with the collision diameter. The difference results from the fact that in this case $(\sigma/V_c^{1/3})_{\text{methane}}$ is quite different from $(\sigma/V_c^{1/3})_{\text{neopentane}}$. In fact this association does not seem to be true unless $Z_{c_i} \cong Z_{c_j}$.

By carrying the value of $(\epsilon_0/k)_{ij}$ from both calculations, 149°K by the use of σ and $(149)(0.898/0.787) = 170°\text{K}$ from $V_c^{1/3}$, the next step is to determine $b_{0_{ij}}$. Since $b_0 = \frac{2}{3}\pi N_0\sigma^3$,

$$b_{0_{ij}} = \{[(b_{0_i})^{1/3} + (b_{0_j})^{1/3}]/2\}^3 = \{[(70.9)^{1/3} + (383)^{1/3}]/8\}^3$$
$$= 185.2 \text{ cm}^3/\text{g mole}$$
$$T_{ij}^* = \begin{cases} (T/(\epsilon_{0_{ij}}/k)) \\ 363.2/149 = 2.44 & \sigma \text{ calculation} \\ 363.2/170 = 2.14 & V_c^{1/3} \text{ calculation} \end{cases}$$

Thus, from Fig. 3-11,

$$B^* = -0.36 \qquad \sigma \text{ calculation}$$
$$B_{ij} = (-0.36)(185) = -66 \text{ cm}^3/\text{g mole}$$
$$B^* = -0.53 \qquad V_c^{1/3} \text{ calculation}$$
$$B_{ij} = (-0.53)(185) = -98 \text{ cm}^3/\text{g mole}$$

Huff and Reed, using Eqs. (3-45) to (3-47) to determine B_{ij}, $T_{c_{ij}}$ from Eq. (7-15), with ϵ_0 proportional to T_c, and P_c from Eq. (7-29) obtain $B_{ij} = -101$ cm³/g mole. From this example and others worked out elsewhere, it would appear that the volume-correction term in Eq. (7-15) is best made from critical volumes rather than from σ^3 values.

Finally, to estimate the mixture virial coefficient from Eq. (7-3),

$$B_m = (0.608)^2(-520) + 2(0.608)(0.392)(-98) + (0.392)^2(-22)$$
$$= -243 \text{ cm}^3/\text{g mole}$$

The experimental value is -265 cm^3/g mole (59), and the error is

$$\{[-243 - (-265)]/-265\} \times 100 = -8.3 \text{ per cent}$$

Example 7-2. Estimate the cross coefficient B_{ij} for mixtures of nitromethane and argon and of nitromethane and acetone at 50°C. Compare with the experimental values of -72 (± 20) and $-2,679$ (± 50) cm^3/g mole (11).

Solution. These two cases illustrate the effect of polar components. From Table 3-1 and Ref. 11, the following pure-component constant are available:

	ϵ_0/k, °K	b_0, cm^3/g mole	t^*	α, cm^3 $\times 10^{25}$	Type of potential parameter
Nitromethane....	290	90.8	1.6	....	Stockmayer
Argon..........	119.8	49.8	...	16.3	Lennard-Jones
Acetone........	428	70.1	0.9	....	Stockmayer

Nitromethane-Acetone Mixture. This is a polar-polar mixture. From Eq. (7-9) (since b_0 is proportional to σ^3) and Eq. (7-16)

$$b_{0_{ij}} = [(b_0)_i^{1/3} + (b_0)_j^{1/3}]^3/8$$
$$= [(90.8)^{1/3} + (70.1)^{1/3}]^3/8 = 80.3 \text{ cm}^3/\text{g mole}$$
$$(\epsilon_0/k)_{ij} = \sqrt{(\epsilon_0/k)_i(\epsilon_0/k)_j} = \sqrt{(290)(428)} = 352°K$$

To determine t_{ij}^* from Eq. (7-20), with Δ_{ij}/σ_{ij} for a nitroketone bond $= 0.04$, then $\sigma_{ij} - \Delta_{ij} = \sigma_{ij}(1 - \Delta_{ij})$. $t_j^* = \mu_j^2/2\sqrt{2}\,\epsilon_{0j}\sigma_j^3$; $b_0 = \frac{2}{3}\pi N_0\sigma^3$, Eq. (7-20) then yields

$$t_{ij}^* = (t_i^* t_j^*)^{1/2}(b_{0_i}b_{0_j})^{1/2}/b_{0_{ij}}[1 - (\Delta_{ij}/\sigma_{ij})]^3$$
$$= \{[(1.6)(0.9)]^{1/2}[(90.8)(70.1)]^{1/2}\}/80.3(1 - 0.04)^3 = 1.34$$
$$T_{ij}^* = (50 + 273.2)/352 = 0.916$$

These values of T_{ij}^* and t_{ij}^* are off the limits of the plot in Fig. 3-14. However, from table II-A of Ref. 64,

$$B^* = -38.3 \qquad B_{ij} = (-38.3)b_{0_{ij}} = (-38.3)(80.3) = -3,070 \text{ cm}^3/\text{g mole}$$

If the Δ_{ij} correction is not employed, $t^* = 1.18$, $B^* = -23.4$, $B_{ij} = -1,880$ cm^3/g mole. Clearly the answer is very sensitive to the t^* value and thus the Δ_{ij} value chosen.

Nitromethane-Argon Mixture. This is an example of a polar-nonpolar mixture. To use Eqs. (7-21) to (7-23), the hybrid values of σ and ϵ_0 for nitromethane first have to be determined from Eqs. (7-24) and (7-25), with critical values from Appendix A,

$$\sigma^* = \sigma_{\text{nitromethane hybrid}} = 0.84V_c^{1/3}$$
$$= (0.84)(173)^{1/3} = 4.67 \text{ A}$$

This compares with a Stockmayer value of $\sigma = 4.18$ A. ΔE_v^* is obtained from Eq. (7-26), with $\Delta Z_v \sim 1.0$, $T_c = 305.4°K$, $T_b = 184.6°K$, $P_c = 48.2$ atm for ethane, the hydrocarbon homomorph of nitromethane. Thus,

$$\Delta E_v^* = (1.987)(305.4)\{[184.6/(305.4 - 184.6)] \ln 48.2 - 0.7\}$$
$$= (607)(5.93 - 0.70) = 3180 \text{ cal/g mole}$$

From Fig. 7-1, $\epsilon_0/k = 230°K$ for the nitromethane hybrid $\equiv [\epsilon_0/k]_j^*$. To determine $K_{\text{nitromethane}}$ recourse can be had to the very approximate estimating scheme suggested by Blanks and Prausnitz (10); in this case K is about 3. However, since this correlation has not been thoroughly tested, assume in this case that K is unity; then the value of ξ_{ij} in Eq. (7-23) (with j = nitromethane, i = argon) is

$$1 + \frac{K_j \alpha_i \mu_j^2}{4 \left(\dfrac{\sigma_i + \sigma_j^*}{2}\right)^6 \sqrt{\epsilon_{0_i} \epsilon_{0_j}^*}} = 1 + \frac{K_j \alpha_i l_j^* \sqrt{8} \, \sigma_j{}^3 \epsilon_{0_j}}{4 \left(\dfrac{\sigma_i + \sigma_j^*}{2}\right)^6 \sqrt{\epsilon_{0_i} \epsilon_{0_j}^*}}$$

$$\xi_{ij} = 1 + \frac{(1)(16.3)(10^{-25})(1.6) \sqrt{8} \, (4.18)^3 (290)}{(4) \left(\dfrac{3.40 + 4.67}{2}\right)^6 \sqrt{(119.8)(230)} \, (10^{-24})} = 1.05$$

and from Eqs. (7-21) and (7-22)

$$\sigma_{ij}' = \tfrac{1}{2}(3.40 + 4.67)(1.05)^{-\frac{1}{6}}$$
$$= 4.05 \text{ A}$$
$$[\epsilon_0/k]_{ij}' = \sqrt{(119.8)(230)} \, (1.05)^2 = 183°K$$
$$T_{ij}^* = (50 + 273.2)/183 = 1.77$$
$$b_{0_{ij}}' = (1.26)(\sigma_{ij}')^3 = 83.5 \text{ cm}^3/\text{g mole}$$

From Fig. 3-10
$$B_{ij}^* = -0.84 \qquad B_{ij} = (-0.84)(b_{0_{ij}}')$$
$$= (-0.84)(83.5) = -70 \text{ cm}^3/\text{g mole}$$

7-9 Pseudocritical Constants for Mixtures

The so-called "law of corresponding states" introduced in Chap. 3 and employed in subsequent chapters was used principally to correlate properties at equal reduced temperatures and pressures. Refinements were introduced to divide pure materials into classes with certain values of the critical compressibility factor, acentric factor, or other characterizing third parameter. Such correlation techniques were, in most instances, convenient and reliable.

The natural course of action has been to extend this method to mixtures. However, to accomplish this task, some technique must be chosen to determine the correct mixture critical properties so that the reduced-state correlations for the pure components may be employed. The use of true-mixture critical properties does not, in general, lead to satisfactory mixture correlations. Consequently, considerable use has been made of the pseudocritical concept. This concept is based on the supposition that a single pure fluid may exist which possesses the same properties as the mixture if each is at the same temperature and pressure. The critical properties of this pure fluid are then the proper pseudocritical properties of the mixture.

The simplest and most widely used rule is due to Kay (74).   In this case the pseudocritical temperature and pressure are chosen simply as mole-fraction averages of pure-component criticals,*

$$T_{c_m}(\mathrm{K}) = \sum_i y_i T_{c_i} \qquad (7\text{-}30)$$

$$P_{c_m}(\mathrm{K}) = \sum_i y_i P_{c_i} \qquad (7\text{-}31)$$

Besides Kay's rule, several other well-known rules have been suggested in the literature.   All are more complex than Kay's but are also more accurate in predicting mixture P-V-T properties, as pointed out in Sec. 7-10.   These rules are summarized below for the general case of a multi-component system; in each case the estimated pseudocritical mixture property is followed by an identifying letter(s) to indicate from which rule it was calculated; for example, $T_{c_m}(\mathrm{K})$ would indicate Kay's rule [Eq. (7-30)].

Summary of Pseudocritical Rules.
Leland-Mueller (83)

$$T_{c_m}(\mathrm{LM}) = \left\{ \frac{\left[\sum_i y_i (Z_{c_i} R T_{c_i}^{(\alpha+1)}/P_{ci})^{1/2} \right]^2}{V_{c_m}(\mathrm{LM})} \right\}^{1/\alpha} \qquad (7\text{-}32)$$

$$P_{c_m}(\mathrm{LM}) = R T_{c_m}(\mathrm{LM}) Z_{c_m}/V_{c_m}(\mathrm{LM}) \qquad (7\text{-}33)$$

$$V_{c_m}(\mathrm{LM}) = \tfrac{1}{8} \sum_i \sum_j y_i y_j [(R Z_{c_i} T_{ci}/P_{ci})^{1/3} + (R Z_{c_j} T_{cj}/P_{cj})^{1/3}]^3$$

$$= \tfrac{1}{8} \sum_i \sum_j y_i y_j (V_{ci}^{1/3} + V_{cj}^{1/3})^3 \qquad (7\text{-}34)$$

$$Z_{c_m} = \sum_i y_i Z_{c_i} \qquad (7\text{-}35)$$

$$\alpha = 2.43 - 0.74\theta \qquad 1.9 > \theta > 0.5$$
$$= 2.2 \qquad\qquad\quad \theta < 0.5$$
$$= 1.0 \qquad\qquad\quad \theta > 1.9 \qquad (7\text{-}36)$$
$$\theta = (P/T)[T_{c_m}(\mathrm{K})/P_{c_m}(\mathrm{K})] \qquad (7\text{-}37)$$

Joffe–Stewart, Burkhardt, and Voo (70, 141)

$$T_{c_n}(\text{J-SBV}) = K^2/J \qquad (7\text{-}38)$$
$$P_{c_m}(\text{J-SBV}) = T_{c_m}(\text{J-SBV})/J \qquad (7\text{-}39)$$
$$K^2 = T_{c_m}^2/P_{c_m} = \left(\sum_i y_i T_{c_i}/P_{c_i}^{1/2} \right)^2 \qquad (7\text{-}40)$$

$$J = T_{c_m}/P_{c_m} = \tfrac{1}{8} \sum_i \sum_j y_i y_j [(T_{c_i}/P_{c_i})^{1/3} + (T_{c_j}/P_{c_j})^{1/3}]^3$$

---

* Several modifications of Kay's rule have also been suggested.   For example, a recent paper by Li, Chen, and Murphy (86a) suggests that $(T_b/T_c)_m$ is a linear mole-fraction average of T_b/T_c for the mixture components; this technique worked well for estimating T_{c_m} from T_{b_m}, T_{b_j}, T_{c_j} for mixtures of halogenated hydrocarbons.

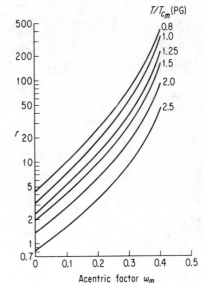

FIG. 7-2. Estimation of r in Eq. (7-47). [From J. M. Prausnitz, and R. D. Gunn, AIChE J., **4**:430 (1958).]

or if Eq. (7-12) is used,

$$J = T_{c_m}/P_{c_m} = \tfrac{1}{3} \sum_i y_i T_{c_i}/P_{c_i} + \tfrac{2}{3} \left[\sum_i y_i (T_{c_i}/P_{c_i})^{\frac{1}{2}} \right]^2 \quad (7\text{-}41)$$

Prausnitz and Gunn (117, 118)

$$T_{c_m}(\text{PG}) = [\beta + \sqrt{\beta^2 + rV_{c_m}(\text{LM})\gamma}]/2sV_{c_m}(\text{PG}) \qquad (7\text{-}42)$$

$$P_{c_m}(\text{PG}) = Z_{c_m}RT_{c_m}(\text{PG})/V_{c_m}(\text{PG}) \qquad (7\text{-}43)$$

$$V_{c_{ij}}(\text{PG}) = \tfrac{1}{2}(V_{c_i} + V_{c_j}) - \Delta V_{c_{ij}} \qquad (7\text{-}44)$$

$$V_{c_{ij}}(\text{PG}) \cong [\tfrac{1}{2}(V_{c_i}^{\frac{1}{3}} + V_{c_j}^{\frac{1}{3}})]^3 \qquad (7\text{-}11)$$

$$\Delta V_{c_{ij}} = 12(V_{c_i}/V_{c_j}) - 30 \quad \text{cm}^3/\text{g mole}, \; V_{c_i}/V_{c_j} \geq 2.5 \quad (7\text{-}45)$$
$$= 0 \qquad\qquad V_{c_i}/V_{c_j} < 2.5$$

$$V_{c_m}(\text{PG}) = \sum_i \sum_j y_i y_j V_{c_{ij}}(\text{PG}) \cong V_{c_m}(\text{LM}) \qquad (7\text{-}46)$$

$$r, s = f[\omega_m, \, T/T_{c_m}(\text{PG})] \qquad (7\text{-}47)$$

as shown in Figs. 7-2 and 7-3.

$$\omega_m = \text{mixture acentric factor} = \sum_i y_i \omega_i \qquad (7\text{-}48)$$

$$\beta = \sum_i \sum_j y_i y_j V_{c_{ij}} T_{c_{ij}} \qquad (7\text{-}49)$$

$$\gamma = \sum_i \sum_j y_i y_j V_{c_{ij}} T_{c_{ij}}^2 \qquad (7\text{-}50)$$

$$T_{c_{ij}} = k_{ij}(T_{c_i} T_{c_j})^{\frac{1}{2}} \qquad (7\text{-}51)$$
$$k_{ij} \cong V_c V_{c_j}/V_{ij}^2(\text{PG}) \qquad (7\text{-}52)$$

and Z_{c_m} and $V_{c_m}(\text{LM})$ are given above in Eqs. (7-35) and (7-34).

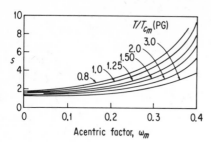

Fig. 7-3. Estimation of s in Eq. (7-47)·
[*From J. M. Prausnitz, and R. D. Gunn, AIChE J.,* **4**:430 (1958).]

Modified Prausnitz and Gunn (118)

$$T_{c_m}(\text{MPG}) = T_{c_m}(\text{K}) = \sum_i y_i T_{c_i} \tag{7-30}$$

$$P_{c_m}(\text{MPG}) = Z_{c_m} R T_{c_m}/V_{c_m} = R \sum_i y_i Z_{c_i} \sum_i y_i T_{c_i}/\sum_i y_i V_{c_i} \tag{7-53}$$

Reduction to Kay's Rule.   No indication is given here of the theory and empiricism that lie behind these pseudocritical rules.   It appears that all may be shown to stem from Eq. (3-30).   It also is possible, with reasonable simplifying assumptions, to collapse the complex rules for pseudocritical temperature to Kay's rule [Eq. (7-30)].   A similar reduction in the pseudocritical-pressure rules to Eq. (7-31) does not, however, appear to be justifiable (126).   The realization that all rules, including Kay's, usually yield about the same value of the pseudocritical temperature can lead to a considerable simplification of any set of calculations and has led to the modified Prausnitz and Gunn rules given above. General, but approximate, criteria follow of how T_{c_m} and P_{c_m} differ (for binary systems) between Kay's rule and those founded on a more theoretical basis:

For T_{c_m}, Kay's rules will differ by less than 2 per cent from other rules if $0.5 < T_{c_1}/T_{c_2} < 2$ and $0.5 < P_{c_1}/P_{c_2} < 2$.

For P_{c_m}, Kay's rule appears to yield values close to other rules if either $P_{c_1} \cong P_{c_2}$ or $V_{c_1} \cong V_{c_2}$.   Differences are usually less than 10 per cent for $0.5 < P_{c_1}/P_{c_2} < 2$ and T_{c_1}/T_{c_2} near unity.   For other ranges, Kay's rule yields considerably different values.

7-10   Discussion and Application of Pseudocritical Rules to Estimate *P-V-T* Relations

There are, of course, no experimental pseudocritical constants with which to compare calculated values.   The calculated values of T_{c_m}, P_{c_m}, Z_{c_m}, ω_m, etc., are used as pure-component constants in reduced-state correlations.   Mixture property estimations using this technique involve the uncertainties in both the pseudocritical concept and the reduced-correlation technique.   Some rules for T_{c_m} and P_{c_m} may be more applica-

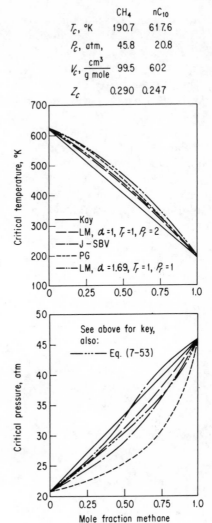

FIG. 7-4. Pseudocritical constants for the system methane–n-decane.

ble for fugacity calculations than volume, or for volume rather than enthalpy deviations, etc.; so it is very difficult to make any reasonable assessment without a fair, comprehensive testing program where the pseudocritical rules, the compound class, the reduced-state correlation, the desired property, and the T_r, P_r range are systematically varied. As noted in the previous section, in some cases the suggested complex pseudocritical rules give about the same values of T_{c_m}. This is usually not true for P_{c_m}. The differences between the rules are emphasized in systems with molecules greatly differing in size, structure, etc. For example, in Fig. 7-4, curves for T_{c_m} and P_{c_m} are drawn for the binary mixture of methane and n-decane. These molecules have widely different critical constants, and none of the pseudocritical rules are well approximated by Kay's rule. In other such tests, the agreement between the calculated T_{c_m} and Kay's rule was better than shown in Fig. 7-4 though poor agreement between the calculated P_{c_m} values with those of Kay's rule was usually found.

All the pseudocritical rules have been tested by estimating P-V-T properties of mixtures. The techniques employed and results obtained are discussed briefly below.

Leland-Mueller [Equations (7-32) to (7-37)]. A total of 58 datum points for saturated liquids and vapors, most at high pressure, containing hydrocarbons, N_2, CO_2, and H_2S, were predicted by calculating the pseudocritical T_{c_m}, P_{c_m}, and Z_{c_m}, determining T_r, P_r, and calculating the mixture volume from known data on a reference substance at the same T_r, P_r as that of the mixture (83). The reference substance was chosen to have a Z_c value close to Z_{c_m}. An overall average error of 2.3 per cent was found by using the Leland-Mueller methods. Kay's rule applied to the same test group yielded errors, usually from two to ten times as large, the difference being caused primarily by the poor approximation of P_{c_m} by Kay's rule. Only nonpolar mixtures were tested.

Joffe-Stewart, Burkhardt, and Voo [Eqs. (7-38) to (7-41)]. Thirty-nine binary and predominantly nonpolar mixtures were studied by Stewart, Burkhardt, and Voo (141) and 1,700 datum points chosen. T_{c_m} and P_{c_m} were calculated, T_r and P_r determined, and the Lydersen, Greenkorn, and Hougen gas-compressibility-factor tables of Appendix B or the liquid-density correlation in Sec. 3-19 (Table 3-6) was used to determine mixture volumes. Z_c was chosen by Eq. (7-35). Both homogeneous gas and liquid mixtures were studied. The average overall error was 4.3 per cent, with much of the error contributed by tests on systems containing CO_2 or H_2S.

Prausnitz and Gunn [Eqs. (7-42) to (7-52)]. Ten nonpolar gas mixtures were studied at high pressure. Values of T_{c_m}, P_{c_m}, and ω_m were determined; then from T_{r_m} and P_{r_m} with ω_m, volumetric properties were determined from compressibility-factor charts of Pitzer (110, 112), Eq. (3-15), and Figs. 3-5 and 3-6. Average overall errors of about 3 per cent were found. [For systems containing hydrogen, special pure-hydrogen critical properties of $T_c = 43.4°K$, $V_c = 50 \text{ cm}^3/\text{g mole}$, and $\omega = 0$ were used (118).] Kay's rule was considerably less accurate. In Prausnitz and Gunn's testing, the value of k_{ij} [Eq. (7-51)] was, in reality, determined from experimental data so that in the general case the expected average error may be larger.

Modified Prausnitz and Gunn [Eqs. (7-30) and (7-53)]. In applying these methods to the same systems noted above, errors of about 5 per cent were found (118). The smallest errors were noted for $T_{r_m} > 1.3$.

Discussion and Recommendations. When tested with nonpolar volumetric-mixture data and the usual three-parameter reduced correlations, all the pseudocritical methods seem to yield about the same error, that is, 3 to 5 per cent. Much of this error may be attributed to the inexactness of the three-parameter volumetric correlation; so the pseudocritical concept appears quite useful and reliable. As suggested in Sec. 7-9 the pseudocritical rules may be considered to be based upon Eq. (3-30), wherein the second virial coefficient is related to the intermolecular potential function. As such, one would not have predicted good agreement at high pressures where third and higher virials are important. There is, however, a good deal of empiricism woven into the rules, and the final result is quite general. All pseudocritical rules have been tested adequately only with nonpolar mixtures. Testing with polar-polar and polar-nonpolar mixtures will undoubtedly show larger errors, but no estimate is possible. Also, in all cases the largest errors occur near T_{c_m}, $P_{c_m} \sim 1$ so that caution should be used in this region.

In formulating specific recommendations, there is wide latitude for judgment; however, those given below seem to be reasonable and can serve as a useful guide:

1. If the ratios of T_{c_i}/T_{c_j} are within the range of $0.5 < T_{c_i}/T_{c_j} < 2$:

    a. Use Kay's rule [Eqs. (7-30) and (7-31)] if all $P_{c_i} \sim P_{c_j}$ *or* $V_{c_i} \sim V_{c_j}$.

    b. Use the modified Prausnitz and Gunn rules [Eqs. (7-30) and (7-53)] if P_{c_i} differs from P_{c_j} by over 20 per cent.

2. If the ratios of T_{c_i}/T_{c_j} are *outside* the range of $0.5 < T_{c_i}/T_{c_j} < 2$, use any of the more complex rules, LM, J-SBV, and PG, outlined in Sec. 7-9.

From the T_{c_m} and P_{c_m} values obtained, calculate T_{r_m} and P_{r_m}, and use any of the volumetric correlations discussed in Chap. 3. If Z_c correlations are to be used, determine Z_{c_m} from Eq. (7-35). Satter and Campbell (129) recommend the J-SBV method as the best general method for all types of gas mixtures; in their tests, the Pitzer acentric-factor correlation was used to predict volumetric data from calculated reduced pseudocritical temperatures and pressures.

Using the recommendations above, errors to be expected will range from 2 to 5 per cent for nonpolar homogeneous gas or liquid mixtures. For mixtures containing polar components, or if T_{r_m} and P_{r_m} are near unity, larger errors are to be expected. The various methods are illustrated later in Example 7-4.

7-11 Equations of State for Mixtures

In Sec. 3-16, a number of equations of state were described. Only the eight-constant Benedict-Webb-Rubin equation has been tested fully with mixtures. This equation is summarized in Appendix E, and constants are listed for many pure compounds. The combination rules to obtain the mixture parameters are also presented. Only light hydrocarbon mixtures (and their mixtures with N_2, CO_2, and SO_2) may be treated. The application of this equation of state to mixtures is discussed in many papers (2, 5, 23, 28, 40, 67, 103, 109, 138), and an excellent description of its development and accuracy is given in a monograph by Opfell, Pings, and Sage (102). Hydrogen mixtures require special consideration (138). No other equation of state has been so thoroughly developed for mixtures, although methods have been presented to obtain mixture coefficients for the Black equation (9, 19), and the simple Redlich-Kwong equation [Eq. (3-51) and Example 3-6]. In the latter case, for a mixture (37),

$$a_m^* = \sum_i y_i a_i^* \qquad (7\text{-}54)$$

$$b_m^* = \sum_i y_i b_i^* \qquad (7\text{-}55)$$

where $a_i^{*2} = 0.4278/T_{r_i}^{2.5} P_{c_i}$, atm^{-1}

$b_i^* = 0.0867/T_{r_i} P_{c_i}$, atm^{-1}

Kay's rules have been used with some success to obtain T_{r_m} and P_{r_m} for use in the generalized Beattie-Bridgman equation (3-57), and recently mixture rules have been suggested for the Martin-Hou equation of state [Eq. (3-66)] (135, 136). This equation of state has been successful in treating CO_2-N_2 gas mixtures but has not, as yet, been tested with other mixtures (135).

None of these latter equations have been sufficiently tested to allow error estimates. Therefore, unless one is dealing with compounds specifically covered by the Benedict-Webb-Rubin equation (as shown in Appendix E), no well-tested mixture equations of state are available. Even the use of the BWR equation is not convenient except for machine computation and is not recommended as particularly accurate for mixtures near the critical point or for reduced densities much greater than about 1.5 to 2 (2, 7, 102).

TABLE 7-3. SUGGESTED COMBINING RULES FOR MARTIN-HOU EQUATION OF STATE [EQ. (3-66)] AS APPLIED TO MIXTURES*

K_m = mixture const
K_i, K_j = pure-component const

Constant	Combining rule
b	$\sum_i y_i K_i$
B_2, B_3, B_5, T_c	$\left(\sum_i y_i K_i^{\frac{1}{2}}\right)^2$
A_2, A_3, A_4, A_5, C_2, C_3, C_5	$\frac{1}{8}\sum_i \sum_j y_i y_j (K_i^{\frac{1}{3}} + K_j^{\frac{1}{3}})^3$

* G. E. Smith, Ph.D. thesis, University of Michigan, Ann Arbor, Mich., 1963.

7-12   Discussion and Recommendations of P-V-T Estimation of Mixtures

The Virial Equation. Z is estimated from Eq. (3-22); estimates of the second virial coefficient are described in Secs. 7-3 to 7-8, the methods being illustrated in Examples 7-1 and 7-2.   Only relatively low-pressure gas mixtures can be handled.   This technique has the best theoretical basis.   However, one cannot estimate accurately third and higher virial coefficients or, in systems with large nonspherical or polar molecules, reliable values of second virial coefficients.   Thus the overall accuracy may suffer.

Pseudocritical-constant Method.   Pseudocritical-constant rules are outlined in Sec. 7-9, and the application of such rules to estimate volumetric properties is given in Sec. 7-10.   Example 7-4 illustrates the method.

This method has the greatest generality for both liquid and gas mixtures, although it has been tested adequately only for nonpolar mixtures.

Mixture Equations of State.   The only mixture equation of state studied in much detail is the Benedict-Webb-Rubin equation outlined in Appendix E.   Only light hydrocarbon mixtures (and mixtures of light hydrocarbons with N_2, CO_2, and SO_2) can be treated.   Several other mixture equations of state are outlined briefly in Sec. 7-11.

In addition to the more complicated rules given above, several empirical rules deserve mention, as they are simple and often completely satisfactory for engineering use.

Dalton's Law.   Defining a partial pressure of component i in a gas mixture as

$$p_i = Py_i \qquad (7\text{-}56)$$

Dalton's law states that the partial pressures are additive if components are mixed at constant volume and temperature.   It may easily be shown that this is equivalent to the assumption that the mixture compressibility factor is a mole-fraction average of the component compressibility factors, the latter being evaluated at the system temperature and *partial pressure* of the component in the final mixture.   This law appears to give reasonably good results for low-pressure (<3 atm) (89, 101) nonpolar gas mixtures.

Amagat's Law.   If the mixture is ideal (see Sec. 7-20), then Amagat's law is valid; i.e., volumes of the pure components are additive at constant pressure and temperature.   Thus,

$$Z_m = \sum_i y_i Z_i \qquad (7\text{-}57)$$

or

$$V_m = \sum_i y_i V_i \qquad (7\text{-}58)$$

where Z_i and V_i are evaluated at the system temperature and *total* pres-

THE PROPERTIES OF GASES AND LIQUIDS

sure of the mixture. This rule appears to be reasonably accurate for nonpolar gas or liquid mixtures at low pressures (<5 atm) or at high reduced pressures and temperatures. For polar liquid mixtures it may be very inaccurate (87).

Other Empirical Rules. Many studies have been made to devise suitable mixture rules (1, 4, 63, 84, 94, 101, 111, 119, 125, 127, 147). Townsend (150) defined an *additivity factor* to correlate Z_m with composition and pure-component compressibility factors, but the method does not appear to have any real advantages. Busch and Canjar (14) presented a correlation between Z_m and $\sum_i y_i Z_i$, and Phillips and Thodos (108) devised an empirical technique to estimate saturated liquid densities of aliphatics, olefins, and naphthenes that is believed accurate to 5 to 10 per cent. Finally, Ritter, Lenoir, and Schweppe (127) suggested a reduced correlation for liquid mixtures. The last is similar to the pseudocritical-rule–corresponding-state technique but is less accurate. An excellent summary of experimental mixture data has been given by Tang (148).

Recommendations for Estimating Volumetric Properties of Mixtures.

1. For low-pressure nonpolar gas or liquid mixtures, a rapid, reasonably accurate rule employs Eqs. (7-57) and (7-58), in which ideal solutions are assumed. Errors are expected to be less than 5 per cent for pressures of a few atmospheres. At high values of both T_r and P_r, the technique is also applicable to gas mixtures.

2. For mixtures of light hydrocarbons with or without N_2, CO_2, and SO_2, the Benedict-Webb-Rubin equation of state summarized in Appendix E is the most accurate. The complexity requires a computer solution, although the nomographs of Hsieh and Zimmerman (67) are often convenient to obtain the mixture constants and mixture density. It is not accurate for liquid volumes far removed from the bubble point (102), nor is it completely reliable near mixture critical points (2). Though not thoroughly tested, the Martin-Hou equation [Eq. (3-56)] with mixture constants from Table 7-3 may also be used.

3. For other hydrocarbon gas or liquid mixtures or for nonpolar mixtures, the best available mixture correlations appear to be those utilizing the pseudocritical concept. It is easy to use with any of the pure-component corresponding-state correlations listed in Chap. 3. The recommended pseudocritical rules are summarized in Sec. 7-9. Accuracies are hard to predict, since the theoretical basis of the rules is so indefinite, but usually errors less than 5 to perhaps 10 per cent are to be expected.

4. For mixtures containing polar components, no reliable methods are available. For reduced pressures [based on Kay's rule, Eq. (7-31)] of less than 0.5, the use of Eq. (3-22), with B_m determined from Eq. (7-1) and interaction virials as described in Secs. 7-5 and 7-6 and summarized

n Table 7-2, is recommended with reservations. For such low pressures, C_m and higher virials are assumed zero. For higher pressures, the pseudo-critical technique outlined in recommendation no. 2 is the only available method. Errors may be large with the former technique and even larger with the latter. Usually 10 to 15 per cent errors may be expected, but, for those cases where there is much association in the mixture, the errors may run to 25 to 50 per cent.

None of the mixture correlations is really satisfactory. Canjar (16) has justifiably criticized all of them. This is an area where more experimental and theoretical work is needed.

7-13 Thermodynamic Properties of Mixtures

It is often necessary to estimate the enthalpy, entropy, energy, heat capacity, or other thermodynamic property of a mixture. Such properties are estimated by three general techniques—the same three as used for volumetric-property estimation—from the virial equation, from the pseudocritical-constant–corresponding-state method, or from an equation of state. None of the techniques has been tested sufficiently to allow accurate error estimates, but in the few tests which have been made all seem to yield reasonable results for nonpolar mixtures. Polar mixtures cannot be treated by any technique to yield reliable estimations. This point will be emphasized later. Fugacities of components in a mixture are discussed in Sec. 7-20.

The three techniques noted above are developed in Secs. 7-14 to 7-16. In Sec. 7-17, the various methods for estimating enthalpies are discussed and compared where possible with experimental data. Recommendations for enthalpy estimation are given in Sec. 7-18. Estimations of mixture entropies and heat capacities are discussed briefly in Sec. 7-19.

7-14 Use of the Virial Equation to Estimate Thermodynamic Properties of Mixtures

From the virial equation of state [Eq. (3-22)] and the thermodynamic relations [Eqs. (6-16), (6-21), and (6-29)], it can be shown (64) that

$$\frac{H_m - H_m^0}{RT} = \frac{1}{V}\left[B_m - T\frac{dB_m}{dT}\right] + \frac{1}{V^2}\left[C_m - \frac{T}{2}\frac{dC_m}{dT}\right] + \cdots \quad (7\text{-}59)$$

$$\frac{S_m - S_{m_s}}{R} = -\ln P_s - \frac{T}{V}\frac{dB_m}{dT} - \frac{B_m{}^2}{2V^2} + \frac{C_m}{2V^2}$$
$$- \frac{T}{2V^2}\frac{dC_m}{dT} - \cdots \quad (7\text{-}60)$$

$$\frac{C_{pm} - C_{pm}^0}{R} = -\frac{T^2}{V}\frac{d^2B_m}{dT^2} + \frac{1}{V^2}\left[\left(B_m - T\frac{dB_m}{dT}\right)^2 - C_m\right.$$
$$\left. + T\frac{dC_m}{dT} - \frac{T^2}{2}\frac{d^2C_m}{dT^2}\right] \quad (7\text{-}61)$$

Equations (7-59) to (7-61) are equally applicable to a pure component. For a mixture, the terms involving C_m are not of much value since it is not now possible to estimate C_m with any accuracy, though, in Example 7-3, this term is included to illustrate a possible calculational technique. B_m is determined from Eq. (7-1); in this equation, both pure and interaction virial coefficients must be obtained.   If ϵ_0/k and b_0 can be estimated (on the assumption of a Lennard-Jones or Stockmayer potential) by the methods discussed in Sec. 2-10, by Table 3-1, or, for interaction parameters, by Table 7-2, then B values may be determined from Fig. 3-10, 3-11, 3-14, or 3-15 or by the tables in Ref. 64. dB/dT may be obtained by differentiating the curves in the figures noted above or directly from the tables in Ref. 64.   In both these cases, one obtains $dB^*/dT^* = d(B/b_0)/d[T/(\epsilon_0/k)] = [(\epsilon_0/k)/b_0](dB/dT)$.

An alternative path, which is somewhat less laborious, is to obtain pure-component second virials from Eqs. (3-45) to (3-47).   These equations are not convenient for estimating interaction virial coefficients since the concept of $P_{c_{ij}}$ is not defined, though Eq. (7-29) may be applicable. Prausnitz and Gunn (117) have rearranged Eqs. (3-45) to (3-47) to allow the estimation of interaction second-virial coefficients as follows:

$$B_{ij}/V_{c_{ij}} = (f^0(T_r)/0.291) + \omega_{ij}\{[0.274f^0(T_r) + f^1(T_r)]/$$
$$(0.291 - 0.08\omega_{ij})\} \quad (7\text{-}62)$$

where $f^0(T_r)$ and $f^1(T_r)$ are given by Eqs. (3-46) and (3-47), ω_{ij} by $(\omega_i + \omega_j)/2$, $V_{c_{ij}}$ by Eq. (7-11), T_r by $T/T_{c_{ij}}$ with $T_{c_{ij}}$ from the analogue of Eq. (7-15),

$$T_{c_{ij}} = (V_{c_i}V_{c_j}/V_{c_{ij}}^2)(T_{c_i}T_{c_j})^{1/2} \quad (7\text{-}63)$$

Equation (7-62) gives about the same results as obtained using the more theoretical (but not necessarily more accurate) method employing ϵ_0/k and b_0, even though the rather poor approximation, Eq. (2-29), has been used to relate Z_c and ω.

However, in Eqs. (7-62), (3-45), (3-46), and (3-47) the derivatives dB_i/dT, dB_j/dT, and dB_{ij}/dT may be obtained analytically for use in Eq. (7-1) and Eqs. (7-59) to (7-61).

Finally, to obtain H_m, S_m, and C_{p_m}, mixture volumes are estimated by methods summarized in Sec. 7-12 and

$$H_m^0 = \sum_i y_i H_i^0 \quad (7\text{-}64)$$

$$C_{p_m}^0 = \sum_i y_i C_{p_i}^0 \quad (7\text{-}65)$$

$$S_{m_s} = \sum_i y_i S_{i_s} - R \sum_i \ln y_i + R \ln P_s \quad (7\text{-}66)$$

where as usual H_i^0 and $C_{p_i}^0$ refer to properties of the pure components at zero pressure and S_{i_s} refers to the entropy of the pure material at some standard pressure P_s.

Except for fugacity, the virial equation is not a convenient one to employ to determine thermodynamic properties. For pure components, there are more accurate and convenient methods. For mixtures, there are not necessarily more accurate methods so that one may be forced to employ this technique to obtain reasonable results. Application of the method is discussed in Sec. 7-17.

7-15 Pseudocritical Method to Estimate Thermodynamic Properties of Mixtures

The estimation of many thermodynamic properties was discussed in some detail in Chap. 6. In most cases the most convenient, general, and accurate technique was a reduced-state correlation based upon T_r, P_r, and a third correlating term such as the critical compressibility or acentric factor. Appendix B lists, for example, tables for determining $H - H^0$.

Exactly the same correlation may be applied to mixtures; however, the critical constants to be used are now the pseudocritical mixture constants. Such rules are summarized in Sec. 7-9. The method should be considered applicable only for nonpolar mixtures, but often it is reasonably accurate for slightly polar mixtures. There is no inherent restriction to the gas phase. The method has not been tested enough to allow any meaningful statement regarding the expected accuracy, but the simplicity of this technique makes it rather appealing. The application of the method is discussed in more detail in Sec. 7-17 and illustrated in Example 7-4.

7-16 Equations of State to Estimate Thermodynamic Properties of Mixtures

From any reliable equation of state for which methods are available to obtain mixture constants, one may use Eq. (6-16), (6-17), (6-20), or (6-29) to obtain the differences between mixture thermodynamic properties and some standard state, e.g., from Eq. (6-16), $H_m - H_m^0$ or $H_m - \sum_i y_i H_i^0$. As noted earlier, only two mixture equations of state have received much attention, the Benedict-Webb-Rubin (Appendix E) and the Redlich-Kwong [Eq. (3-51)]. Thus only these two equations have been used for mixture thermodynamic-property estimations. The "straightforward" method indicated above is, however, rather complex to use, and computer facilities are desirable. In Appendix E, the equations derived from the BWR equation are summarized for convenient reference.

Rather than use the technique noted above, a somewhat different technique has been commonly utilized to determine mixture enthalpies; i.e., the difference between the partial molal enthalpy of each component and that of the pure component at zero pressure is first determined, and then the mixture enthalpy is obtained as

$$H_m = \sum_i y_i(\bar{H}_i - H_i^0) + \sum_i y_i H_i^0 \qquad (7\text{-}67)$$

The second term involves only pure-component ideal-gas values, and these can be estimated from some enthalpy base value, with ideal-gas heat capacities obtained as discussed in Chap. 5. The first term accounts for the nonideality of both the mixture and the pure components and is zero for ideal-gas mixtures. It is determined from the component fugacity coefficient $\bar{f}_i/y_i P$, from the thermodynamic relation

$$\{\partial[\ln(\bar{f}_i/y_i P)]/\partial T\}_{P,y} = (H_i^0 - \bar{H}_i)/RT^2 \qquad (7\text{-}68)$$

As shown in Sec. 7-23, the logarithm of the fugacity ratio can be obtained from an equation of state; when it is differentiated with respect to temperature, the term $H_i^0 - \bar{H}_i$ results.

Both these techniques which use equations of state are discussed in Sec. 7-17 and certain simple estimating rules for enthalpies presented.

The estimated values of thermodynamic properties of mixtures obtained with the equation-of-state approach can be only as good as the equation used. Usually, though, *more* error is expected, as first and sometimes (for $C_{p_m} - C_{p_m}^0$) second derivatives of the equation of state are necessary. It does not always follow that good equations of state yield accurate partial derivatives between P, V, T, though the BWR and RK equations referred to above are rather reliable in this respect. Similar conclusions are probably valid for the Martin-Hou equation.

7-17 Discussion of Estimating Techniques for Mixture Thermodynamic Properties

Enthalpy. Hobson and Weber (65) reviewed mixture-enthalpy estimation techniques to 1957. Since then a number of other studies of this problem have appeared. Brewer and Geist (12) used the virial-equation approach (Sec. 7-14) to estimate the enthalpy variation with pressure of high-pressure methane-nitrogen gas mixtures. Equation (7-59) was used, and, owing to the high pressures studied, the third virial term was retained. The method is illustrated in Example 7-3. Small errors were reported by Brewer and Geist (average 2.8 per cent), but the error found in Example 7-3 is considerably larger.* Better results were obtained with the pseudocritical–corresponding-state method illus-

---

* See, however, the note at the end of Example 7-3.

trated in Example 7-4.   Brewer and Geist report similarly good results with this latter approach.   Tooke and Hays (149) and Lambert et al. (80) also discuss the virial method to determine mixture enthalpies of nonpolar mixtures, and Blanks and Prausnitz (10) have used the same method to determine enthalpies of mixtures containing one or more polar components.   In the last case, the pure-component and interaction parameters and second virials are determined as illustrated in Example 7-2.   Good results were claimed for the systems ethanol-pentane and ethanol-benzene.

Other studies of polar mixtures, primarily by Storvick and Smith (91, 92, 144–146) have shown that the usual nonpolar corresponding-state methods with pseudocritical temperatures and generalized enthalpy-deviation tables (such as shown in Appendix B) do not usually yield accurate enthalpy predictions.   These authors have approached the problem by splitting the enthalpy deviation into two parts; one accounts for the nonpolar type of gas nonideality and the other for enthalpy changes due to association of the polar components.   For a few n-alcohol–nonpolar systems, methods have been presented to estimate association enthalpies and entropies, but the method has not been generalized.

Example 7-3.   Estimate the isothermal enthalpy change at $200°K$ ($-100°F$) from zero pressure to 68 atm (1,000 psia) for a methane-nitrogen gas mixture containing 70 mole % methane.   The (experimental) value quoted by Brewer and Geist is -580 cal/g mole (12).

Solution.   Pure-component properties (Appendix A) are as shown in the tabulation.

	Methane	Nitrogen
T_c, °K	190.7	126.2
P_c, atm	45.8	33.5
V_c, cm³/g mole	99.5	90.1
T_b, °K	111.7	77.3
ω	0.013	0.040
Z_c	0.290	0.291
ϵ_0/k, °K	144.5	96.8
σ, A	3.83	3.68
b_0, cm³/g mole	70.9	63.1

The Lennard-Jones parameters, estimated from Eqs. (2-42), (2-43) and (2-45), agree well with the literature values (64).

(a) *Pure-component Second Virials.*   Two techniques will be illustrated:

(a1) $T^* = T/(\epsilon_0/k)$

For CH_4: $T^* = 200/144.5 = 1.38$ $B^* = -1.41$
For N_2: $T^* = 200/96.8 = 2.07$ $B^* = -0.58$

where B^* is found from Figs. 3-10 and 3-11.

CH_4: $B = b_0 B^* = (70.9)(-1.41) = -100$ cm³/g mole
N_2: $B = b_0 B^* = (63.1)(-0.58) = -37$ cm³/g mole

($a2$) From Eqs. (3-45) to (3-47),

	T_r	B^0	B^1	B, cm³/g mole
CH₄	1.049	−104.7	−10.6	−105
N₂	1.585	− 37.6	−37.9	− 36

Agreement between the two methods is good.   Method $a2$ is believed to be slightly more accurate, and these values will be used.

(b) *Pure-component Third-virial Coefficients.*   For the same value of T^* as in ($a1$). From Fig. 3-12,

$$C^*_{CH_4} = 0.57 \qquad C^*_{N_2} = 0.425$$
$$C_{CH_4} = C^* b_0{}^2 = (0.57)(70.9)^2 = 2{,}860 \text{ cm}^6/(\text{g mole})^2$$
$$C_{N_2} = C^* b_0{}^2 = (0.425)(63.1)^2 = 1{,}690 \text{ cm}^6/(\text{g mole})^2$$

(c) *Second-virial Cross Coefficient.*   Two methods will be illustrated:

($c1$) As both molecules are nonpolar and $0.5 < V_c(CH_4)/V_c(N_2) < 2$, then, from the recommendations in Table 7-2,

$$\sigma_{(CH_4\text{-}N_2)} = (3.83 + 3.68)/2 = 3.76 \text{ A} \qquad (\text{Eq. 7-9})$$
$$(\epsilon_0/k)_{(CH_4\text{-}N_2)} = \sqrt{(144.5)(96.8)} = 118°K$$
$$b_{0(CH_4\text{-}N_2)} = \tfrac{2}{3}\pi N_0\sigma^3_{(CH_4\text{-}N_2)} = 1.26\sigma^3$$

if σ is in angstroms and b_0 in cubic centimeters per gram mole

$$= (1.26)(3.76)^3 = 67.0 \text{ cm}^3/\text{g mole}$$
$$T^*_{(CH_4\text{-}N_2)} = {}^{200}\!/_{118} = 1.69 \qquad B^*_{(CH_4\text{-}N_2)} = -0.93$$
$$B_{(CH_4\text{-}N_2)} = (-0.93)(67.0) = -62 \text{ cm}^3/\text{g mole}$$

($c2$) The second method is described in Sec. 7-15 by Eqs. (7-62), (7-63), and (7-11). From Eq. (7-11), $V_{c(N_2\text{-}CH_4)} = 94.8$ cm³/g mole [note that in this case, since $V_{c_{N_2}} \sim V_{c_{CH_4}}$, Eq. (7-13) would have given exactly the same value, i.e., 94.8].   From Eq. (7-63),

$$T_{c(CH_4\text{-}N_2)} = \{[(99.5)(90.1)]/(94.8)^2\}[(190.7)(126.2)]^{1/2}$$
$$= (0.998)(155.2) = 155°K$$
$$\omega_{(CH_4\text{-}N_2)} = \tfrac{1}{2}(0.013 + 0.040) = 0.027$$
$$T_{r(CH_4\text{-}N_2)} = {}^{200}\!/_{155} = 1.29$$
$$f^0(T_{r(CH_4\text{-}N_2)}) = -0.021 \qquad \text{from Eq. (3-46)}$$
$$f^1(T_{r(CH_4\text{-}N_2)}) = +0.083 \qquad \text{from Eq. (3-47)}$$

and, from Eq. (7-62), $B_{(CH_4\text{-}N_2)} = -63$ cm³/g mole, a value very close to that obtained in ($c1$).

(d) *Third-virial Cross Coefficients*

$$(\epsilon_0/k)_{(CH_4\text{-}CH_4\text{-}N_2)} = [(144.5)(144.5)(96.8)]^{1/3} = 126°K$$
$$(\epsilon_0/k)_{(CH_4\text{-}N_2\text{-}N_2)} = [(144.5)(96.8)(96.8)]^{1/3} = 111°K$$
$$\sigma_{(CH_4\text{-}CH_4\text{-}N_2)} = \tfrac{1}{3}(3.83 + 3.83 + 3.68) = 3.78 \text{ A}$$
$$\sigma_{(CH_4\text{-}N_2\text{-}N_2)} = \tfrac{1}{3}(3.83 + 3.68 + 3.68) = 3.73 \text{ A}$$
$$b_{0(CH_4\text{-}CH_4\text{-}N_2)} = (1.26)(3.78)^3 = 68.0 \text{ cm}^3/\text{g mole}$$
$$b_{0(CH_4\text{-}N_2\text{-}N_2)} = (1.26)(3.73)^3 = 65.4 \text{ cm}^3/\text{g mole}$$
$$T^*_{(CH_4\text{-}CH_4\text{-}N_2)} = {}^{200}\!/_{126} = 1.59 \qquad C^*_{(CH_4\text{-}CH_4\text{-}N_2)} = 0.52$$
$$T^*_{(CH_4\text{-}N_2\text{-}N_2)} = {}^{200}\!/_{111} = 1.80 \qquad C^*_{(CH_4\text{-}N_2\text{-}N_2)} = 0.47$$
$$C_{(CH_4\text{-}CH_4\text{-}N_2)} = C^* b_0{}^2 = (0.52)(68.0)^2 = 2{,}400 \text{ cm}^6/(\text{g mole})^2$$
$$C_{(CH_4\text{-}N_2\text{-}N_2)} = C^* b_0{}^2 = (0.47)(65.4)^2 = 2{,}000 \text{ cm}^6/(\text{g mole})^2$$

(e) *Second-virial Mixture Coefficient.* From Eq. (7-1) with $y_{CH_4} = 0.7$.

$$B_m = (y_{CH_4})^2 B_{CH_4} + 2(y_{CH_4})(y_{N_2}) B_{(CH_4-N_2)} + (y_{N_2})^2 B_{N_2}$$
$$= (0.70)^2(-105) + (2)(0.7)(0.3)(-63) + (0.30)^2(-36)$$
$$= -81 \text{ cm}^3/\text{g mole}$$

(f) *Third-virial Mixture Coefficient.* From Eq. (7-2),

$$C_m = (y_{CH_4})^3 C_{CH_4} + 3(y_{CH_4})^2 y_{N_2} C_{(CH_4-CH_4-N_2)} + 3 y_{CH_4}(y_{N_2})^2 C_{(CH_4-N_2-N_2)} + (y_{N_2})^3 C_{N_2}$$
$$= (0.70)^3(2,860) + (3)(0.70)^2(0.30)(2,400) + (3)(0.70)(0.30)^2(2,000)$$
$$+ (0.30)^3(1,690) = 2,460 \text{ cm}^6/(\text{g mole})^2$$

(g) *Mixture Volume.* From Eq. (3-22)

$$Z_m = PV/RT = 1 + B_m/V + C_m/V^2$$
$$= [(68)(V)]/[(82.06)(200)] = 1 - 81/V + 2,460/V^2$$
$$V = 120 \text{ cm}^3/\text{g mole} \qquad Z_m = 0.497$$

(h) *Temperature Derivatives of Second-virial Coefficients.* Equations (3-45) to (3-47) may be differentiated with respect to temperature to obtain the various dB/dT values. However, Hirschfelder, Curtiss, and Bird (64) have tabulated values of Lennard-Jones $T^*(dB^*/dT^*)$ for various T^* in their table 1-B, and these will be used here.

$$T^*(dB^*/dT^*) = T(dB/dT)/b_0$$

	T^*	$T^*(dB^*/dT^*)$	b_0	$T(dB/dT)$, cm³/g mole
CH$_4$	1.38	2.72	70.9	193
CH$_4$-N$_2$	1.69	2.04	67.0	137
N$_2$	2.07	1.55	63.1	97.8

(i) *Temperature Derivatives of Third-virial Coefficients.* Reference 64 tabulates $T^*(dC^*/dT^*)$ as functions of T^* in their table 1-C. Since

$$T^*(dC^*/dT^*) = T(dC/dT)/b_0^2$$

we have the accompanying tabulation.

	T^*	$T^*(dC^*/dT^*)$	b_0	$T(dC/dT)$, cm⁶/(g mole)²
CH$_4$	1.38	-0.306	70.9	-1,540
CH$_4$-CH$_4$-N$_2$	1.59	-0.396	68.0	-1,830
CH$_4$-N$_2$-N$_2$	1.80	-0.364	65.4	-1,560
N$_2$	2.07	-0.293	63.1	-1,170

(j) *Temperature Derivatives of Mixture Virials.* Obtain $T(dB_m/dT)$ and $T(dC_m/dT)$ in Eq. (7-59), by differentiating Eqs. (7-1) and (7-2),

$$T(dB_m/dT) = (y_{CH_4})^2(T)(dB_{CH_4}/dT) + 2 y_{CH_4} y_{N_2}(T)(dB_{(CH_4-N_2)}/dT)$$
$$+ (y_{N_2})^2(T)(dB_{N_2}/dT)$$
$$= (0.70)^2(193) + (2)(0.70)(0.30)(137) + (0.30)^2(97.8)$$
$$= 160 \text{ cm}^3/\text{g mole}$$

In a similar manner,

$$T(dC_m/dT) = (y_{CH_4})^3(T)(dC_{CH_4}/dT) + 3(y_{CH_4})^2(y_{N_2})(T)(dC_{(CH_4\text{-}CH_4\text{-}N_2)}/dT)$$
$$+ 3(y_{CH_4})(y_{N_2})^2(T)(dC_{(CH_4\text{-}N_2\text{-}N_2)}/dT) + (y_{N_2})^3(T)(dC_{N_2}/dT)$$
$$= (0.70)^3(-1,540) + (3)(0.70)^2(0.30)(-1,830)$$
$$+ (3)(0.70)(0.30)^2(-1,560) + (0.30)^3(-1,170)$$
$$= -1,662 \text{ cm}^6/(\text{g mole})^2$$

(k) *Calculation of* $H_m - H_m^0$. From Eq. (7-59) with the terms obtained above,

$$(H_m - H_m^0)/RT = \frac{1}{120}(-81 - 160) + (\frac{1}{120^2})(2,460 + 1,662/2)$$
$$= -2.00 + 0.23 = -1.77$$
$$H_m - H_m^0 = (1.987)(200)(-1.77) = -704 \text{ cal/g mole}$$

NOTE: Brewer and Geist (12) report a calculated value of $H_m - H_m^0 = 602$ cal/g mole. It appears that the difference in their calculated value and the one shown above is that third-virial coefficients were determined by a correlation due to Prausnitz (114) where C/V_c^2 is correlated with T_r and ω. Use of this correlation also leads to an estimate of the volume as 146 cm³/g mole, a value close to the experimental value of about 143 cm³/g mole. This disagreement illustrates the present state of uncertainty in estimating third-virial coefficients.

Example 7-4. Repeat Example 7-3, using the pseudocritical technique.

Solution. The critical properties of the pure components are shown in Example 7-3.

Kay's Rule [*Eqs.* (7-30) *and* (7-31)]

$$T_{c_m} = (0.70)(190.7) + (0.30)(126.2) = 171°K$$
$$P_{c_m} = (0.70)(45.8) + (0.30)(33.5) = 42.1 \text{ atm}$$
$$T_{r_m}(K) = \frac{200}{171} = 1.17$$
$$P_{r_m}(K) = 68/42.1 = 1.62$$

Joffe-Stewart, Burkhardt, and Voo Rule [*Eqs.* (7-38) *to* (7-41)]

$$(T_c/P_c)_{CH_4} = 4.16 \qquad (T_c/P_c)_{N_2} = 3.77°K/\text{atm}$$
$$(T_c/P_c^{\frac{1}{2}})_{CH_4} = 28.2 \qquad (T_c/P_c^{\frac{1}{2}})_{N_2} = 21.8°K/\text{atm}^{\frac{1}{2}}$$
$$K^2 = T_{c_m}^2/P_{c_m} = [(0.70)(28.2) + (0.30)(21.8)]^2 = 691°K^2/\text{atm}$$
$$J = T_{c_m}/P_{c_m} = \frac{1}{3}[(0.70)(4.16) + (0.30)(3.77)]$$
$$+ \frac{2}{3}[(0.70)(4.16)^{\frac{1}{2}} + (0.30)(3.77)^{\frac{1}{2}}]^2 = 4.02°K/\text{atm}$$
$$T_{c_m} = K^2/J = 691/4.02 = 172°K$$
$$P_{c_m} = T_{c_m}/J = 172/4.02 = 42.8 \text{ atm} \qquad T_{r_m} = \frac{200}{172} = 1.16$$
$$P_{r_m} = 68/42.8 = 1.59$$

Leland-Mueller Rule [*Eqs.* (7-32) *to* (7-37)]

$$\theta = P_{r_m}(K)/T_{r_m}(K) = 1.62/1.17 = 1.38, \qquad \text{Eq. (7-37)}$$
$$\alpha = 2.43 - (0.74)(1.38) = 1.40 \qquad \text{by Eq. (7-36)}$$
$$V_{c_m} = y_{CH_4}^2 V_{c_{CH_4}} + \frac{1}{4}y_{CH_4}y_{N_2}(V_{c_{CH_4}}^{\frac{1}{3}} + V_{c_{N_2}}^{\frac{1}{3}})^3 + y_{N_2}^2 V_{c_{N_2}}$$
$$= (0.70)^2(99.5) + \frac{1}{4}(0.70)(0.30)[(99.5)^{\frac{1}{3}} + (90.1)^{\frac{1}{3}}]^3 + (0.30)^2(90.1)$$
$$= 96.7 \text{ cm}^3/\text{g mole} \qquad \text{by Eq. (7-34)}$$

Equation (7-32) may be written

$$T_{c_m} = \left(\frac{\{(y_{CH_4})[V_c T_c^\alpha]_{CH_4}^{\frac{1}{2}} + (y_{N_2})[V_c T_c^\alpha]_{N_2}^{\frac{1}{2}}\}^2}{V_{c_m}} \right)^{1/\alpha}$$
$$= \left\{ \frac{[(0.70)(99.5)^{0.5}(190.7)^{0.7} + (0.30)(90.1)^{0.5}(126.2)^{0.7}]^2}{96.7} \right\}^{1/1.4} = 171°K$$
$$Z_{c_m} = (0.70)(0.290) + (0.30)(0.291) = 0.290$$
$$P_{c_m} = (171)(0.290)(82.07)/96.7 = 42.1 \text{ atm}$$
$$T_{r_m} = \frac{200}{171} = 1.17 \qquad P_{r_m} = 68/42.1 = 1.62$$

Prausnitz-Gunn [Eqs. (7-42) to (7-52)]

$$V_{c_m} = 96.7$$

as by Leland-Mueller method.

$$\omega_m = (0.70)(0.013) + (0.30)(0.040) = 0.021$$
$$T_{c_{ij}} = (T_{c_{CH_4}}T_{c_{N_2}})^{\frac{1}{2}} = [(190.7)(126.2)]^{\frac{1}{2}} = 155°K$$

since $k_{ij} \cong 1.0$.

$$V_{c_{ij}} = 94.8 \text{ cm}^3/\text{g mole}$$

as shown in (c2) of Example 7-3.

$$\beta = y_{CH_4}^2(V_cT_c)_{CH_4} + 2y_{CH_4}y_{N_2}(V_cT_c)_{(CH_4-N_2)} + y_{N_2}^2(V_cT_c)_{N_2}$$
$$= (0.70)^2(99.5)(190.7) + (2)(0.70)(0.30)(94.8)(155)$$
$$+ (0.30)^2(90.1)(126.2) = 16,500 \text{ cm}^3\text{-}°K/\text{g mole}$$
$$\gamma = y_{CH_4}^2(V_cT_c^2)_{CH_4} + 2y_{CH_4}y_{N_2}(V_cT_c^2)_{(CH_4-N_2)} + 2y_{N_2}(V_cT_c^2)_{N_2}$$
$$= (0.70)^2(99.5)(190.7)^2 + 2(0.70)(0.30)(94.8)(155)^2$$
$$+ (0.30)^2(90.1)(126.2)^2 = 2.86 \times 10^6 \text{ cm}^3\text{-}°K^2/\text{g mole}$$

A value of T_{c_m} is needed to obtain r and s. As a first approximation, let

$$T_{c_m} \sim \beta/V_{c_m} = 16,500/96.7 = 171°K$$

Then $T/T_{c_m} = 1.17$, $r = 3.1$, $s = 1.5$ from Figs. 7-2 and 7-3. From Eq. (7-42),

$$T_{c_m} = \frac{16,500 + \sqrt{(16,500)^2 + (3.1)(96.7)(2.86)(10^6)}}{(2)(1.5)(96.7)} = 172°K$$

and so the original assumption of 171°K is satisfactory.

$$P_{c_m} = (0.290)(172)(82.06)/(96.7) = 42.3 \text{ atm}$$
$$T_{r_m} = {}^{200}\!/_{172} = 1.16 \quad \text{and} \quad P_{r_m} = 68/42.3 = 1.61$$

It is instructive to note that all rules give nearly the same pseudocritical constants even though the critical pressures and temperatures of methane and nitrogen are quite different. This is due to the fact that the critical volumes are quite similar, and as indicated in Sec. 7-10, such behavior would have been predicted (126).

To obtain $H_m - H_m^0$ values, choose $T_{r_m} = 1.17$, $P_{r_m} = 1.60$, $Z_{c_m} = 0.290$. From Appendix B,

$$(H_m - H_m^0)/T_c = -3.46$$
$$H_m - H_m^0 = (-3.46)(172) = -595 \text{ cal/g mole}$$

Other enthalpy-deviation studies using the pseudocritical concept with generalized charts have led to the set of nomographs of liquid and vapor light hydrocarbon enthalpies for both pure components and mixtures, as presented by Scheibel and Jenny (132), and also to a technique to estimate saturated-vapor and liquid enthalpies of mixtures of normal paraffins by Stevens and Thodos (142). In the latter paper, the Lydersen-Greenkorn-Hougen tables were used with reduced temperatures based on both Kay's pseudocritical temperatures and the actual mixture critical temperature estimated as shown in Sec. 7-28. Good results were obtained with both critical temperatures, but slightly better results were found by using the true value.

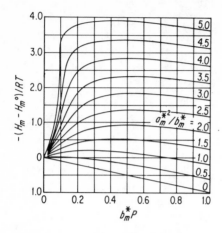

FIG. 7-5. Redlich-Kwong estimation of mixture enthalpies. [W. C. Edmister, R. E. Thompson, and L. Yarborough, AIChE J., 9:116 (1963).]

Mixture enthalpies have been estimated from equations of state, though most correlations are limited to hydrocarbon mixtures and only the Redlich-Kwong and Benedict-Webb-Rubin equations have been extensively employed. Of the many papers presented in this area (17, 33, 40, 106), several appear to deserve detailed mention as rather general methods. Edmister, Thompson, and Yarborough (37) employed Eq. (7-68) and the Redlich-Kwong equation to express fugacity coefficients for mixtures. The expressions obtained are rather complex but were programmed and run successfully on a computer. For hand calculations, the method was reduced to three charts, from which it is possible to obtain partial enthalpies or mixture enthalpies at various temperatures and pressures. These charts are given as Figs. 7-5 to 7-7, and the method is illustrated in Example 7-5. In this example, the system methane-nitrogen is chosen, although the method is stated to be applicable for hydrocarbon mixtures. The result is in good agreement with experi-

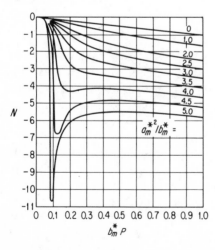

FIG. 7-6. N as a function of a^{*2}/b_m^* and b_m^*P for Eq. (7-70). [W. C. Edmister, R. E. Thompson, and L. Yarborough, AIChE J., 9:116 (1963).]

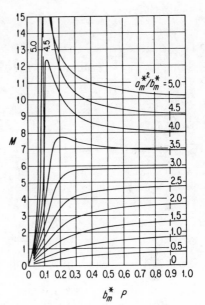

FIG. 7-7. M as a function of a_m^{*2}/b_m^* and $b_m P$ for Eq. (7-70). [*W. C. Edmister, R. E. Thompson, and L. Yarborough, AIChE J.*, **9**:116 (1963).]

mental data and can be readily compared with the methods illustrated in Examples 7-3 and 7-4. The simplicity is appealing. The accuracy is stated to be about 5 per cent up to 2,500 psia, and best agreement is found if the temperature is well above the critical temperature of the more abundant component. Note that this is not the case in Example 7-5.

Example 7-5. Repeat Example 7-3, using the Edmister, Thompson, and Yarborough method.

Solution. The parameters a_m^* and b_m^* are necessary in the solution. They are calculated as outlined below, where

$$a_i^{*2} = 0.4278/T_{r_i}^{2.5}P_{c_i}$$
$$b_i^* = 0.0867/T_{r_i}P_{c_i}$$

	CH$_4$	Mixture	N$_2$
T_c, °K	190.7	....	126.2
P_c, atm	45.8	....	33.5
T_r (at 200°K)	1.05	....	1.58
$T_r^{2.5}$	1.13	....	3.14
$a^{*2} \times 10^3$, atm^{-1}	8.28	....	4.07
$b^* \times 10^3$, atm^{-1}	1.80	....	1.64
$a^* \times 10^2$, atm$^{-\frac{1}{2}}$	9.08	....	6.36
a_m^* [Eq. (7-54)], atm$^{-\frac{1}{2}}$	......	8.26×10^{-2}	
b_m^* [Eq. (7-55)], atm^{-1}	......	1.75×10^{-3}	
$b_m^* P$	......	0.119	
a_m^{*2}/b_m^*	......	3.90	

From Fig. 7-5,

$$-(H_m - H_m{}^0)/RT = 1.50$$
$$H_m - H_m{}^0 = -(1.987)(200)(1.50) = -597 \text{ cal/g mole}$$

Figure 7-5 may be approximated in an analytical manner as (34)

$$-(H_m - H_m{}^0)/RT = (1 - Z_m) + 1.5(a_m^{*2}/b_m^*) \ln (1 + b_m^* P) \qquad (7\text{-}69)$$

Figures 7-6 and 7-7 allow a calculation of partial molal enthalpies by means of Eq. (7-70),

$$\overline{\Delta H}_i/RT = (\bar{H}_i - H_i{}^0)/RT = (H_m - H_m{}^0)/RT - (a_i^*/a_m^* - 1)M - (b_i^*/b_m^* - 1)N \qquad (7\text{-}70)$$

where the first term is obtained from Fig. 7-5 and the parameters M and N from Figs. 7-6 and 7-7. For example, in the present problem,

$$-(H_m - H_m{}^0)/RT = 1.50$$
$$N = \text{(about)} -2.2$$
$$M = \text{(very difficult to read in this range)} \cong 12$$
$$\overline{\Delta H}_{CH_4}/RT = -1.50 - \{[(9.08)(10^{-2})]/[(8.26)(10^{-2})] - 1\}(12)$$
$$\qquad\qquad - \{[(1.80)(10^{-3})]/[(1.75)(10^{-3})] - 1\}(-2.2)$$
$$= -1.50 - 1.2 + 0.06 \cong -2.5$$
$$\overline{\Delta H}_{CH_4} = -1000 \text{ cal/g mole}$$

This is probably a poor result, since the point used in Fig. 7-7 for obtaining M is on a very sensitive part of the diagram. In a similar way $\overline{\Delta H}_{N_2} > 0$. As this is not likely, the method is not believed applicable in this case.

Another technique applicable to hydrocarbon mixtures in both liquid and vapor states has been proposed by Canjar and Peterka (18). In this method, the molal average boiling point (MABP) of the mixture at 1 atm is used as the characterizing factor. The value of $H_m - H_m{}^0$ for the vapor may be determined directly from Fig. 7-8 with values of the MABP and the pressure. For the liquid phase, the enthalpy difference between the liquid and ideal gas is first determined at 1,500 psia from Fig. 7-9 as a function of the MABP and temperature. This liquid-mixture enthalpy is then corrected to the desired pressure by means of Fig. 7-10. For example, if the liquid enthalpy at 300 psia and 85°F were desired for a light hydrocarbon mixture with an MABP of -30°F, then, from Fig. 7-9, $(H_m - H_m{}^0) = -152$ Btu/lb at 1,500 psia. To obtain a value at 300 psia, the correction from Fig. 7-10 is about -1 Btu/lb; thus the value of $H_m - H_m{}^0$ at 300 psia is -153 Btu/lb.

Two other papers dealing with hydrocarbon mixtures are worth noting. Edmister and Yarborough (38) used both the RK and BWR equations of state to calculate gas-mixture enthalpies and concluded that both yielded results of comparable accuracy. These same workers present a general correlation for enthalpies of gaseous hydrocarbon mixtures containing methane. In another paper, by Edmister, Persyn, and Erbar (34), a rather complete scheme is proposed to determine enthalpies of hydrocarbon

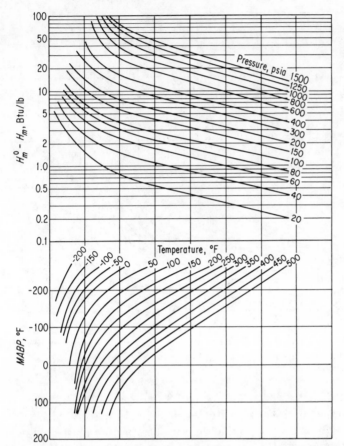

Fig. 7-8. Pressure correction to enthalpies of hydrocarbon mixtures in ideal-gas state, vapor phase. [*L. N. Canjar and V. J. Peterka, AIChE J.*, **2**:343 (1956).]

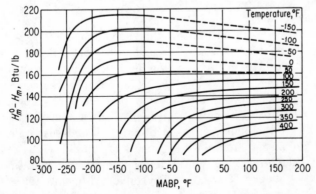

Fig. 7-9. Pressure correction of 1,500 psia to enthalpies of hydrocarbon mixtures in the liquid phase. [*L. N. Canjar and V. J. Peterka, AIChE J.*, **2**:343 (1956).]

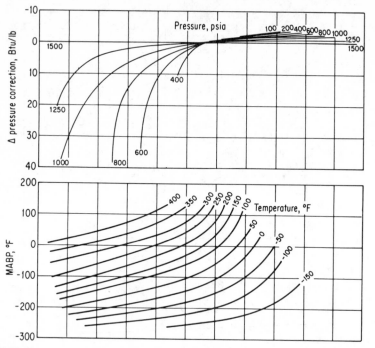

Fig. 7-10. Pressure correction to Fig. 7-9.   [L. N. Canjar and V. J. Peterka, AIChE J. **2**:343 (1956).]

mixtures in both saturated-vapor and liquid states.   The vapor-phase correlation is identical to that described earlier and illustrated in Example 7-5.   In the liquid phase, a technique was used to determine the partial molal enthalpy and mixture enthalpy from the Hildebrand solubility parameter.   Although rather good results were obtained, it is felt that the Canjar-Peterka technique described earlier is as accurate and somewhat easier to use.

In the discussion of mixture enthalpies, some mention should be made of the fact that considerable time and effort have been expended to measure and correlate heats of mixing in nonideal-liquid solutions.   The available data were reviewed to 1960 (73, 151); it was concluded that there were no reliable estimation techniques for nonhydrocarbon mixtures.   For hydrocarbon mixtures, the methods described earlier in this section indicate the approach taken to obtain liquid-mixture enthalpies. The most promising effort on liquid heats of solution (123) utilized the Scatchard-Hildebrand equation to determine internal energies of mixing at constant volume.   These were then converted to enthalpies of mixing. Even in this case, mixtures which are not comprised of approximately spherically symmetric molecules cannot be treated.

Latent-heat Effects. Quite frequently, it is only the latent heat of vaporization or condensation of a mixture that is desired. For example, in distillation calculations the variation of the mixture molal latent heat from plate to plate determines the validity of the assumption of constant-molal overflow. In discussing such latent heat, it is necessary to recognize that there are several ways of defining it. In the example given above for distillation calculations, the latent heat of interest is that at constant pressure and temperature, i.e., for vaporization the enthalpy difference for 1 mole of mixture (with the composition of the vapor) from liquid to vapor; for condensation, the composition corresponds to the liquid phase. This latent heat is conceptually different (though often not much different numerically) from the difference between saturated-liquid enthalpies of vapor and liquid. Other types of mixture latent heats are of interest in different practical situations. A description of the more common types is given by Gambill (45). It is possible to calculate rigorously the various types of mixture latent heats from thermodynamics (27, 29, 45, 66), usually by employing variations of the Clausius-Clapeyron equation, but to do so a rather complete set of vapor-liquid composition -P-T data is ordinarily required. In fact there seem to be no simple estimation techniques which will account for nonideal effects in the vapor and liquid. For hydrocarbon mixtures, the correlations presented earlier to determine mixture vapor and liquid enthalpies may be used. For other types of mixtures, at low pressures, it is usually sufficiently accurate to neglect entirely all nonideal effects and to calculate mixture latent heats by a mole-fraction average of the pure-component latent heats. For example, if 1 mole of vapor is to be formed with a composition y_1, y_2, . . . from a sufficiently large amount of liquid so that the composition of the liquid is not appreciably changed, then $\Delta H_{v_m} = \sum_i y_i \, \Delta H_{v_i}$, where ΔH_{v_i} is the

pure-component latent heat at the temperature in question. If the temperature varies, an average temperature may be used or a thermodynamic cycle outlined to account for the temperature change (140). These rules appear somewhat loose and inexact. They are, but the saving grace is that the ΔH_v terms are usually so much larger than heats of mixing (vapor and liquid) or ΔH terms due to temperature effects that small errors result in employing this approximation.

7-18 Recommendations for Estimating the Enthalpy of Mixtures

1. For a given mixture, a base-enthalpy value of each pure component is chosen at some reference temperature and pressure. A convenient base pressure is zero absolute, since the mixture then behaves as an ideal gas.

2. This zero reference pressure being assumed, the enthalpies of the pure components are first calculated at the system temperature and

reference pressure from

$$H_{T^0} - H_{T_{ref}}^0 = \int_{T_{ref}}^{T} C_P^0 \, dT \qquad (7\text{-}71)$$

where C_P^0 is obtained from experimental data or is evaluated by methods discussed in Sec. 5-8.

3. At the temperature T, $P = 0$, the mixture enthalpy H_m^0 is determined, per mole, from Eq. (7-64).

4. The mixture enthalpy at the system pressure is then determined by calculating the isothermal enthalpy deviation,

$$H_m = (H_m - H_m^0) + H_m^0 \qquad (7\text{-}72)$$

5. The isothermal enthalpy deviation $H_m - H_m^0$ may be determined as follows:

a. For vapor mixtures of light hydrocarbons, use the method of Edmister, Thompson, and Yarborough with Figs. 7-5 to 7-7. This method is illustrated in Example 7-5. Errors of 2 to perhaps 10 per cent are to be expected up to pressures of 2,500 psia if temperatures are above the critical temperature of the more abundant component.

b. For liquid mixtures of light hydrocarbons and for vapor mixtures at low temperatures, use the method of Canjar and Peterka as shown in Figs. 7-8 to 7-10. The method of application is discussed earlier in the text.

c. For machine computation of mixture enthalpies, any reliable equation of state for mixtures may be used with Eq. (6-16) to obtain the isothermal enthalpy deviation. Such equations are illustrated for the BWR equation in Appendix E, and a good description of the use of the RK equation is given in Ref. 137. If the equation of state is reliable for the range of interest, both techniques should lead to errors of only a few per cent.

d. For the broad class of nonpolar mixtures either the virial approach (Example 7-3) or the pseudocritical technique (Example 7-4) can be used. The latter is somewhat easier to use and appears to yield reliable results though of less accuracy than (a), (b), (c) above for hydrocarbon mixtures. It is impossible to estimate errors; they are perhaps ± 10 per cent for most vapor-phase estimations and ± 20 per cent for liquid-phase enthalpy values.

e. For mixtures containing polar components, no reliable method is available. For the special case of n-alcohols–hydrocarbons in the vapor phase, an approximate method to determine the isothermal enthalpy deviation is available (145), but the only general methods are the virial approach and the pseudocritical-constant method. In the former, the correct interaction-parameter rules are given in Table 7-2. In the latter, the method is used in an identical manner as for nonpolar mixtures. Errors may be large.

f. If only values of ΔH_{v_m} are desired, these may be approximated within a few per cent error by a mole-fraction average of the pure-component latent heats at the temperature of the system. Nonideality effects are neglected compared with the large values of ΔH_v of the pure components. This method is probably reliable for most engineering calculations and is better at lower pressures and for systems which have small heats of mixing.

7-19 Estimation of Thermodynamic Properties of Mixtures (Other than Enthalpy)

The estimation of isothermal deviations of mixture entropy, internal energy, and heat capacity from the ideal-gas state has not been investigated in any detail, probably because these properties are of less practical value than enthalpies. Values for ideal-gas mixtures may be obtained from Eqs. (7-65) and (7-66) and real-gas or -liquid values from Eqs. (6-20) and (6-29) with a reliable mixture equation of state. The results obtained by using the BWR equation are given, for example, in Appendix E. Presumably other equations of state could also be used.

In hand-calculation methods, the virial approach may be used, as illustrated in Example 7-3, except that the isothermal deviations are determined from Eq. (7-60) or (7-61), and, in a similar manner, the pseudocritical method can be used, as illustrated in Example 7-4, except that generalized correlations for entropy or heat capacity would then be used. Such correlations are described in Secs. 6-6 and 6-8. Errors by the use of these techniques are not known. Presumably entropy estimations would be in the same range of accuracy as enthalpy estimations, but larger errors would be expected for heat capacity because a second differentiation of the equation of state is involved.

7-20 Fugacities of Components in a Mixture

The fugacity of component i in a mixture $\bar{f}_i$ is closely related to the chemical potential by the definition (13, 85)

$$\mu_i \equiv (\partial \underline{F} / \partial N_i)_{T,P,N(\neq i)} = \bar{F}_i = RT \ln \bar{f}_i + \varphi_i(T) \qquad (7\text{-}73)$$

It is then analogous to a partial molal quantity. A second part of the definition is

$$\bar{f}_i \rightarrow p_i = Py_i \qquad \text{as } P \rightarrow 0 \qquad (7\text{-}74)$$

The advantage of using $\bar{f}_i$ rather than μ_i lies in the fact that an absolute numerical value may be obtained, whereas μ_i cannot be evaluated except relative to some base value; also, μ_i becomes negative infinite as $y_i \rightarrow 0$, whereas under such conditions $\bar{f}_i \rightarrow 0$. The units of fugacity are pressure, and the apparent dimensional difficulty of Eq. (7-73) is eliminated by noting that the unknown temperature function $\varphi_i(T)$ has the dimensions of energy/(mole) [ln (standard pressure)].

The quantities μ_i and $\bar{f}_i$ are useful only for situations involving chemical, phase, or other equilibrium. For example, in phase equilibrium the criteria are equality of temperature, pressure, and fugacity (or chemical potential) of each component between the phases in equilibrium. Likewise, in homogeneous chemical-reaction equilibrium, the criterion for equilibrium is the equality of the sum of chemical potentials (times the appropriate stoichiometric multiplier) between reactants and products. In terms of fugacity, these very important relations become:

$$\bar{f}_i^{\mathrm{I}} = \bar{f}_i^{\mathrm{II}}, \text{ phase equilibrium between phases I and II} \qquad (7\text{-}75)$$

$$K = e^{-\Delta F^0/RT} = \{[\bar{f}/f^0]_C{}^c/[\bar{f}/f^0]_A{}^a\}\{[\bar{f}/f^0]_D{}^d/[\bar{f}/f^0]_B{}^b\}(\cdots / \cdots) \qquad (7\text{-}76)$$

where the latter expresses the *equilibrium constant* for the general reaction

$$aA + bB + \cdots \rightleftharpoons cC + dD + \cdots \qquad (7\text{-}77)$$

The superscript zeros on f and ΔF refer to values in some arbitrarily chosen standard state. A thorough discussion of the use of Eqs. (7-75) and (7-76) will be found in thermodynamics texts. These equations are noted here to indicate the value of obtaining expressions relating $\bar{f}_i$ to temperature, pressure and composition, so that chemical- or phase-equilibrium compositions can be calculated.

The basic equations employed to calculate $\bar{f}_i$ may be readily derived from thermodynamics and are usually of one or two forms,

$$RT \ln (\bar{f}_i/y_i f_i{}^0) = RT \ln \gamma_i = \int_0^P (\bar{V}_i - V_i{}^0)\, dP \qquad (7\text{-}78)$$

or $\qquad RT \ln (\bar{f}_i/y_i P) = RT \ln \phi_i = \int_0^P (\bar{V}_i - RT/P)\, dP \qquad (7\text{-}79)$

Equation (7-78) defines an activity coefficient γ_i and requires the calculation of the fugacity of pure i, $f_i{}^0$ at the same temperature and pressure and in the same state of aggregation (liquid, gas, . . .) as the mixture (see Sec. 6-5). Equation (7-79) defines a fugacity coefficient ϕ_i. Both forms are useful. The first is very often used when ideal or nearly ideal solutions are being studied. Ideal solutions are defined in such a way that

$$\mu_i = \mu_i{}^0 + RT \ln y_i \qquad (7\text{-}80)$$

where $\mu_i{}^0$ is the chemical potential of pure i at the temperature and pressure of the mixture. From Eq. (7-80) it is easily shown that, for ideal solutions, $\gamma_i = 1.0$; thus, from Eq. (7-78),

$$\bar{f}_i = y_i f_i{}^0 \qquad \text{ideal solutions} \qquad (7\text{-}81)$$

Equation (7-81) is called the *Lewis and Randall rule*. It is very easy to employ and is probably the way most often used to determine $\bar{f}_i$. For ideal-gas mixtures, the fugacity of the pure component, f_i^0, becomes equal to the pressure, and, from Eq. (7-81),

$$\bar{f}_i = y_i P = p_i \qquad \text{ideal gases} \qquad (7\text{-}82)$$

The accuracy of Eqs. (7-81) and (7-82) will be discussed later, but it may be noted here that Eq. (7-81) is rigorous for ideal solutions and for most real-nonpolar-gas mixtures it provides a good approximation *at any pressure* as long as component i is present in excess over all other components or as long as the constituents of the mixture are similar. There is one serious disadvantage to Eq. (7-78) or to the idealized form [Eq. (7-81)] for fugacity calculations in saturated-liquid and -vapor mixtures. That is, in mixtures at their dew or bubble point, all components are stable as either a gas or a liquid when considered in the pure state for determining f_i^0. Thus for a saturated-vapor mixture, if pure i is stable as a liquid for this particular P and T, still f_i^0 must be evaluated as vapor at P and T for use in Eq. (7-78). Such a problem robs the equation of some degree of reality, since now the necessity of defining hypothetical pure states with properties of subcooled vapors or superheated liquids must be faced.* Other such problems arise if, for the liquid, one of the components, pure, is at a temperature greater than the critical. Here, some arbitrary rule must be established to define $f_{i_L}^0$ for such a component. Some of these problems are considered later, and a lucid article discussing the situation is available (115).

Several approaches are available to determine $\bar{f}_i$ from Eq. (7-78) or (7-79). These are discussed in Secs. 7-21 to 7-25 and recommendations presented in Sec. 7-26.

7-21 Component Mixture Vapor Fugacities from the Virial Equation

When using Eq. (7-79) with the virial equation [Eq. (3-22)], it may be shown that (114, 128),

$$\ln \phi_i = (2/V) \sum_j y_j B_{ij} + (3/2V^2) \sum_j \sum_k y_j y_k C_{ijk} + \cdots - \ln Z_m \qquad (7\text{-}83)$$

The pure component and cross virial coefficients are estimated by techniques described in Sec. 7-8 and illustrated in Example 7-3. The applica-

---

* This problem is often eliminated by defining f_i^0, not as the fugacity of the pure component, but for some definite specified state in the solution. γ then is also changed. For volatile components in liquid solutions, a common definition of f_i^0 is

$$f_i^0 = \lim_{x_i \to 0} (f_i/x_i) = \mathfrak{IC}_i$$

where $\mathfrak{IC}_i$ is Henry's-law constant for component i. In this case f_i^0 or $\mathfrak{IC}_i$ is not an imaginary value but can be obtained from experimental data; f_i^0 or $\mathfrak{IC}_i$ is now a function of the solvent medium in addition to temperature and pressure.

tion of Eq. (7-83) to nonpolar systems has been thoroughly discussed by Prausnitz (114). Reasonable results have been obtained for polar systems (10, 114) and for cryogenic mixtures where the Kihara potential function is applicable (120). Example 7-2 shows one possible way to obtain the virial coefficients for such systems.

7-22 Component Mixture Vapor Fugacities from the Pseudocritical-constant Method

If pseudocritical constants are determined for a mixture by methods described in Sec. 7-9, it is possible to estimate the fugacity *of the mixture* as though it were a pure component. Techniques described in Sec. 6-5 would be employed. However, to determine component fugacities, a different approach is necessary. The general method for determining $\bar{V}_i$, $\bar{H}_i$, and ϕ_i (46–48) was first suggested by Gamson and Watson; modifications were later discussed by Joffe (71) and by Comings (21). The technique is described in Appendix F, where various pseudocritical rules are considered. The original work of Gamson and Watson considered only Kay's and J-SBV's rules. The procedure has been extended to allow all properties such as $\bar{f}_i/P$, $\bar{V}_i$, $\bar{H}_i - H_i^0$, etc., to be expressed as functions of T_r, P_r, and the acentric factor ω. To indicate the type of result used to determine $\bar{f}_i/Py_i = \phi_i$, by using the modified Prausnitz and Gunn pseudocritical rules [Eqs. (7-30) and (7-53)], then, from Appendix F with Eqs. (7-5), (F-11), (F-17), and (F-13) and the table in Appendix F,

$$
\ln \phi_i = \ln (\bar{f}_i/y_iP) = \ln (f_m/P) + \{[(H_m - H_m^0)/RT](T_{c_i} - T_{c_m})\} \\
+ (Z_m - 1)[(V_{c_i} - V_{c_m})/V_{c_m} - (Z_{c_i} - Z_{c_m})/Z_{c_m} - (T_{c_i} - T_{c_m})/T_{c_m}] \\
+ \ln (f/P)^1(\omega_i - \omega_m) \quad (7\text{-}84)
$$

In Eq. (7-84) values of T_{c_m}, Z_{c_m}, V_{c_m} are found from the modified Prausnitz and Gunn rules, $H_m - H_m^0$ and Z_m from mixture correlations described earlier in this chapter, f_m/P from Sec. 6-5, the mixture being assumed a pure component with critical properties equal to the calculated pseudocritical values. The expression $\ln (f/P)^1$ is a function of T_{r_m} and P_{r_m} as given in Ref. 86. The $\ln (f/P)^1$ function is similar in nature to the Z^1 group of Pitzer as given in Eq. (3-15). Usually this term is small, and the multiplier $\omega_i - \omega_m$ is also small, so that the product may often be neglected.

Gamson (46) found that Kay's rule, when employed with this method, required empirical modification to give calculated fugacities near experimental values, though J-SBV's rule yielded better results. Too few tests were made to be conclusive. Edmister (31) shows plots to use the uncorrected Kay's rule to minimize calculational effort.

Leland, Chappelear, and Gamson (81) have used the Leland and Mueller pseudocritical rules to test this method (actually vapor-liquid equilibrium values were determined) (99), with good results. In this case, generalized $H_m - H_m^0$, Z_m, etc., correlations were not used, but such properties were calculated from known values of a reference substance with "molecular similarity," e.g., with $Z_c(\text{ref.}) = Z_{c_m}$. This technique is probably more reliable than generalized corresponding-state correlations.

In any case, the technique outlined above has never been methodically tested, and the reliability and accuracy are, at present, impossible to assess.

7-23 Component Mixture Vapor Fugacities from Equations of State

The fugacity coefficient for component i in the vapor phase is obtained from Eq. (7-79), provided that a mixture equation of state is available to determine $\bar{V}_i$. ϕ_i has been evaluated in most studies from the Redlich-Kwong [Eq. (3-51) or (3-52) with (7-54) and (7-55)] or Benedict-Webb-Rubin equations (Appendix E), though the Black equation (9, 19) and Martin-Hou equation (135, 136) have also been suggested.

Redlich-Kwong Equation of State. Using this equation

$$\ln \phi_i = (Z_m - 1)(b_i^*/b_m^*) - \ln (Z_m - b_m^* P) \\ - (a_m^{*2}/b_m^*)(2a_i^*/a_m^* - b_i^*/b_m^*) \ln (1 + b_m^* P/Z_m) \quad (7\text{-}85)$$

where the constants are defined by means of Eqs. (7-54) and (7-55) and Z_m is the mixture compressibility factor from Eq. (3-51) or (3-52). Equation (7-85) has been used by several writers to determine ϕ_i for vapors (31, 34, 37, 52, 122, 143), with good results. Chao and Seader, among others, have developed a consistent method to determine phase-equilibrium constants for hydrocarbon mixtures, with Eq. (7-85) to determine the vapor-phase component fugacity. They place rather definite restrictions of temperature and pressure on the technique, and it is not obvious to what extent these result from the use of Eq. (7-85). However, it is stated that this method of determining ϕ_i is almost, if not quite, as good as the more complex BWR form (see below), though the accuracy decreases as the pressure approaches the mixture critical pressure. From more recent studies by Grayson and Streed (52), the tentative restrictions of the method may be stated as follows: temperatures of about 800°F to $T_{r_i} = 0.5$ (except for H_2 and CH_4, where the lower limits are about $-100°F$), pressures up to about 3,000 psia. This method is also discussed in Sec. 7-25, where liquid-phase component fugacities are discussed.

Benedict-Webb-Rubin Equation of State. In contrast to the RK equation, which is applicable only for vapors, the BWR equation can be used both for the vapor and saturated-liquid states. Consequently, the principal use of the BWR equation has been to determine phase-equilibrium constants, since the equations for fugacity given in Appendix E hold for both the liquid and vapor phases. Very seldom is the BWR equation used to determine only vapor-phase fugacities, although it could be so used if desired. However, the RK vapor-phase fugacity correlation [Eq. (7-85)] is simpler and almost as accurate for ϕ_{i_v}, so that it is ordinarily used for calculations involving only the vapor. Calculations of equilibrium constants from the BWR equation are discussed later, in Sec. 7-25.

7-24 Miscellaneous Methods to Determine Component Fugacities in Mixtures

Intercept Rule. From thermodynamics, it is possible to show that

$$\ln \phi_j = \ln (f_m/P) + \{\partial[\ln (f_m/P)]/\partial y_j\}_{T,P,y_r \ (r \neq i,j)}$$
$$- \sum_k y_k \{\partial[\ln (f_m/P)]/\partial y_k\}_{T,P,y_r \ (r \neq k,i)} \qquad (7\text{-}86)$$

where j is any component and i the component eliminated as $y_i = 1 - \Sigma y_k$. An expression similar to Eq. (7-86) may be written for the ith component, but the second term on the right side disappears. In a binary of 1 and 2, these equations become simply

$$\ln \phi_1 = \ln (f_m/P) - y_2 \{\partial[\ln (f_m/P)]/\partial y_2\}_{T,P} \qquad (7\text{-}87)$$

and similarly for 2 with the subscripts 1 and 2 reversed. Equations (7-86) and (7-87) are the basis of the *intercept rule*, so called because a graph of $\ln (f_m/P)$ versus y_2 will yield a curve the tangent to which at any point will give intercepts on the $\ln (f_m/P)$ axis of $\ln \phi_1$ at $y_2 = 0$ and $\ln \phi_2$ at $y_2 = 1$. In reality, these equations represent but a different way of expressing the pseudocritical equations given in Appendix F. The value of $\ln (f_m/P)$ is found from pure-component correlations by using mixture pseudocritical constants to determine reduced values. This intercept rule for fugacity has been found to be reasonably accurate for calculating ϕ_j in binary mixtures of ethylene with nitrogen, hydrogen, and ethane (50).

Mehra, Brown, and Thodos Technique (97). These workers propose a graphical, empirical technique to estimate the ratio of activity coefficients [see Eq. (7-78) for definition of γ] in the liquid and vapor phases for binary hydrocarbon systems up to and including the true mixture critical. That is,

$$K_j \equiv y_j/x_j = (f_{jL}^0/f_{jv}^0)(\gamma_{jL}/\gamma_{jv}) \qquad (7\text{-}88)$$

Fugacities of the pure components at the system P and T are given as f_{jL}^0 and f_{jv}^0 in the liquid and vapor phases. The difficulties noted earlier regarding unstable states for one of these two pure-component fugacities are still present. The activity-coefficient ratio is correlated with the pure-component normal boiling points and critical points in a series of graphs. Good results were obtained when the method was used to predict K values for light hydrocarbon binary mixtures in the vicinity of the critical point, deviations being less than 10 per cent.

Other Methods. The Chao-Seader method also predicts equilibrium constants for hydrocarbon mixtures; this technique is discussed in Sec. 7-25. Prausnitz (113) proposes a simple method based on the corresponding-state concept to predict $\bar{f}_{j_v}$ at moderate densities. Gilliland and Sullivan (50) review other techniques.

7-25 Estimation of Component Fugacities in Liquid Mixtures

The value of a component fugacity in a liquid mixture is equal to the fugacity in the coexisting vapor phase in equilibrium, that is, $\bar{f}_{i_L} = \bar{f}_{i_v}$. In Secs. 7-20 to 7-24 the relationship of $\bar{f}_{i_v}$ to pressure, temperature, and vapor composition has been discussed. To relate $\bar{f}_{i_L}$ to liquid-phase properties, Eq. (7-78) is usually employed, i.e.,

$$\bar{f}_{i_L} = x_i f_{i_L}^0 \gamma_{i_L} \qquad (7\text{-}78)$$

where γ_{i_L} is the liquid-phase activity coefficient at T, P and with composition $x_i \cdots$. The $f_{i_L}^0$ refers to the fugacity of the pure component i under the pressure and temperature of the liquid *and as a liquid*. As before, pure i may or may not be stable as a liquid at the T and P considered. It is stable if $P > P_{vp_i}$; then since $f_{i_L}^0$ refers to the fugacity of a subcooled liquid, it can be estimated readily from the fugacity of the pure component, saturated at T, and the Poynting correction, i.e.,

$$f_{i_L}^0 = f_{i_{vp}}^0 \exp\left[(1/RT) \int_{P_{vp}}^{P} V_{i_L}^0 \, dp \right]_{P > P_{vp}} \qquad (7\text{-}89)$$

Except at very high pressures the exponential term is nearly unity. The fugacity $f_{i_{vp}}^0$ can be estimated from the techniques described in Sec. 6-5. If the pure saturated vapor behaves as an ideal gas at P_{vp}, T, then $f_{i_{vp}}^0 \sim P_{vp}$.

If, for component i, $P < P_{vpi}$, then $f_{i_L}^0$ refers to the fugacity of a superheated pure liquid. No good theoretical ways have been suggested to determine this value. Equation (7-89) is still applicable, but now $V_{i_L}^0$ refers to volumes of a *superheated liquid*. As a first approximation Eq. (7-89) is simplified by neglecting the exponential term. For high-pressure hydrocarbon mixtures a different technique is used, as described below. Finally, one other difficulty arises in determining f_i^0 in Eq. (7-78). If $T > T_{c_i}$, then i, pure, cannot exist as a liquid. To obtain a value, the vapor-pressure–temperature relation of i is usually extrapolated to the temperature of the system by some simple technique, as by the Cox chart or by the relation $\log P_{vp} = A/T + B$ (see Chap. 4). This fictitious vapor pressure is then employed. The crudeness of this technique is absorbed in the determination of γ_{i_L}.

Phase-equilibrium Constants. As pointed out earlier, the fugacity concept is used to determine vapor-liquid equilibrium constants.

$$K_i \equiv y_i/x_i = \gamma_{iL}(f^0_{iL}/P)/\phi_i \qquad (7\text{-}90)$$

In this relation, ϕ_i is the fugacity coefficient of i in the vapor phase; estimation methods were discussed in Secs. 7-20 to 7-24. It is equal to unity for ideal-gas mixtures and to $f^0_{i_v}/P$ for an ideal solution in the vapor. The term f^0_{iL}/P has been discussed above, and many of the problems encountered in the actual calculation were pointed out. The latter is not a function of composition and equals P_{vp_i}/P if the saturated vapor is ideal and the Poynting correction neglected. For hydrocarbon mixtures Chao and Seader (20) have proposed that this ratio be determined as a function of T_r, P_r, and $\bar{\omega}$ as follows:

$$\log (f^0_{iL}/P) = \log \nu = \log \nu^0 + \bar{\omega} \log \nu^1 \qquad (7\text{-}91)$$
$$\text{where} \quad \log \nu^0 = A_0 + A_1/T_r + A_2 T_r + A_3 T_r{}^2 + A_4 T_r{}^3 + (A_5 + A_6 T_r$$
$$+ A_7 T_r{}^2)P_r + (A_8 + A_9 T_r)P_r{}^2 - \log P_r \qquad (7\text{-}92)$$
$$\log \nu^1 = -4.23893 + 8.65808 T_r - 1.22060/T_r$$
$$- 3.15224 T_r{}^3 - 0.025(P_r - 0.6) \qquad (7\text{-}93)$$

The constants A_0 through A_9 have been obtained by Grayson and Streed and are shown in Table 7-4 (52). These values were obtained from experimental K data by working backward from Eq. (7-90), ϕ_i being determined from the Redlich-Kwong method [Eq. (7-85)] and γ_{iL} as by Eq. (7-94). Values of $\bar{\omega}$ to be used are tabulated in Table 7-5. The use of Eq. (7-91) with Table 7-4 is reported to be valid up to 800°F and 3,000 psia (52). For compounds other than hydrocarbons, Eqs.

TABLE 7-4. COEFFICIENTS IN EQ. (7-92)*

	Simple fluid	Methane	Hydrogen
A_0	2.05135	1.36822	1.50709
A_1	−2.10899	−1.54831	2.74283
A_2	0	0	−0.02110
A_3	−0.19396	0.02889	0.00011
A_4	0.02282	−0.01076	0
A_5	0.08852	0.10486	0.008585
A_6	0	−0.02529	0
A_7	−0.00872	0	0
A_8	−0.00353	0	0
A_9	0.00203	0	0

* H. G. Grayson and C. W. Streed, Paper 20-P07, sixth World Petroleum Conference, Frankfurt, June, 1963.

(7-91) to (7-93) may be used if they conform to a simple three-parameter corresponding-state correlation such as that suggested by Pitzer and discussed in Chap. 3.

Finally, in Eq. (7-90), the liquid-phase activity coefficient must be determined. It is unity for ideal-liquid solutions. For nonideal solutions, especially for those containing polar components, it is difficult to estimate with any accuracy. A thorough discussion of the estimation of liquid-phase activity coefficients would necessitate a discussion of liquid-solution theory and would form a separate monograph. This field of investigation is quite active, and references to a few typical papers indicating the approaches are given, though by no means is such a list to be considered at all complete (8, 43, 51, 62, 100, 116, 121, 153).

As one example of a γ_L estimating technique, the *regular-solution* concept is briefly outlined (32, 62, 122, 130, 131). In such a solution, the entropy of mixing is equal to that of an ideal solution. Liquid hydrocarbon or other nonpolar compounds often form mixtures that resemble regular solutions. In such solutions,

$$\ln \gamma_{i_L} = V_i^*(\delta_i - \bar{\delta})^2/RT \qquad (7\text{-}94)$$

δ is a solubility parameter, defined by Hildebrand (62) as

$$\delta = (\Delta E_v/V^*)^{\frac{1}{2}} \qquad (7\text{-}95)$$

The value of $\bar{\delta}$ represents the average solubility parameter for the mixture,

$$\bar{\delta} = \sum_i x_i V_i^* \delta_i \Big/ \sum_i x_i V_i^* \qquad (7\text{-}96)$$

The values of δ_i for 59 compounds are given in Table 7-5 from a tabulation by Cavett (19). The difference $\delta_i - \bar{\delta}$ is assumed to be independent of temperature.

V_i^* is often considered to be simply the molal liquid volume at 25°C, but it may be considered variable with temperature and may be determined by Eq. (7-97) (32),

$$V_i^* = (V_\omega)(5.7 + 3.0T_{r_i}) \qquad (7\text{-}97)$$

where V_ω is a constant for each compound, values for which are also tabulated in Table 7-5. A more thorough discussion of the use of Eq. (7-94) is given by Prausnitz, Edmister, and Chao (122).

Chao-Seader Estimation of Equilibrium Constants. To estimate equilibrium constants for hydrocarbon mixtures, Eq. (7-90) is used. ϕ_i may be obtained in any of the ways discussed in Secs. 7-20 to 7-24, but Eq. (7-85) is recommended. $f_{i_L}^0/P$ is determined from Eqs. (7-91) to

TABLE 7-5. PARAMETERS FOR USE IN EQS. (7-94), (7-96), AND (7-97)*

Name	$\bar{\omega}$	δ, (cal/cm^3)$^{1/2}$	V_ω, cm^3/g mole
Methane.................	0	5.450	5.000
Ethane..................	0.1064	5.880	7.880
Propane.................	0.1538	6.000	10.350
n-Butane...............	0.1953	6.730	13.000
i-Butane................	0.1825	6.240	13.370
n-Pentane...............	0.2518	7.021	15.270
i-Pentane...............	0.2104	6.710	15.360
Neopentane..............	0.1969	6.116	15.890
n-Hexane...............	0.2972	7.266	17.640
2-Methylpentane.........	0.2771	7.018	17.730
3-Methylpentane.........	0.2746	7.132	17.480
2,2-Dimethylbutane........	0.2314	6.712	17.760
2,3-Dimethylbutane........	0.2466	6.967	17.520
n-Heptane...............	0.3403	7.430	20.050
n-Octane................	0.3992	7.551	22.490
n-Nonane................	0.4439	7.649	24.940
n-Decane................	0.4869	7.721	27.420
n-Undecane..............	0.5210	7.790	29.900
n-Dodecane..............	0.5610	7.840	32.390
n-Tridecane..............	0.6002	7.890	34.880
n-Tetradecane............	0.6399	7.920	37.390
n-Pentadecane...........	0.6743	7.960	39.890
n-Hexadecane............	0.7078	7.990	42.410
Ethylene................	0.0949	5.800	6.880
Propylene...............	0.1451	6.200	9.690
1-Butene................	0.1917	6.760	12.170
cis-2-Butene.............	0.2607	7.250	11.710
trans-2-Butene...........	0.2638	7.030	12.000
i-Butene................	0.1975	6.790	12.170
1-Pentene...............	0.2198	7.055	14.550
cis-2-Pentene.............	0.2060	7.346	14.260
trans-2-Pentene...........	0.2090	7.284	14.410
2-Methyl-1-butene........	0.2000	7.169	14.310
3-Methyl-1-butene........	0.1490	6.729	14.770
2-Methyl-2-butene........	0.2120	7.418	14.140
1-Hexene................	0.2463	7.400	16.900
1-Heptene...............	0.3471	7.168	19.230
Propadiene..............	0.1193	6.854	9.650
1,2-Butadiene............	0.0987	7.950	10.940
1,3-Butadiene............	0.2028	6.940	11.270
Cyclopentane............	0.2051	8.107	12.720
Methylcyclopentane.......	0.2346	7.849	15.330
Ethylcyclopentane........	0.2709	7.739	17.720
Cyclohexane.............	0.2032	8.196	14.870
Methylcyclohexane........	0.2421	7.826	17.670
Ethylcyclohexane.........	0.3046	7.743	19.920

Table 7-5. Parameters for Use in Eqs. (7-94), (7-96), and (7-97)* *(Continued)*

Name	$\bar{\omega}$	δ, $(\text{cal/cm}^3)^{\frac{1}{2}}$	V_ω $\text{cm}^3/\text{g mole}$
Benzene.................	0.2130	9.158	12.260
Toluene.................	0.2591	8.915	14.830
o-Xylene................	0.2904	8.987	17.030
m-Xylene................	0.3045	8.818	17.280
p-Xylene................	0.2969	8.769	17.340
Ethylbenzene............	0.2936	8.787	17.230
Hydrogen...............	0	3.250	0.955
Nitrogen................	0.0206	2.580	2.534
Oxygen.................	0.0299	4.000	2.871
Carbon monoxide..........	−0.0067	3.130	2.584
Carbon dioxide...........	0.1768	6.000	6.365
Hydrogen sulfide.........	0.0868	5.634	5.081
Sulfur dioxide...........	0.2402	6.000	6.516

* R. H. Cavett, paper presented to Session on Computer Applications, Twenty-seventh Midyear Meeting of the API, Division of Refining, May 15, 1962.

(7-93) with Tables 7-4 and 7-5. γ_{i_L} is found from Eqs. (7-94) and (7-96) with Table 7-5. Good results have been reported for all types of hydrocarbon mixtures (which includes those containing hydrogen). Usually the experimental values differed by less than 10 per cent from calculated values. The correlation is valid for temperatures up to about 800°F and 1500 psia (52). A similar technique is being developed by Edmister, Thompson, and Stuckey (36), and a good summary of the method with a detailed set of equations and computer directions has been published by Cavett (19).

Pseudocritical-constant Method. In Appendix F, generalized techniques are developed to estimate mixture fugacities by combining various pseudocritical rules with the law of corresponding states. These techniques allow $\bar{f}_i$ to be related to composition and mixture properties such as $H_m - H_m^0$, Z_m, etc., the latter being obtained from pure-component correlations and reduced temperatures and pressures of the mixture as determined from the pseudocritical values. The fugacity equations in Appendix F can be applied to both the liquid and the gas phase. By equating the values of $\bar{f}_{i_L}$ to $\bar{f}_{i_v}$ an equilibrium constant may be formulated. The expressions are somewhat complex, but Leland, Chappelear, and Gamson (81) have successfully demonstrated the technique, using the Leland and Mueller pseudocritical-constant rules [Eqs. (7-32) to (7-37)]. In simple molecule systems (hydrocarbons with H_2S and CO_2) values of K were estimated at high pressures over a range of temperatures usually within 20 to 30 per cent and often within 10 per cent. A similar approach using a modified form of Kay's rule to predict pseudocritical constants was presented earlier by Gamson and Watson (48). At pressures exceeding 1,500 psia, the Leland et al. method referred to above has been shown to be more accurate than the Chao-Seader method (40*a*).

Benedict-Webb-Rubin Equation. The BWR equation (Appendix E) has often been used to determine equilibrium constants for mixtures of light hydrocarbons (6, 124). Similar studies with N_2-CO and CO_2-propane systems are also available (23, 133). The equation used is (E-14) in Appendix E, with the usual criteria of $T, P, \bar{f_i}$ equality between phases. The method is complex and usually requires a computer to make the technique useful.

Edmister (30) and Edmister and Ruby (35) have simplified the use of the BWR equation to allow both vapor and liquid fugacities to be determined graphically from the reduced temperatures and pressures of each component and the molal average boiling point of the mixture. These charts and others prepared by DePriester (26) considerably simplify the use of the BWR equation for determining fugacities and equilibrium constants in light hydrocarbon mixtures.

7-26 Recommendations for Estimating Component Fugacity and Equilibrium Constant

1. Gas-phase fugacities.
    a. For ideal-gas mixtures, e.g., mixtures of nonpolar molecules at low pressures and high temperatures,

$$\bar{f}_{i_v} = p_i = Py_i \qquad (7\text{-}82)$$

    b. For nonideal-gas mixtures, at any pressure, if a component i is present in excess or if all the constituents are similar chemically, Amagat's rule is satisfactory and the mixtures may be approximated as ideal solutions,

$$\bar{f}_{i_v} = y_i f_i^0 \qquad (7\text{-}81)$$

    c. For nonideal solutions not in category *b*, several methods are applicable, though more tedious than Eq. (7-81),
    (1) For nonpolar mixtures, and even slightly polar mixtures, the virial equation [Eq. (7-83)] may be used. Pressures should probably be less than about 0.8 of the true-mixture critical pressure.
    (2) For nonpolar and slightly polar mixtures, the pseudocritical technique, such as illustrated by Eq. (7-84), is applicable, though no reliable tests have been made of its accuracy. The intercept rule [Eqs. (7-86) and (7-87)] is a special case of this method.
    (3) Most reliable results are to be expected with the RK, BWR, or

other accurate equations of state, e.g., Eq. (7-85) or (E-14) and Appendix E. The RK equations are simple to use and have proved reliable in estimating $\bar{f}_i$ for the calculation of liquid-vapor equilibrium constants. The BWR is more complex to use. The RK method is applicable to nonpolar or slightly polar compounds, and its accuracy increases at the higher temperatures. The convenient fugacity charts of Edmister and Ruby (30, 35), obtained from BWR equation calculations, are often useful for hydrocarbon mixtures.

(4) In polar mixtures, no method is suitable, or at least none has been adequately tested. The virial, pseudocritical, and RK methods were not developed to handle such cases, but they can be used, as can Eq. (7-81), if it is realized that large errors may result.

2. Liquid-phase fugacities and liquid-vapor equilibrium constants.

 a. For ideal gases, ideal-liquid solutions, Eq. (7-90) reduces to

$$K_i = P_{vp_i}/P$$

Such an approximation is seldom valid except for low-pressure mixtures of nonpolar, similar molecules.

 b. For hydrocarbon (with or without hydrogen) mixtures, the well-developed method of Chao and Seader is recommended for the determination of equilibrium constants. This method is described in Sec. 7-25. If the mixture is near the critical point, a convenient technique is that due to Mehra, Brown, and Thodos [Eq. (7-88)], and for light hydrocarbon mixtures, the BWR equations (Appendix E) or the simplified plots of Edmister and Ruby (30, 35) are often used with excellent results. These methods usually predict K within 10 per cent over wide temperature and pressure ranges.

 c. For mixtures containing components other than hydrocarbons, it is best to use Eq. (7-90) to determine K_i, with ϕ_i obtained by methods described in Secs. 7-20 to 7-24, f_i^0/P from pure-component fugacity correlations, and γ_{i_L} from experimental data or some vapor-liquid correlation such as the van Laar or Margules, where the constants have been found experimentally or calculated separately by some empirical correlation such as suggested by Gilmont, Zudkevitch, and Othmer (51), Wilson and Deal (153), or Black (8). These γ_L correlations are not evaluated in this book.

 d. In default of any γ_{i_L} data or suitable correlations, it is recommended that the pseudocritical-constant method be used to determine K by the use of fugacity values as outlined in Appendix F and to equate $\bar{f}_{i_L} = \bar{f}_{i_v}$ to solve for K. This technique is algebraically complex and probably would require machine-computation assistance; it is illustrated in detail in Ref. 81.

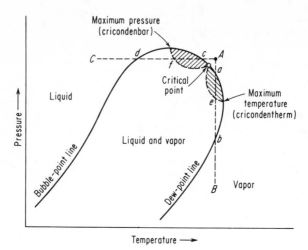

FIG. 7-11. Vapor-liquid behavior of a multicomponent mixture in the critical region. [*E. D. Silverman and G. Thodos, Ind. Eng. Chem. Fundamentals,* **1**:299 (1962).]

For polar mixtures the only applicable method is (*c*). For nonpolar mixtures, (*b*) is preferable for hydrocarbons, and either (*c*) or (*d*) (in order of choice) is recommended for systems containing one or more nonhydrocarbon components. Adler and Palazzo summarize in convenient form many of the thermodynamic ways to express K (3).

7-27   True Critical Points for Mixtures

The critical region for a mixture has been sketched in an informative way by Silverman and Thodos (134) and is shown schematically in Fig. 7-11. The solid line, representing a single fixed composition, shows three critical points. The true critical point represents the maximum temperature and pressure where two phases can exist. However, two phases may exist under conditions of higher pressure and lower temperature, and vice versa. The maximum pressure and temperature limits for the mixture are usually called the *cricondenbar* and *cricondentherm*, respectively. The shaded portions represent schematically the regions where retrograde condensation can occur. That is, from *A* to *C*, the two-phase envelope is entered at *C* from the liquid region. Vaporization occurs as temperature is *decreased* at constant pressure. At the limit of the shaded area (point *f*) maximum vaporization results, and condensation occurs from this point to the bubble-point curve. At point *d* on the bubble-point curve, the mixture is entirely liquid. A similar sequence of events occurs from *A* to *B*, but in this case condensation occurs over a region of *decreasing* pressure at constant temperature. Comings (21) gives a very lucid summary of multicomponent-mixture behavior in the region of the critical point.

To understand the behavior of mixtures in the critical region, estimating techniques are needed to predict the critical point and the points of maximum temperature and pressure. Such estimating techniques are summarized in Secs. 7-28 to 7-30. Recommendations are presented in Sec. 7-31.

7-28   Estimation of the True Critical Temperatures and Pressures of Mixtures

Numerous experimental studies have reported the critical point for hydrocarbon mixtures, including simple molecules such as CO, N_2, etc., but almost no data are available for other systems, especially those with one or more polar components. Consequently at the present time, all critical-point estimating methods are limited to hydrocarbons and, in some cases, a few of the usual inorganic gases often associated with natural gas. Often it is a good approximation to use Kay's rule [Eq. (7-30)] to determine true-mixture critical temperatures, but Kay's rule [Eq. (17-31)] gives poor predictions of the true-mixture critical pressures.

Examination of some recent critical temperatures for 15 binaries made up from aliphatic hydrocarbons, naphthenes, and benzene (107) and 10 binaries comprised of N_2, CO, O_2, CH_4, and A (72) showed that Kay's rule, i.e., a mole-fraction average of the pure critical temperatures, predicted the true critical temperature usually within 10°K. The least error was found for aliphatic-aliphatic binaries and the most for aliphatic-aromatic binaries. However, for dissimilar systems, Kay's rule is at best only an approximation for critical pressures.

Many empirical methods have been suggested to estimate true values of the critical constants T'_{c_m} and P'_{c_m} (22, 24, 32, 39, 53, 56, 74, 78, 79, 96, 104, 105, 137), and most are reviewed by Grieves and Thodos (53). Other than these empirical methods, Ackerman (2) discusses the use of the Redlich-Kwong and Benedict-Webb-Rubin equations of state as a means to determine mixture criticals. The results are quite complex, but good results were obtained for T'_{c_m} and reasonable results for P'_{c_m} for 26 binaries. In the estimation of P'_{c_m}, the choice of the BWR constants employed for the pure materials significantly affects the final results.

Most binaries show a pronounced maximum critical pressure at some intermediate composition. Both the RK and BWR predict the general shape, though considerable error is possible. Actually, the simpler RK equation usually gives more accurate results. For most systems, however, empirical methods appear preferable at the present time.

Grieves and Thodos Method for Critical Temperature. A general method to predict critical temperatures of multicomponent hydrocarbon systems has been presented by Grieves and Thodos (54). The correlating parameter is the ratio of the normal boiling points of the pure compo-

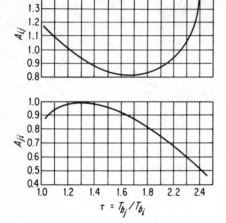

FIG. 7-12. Relationships between binary temperature coefficients and normal boiling-point ratio (nonmethane systems). [R. B. Grieves and G. Thodos, AIChE J., 8:550 (1962).]

nents, and the general expression is

$$T'_{c_m} = \sum_{i=1}^{n} \left\{ T_{c_i} / \left[1 + (1/x_i) \sum_{\substack{j=1 \\ j \neq i}} A_{ij}x_j \right] \right\} \qquad (7\text{-}98)$$

where x is the mole fraction and A_{ij} and A_{ji} parameters are read from Fig. 7-12 or 7-13 as a function of $\tau = T_{b_j}/T_{b_i}$, $\tau > 1$. For a binary, Eq. (7-98) reduces to

$$T'_{c_m} = T_{c_1}/[1 + (x_2/x_1)A_{12}] + T_{c_2}/[1 + (x_1/x_2)A_{21}] \qquad (7\text{-}99)$$

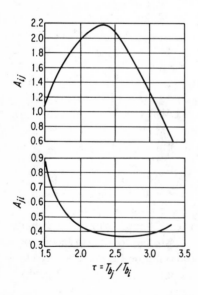

FIG. 7-13. Relationships between binary temperature coefficients and normal boiling-point (methane systems). [R. B. Grieves and G. Thodos, AIChE J., 8:550 (1962).]

Figure 7-13 is applicable to hydrocarbon systems not containing methane; if i or j refers to methane, then A_{ij} and A_{ji} should be found from Fig. 7-13.* This correlation is also applicable to systems containing aromatic hydrocarbons if the pure aromatic critical temperature is adjusted by the following rules:

$$T_c(\text{corrected}) = \begin{cases} T_c(\text{true}) - 15 & \text{when } x_{\text{aromatic}} > 0.6 \\ T_c(\text{true}) - 40 & \text{when } x_{\text{aromatic}} < 0.6 \end{cases} \quad (7\text{-}100)$$

where T is in degrees Rankine. In testing 41 binaries having 208 different compositions, the average maximum deviation between T'_{c_m} calculated and experimental (based on absolute temperature) was 0.91 per cent. In 28 multicomponent systems, a similar average error was 1.03 per cent. Example 7-6, from Ref. 54, illustrates the technique.

Example 7-6. Establish the critical temperature of a quaternary hydrocarbon mixture having the following composition:†

		Mole fraction	T_b, °R	T_c, °R	P_c, psia
1	Ethane.........	0.254	331.7	549.5	707.1
2	Propane.........	0.255	416.1	666.0	617.4
3	n-Butane.........	0.255	491.6	765.7	550.1
4	n-Pentane........	0.236	556.6	847.1	494.2
		1.000			

Solution. For this system there exist six binary pairs, each of which determines a set of binary coefficients. These coefficients are obtained from Fig. 7-12 and are listed below, together with the values of τ.

	τ		
Ethane-propane..............	1.254	$A_{12} = 0.966$	$A_{21} = 0.986$
Ethane-n-butane.............	1.482	$A_{13} = 0.849$	$A_{31} = 0.960$
Ethane-n-pentane............	1.678	$A_{14} = 0.813$	$A_{41} = 0.883$
Propane-n-butane............	1.181	$A_{23} = 1.017$	$A_{32} = 0.973$
Propane-n-pentane..........	1.338	$A_{24} = 0.914$	$A_{42} = 0.986$
n-Butane-n-pentane..........	1.132	$A_{34} = 1.059$	$A_{43} = 0.955$

* The single exception found was the system methane–n-butane. In this special case the constants $A_{12} = 0.86$, $A_{21} = 0.60$ (1 = methane, 2 = n-butane) should be used.

† These values differ slightly (usually in the fourth place) from those tabulated in Appendix A. They will be employed here to preserve the numerical values used by Grieves and Thodos.

These values are substituted into the expanded form of Eq. (7-98) for a quarternary mixture,

$$T'_{c_m} = \frac{T_{c_1}}{1 + \dfrac{x_2}{x_1}A_{12} + \dfrac{x_3}{x_1}A_{13} + \dfrac{x_4}{x_1}A_{14}} + \frac{T_{c_2}}{1 + \dfrac{x_1}{x_2}A_{21} + \dfrac{x_3}{x_2}A_{23} + \dfrac{x_4}{x_2}A_{24}}$$

$$+ \frac{T_{c_3}}{1 + \dfrac{x_1}{x_3}A_{31} + \dfrac{x_2}{x_3}A_{32} + \dfrac{x_4}{x_3}A_{34}} + \frac{T_{c_4}}{1 + \dfrac{x_1}{x_4}A_{41} + \dfrac{x_2}{x_4}A_{42} + \dfrac{x_3}{x_4}A_{43}}$$

Upon substituting the values tabulated above, T'_{c_m} is found to be 734°R. Etter and Kay (41) report a critical temperature of 731°R for this mixture.

Grieves and Thodos Method for Critical Pressures (55). The key correlating parameters in this method for estimating mixture critical pressures are the molal average boiling point T_{mabp} and the mixture normal boiling point T_{b_m}. These values are determined as

$$T_{\text{mabp}} = \sum_i x_i T_{b_i} \qquad (7\text{-}101)$$

$$T_{b_m} = \text{temperature at which} \sum_i x_i p_{vp_i} = 1 \text{ atm} \qquad (7\text{-}102)$$

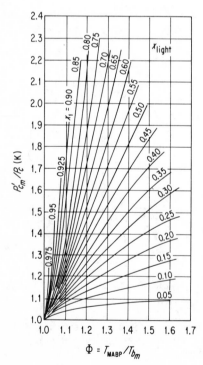

FIG. 7-14. True-mixture critical pressures for nonmethane systems. [R. B. Grieves and G. Thodos, AIChE J., **9**:25 (1963).]

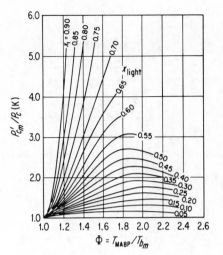

FIG. 7-15. True-mixture critical pressures for binary systems containing methane. [*R. B. Grieves and G. Thodos, AIChE J.*, **9**:25 (1963).]

In Eq. (7-102), T_{b_m} is calculated by assuming Raoult's law, and the vapor pressures are evaluated at T_{b_m}; a trial-and-error calculation is necessary. In the mixture, Φ is defined as

$$\Phi = T_{\text{mabp}}/T_{b_m} \qquad (7\text{-}103)$$

Binary Systems. For binary systems, Φ is plotted against $P'_{c_m}/P_c(\text{K})$ in Fig. 7-14, with curves of constant composition of the lighter component. Figure 7-14 is employed for non-methane-hydrocarbon systems and Fig. 7-15 for methane binaries. $P_c(\text{K})$ is Kay's pseudocritical pressure, i.e., the mole-fraction average critical pressure.

Aromatic, Acetylenic, and Naphthenic Corrections. If the binary contains an aromatic, an acetylene, or a naphthene as a component, it is necessary to apply a correction factor to the calculated value of Φ. These correction factors are given in Fig. 7-16.

Multicomponent Systems. To estimate the critical pressure in a multicomponent system, the technique recommended is to proceed in a stepwise manner. First, the binary composed of the two highest boiling components is considered and the critical pressure calculated by using the relative compositions (free of lower-boiling components) of the two high boilers. Next, the ternary of the three highest boilers is considered, with use of relative compositions free of any lower component. Φ is calculated and corrected, if need be, by Fig. 7-16. Then $P'_{c_m}/P_c(\text{K})$ is determined from Fig. 7-14 (or Fig. 7-15 if the low boiler is CH_4). Note that $P_c(\text{K})$ in this case is *not* a mole-fraction average critical pressure. Rather, it is the mole-fraction average of the low boiler P_c and the calculated

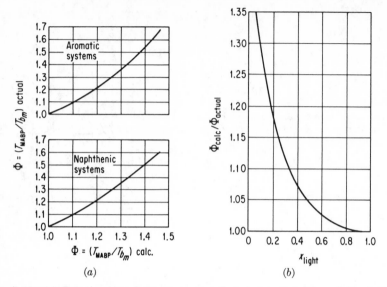

FIG. 7-16. (a) Relationships between corrected and actual values of the boiling parameter for naphthenic and aromatic systems. (b) Ratio of corrected boiling parameter to actual boiling parameter versus x_L, mole fraction of low-boiling component for acetylene systems. [R. B. Grieves and G. Thodos, AIChE J., **9**:25 (1963).]

P'_{c_m} of the high-boiling binary calculated previously. Example 7-7 from Ref. 55 illustrates the technique used for a quaternary system. It was found empirically that, when methane and ethane were present in the same mixture, better results were obtained if a fictitious boiling point of methane and ethane were chosen as 116.6°K (210°R) and 194.4°K (350°R), respectively.

The errors found by Grieves and Thodos using this method were about 1 per cent for binary systems and 2 per cent for multicomponent systems.

Example 7-7. Repeat Example 7-6 to determine the true-mixture critical pressure.
Solution. The properties of the pure components are tabulated in the solution of Example 7-6.

(a) Calculate the mixture critical pressure of the highest-boiling binary. In this case, the pair is n-butane–n-pentane. The compositions of the high-boiling binary are

$$x_{C_4} = 0.255/(0.255 + 0.236) = 0.519 \qquad x_{C_5} = 0.481$$
$$T_{mabp} = (0.519)(491.6) + (0.481)(556.6) = 522.8°R$$

From vapor pressures and Eq. (7-102),

$$T_{b_m} = 513.0°R$$
$$\Phi_{(C_4\text{-}C_5)} = (522.8)/(513.0) = 1.019$$

From Fig. 7-14 with $x = 0.519$, $P'_{c_m}/P_c(K) = 1.035$,

$$P_c(K) = (0.519)(550.1) + (0.481)(494.2) = 523.2 \text{ psia}$$

Thus $\qquad P'_{c_m} = (1.035)(523.2) = 541.5 \text{ psia}$

(b) Next consider the ternary of propane, n-butane, and n-pentane.

$$x_{C_3} = 0.255/(0.255 + 0.255 + 0.236) = 0.342 \qquad x_{C_4} = 0.342 \qquad x_{C_5} = 0.316$$

Following the same procedure as in (a), $T_{\text{mabp}} = 486.3°\text{R}$, $T_{b_m} = 455.0°\text{R}$, $\Phi = 1.069$, $P'_{c_m}/P_c(K) = 1.095$ at $x_{\text{light}} = 0.342$.

$$P_c(K) = (0.342)(617.4) + (0.342 + 0.316)(541.5)$$
$$= 567.4 \text{ psia}$$

Thus $\qquad P'_{c_m} = (1.095)(567.4) = 621.3 \text{ psia}.$

(c) Repeat (b) for the quaternary, now using the original compositions. Here $x_{\text{light}} = x_{C_2} = 0.254$, $T_{\text{mabp}} = 446.5°\text{R}$, $T_{b_m} = 381.0°\text{R}$, $\Phi = 1.172$, and P'_{c_m}/P_c (K) $= 1.176$.

$$P_c(K) = (0.254)(707.1) + (1 - 0.254)(621.3) = 642.9 \text{ psia}$$
$$P'_{c_m} = (1.176)(642.9) = 756.1 \text{ psia}.$$

The reported experimental value is 742 psia (41).

7-29 Estimation of the True Critical Density for Binary Hydrocarbon Mixtures

Critical densities for hydrocarbon mixtures may be estimated from $P'_{c_m}/Z_{c_m}RT'_{c_m}$, where P'_{c_m} and T'_{c_m} are found from the methods described in Sec. 7-28 and Z_{c_m} approximated as $\sum_i x_i z_{c_i}$. Another technique utilizes the Φ parameter defined by Eq. (7-103) (55). Figure 7-17 shows a plot of Φ as a function of $\rho'_{c_m}V_c(K)$ for various mole fractions of the light

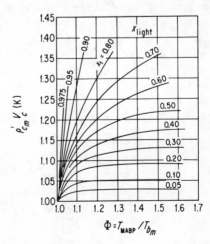

FIG. 7-17. Relationship between $\rho'_{c_m}V_c(K)$ and Φ for nonmethane hydrocarbon systems. [R. B. Grieves and G. Thodos, AIChE J., 9:25 (1963).]

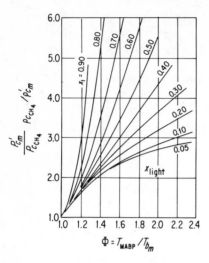

FIG. 7-18. Relationship between $(P'_{c_m}/ P_{c_{CH_4}})(\rho_{c_{CH_4}}/\rho'_{c_m})$ and Φ for binary systems containing methane. [*R. B. Grieves* and *G. Thodos, AIChE J.*, **9**:25 (1963).]

component. The $V_c(\mathrm{K})$ is the Kay's-rule analogue for critical volume, i.e.,

$$V_c(\mathrm{K}) = V_{c_1}x_1 + V_{c_2}x_2 \qquad (7\text{-}104)$$

Figure 7-17 is to be used for binary systems not containing methane. If methane is one of the components, Fig. 7-18 should be used. In this case the ordinate is

$$(P'_{c_m}/P_{c_{CH_4}})(\rho_{c_{CH_4}}/\rho'_{c_m})$$

where P'_{c_m} is the true critical pressure of the binary as determined in Sec. 7-28 and $P_{c_{CH_4}}$, $\rho_{c_{CH_4}}$ are the true critical pressures and densities of pure methane. The lines of constant composition in Fig. 7-18 are the mole fractions of methane in the mixture.

In testing five binary systems having 23 compositions, Grieves and Thodos report an average error of about 1 to 2 per cent in the estimation of critical densities. The method is presumably applicable to multi-component systems if a stepwise procedure similar to that used for the estimation of critical pressures (Sec. 7-28) is followed.

7-30   Estimation of Cricondentherms and Cricondenbars

This estimation problem has been attacked in three recent papers (41, 57, 134). Etter and Kay (41) have obtained accurate empirical equations for both cricondentherm and cricondenbar for multicomponent mixtures of normal paraffins. The more general techniques were proposed by Grieves and Thodos (57) and by Silverman and Thodos (134), and these are described below.

Cricondentherm and Cricondenbar Temperatures. The temperature at points of maximum temperature and maximum pressure are designated T_t and T_p and are estimated by the following empirical equations (57):

$$T_t/T_c(\text{K}) = 1.01 + (T_{\text{mabp}}/T_{b_m} - 1)\, e^{5.40x_L - 3.39} \qquad 0 < x_L \leq 0.55$$
$$(7\text{-}105)$$

$$T_t/T_c(\text{K}) = 1.256 + [(T_{\text{mabp}}/T_{b_m} - 1)\, e^{6.38x_L - 4.38}] - 0.418\, x_L$$
$$0.55 < x_L \leq 0.925 \quad (7\text{-}106)$$

$$T_p/T_c(\text{K}) = 1.008 + (T_{\text{mabp}}/T_{b_m} - 1)\, e^{4.33x_L - 3.62}$$
$$0 < x_L \leq 0.7 \quad (7\text{-}107)$$

$$T_p/T_c(\text{K}) = 1.116 + [(T_{\text{mabp}}/T_{b_m} - 1)\, e^{6.33x_L - 5.14}] - 0.165x_L$$
$$0.7 < x_L \leq 0.925 \quad (7\text{-}108)$$

where $T_c(\text{K})$ is the Kay's-rule temperature, i.e., the molal average mixture critical temperature, T_{mabp} the molal average boiling point, T_{b_m} the atmospheric bubble point of the mixture [Eq. (7-102)], and x_l the mole fraction of the lowest-boiling component. The definition of x_L causes no difficulty in dealing with binary systems, but for systems containing three or more components one must use a stepwise method similar to that suggested for P'_{c_m} in Sec. 7-28. That is, in a ternary system, the binary composing the two high-boiling compounds is considered first. The values of T_t and T_p are calculated by using the relative mole fractions of these high boilers on a low-boiler-free basis. This binary is then considered to be a pure component with a critical temperature equal to the calculated T_t or T_p (depending upon whether the ternary T_t or T_p is to be calculated) to determine $T_c(\text{K})$. x_L in the first calculation (of the high-boiler binary) is the mole fraction of the low boiler in the high-boiler pair; in the ternary calculation, it is the true low boiler in the ternary. The method is illustrated in Example 7-8 with a quaternary calculation taken from the article by Grieves and Thodos (57). The average deviation of the method in calculating T_t for 22 binary mixtures (123 compositions) was 0.87 per cent and for T_p with 18 binaries (104 compositions) 0.78 per cent. Slightly higher errors were found for multicomponent mixtures, but in general they were less than 1.5 per cent.

Example 7-8. Estimate the cricondentherm and cricondenbar temperatures for the mixture considered in Example 7-6.
Solution. (a) Determine T_t and T_p for the highest-boiling binary, i.e., one consisting of n-butane and n-pentane.

$$x_L = x_{C_4} = 0.255/(0.255 + 0.236) = 0.519 \qquad x_{C_5} = 0.481$$
$$T_{\text{mabp}} = (0.519)(491.6) + (0.481)(556.6) = 522.8°\text{R}$$
$$T_{b_m} = 513°\text{R [from vapor pressures and Eq. (7-102)]}$$
$$T_c(\text{K}) = (0.519)(765.7) + (0.481)(847.1) = 804.9°\text{R}$$

From Eqs. (7-105) and (7-107) with $T_{mabp}/T_{b_m} = 1.02$,

$$T_t/T_c(K) = 1.01 \qquad T_t = 812.9°R$$
$$T_p/T_c(K) = 1.007 \qquad T_p = 810.5°R$$

(b) Determine T_t and T_p for the ternary C_3—C_4—C_5.

$$x_L = x_{C_3} = 0.255/(0.255 + 0.255 + 0.236) = 0.342$$
$$x_{C_4} = 0.342 \qquad \text{and} \qquad x_{C_5} = 0.316$$
$$T_{mabp} = (0.342)(416.1) + (0.342)(491.6) + (0.316)(556.6) = 486.3°R$$
$$T_{b_m} \text{ [from vapor pressures and Eq. (7-102)]} = 455°R$$
$$T_c(K) \text{ (for estimating } T_t) = (0.342)(666) + (0.342 + 0.316)(812.9) = 762.7°R$$
$$T_c(K) \text{ (for estimating } T_p) = (0.342)(666) + (0.342 + 0.316)(810.5) = 761.1°R$$

From Eqs. (7-105) and (7-107) with $T_{mabp}/T_{b_m} = 1.069$,

$$T_t/T_c(K) = 1.023 \qquad T_t = (1.023)(762.7) = 780.2°R$$
$$T_p/T_c(K) = 1.017 \qquad T_p = (1.017)(761.1) = 774.0°R$$

(c) Determine T_t and T_p for quaternary C_2—C_3—C_4—C_5.

$$T_{mabp} = (0.254)(331.7) + (0.255)(461.1) + (0.255)(491.6) + (0.236)(556.6) = 446.5°R$$
$$T_{b_m} \text{ [from vapor pressures and Eq. (7-102)]} = 381°R$$
$$T_c(K) = (0.254)(549.5) + (0.255 + 0.255 + 0.236)(780.2)$$
$$= 721.6°R \qquad \text{for estimating } T_t$$
$$T_c(K) = (0.254)(549.5) + (0.255 + 0.255 + 0.236)(774.0)$$
$$= 717.0°R \qquad \text{for estimating } T_p$$

From Eqs. (7-105) and (7-107) with $T_{mabp}/T_{b_m} = 1.172$,

$$T_t/T_c(K) = 1.035 \qquad T_t = (1.035)(721.6) = 746.9°R$$
$$T_p/T_c(K) = 1.025 \qquad T_p = (1.025)(717.0) = 734.9°R$$

The experimental values are 738 and 726°R (41).

Cricondentherm and Cricondenbar Pressures. The pressures at the cricondentherm and cricondenbar, P_t and P_p, can be estimated only for binary hydrocarbon mixtures. The technique suggested by Silverman and Thodos (134) is empirical and is developed by an analysis of existing experimental data. The method is also applicable to estimate T_t and T_p and, though slightly less accurate than Eqs. (7-105) to (7-108), is more easily used; so the description given below will include the estimation of both T and P at the cricondentherm and cricondenbar points.
Let

$$\xi \equiv [\eta - \eta(K)]/y_1 y_2 = A + B y_1 + C y_1^2 + D y_1^3 \qquad (7\text{-}109)$$

where η can be T_t, P_t, T_p, or P_p and where $\eta(K)$ is the corresponding mole-fraction average of either T_c or P_c of the pure components and y_1 is the mole fraction of the light component. The polynomial constants

A, B, ... are functions of $\tau = T_{b_2}/T_{b_1}$, $\tau > 1$, as given in Table 7-6. The method is illustrated in Example 7-9. Note that, as arranged, the values of η should be in pounds per square inch absolute or degrees Rankine if Table 7-6 is used. In testing with 14 binary systems, not including those containing methane, where erratic results were sometimes obtained, but including one system with H_2S, errors less than 5 per cent were usually noted.

Example 7-9. Estimate the cricondentherm pressure for a mixture of ethane and i-butane containing 0.6577 mole-fraction ethane.
Solution. The value of τ for this system is $T_b(C_4)/T_b(C_2) = 1.478$.

$$\text{Value of } \eta(K) = P_c(K) = (0.6577)[P_c(C_2)] + (0.3423)[P_c(C_4)]$$
$$= 654.3 \text{ psia}$$

From Table 7-6, with $\tau = 1.478$, $A = 329.64$, $B = 46.22$,

$$C = 103.76 \quad \text{and} \quad D = 382.43$$

TABLE 7-6. SUMMARY OF ANALYTICAL EXPRESSIONS FOR DETERMINATION OF
COMPOSITION COEFFICIENTS OF EQ. (7-109), $\xi = A + By_1 + Cy_1^2 + Dy_1^3$*

Cricondentherm (maximum temperature):

Temperature, °R

$A = -0.60 + 202.2(\tau - 1) + 32.0(\tau - 1)^2 + 78.0(\tau - 1)^3$
$B = 1.61 + 158.3(\tau - 1) - 238.4(\tau - 1)^2 + 448.2(\tau - 1)^3$
$C = 0.76 - 104.6(\tau - 1) + 0.10(\tau - 1)^2 - 496.2(\tau - 1)^3$
$D = 1.47 + 124.8(\tau - 1) + 271.9(\tau - 1)^2 + 1,022.1(\tau - 1)^3$

Pressure, psia

$A = -11.74 + 660.8(\tau - 1) + 327.0(\tau - 1)^2 - 449.9(\tau - 1)^3$
$B = -0.79 + 145.8(\tau - 1) - 74.9(\tau - 1)^2 - 51.4(\tau - 1)^3$
$C = 1.94 - 384.4(\tau - 1) + 1,199.0(\tau - 1)^2 + 111.8(\tau - 1)^3$
$D = -28.75 + 979.4(\tau - 1) + 163.0(\tau - 1)^2 - 863.6(\tau - 1)^3$

Cricondenbar (maximum pressure):

Temperature, °R

$A = -0.62 + 140.3(\tau - 1) + 70.2(\tau - 1)^2 + 9.95(\tau - 1)^3$
$B = -3.23 + 571.3(\tau - 1) - 1,884.8(\tau - 1)^2 + 2,573.7(\tau - 1)^3$
$C = 19.98 - 2,171.7(\tau - 1) + 7,196.4(\tau - 1)^2 - 9,808.1(\tau - 1)^3$
$D = -12.25 + 1,680.8(\tau - 1) - 5,265.1(\tau - 1)^2 + 8,336.6(\tau - 1)^3$

Pressure, psia

$A = -4.24 + 564.2(\tau - 1) - 107.6(\tau - 1)^2 + 154.4(\tau - 1)^3$
$B = 6.34 - 229.0(\tau - 1) + 1,262.8(\tau - 1)^2 + 2,249.7(\tau - 1)^3$
$C = -8.74 + 2,128.6(\tau - 1) - 2,268.8(\tau - 1)^2 - 7,125.3(\tau - 1)^3$
$D = 15.48 - 1,991.0(\tau - 1) + 4,882.6(\tau - 1)^2 + 7,693.4(\tau - 1)^3$

* E. D. Silverman and G. Thodos, *Ind. Eng. Chem. Fundamentals*, **1**:299 (1962).

Thus

$$\xi = \frac{P_t - P_c(\mathrm{K})}{y_{c_2} y_{c_4}} = 329.64 + (46.22)(0.6577) + (103.76)(0.6577)^2$$

$$+ (382.43)(0.6577)^3 = 513.9$$

$$P_t = (513.96)(0.6577)(0.3423) + 654.3 = 770 \text{ psia}$$

The experimental value is 779 psia (75).

7-31   Summary of Recommended Methods for Estimating Critical Points of Mixtures

Only hydrocarbons can be treated, though hydrocarbon mixtures with inert gases may possibly also fit the correlations.

For T'_{c_m}, use Eq. (7-98) with Figs. 7-12 and 7-13 and the correction for aromatics as noted in Eq. (7-100).

For P'_{c_m}, use Figs. 7-14 to 7-16, where the various terms are defined in Eqs. (7-101) to (7-103). Note that corrections are required if aromatics or naphthenes are present.

For V'_{c_m}, use Figs. 7-17 and 7-18 with Φ defined in Eq. (7-103).

For T_t *and* T_p, use Eqs. (7-105) to (7-108).

For P_t *and* P_p, use Eq. (7-109) and Table 7-6. T_t and T_p may also be calculated. Only binary mixtures can be handled.

The errors associated with these methods are discussed in the same sections in which the methods are described.

NOMENCLATURE FOR CHAPTER 7

a = van der Waals' constant

a^* = Redlich-Kwong equation-of-state constant [see Eq. (7-54)]

A_{ij}, A_{ji} = parameter in Eq. (7-98)

b = van der Waals' constant

b^* = Redlich-Kwong equation-of-state constant [see Eq. (7-55)]

b_0 = hard-sphere volume, $\frac{2}{3}\pi N_0 \sigma^3$, cm^3/g mole

B = second-virial coefficient, cm^3/g mole; $B^* = B/b_0$

C = third-virial coefficient, cm^6/(g mole)^2; $C^* = C/b_0^2$

C_p = heat capacity, cal/(g mole)($^\circ$K); C_p^o, at zero pressure

ΔE_v^* = internal energy of vaporization of the hydrocarbon homomorph at $T_r = 0.7$, kcal/g mole

f = fugacity, atm; $\bar{f}_i$ fugacity of component i in the mixture; f_i^0, in a standard state or a pure component

F = total free energy, cal

ΔF^0 = standard free-energy change in reaction, cal/g mole

H = enthalpy, cal/g mole; H^0, in a reference state, usually zero pressure; $\bar{H}_i$, partial molal enthalpy

ΔH_v = enthalpy of vaporation, cal/g mole

$\mathcal{H}$ = Henry's-law constant, $\bar{f}_i/x_i$

I = ionization potential

J = parameter in J-SBV method, defined in Eq. (7-41)

k = Boltzmann's constant

k_{ij} = parameter in Eq. (7-51), defined in Eq. (7-52)

K = parameter defined in J-SBV method, Eq. (7-40); equilibrium constant, y/x

K_j = polar constant in Eq. (7-23)

(K) = symbol after T_c, P_c, etc., signifying Kay's rule, i.e., a mole-fraction average

M = parameter in Eq. (7-70)

MABP = designation for molal average boiling point

N = parameter in Eq. (7-70); N_i, moles of i

N_0 = Avogadro's number = 6.023×10^{23}

p = partial pressure, yP, atm

P = pressure, atm; P_c, critical pressure; P_{c_m}, pseudocritical pressure of mixture; P'_{c_m}, true critical pressure of mixture; P_s, standard-state pressure

r = distance between molecules; parameter in Eq. (7-47) and Fig. 7-2

R = gas constant

s = parameter in Eq. (7-47) and Fig. 7-3

S = entropy, cal/(g mole)(°K); S_s, entropy in a standard state at P_s

t^* = parameter in Eqs. (7-19) and (7-20)

T = temperature, °K; T_c, critical temperature; T_{c_m}, pseudocritical temperature of mixture; T'_{c_m}, true critical temperature of mixture

$T^* = T/(\epsilon_0/k)$

V = volume, cm³/g mole; V^*, characteristic value in Eq. (7-97); V_c, critical volume; V_{c_m}, pseudocritical volume of mixture; V'_{c_m}, true critical volume of mixture; $\bar{V}_i$, partial molal volume of i

x = mole fraction, usually liquid

y = mole fraction, usually vapor

Z = compressibility factor; $\Delta Z_v = (Z_v - Z_L)$; Z_c, critical compressibility factor

Greek

α = polarizability; parameter in LM's rule [Eq. (7-32)]

β = parameter in PG's rule [Eq. (7-49)]

γ = parameter in PG's rule [Eq. (7-50)]; γ_i, activity coefficient of i [Eq. (7-78)]

δ = solubility parameter [Eq. (7-95)]

Δ = correction factor for intermolecular distance (Table 7-1)

ϵ_0 = potential-energy parameter; ϵ'_0, modified L-J parameter in Eq. (7-22); ϵ_0^*, modified polar potential parameter in Eq. (7-25)

η = parameter in Eq. (7-109), representing T_t, P_t, . . .

$\theta = (P/T)[T_{c_m}(\mathrm{K})/P_{c_m}(\mathrm{K})]$

μ = chemical potential

$\nu = (f^0/P)_L$

ξ = parameter in Eq. (7-109); ξ_{ij}, a correction factor for σ and ϵ_0 in Eq. (7-23)

ρ = density, g moles/cm³; ρ_c, critical density; ρ_{c_m}, pseudocritical density for mixture; ρ'_{c_m}, true critical density for mixture

σ = parameter representing molecular diameter; σ', modified L-J parameter in Eq. (7-21); σ_j^*, modified polar potential in Eq. (7-24)

$\tau = T_{b_2}/T_{b_1}$, $\tau > 1$

$\varphi(T)$ = function of temperature in Eq. (7-73)

ϕ_i = fugacity coefficient (Eq. (7-79)]

$\Phi = T_{\mathrm{mabp}}/T_{b_m}$

ω = acentric factor; $\bar{\omega}$, modified acentric factor in Eq. (7-91) and Table 7-5

Subscripts

b = normal boiling point

c = critical point

i, j = components i or j

ij = interaction between i and j
L = liquid
m = mixture
p = cricondenbar point
r = reduced
s = standard state
t = cricondentherm point
v = vapor

REFERENCES FOR CHAPTER 7

1. Abraham, W. H., and C. O. Bennett: *AIChE J.*, **6**:257 (1960).
2. Ackerman, F. J.: M.S. thesis, UCRL-10650, University of California, Berkeley, Calif., February, 1963.
3. Adler, S. B., and D. F. Palazzo: *Chem. Eng.*, **66**(6):95, (7):123 (1959).
4. Barker, J. A., and M. Linton: *J. Chem. Phys.*, **38**:1853 (1963).
5. Benedict, M., G. B. Webb, and L. C. Rubin: *Chem. Eng. Progr.*, **47**:419 (1951).
6. Benedict, M., G. B. Webb, and L. C. Rubin: *Chem. Eng. Progr.*, **47**:449 (1951).
7. Benedict, M., G. B. Webb, L. C. Rubin, and L. Friend: *Chem. Eng. Progr.*, **47**:419, 449, 571, 609 (1951).
8. Black, C.: *AIChE J.*, **5**:249 (1959).
9. Black, C.: *Ind. Eng. Chem.*, **50**:391 (1958).
10. Blanks, R. F., and J. M. Prausnitz: *AIChE J.*, **8**:86 (1962).
11. Bottomley, G. A., and T. H. Spurling: *Australian J. Chem.*, **16**:1 (1963).
12. Brewer, J., and J. M. Geist: *J. Chem. Eng. Data*, **6**:405 (1961).
13. Burnside, H. E. W.: Sc.D. thesis in chemical engineering, Massachusetts Institute of Technology, 1938.
14. Busch, J. S., and L. N. Canjar: *AIChE J.*, **7**:343 (1961).
15. Canfield, F. B.: Ph.D. dissertation, Rice University, May, 1962.
16. Canjar, L. N.: *Petrol. Refiner*, **35**:(2):113 (1956).
17. Canjar, L. N., and W. C. Edmister: *Chem. Eng. Progr., Symp. Ser.*, **49**(7):73 (1953).
18. Canjar, L. N., and V. J. Peterka: *AIChE J.*, **2**:343 (1956).
19. Cavett, R. H.: Paper presented to Session on Computer Applications, Twenty-seventh Midyear Meeting of the API Division of Refining, May 15, 1962.
20. Chao, K. C., and J. D. Seader: *AIChE J.*, **7**:598 (1961).
21. Comings, E. W.: "High Pressure Technology," McGraw-Hill Book Company, New York, 1956.
22. Cota, H., and G. Thodos: *J. Chem. Eng. Data*, **7**:63 (1962).
23. Cullen, E. J., and K. A. Kobe: *AIChE J.*, **1**:452 (1955).
24. Davis, P. C., A. F. Bertuzzi, T. L. Gore, and F. Kurata: *J. Petrol. Technol.*, **6**(10):37 (1954).
25. Denbigh, K. G.: *Trans. Faraday Soc.*, **36**:936 (1940).
26. DePriester, C. L.: *Chem. Eng. Progr. Sym. Ser.*, **49**(7):1 (1953).
27. Dodge, B. F.: "Chemical Engineering Thermodynamics," McGraw-Hill Book Company, New York, 1944.
28. Eakin, B. E., and R. T. Ellington: "Thermodynamic and Transport Properties of Gases, Liquids and Solids," p. 195, McGraw-Hill Book Company, New York, 1959.
29. Edmister, W. C. *AIChE J.*, **1**:38 (1955).
30. Edmister, W. C.: *Petrol. Refiner*, **39**(7):133 (1960).
31. Edmister, W. C.: *Petrol. Refiner*, **39**(11):233 (1960).

32. Edmister, W. C.: *Petrol. Refiner*, **39**(12):159 (1960).
33. Edmister, W. C., and L. N. Canjar.: *Chem. Eng. Progr., Symp. Ser.*, **49**(7):85 (1953).
34. Edmister, W. C., C. L. Persyn, and J. H. Erbar: Paper presented at the Forty-second Annual Convention, National Gas Processors Association, Houston, Tex., Mar. 20–22, 1963.
35. Edmister, W. C., and C. L. Ruby: *Chem. Eng. Progr.*, **51**:95-F (1955).
36. Edmister, W. C., R. E. Thompson, and A. N. Stuckey Jr.: Paper presented at the Forty-first Annual Convention, National Gas Processors Association, Denver, Colo., Apr. 25, 1962.
37. Edmister, W. C., R. E. Thompson, and L. Yarborough: *AIChE J.*, **9**:116 (1963).
38. Edmister, W. C., and L. Yarborough: *AIChE J.*, **9**:240 (1963).
39. Eilerts, C. K., et al.: "Phase Relations of Gas-Condensate Fluids," *U.S. Bur. Mines Monograph* 10, vol. 1, pp. 101–154, 1957.
40. Ellington, R. T., O. T. Bloomer, B. E. Eakin, and D. C. Gami: "Thermodynamic and Transport Properties of Gases, Liquids, and Solids," p. 102, McGraw-Hill, Book Company, New York, 1959.
40a. Emanuel A. S.: Internal Report, California Research Corp., La Habra, Calif., 1964.
41. Etter, D. O., and W. B. Kay: *J. Chem. Eng. Data*, **6**:409 (1961).
42. Fender, B. E. F., and G. D. Halsey: *J. Chem. Phys.*, **36**:1881 (1962).
43. Finch, R. N., and M. van Winkle: *AIChE J.*, **8**:455 (1962).
44. Fox, J. H. P., and J. D. Lambert: *Proc. Roy. Soc. (London)*, **A210**:557 (1952).
45. Gambill, W. R.: *Chem. Eng.*, **65**(2):137(1958).
46. Gamson, B. W.: *Ind. Eng. Chem.*, **40**:2439 (1948).
47. Gamson, B. W., and K. M. Watson: *Natl. Petrol. News, Tech. Sec.*, **36**:R-556 (1944).
48. Gamson, B. W., and K. M. Watson: *Natl. Petrol. News, Tech. Sec.*, **36**:R-623 (1944).
49. Gilbert, L. L.: M.S. thesis, Rice University, May, 1963.
50. Gilliland, E. R., and T. E. Sullivan: *Chem. Eng. Progr., Symp. Ser.*, **48**(2):18 (1952).
51. Gilmont, R., D. Zudkevitch, and D. F. Othmer: *Ind. Eng. Chem.*, **53**:223 (1961).
52. Grayson, H. G., and C. W. Streed: Paper 20-PD7, Sixth World Petroleum Conference, Frankfurt, June, 1963.
53. Grieves, R. B., and G. Thodos: *AIChE J.*, **6**:561 (1960).
54. Grieves, R. B., and G. Thodos: *AIChE J.*, **8**:550 (1962).
55. Grieves, R. B., and G. Thodos: *AIChE J.*, **9**:25 (1963).
56. Grieves, R. B., and G. Thodos: *Ind. Eng. Chem. Fundamentals*, **1**:45 (1962).
57. Grieves, R. B. and G. Thodos: *Soc. Petrol. Eng. J.*, **3**:287 (1963).
58. Guggenheim, E. A., and M. L. McGlashan: *Proc. Roy. Soc. (London)*, **A206**:448 (1951).
59. Hamann, S. D., J. A. Lambert, and R. B. Thomas; *Australian J. Chem.*, **8**:149 (1955).
60. Hecht, C. E.: *J. Chem. Phys.*, **37**:679 (1962).
61. Hecht, C. E.: *J. Chem. Phys.*, **38**:1008 (1963).
62. Hildebrand, J. H., and R. L. Scott: "The Solubility of Nonelectrolytes," 3d ed., Reinhold Publishing Corporation, New York, 1950.
63. Hirschfelder, J. O., and R. J. Buehler: The Properties of a Gaseous or Liquid Mixture (Preliminary Study), TR WIS-00R-17, Jan. 9, 1957.
64. Hirschfelder, J. O., C. F. Curtiss, and R. B. Bird: "Molecular Theory of Gases and Liquids," John Wiley & Sons, Inc., New York, 1954.
65. Hobson, M., and J. H. Weber: *Chem. Eng.*, **64**(12):272 (1957).

66. Hobson, M., and J. H. Weber: *Petrol. Processing*, **12**:15 (September, 1957).
67. Hsieh, J. S., and R. H. Zimmerman: *J. Chem. Eng. Data*, **3**:194 (1958).
68. Hudson, G. H., and J. C. McCoubrey: *Trans. Faraday Soc.*, **56**:761 (1960).
69. Huff, J. A., and T. M. Reed, III: *J. Chem. Eng. Data*, **8**:306 (1963).
70. Joffe, J.: *Ind. Eng. Chem.*, **39**:837 (1947).
71. Joffe, J.: *Ind. Eng. Chem.*, **40**:1738 (1948).
72. Jones, I. W., and J. S. Rowlinson: *Trans. Faraday Soc.*, **59**:1702 (1963).
73. Katz, G.: S. M. thesis in chemical engineering, Massachusetts Institute of Technology, 1960.
74. Kay, W. B.: *Ind. Eng. Chem.*, **28**:1014 (1936).
75. Kay, W. B.: *Ind. Eng. Chem.*, **32**:353 (1940).
76. Kay, W. B., and T. D. Nevens: *Chem. Eng. Progr., Symp. Ser.*, **48**(3):108 (1952).
77. Kirkwood, J. G.: *Z. Physik*, **33**:57 (1932).
78. King, M. B.: *Trans. Faraday Soc.*, **54**:149 (1958).
79. Kurata, F., and D. L. Katz: *Trans. AIChE.* **38**:995 (1942).
80. Lambert, J. D., J. S. Clarke, J. F. Duke, C. L. Hicks, S. D. Lawrence, D. M. Morris, and M. G. T. Shone: *Proc. Roy. Soc. (London)*, **A249**:414 (1959).
81. Leland, T. W., Jr., P. S. Chappelear, and B. W. Gamson: *AIChE J.*, **8**:482 (1962).
82. Leland, T. W., Jr., R. Kobayashi, and W. H. Mueller: *AIChE J.*, **7**:535 (1961).
83. Leland, T. W., Jr., and W. H. Mueller: *Ind. Eng. Chem.*, **51**:597 (1959).
84. Lenoir, J. M.: *Petrol. Refiner*, **39**(8):136 (1960).
85. Lewis, G. N., and M. Randall: "Thermodynamics and the Free Energy of Chemical Substances," McGraw-Hill Book Company, New York, 1923.
86. Lewis, G. N., and M. Randall: "Thermodynamics," rev. by K. S. Pitzer and L. Brewer, McGraw-Hill Book Company, New York, 1961.
86a. Li, C. C., T. Y. Chen, and K. P. Murphy: Paper presented at the Las Vegas American Institute of Chemical Engineers meeting, September, 1964.
87. Ling, T. D., and M. van Winkle: *J. Chem. Eng. Data*, **3**:88 (1958).
88. London, F.: *Z. Physik*, **63**:245 (1930), **60**:491 (1930).
89. Luker, J. A., and T. A. Gniewek: *Syracuse Univ. Research Inst. Rept.* 273–557 F, July 29, 1955, 273–558 F, Aug. 2, 1955.
90. Luker, J. A., and T. A. Gniewek: *Syracuse Univ. Research Inst.* Ch.E. 273–558, August, 1955; Ch.E. 273-557 F, July, 1955.
91. McCracken, P. G., and J. M. Smith: *AIChE J.*, **2**:498 (1956).
92. McCracken, P. G., T. S. Storvick, and J. M. Smith: *J. Chem. Eng. Data*, **5**:130 (1960).
93. Magasanik, D., and R. T. Ellington: Paper presented to the National Meeting, of the American Institute of Chemical Engineers, Houston, Tex., December 1963.
94. Mason, D., and B. E. Eakin: *J. Chem. Eng. Data*, **6**:499 (1961).
95. Mayer, J. E.: *J. Phys. Chem.*, **43**:71 (1939).
96. Mayfield, F. D.: *Ind. Eng. Chem.*, **34**:843 (1942).
97. Mehra, V. S., G. M. Brown, and G. Thodos: *Chem. Eng. Sci.*, **17**:33 (1962).
98. Miller, A.: *Proc. Roy. Soc. (London)*, **A154**:624 (1936).
99. Mueller, W. H., T. W. Leland, Jr., and R. Kobayashi: *AIChE J.*, **7**:267 (1961).
100. Nagata, I.: *J. Chem. Eng. Data*, **6**:586 (1961).
101. Obert, E. F., and R. L. Young: Generalized Compressibility Charts for Industrial Problems, *Technol. Inst., Northwestern Univ., Research Rept.* M101, Evanston, Ill., 1951.
102. Opfell, J., C. J. Pings, Jr., and B. H. Sage: API Research Project 37, Monograph on "Equations of State for Hydrocarbons," American Petroleum Institute, 1959.
103. Opfell, J., W. G. Schlinger, and B. H. Sage: *Ind. Eng. Chem.*, **46**:1286 (1954).

104. Organick, E. I.: *Chem. Eng. Progr., Symp. Ser.*, **49**(6):81 (1953).
105. Organick, E. I., and G. G. Brown: *Chem. Eng. Progr., Symp. Ser.*, **48**(2):97 (1952).
106. Papadopoulos, A., R. L. Pigford, and L. Friend: *Chem. Eng. Progr. Symp. Ser.*, **49**(7):119 (1953).
107. Partington, E. J., J. S. Rowlinson, and J. F. Weston: *Trans. Faraday Soc.*, **56**:479 (1960).
108. Phillips, E. M., and G. Thodos: *AIChE J.*, **7**:413 (1961).
109. Pings, C. J., Jr., and B. H. Sage: *J. Chem. Eng. Data*, **1**:56 (1956).
110. Pitzer, K. S.: *J. Am. Chem. Soc.*, **77**:3427 (1955).
111. Pitzer, K. S., and G. O. Hultgren: *J. Am. Chem. Soc.*, **80**:4793 (1958).
112. Pitzer, K. S., D. Z. Lippmann, R. F. Curl, C. M. Huggins, and D. E. Petersen: *J. Am. Chem. Soc.*, **77**:3433 (1955).
113. Prausnitz, J. M.: *Chem. Eng. Sci.*, **6**:112 (1957).
114. Prausnitz, J. M.: *AIChE J.*, **5**:3 (1959).
115. Prausnitz, J. M.: *AIChE J.*, **6**:78 (1960).
116. Prausnitz, J. M., and R. Anderson: *AIChE J.*, **7**:96 (1961).
117. Prausnitz, J. M., and R. D. Gunn: *AIChE J.*, **4**:430 (1958).
118. Prausnitz, J. M., and R. D. Gunn: *AIChE J.*, **4**:430, 494 (1958).
119. Prausnitz, J. M., and R. D. Gunn: *AIChE J.*, **4**:494 (1958).
120. Prausnitz, J. M., and A. L. Myers: *AIChE J.*, **9**:5 (1963).
121. Prausnitz, J. M., and F. H. Shair: *AIChE J.*, **7**:682 (1961).
122. Prausnitz, J. M., W. C. Edmister, and K. C. Chao: *AIChE J.*, **6**:214 (1960).
123. Prengle, H. W., F. L. Worley, Jr., and C. E. Mauk: *J. Chem. Eng. Data*, **6**:395 (1961).
124. Reamer, H. H., B. H. Sage, and W. N. Lacey: *Ind. Eng. Chem.*, **43**:2515 (1951).
125. Redlich, O., and A. K. Dunlop: *Chem. Eng. Progr. Symp. Ser.*, **59**(44):95 (1963).
126. Reid, R. C., and T. W. Leland, Jr.: *AIChE J.*, **11**:228 (1965).
127. Ritter, R. B., J. M. Lenoir, and J. L. Schweppe: *Petrol. Refiner*, **37**(11):225 (1958).
128. Rowlinson, J. S.: "Encyclopedia of Physics," vol. 12, p. 1, Springer-Verlag OHG, Berlin, 1958.
129. Satter, A., and J. M. Campbell: *Soc. Petrol. Eng. J.*, **3**:333 (1963).
130. Scatchard, G.: *Chem. Revs.*, **8**:321 (1931).
131. Scatchard, G.: *J. Am. Chem. Soc.*, **56**:995 (1934).
132. Scheibel, E. G., and F. J. Jenny: *Ind. Eng. Chem.*, **37**:990 (1945).
133. Schiller, F. C., and L. N. Canjar: *Chem. Eng. Progr., Symp. Ser.*, **49**(7):67 (1953).
134. Silverman, E. D., and G. Thodos: *Ind. Eng. Chem. Fundamentals*, **1**:299 (1962).
135. Smith, G. E.: Ph.D. thesis, University of Michigan, Ann Arbor, Mich., 1963.
136. Smith, G. E., R. E. Sonntag, and G. J. VanWyler: *Advances in Cryogenic Eng.*, **8**:162 (1963).
137. Smith, R. L., and K. M. Watson: *Ind. Eng. Chem.*, **29**:1408 (1937).
138. Solbrig, C. W. and R. T. Ellington: *Chem. Eng. Progr. Sym. Ser.*, **59**(44):127 (1963).
139. Srivastava, B. N., and M. P. Madan: *Proc. Phys. Soc. (London)*, **A166**:277 (1953).
140. Stein, F. P., and J. J. Martin: *Chem. Eng. Progr., Symp. Ser.*, **59**(44):112 (1963).
141. Stewart, W. E., S. F. Burkhardt, and D. Voo: Paper presented at the National Meeting of the American Institute of Chemical Engineers, Kansas City, Mo., May 18, 1959.
142. Stevens, W. F., and G. Thodos: *AIChE J.*, **9**:293 (1963).
143. Stiehl, J. G., M. Hobson, and J. H. Weber: *AIChE J.*, **2**:389 (1956).
144. Storvick, T. S., and J. M. Smith: *J. Chem. Eng. Data*, **5**:133 (1960).
145. Storvick, T. S., and J. M. Smith: *J. Chem. Eng. Data*, **6**:28 (1961).

146. Storvick, T. S., and J. M. Smith: *J. Chem. Eng. Data*, **6**:28 (1961).
147. Su, Gouq-Jen, P. H. Huang, and Y.-M. Chang: *J. Am. Chem. Soc.*, **68**:1403 (1946).
148. Tang, W. K.: Properties of Gaseous and Liquid Mixtures, TR-WIS-OOR-13, Aug. 9, 1956.
149. Tooke, J. F., and G. E. Hays: Paper presented at the Forty-second National Gas Processors Association Annual Convention, Houston, Tex., March, 1963.
150. Townsend, P. W.: Ph.D. thesis, Columbia University, 1959; *Dissertation Abstr.*, **20**:240 (1959).
151. Warner, H. R.: S.B. thesis in chemical engineering, Massachusetts Institute of Technology, 1958.
152. Watson, K. M.: *Ind. Eng. Chem.*, **35**:398 (1943).
153. Wilson, G. M., and C. H. Deal: *Ind. Eng. Chem. Fundamentals*, **1**:20 (1962).

CHAPTER 8

SURFACE TENSION

8-1 Scope

Reliable techniques to estimate the surface tension of a pure liquid are discussed in Secs. 8-3 to 8-6. The variation of surface tension with temperature is covered in Sec. 8-7 and with pressure in Sec. 8-8. Recommendations are given in Sec. 8-9.

Surface-tension estimation methods for nonaqueous mixtures are presented in Sec. 8-10 and for aqueous mixtures in Sec. 8-11. Interfacial tensions are considered briefly in Sec. 8-12.

8-2 Introduction

The boundary layer between liquid and gas phases may, in some ways, be considered to be a third phase with properties intermediate between those of a liquid and a gas. There exist very large density gradients in this layer or film, and as Michaels (24) has recently pointed out in an excellent review paper, there also exist very large gradients in molecular energy. The effective thickness of the surface film is only a few molecules, and it is in these layers that the properties of the material change from those of a bulk liquid to those of a gas.

A qualitative microscopic picture of the surface layer shows that there are unequal forces acting upon the molecules; i.e., at low gas densities, the surface molecules are attracted sidewise and toward the bulk liquid but experience considerably less attraction in the direction of the gas phase. Thus the surface layer is in tension and tends to contract to the smallest area compatible with the mass of material and container walls.

A quantitative index of this tension may be presented in various ways, the most common being the surface tension γ. γ is defined simply as the force exerted in the plane of the surface, per unit length. Contrary to the usual concept of tension in a solid, it is independent of the amount of distension (17). By virtue of the definition, one may devise a reversible isothermal process whereby surface areas are increased by pulling the surface apart and allowing the molecules from the bulk liquid to enter this layer. The differential reversible work is then $\gamma \, dA$; in this case γ is the surface free energy per unit of area. As equilibrium systems tend to a state of minimum free energy (at constant temperature and pressure) the product γA also tends to a minimum or to a state of minimum area. This alternative concept therefore leads to the same conclusion as noted above when γ was considered mechanically as a tension force per unit length.

γ considered as a tension is usually expressed in dynes per centimeter, while from the thermodynamic point of view as a surface free energy per unit area it ordinarily has the units of ergs per square centimeter. These units and numerical values of γ are identical, though the method of defining γ is different.

The thermodynamics of surface layers furnishes a fascinating study. Guggenheim (10) and Gibbs (9) have formulated treatments which differ considerably but eventually reduce to similar equations relating macroscopically measurable quantities. In addition to the thermodynamic aspect, a detailed treatment of the physics and chemistry of surfaces has been recently published by Adamson (1). These areas are not covered here; rather, the emphasis is placed upon the few reliable methods available to estimate γ, either from theory or from empirical equations.

8-3   Estimation of the Surface Tension of a Pure Liquid

As pointed out by Gambill (7), surface tensions of most organic materials are all approximately the same at about room temperature; i.e., the range found is from about 25 to 40 dynes/cm. Water has a higher value of 72.75 dynes/cm at 20°C, and liquid-metal values commonly are between 300 and 600 dynes/cm; e.g., mercury at 20°C has a value of about 476. With increasing temperature, reflecting the decreased liquid density, there is less pull on the surface molecules, and surface tensions decrease. At the critical temperature, $\gamma = 0$; Rice (32) discusses this region in some detail.

The very early estimation techniques were based on the empirical Eötvös equation

$$\gamma = k_E(T_c - T)/V^{2/3} \tag{8-1}$$

where k_E is a specific constant for each material and V the molal liquid volume [see Eq. (2-15) for a recent correlation using this equation]. Values of k_E are often about constant at 2.12 for nonpolar low-molecular-weight materials but are smaller than 2.12 for polar materials and larger than 2.12 for high-molecular-weight compounds (7).* If Eq. (8-1) is modified by replacing $T_c - T$ by $T_c - T - 6$, the correlation is called the *Ramsey-Shield-Eötvös correlation*.

---

* These numerical values of k_E assume γ in dynes per centimeter, T in degrees Kelvin or Centigrade and V in cubic centimeters per gram mole.

A more accurate way to account for the variation of γ with temperature was suggested by van der Waals in 1894 (43) as

$$\gamma = k T_c^{1/3} P_c^{2/3} (1 - T_r)^{n_\gamma} \qquad (8-2)$$

where k and n_γ are supposedly universal constants for all materials. This equation is the precursor of most of the reliable correlations in this chapter; in fact it may be noted that the group $\gamma/T_c^{1/3} P_c^{2/3}$ may be considered as a dimensionless surface tension for incorporation into a framework of the law of corresponding states. Such a step is described later in this section.

Macleod-Sugden Correlation. Macleod (19) in 1923 suggested an empirical relation between γ and the densities of the liquid and vapor.* One specific constant was required. Ferguson pointed out in the discussion following the article that such a correlation was but another variation of Eq. (8-2), and later Sugden (36) traced the relationship in detail. Macleod's original equation is given below as Eq. (8-3), where the constant is designated as $[P]$ and called the "parachor" by Sugden (37).

$$\gamma^{1/4} = [P](\rho_L - \rho_v) \qquad (8-3)$$

At low vapor densities, the parachor may be visualized as a comparative volume between two liquids of equal surface tensions. The parachor has been shown to be an additive function of the atoms and groups in the molecule and to be approximately temperature-independent. The first group-contribution tabulation was suggested by Sugden (36), and others have since been proposed. The most detailed study of the relationship between the parachor and structure was carried out by Quale (29), and his values are shown in Table 8-1. Values of the parachor calculated from this table are to be used in Eq. (8-3) when γ is expressed as dynes per centimeter and the densities as gram moles per cubic centimeter. An alternative approach to correlate the parachor has been to relate it to Lennard-Jones potential parameters (4, 14).

There are many possible variations of the Macleod-Sugden relation. For example, the values of ρ_L and ρ_v may be replaced with relations involving P_r, T_r, and Z_c, as shown in Chap. 3. A common variation relates γ to the liquid viscosity μ (in centipoises) as (5, 26, 41)

$$\log \log 10\mu_L = m\gamma^{1/4} - 2.900 \qquad (8-4)$$

But from Souder's correlation [Eq. (9-51)] Eq. (8-4) becomes

$$\gamma^{1/4} = (I/m)\rho_L$$

* Apparently a similar equation was proposed by Kleeman (15) in 1911, but the credit is generally given to Macleod.

TABLE 8-1. RECOMMENDED ATOMIC AND STRUCTURAL CONTRIBUTIONS TO
CALCULATE THE PARACHOR*

CH_2 in—$(CH_2)_n$:

$n < 12$	40.0
$n > 12$	40.3†
C	9.0
H	15.5
In OH	10.0
In HN	12.5
O	19.8
O_2 in esters	54.8
N	17.5
S	49.1
P	40.5
F	26.1
Cl	55.2
Br	68.0
I	90.3
Se	63
Si	31
Al	55
Sn	64.5
As	54

Ethylenic bond:

Terminal	19.1
2,3 position	17.7
3,4 position	16.3
Triple bond	40.6

Carbonyl bond in ketones:

Total number of carbon atoms =		
	3	22.3
	4	20.0
	5	18.5
	6	17.3
	7	17.3
	8	15.1
	9	14.1
	10	13.0
	11	12.6

Single bond	0.0
Semipolar bond	0.0
Singlet linkage	−9.5
Hydrogen bridge	−14.4‡
Chain branching, per branch	−3.7§
Secondary-secondary adjacency	−1.6
Secondary-tertiary adjacency	−2.0
Tertiary-tertiary adjacency	−4.5

Alkyl groups:¶

1-Methylethyl	133.3
1-Methylpropyl	171.9
1-Methylbutyl	211.7
2-Methylpropyl	173.3
1-Ethylpropyl	209.5

TABLE 8-1. RECOMMENDED ATOMIC AND STRUCTURAL CONTRIBUTIONS TO
CALCULATE THE PARACHOR* (*Continued*)

1,1-Dimethylethyl	170.4
1,1-Dimethylpropyl	207.5
1,2-Dimethylpropyl	207.9
1,1,2-Trimethylpropyl	243.5
Position differences in benzene:	
Ortho-meta	1.8–3.4
Meta-para	0.2–0.5
Ortho-para	2.0–3.8
Ring closure:	
3-membered ring	12.5
4-membered ring	6.0
5-membered ring	3.0
6-membered ring	0.8
7-membered ring	4.0

* From O. R. Quale, *Chem. Revs.*, **53**:439 (1953).
† Somewhat greater beyond 20 —CH_2—.
‡ Includes any ortho effect.
§ Varies from −2.1 to −6.5.
¶ Complete group, including branching.

with I the Souder's viscosity constant. However, as calculated

$$m = I/[P]$$

so insertion of this relation yields Eq. (8-3) with the assumption that $\rho_L \gg \rho_v$.

A convenient nomograph of Eq. (8-3) as prepared by Johnson is available (7).

The use of the empirical exponent of ¼ in Eq. (8-3) has been criticized by Wright (45). That is, by writing Eq. (8-3) as

$$\gamma^{1/p} = [P]'(\rho_L - \rho_v) \tag{8-5}$$

where p and $[P]'$ are constants for a given material, he showed by a regression analysis of experimental data at various temperatures that for different materials the best value of p varied from 3.5 to 4.5 and $[P]'$ differed from the Sugden parachor. No general correlation of p or $[P]'$ was, however, attempted.

Surface-tension values estimated with Eq. (8-3) are compared with a few experimental values in Table 8-4. It is seen that, except for methyl alcohol, the errors are usually less than 3 or 4 per cent over the small temperature range chosen. The relation is not suitable for water, HCN, or other highly polar compounds. Example 8-1 illustrates the technique.

Example 8-1. Estimate the surface tension of ethyl acetate at 20°C, using the Macleod-Sugden correlation. The experimental value reported is 23.75 dynes/cm (29, 39).

Solution. From Table 8-1, the parachor is determined as

$$[P] = 3C + 6H + (CH_2)_{n<12} + O_2 \text{ ester}$$
$$= 3(9.0) + 6(15.5) + 40.0 + 54.8$$
$$= 214.8$$
$$M = 88.10$$
$$\rho_L = 0.9001 \text{ g/cm}^3 = 0.9001/88.1 \text{ g mole/cm}^3$$

From Eq. (8-3)

$$\gamma = [(214.8)(0.9001/88.10)]^4 = 23.24 \text{ dynes/cm}$$
$$\text{Error} = [(23.24 - 23.75)/23.75] \times 100 = -2.1\%$$

Molar-refraction Modification of the Macleod-Sugden Correlation. The molar refraction $[R_\lambda]$ is related to the refractive index n_λ at a wavelength λ by the Lorenz-Lorenz expression

$$[R_\lambda] = (1/\rho_L)(n_\lambda^2 - 1)/(n_\lambda^2 + 2) \qquad (8\text{-}6)$$

where ρ_L is the molal liquid density. The wavelength of light chosen for n_λ is usually that of the sodium D line; thus the molar refraction is denoted as $[R_D]$, but the refractive index is simply noted as n. Combining Eq. (8-6) with (8-3), where the assumption $\rho_L \gg \rho_v$ is made (40),

$$\gamma = \left\{ \frac{[P]}{[R_D]} \frac{(n^2 - 1)}{(n^2 + 2)} \right\}^4 \qquad (8\text{-}7)$$

The molar refraction $[R_D]$ has been shown to be similar to $[P]$ in that it is an additive constant and not a strong function of temperature. A table of contributions is given in Table 8-2 (6).

Equation (8-7) is normally applied only near room temperature as it is in this range where refractive indices are normally available. Within the restrictions that $\rho_L \gg \rho_v$ and $[P]$ and $[R_D]$ are temperature-independent, it could be applied to other temperature ranges provided values of n are available. Probably, however, it had best be considered to apply only in the 20 to 30°C range, and temperature extrapolation techniques described in Sec. 8-4 had best be used to obtain values at other temperatures.

For estimating values of γ at or near room temperature Gambill (7) has found Eq. (8-7) to be the most accurate of those he tested. Generally errors of less than 2 to 3 per cent are to be expected. Some calculated values are compared with experimental surface tensions in Table 8-4; the method is illustrated in Example 8-2. From the few tests shown in Table 8-4, the per cent errors found were in most cases very near to those from the Macleod-Sugden equation (8-3). Estimating γ with Eq. (8-7) does have the advantage that no density data need be known, though in many cases densities may be more readily available than refractive indices.

TABLE 8-2. ATOMIC AND STRUCTURAL CONTRIBUTIONS TO THE
MOLAR REFRACTION $[R_D]$*

Increment

C	2.418
H	1.100
—CH$_2$—	4.618
O (hydroxyl)	1.525
O (ether)	1.643
O (carboxyl)	2.211†
COO—(ester)	6.154
Cl	5.967
Br	8.865
I	13.90
N (primary amine)	2.322
N (secondary amine)	2.502
N (tertiary amine)	2.840
N (nitrile)	5.516
3-membered ring	0
4-membered ring	0
5-membered ring	0
6-membered ring	0
7-membered ring	0
Double bond	1.733
Semipolar double bond	1.733
Triple bond	2.398

* Based on the sodium D line, from F. Eisenlohr, *Z. physik. Chem.*, **75**:585 (1910).
† Includes allowance for double bond.

Example 8-2. Repeat Example 8-1, using Eq. (8-7).
Solution. The molar refraction is calculated from Table 8-2.

$$[R_D] = 3C + 8H + (COO)_{ester}$$
$$= 3(2.418) + 8(1.100) + 6.154 = 22.208$$
$$[P] \text{ (from Example 8-1)} = 214.8$$
$$n = 1.37216 \quad \text{at } 20°C \text{ (12)}$$

Thus from Eq. (8-7)

$$\gamma = ((214.8/22.208) \times \{[(1.37216)^2 - 1]/[(1.37216)^2 + 2]\})^4 = 23.36 \text{ dynes/cm}$$
$$\text{Error} = [(23.36 - 23.75)/23.75] \times 100 = -1.6\%$$

Corresponding-state Correlation. As pointed out earlier, the group $\gamma/P_c^{2/3}T_c^{1/3}$ is dimensionless except for a numerical constant which depends upon the units of γ, P_c, and T_c.* Brock and Bird (4) have proposed an estimating method wherein this dimensionless group is correlated by the principle of corresponding states.

$$\gamma/P_c^{2/3}T_c^{1/3} = (0.133\alpha_c - 0.281)(1 - T_r)^{11/9} \qquad (8-8)$$

* If γ is in dynes per centimeter, P_c in atmospheres, and T_c in degrees Kelvin, the group $\gamma/P_c^{2/3}T_c^{1/3}$ must be multiplied by 0.227×10^{-6} to be truly dimensionless.

T_r is the reduced temperature, α_c the Riedel factor discussed in Sec. 2-8, and P_c and T_c are the critical pressure and temperature in atmospheres and degrees Kelvin.   Brock and Bird have correlated surface tensions of 84 widely different nonpolar organic compounds and permanent gases with an average deviation of about 3 per cent.   Hydrogen and helium (which exhibit quantum effects) and polar molecules cannot be treated satisfactorily with this correlation.   A similar correlation has also been suggested by Riedel (33), but extensive testing indicates Eq. (8-8) to be slightly more accurate.

Some values of calculated surface tensions are compared with experimental values in Table 8-4, and the method is illustrated in Example 8-3. In general, the method is slightly less accurate than either Eq. (8-3) or (8-7), but it requires no data such as densities or refractive indices.   To illustrate the large errors possible for polar compounds, the method was also applied to these types in Table 8-4; it is clear that the restriction to nonpolar materials made earlier is valid.

Example 8-3.   Estimate the surface tension of benzene at 120°C by means of Eq. (8-8).   The experimental value reported is 16.42 dynes/cm (39).

Solution.   The critical constants for benzene are $P_c = 48.6$ atm, $T_c = 562.1°K$, and $\alpha_c = 6.83$ (Appendix A).

Thus

$$T_r = (120 + 273.2)/562.1 = 0.70$$

From Eq. (8-8)

$$\gamma = (48.6)^{2/3}(562.1)^{1/3}[(0.133)(6.83) - 0.281](1 - 0.70)^{11/9}$$
$$= 15.74 \text{ dynes/cm}$$
$$\text{Error} = [(15.74 - 16.42)/16.42] \times 100 = -4.1\%$$

8-4   Variation of Surface Tension with Temperature

Most relations which show the variation of surface tension with temperature have the form of Eq. (8-2).   For example, Eq. (8-8) assumes n_γ to have a value of $11/9$ or 1.22.   Other authors have proposed values around 1.2 (8, 21).   To relate surface tensions at temperatures 1 and 2,

$$\gamma_1/\gamma_2 = [(1 - T_{r_1})/(1 - T_{r_2})]^{1.2} \tag{8-9}$$

Kharbarda's nomograph (13) of Eq. (8-9) is given by Gambill (8).   The exponent 1.2 (or 1.22) is strictly applicable for nonpolar compounds, and for polar materials it is usually different.   One way to estimate n_γ for such polar compounds is illustrated in Sec. 2-3, Example 2-2.   Wright (45) has criticized the universal and indiscriminate use of 1.2 and in an examination of many compounds (primarily ketones and nitriles) has found the best value of the exponent to vary between 0.99 and 1.23, with a mean of about 1.16.

Other temperature correlations have been reviewed (8), but none appear more accurate than, nor do they have the appealing simplicity of, Eq. (8-9). A convenient nomograph to determine γ at various temperatures for about 100 common organic chemicals is given in Fig. 8-1 (27), to be used in conjunction with Table 8-3.

8-5 Variation of Surface Tension with Pressure

Values of γ are usually reported for surfaces in contact with the pure vapor of the liquid being studied or with air. At low pressures both values are about the same. At higher pressures, the pressure usually denotes the vapor pressure of the pure material, and air or other "inert" gases are excluded. If such gases were present, the increased solubility of this pressurizing gas in the liquid would result in a binary mixture and significant changes in the surface tension would be possible by virtue of a preferential concentration of the dissolved gas near the surface. As it is impossible to exceed the vapor pressure in a two-phase single-component system, studies under very high pressures have always involved the use of a pressurizing gas. Invariably in such a pressurization there is a marked reduction in the measured surface tension. For example, some typical results for water are shown in Fig. 8-2 (35). Similar results were obtained for hexane. No good quantitative estimation of the effect of pressure is yet available, but Slowinski et al. (35) suggest on the basis of water and hexane experiments that

$$\gamma_P/\gamma_{\text{pure}} = 1 - KP \qquad T = \text{const} \tag{8-10}$$

where K is independent of the liquid being pressurized and depends only upon the temperature and nature of the pressurizing gas. It would be surprising if this simple Henry's-law analogy were general, but it is the best relation to date. Approximate K values at 25°C for a few gases over water may be obtained from Fig. 8-2; that is, the slopes of the lines for the several gases are equal to $-K$.

8-6 Discussion and Recommendation of Surface-tension Estimation Techniques for Pure Liquids

Only the more reliable estimation techniques have been discussed in previous sections. Gambill (7, 8) has considered several other methods, but these do not appear to offer any real advantage over those presented above. Also, Reich (30) has approximated surface tensions by a relationship involving vapor pressures and liquid densities which is often quite accurate below T_b for nonpolar materials. In somewhat different approaches Simmons and Wilson relate surface tensions to viscosity,

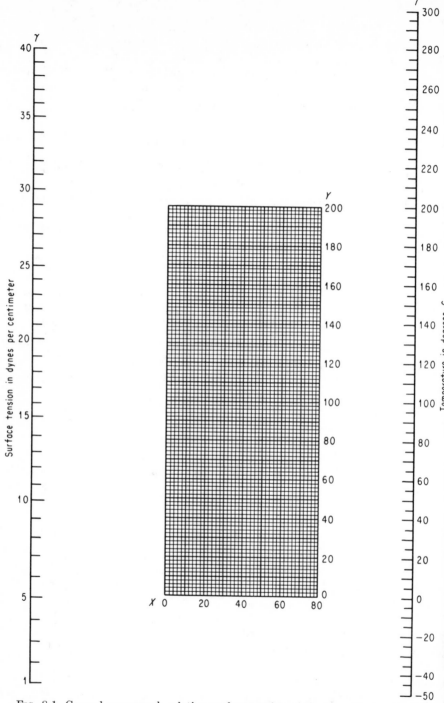

FIG. 8-1. General nomograph relating surface tension of liquids with temperature. Values for X and Y, taken from Table 8-3, are used for any particular compound to give a point on the central grid. By using this point as a pivot for a straight line, the value of the surface tension may be read from the intersection of this line with the γ scale against the value of the temperature read from the intersection of this line with the T scale. [*D. F. Othmer, S. Josefowitz, and Q. F. Schmutzler, Ind. Eng. Chem.,* **40**:886 (1948).]

TABLE 8-3. X AND Y VALUES FOR SURFACE-TENSION NOMOGRAPH*

Compound	X	Y	Compound	X	Y
Acetal	19	88	Ethyl isobutyrate	20.9	93.7
Acetaldehyde	33	78	Ethyl ether	27.5	64
Acetaldoxime	23.5	127	Ethyl formate	30.5	88.8
Acetamide	17	192.5	Ethyl iodide	28	113.2
Acetic acid	17.1	116.5	Ethyl mercaptan	35	81
Acetic anhydride	25	129	Ethyl propionate	22.6	97
Acetone	28	91	Ethylamine	11.2	83
Acetonitrile	33.5	111	Ethylbenzene	22	118
Acetophenone	18	163	Ethylene chloride	32	120
Allyl alcohol	12	111.5	Ethylene oxide	42	83
Anethole	13	158.1	n-Hexane	22.7	72.2
Aniline	22.9	171.8	Hydrogen cyanide	30.6	66
Anisole	24.4	138.9	Mesitylene	17	119.8
Ammonia	56.2	63.5	Methyl acetate	34	90
Isoamyl acetate	16.4	103.1	Methyl alcohol	17	93
Isoamyl alcohol	6	106.8	Methyl n-butyrate	25	88
Benzene	30	110	Methyl isobutyrate	24	93.8
Benzonitrile	19.5	159	Methyl chloride	45.8	53.2
Benzylamine	25	156	Methyl ether	44	37
Bromobenzene	23.5	145.5	Methyl ethyl ketone	23.6	97
Isobutyl acetate	16	97.2	Methyl formate	38.5	88
n-Butyl alcohol	9.6	107.5	Methyl propionate	29	95
Isobutyl alcohol	5	103	Methylamine	42	58
n-Butyric acid	14.5	115	Naphthalene	22.5	165
Isobutyric acid	14.8	107.4	Nitroethane	25.4	126.1
n-Butyronitrile	20.3	113	Nitromethane	30	139
Carbon disulfide	35.8	117.2	Nitrosyl chloride	38.5	93
Carbon tetrachloride	26	104.5	Nitrous oxide	62.5	0.5
Chloral	30	113	n-Octane	17.7	90
Chlorine	45.5	59.2	Paraldehyde	22.3	103.8
Chlorobenzene	23.5	132.5	Phenetole	20	134.2
p-Chlorobromobenzene	14	162	Phenol	20	168
Chloroform	32	101.3	Phosphorus oxychloride	26	125.2
p-Chlorotoluene	18.7	134	Piperidine	24.7	120
o-Cresol	20	161	Propionic acid	17	112
m-Cresol	13	161.2	Propionitrile	23	108.6
p-Cresol	11.5	160.5	n-Propyl acetate	23	97
Cyclohexane	42	86.7	n-Propyl alcohol	8.2	105.2
Diethyl ketone	20	101	n-Propyl formate	24	97
Diethyl oxalate	20.5	130.8	n-Propylamine	25.5	87.2
Diethyl sulfate	19.5	139.5	p-Isopropyl toluene	12.8	121.2
Diethyl aniline	17	142.6	Pyridine	34	138.2
Dimethyl sulfate	23.5	158	Quinoline	19.5	183
Dimethylamine	16	66	Thiophene	35	121
Dimethyl aniline	20	149	Toluene	24	113
Ethyl acetate	27.5	92.4	Triethylamine	20.1	83.9
Ethyl acetoacetate	21	132	Trimethylamine	21	57.6
Ethyl alcohol	10	97	Tripalmitin	2	151
Ethyl benzoate	14.8	151	Triphenyl methane	12.5	182.7
Ethyl bromide	31.6	90.2	m-Xylene	20.5	118
Ethyl n-butyrate	17.5	102	p-Xylene	19	117

* D. F. Othmer, Samuel Josefowitz, and Q. F. Schmutzler, *Ind. Eng. Chem.*, **40**:886 (1948).

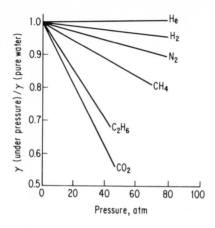

FIG. 8-2. Effect of gas pressurization of a water surface on the surface tension at 25°C. [E. J. Slowinski, Jr., E. F. Gates, and C. E. Waring, J. Phys. Chem., **61**:808 (1957).]

energy of vaporization, and boiling points (34) and Mayer to liquid compressibility (22).

Based on the discussion given previously and the results in Table 8-4:

For nonpolar materials, either the Macleod-Sugden correlation [Eq. (8-3)] or the Brock and Bird corresponding-state technique [Eq. (8-8)] should be used. The choice of one or the other method will probably be dictated by the available data. If accurate liquid and vapor densities are known, Eq. (8-3) is probably preferable, though at high temperatures there may be some variation in the parachor with temperature. If liquid densities have to be estimated, then the fourth power of the density in Eq. (8-3) will cause the final errors to be larger and in this case Eq. (8-8) is preferable. At high reduced temperatures, Eq. (8-8) is also recommended.

For polar materials, no reliable method is available. Equation (8-3) is as good as any, but the large errors possible for some polar compounds (see Table 8-4) should be noted.

If a single surface-tension datum point is available and values are desired at other temperatures, Eq. (8-9) should be used (the exponent 1.2 is often taken as 1.22). For polar materials, this technique may not be reliable, as the exponent is often a function of temperature.

The effect of pressure on the surface tension of a liquid may be approximated in a very rough manner by means of Eq. (8-10), with K determined from Fig. 8-2 for a few gases over water.

8-7 Surface Tensions of Nonaqueous Mixtures

In liquid mixtures, the concentrations usually specified refer to bulk values. The surface tension is, however, primarily influenced by the surface concentrations. It is surprising, therefore, that there are, in fact, any simple, reliable estimating techniques for mixture surface ten-

TABLE 8-4. COMPARISON OF CALCULATED AND EXPERIMENTAL VALUES OF
SURFACE TENSION OF PURE LIQUIDS

Compound	T, °C	γ exp., dynes/cm	Ref.	γ calc., dynes/cm					
				Macleod-Sugden eq. (8-3)	% Error*	Mod. Macleod-Sugden eq. (8-7)	% Error*	Brock and Bird eq. (8-8)	% Error*
Acetic acid..........	15	27.95	39	.....	......	.....	......	43.01	+59
	20	27.42	39	26.04	− 5.0	26.26	− 4.2	42.15	+54
	30	26.34	39	24.95	− 5.3	.....	......	40.46	+54
Acetone.............	15	23.92	39	24.36	+ 1.8	.....	......	25.87	+ 8.1
	20	23.32	39	23.70	+ 1.6	24.28	+ 4.1	25.16	+ 7.9
	40	21.16	29	21.09	− 0.3	.....	......	22.34	+ 5.6
Aniline.............	10	44.00	39	42.89	− 2.5	.....	......	48.62	+11
	20	43.00	39	41.51	− 3.5	41.67	− 3.1	47.19	+ 7.7
	50	40.10	39	.....	......	.....	......	42.96	+ 7.1
Benzene.............	10	30.26	39	29.27	− 3.3	.....	......	29.29	− 3.2
	20	28.88	39	27.89	− 3.4	27.92	− 3.3	28.01	− 3.0
	90	20.13	39	.....	......	.....	......	19.38	− 3.7
	120	16.42	39	15.74	− 4.1	.....	......	15.87	− 3.4
n-Butyl alcohol......	15	25.00	39	25.76	+ 3.0	.....	......	34.31	+37
	20	24.57	39	25.29	+ 2.9	25.10	+ 2.2	33.55	+37
	30	23.75	39	24.36	+ 2.6	.....	......	32.04	+35
Carbon disulfide.....	15	33.07	39	34.66	+ 4.9	.....	......	34.00	+ 2.8
	20	32.25	39	33.86	+ 5.0	33.87	+ 5.0	33.22	+ 3.0
	30	30.79	39	32.28	+ 4.8	.....	......	31.66	+ 2.8
Carbon tetrachloride .	10	28.05	39	28.48	+ 1.5	.....	......	27.09	− 3.4
	20	26.76	39	27.14	+ 1.4	27.13	+ 1.4	25.88	− 3.3
	50	23.22	39	23.41	+ 0.8	.....	......	22.33	− 3.8
Chlorobenzene.......	15	33.86	39	33.73	− 0.4	.....	......	33.65	− 0.6
	20	33.28	39	33.06	− 0.7	32.88	− 1.2	33.05	− 0.7
	50	29.60	29	29.40	− 0.7	.....	......	29.51	− 0.3
Cyclohexane.........	15	25.64	39	24.87	− 3.0	.....	......	24.62	− 4.0
	20	24.99	39	24.30	− 2.8	24.29	− 2.8	24.06	− 3.7
	30	23.82	39	23.16	− 2.8	.....	......	22.93	− 3.7
Cyclopentane........	15	23.16	39	22.25	− 3.9	.....	......	22.61	− 2.4
	20	22.42	39	21.67	− 3.4	21.65	− 3.4	21.99	− 1.9
	30	21.17	39	20.57	− 2.8	.....	......	20.77	− 1.9
Diethyl ether........	15	17.62	39	17.51	− 0.6	.....	......	17.58	− 0.2
	20	17.06	39	16.96	− 0.5	17.02	− 0.2	16.98	− 0.5
	30	15.95	39	15.89	− 0.4	.....	......	15.79	− 1.0
Ethyl acetate........	15	24.36	39	23.87	− 2.0	.....	......	24.92	+ 2.3
	20	23.75	39	23.24	− 2.1	23.36	− 1.6	24.28	+ 2.2
	30	22.55	39	22.02	− 2.4	.....	......	22.99	+ 2.0
Ethyl bromide.......	15	24.83	39	23.71	− 4.5	.....	......	28.06	+13
	20	24.15	39	22.98	− 4.8	22.97	− 4.9	27.27	+13
	30	22.83	39	21.80	− 4.5	.....	......	25.69	+12

TABLE 8-4. COMPARISON OF CALCULATED AND EXPERIMENTAL VALUES OF
SURFACE TENSION OF PURE LIQUIDS (*Continued*)

Compound	T, °C	γ exp., dynes/cm	Ref.	γ calc., dynes/cm					
				Macleod-Sugden eq. (8-3)	% Error*	Mod. Macleod-Sugden eq. (8-7)	% Error*	Brock and Bird eq. (8-8)	% Error*
n-Heptane	10	21.12	39	21.28	+ 0.6	.....	......	20.30	− 4.0
	20	20.31	29	20.28	− 0.2	20.26	− 0.3	19.33	− 4.8
	50	17.20	39	17.32	+ 0.7	.....	......	16.51	− 4.0
n-Hexane	15	18.94	39	18.95	+ 0.1	.....	......	18.90	− 0.2
	20	18.42	39	18.42	0	18.48	+ 0.3	18.37	− 0.3
	40	16.35	39	16.35	− 0.1	.....	......	16.30	− 0.3
Methyl alcohol	15	22.99	39	20.18	−12	.....	......	45.40	+98
	20	22.55	39	19.72	−13	20.09	−11	44.16	+96
	30	21.69	39	18.78	−13	.....	......	41.73	+93
Phenol	20	40.90	39	36.42	−11	36.42	−11	54.10	+32
	30	39.88	39	.....	......	.....	......	52.46	+32
	50	37.74	39	35.41	− 6.2	.....	......	49.20	+30
n-Octane	10	22.73	39	22.69	− 0.2	.....	......	22.68	− 0.2
	20	21.77	39	21.74	− 0.1	21.70	− 0.3	21.71	− 0.3
	50	18.82	39	18.82	0	.....	......	18.86	+ 0.2
Toluene	15	29.10	39	28.53	− 2.0	.....	......	29.72	+ 2.1
	20	28.52	39	27.91	− 2.1	27.92	− 2.1	29.11	+ 2.1
	30	27.40	39	26.76	− 2.3	.....	......	27.93	+ 1.9
2,2,3-Trimethylbutane.	20	18.76	29	18.20	− 3.0	18.19	− 3.0	19.19	+ 2.3
	30	16.81	29	.....	......	.....	......	18.21	+ 8.3

* % Error = [(calc. − exp.)/exp.] × 100.

sions. The several correlations discussed below are all modifications of those described earlier for pure-component estimations. The modifications are usually elementary, and the very fact that they produce reasonable answers is probably due to the small range of pure-liquid surface tensions and the fact that most surface-tension–composition curves are approximately linear.

Macleod-Sugden Correlation. For mixtures, Eq. (8-3), with $\rho_{L_m} \gg \rho_{v_m}$, becomes

$$\gamma_m^{1/4} = [P_m](\rho_{L_m}) \tag{8-11}$$

where ρ_{L_m} refers to the actual mixture liquid molal density and the mixture parachor is assumed to be given by

$$[P_m] = \sum_j x_j[P_j] \tag{8-12}$$

This form was suggested by Hammick and Andrews (11) and has been tested by Bowden and Butler (3) with good results for methyl (and ethyl) carbonate mixtures with benzene, chloroform, and nitrobenzene. Gambill also reports errors less than 4 per cent even for mixtures of associated liquids (8). To use Eq. (8-11), mixture-density data must be available.

If the effect of vapor density is included, Eq. (8-11) becomes

$$\gamma_m{}^{1\!/4} = \rho_{L_m} \sum_j [P_j] x_j - \rho_{v_m} \sum_j [P_j] y_j \qquad (8\text{-}13)$$

where densities are those on a molal basis and x and y are equilibrium liquid and vapor mole fractions. The more complex form of the Macleod-Sugden equation for mixtures is necessary only for high-temperature–high-pressure systems. For example, Weinaug and Katz (44) used it for the methane-propane system to calculate surface tensions from 5 to 194°F. It has also been used for the system nitrogen-butane (and heptane) by Reno and Katz (31). In the latter study the best value of $[P]_{N_2}$ was found to be 60 for the butane system and 41 for the heptane system. This variability of the parachor violates the usually accepted principle that the parachor is a true characteristic constant for a material.

Modified Macleod-Sugden Correlation. For mixtures, Eq. (8-7) becomes

$$\gamma_m = ([P_m]/[R_{D_m}])[(n_m{}^2 - 1)/(n_m{}^2 + 2)] \qquad (8\text{-}14)$$

where $[P_m]$, $[R_{D_m}]$, and n_m are all given by the form of Eq. (8-12), that is, a mole-fraction average. This form was suggested by Meissner and Michaels (23); when it was tested with nonaqueous solutions, errors less than 7 per cent were found. Included in the list were many polar-nonpolar binaries. The equation was later shown to be reasonably accurate (25) for ternary liquid systems containing mixtures of benzene, isopropyl alcohol, n-propyl alcohol, nitrobenzene, furfural, ethyl acetate, toluene, and benzyl alcohol.

Corresponding-state Correlation. Equation (8-8) may be applicable for mixtures if pseudocritical constants are employed. This pseudocritical concept is developed in detail in Sec. 7-9. The simplest procedure would be to assume that P_{c_m}, T_{c_m}, and α_{c_m} are all mole-fraction averages (i.e., Kay's pseudocritical rule is applicable). Such a calculation was made for most of the same binaries tested by Meissner and Michaels, and comparable results were obtained; i.e., this technique, compared with Eq. (8-14), showed no significant difference in errors calculated.

Discussion of the Nonaqueous-mixture Surface-tension Estimation Techniques. To give an idea of the type of results obtained with Eqs. (8-14) and (8-8), Fig. 8-3 has been drawn showing a few experimental

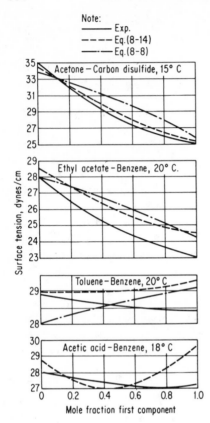

FIG. 8-3. Calculated and experimental mixture surface tensions.

and calculated curves. Several points should be noted. First, even though the systems represent quite different chemical types, the γ-x curves are not grossly different from a linear form. This seems to be typical of most γ-x plots. Second, the mixture-estimating techniques have no built-in control to yield the correct values for the pure components. Experimental values of the pure components are often available, and a technique is desired to determine the effect of varying composition. In general the estimating techniques give the correct trend with composition (benzene-toluene excepted), but the predictions are not overimpressive. In fact, in many (if not most) cases, one would not be far in error by employing the simple form

$$\gamma_m = \sum_j x_j \gamma_j \tag{8-15}$$

For a binary, this would indicate γ_m to be linear in composition.

Finally, in comparing some of the pure-component values of Fig. 8-3 with those tabulated in Table 8-4, one will find occasional discrepancies.

The data from Table 8-4 were taken mostly from the new edition of Timmerman's book (39), whereas those in Fig. 8-3 were obtained from miscellaneous sources quoted by Meissner and Michaels (23). There does not yet seem to be a good reference set of mixture properties which is universally accepted. Timmerman's is probably the best to date, and recent publications such as that by Ling and Van Winkle (18) are representative of some accurate studies.

Recommendations. To determine the surface tension of a nonaqueous organic mixture, use Eq. (8-11) (low pressure) or Eq. (8-13) (high pressure), or Eq. (8-14) or Eq. (8-8) with pseudocritical constants. There is little difference in accuracy among these three methods, and the choice is probably to be dictated by the available data for the mixture in question. For example, if accurate mixture-density data were available, Eq. (8-11) or (8-13) would be used. If refractive indices of the pure components were known but liquid densities were not known, Eq. (8-14) might be used. Equation (8-8) requires no particular properties other than pure critical constants, but it has not been thoroughly tested. For rapid estimates, if values of γ for the pure substances are available, Eq. (8-15) is convenient. All the methods will usually yield maximum errors only slightly greater than errors found in using the method to determine the surface tensions of the pure components.

If one desires a more accurate mixture-surface-tension estimation method and if the mixture is nonpolar, reference may be made to a recent correlating technique based upon a cell model of the vapor-liquid interface (5a). The method has the best theoretical base of all mixture correlation methods, but to obtain accurate results, the liquid-phase activity coefficients must be known.

8-8 Surface Tensions of Aqueous Solutions

Whereas for nonaqueous solutions the mixture often approximated a linear dependence with mole fraction, aqueous solutions show pronounced nonlinear characteristics. A typical case is shown in Fig. 8-4 for acetone-water at 50°C (20). The surface tension of the mixture is represented

FIG. 8-4. Surface tension of acetone-water solutions at 50°C. [R. A. McAllister and K. S. Howard, AIChE J., **3**:325 (1957).]

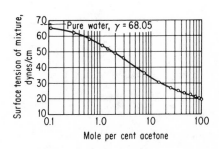

by an approximate straight line on semilogarithmic coordinates. This behavior is typical of organic-aqueous systems, where small concentrations of the organic material may significantly affect the mixture surface tension. The hydrocarbon portion of the organic molecule behaves as a hydrophobic material and tends to be rejected from the water phase by preferentially concentrating on the surface. In such a case, the bulk concentration is not the important variable; rather, one should use the "surface" concentration. Unfortunately, the latter is not amenable to direct measurement. Meissner and Michaels (23) show graphs similar to Fig. 8-4 for a variety of dilute solutions of organic materials in water and suggest that the general behavior is approximated by the Szyszkowski equation, which they modify to the form:

$$\gamma/\gamma_w = 1 - 0.411 \log (1 + x/a) \qquad (8\text{-}16)$$

where γ_w = surface tension of pure water, x is the mole fraction of organic material, and a is a constant characteristic of the organic material. Values of a are listed in Table 8-5 for a few compounds. This equation should not be used if the mole fraction of the organic solute exceeds 0.01.

To estimate the surface tensions of aqueous binary mixtures over wide concentration ranges of the dissolved organic material and for both low and high-molecular-weight organic-aqueous systems, the proposed method of Tamura, Kurata, and Odani (38) may be used. Equations (8-11) and (8-12) are assumed as a starting point, but the significant densities and concentrations are taken to be those characteristic of the surface layer; i.e., in Eq. (8-11), the mixture density becomes,

$$1/\rho_{L_m} = V_s = \sum_j x_{s_j} V_j \qquad (8\text{-}17)$$

where V_s is the molal volume of the surface layer and x_{s_j} is the mole fraction of j in this surface layer. V_j is, however, chosen as the pure-component molal volume of j. Thus, from Eqs. (8-11), (8-12), and (8-3) (with $\rho_L \gg \rho_v$), with subscript w representing water and o the organic component,

$$V_s\gamma_m{}^{1/4} = x_{s_w}[P_w] + x_{s_o}[P_o] = x_{s_w}V_w\gamma_w{}^{1/4} + x_{s_o}V_o\gamma_o{}^{1/4} \qquad (8\text{-}18)$$

and
$$\gamma_m{}^{1/4} = \varphi_{s_w}\gamma_w{}^{1/4} + \varphi_{s_o}\gamma_o{}^{1/4} \qquad (8\text{-}19)$$

where φ_{s_w} = superficial volume-fraction water in surface layer

$$\varphi_{s_w} = x_{s_w}V_w/V_s \qquad (8\text{-}20)$$

and similarly for φ_{s_o}.

TABLE 8-5. CONSTANTS FOR THE SZYSZKOWSKI EQUATION (8-16)*

Compound	$a \times 10^4$
Propionic acid	26
n-Propyl alcohol	26
Isopropyl alcohol	26
Methyl acetate	26
n-Propyl amine	19
Methyl ethyl ketone	19
n-Butyric acid	7.0
Isobutyric acid	7.0
n-Butyl alcohol	7.0
Isobutyl alcohol	7.0
Propyl formate	8.5
Ethyl acetate	8.5
Methyl propionate	8.5
Diethyl ketone	8.5
Ethyl propionate	3.1
Propyl acetate	3.1
n-Valeric acid	1.7
Isovaleric acid	1.7
n-Amyl alcohol	1.7
Isoamyl alcohol	1.7
Propyl propionate	1.0
n-Caproic acid	0.75
n-Heptanoic acid	0.17
n-Octanoic acid	0.034
n-Decanoic acid	0.0025

* H. P. Meissner and A. S. Michaels, *Ind. Eng. Chem.*, **41**:2782 (1949).

Equation (8-19) is the final correlation. To obtain values of the superficial surface volume fractions φ_{s_w} and φ_{s_o}, an equilibrium is assumed between the surface and bulk liquid molecules of water and the organic substance (16, 28). The standard free-energy change for this equilibrium is taken as proportional to the difference in surface free energies (surface tensions) between water and the organic material. The final equation is rather complex, and after rearrangement it may be written in the following set of equations,

$$\mathcal{B} = \log \left(\varphi_w^q / \varphi_o \right) \tag{8-21}$$

$$\mathcal{C} = \log \left(\varphi_{sw}^q / \varphi_{s_o} \right) \tag{8-22}$$

$$\mathcal{C} = \mathcal{B} + Q \tag{8-23}$$

$$Q = 0.441(q/T)(\gamma_o V_o^{2/3}/q - \gamma_w V_w^{2/3}) \tag{8-24}$$

where φ_{s_w} was defined by Eq. (8-20) and φ_w, φ_o are the superficial bulk volume fractions of water and organic material, i.e.,

$$\varphi_w = x_w V_w / (x_w V_w + x_o V_o) \qquad (8\text{-}25)$$
$$\varphi_o = x_o V_o / (x_w V_w + x_o V_o)$$

x_w, x_o refer to the bulk mole fractions; V_w, V_o to the molal volumes; and γ_w, γ_o to the surface tensions of the pure water and organic material. T is in degrees Kelvin, and q is a constant depending upon the type and size of the organic constituent.   The accompanying tabulation indicates q for various materials.

Materials	q	Example
Fatty acids, alcohols.....	Number of carbon atoms	Acetic acid, $q = 2$
Ketones................	One less than the number of carbon atoms	Acetone, $q = 2$
Halogen derivatives of fatty acids............	Number of carbons times ratio of molal volume of halogen derivative to parent fatty acid	Chloroacetic acid

The method is illustrated in Example 8-4.   Tamura et al. (38) tested the method with some 14 aqueous systems and 2 alcohol-alcohol systems;* the percentage errors were less than 10 per cent when q was less than 5 and within 20 per cent for q greater than 5.

Example 8-4.   Estimate the surface tension of a mixture of methyl alcohol and water at 30°C when the mole-fraction alcohol is 0.122.   The experimental value reported is 46.1 dynes/cm (38).
Solution.   At 30°C (12) (o represents methyl alcohol, w water), $\gamma_w = 71.18$ dynes/cm, $\gamma_o = 21.75$ dynes/cm, $V_w = 18$ cm³/g mole, $V_o = 41$ cm³/g mole, and q = number of carbon atoms = 1.

From Eqs. (8-25),
$$\varphi_w / \varphi_o = (0.878)(18)/(0.122)(41) = 3.16$$
and from Eq. (8-21),
$$\mathcal{B} = \log 3.16 = 0.50$$
$$Q \text{ [from Eq. (8-24)]} = (0.441)(\tfrac{1}{303})[(21.75)(41)^{2/3} - (71.18)(18)^{2/3}]$$
$$= -0.34$$

Hence $\mathcal{Q}$ [from Eq. (8-23)] $= \mathcal{B} + Q = 0.50 - 0.34 = 0.16$
$$= \log (\varphi_{s_w} / \varphi_{s_o}) \qquad \text{from Eq. (8-22)}$$
Since $\varphi_{s_w} + \varphi_{s_o} = 1$, then
$$\varphi_{s_w} / (1 - \varphi_{s_o}) = 10^{0.16} = 1.45$$
or $$\varphi_{s_w} = 0.59 \qquad \varphi_{s_o} = 0.41$$

* For nonaqueous systems between polar molecules, the method is unchanged except that in this case q = ratio of molal volumes of the solute to solvent.

Finally, from Eq. (8-19),

$$\gamma_m = [(0.59)(71.18)^{\frac{1}{4}} + (0.41)(21.75)^{\frac{1}{4}}]^4 = 46 \text{ dynes/cm}$$
$$\text{Error} = [(46 - 46.1)/46.1] \times 100 = -0.2\%$$

Recommendations. For estimating the surface tension of binary organic-aqueous mixtures, use the method of Tamura, Kurata, and Odani as given by Eqs. (8-17) to (8-25) and illustrated in Example 8-4. Errors should normally not exceed 10 to 15 per cent. If the organic compound has five or more carbon atoms, the solubility in water will be low and the Szyszkowski equation (8-16) as developed by Meissner and Michaels should be used.

For binary mixtures of highly polar materials, such as alcohols, the method of Tamura et al. noted above can be used.

8-9 Interfacial Tension

In a system of two or more immiscible or partially miscible *liquid* phases, there is an interfacial tension (or surface free energy) at each interface. This interfacial tension is analogous to the surface tension between liquid and vapor, though numerically values are usually less than the larger of the pure-liquid surface tensions.

Gambill (8) has presented an excellent concise summary of the literature dealing with the estimation of interfacial tension. He discusses the only useful estimation technique, the Antonoff rule (2), in some detail. This is

$$\gamma_i = |\gamma_1 - \gamma_2| \tag{8-26}$$

where γ_i = interfacial tension
  γ_1, γ_2 = surface tension of *mutually saturated phases* as measured against a common gas

Pure-component surface tensions should not be used: γ_1, γ_2 refer to values of the liquid saturated with respect to the other component. Earlier in this chapter (Sec. 8-5 and particularly Sec. 8-8) it was seen that small bulk concentrations of a chemically dissimilar molecule in a solvent often profoundly lower the surface tension of the solvent. It is this mixture surface tension which is to be used in Eq. (8-26) for γ_1, γ_2. Gambill discusses the errors expected in the use of Eq. (8-26); he found average errors of about 3.3 per cent for eight organic-water partially miscible systems in the range 17 to 26°C. The maximum error found was near 15 per cent.

Little recent work has been published on interfacial tensions, though Valentine and Heideger (42) have recently presented an interesting study where γ_i was measured for aqueous multicomponent organic mixtures. No general correlation was obtained from the data. It is interesting to note that γ_i is time-dependent approaching an asymptotic value for an "aged" surface. Both aged and freshly formed surfaces were studied by Valentine and Heideger; i.e., the latter pertained to surfaces wherein the equilibrium surface concentrations had not yet been obtained. These two measurements differed in many cases by 20 to 30 per cent, the value for the aged surface being larger. This phenomenon is important in interpreting interfacial-tension data. The estimated values from Eq. (8-26) presumably refer to aged surfaces; for application in many agitated mass-transfer processes, freshly formed surfaces are present, and γ_i for this condition is the relevant value.

NOMENCLATURE FOR CHAPTER 8

a = constant in Eq. (8-16)

α = parameter in Eq. (8-22)

$\mathcal{B}$ = parameter in Eq. (8-21)

I = Souders viscosity constant (see Sec. 9-12)

k = constant in Eq. (8-2)

k_E = Eötvös constant in Eq. (8-1)

K = pressure constant in Eq. (8-10)

m = constant in Eq. (8-4) = $I/[P]$

M = molecular weight

n = refractive index as measured with the wavelength of the sodium D line; n_λ, measured at wavelength λ; n_γ, exponent in Eq. (8-2)

p = constant in Eq. (8-5)

P = pressure, atm

P_{c_m} = pseudocritical pressure for a mixture, atm

$[P]$ = parachor (see Table 8-1)

$[P]'$ = constant in Eq. (8-5)

q = parameter in Eq. (8-24)

Q = parameter defined by Eq. (8-24)

$[R_D]$ = molar refraction referred to the D line of sodium; $[R_\lambda]$, referred to wavelength λ

T = temperature, °K

T_{c_m} = pseudocritical temperature for a mixture, °K

V = molal volume, cm³/g mole

x = mole fraction, liquid

y = mole fraction, vapor

Greek

α_c = Riedel factor (see Sec. 2-8)

γ = surface tension, dynes/cm

μ = viscosity, centipoises

ρ = density, g moles/cm³

φ = superficial volume fraction

Subscripts

c = critical state

i = interfacial, between liquid phases

j = component j

L = liquid

m = mixture

o = organic constituent
p = under pressure
r = reduced state
s = surface phase
v = vapor phase
w = water

REFERENCES FOR CHAPTER 8

1. Adamson, A. W.: "Physical Chemistry of Surfaces," Interscience Publishers, Inc., New York, 1960.
2. Antonoff, G. N.: *J. Russ. Phys.-Chem. Soc.*, **39**:342 (1907).
3. Bowden, S. T., and E. T. Butler: *J. Chem. Soc.*, **1939**:79.
4. Brock, J. R., and R. B. Bird: *AIChE J.*, **1**:174 (1955).
5. Buehler, C. A.: *J. Phys. Chem.*, **42**:1207 (1938).
5a. Eckert, C. A., and J. M. Prausnitz: *AIChE J.*, **10**:677 (1964).
6. Eisenlohr, F.: *Z. physik. Chem.*, **75**:585 (1910).
7. Gambill, W. R.: *Chem. Eng.*, **64**(4):146 (1958).
8. Gambill, W. R.: *Chem. Eng.*, **64**(5):143 (1958).
9. Gibbs, J. W.: "The Collected Works of J. Willard Gibbs," vol. I, Thermodynamics, Yale University Press, New Haven, Conn., 1957.
10. Guggenheim, E. A.: "Thermodynamics," 4th ed., North Holland Publishing Company, Amsterdam, 1959.
11. Hammick, D. L., and L. W. Andrew: *J. Chem. Soc.*, **1929**:754.
12. International Critical Tables, vol. IV, pp. 447, 448, McGraw-Hill Book Company, New York, 1928.
13. Kharbarda, O. P.: *Indian Chemist*, **31**(4):187 (1955).
14. Kirkwood, J. G., and F. P. Buff: *J. Chem. Phys.*, **17**:338 (1949).
15. Kleeman, R. D.: *Phil. Mag.*, **21**:99 (1911).
16. Kurata, Michio: *Busseiron Kenkyu (Researches on Chem. Phys.)*, **56**:60 (1952).
17. Lewis, W. K., L. Squires, and G. Broughton: "Industrial Chemistry of Colloidal and Amorphous Materials," chap. III, The Macmillan Company, New York, 1949.
18. Ling, T. D., and M. Van Winkle: *J. Chem. Eng. Data*, **3**:88 (1958).
19. Macleod, D. B.: *Trans. Faraday Soc.*, **19**:38 (1923).
20. McAllister, R. A., and K. S. Howard: *AIChE J.*, **3**:325 (1957).
21. McConnell, H. M.: *J. Chem. Phys.*, **23**:2454 (1955).
22. Mayers, S. W.: *J. Chem. Phys.*, **38**:1803 (1963).
23. Meissner, H. P., and A. S. Michaels: *Ind. Eng. Chem.*, **41**:2782 (1949).
24. Michaels, A. S.: Fundamentals of Surface Chemistry and Physics, *ASTM Spec. Tech. Publ.* 340, 1962.
25. Michaels, A. S., R. S. Alexander, and C. L. Becker: *Ind. Eng. Chem.*, **42**:2332 (1950).
26. Móritz, P.: *Periodica Polytech.*, **3**:167 (1959).
27. Othmer, D. F., S. Josefowitz, and Q. F. Schmutzler: *Ind. Eng. Chem.*, **40**:886 (1948).
28. Prigogine, I., and J. Marechal: *J. Colloid. Sci.*, **7**:122 (1952).
29. Quale, O. R.: *Chem. Revs.*, **53**:439 (1953).
30. Reich, I.: *J. Colloid. Sci.*, **14**:562 (1959).
31. Reno, G. J., and D. L. Katz: *Ind. Eng. Chem.*, **35**:1091 (1943).
32. Rice, O. K.: *J. Phys. Chem.*, **64**:976 (1960).
33. Riedel, L.: *Chem.-Ing.-Tech.*, **27**:209 (1955).

394   THE PROPERTIES OF GASES AND LIQUIDS

34. Simmons, J. H., and W. H. Wilson: *J. Chem. Phys.*, **23**:613 (1955).
35. Slowinski, E. J., Jr., E. F. Gates, and C. E. Waring: *J. Phys. Chem.*, **61**:808 (1957).
36. Sugden, S.: *J. Chem. Soc.*, **1924**:32.
37. Sugden, S.: *J. Chem. Soc.*, **1924**:1177.
38. Tamura, M., M. Kurata, and H. Odani: *Bull. Chem. Soc. Japan*, **28**:83 (1955).
39. Timmermans, J.: "Physico-chemical Constants of Pure Organic Compounds," Elsevier Publishing Company, Amsterdam, 1950.
40. Tripathi, R. C.: *J. Indian Chem. Soc.*, **18**:411 (1941).
41. Tripathi, R. C.: *J. Indian Chem. Soc.*, **19**:51 (1942).
42. Valentine, R. S., and W. J. Heideger: *J. Chem. Eng. Data*, **8**:27 (1963).
43. van der Waals, J. D.: *Z. physik. Chem.*, **13**:716 (1894).
44. Weinaug, C. F.: *Ind. Eng. Chem.*, **35**:239 (1943).
45. Wright, F. J.: *J. Appl. Chem.*, **11**:193 (1961).

CHAPTER 9

VISCOSITY

9-1 Scope

The first part of this chapter deals with the viscosity of gases and the second with the viscosity of liquids. In each part, methods are recommended for (1) correlating low-pressure viscosity data with temperature, (2) estimating viscosities when no experimental data are available, (3) estimating the effect of pressure on viscosity, and (4) estimating the viscosities of mixtures. The molecular theory of viscosity is considered briefly.

9-2 Definition and Units of Viscosity

If a shearing stress is applied to any portion of a confined fluid, the fluid will move, and a velocity gradient will be set up within the fluid, with a maximum velocity at the point where the stress is applied. The viscosity of the medium is defined as the ratio of the shear stress per unit area at any point to the velocity gradient. Viscosity is a measure of the internal fluid friction, which tends to oppose any dynamic change in the fluid motion; i.e., if the friction between layers of fluid is small (low viscosity), an applied shearing force will result in a large velocity gradient. As the viscosity increases, each fluid layer exerts a larger frictional drag on adjacent layers and the velocity gradient decreases.

It is to be noted that viscosity differs in one important respect from the properties discussed previously in this book; namely, viscosity is a dynamic nonequilibrium property on a macro scale. Density, for example, is a static equilibrium property. On a micro scale, both properties reflect the effect of molecular motions and interaction. Viscosity is a nonequilibrium, or "transport," property, but it is a function of the state of the fluid, as are temperature, pressure, and volume, and may be used to define the state of the material.*

* This discussion is limited to Newtonian fluids, i.e., those fluids in which the viscosity, as defined, is independent of the magnitude either of the shearing stress or of the velocity gradient (rate of shear). Newtonian fluids include most pure liquids, simple mixtures, and gases. Non-Newtonian fluids are characterized by the fact that the viscosity is not independent of the shearing stress or rate of shear and are grouped as being associated with three types of flow: pseudoplastic, dilatant, and plastic (150). Paper-pulp slurries, paints, polymer solutions, etc., are included in the non-Newtonian class.

The mechanism, or theory, of gas viscosity has been reasonably well clarified by the application of the kinetic theory of gases, but the theory of liquid viscosity is poorly developed.   Brief résumés of both theories will be presented later.

Since viscosity is defined as a shearing stress per unit area divided by a velocity gradient, it should have the dimensions of force-time/(length)^2 or mass/(length)(time).   Both dimensional groups are used, although for most scientific work viscosities are expressed in terms of poises, centipoises, micropoises, etc.   A poise denotes a viscosity of 1 dyne-sec/cm^2 or 1 g mass/(sec)(cm), and 1.0 centipoise = 0.01 poise.   The following conversion factors apply to the conversion of viscosity units:

$$1 \text{ poise} = 1.000 \times 10^2 \text{ centipoises}$$
$$= 1.000 \times 10^6 \text{ micropoises}$$
$$= 6.72 \times 10^{-2} \text{ lb mass/(ft)(sec)}$$
$$= 242 \text{ lb mass/(ft)(hr)}$$
$$= 2.09 \times 10^{-3} \text{ lb force-sec/ft}^2$$

For example, if a gas has a viscosity of 0.015 centipoise, the viscosity in lb mass/(ft)(sec) = $0.015[(6.72/10^2) \times 10^{-2}] = 1.01 \times 10^{-5}$.

9-3   Theory of Gas Viscosity and Other Transport Properties

The theory is simply stated but is quite complex to express in equations which may be used directly to calculate viscosities.   In simple terms, when a gas undergoes a shearing stress so that there is some bulk motion, the molecules at any one point have the bulk-velocity vector added to their own random-velocity vector.   Molecular collisions cause an interchange of momentum throughout the fluid, and this bulk-motion velocity (or momentum) becomes distributed.   Near the source of the applied stress, the bulk-velocity vector is high, but as the molecules move away from the source, they are "slowed down" (in the direction of bulk flow), causing the other sections of the fluid to move in the direction of bulk flow. This random molecular-momentum interchange is the predominant cause of the phenomenon of gas viscosity.

Elementary Kinetic Theory.   If the gas is modeled in the simplest manner, it is possible to show easily the general relationship of viscosity to temperature, pressure, and molecular size.   More rigorous treatments will yield similar relationships, but containing important correction factors. The elementary gas model assumes all molecules to be noninteracting rigid spheres of diameter σ (with mass m), moving randomly at a mean velocity v.   The density is n molecules in a unit volume.   Molecules move in the gas, collide, and may transfer momentum or energy if there are velocity or temperature gradients; such processes also result in a transfer of molecular species if a concentration gradient exists. The net flux of momentum, energy, or component mass between two layers is assumed proportional to the momentum, energy, or mass density gradient, i.e.,

$$\text{Flux } \alpha(-d\rho'/dz) \tag{9-1}$$

where the density ρ' decreases in the $+z$ direction and ρ' may be ρ_i, mass density, nmv_y, momentum density, or $C_v nT$, energy density. The coefficient of proportionality for all these fluxes is given by elementary kinetic theory as $vL/3$, where v is the average molecular speed and L the mean free path.

Equation (9-1) is also used to define the transport coefficients of diffusivity, viscosity, and thermal conductivity, i.e.,

$$\text{Mass flux} = -Dm(dn_i/dz) = (-vL/3)(d\rho_i/dz) \tag{9-2}$$
$$\text{Momentum flux} = -\mu(dv_y/dz) = (-vL/3)mn(dv_y/dz) \tag{9-3}$$
$$\text{Energy flux} = -k(dT/dz) = (-vL/3)C_v n(dT/dz) \tag{9-4}$$

Equations (9-2) to (9-4) define the transport coefficients μ, D, and k. If the average speed is proportional to $(RT/M)^{1/2}$ and the mean free path to $1/n\sigma^2$, then,

$$D = vL/3 = \text{const } (T^{3/2}/M^{1/2}P\sigma^2) \tag{9-5}$$
$$\mu = m\rho vL/3 = \text{const } (T^{1/2}M^{1/2}/\sigma^2) \tag{9-6}$$
$$k = vLC_v\rho/3 = \text{const } (T^{1/2}/M^{1/2}\sigma^2) \tag{9-7}$$

The constant multipliers in Eqs. (9-5) to (9-7) are different in each case; the interesting facts to note from these results is the dependency of the various transfer coefficients on T, P, M, and σ. A similar treatment with inert molecules (i.e., ideal gases) having a Maxwellian velocity distribution yields the same final equations but with slightly different numeral constants.

The viscosity equation [Eq. (9-6)], as determined from a rigorous solution of the rigid, noninteracting sphere model, is

$$\mu = 0.002669 \sqrt{MT}/\sigma^2 \quad \text{(centipoise)} \tag{9-8}$$

where μ is in centipoises, M is the molecular weight, T the temperature in degrees Kelvin, and σ the hard-sphere diameter in angstroms. The equations for k and D are discussed in Chaps. 10 and 11.

Spherical Model with Intermolecular Forces. The major step forward in the calculation of transport coefficients from theory is due to Chapman and Enskog (38, 97, 98). The important assumptions in this development are: (1) the gas is sufficiently dilute so that only binary collisions occur, (2) the motion of the molecules during a collision can be described by classical mechanics, (3) only elastic collisions occur, and (4) the inter-molecular forces act only between fixed centers of the molecules, i.e., the intermolecular potential function is spherically symmetric. With these restrictions it would appear that the resulting theory should be applicable only to low-pressure high-temperature monatomic gases. The pressure and temperature restrictions are valid, but for lack of tractable, alternative models it is very often applied to polyatomic gases, except in the case of thermal conductivity, where a correction for internal-energy transfer and storage must be included (see Chap. 10).

The Chapman-Enskog treatment considers in detail the interactions between colliding molecules, with allowance for a potential energy $\varphi(r)$. The equations are well known (38), but their solution is often very difficult. Each choice of an intermolecular potential $\varphi(r)$ must be solved separately. In general terms, the solution for viscosity is written as

$$\mu = 0.002669 \sqrt{MT}/\sigma^2 \Omega_v \qquad \text{(centipoise)} \qquad (9\text{-}9)$$

which is identical to Eq. (9-8) except for the inclusion of the "collision integral" Ω_v. Obviously Ω_v must be unity if the molecules do not interact. It may be calculated if $\varphi(r)$ is specified, though, as noted above, the actual calculation may be difficult. The values of Ω_v for the Lennard-Jones and Stockmayer potential functions are discussed in detail in Sec. 9-4. These two potential functions are of the greatest interest to engineers, since values of the characterizing potential parameters σ and ϵ_0 are often available or may be estimated. However, considerable effort is now being made to evaluate Ω_v for other, more realistic potential functions (117, 129).

Discussion. The derivation of Eq. (9-9) (or similar ones for k and D given in Chaps. 10 and 11) is a major achievement. Extensive use has been made of this type of equation to calculate transport coefficients in temperature ranges far in excess of convenient laboratory experimental conditions, i.e., at thousands of degrees, in plasmas, etc. (3, 4, 46), and Svehla (197) has tabulated such calculated values for many gases from 100 to 5000°K (197).

The theory of low-pressure gas-transport properties is, however, by no means complete. Besides the studies mentioned above dealing with other spherically symmetric intermolecular potentials, currently extensive investigations deal with polar molecules with orientation-dependent forces. Mason and Monchick (142), Dahler (46), and Liley (127, 128) have published excellent summaries of the current developments.

9-4 Estimation of Low-pressure Gas Viscosity

The most promising methods for estimating the viscosity of a gas at low pressure, in the absence of experimental data, are summarized below.

Estimated viscosity values are compared with experimental data in Table 9-3, and recommendations are summarized later in this section.

Theoretical Method. The theory of gas-transport properties was reviewed very briefly in Section 9-3. For viscosity, the result of the Chapman-Enskog solution was given by Eq. (9-9), and, as was noted there, the functional dependence of Ω_v on temperature and other molecular parameters varied with the intermolecular potential chosen. Two cases are discussed here; nonpolar gases as represented by the Lennard-Jones potential, and polar gases as represented by the Stockmayer potential.

TABLE 9-1. VALUES OF THE COLLISION INTEGRAL Ω_v FOR VISCOSITY AND OF THE VISCOSITY TEMPERATURE FUNCTION $f_1(kT/\epsilon_0)$†

Based on the Lennard-Jones potential

$T^* = kT/\epsilon_0$‡	Ω_v‡	$f_1(kT/\epsilon_0)$	kT/ϵ_0	Ω_v	$f_1(kT/\epsilon_0)$	kT/ϵ_0	Ω_v	$f_1(kT/\epsilon_0)$
0.30	2.785	0.1969	1.65	1.264	1.0174	4.0	0.9700	2.0719
0.35	2.628	0.2252	1.70	1.248	1.0453	4.1	0.9649	2.1090
0.40	2.492	0.2540	1.75	1.234	1.0729	4.2	0.9600	2.1457
0.45	2.368	0.2834	1.80	1.221	1.0999	4.3	0.9553	2.1820
0.50	2.257	0.3134	1.85	1.209	1.1264	4.4	0.9507	2.2180
0.55	2.156	0.3440	1.90	1.197	1.1529	4.5	0.9464	2.2536
0.60	2.065	0.3751	1.95	1.186	1.1790	4.6	0.9422	2.2888
0.65	1.982	0.4066	2.00	1.175	1.2048	4.7	0.9382	2.3237
0.70	1.908	0.4384	2.1	1.156	1.2558	4.8	0.9343	2.3583
0.75	1.841	0.4704	2.2	1.138	1.3057	4.9	0.9305	2.3926
0.80	1.780	0.5025	2.3	1.122	1.3547	5.0	0.9269	2.4264
0.85	1.725	0.5346	2.4	1.107	1.4028	6.0	0.8963	2.751
0.90	1.675	0.5666	2.5	1.093	1.4501	7.0	0.8727	3.053
0.95	1.629	0.5985	2.6	1.081	1.4962	8.0	0.8538	3.337
1.00	1.587	0.6302	2.7	1.069	1.5417	9.0	0.8379	3.607
1.05	1.549	0.6616	2.8	1.058	1.5861	10	0.8242	3.866
1.10	1.514	0.6928	2.9	1.048	1.6298	20	0.7432	6.063
1.15	1.482	0.7237	3.0	1.039	1.6728	30	0.7005	7.880
1.20	1.452	0.7544	3.1	1.030	1.7154	40	0.6718	9.488
1.25	1.424	0.7849	3.2	1.022	1.7573	50	0.6504	10.958
1.30	1.399	0.8151	3.3	1.014	1.7983	60	0.6335	12.324
1.35	1.375	0.8449	3.4	1.007	1.8388	70	0.6194	13.615
1.40	1.353	0.8744	3.5	0.9999	1.8789	80	0.6076	14.839
1.45	1.333	0.9036	3.6	0.9932	1.9186	90	0.5973	16.010
1.50	1.314	0.9325	3.7	0.9870	1.9576	100	0.5882	17.137
1.55	1.296	0.9611	3.8	0.9811	1.9962	200	0.5320	26.80
1.60	1.279	0.9894	3.9	0.9755	2.0343	400	0.4811	41.90

† From J. O. Hirschfelder, C. F. Curtiss, and R. B. Bird, "Molecular Theory of Gases and Liquids," John Wiley & Sons, Inc., New York, 1954, and L. A. Bromley and C. R. Wilke, *Ind. Eng. Chem.*, **43**:1641 (1951).

‡ Hirschfelder, Curtiss, and Bird use the symbol T^* for kT/ϵ_0 and $\Omega^{(2.2)*}$ for Ω_v. Bromley and Wilke use $(kT/\epsilon)^{1/2}V/W^2(2)$ for $f_1(kT/\epsilon_0)$. More complete tables of these functions are given in the two references cited.

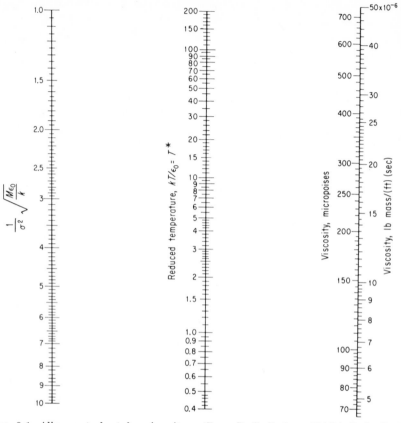

FIG. 9-1. Alignment chart for viscosity. (*From R. S. Brokaw, NASA Tech. Rept. R-81, 1961.*) The group $\sqrt{M\epsilon_0/k}/\sigma^2$ falls between 1 and 10. This range covers almost all cases. However, if $\sqrt{M\epsilon_0/k}/\sigma^2$ is greater than 10, then the same scale is used but the actual value of $\sqrt{M\epsilon_0/k}/\sigma^2$ is divided by 10 and the final viscosity multiplied by 10. Similar, but opposite, statements hold if the group is less than 1.0.

Nonpolar Gases. On the assumption that the Lennard-Jones potential describes adequately the interaction between nonpolar molecules, the collision integral Ω_v in Eq. (9-9) has been calculated and tabulated as a function of T^*, i.e., kT/ϵ_0, by Hirschfelder, Curtiss, and Bird (98); the dependence is shown in Table 9-1. The parameters ϵ_0 (or ϵ_0/k) and σ are the Lennard-Jones potentials discussed in Sec. 2-10 and tabulated in Appendix G. The values in Appendix G have been back-calculated (usually from experimental viscosity data) and are always to be preferred to those estimated by methods described in Sec. 2-10.

Luft and Kharbanda (131) have approximated the relationship between Ω_v and T^* as

$$1/\Omega_v = 0.697(1 + 0.323 \ln T^*) \tag{9-10}$$

but deviations of 1 or 2 per cent are found. More convenient is a nomograph for Eq. (9-9) as given by Brokaw (29) and shown in Fig. 9-1. A similar nomograph was suggested earlier by Bromley and Wilke (30).

Section 2-10 discussed the discrepancies between various sets of values of σ and ϵ_0 as determined by different investigators from the same experimental viscosity data. It was pointed out that these discrepancies were not often serious in viscosity calculations, as there is a compensating effect between σ and ϵ_0. As a case in point, Flynn and Thodos (62) suggest for n-butane the Lennard-Jones parameters $\sigma = 5.869$ A, $\epsilon_0/k = 208°$K, whereas Svehla (see Appendix G) suggests the very different values of 4.730 A and 513.4°K. Figure 9-2 shows the calculated values of the low-pressure n-butane viscosity from Eq. (9-9), using both of these sets of potential parameters (198). The compensation effect is striking, and the ability of this equation to reproduce experimental data is also encouraging.

A number of calculated values of the viscosity obtained from Eq. (9-9), Appendix G, and Table 9-1 are compared with experimental values in Table 9-3. The Lennard-Jones potential was employed in calculating viscosity in the case of those gases listed as nonpolar. In general, errors less than 2 per cent are noted. The error is usually greater if σ and ϵ_0/k are estimated by the methods suggested in Sec. 2-10.

The estimation technique is illustrated in Example 9-1.

Polar Gases. Monchick and Mason (152) have determined the collision integral term of Eq. (9-9) by using the Stockmayer potential discussed in

FIG. 9-2. Comparison of calculated and experimental low-pressure gas viscosity of n-butane.

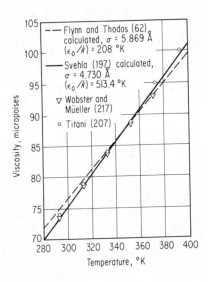

Sec. 3-13.* In that section the tabulation of known Stockmayer potentials is given; that is, σ, ϵ_0/k, and δ. The last parameter allows for the molecular dipole moment μ_p and is defined as

$$\delta = \mu_p^2/2\epsilon_0\sigma^3 \qquad (9-11)$$

To determine the Stockmayer collision integral Ω_v, Table 9-2 should be used.

Table 9-3 shows a few calculated values of polar-gas viscosities calculated from Eq. (9-9), with Tables 3-1 and 9-2. The gases are noted as polar, indicating that the Stockmayer potential was assumed applicable. The errors are again usually less than 2 per cent; no values for σ and ϵ_0 were available for acetic acid. Also it can be noted that the concept "polar" was extended to cover borderline materials such as the ethers, esters, and certain halogenated hydrocarbons.

The method is illustrated in Example 9-2.

Modifications of the Theoretical Method. Most modifications of Eq. (9-9) have employed empirical rules to express σ and ϵ_0 in terms of critical properties. One of the best known is due to Bromley and Wilke (130), who suggested that, for nonpolar gases, ϵ_0/k be replaced by $0.75T_c$ as shown in Eq. (2-46) and σ by $\frac{5}{6}V_c^{1/3}$. The resulting equation then becomes,

$$\mu = [0.00333(MT_c)^{1/2}f_1(1.33T_r)]/V_c^{2/3} \qquad (9-12)$$

where μ = nonpolar gas viscosity, centipoises
M = molecular weight
T_c = critical temperature, °K
V_c = critical volume, cm³/g mole
T_r = reduced temperature, T/T_c
$f_1(1.33T_r)$ = function obtained in Table 9-1 in which kT/ϵ_0 is approximated by $1.33T_r$

Calculated viscosities are shown in Table 9-3 and compared with experimental data. Equation (9-12) was applied to both polar and nonpolar gases, even though it should probably not be used for the latter. Errors averaging around 5 per cent are noted.

This technique of making proportionalities between both ϵ_0/k and σ and critical constants could be extended by using the other rules suggested in Sec. 2-10 for nonpolar gases and Sec. 3-13 for polar gases. Errors of around 2 to 3 per cent would be expected in the calculated viscosities. This method is not pursued further here, as the corresponding-state methods discussed below are more reliable if potential parameters are not available.

---

* Actually their result also contains a correction-factor multiplier to the right-hand side of Eq. (9-9), but this factor is nearly unity.

TABLE 9-2. COLLISION INTEGRALS Ω_v FOR VISCOSITY AS CALCULATED BY
USE OF THE STOCKMAYER POTENTIAL[†]

$$\delta = (\text{dipole moment})^2/2\epsilon_0\sigma^3$$
$$T^* = kT/\epsilon_0$$

T^* \ δ	0‡	0.25	0.50	0.75	1.0	1.5	2.0	2.5
0.1	4.1005	4.266	4.833	5.742	6.729	8.624	10.34	11.89
0.2	3.2626	3.305	3.516	3.914	4.433	5.570	6.637	7.618
0.3	2.8399	2.836	2.936	3.168	3.511	4.329	5.126	5.874
0.4	2.5310	2.522	2.586	2.749	3.004	3.640	4.282	4.895
0.5	2.2837	2.277	2.329	2.460	2.665	3.187	3.727	4.249
0.6	2.0838	2.081	2.130	2.243	2.417	2.862	3.329	3.786
0.7	1.9220	1.924	1.970	2.072	2.225	2.614	3.028	3.435
0.8	1.7902	1.795	1.840	1.934	2.070	2.417	2.788	3.156
0.9	1.6823	1.689	1.733	1.820	1.944	2.258	2.596	2.933
1.0	1.5929	1.601	1.644	1.725	1.838	2.124	2.435	2.746
1.2	1.4551	1.465	1.504	1.574	1.670	1.913	2.181	2.451
1.4	1.3551	1.365	1.400	1.461	1.544	1.754	1.989	2.228
1.6	1.2800	1.289	1.321	1.374	1.447	1.630	1.838	2.053
1.8	1.2219	1.231	1.259	1.306	1.370	1.532	1.718	1.912
2.0	1.1757	1.184	1.209	1.251	1.307	1.451	1.618	1.795
2.5	1.0933	1.100	1.119	1.150	1.193	1.304	1.435	1.578
3.0	1.0388	1.044	1.059	1.083	1.117	1.204	1.310	1.428
3.5	0.99963	1.004	1.016	1.035	1.062	1.133	1.220	1.319
4.0	0.96988	0.9732	0.9830	0.9991	1.021	1.079	1.153	1.236
5.0	0.92676	0.9291	0.9360	0.9473	0.9628	1.005	1.058	1.121
6.0	0.89616	0.8979	0.9030	0.9114	0.9230	0.9545	0.9955	1.044
7.0	0.87272	0.8741	0.8780	0.8845	0.8935	0.9181	0.9505	0.9893
8.0	0.85379	0.8549	0.8580	0.8632	0.8703	0.8901	0.9164	0.9482
9.0	0.83795	0.8388	0.8414	0.8456	0.8515	0.8678	0.8895	0.9160
10.0	0.82435	0.8251	0.8273	0.8308	0.8356	0.8493	0.8676	0.8901
12.0	0.80184	0.8024	0.8039	0.8065	0.8101	0.8201	0.8337	0.8504
14.0	0.78363	0.7840	0.7852	0.7872	0.7899	0.7976	0.8081	0.8212
16.0	0.76834	0.7687	0.7696	0.7712	0.7733	0.7794	0.7878	0.7983
18.0	0.75518	0.7554	0.7562	0.7575	0.7592	0.7642	0.7711	0.7797
20.0	0.74364	0.7438	0.7445	0.7455	0.7470	0.7512	0.7569	0.7642
25.0	0.71982	0.7200	0.7204	0.7211	0.7221	0.7250	0.7289	0.7339
30.0	0.70097	0.7011	0.7014	0.7019	0.7026	0.7047	0.7076	0.7112
35.0	0.68545	0.6855	0.6858	0.6861	0.6867	0.6883	0.6905	0.6932
40.0	0.67232	0.6724	0.6726	0.6728	0.6733	0.6745	0.6762	0.6784
50.0	0.65099	0.6510	0.6512	0.6513	0.6516	0.6524	0.6534	0.6546
75.0	0.61397	0.6141	0.6143	0.6145	0.6147	0.6148	0.6148	0.6147
100.0	0.58870	0.5889	0.5894	0.5900	0.5903	0.5901	0.5895	0.5885

† L. Monchick and E. A. Mason, *J. Chem. Phys.*, **35**:1676 (1961).

‡ The values of Ω_v in this column differ slightly from values in Table 9-1 at low values of T^*.

Example 9-1. Estimate the viscosity of n-hexane gas at low pressure and at 150°C. The experimental value from Table 9-3 is 0.00934 centipoise.

Solution. n-Hexane is a nonpolar gas. From Appendix G, $\sigma = 5.949$ A, $\epsilon_0/k = 399.3$°K. Thus $T^* = kT/\epsilon_0 = (150 + 273)/399.3 = 1.06$. From Table 9-1, $\Omega_v = 1.541$. Then from Eq. (9-9), with $M = 86.2$,

$$\mu = [0.002669\ \sqrt{(423)(86.2)}]/[(5.949)^2(1.541)] = 0.00935 \text{ centipoise}$$
$$\text{Error} = [(0.00935 - 0.00934)/0.00934] \times 100 = +0.1\%$$

Alternatively, from Fig. 9-1 with $\sqrt{M\epsilon_0/k}/\sigma^2 = \sqrt{(86.2)(399.3)}/(5.949)^2 = 5.2$ and $kT/\epsilon_0 = T^* = 1.06$,

$$\mu = 93 \text{ micropoises} = 0.0093 \text{ centipoise}$$

From Eq. (9-12), with $T_c = 507.3$°K, $V_c = 368$ cm^3/g mole,

$$T_r = 423/507.3 = 0.834 \qquad 1.33T_r = 1.10 \qquad f_1(1.33T_r) = 0.6928$$

From Table 9-1, then,

$$\mu = 0.00333\{[\sqrt{(86.2)(507.3)}\ (0.6928)]/(368)^{2/3}\} = 0.00935 \text{ centipoise}$$

Example 9-2. Estimate the viscosity of ethyl alcohol at 150°C and low pressure. The experimental value given in Table 9-3 is 0.01232 centipoise.

Solution. Ethyl alcohol is a polar gas, and the Stockmayer potential should be applicable. From Table 3-1, $\epsilon_0/k = 431$°K, $\sigma = 4.31$ A, $\delta = 0.3$. $T^* = kT/\epsilon_0 = {}^{423}\!/_{431} = 0.981$, and Ω_v from Table 9-2 is 1.63. Thus from Eq. (9-9), with $M = 46.1$

$$\mu = [0.002669\ \sqrt{(46.1)(423)}]/[(4.31)^2(1.63)] = 0.0123 \text{ centipoise}$$
$$\text{Error} = [(0.0123 - 0.0123)/0.0123] \times 100 = 0\%$$

If Eq. (9-12) is used, the calculated value is 0.0117 centipoise and the error is -5 per cent.

Corresponding-state Method. The form of Eq. (9-12) suggests that the dimensionless group $\mu V_c^{2/3}/(MT)^{1/2}$ may be a function only of reduced temperature, and just this type of correlation was proposed by Whalley (214). By eliminating the quantity V_c by Eq. (3-2), the functional grouping becomes

$$\mu\xi = \mu(T_c^{1/6}/M^{1/2}P_c^{2/3}) = f(T_r, Z_c) \qquad (9-13)$$

This type of correlation has been extensively studied by Stiel and Thodos (192, 193, 195) for nonpolar and polar gases, by Flynn and Thodos (63) for hydrocarbons, by Mathur and Thodos (143) for high-temperature gases, dissociated and undissociated, and by Helfand and Rice (93) as expressed in molecular units (that is, ϵ_0/k, σ, etc.), instead of critical properties. Experimental data fitted to Eq. (9-13) have yielded the following equations, which appear to be the best available (193, 194):

Nonpolar gases

$$\mu\xi = (34.0)(10^{-5})T_r^{0.94} \qquad\qquad T_r \le 1.5 \qquad (9\text{-}14)$$
$$\mu\xi = (17.78)(10^{-5})(4.58T_r - 1.67)^{5\!/\!8} \qquad T_r > 1.5 \qquad (9\text{-}15)$$

Polar gases.   Hydrogen-bonding types, $T_r < 2.0$

$$\mu\xi = (7.55T_r - 0.55)(10^{-5})Z_c^{-5\!/\!4} \qquad\qquad (9\text{-}16)$$

Non-hydrogen-bonding types, $T_r < 2.5$

$$\mu\xi = (1.90T_r - 0.29)^{4\!/\!5}(10^{-4})Z_c^{-2\!/\!3} \qquad\qquad (9\text{-}17)$$

In the foregoing equations μ = viscosity, centipoises

$$\xi = T_c^{1\!/\!6}/M^{1\!/\!2}P_c^{2\!/\!3}$$

T_c = critical temperature, °K

P_c = critical pressure, atm

M = molecular weight

T_r = reduced temperature, T/T_c

These simple equations are applicable to all nonpolar and polar gases except hydrogen, helium, fluorine, bromine, and iodine.   Stiel and Thodos (193) present special techniques to calculate viscosities for these gases. Also, although acetic acid is known to exhibit hydrogen bonding, its predicted behavior from Eq. (9-16) is anomalous; probably cyclic dimers are formed, and it had best be considered a polar gas without hydrogen bonds.

Calculated values of viscosity by using these equations are compared with experimental data in Table 9-3 for a few typical gases at various temperatures.   An average error of only 1.8 per cent was found for the nonpolar gases and 3.2 per cent for the polar gases.   The method is illustrated in Example 9-3.

Miscellaneous Methods.   Gambill (74) has reviewed most of the estimation techniques up to 1958 and summarizes the expected errors. Several workers (10, 126) have employed the Sutherland viscosity equation (see Sec. 9-5) as a starting point for their development.   However, when the estimating equations were tested, they were found to be less accurate than those discussed above.

Example 9-3.   Estimate the low-pressure viscosity of toluene at 250°C, using the method of corresponding states.   The experimental value from Table 9-3 is 0.01227 centipoise.

Solution.   From Appendix A, $T_c = 592.0°K$, $P_c = 41.6$ atm, $M = 92.13$.   Since $T_r = (250 + 273)/592 = 0.883$, and as toluene is nonpolar, Eq. (9-14) is to be used.

$$\xi = T_c^{1\!/\!6}/M^{1\!/\!2}P_c^{2\!/\!3} = (592.0)^{1\!/\!6}/[(92.13)^{1\!/\!2}(41.6)^{2\!/\!3}] = 0.0252$$
$$\mu = [(34.0)(10^{-5})(0.883)^{0.94}]/0.0252 = 0.0120 \text{ centipoise}$$
$$\text{Error} = [(0.0120 - 0.01227)/0.01227] \times 100 = -2.2\%$$

TABLE 9-3. COMPARISON BETWEEN CALCULATED AND EXPERIMENTAL VALUES OF
LOW-PRESSURE GAS VISCOSITY
Values of viscosity in centipoises $\times$ 100

Compound	T, °C	Experimental* viscosity	Values calculated by methods of					
			Theoretical Eq. (9-9)†		Bromley and Wilke Eq. (9-12)		Stiel and Thodos Eqs. (9-14) to (9-17)	
			Calc.	% Error‡	Calc.	% Error‡	Calc.	% Error‡
Nonpolar Gases:								
Acetylene..........	20	1.020	1.013	− 0.7	1.013	− 0.7	0.9886	−3.1
	50	1.113	1.111	− 0.2	1.112	− 0.1	1.084	−2.6
	80	1.20	1.208	+ 0.7	1.21	+ 0.8	1.178	−1.8
	120	1.32	1.329	+ 0.7	1.33	+ 0.8	1.303	−1.3
Benzene...........	20	0.746	0.7468	+ 0.1	0.746	0.0	0.7553	+1.2
	77.8	0.870	0.8958	+ 3.0	0.901	+ 3.5	0.8946	+2.8
	150	1.070	1.085	+ 1.4	1.082	+ 1.1	1.067	−0.3
	250	1.311	1.335	+ 1.8	1.338	+ 2.1	1.302	−0.7
n-Butane...........	20	0.739	0.7705	+ 4.3	0.753	+ 1.9	0.7465	+1.0
	60	0.839	0.8763	+ 4.4	0.855	+ 1.9	0.8419	+0.3
	120	0.998	1.037	+ 3.9	1.007	+ 0.9	0.9837	−1.4
1-Butene..........	20	0.761	0.7636	+ 0.3	0.774	+ 1.7	0.7730	+1.6
	60	0.863	0.8676	+ 0.5	0.879	+ 1.8	0.8719	+1.0
	120	1.020	1.013	− 0.7	1.034	+ 1.4	1.019	−0.1
Carbon dioxide.....	−100	0.856	0.8879	+ 3.7	0.879	+ 2.7	0.8933	+4.4
	0	1.370	1.391	+ 1.5	1.391	+ 1.5	1.371	+0.1
	100	1.828	1.843	+ 0.8	1.865	+ 2.0	1.839	+0.6
	300	2.645	2.612	− 1.2	2.694	+ 1.7	2.668	+0.9
	500	3.303	3.261	− 1.3	3.391	+ 2.7	3.341	+1.2
	800	4.135	4.097	− 0.9	4.299	+ 3.5	4.220	+2.1
Carbon disulfide....	100	1.254	1.257	+ 0.2	1.261	+ 0.6	1.308	+4.3
	200	1.595	1.602	+ 0.4	1.597	+ 0.1	1.636	+2.6
	300	1.936	1.930	− 0.3	1.921	− 0.8	1.959	+1.2
Carbon tetrachloride	125	1.326	1.302	− 1.8	1.388	+ 4.6	1.358	+2.4
	200	1.560	1.533	− 1.7	1.647	+ 5.5	1.597	+2.4
	300	1.859	1.829	− 1.6	1.984	+ 6.7	1.913	+2.9
Cyclohexane........	35	0.723	0.7232	0.0	0.721	− 0.2	0.7344	+1.6
	77.8	0.811	0.8209	+ 1.2	0.823	+ 1.5	0.8300	+2.3
	100	0.873	0.8715	− 0.2	0.879	+ 0.7	0.8792	+0.7
	200	1.086	1.089	+ 0.3	1.113	+ 2.5	1.099	+1.2
	300	1.292	1.288	− 0.3	1.338	+ 2.8	1.316	+1.9
Ethane............	20	0.909	0.9251	+ 1.8	0.970	+ 6.7	0.9155	+0.7
	50	0.998	1.013	+ 1.5	1.065	+ 6.7	1.003	+0.5
	100	1.142	1.157	+ 1.3	1.215	+ 5.8	1.149	+0.6
	250	1.526	1.537	+ 0.7	1.630	+ 6.8	1.552	+1.7

TABLE 9-3. COMPARISON BETWEEN CALCULATED AND EXPERIMENTAL VALUES OF
LOW-PRESSURE GAS VISCOSITY (*Continued*)

Compound	T, °C	Experimental* viscosity	Values calculated by methods of					
			Theoretical Eq. (9-9)†		Bromley and Wilke Eq. (9-12)		Stiel and Thodos Eqs. (9-14) to (9-17)	
			Calc.	% Error‡	Calc.	% Error‡	Calc.	% Error‡
Ethylene............	− 80	0.714	0.6596	− 7.6	0.689	− 3.5	0.6701	−6.1
	0	0.945	0.9327	− 1.3	0.970	+ 2.6	0.9282	−1.8
	50	1.106	1.094	− 1.1	1.136	+ 2.7	1.087	−1.7
	150	1.407	1.398	− 0.6	1.442	+ 2.5	1.401	−0.4
	250	1.680	1.669	− 0.7	1.722	+ 2.5	1.710	+1.8
Hexane............	35	0.709	0.6770	− 4.5	0.693	− 2.3	0.6737	−5.0
	77.8	0.795	0.7719	− 2.9	0.793	− 0.3	0.7613	−4.2
	150	0.934	0.9345	+ 0.1	0.935	+ 0.1	0.9077	−2.8
	225	1.098	1.095	− 0.3	1.122	+ 2.2	1.058	−3.6
	300	1.251	1.251	0.0	1.281	+ 2.4	1.207	−3.5
Isobutane..........	20	0.744	0.7404	− 0.5	0.753	+ 1.2	0.7602	+2.2
	60	0.845	0.8442	− 0.1	0.856	+ 1.3	0.8573	+1.5
	120	0.995	0.9933	− 0.2	1.006	+ 1.1	1.002	+0.7
Methane...........	20	1.089	1.097	+ 0.7	1.060	− 2.7	1.086	−0.3
	100	1.331	1.339	+ 0.6	1.292	− 2.9	1.315	−1.2
	200	1.602	1.609	+ 0.4	1.553	− 2.9	1.571	−1.9
	300	1.847	1.853	+ 0.3	1.788	− 3.2	1.805	−2.3
	500	2.265	2.286	+ 0.9	2.197	− 3.0	2.224	−1.8
n-Pentane..........	125	0.917	0.9185	+ 0.2	0.950	+ 3.6	0.9182	+0.1
	175	1.03	1.032	+ 0.2	1.07	+ 3.9	1.026	−0.4
	225	1.14	1.137	− 0.3	1.18	+ 3.5	1.134	−0.5
	300	1.30	1.298	− 0.2	1.34	+ 3.1	1.293	−0.5
Propane............	20	0.806	0.8089	+ 0.4	0.833	+ 3.3	0.8181	+1.5
	60	0.922	0.9133	− 0.9	0.943	+ 2.3	0.9226	+0.7
	125	1.066	1.079	+ 1.2	1.118	+ 4.9	1.091	+2.3
	200	1.246	1.251	+ 0.4	1.309	+ 5.1	1.283	+3.0
	275	1.419	1.414	− 0.4	1.489	+ 4.9	1.474	+3.9
Propylene..........	20	0.843	0.8460	+ 0.4	0.876	+ 3.9	0.8541	+1.3
	50	0.933	0.9313	− 0.2	0.965	+ 3.4	0.9360	+0.3
	150	1.210	1.205	− 0.4	1.245	+ 2.9	1.206	−0.3
	250	1.467	1.466	− 0.1	1.505	+ 2.6	1.472	+0.3
Sulfur dioxide......	10	1.200	1.227	+ 2.3	1.234	+ 2.8	1.215	+1.3
	40	1.350	1.362	+ 0.9	1.366	+ 1.1	1.336	−1.0
	100	1.630	1.619	− 0.7	1.628	− 0.1	1.576	−3.3
	300	2.461	1.435	− 1.1	2.435	− 1.0	2.359	−4.1
	500	3.15	3.132	− 0.6	3.14	− 0.3	3.053	−3.1
	700	3.76	3.762	+ 0.1	3.76	0.0	3.639	−3.2
	900	4.32	4.328	+ 0.2	4.33	+ 0.2	4.173	−3.4

TABLE 9-3. COMPARISON BETWEEN CALCULATED AND EXPERIMENTAL VALUES OF LOW-PRESSURE GAS VISCOSITY (*Continued*)

Compound	T, °C	Experimental* viscosity	Values calculated by methods of					
			Theoretical Eq. (9-9)†		Bromley and Wilke Eq. (9-12)		Stiel and Thodos Eqs. (9-14) to (9-17)	
			Calc.	% Error‡	Calc.	% Error‡	Calc.	% Error‡
Toluene............	60	0.789	0.7701	− 2.4	0.791	+ 0.3	0.7876	−0.2
	150	1.008	0.9763	− 3.1	1.011	+ 0.3	0.9860	−2.2
	250	1.227	1.193	− 2.8	1.247	+ 1.6	1.204	−1.9
Average error.....	......	......	......	1.2	.....	2.4	......	1.8
Polar Gases:								
Acetone	100	0.933	0.9918	+ 6.3	0.979	+ 4.9	0.9917	+6.3
	150	1.075	1.129	+ 5.0	1.100	+ 2.4	1.180	+9.8
	225	1.275	1.336	+ 4.8	1.300	+ 2.0	1.315	+3.1
	325	1.530	1.602	+ 4.7	1.541	+ 0.7	1.560	+2.0
Acetic acid.........	150	1.175	......	......	1.220	+ 3.8	1.215§	+3.4
	250	1.506	......	......	1.510	+ 0.3	1.500§	−0.4
Ammonia..........	0	0.900	0.9332	+ 3.7	0.902	+ 0.2	0.9385	+4.3
	100	1.310	1.278	− 2.4	1.231	− 6.1	1.324	+1.1
	200	1.69	1.618	− 4.3	1.54	− 8.9	1.709	+1.1
	400	2.51	2.259	−10.0	2.10	−16	2.480	−1.2
Chloroform.........	20	1.000	1.003	+ 0.3	1.024	+ 2.4	0.9817	−1.8
	50	1.095	1.110	+ 1.4	1.134	+ 3.5	1.112	+1.6
	100	1.250	1.281	+ 2.5	1.312	+ 5.0	1.269	+1.5
	200	1.585	1.616	+ 2.0	1.665	+ 5.0	1.607	+1.4
	350	2.08	2.087	+ 0.3	2.16	+ 3.7	2.084	+0.2
Dimethyl ether.....	20	0.909	0.8936	− 1.7	0.909	0.0	0.8760	−3.6
	60	1.044	1.019	− 2.4	1.033	− 1.1	0.9949	−4.7
	120	1.228	1.207	− 1.7	1.214	− 1.1	1.167	−5.0
Ethyl acetate.......	125	1.008	1.014	+ 0.6	1.061	+ 5.3	1.048	+4.0
	175	1.139	1.144	+ 0.4	1.192	+ 4.7	1.177	+3.3
	250	1.333	1.333	0.0	1.384	+ 3.8	1.366	+2.5
	325	1.528	1.525	− 0.2	1.570	+ 3.8	1.548	+1.3
Ethyl alcohol.......	110	1.113	1.116	+ 0.3	1.059	− 4.9	1.095	−1.6
	150	1.232	1.233	+ 0.1	1.170	− 5.0	1.222	−0.8
	200	1.374	1.374	0.0	1.306	− 4.9	1.380	+0.4
	300	1.646	1.658	+ 0.7	1.566	− 4.9	1.697	+3.1
Ethyl ether.........	125	0.991	0.9958	+ 0.5	1.037	+ 4.6	1.048	+5.8
	175	1.119	1.092	− 2.4	1.161	+ 3.5	1.174	+4.9
	225	1.239	1.242	+ 0.2	1.286	+ 3.8	1.297	+4.7
	300	1.407	1.416	+ 0.6	1.463	+ 4.0	1.477	+5.0
Isopropyl alcohol....	120	1.030	1.031	+ 0.1	1.024	− 0.6	1.080	+4.9
	160	1.144	1.139	− 0.4	1.127	− 1.5	1.202	+5.1
	220	1.302	1.300	− 0.2	1.280	− 1.7	1.384	+6.3
	300	1.498	1.507	− 0.6	1.474	− 1.6	1.626	+8.5

TABLE 9-3. COMPARISON BETWEEN CALCULATED AND EXPERIMENTAL VALUES OF LOW-PRESSURE GAS VISCOSITY (*Continued*)

Compound	T, °C	Experi-mental* viscosity	Values calculated by methods of					
			Theoretical Eq. (9-9)†		Bromley and Wilke Eq. (9-12)		Stiel and Thodos Eqs. (9-14) to (9-17)	
			Calc.	% Error‡	Calc.	% Error‡	Calc.	% Error‡
Methyl alcohol.....	35	1.013	1.015	+ 0.2	0.890	−12	0.9586	−5.4
	65	1.114	1.119	+ 0.4	0.975	−12	1.065	−4.4
	120	1.290	1.298	+ 0.6	1.140	−12	1.260	−2.3
	160	1.428	1.428	0.0	1.253	−13	1.401	−1.9
	240	1.692	1.689	− 0.2	1.478	−12	1.685	−0.4
	320	1.945	1.942	− 0.2	1.692	−13	1.968	+1.2
Methyl chloride.....	20	1.061	1.067	+ 0.6	1.083	+ 2.1	1.039	−2.1
	50	1.194	1.177	− 1.4	1.193	− 0.1	1.146	−4.0
	80	1.287	1.287	0.0	1.303	+ 1.2	1.251	−2.8
	130	1.471	1.470	− 0.1	1.482	+ 0.7	1.421	−3.4
Methylene chloride..	20	0.985	1.024	+ 4.0	1.034	+ 5.0	1.014	+2.9
	100	1.265	1.307	+ 3.3	1.320	+ 4.3	1.306	+3.2
	200	1.600	1.666	+ 4.1	1.668	+ 4.3	1.612	+0.8
	300	1.925	2.014	+ 4.7	2.002	+ 4.0	1.975	+2.6
n-Propyl alcohol....	125	1.035	1.044	+ 0.9	1.026	− 0.9	1.058	+2.2
	200	1.240	1.244	+ 0.3	1.218	− 1.7	1.279	+3.1
	275	1.440	1.437	− 0.2	1.404	− 2.5	1.500	+4.2
Average error.....				1.7		4.4		3.2

* Experimental values were taken from P. M. Craven and J. D. Lambert, *Proc. Roy. Soc. (London)*, **A205**:439 (1951) and "Landolt-Börnstein Tables," vol. 4, pt. 1, Springer-Verlag OHG, Berlin, 1955.

† For the calculated values from Eq. (9-9), if the Lennard-Jones potentials were not available from Appendix G, they were estimated from Eqs. (2-42) and (2-43).

‡ % Error = [(calculated − experimental)/experimental] × 100.

§ Acetic acid taken as non-hydrogen-bonding.

Recommendations: Viscosities of Pure Gases at Low Pressure. If Lennard-Jones or Stockmayer potential parameters are available from Appendix G or Table 3-1, use Eq. (9-9), with Ω_v determined from Table 9-1 or 9-2. Errors less than 2 per cent are to be expected over a temperature range from near the freezing point to reduced temperatures around 10 or higher. At sufficiently high temperatures, where the gas begins to dissociate, it should be treated as a mixture (see Secs. 9-7 and 9-8) or by special methods; e.g., see Ref. 143.

If potential parameters are not available, use the corresponding-state methods of Stiel and Thodos [Eqs. (9-14) to (9-17)], with critical properties from Appendix A or estimated by methods outlined in Chap. 2. Errors are expected to be 2 to 4 per cent. Hydrogen, helium, fluorine, bromine, and iodine should not be treated by this method.

9-5   Effect of Temperature on Low-pressure Gas Viscosity

Viscosities of low-pressure gases increase with temperature. Viscosity may be said to be proportional to T^n, where n is near unity at low temperatures and approaches the value 0.5, as called for by simple kinetic theory, at very high temperatures (126).

The corresponding-state correlations [Eqs. (9-14) to (9-17)] indicate that, below a reduced temperature of 1.5 to 2, μ is proportional to $T +$ constant for polar materials and to $T^{0.94}$ for nonpolar gases. For reduced temperatures greater than 1.5 to 2, μ is proportional to $T^{0.625} +$ constant. No comparable corresponding-state correlation is available for polar gases at high reduced temperatures.

Similar results are obtained by examining Eq. (9-9). By rearrangement,

$$\mu = K(kT/\epsilon_0)^{\frac{1}{2}}/\Omega_v = \frac{KT^{*\frac{1}{2}}}{\Omega_v} = Kf_1(T^*) \qquad (9\text{-}18)$$

where K is a temperature-independent constant. From Tables 9-1 and 9-2 it can be noted that Ω_v decreases as T^* increases, so that the viscosity exponent on temperature is greater than $\frac{1}{2}$.

If a single value of viscosity is available, it is probably best to extrapolate to other temperatures with Eq. (9-18) and either Tables 9-1 or 9-2, i.e.,

$$\mu_1/\mu_2 = (T_1^*/T_2^*)^{\frac{1}{2}}/(\Omega_{v_1}/\Omega_{v_2}) = f_1(T_2^*)/f_1(T_1^*) \qquad (9\text{-}19)\dagger$$

Values of ϵ_0/k must be available or must be estimated. Appendix G and Table 3-1 list experimental values of ϵ_0/k for nonpolar and polar gases, and estimation techniques are presented in Secs. 2-10 and 3-13. Alternatively, Eqs. (9-14) to (9-17) may be used where ξ is treated as a constant to be determined from the one experimental datum point.

If two or more experimental data points are available, any of the recommended gas-viscosity methods discussed in Sec. 9-4 may be employed and the error adjusted by some weighting technique. Alternatively, the two-constant Sutherland equation has been shown to be highly reliable in correlating viscosity-temperature data (126). In this equation,

$$\mu = bT^{\frac{3}{2}}/(S + T) \qquad (9\text{-}20)$$

† $f_1(T^*)$ functions are shown only in Table 9-1. They may easily be found from values in Table 9-2 by $f_1(T^*) = T^{*\frac{1}{2}}/\Omega_v$.

so that a plot of $T^{3/2}/\mu$ against T should give a straight line with a slope of $1/b$ and an intercept of S/b, the so-called "Sutherland constant."

Various other viscosity-temperature relations, many with three or more undetermined constants, have been suggested (143). Gambill (75) has reviewed most of them, but none is believed more reliable than the rather simple methods presented above.

Recommendations: Estimation of the Variation of Gas Viscosity with Temperature. The temperature variation of low-pressure gases is most easily visualized from the corresponding-state correlations as given in Eqs. (9-14) to (9-17). If a single datum point is available and values are desired at other temperatures, use Eq. (9-19), with ϵ_0/k from Appendix G or Table 3-1 and Ω_v from Table 9-1 or 9-2, depending upon whether the gas is assumed to be nonpolar and characterized by the Lennard-Jones potential or polar and characterized by the Stockmayer potential.

If two or more data points are available, an accurate and simple temperature correlation is the Sutherland equation (9-20).

Example 9-4. The viscosity of carbon dioxide at 1 atm is 0.01370 centipoise at 0°C. Estimate the viscosity at 800°C and 1 atm.

Solution. From Appendix G, $\epsilon_0/k = 195.2$°K. Thus $T^* = kT/\epsilon_0 = 273.2/195.2 = 1.40$ at 0°C and $1,073/195.2 = 5.5$ at 800°C. From Table 9-1, $\Omega_v = 1.353$ at 0°C and 0.912 at 800°C. Substituting in Eq. (9-19),

$$\mu_{800} = (0.01370)[(5.5/1.4)^{1/2}/(0.912/1.353)] = 0.0404 \text{ centipoise}$$

The same result is obtained if the $f_1(T^*)$ values are used in Table 9-1, that is,

$$\mu_{800} = (0.01370)[f_1(T^*_{800})/f_1(T^*_0)] = (0.01370)[(2.58)/(0.874)] = 0.0404 \text{ centipoise}$$

The experimental value at 800°C is 0.0414 centipoise.

Example 9-5. Given the viscosity of carbon dioxide at 1 atm as 0.01370 centipoise at 0°C and 0.0330 at 500°C, what is the estimated value at 800°C?

Solution. At $T = 273$ and 773, the values of $T^{3/2}/\mu$ are 3.29×10^5 and 6.51×10^5. From Eq. (9-20), plotting these values versus T and extrapolating to 1073°K, $T^{3/2}/\mu$ is 8.44×10^5, whence $\mu = 0.0416$ centipoise. The experimental value is 0.0414 centipoise.

9-6   Effect of Pressure on the Viscosity of Pure Gases

The title of this section is something of a misnomer, as it will be shown below that most dense-gas correlations relate viscosity to density rather than to pressure explicitly. If the density is not available, it must be estimated separately by methods outlined in Chap. 3.

There have been many excellent reviews of the methods proposed to estimate or correlate dense-gas viscosities (57, 75, 82, 188, 190). As shown in these reviews, there appears to be no accurate theory upon which to base estimation techniques. For pressures up to a few atmospheres or as low as a few hundredths of an atmosphere, the estimation of viscosity is to be made as indicated in Sec. 9-5. At high pressures, however, the viscosity increases with pressure or density.

Enskog Dense-gas Theory. The Enskog theory, which is treated in detail by Chapman and Cowling (38), was the first dense-gas theory to be developed. Rigid spherical molecules with no intermolecular forces were assumed. The Enskog equation is,

$$\mu/\mu^0 = b_0\rho(1/b_0\rho\chi + 0.80 + 0.761b_0\rho\chi) \tag{9-21}$$

where μ = viscosity, centipoises

μ^0 = low-pressure viscosity at the same temperature, centipoises

b_0 = hard-sphere volume = $\frac{2}{3}\pi N_0\sigma^3$, cm³/g mole

N_0 = Avogadro's number

σ = hard-sphere diameter, A

ρ = molal density g moles/cm³

χ = correction factor accounting for the probability of collisions

This relation, with b_0 and χ suitably evaluated from experimental data (57), has been shown to correlate high-pressure nitrogen data very well, but not argon (145).   The product $b_0\rho\chi$, often called the *Enskog modulus*, can be estimated by a technique suggested by Damasius and Thodos (47). The Enskog method does not appear to provide an accurate basis for dense-gas viscosity prediction. It is, however, instructive to note that the Enskog relation predicts that the ratio μ/μ^0 is a function only of gas density. This conclusion is also reached in many other estimation techniques.

Other more detailed and less easily stated dense-gas theories often arrive at a result which allows a separation of the viscosity into two terms, one accounting for momentum transfer due to intermolecular force fields and the other for momentum transfer to collisions occurring in the absence of such fields. The first can be shown to be more important at high density, while the latter predominates at low density and is primarily dependent on temperature. It has been suggested that the latter is close to the low-pressure viscosity μ^0 discussed in Sec. 9-5 (57), whereupon one may write $\mu - \mu^0 = f(\rho)$.

This type of dense-gas correlation is considerably different from that shown in Eq. (9-21). Both types of dependence have, however, been extensively used in dense-gas viscosity correlations. Starling and Ellington (190) have recently summarized the evidence for and against the above equation, and Giddings and Kobayashi (82) have concluded that there is no theoretical justification for this particular type of expression.

Correlations Based on Residual-viscosity Concepts. The residual viscosity $\mu - \mu^0$ has been correlated with density by numerous investigators (54, 57, 82, 109, 113, 188, 196).   A convenient, general, and rather accurate form of the correlation is given below in Eqs. (9-22) to (9-27):

Nonpolar gases (109)

$$(\mu - \mu^0)\xi = (23.12e^{1.079\rho_r} - 25)(10^{-5}) \qquad 0.3 \le \rho_r \le 2.0 \quad (9\text{-}22)$$
$$(\mu - \mu^0)\xi = (11.0e^{1.584\rho_r} - 11.0)(10^{-5}) \qquad \rho_r < 0.3 \qquad\qquad (9\text{-}23)$$

The correlation presented by Jossi, Stiel, and Thodos actually covers the range $0.1 < \rho_r < 3$, but Eq. (9-22) does not cover the high-density range of ρ_r between 2 and 3. This range is, however, important in correlating liquid viscosities. Equation (9-24), though more complex than Eqs. (9-22) and (9-23), will adequately cover the entire range of ρ_r between 0.1 and 3.

$$[(\mu - \mu^0)\xi + 10^{-4}]^{0.25} = 0.10230 + 0.023364\rho_r + 0.058533\rho_r^2$$
$$- 0.040758\rho_r^3 + 0.0093324\rho_r^4 \quad (9\text{-}24)$$

In these equations, μ = viscosity, centipoises
μ^0 = low-pressure viscosity at the same temperature, centipoises
$\xi = T_c^{1/6}/M^{1/2}P_c^{2/3}$ [see Eqs. (9-14) to (9-17) for dimensions]
ρ_r = reduced density, $\rho/\rho_c = V_c/V$

Equation (9-24) is represented graphically by the lower curve in Fig. 9-3.

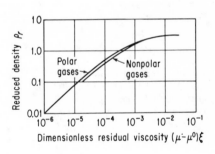

FIG. 9-3. Dense-gas viscosity correlation based on residual-viscosity concept. [*From J. A. Jossi, L. I. Stiel, and G. Thodos, AIChE J.* **8**:59 (1962); *Stiel, L. I., and G. Thodos, AIChE J.,* **10**:275 (1964)]

Polar gases (196)

$$(\mu - \mu^0)\xi = (16.56)(10^{-5})\rho_r^{1.111} \qquad \rho_r \le 0.1 \qquad (9\text{-}25)$$
$$(\mu - \mu^0)\xi = (0.607)(10^{-5})(9.045\rho_r + 0.63)^{1.739} \qquad 0.10 \le \rho_r \le 0.90 \qquad (9\text{-}26)$$
$$\log\,[-\log\,(\mu - \mu^0)\xi] = 0.6439 - 0.1005\rho_r - \Delta \qquad 0.9 \le \rho_r < 2.6 \qquad (9\text{-}27)$$

where $\Delta = \begin{cases} 0, & 0.9 \le \rho_r \le 2.2 \\ (4.75)(10^{-4})(\rho_r^3 - 10.65)^2 & 2.2 < \rho_r < 2.6 \end{cases}$

Also, $(\mu - \mu^0)\xi = 0.00900$ and 0.0250 at $\rho_r = 2.8$ and 3.0, respectively.

The variables are defined under Eq. (9-24) and the correlation is shown as the upper curve in Fig. 9-3.

Discussion. As Fig. 9-3 indicates, this viscosity relationship is very sensitive to density at high densities. In Sec. 9-12, this high-density range of the correlation is applied to liquids to yield an approximate liquid-viscosity correlation.

Brebach and Thodos (26) have applied this type of correlation specifically to the diatomic gases, Shimotake and Thodos (180) to the inert gases, Eakin and Ellington (54) to the light hydrocarbons, and Kestin and Moszynski (113) to steam.

It is difficult to assess the accuracy of the correlations represented by Eqs. (9-22) to (9-27), as they have not been extensively tested. Errors to be expected are probably less than 10 to 15 per cent. To indicate the type of errors found, Table 9-4 compares calculated and experimental dense-gas viscosity values for a few materials. The method is illustrated by Example 9-6.

Example 9-6. Estimate the viscosity of ammonia at 150°C and 272 atm. The experimental value is 0.0417 centipoise (180).

Solution. Ammonia is a polar gas, and Eqs. (9-25) to (9-27) apply. First, however, the reduced density must be determined. From Appendix A, $T_c = 405.6°K$, $P_c = 111.5$ atm, $V_c = 72.5$ cm^3/g mole, $Z_c = 0.242$, and $\omega = 0.250$. Thus $T_r = 423/405.6 = 1.04$, $P_r = 272/111.5 = 2.44$. If the compressibility factor Z is determined from Pitzer's correlation [Eq. (3-15)], with Z^0 and Z^1 determined from Figs. 3-5 and 3-6 as $Z^0 = 0.397$, $Z^1 = -0.09$, then $Z = Z^0 + \omega Z^1 = 0.397 + (0.250)(-0.09) = 0.374$, and

$$\rho_r = \rho/\rho_c = \rho V_c = PV_c/ZRT = [(272)(72.5)]/(0.374)(82.07)(423) = 1.53$$

Thus Eq. (9-27) should be used with $\Delta = 0$. Next ξ is determined as $T_c^{1/6}/M^{1/2}P_c^{2/3} = (405.6)^{1/6}/(17.0)^{1/2}(111.5)^{2/3} = 0.0285$. μ^0 is determined from Eq. (9-16) as 0.0152 centipoise. Using these values in Eq. (9-27),

$$\log [- \log (\mu - 0.0152)(0.0285)] = 0.6439 - 0.1005(1.53)$$
$$\mu = 0.0438 \text{ centipoise}$$
$$\text{Error} = [(0.0438 - 0.0417)/0.0417] \times 100 = +5.0\%$$

It is interesting to note that, if the experimental value of reduced density were used, $\rho_r = 1.775$ (180), then μ(calc.) = 0.0573 centipoise and the error becomes +27 per cent. Clearly in this reduced density range the estimated value of viscosity is sensitive to the density value chosen.

Correlations Based on Viscosity Ratios. A very common dense-gas-viscosity correlating technique assumes that the ratio μ/μ^0, μ/μ_c^0, or μ/μ_c may be correlated in terms of reduced properties. μ^0 is the low-pressure viscosity at the system temperature, μ_c^0 is the low-pressure viscosity at the critical temperature, and μ_c is the viscosity at the critical point.

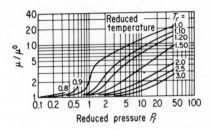

FIG. 9-4. μ/μ^0 as a function of P_r and T_r.

Comings, Mayland, and Egly (41–43) were the first to suggest the relationship

$$\mu/\mu^0 = f(P_r, T_r) \qquad (9\text{-}28)$$

where μ = viscosity, centipoises

μ^0 = viscosity at low pressure at the system temperature, centipoises

$P_r = P/P_c$, reduced pressure

$T_r = T/T_c$, reduced temperature

A fair correlation was obtained, the deviations of the data being less than 20 per cent.

Uyehara and Watson (209) modified this approach by using μ/μ_c instead of μ/μ^0. They listed a number of values for μ_c for use with the correlation obtained. Bromley and Wilke (30) rearranged the Uyehara and Watson correlation, putting it in the form of Eq. (9-28), since values of μ^0 are generally more available than those of μ_c. Their result is a graph relating μ/μ^0 to T_r and P_r, similar to the earlier correlation of Comings, Mayland, and Egly. Carr, Parent, and Peck (36) have extended this type of correlation to higher values of P_r.

Figure 9-4 summarizes the results of these workers in the form of a graph of μ/μ^0 versus P_r, with T_r as a parameter. It is based primarily on Bromley and Wilke and on Carr, Parent, and Peck, who agree fairly well in the range in which they overlap. Because high-pressure-gas viscosity data are meager and often questionable, Fig. 9-4 is probably not generally reliable to better than 10 to 20 per cent and may be seriously in error in the region of the critical.

It is evident that μ/μ^0 varies rapidly with temperature near the critical, and the type of correlation represented by Fig. 9-4 is unreliable in this region. Grunberg and Nissan (87) attempt to get around this difficulty by correlating μ/μ^0 as a function of ρ_r and T_r. Their result is represented by the nomograph of Fig. 9-5.

μ/μ_c^0 correlated as a function of density has been used for the inert gases (180) and for the diatomic gases (26), and similar correlations were presented for μ/μ_c for many diverse gases (192). For the latter type of correlation (which is similar to the Uyehara and Watson method men-

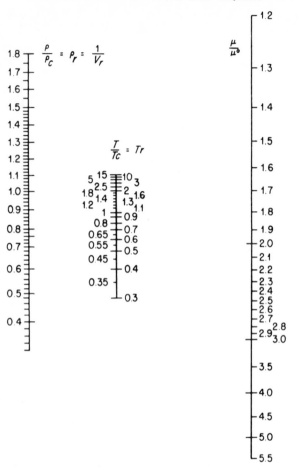

FIG. 9-5. Density correction to gaseous viscosity. [*From L. Grunberg and A. H. Nissan, Ind. Eng. Chem.,* **42**:886 (1950).]

tioned earlier), the critical viscosity must be known or estimated. For nonpolar gases it has been suggested (126) that

$$\mu_c \xi = (77.0)(10^{-5}) \tag{9-29}$$

Although only an approximation, this relation reduces to Eqs. (9-14) and (9-22) for $\mu = \mu_c$, $\mu^0 = \mu_c^0$, $\rho_r = 1$, $T_r = 1$.

Other dense-gas viscosity correlations based upon μ/μ^0 (9, 40, 146, 212) do not show any real advantage over the methods discussed above. However, a similar correlation by Coremans and Beenakker (44) has been found to be quite accurate for many low-molecular-weight gases and shows promise of being useful for other gases. This correlation may be expressed as

$$\mu/\mu^0 = 1 + (0.55\rho^* + 0.96\rho^{*2} + 0.61\rho^{*3})T^{*(-0.59)} \qquad (9\text{-}30)$$

where μ = viscosity, centipoises

μ^0 = low-pressure viscosity at the same temperature, centipoises

$T^* = kT/\epsilon_0$, where ϵ_0/k is the Lennard-Jones potential parameter (see Sec. 2-10 and Appendix G)

$\rho^* = \rho b_0$, with ρ in g moles/cm³ and b_0 the hard-sphere volume, $\frac{2}{3}\pi N_0\sigma^3$; b_0 values are tabulated in Appendix G

Table 9-4 shows a few dense-gas viscosities calculated from Eq. (9-30); when these were compared with experimental data, errors were found to be variable with best agreement for simple nonpolar molecules. The method is illustrated in Example 9-7.

Example 9-7. Estimate the viscosity of propane at 6,000 psia (408 atm) and 275°F (408°K) by Coremans and Beenakker's method. The experimental value is 0.0800 centipoise (13).

Solution. From Appendix G, $b_0 = 169.2$ cm³/g mole, and $\epsilon_0/k = 237.1°$K. To estimate ρ, use Pitzer's method [Eq. (3-15)]. Appendix A shows $T_c = 369.9°$K, $P_c = 42.0$ atm, $\omega = 0.152$. Thus $T_r = 408/369.9 = 1.10$, $P_r = 408/42.0 = 9.72$. From Figs. 3-5 and 3-6, $Z^0 = 1.15$, $Z^1 = -0.30$, whence

$$Z = Z^0 + \omega Z^1 = 1.15 + (0.152)(-0.30) = 1.10$$

and

$$\rho = P/ZRT = 408/[(1.10)(82.07)(408)] = 0.011 \text{ g mole/cm}^3$$
$$\rho^* = \rho b_0 = (169.2)(0.011) = 1.87$$
$$T^* = kT/\epsilon_0 = 408/237.1 = 1.72$$

μ^0 is estimated from Eq. (9-9) with Table 9-1 to be 0.011 centipoise. Then, from Eq. (9-30),

$$\mu/0.011 = 1 + [(0.55)(1.87) + (0.96)(1.87)^2 + (0.61)(1.87)^3](1.72)^{-0.59}$$
$$\mu = 0.078 \text{ centipoise}$$
$$\text{Error} = [(0.078 - 0.080)/0.080] \times 100 = -2.5\%$$

Recommendations: Viscosity of Gases at Elevated Pressure. A quick, approximate estimate of the ratio μ/μ^0 may be obtained from Figures 9-4 or 9-5 from reduced temperature and pressure or density. μ^0, the low-pressure viscosity, may be estimated by methods described in Sec. 9-4.

A more accurate estimation may be made by means of Eqs. (9-22) to (9-27) or Eq. (9-30). Both methods require knowledge of the gas density, but the former is based upon critical properties, whereas the latter is based on Lennard-Jones potential parameters. Both appear to yield comparable errors, as shown in Table 9-4. Equations (9-22) to (9-27) have been more extensively tested with complex molecules.

TABLE 9-4. COMPARISON BETWEEN CALCULATED AND EXPERIMENTAL DENSE-GAS VISCOSITIES

Compound	T, °C	P, atm	μ exp., centipoise	Ref.	ρ_r reduced density	Coremans and Beenakker		Jossi, Stiel, and Thodos			
						μ calc., centipoise	% Error*	μ calc., centipoise	Eq. used to calc.	μ° centipoise, calc. by	% Error*
Ammonia..........	171.1	13.6	0.0157	33	0.0279	0.0154	− 2.2	0.0161	(9-25)	0.0160 by (9-16)	+ 2.5
		40.8	0.0157		0.0898	0.0156	− 0.8	0.0161	(9-25)		+ 2.2
		68.0	0.0162		0.1622	0.0160	− 1.0	0.0167	(9-26)		+ 3.7
		136.1	0.0197		0.4517	0.0179	− 9.1	0.0191	(9-26)		− 3.0
		204.1	0.0317		0.9949	0.0243	−23	0.0271	(9-27)		−14
		340.2	0.0500		2.218	0.0572	+14	0.0972	(9-27)		+94
n-Butane......	171.1	6.8	0.0113	51	0.050	0.0114	+ 0.9	0.0113	(9-23)	0.0110 by (9-14)	+ 0.2
		34.0	0.0134		0.355	0.0129	− 3.7	0.0138	(9-22)		+ 3.1
		68.0	0.0405		1.528	0.0274	−32	0.0407	(9-22)		+ 0.5
		340.2	0.0938		2.203	0.0447	−52	0.0834	(9-24)		−11
		680.5	0.1325		2.380	0.0507	−62	0.110	(9-24)		−17
Carbon dioxide......	50	41.2	0.0170	114	0.1786	0.0173	+ 1.5	0.0128	(9-23)	0.0112 by (9-14)	−25
		70.0	0.0190		0.3764	0.0196	+ 3.0	0.0155	(9-22)		−18
		89.9	0.0237		0.6304	0.0238	+ 0.5	0.0204	(9 22)		−14
		100.2	0.0295		0.8631	0.0294	− 0.3	0.0263	(9-22)		−11
		116.7	0.0425		1.229	0.0423	− 0.5	0.0389	(9-22)		− 8.4

TABLE 9-4. COMPARISON BETWEEN CALCULATED AND EXPERIMENTAL DENSE-GAS VISCOSITIES (*Continued*)

Compound	T, °C	P, atm	μ exp., centipoise	Ref.	ρ_r reduced density	Coremans and Beenakker		Jossi, Stiel, and Thodos			
						μ calc., centipoise	% Error*	μ calc., centipoise	Eq. used to calc.	μ° centipoise, calc. by	% Error*
Nitrogen........	25	35.0	0.0185	170	0.1293	0.0181	− 2.2	0.0180	(9-23)	0.0174 by (9-15)	− 2.5
		69.0	0.0190		0.2547	0.0187	− 1.6	0.0188	(9-23)		− 1.4
		137.1	0.0208		0.4957	0.0205	− 1.7	0.0210	(9-22)		+ 0.7
		341.2	0.0286		1.0627	0.0283	− 1.0	0.0292	(9-22)		+ 1.9
		681.5	0.0415		1.5680	0.0412	− 0.8	0.0421	(9-22)		+ 1.4
Sulfur dioxide........	200	18.0	0.0228	180	0.0529	0.0206	− 9.8	0.0122	(9-25)	0.0118 by (9-17)	−47
		52.1	0.0250		0.1826	0.0216	−13	0.0132	(9-26)		−47
		69.1	0.0263		0.2594	0.0229	−13	0.0140	(9-26)		−47
		137.1	0.0346		0.9779	0.0366	+ 6.0	0.0281	(9-27)		−19
		205.2	0.0565		1.6265	0.0644	+14	0.0621	(9-27)		+ 9.9
Av. error........	......	......	......	...	......	......	10	......	......	......	15

* Per cent error = [(calc. − exp.)/exp.] × 100.

9-7   Viscosities of Gas Mixtures at Low Pressure

The viscosities of binary gas mixtures are usually not linear in composition, and mixture viscosities are often larger than predicted by a mole-fraction average. Such an observation reflects the greater "persistence" of the heavier molecule in a collision (193). Viscosity maxima are, however, not uncommon, the maximum being greater than the value for either pure component. No experimental cases of a viscosity minimum have been reported. The occurrence of a viscosity maximum has been studied in detail (99, 171), and it appears that such maxima are most likely to occur in a mixture of polar and nonpolar gases of quite different molecular weights when the viscosities of the pure components are about equal.

The extension of the rigorous kinetic theory of Chapman and Enskog may be employed to express the viscosity of a low-pressure multicomponent gas mixture (19, 38, 98). The expressions are quite complicated and consist of the ratio of two determinants which contain terms involving mole fractions, molecular weights, pure-component viscosities, temperature, and various collision integrals. For a pure component, the determinant ratio collapses to Eq. (9-9). In general, this rigorous equation has been expanded in an approximate-series form, and various correction terms have been discussed (28, 140, 176, 177). For a n-component mixture at low pressures, the kinetic-theory result may be approximated as follows, second-order effects being neglected:

$$\mu_m = \sum_{i=1}^{n} \mu_i / [1 + \sum_{\substack{j=1 \\ j \neq i}}^{n} \phi_{ij}(y_j/y_i)] \qquad (9\text{-}31)$$

where
$$\phi_{ij} = \tfrac{6}{5} A_{ij}^*(RT/PM_i)(\mu_i/D_{ij}) \qquad (9\text{-}32)$$

and where $A_{ij}^* = \Omega_{v_{ij}}/\Omega_{D_{ij}}$

R = gas constant

T = temperature, °K

P = pressure, atm

M_i = molecular weight of i

$\Omega_{v_{ij}}$ = collision integral for viscosity as tabulated in either Table 9-1 or Table 9-2 for a mixture of components i and j

$\Omega_{D_{ij}}$ = collision integral for diffusion as tabulated in Table 11-1 for a mixture of i and j

To obtain the ij collision integrals, values of $\epsilon_{0_{ij}}$ must be obtained; usually these are estimated by means of Eq. (7-16). A_{ij}^* is a number close to unity and is often about 1.1 (28). However, if A_{ji}^* is called a constant and Eq. (9-32) rearranged,

$$\phi_{ij} = \tfrac{6}{5}A_{ij}^*(\mu_i/\rho_i D_{ij}) \qquad (9\text{-}33)$$

methods of estimating D_{ij} are given in Chap. 11.

An evaluation of experimental data showed that the group $\tfrac{6}{5}A_{ij}^*$ was close to 1.385 (32) [note that $(1.1)(\tfrac{6}{5}) = 1.32$], so that as an approximation

$$\phi_{ij} = 1.385(\mu_i/\rho_i D_{ij}) \qquad (9\text{-}34)$$

Ranz and Brodowsky (165) present an excellent summary of the development of mixture viscosity equations.

Wilke Estimation Method. Wilke (215) greatly increased the ease of application of Eq. (9-31) by approximating the diffusion coefficient from Sutherland's kinetic-theory model, to yield,

$$\phi_{ij} = [1 + (\mu_i/\mu_j)^{1/2}(M_j/M_i)^{1/4}]^2/\{\sqrt{8}\,[1 + (M_i/M_j)]^{1/2}\} \qquad (9\text{-}35)$$

ϕ_{ji} is found by interchanging subscripts or by

$$\phi_{ji} = (\mu_j/\mu_i)(M_i/M_j)\phi_{ij} \qquad (9\text{-}36)$$

This expression of ϕ, which is now based on rather tenuous theoretical grounds, is the best known and one of the most accurate methods for the estimation of viscosities of gas mixtures. For a binary system of 1 and 2 the equations become

$$\mu_m = \mu_1/[1 + (y_2/y_1)\phi_{12}] + \mu_2/[1 + (y_1/y_2)\phi_{21}] \qquad (9\text{-}37)$$

where μ_m = viscosity of mixture at low pressure, centipoises

$\mu_1,\ \mu_2$ = low-pressure viscosity of pure components, centipoises

$y_1,\ y_2$ = mole fractions

$\phi_{12} = [1 + (\mu_1/\mu_2)^{1/2}(M_2/M_1)^{1/4}]^2/[\sqrt{8}\,(1 + M_1/M_2)^{1/2}]$

$\phi_{21} = [1 + (\mu_2/\mu_1)^{1/2}(M_1/M_2)^{1/4}]^2/[\sqrt{8}\,(1 + M_2/M_1)^{1/2}]$

$\qquad\qquad = \phi_{12}(\mu_2/\mu_1)(M_1/M_2)$

The ϕ factors may be conveniently determined from the nomograph developed by Brokaw (29) and shown in Fig. 9-6.

Equation (9-31), with ϕ given by (9-35), has been extensively tested. Wilke (215) compared calculated values with data on 17 binary systems and reports an average deviation of less than 1 per cent; several cases in which μ_m passed through a maximum were included. This equation has been discussed by others (30, 39, 46, 80, 165, 174, 175, 178, 219). Even for mixtures of He with A at temperatures up to 15,000°K, Amdur and

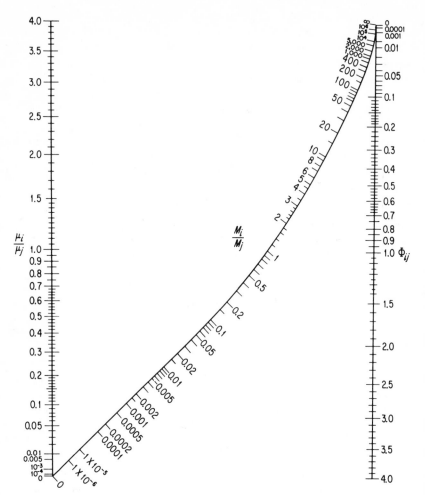

FIG. 9-6. Alignment chart for Φ_{ij} from viscosity.   (*From R. S. Brokaw, NASA Tech. Rept.* R-81, 1961.)

Mason (4) found deviations of less than 4 per cent between values calculated from Wilke's equation and those calculated from more rigorous theory; slightly larger deviations were found for mixtures of H and H_2 in frozen equilibrium at high temperatures (211).   Cheung (39) compared Wilke's equation with data on 20 binary systems and 9 ternary systems and found average errors of 2.0 and 1.6 per cent.   Wilke's equation has proved reliable even when tested with binary polar-polar gas mixtures such as *n*-butanol with methyl, ethyl, and propyl alcohols (169). Table 9-5 illustrates the fit of the equation for three low-pressure gas mixtures, methane-propane, sulfur hexafluoride–carbon tetrachloride, and nitrogen–carbon dioxide. The errors noted are typical; i.e., usually they are less than 1 per cent but may range up to 3 to 4 per cent in some cases. Wilke's method may, however, lead to predicted mixture viscosities greater than experimental for mixtures containing hydrogen or helium with a heavier gas; the mixture H_2-N_2 is a case in point. For this mixture, predicted values may be as much as 50 per cent greater than those found experimentally.

Example 9-8. Estimate the viscosity of a mixture of methane and n-butane containing 70 mole per cent of the former at 1 atm and 100°F.

Solution. Assume the viscosities of the pure components to be unknown. From Eq. (9-9) with Table 9-1 and Appendix G, as illustrated in Example 9-1, μ(methane) = 0.0155 and μ(n-butane) = 0.00786 centipoise. To apply Eq. (9-31) or in this case (9-37) with 1 as methane and 2 as n-butane when $M_1 = 16.04$, $M_2 = 58.12$,

$$\phi_{12} = [1 + (0.0115/0.00786)^{1/2}(58.12/16.04)^{1/4}]^2/[\sqrt{8}\,(1 + 16.04/58.12)^{1/2}] = 2.233$$
$$\phi_{21} = 2.233(0.00786/0.0115)(16.04/58.12) = 0.420$$

(Similar results are obtained from Fig. 9-6.) Then, from Eq. (9-37),

$$\mu_m = 0.0115/[1 + (0.3/0.7)(2.233)] + 0.00786/[1 + (0.7/0.3)(0.420)]$$
$$= 0.00987 \text{ centipoise}$$

The experimental value is 0.00982 centipoise (50).

$$\text{Error} = [(0.00987 - 0.00982)/0.00982] \times 100 = +0.5\%$$

Herning and Zipperer Estimation Method. This simple rule (95) is discussed by Gambill (76) and Godridge (85), who indicate that it is often accurate to within 3 per cent except for hydrogen-rich mixtures.

$$\mu_m = \left[\sum_{i=1} y_i\mu_i(M_i)^{0.5}\right] / \left[\sum_{i=1} y_i(M_i)^{0.5}\right] \qquad (9\text{-}38)$$

As written, Eq. (9-38) cannot be used for mixtures exhibiting maxima in the viscosity-composition curve. Calculated values are compared with experimental data for several mixtures in Table 9-5. Surprisingly low errors were found in this test. A similar equation has been studied by Carr (34) and Eakin (57). The method is illustrated in Example 9-9.

Example 9-9. Repeat Example 9-8, using the method of Herning and Zipperer.

Solution. As before, letting 1 be methane and 2 be n-butane, and $y_1 = 0.7$, $y_2 = 0.3$, $\mu_1 = 0.0115$ centipoise, $\mu_2 = 0.00786$ centipoise, $M_1 = 16.04$, $M_2 = 58.12$, from Eq. (9-38),

$$\mu_m = [(0.7)(0.0115)(16.04)^{1/2} + (0.3)(0.00786)(58.12)^{1/2}]/[(0.7)(16.04)^{1/2}$$
$$+ (0.3)(58.12)^{1/2}] = 0.00987 \text{ centipoise}$$
$$\text{Error} = [(0.00987 - 0.00982)/0.00982] \times 100 = +0.5\%$$

Dean and Stiel Estimation Method. In a somewhat different approach, Dean and Stiel (49) suggested that Eqs. (9-14) and (9-15) might be applicable to low-pressure gas mixtures if, in evaluating ξ, suitable pseudocritical constants were used. After a careful study of low-pressure data, it was recommended that Eqs. (9-14) and (9-15) be modified slightly to give

$$\mu_m \xi_m = (34.0)(10^{-5}) T_r^{\,8\!/\!9} \qquad\qquad T_r \leq 1.5 \qquad (9\text{-}39)$$

$$\mu_m \xi_m = (166.8)(10^{-5})(0.1338 T_r - 0.0932)^{5\!/\!9} \qquad T_r > 1.5 \qquad (9\text{-}40)$$

where
$$\xi_m = T_{c_m}^{1\!/\!6} \Big/ \Big[\Big(\sum_i y_i M_i \Big)^{1\!/\!2} P_{c_m}^{2\!/\!3} \Big]$$

T_{c_m} and P_{c_m} are pseudocritical values and are to be determined from the modified Prausnitz and Gunn rule [Eqs. (9-43) to (9-46)] and Sec. 7-9.

Dean and Stiel tested Eqs. (9-39) and (9-40) on 22 binary low-pressure nonpolar gas mixtures containing monatomic and diatomic gases, hydrocarbons, and carbon dioxide. With 339 data points, Eqs. (9-39) and (9-40), yielded an average error of 1.7 per cent. Larger errors were found if Kay's or Joffe and Stewart, Burkhardt, and Voo's pseudocritical rules (see Sec. 7-9) were used. For this same data set, Wilke's method yielded an error of 1.0 per cent and that of Herning and Zipperer 1.6 per cent. Similar errors were found in testing with multicomponent mixtures.

Equations (9-39) and (9-40) are applicable only to nonpolar low-pressure gas mixtures which do not contain hydrogen or helium. Unlike the other mixture rules presented earlier, there is no built-in mechanism to force the pure-component viscosities to be predicted exactly. That is, if pure-component values are available, there is no way to take advantage of such data. A few calculated values are compared with experimental data in Table 9-5, and the method is illustrated in Example 9-10.

Example 9-10. Repeat Example 9-8 using the method of Dean and Stiel.
Solution. As before, with methane as component 1 and n-butane as component 2, from Appendix A, $T_{c_1} = 190.7°K$, $T_{c_2} = 425.2°K$, $V_{c_1} = 99.5$ cm^3/g mole, $V_{c_2} = 255$ cm^3/g mole, $Z_{c_1} = 0.290$, and $Z_{c_2} = 0.274$.
Using modified Prausnitz and Gunn pseudocritical rules,

$$T_{c_m} = y_1 T_{c_1} + y_2 T_{c_2} = (0.7)(190.7) + (0.3)(425.2) = 261°K$$
$$V_{c_m} = y_1 V_{c_1} + y_2 V_{c_2} = (0.7)(99.5) + (0.3)(255) = 146.1 \text{ cm}^3/\text{g mole}$$
$$Z_{c_m} = y_1 Z_{c_1} + y_2 Z_{c_2} = (0.7)(0.290) + (0.3)(0.274) = 0.285$$
$$P_{c_m} = Z_{c_m} R T_{c_m} / V_{c_m} = [(0.285)(82.06)(261)]/(146.1) = 41.8 \text{ atm}$$
$$T = 100°F = 311°K \qquad T_r = {}^{311}\!/\!{}_{261} = 1.19$$

Thus Eq. (9-39) is to be used.

$$\xi_m = T_{c_m}^{1\!/\!6} / [(y_1 M_1 + y_2 M_2)^{1\!/\!2} P_{c_m}^{2\!/\!3}]$$
$$= 261^{1\!/\!6} / \{[(0.7)(16.04) + (0.3)(58.12)]^{1\!/\!2}(41.8)^{2\!/\!3}\} = 0.0394$$

and

$$\mu_m(0.0394) = (34.0)(10^{-5})(1.19)^{3/9} = 0.0101 \text{ centipoise}$$
$$\text{Error} = [(0.0101 - 0.00982)/0.00982] \times 100 = +3.0\%$$

Other Methods to Estimate Low-pressure Gas-mixture Viscosity. A number of other methods of estimating the viscosity of a gas mixture at low pressures have been suggested (76, 82). Strunk et al. (196a) use Eq. (9-9) and define rules to determine Lennard-Jones potential parameters for mixtures. Francis (64) proposes Eq. (9-31), with ϕ_{ij} given by an expression very similar to Wilke's form [Eq. (9-35)], except that in both the numerator and denominator there appears the ratio of collision

TABLE 9-5. COMPARISON BETWEEN CALCULATED AND EXPERIMENTAL
GAS-MIXTURE VISCOSITIES
Viscosity values in centipoise. Pressures are near atmospheric

System	T, °C	Mole fraction first component	Experimental viscosity μ_m	Ref.	Viscosity calculated by method of					
					Wilke		Herning and Zipperer		Dean and Stiel	
					μ_m	% Error*	μ_m	% Error*	μ_m	% Error*
Methane-propane....	25	0	0.0081	16					0.00841	+ 3.1
		0.2	0.0085		0.00847	−0.4	0.00848	−0.2	0.00883	+ 3.9
		0.4	0.00899		0.00891	−0.9	0.00893	−0.7	0.00929	+ 3.3
		0.6	0.0095		0.00946	−0.4	0.00948	−0.2	0.00979	+ 3.0
		0.8	0.0102		0.01014	−0.6	0.01015	−0.5	0.0103	+ 1.0
		1.0	0.0110						0.0108	− 1.8
	225	0	0.0131	16					0.0133	+ 1.5
		0.2	0.0136		0.0136	0	0.0136	0	0.0139	+ 2.1
		0.4	0.0142		0.0142	0	0.0141	−0.7	0.0147	+ 3.5
		0.6	0.0149		0.0149	0	0.0148	−0.6	0.0155	+ 4.0
		0.8	0.0157		0.0157	0	0.0157	0	0.0162	+ 3.3
		1.0	0.0167						0.0167	0
Sulfur hexafluoride–carbon tetrachloride	30	0	0.01767	166					0.01992	+12.7
		0.246	0.01643		0.01718	+4.6	0.01715	+4.4	0.01716	+ 4.4
		0.509	0.01615		0.01670	+3.4	0.01666	+3.2	0.01711	+ 5.9
		0.743	0.01599		0.01630	+1.9	0.01627	+1.8	0.01690	+ 5.7
		1.0	0.01590						0.01673	+ 5.2
Nitrogen–carbon dioxide	20	0	0.01466	112					0.01469	+ 0.2
		0.2130	0.01535		0.01516	−1.3	0.01518	−1.1	0.01506	− 1.9
		0.3432	0.01571		0.01548	−1.5	0.01552	−1.2	0.01533	− 2.4
		0.4946	0.01618		0.01590	−1.8	0.01594	−1.5	0.01570	− 3.0
		0.6248	0.01670		0.01628	−2.5	0.01633	−2.2	0.01595	− 4.5
		0.7667	0.01721		0.01674	−2.8	0.01678	−2.5	0.01663	− 3.4
		1.0	0.01758						0.01756	− 0.1

* Per cent error = [(cal. − exp.)/exp.] × 100.

integrals for the pure components and for the interaction collision integral $\Omega_{v_{ij}}$ defined in terms of $\epsilon_{0_{ij}}$ [see Eq. (7-16)]. Excellent results are claimed by Francis for mixtures of components differing widely in molecular weight. Mason and Monchick (141) have applied the rigorous kinetic theory to calculate viscosities of low-pressure polar-nonpolar gas mixtures and obtained excellent agreement between calculated and experimental values. For the polar component, Stockmayer potential parameters were used, while, for the nonpolar component and all mixture properties, the Lennard-Jones potential parameters were chosen.

Recommendations: Viscosities of Gas Mixtures at Low Pressures. Seldom in this book have there been such excellent theoretical and accurate relations to determine a property as in this case of gas-mixture viscosities. However, these rigorous equations have not been presented; Eq. (9-31) is only an approximation to the rigorous form discussed in detail in Ref. 98. The Wilke form of this approximation is much easier to employ and is almost equal in accuracy to the rigorous form. It is, therefore, the estimation technique recommended for low-pressure gas-mixture viscosities. There are other methods of comparable accuracy [see especially (64) and (141)], but the data required for Wilke's method are more readily available and it has been found reliable in almost all cases in which it has been used.

9-8 Viscosities of Gas Mixtures at High Pressures

Estimation of high-pressure gas-mixture viscosities is possible by a number of techniques (35, 76). The most accurate method at present appears to be a modification of the residual-viscosity technique discussed in Sec. 9-6. Two recent papers discuss this particular method (49, 82), and both have presented correlations of the form of Eqs. (9-22) to (9-24),

$$(\mu_m - \mu_m{}^0)\xi_m = f(\rho_{r_m}) \tag{9-41}$$

In particular, Dean and Stiel express Eq. (9-41) explicitly as

$$(\mu_m - \mu_m{}^0)\xi_m = (10.8)(10^{-5})(e^{1.439\rho_{rm}} - e^{-1.111\rho_{rm}{}^{1.858}}) \tag{9-42}$$

where μ_m = high-pressure mixture viscosity, centipoises
    $\mu_m{}^0$ = low-pressure mixture viscosity, centipoises
    ρ_{r_m} = pseudoreduced mixture density, ρ_m/ρ_{c_m}
    ρ_m = mixture density, g moles/cm^3
    ρ_{c_m} = pseudocritical mixture density, g moles/cm^3
       = $P_{c_m}/Z_{c_m}RT_{c_m}$
    ξ_m = $T_{c_m}^{1/6}/M_m^{1/2}P_{c_m}^{2/3}$

The mixture molecular weight M_m is, of course, a mole-fraction average. The pseudocritical mixture parameters Z_{c_m}, T_{c_m}, and P_{c_m} must be calculated from some assumed pseudocritical-constant rule. After some study and comparison between calculated and experimental results, Dean and Stiel chose the modified Prausnitz and Gunn rules (Sec. 7-9),

$$T_{c_m} = \sum_i y_i T_{c_i} \tag{9-43}$$

$$Z_{c_m} = \sum_i y_i Z_{c_i} \tag{9-44}$$

$$V_{c_m} = \sum_i y_i V_{c_i} \tag{9-45}$$

$$P_{c_m} = Z_{c_m} R T_{c_m} / V_{c_m} \tag{9-46}$$

These pseudocritical values are then used to calculate ρ_{c_m} and ξ_m.

Equation (9-42) is to be used only for nonpolar mixtures; it may be applied to both gases at high pressures and liquids at high temperatures, but the accuracy for liquids with reduced densities greater than about 2 is expected to be poor. Actually, the equation has never been tested in any detail in the liquid region. When it was tested on 9 gas mixtures at various densities (1,396 different data points), the average error found was 3.7 per cent; most mixtures were composed of light hydrocarbons or hydrocarbon-inert gases. The technique is illustrated in Example 9-11.

A very similar correlation has been independently proposed by Giddings and Kobayashi (82). In this case the Leland and Mueller rules (Sec. 7-9) were chosen to determine the pseudocritical constants. A good correlation was obtained for light hydrocarbon mixtures; it was also found that the correlation could be improved if the mole-fraction molecular weight were employed as a third correlating parameter.

Example 9-11. Estimate the viscosity of a mixture of 18.65 mole % ethylene and 81.35 mole % ethane at 150°C and 120 atm. Dean and Stiel report the experimental value to be 0.01882 centipoise.

Solution. Letting ethylene be component 1 and ethane component 2, from Appendix A, $T_{c_1} = 283.1°K$, $T_{c_2} = 305.4°K$, $M_1 = 28.05$, $M_2 = 30.07$, $Z_{c_1} = 0.270$, $Z_{c_2} = 0.285$, $V_{c_1} = 124$ cm³/g mole, $V_{c_2} = 148$ cm³/g mole, $\omega_1 = 0.073$, $\omega_2 = 0.105$.

$$T_{c_m} = (0.1865)(283.1) + (0.8135)(305.4) = 301°K$$
$$M_m = (0.1865)(28.05) + (0.8135)(30.07) = 29.69$$
$$V_{c_m} = (0.1865)(124) + (0.8135)(148) = 143.5 \text{ cm}^3/\text{g mole}$$
$$Z_{c_m} = (0.1865)(0.270) + (0.8135)(0.285) = 0.282$$
$$\omega_m = (0.1865)(0.073) + (0.8135)(0.105) = 0.098$$
$$P_{c_m} = Z_{c_m} R T_{c_m} / V_{c_m} = [(0.282)(82.06)(301)] / 143.5 = 48.6 \text{ atm}$$
$$\xi_m = T_{c_m}^{1/6} / M_m^{1/2} P_{c_m}^{2/3} = (301)^{1/6} / (29.69)^{1/2}(48.6)^{2/3} = 0.03568$$

To determine ρ_m, Pitzer's correlation [Eq. (3-15)], Figs. 3-5 and 3-6, with $T_{r_m} = {}^{423}\!/_{301} = 1.40$,

$$P_{r_m} = 120/48.6 = 2.47 \qquad Z_m{}^0 = 0.74 \qquad Z_m{}^1 = 0.20$$
$$Z_m = Z_m{}^0 + \omega Z_m{}^1 = 0.74 + (0.098)(0.20) = 0.76$$
$$V_m = Z_m R T / P = [(0.76)(82.06)(423)] / 120 = 220 \text{ cm}^3/\text{g mole}$$
$$\rho_{r_m} = V_{c_m} / V_m = 143.5/220 = 0.65$$

The low-pressure mixture viscosity may be determined by any of the techniques discussed in Sec. 9-7. As long as Dean and Stiel's high-pressure method is being illustrated here, for consistency, their low-pressure value is employed; i.e., from Eq (9-39), $\mu_m{}^0 = 0.01299$ centipoise. Then, from Eq. (9-42),

$$(\mu_m - \mu_m{}^0)\xi_m = (\mu_m - 0.01299)(0.03568)$$
$$= (10.8)(10^{-5})[(e^{(1.439)(0.65)}) - (e^{(-1.111)(0.65)^{1.858}})]$$
$$\mu_m = 0.0189 \text{ centipoise}$$
$$\text{Error} = [(0.0189 - 0.0188)/0.0188] \times 100 = +0.5\%$$

Recommendations: Viscosities of Gas Mixtures at Elevated Pressures. To estimate the viscosities of nonpolar gas mixtures, use Eq. (9-42) with pseudocritical constants determined from the modified Prausnitz and Gunn rules. Errors are expected to be less than 5 per cent for mixtures of low-molecular-weight gases. For high-molecular-weight nonpolar gas mixtures, and for mixtures containing one or more polar components, no satisfactory method has yet been devised. Equation (9-42) may still be used, but with the realization that larger errors may be expected.

9-9 Liquid Viscosities

Gas viscosities at low pressures may be estimated by techniques based on sound theory, but there is no comparable theoretical basis for the estimation of the viscosity of liquids. Certainly the viscosities of liquids are considerably different from those of gases, i.e., they are much larger numerically, and they decrease sharply with an increase in temperature. The phenomenon of low-pressure gas viscosity is due primarily to the transfer of momentum by individual collisions between molecules moving randomly between layers with different velocities. A similar momentum transfer may also exist in liquids, though it is usually overshadowed by the interacting force fields between the close-packed liquid molecules. The densities of liquids are such that the average molecular-separation distance is not greatly different from the effective range of such force fields. This qualitative concept of liquid viscosity is often expressed by (190)

$$\mu_L = \mu_K + \mu_F \tag{9-47}$$

where μ_K represents the viscosity contribution as described by a "kinetic-theory" picture of momentum transfer and μ_F is that part resulting from the action of intermolecular forces. The first may be determined by the theoretical techniques described earlier in this chapter, e.g., Eq. (9-9); the latter must be determined primarily from some theory of the liquid state. At the present time, this cannot be done in an accurate manner. Brush (31) summarizes the state of the art as follows:

The statement that (liquid) viscosity is due to interatomic forces by no means constitutes a scientific theory. It is necessary to show that the assumption of some specific type of force law, not too different from the laws assumed in other successful theories, leads to correct predictions of the value of the viscosity coefficient over the entire range of temperatures and pressures. We are certainly nowhere near having achieved this, at least if one judges by the standards applicable to gas theory. Instead, we have a large number of competing "theories of viscosity," ranging from those which do no more than suggest explanations for the factors introduced into empirical formulas, to those which subject the unfortunate reader to hundreds of complex mathematical equations without rewarding him with any real solution to the problem. As yet, there is no general agreement on whether viscosity is essentially due to attractive or repulsive forces; furthermore, although one of the most popular theories uses quantum-mechanical concepts such as tunneling through potential barriers and virtual intermediate states, it has not been proved that the introduction of quantum mechanics is really necessary in order to explain viscosity at ordinary temperatures.

In general, the prevailing theories of liquid viscosity can be divided somewhat arbitrarily into those based on a gaslike liquid and those based on a solidlike liquid. In the former, the liquid is considered ordered in a short-range sense but disordered in a long-range view. Distribution functions are calculated from such models and expressions for viscosity obtained. Numerical values of viscosity cannot yet be calculated, owing to mathematical difficulties.

In the latter type of theory, the liquid is assumed to exist as a regular lattice, momentum transfer resulting from molecules vibrating within the lattice structure, or moving into nearby holes, or combinations of these two events. The lattices chosen have varied greatly from cubic to types resembling parallel tunnels. In one widely accepted theory,* the movement from a lattice site to a hole has been considered analogous to an activated chemical reaction.

Unfortunately, as noted in the quotation given above, no theory reduces to a simple form which allows liquid viscosities to be a priori calculated, and empirical (and often inaccurate) estimation techniques must be used. These methods do not conflict with theory: they merely allow some of the unknown or incalculable theoretical constants to be approximated from structure or other physical properties.

The reader interested in probing deeper into some of the quantitative aspects of liquid viscosity can easily do so. Brush (31) has published a well-written, thoroughly documented (584 references) review on the theories of liquid viscosity. Four very readable discussions are also available which summarize most of the key concepts (6, 81, 98, 125); for more specific studies, Refs. 14, 19, 25, 53, 60, 65, 72, 134 to 136, 156, 162, 179, 190 and 216 are recommended.

The emphasis in the following sections is placed upon ways to calculate

---

* An excellent, readable monograph describing lattice theories has recently been published (12).

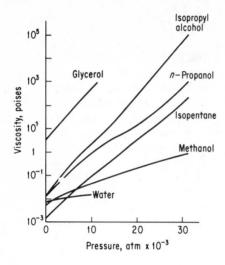

FIG. 9-7. Approximate variation of liquid viscosity with pressure at room temperature. [*From D. C. Munro, in R. S. Bradley (ed.) "High Pressure Physics and Chemistry,"* p. 18, *Academic Press, New York*, 1963.]

liquid viscosities for pure materials and mixtures at various temperatures and pressures; most methods have no definite liquid model as a basis but were suggested from a study of experimental data.

9-10   Effect of High Pressure on Low-temperature Liquid Viscosity

The viscosity of liquids below the normal boiling point is not particularly affected by moderate pressures, but under very high pressures, large increases have been noted.*   The pressure effect is illustrated for some simple liquids in Fig. 9-7 (24); it is obvious that, under large pressures, order-of-magnitude increases in liquid viscosity are possible.   It seems to be a rather general rule that, the more complex the molecular structure, the larger the effect of pressure (86, 107, 121, 130, 167).   For example, from the detailed experiments of Bridgman (27) carried out to pressures of about 12,000 atm, the fractional increase in the viscosity of liquid mercury was only about 0.32, for isobutyl alcohol 790, and for the complicated molecule eugenol about 10^7.   Figure 9-7 illustrates similar increases.   Water presents an anomaly, increasing only a little over twofold from 1 to 10,000 atm.   Most of Bridgman's results indicate that a viscosity-pressure plot is linear to a few thousand atmospheres, but at higher pressures the plot would be nearly linear if $\ln \mu_L$ were plotted against P as shown in Fig. 9-7.   This semilogarithmic correlation is said to be predicted by the hole theory of liquids (134).

* The discussion in this section is limited to low temperatures, since practically all experimental, very-high-pressure data have been obtained in this temperature region; also, high-pressure high-temperature liquid viscosities are estimated by different types of correlations, i.e., those discussed in Sec. 9-12.

There seems to be no reliable way to estimate low-temperature high-pressure liquid viscosities. Andrade (162) suggested a relationship involving the ratios of the specific volumes and adiabatic-compressibility factors for the compressed and uncompressed liquids, but the relationship is only approximate in the linear portion of the μ_L-P curve and does not even approximate the true situation at high pressures. This formula is also discussed briefly by Gambill in a review article (78).

9-11   Effect of Temperature on Liquid Viscosity

Liquid viscosities are very sensitive to temperature. At temperatures near or somewhat below the normal boiling point the behavior is well represented by the relation,

$$\mu_L = A e^{B/T} \tag{9-48}$$

where A and B are positive. A is of the same order of magnitude as the gas viscosity, and B is very approximately represented as the heat of fusion divided by the gas constant (105). Equation (9-48) resembles superficially the integrated Clapeyron equation for vapor pressures; in fact, it is believed that it was originally chosen for this reason by de Guzman (6). It has since become known as the Andrade equation, as it was Andrade who first suggested this form from an analysis of the mechanism of liquid viscosity (7, 8). In the intervening years since Eq. (9-48) was first suggested, literally hundreds of other viscosity-temperature relations have been proposed. Those most often quoted are of two types: first, there is introduced a volume dependency resulting in forms such as

$$\mu_L V^x = A e^{B/V^y T} \tag{9-49}$$

where V is the molar volume and the values of both x and y range from 0 to unity (184, 187, 218); second, there are those modifications of Eq. (9-48) which introduce another unknown constant to improve the fit to experimental data (18, 45, 58, 89, 102, 108, 139, 147, 148, 149, 204, 210). A typical example is the Girifalco form (83),

$$\log \mu_L = C/T^2 + B/T + A \tag{9-50}$$

where C is about zero except for polar or associated liquids. Equation (9-50) appears also to be a suitable empirical relation for mixtures (151).

Extensive testing of these and other forms has shown that, for a two-constant relation, Eq. (9-48) is reasonably accurate and, compared with others, is usually much more convenient to use (78, 94, 107, 115, 116, 134). It may not be suitable for complex compounds or for very low or very high temperatures, but no other simple relation has been proved reliable under such conditions. The fact is, the $\log \mu_L$-$1/T$ linearity is only approximate over a range from somewhat above the normal boiling tem-

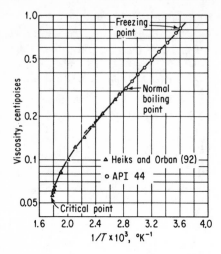

FIG. 9-8. Experimental data on the viscosity of liquid for benzene.

perature to a temperature near, but greater than, the freezing point. Figure 9-8 has been drawn for benzene from the freezing point to the critical point (92). At a temperature above T_b the viscosity begins to decrease very rapidly with temperature, and Eq. (9-48) is certainly not applicable. Though not shown for benzene, it is commonly found that near the freezing point the slope also changes and becomes much larger.

The high-temperature range (above a T_r of about 0.8) is best fitted by the Stiel and Thodos correlation discussed in Section 9-12. Below $T_r = 0.8$, Eq. (9-48) is recommended.

Various attempts have been made to relate A and B to vapor pressure, latent heat of vaporization, or other physical properties of the substance (59, 106, 156), but these have not been generally successful.

Deviations from the exponential function may be allowed for by the use of a graph similar to the Cox chart of vapor pressures. Irany (103–105, 163) describes such a graph in which viscosity is represented on a scale distorted in such a way as to force the μ_L-T relation to be linear for some substances for which viscosity data are available. Graphs of μ_L versus T for similar compounds are then found to be linear when the special μ_L scale prepared in this way is used. This is the basis of the ASTM viscosity graph paper (213) widely employed in the petroleum industry for representing the viscosity of oils as a function of temperature. The corresponding adaptation of Dühring's rule (Sec. 4-10) may also be used. Perry (160) gives an alignment chart which represents the vicosity-temperature function for each of 110 pure liquids at 1 atm.

Equation (9-48) requires two viscosity-temperature data points to fix values of the two constants. If only one is available, one of the few ways to extrapolate this value is to employ the approximate Lewis and Squires chart (125), which is based on the empirical fact that the variation of

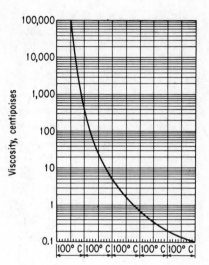

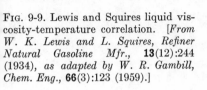

Fig. 9-9. Lewis and Squires liquid viscosity-temperature correlation. [*From W. K. Lewis and L. Squires, Refiner Natural Gasoline Mfr.*, **13**(12):244 (1934), *as adapted by W. R. Gambill, Chem. Eng.*, **66**(3):123 (1959).]

viscosity with temperature seems to depend primarily upon the value of the viscosity. This chart, shown in Fig. 9-9 (78), may be used by locating the known value of viscosity on the ordinate and then extending the abscissa by the required number of degrees to find the new viscosity. For example, if the viscosity were 0.7 centipoise at 0°C, then at 100°C it would be about 0.2 centipoise, etc. Gambill (78) mentions several other approximate one-data-point extrapolation formulas; the estimation techniques discussed in the next section may also be so used by employing single viscosity point to yield the structural constant.

Recommendations: Estimation of the Variation of the Viscosity of a Liquid with Temperature. From the freezing point to slightly above the normal boiling point, Eq. (9-48) is the best simple temperature-liquid viscosity function. Two data points are required. If more data points are available, they may be fitted to equations similar to Eq. (9-50). If only one datum point is known, a rough approximation of the viscosity at other temperatures may be obtained from Fig. 9-9.

Above the normal boiling point, no good temperature-viscosity correlations are available. The technique of Stiel and Thodos, discussed in Sec. 9-12, is probably the best available.

9-12 Estimation of Liquid Viscosity When No Experimental Data Are Available

Much effort has been expended to relate viscosities to molecular structure (5, 17, 115, 130, 134, 154, 155, 173, 191, 218), and a particularly thorough discussion has been published by Bondi (20). In a comparative way, increasing the molecular weight, the degree of branching, or the ability of the molecule to associate with its neighbors will increase both the viscosity and the sensitivity of the viscosity to temperature changes. Introducing double bonds usually reduces the viscosity, since even though the resulting molecule is less flexible, there is also less hindrance from the missing hydrogen atoms.   Many rules of thumb have been formulated to relate structural characteristics to viscosity, but to date no reliable quantitative relations have been suggested.   Consider Eq. (9-48), which is the best low-temperature two-constant liquid-viscosity correlation.   All attempts to estimate A or B from group contributions have met with indifferent success (18).   For example, Kierstead and Turkevitch (115) studied this problem for the simple case of pure hydrocarbons but could not develop any useful quantitative basis for predicting either A or B from structure alone.   To indicate the complexity involved, their conclusions may be worth summarizing.   In homologous series, $1/A$ appears to be a linear function of the number of carbon atoms, but B increases slowly as the number of carbons in the skeleton increases. A decreases but B increases with branching, but the effect of the branching varies; i.e., each branch appears to have more effect than the preceding.   Unsaturation increases A and decreases B for similar compounds; cyclic compounds have larger values of B and A than the corresponding aliphatic compounds.   Other generalizations could be made, but as yet A and B have not been successfully related to molecular structure, though the additive constant Θ in Eq. (9-52) may be shown to approximate B (see discussion under Thomas's Method).

Various attempts have been made to predict viscosities: none is reliable; all are empirical.   Three are presented here as the best estimations available, but to judge from the errors to be expected in their use (see Table 9-8), it must be stressed that they should be used only as a last resort when no experimental viscosity data can be obtained.

Souders's Method (185).   This method is based on the empirical relation

$$\log (\log 10\mu_L) = m\rho_L - 2.9 \qquad (9\text{-}51)$$

where μ_L = viscosity, centipoises

ρ_L = density, g/cm³

m = constant = I/M

I = viscosity constant calculated from atomic and structural constants given in Table 9-6

M = molecular weight

Use of Eq. (9-51) to calculate liquid viscosity involves several difficulties:

1. The temperature effect is felt in the density change alone, and, while the temperature level is usually known, the corresponding accurate density is not.

2. The constant 2.9, per se, cannot be used in the calculation since if only two-place accuracy were present initially, two antilogarithms would remove both places as characteristics and yield only an order-of-magnitude answer.

3. m (or I, since M can be accurately determined) must be known very precisely since it appears as an exponential multiplier to an exponential in the calculation of viscosity.

Even with these faults, Eq. (9-51) does provide an approximate method for the calculation of liquid viscosities up to and slightly above the normal boiling point. Compounds containing sulfur cannot be treated. Table 9-8 presents a comparison of calculated and experimental viscosities, based on the use of 2.900 as the constant in Eq. (9-51). Aromatic and alicyclic compounds yield the least error (up to 10 per cent). Hydrocarbons, except for low-molecular-weight n-paraffins, unsaturates, and branched compounds, may be expected to yield values in error up to 20 per cent. Calculated viscosities for alcohols and multihalogenated compounds are usually much larger than experimental, while the opposite is true for acids. Esters may be treated satisfactorily, as may freons (153). The method is illustrated in Example 9-12.

Example 9-12. Estimate the viscosity of acetic acid at 40°C by Souders's method. The density at this temperature is 1.027 g/cm³.

Solution. From Table 9-6, the value of I obtained is

$$I = C + 3H + COOH = 50.2 + 3(2.7) + 104.4 = 162.7$$
$$M = 60.05$$

Thus $(I/M)\rho_L = (2.709)(1.027) = 2.782$

Substituting in Eq. (9-51),

$$\log (\log 10\mu_L) = 2.782 - 2.900 = -0.118$$

and $\mu_L = 0.578$ centipoise

This is 36 per cent less than the experimental value, 0.91 centipoise (123).

Thomas's Method (206). Thomas has suggested that liquid viscosities at temperatures below the normal boiling point may be calculated from the empirical expression

$$\log [8.569(\mu_L/\rho_L^{1/2})] = \Theta \left[\frac{1}{T_r} - 1 \right] \tag{9-52}$$

where μ_L = viscosity of liquid, centipoises
ρ_L = density, g/cm³
Θ = viscosity constant calculated from values in Table 9-7
T_r = reduced temperature = T/T_c

TABLE 9-6. SOUDERS'S ATOMIC AND STRUCTURAL CONSTANTS TO CALCULATE I*

CH_2	55.6	OH	57.1	N	37
H	2.7	COO	90	Cl	60
C	50.2	COOH	104.4	Br	79
O	29.7	NO_2	80	I	110

Structural Values

Double bond...........	-15.5	$\begin{array}{cc} R & R \\ \diagdown & \diagup \\ CHCH \\ \diagup & \diagdown \\ R & R \end{array}$	$+8$	$-CH{=}CHCH_2X$†	$+4$
5-C ring..............	-24				
6-C ring..............	-21				
Side group on 6-C ring:		$\begin{array}{c} R \\ \mid \\ R{-}C{-}R \\ \mid \\ R \end{array}$	$+13$	$\begin{array}{c} R \\ \mid \\ \diagdown \\ CHX† \\ \diagup \\ R \end{array}$	$+6$
Molecular weight less than 17...........	-9				
Molecular weight more than 16...........	-17	$\begin{array}{c} H{-}C{-}R \\ \parallel \\ O \end{array}$	$+10$		
Ortho and para........	$+3$				
Meta.................	$+1$	$\begin{array}{c} CH_3{-}C{-}R \\ \parallel \\ O \end{array}$	$+5$		

* M. Souders, *J. Am. Chem. Soc.*, **60**:154 (1938).
† X is a negative group.

Davis's (48) nomograph to solve Eq. (9-51) clearly illustrates the importance of obtaining accurate values of I and ρ_L. Lagemann (122) has related I to $[R]$, the molar refraction, in a simple nomograph.

The additive constant Θ is related to B in Eq. (9-48), as can be shown by differentiating Eq. (9-52) with respect to $1/T$,

$$d(\ln \mu_L)/d(1/T) = B = (1/T_c)\{\tfrac{1}{2}[d(\ln \rho_r)/d(1/T_r)] + 2.303\Theta\}$$

For temperatures near or slightly below T_b (that is, around $T_r = 0.6$), the first term in the brackets is of the order of 0.1 to 0.2, whereas the term 2.303Θ varies from about 1.3 to 2. Thus the value of B is of the same order of magnitude as $2.303\Theta/T_c$ and is thereby related very approximately to structure.

Experimental values of liquid viscosity are compared with calculated values in Table 9-8. The errors are quite variable but generally indicate that aromatics (except benzene), monohalogenated compounds, unsaturates, and high-molecular-weight n-paraffins can be treated with errors usually less than 15 per cent. This method should not be used for alcohols, acids, naphthenes, heterocyclics, amines, aldehydes, or multihalogenated compounds. The method is illustrated in Example 9-13.

TABLE 9-7. THOMAS'S CONTRIBUTIONS TO CALCULATE Θ IN EQ. (9-52)*

C	-0.462
H	$+0.249$
O	$+0.054$
Cl	$+0.340$
Br	$+0.326$
I	$+0.335$
Double bond	$+0.478$
C_6H_5	$+0.385$
S	$+0.043$
CO	$+0.105$ (ketones and esters)
CN	$+0.381$ (nitriles)

* L. H. Thomas, *J. Chem. Soc. (London)*, **1946**:573.

Example 9-13. Estimate the viscosity of chloroform at 60°C by Thomas's method. The density at this temperature is 1.413 g/cm³.

Solution. The critical temperature of chloroform is 536.6°K, whence T_r is $(273.1 + 60)/536.6 = 0.621$. Referring to Table 9-7, Θ is determined to be (-0.462) $+ 3(0.340) + 0.249 = 0.807$. Substituting in Eq. (9-52),

$$\log (8.569\mu_L/1.413^{\frac{1}{2}}) = 0.807(1/0.621 - 1.000) = 0.492$$

whence $\mu_L = 0.431$ centipoise, which is 11 per cent greater than the experimental value, 0.390 centipoise (123).

Stiel and Thodos's Method. The corresponding-state relations suggested by Stiel and Thodos (109, 189, 193, 196) for dense gases (Sec. 9-6) may also be used for the liquid phase if the density limits placed on the correlation are not exceeded. For example, for nonpolar gases, Eq. (9-24) should be applicable for reduced densities less than 3. To visualize these relations, they may be solved in a general manner for saturated liquids by assuming the Lydersen et al. liquid-density correlation [Eq. (3-74)] and Table 3-6 to yield a relation of the form

$$\mu_L \xi = f(Z_c, T_r) \tag{9-53}$$

as shown in Fig. 9-10. At high values of T_r the value of $\mu_L \xi$ is not particularly sensitive to the value of Z_c, whereas at lower values of T_r the reverse is true. At the lower temperatures, liquid viscosities become particularly sensitive to structure, and this is reflected partially by different Z_c values. Figure 9-10 is not suggested as an accurate method to estimate liquid viscosities at low temperatures (below the normal boiling point), but it is reasonably good for the calculation of viscosities of saturated liquids at temperatures between T_b and T_c. Preferably, experimental liquid densities should be used with Eqs. (9-22) to (9-24), but if these are not known, Fig. 9-10 may be used. Figures 9-11 to 9-13 have been drawn to illustrate the fit of this correlation for propane,

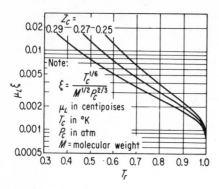

FIG. 9-10. Generalized liquid-viscosity correlation.

n-heptane, and benzene. The solid curves are obtained directly from Eqs. (9-22) to (9-24), experimentally reported saturated-liquid-density data being employed. The dashed lines have been obtained from Eq (9-53) and Fig. 9-10. (In the n-heptane case, the two calculational methods gave identical results; i.e., for n-heptane the generalized liquid density correlation in Table 3-6 is very accurate.)

The Stiel and Thodos method was not designed for the estimation of liquid viscosities at low temperatures, and it is remarkable that the fi of the calculated and experimental curves is as good as shown.   In some other tests, rather erratic results were obtained indicating that the corre lating parameters ξ, Z_c, and T_r are not sufficient to characterize liquid viscosity behavior at the low temperatures (T_b and below).   However this type of treatment, i.e., correlation of a dimensionless liquid viscosity has been suggested by several other investigators (22, 23, 93, 205, 209)

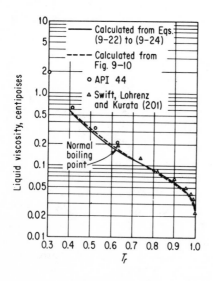

FIG. 9-11. Comparison between calculated and experimental liquid viscosities of propane.

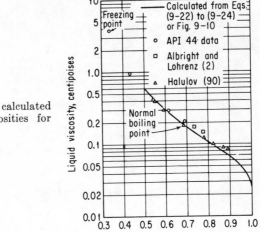

FIG. 9-12. Comparison between calculated and experimental liquid viscosities for n-heptane.

hough in most instances the dimensionless group is $\mu_L \sigma^2/\epsilon_0^{1/2} M^{1/2}$ rather han $(\mu_L T_c^{1/6}/P_c^{2/3} M^{1/2})$. σ and ϵ_0 are the usual potential parameters in ome two-constant intermolecular energy-distance relations (such as the Lennard-Jones). The two dimensionless groups reduce to the same form f some proportionality between σ^3 and V_c and between ϵ_0 and T_c is assumed (see Sec. 2-10). A similar approach for the transport properties of cryogenic fluids has been successfully demonstrated by Kerrisk, Rogers, and Hammel (111); in this case, a quantum-mechanical characterizing group was also necessary, that is, $h/\sigma(m\epsilon_0)^{1/2}$.

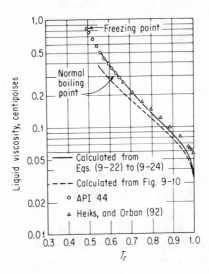

FIG. 9-13. Comparison between calculated and experimental liquid viscosities for benzene.

Example 9-14. Using the method of Stiel and Thodos, estimate the viscosity of liquid n-heptane at the normal boiling point of $372°K$. The experimental value is about 0.195 centipoise (90).

Solution

$$T_c = 540.3°K \qquad P_c = 27.0 \text{ atm} \qquad V_c = 426 \text{ cm}^3/\text{g mole} \qquad M = 100.2$$
$$Z_c = 0.259 \qquad \xi = (540.3)^{\frac{1}{6}}/(100.2)^{\frac{1}{2}}(27.0)^{\frac{2}{3}} = 0.0317$$

(a) From Fig. 9-10, with $T_r = 372/540.3 = 0.686$,

$$\mu_L \xi = 0.0061$$
$$\mu_L = 0.0061/0.0317 = 0.192 \text{ centipoise}$$
$$\text{Error} = [(0.192 - 0.195)/0.195] \times 100 = -1.5\%$$

(this error is smaller than usually found.)

(b) Since the liquid volume is $V_b = 162 \text{ cm}^3/\text{g mole}$ (experimental), then

$$\rho_r = {}^{426}\!/_{162} = 2.63$$

and from Eq. (9-24) or Fig. 9-3

$$(\mu_L - \mu^0)\xi \times 10^5 = 550$$
or $\qquad\qquad \mu_L - \mu^0 = (550/0.0317) \times 10^{-5} = 0.174 \text{ centipoise}$
From Eq. (9-14), $\qquad \mu^0 = 0.0075 \text{ centipoise} \qquad$ at $T_r = 0.686$
and $\qquad\qquad \mu_L = 0.174 + 0.0075 = 0.182 \text{ centipoise}$
$$\text{Error} = [(0.182 - 0.195)/0.195] \times 100 = -6.7\%$$

Other Correlations. Many other empirical estimation techniques have been suggested. Gambill (77) has reviewed many of them and suggested a new one based on the molal latent heat of vaporization at the normal boiling point. Friend and Hargreaves have tried to relate an additive parameter called the *rheochor* to the viscosity at T_b (67–71, 181). Albright and Lohrenz (2) have suggested the correlating parameter ZZ_c, and other workers have, at various times, proposed relations involving μ_L, T, and one or more of the following: T_b, M, vapor density, surface tension, sonic velocity, van der Waals' volumes, vapor pressure, etc. (1, 60, 66, 118, 137, 154, 155, 157–159, 164, 182, 190, 200, 203).

A particularly interesting correlation was proposed by Bondi (21), who correlated a dimensionless viscosity with a reduced temperature [identical to that shown in Eq. (3-78) in an equation of the form of Eq. (9-48)]. The values of A and B were found to be constant for several homologous series and, in fact, were almost the same for most families. The parameters used to nondimensionalize μ_L and T were found to be additive functions of the various characterizing groups comprising the molecule.

Most of these methods are valid only at temperatures near the normal boiling point. For higher temperatures, in addition to the Stiel and Thodos correlation presented earlier, Grunberg and Nissan (88) have proposed a nomograph relating μ_L, μ^0, T_r, and ρ_r, where μ^0 is the low-pressure gas viscosity. Uyehara and Watson (209) included a liquid region in the μ_L/μ_c-T_r-P_r correlation described briefly in Sec. 9-6 (55, 189). Smith and Brown (183) and others (201) represented the viscosity of saturated liquids (and vapors) by a series of curves each for a particular homologous series.

Andrade's (6) well-known technique to estimate viscosities at the melting point was recently studied by Matsen and Johnson (144), who expressed it as $\mu_L = \beta\rho^{2/3}T^{1/2}/M^{1/6}$, where μ_L at the melting point is expressed in centipoises, ρ in grams per cubic centimeter, and T in degrees Kelvin and where M is the molecular weight. The minimum value of β was suggested as 0.051 by Andrade, from theoretical considerations. Matsen and Johnson found that actual values were much higher; they tabulated a set of β values for a large number of compounds. There was definitely a correlation of β with structure, the simple, symmetrical monatomic liquids approaching the theoretical value but increasing, often by orders of magnitude, for complex unsymmetrical structures. For example, the β values for the n-alkane series oscillated between 0.058 for methane to 2.78 for propane, though β for most compounds up to eicosane fell in the range 0.3 to 0.7.

Recommendations: Estimation of the Viscosity of Pure Liquids. For liquids near or below the normal boiling point use either Souders's or Thomas's method. Neither is very reliable, as can be seen from the results in Table 9-8. Usually errors do not exceed 30 per cent, but not infrequently the methods fail to yield a reasonable value.

For liquids at temperatures greater than the normal boiling point, use the method of Stiel and Thodos described in Sec. 9-6 or approximated by Fig. 9-10. Errors are usually less than 10 to 15 per cent if experimental liquid densities are used.

9-13 Estimation of Liquid-mixture Viscosity

As discussed in Sec. 9-12, there is no reliable method to estimate the viscosity of a pure liquid, and only very approximate empirical rules are available. This same situation exists for liquid mixtures and will continue until a quantitative theory is established for pure materials; only then is there hope that good mixture techniques can be formulated.

To discuss qualitatively the concept of liquid-mixture viscosity, one should formulate some picture of the actual molecular processes taking place. In a binary of A and B, molecular interactions are of both the A-A and B-B types. There are, in addition, the A-B type of interactions. The introduction of the A-B type of effects invariably leads to undetermined mixture constants. A good example of such an approach is due to McAllister (133), who adopted the semitheoretical Eyring approach (84). In this mechanistic picture, the interaction between layers of molecules in the velocity gradient involves "activated" jumps of molecules

TABLE 9-8. COMPARISON OF CALCULATED AND EXPERIMENTAL
VISCOSITIES OF LIQUIDS
Values of viscosity in centipoises

Compound	T, °C	Exp.* μ	Thomas μ	Thomas % Error†	Souders μ	Souders % Error†	Stiel and Thodos μ	Stiel and Thodos % Error†
Acetone.............	− 90	2.075	1.76	−15	1.70	− 18		
	− 60	0.892	0.944	+ 5.8	0.875	− 1.9		
	0	0.389	0.402	+ 3.3	0.393	+ 1.0	0.657	+ 69
	30	0.292	0.294	+ 0.7	0.288	− 1.4	0.359	+ 23
	60	0.226	0.227	+ 0.5	0.225	− 0.4	0.237	+ 4.9
Acetic acid..........	10	1.45	0.707	−51	0.875	− 41	1.16	− 20
	40	0.901	0.460	−49	0.578	− 36	0.653	− 28
	80	0.561	0.345	−37	0.376	− 32	0.359	− 36
	110	0.416	0.274	−36	0.294	− 29	0.272	− 35
Aniline..............	− 5	13.43	.....	.....	5.62	− 58		
	20	4.38	.....	.....	3.23	− 26	1.185	− 73
	60	1.52	.....	.....	1.54	+ 1.3	0.665	− 56
	120	0.658	.....	.....	0.686	+ 4.2	0.363	− 45
Benzene.............	5	0.826	0.491	−41	0.828	+ 0.2	0.626	− 24
	40	0.492	0.344	−31	0.507	+ 3.0	0.430	− 13
	80	0.318	0.250	−21	0.323	+ 1.6	0.288	− 9.4
	120	0.219	0.191	−13	0.225	+ 2.7	0.196	− 10.5
	160	0.156	0.152	− 2.5	0.171	+ 9.7	0.140	− 10
	190	0.121	0.131	+ 8.3	0.153	+ 26	0.119	− 1.7
n-Butane.............	− 90	0.63	0.68	+ 8.0	0.45	− 29	0.559	− 11
	− 60	0.403	0.414	+ 2.7	0.316	− 21	0.385	− 4.5
	− 30	0.282	0.280	− 0.7	0.239	− 15	0.255	− 9.6
	0	0.210	0.205	− 2.4	0.191	− 9.0	0.178	− 15
1-Butene.............	−110	0.79	0.95	+19	0.46	− 42		
	− 80	0.45	0.53	+18	0.35	− 22	0.595	+ 32
	− 40	0.26	0.30	+15	0.21	− 19	0.267	+ 2.7
n-Butyl alcohol........	0	5.14	0.57	−89	5.32	+ 3.5		
	40	1.77	0.37	−78	2.23	+ 28	0.694	− 61
	80	0.762	0.261	−66	1.09	+ 43	0.398	− 48
	120	0.394	0.198	−50	0.628	+ 62	0.277	− 30
Carbon tetrachloride...	0	1.369	1.353	− 0.1	11.9	+770	0.721	− 47
	30	0.856	0.872	+ 1.9	3.98	+360	0.519	− 39
	70	0.534	0.544	+ 1.9	1.29	+140	0.354	− 34
	100	0.404	0.404	0	0.700	+ 74	0.278	− 31
Chlorobenzene........	0	1.054	1.215	+15	1.038	− 1.7		
	40	0.639	0.667	+ 4.4	0.612	− 4.2	0.678	+ 6.1
	80	0.441	0.447	+ 1.4	0.405	− 8.2	0.476	+ 7.9
	120	0.326	0.322	− 1.2	0.292	− 10	0.339	+ 4.0

THE PROPERTIES OF GASES AND LIQUIDS

TABLE 9-8. COMPARISON OF CALCULATED AND EXPERIMENTAL
VISCOSITIES OF LIQUIDS (*Continued*)

Compound	T, °C	Exp.* μ	Thomas		Souders		Stiel and Thodos	
			μ	% Error†	μ	% Error†	μ	% Error†
Chloroform...........	0	0.700	0.870	+24	1.56	+120		
	30	0.502	0.590	+18	0.929	+ 84	1.051	+109
	60	0.390	0.431	+10	0.524	+ 34	0.592	+ 52
Cyclohexane..........	5	1.300	......	......	1.260	− 3.1	0.449	− 65
	30	0.826	......	......	0.802	− 2.9	0.344	− 58
	60	0.528	......	......	0.507	− 4.0	0.259	− 51
	80	0.411	......	......	0.412	+ 0.2	0.226	− 42
Cyclopentane.........	− 20	0.72	......	......	0.73	+ 1.4	0.453	− 37
	20	0.439	......	......	0.429	− 2.3	0.298	− 32
	50	0.323	......	......	0.311	− 3.7	0.228	− 29
2,2-Dimethylpropane..	− 15	0.431	0.268	−37	0.310	− 28	0.186	− 57
	0	0.328	0.229	−31	0.265	− 19	0.161	− 51
	10	0.281	0.207	−26	0.237	− 16	0.141	− 50
Ethane..............	−175	0.985	1.521	+54	0.288	− 72		
	−120	0.257	0.330	+27	0.173	− 33	0.324	+ 26
	− 85	0.162	0.194	+20	0.144	− 11	0.175	+ 8.0
Ethylene bromide.....	20	1.714	1.304	−24	4.732	+170	0.646	− 62
	60	0.995	0.824	−18	1.879	+ 88	0.463	− 53
	120	0.562	0.487	−12	0.686	+ 22	0.309	− 45
Ethylene chloride.....	0	1.123	0.914	−19	1.758	+ 57	0.766	− 32
	40	0.644	0.563	−13	0.805	+ 25	0.420	− 35
	80	0.417	0.381	− 8.6	0.449	+ 7.7	0.285	− 32
Ethyl alcohol.........	0	1.770	0.375	−79	0.138	− 92	0.614	− 65
	40	0.826	0.266	−68	0.137	− 83	0.578	− 30
	75	0.465	0.209	−55	0.137	− 70	0.549	+ 18
Ethyl acetate.........	20	0.458	0.442	− 3.5	0.474	+ 3.5	0.613	+ 34
	80	0.246	0.247	+ 0.4	0.252	+ 2.4	0.241	− 2.0
	140	0.153	0.160	+ 4.5	0.161	+ 5.2	0.126	− 18
	190	0.0998	0.118	+19	0.130	+ 30	0.0822	− 18
Ethylbenzene.........	− 20	1.24	1.17	− 5.6	1.21	− 2.4		
	40	0.535	0.528	− 1.3	0.519	− 3.0	0.625	+ 17
	100	0.308	0.304	− 1.3	0.296	− 3.9	0.341	+ 11
	140	0.231	0.230	− 0.4	0.232	+ 0.5	0.252	+ 9.1
Ethyl bromide........	20	0.395	0.411	+ 4.0	0.304	− 23	0.746	+ 89
	60	0.269	0.294	+ 9.3	0.221	− 18	0.410	+ 52
	100	0.199	0.223	+12	0.175	− 12	0.267	+ 34
	160	0.126	0.159	+26	0.138	+ 9.5	0.167	+ 33
Ethylene.............	−170	0.70	0.86	+23	0.17	− 76	0.360	− 49
	−140	0.31	0.37	+19	0.14	− 55	0.185	− 40
	−100	0.15	0.19	+27	0.095	− 37	0.110	− 27

TABLE 9-8. COMPARISON OF CALCULATED AND EXPERIMENTAL
VISCOSITIES OF LIQUIDS (*Continued*)

Compound	T, °C	Exp.* μ	Thomas μ	Thomas % Error†	Souders μ	Souders % Error†	Stiel and Thodos μ	Stiel and Thodos % Error†
Ethyl ether	0	0.289	0.311	+ 7.6	0.284	− 1.7	0.241	− 17
	20	0.236	0.254	+ 7.6	0.239	+ 1.3	0.191	− 19
	60	0.167	0.181	+ 8.4	0.181	+ 8.4	0.131	− 22
	100	0.118	0.137	+16	0.148	+ 25	0.095	− 19
Ethyl formate	0	0.507	0.479	− 5.5	0.553	+ 9.1	0.676	+ 33
	30	0.362	0.343	− 5.2	0.345	− 4.7	0.342	− 5.5
	55	0.288	0.280	− 2.7	0.238	− 17	0.216	− 25
Heptane	− 90	3.77	2.78	−26	2.55	− 32		
	− 40	0.965	0.966	+ 0.1	0.948	− 1.8		
	20	0.418	0.413	− 1.2	0.425	+ 1.7	0.397	− 5.0
	60	0.287	0.274	− 4.5	0.284	− 1.0	0.247	− 14
	100	0.209	0.206	− 1.4	0.212	+ 1.4	0.173	− 17
Hexane	− 60	0.888	0.963	+ 8.5	0.845	− 4.8		
	0	0.381	0.393	+ 3.2	0.379	− 0.5	0.370	− 2.9
	40	0.262	0.260	− 0.8	0.262	0.0	0.235	− 10
	70	0.205	0.201	− 2.0	0.208	+ 1.5	0.175	− 15
Hydrogen chloride	−115	0.581	0.549	− 5.5	0.156	− 73		
	− 85	0.458	0.339	−24	0.138	− 70	0.507	+ 11
Hydrogen sulfide	− 80	0.511	0.374	−27	....	....	0.363	− 29
	− 65	0.443	0.312	−29	....	....	0.305	− 31
Isobutane	− 80	0.628	0.493	−22	0.319	− 49	0.499	− 21
	− 40	0.343	0.280	−18	0.226	− 34	0.290	− 15
	− 10	0.239	0.203	−15	0.183	− 23	0.196	− 18
Isopropyl alcohol	10	3.319	0.350	−90	2.992	− 9.8	0.544	− 84
	30	1.811	0.288	−84	1.901	+ 4.9	0.401	− 78
	50	1.062	0.244	−77	1.256	+ 18	0.316	− 70
Methane	−185	0.226	0.330	+46	0.117	− 48	0.202	− 11
	−160	0.115	0.176	+53	0.113	− 1.7	0.123	+ 7.0
Methyl alcohol	5	0.746	0.328	−56	1.016	+ 36	0.749	+ 0.4
	20	0.592	0.287	−51	0.775	+ 31	0.559	− 5.6
	60	0.350	0.210	−40	0.435	+ 24	0.304	− 13
2-Methylbutane	− 50	0.55	0.51	− 7.3	0.49	− 11	0.476	− 13
	− 20	0.353	0.341	− 3.4	0.310	− 12	0.289	− 18
	30	0.205	0.205	0.0	0.202	− 1.5	0.167	− 19
Pentane	−120	2.35	2.55	+ 8.6	1.40	− 40		
	− 80	0.791	0.921	+16	0.673	− 15		
	− 40	0.428	0.471	+10	0.402	− 6.1	0.434	+ 1.4
	0	0.279	0.289	+ 3.6	0.271	− 2.8	0.265	− 5.0
	30	0.216	0.216	0.0	0.212	− 1.8	0.192	− 11

TABLE 9-8. COMPARISON OF CALCULATED AND EXPERIMENTAL
VISCOSITIES OF LIQUIDS (*Continued*)

Compound	T, °C	Exp.* μ	Thomas		Souders		Stiel and Thodos	
			μ	% Error†	μ	% Error†	μ	% Error†
Phenol..............	50	3.020	0.725	−76	10.4	+240	0.913	− 70
	70	1.614	0.589	−63	5.83	+260	0.688	− 57
	100	0.783	0.453	−42	2.88	+270	0.493	− 37
Propane..............	−190	13.8	12.2	−12	0.841	− 94		
	−140	0.984	1.15	+17	0.398	− 60		
	− 80	0.327	0.332	+ 1.5	0.222	− 32	0.290	− 11
	− 40	0.205	0.199	− 2.9	0.169	− 18	0.170	− 17
n-Propyl alcohol.......	10	2.897	0.412	−86	2.812	− 2.9	0.699	− 76
	40	1.400	0.306	−78	1.400	0.0	0.419	− 70
	100	0.443	0.194	−56	0.493	+ 11	0.217	− 51
Pyridine..............	20	0.974	......	......	7.43	+670		
	40	0.735	......	......	4.08	+450		
	90	0.443	......	......	1.29	+190		
Toluene..............	− 20	1.07	0.88	−18	1.11	+ 3.7		
	20	0.587	0.530	− 9.2	0.607	+ 3.4	0.607	+ 3.4
	60	0.380	0.357	− 6.1	0.391	+ 2.9	0.402	+ 5.8
	110	0.249	0.241	− 3.2	0.258	+ 3.6	0.256	+ 2.8
o-Xylene.............	0	1.108	0.936	−16	1.20	+ 8.2		
	40	0.625	0.564	− 9.8	0.659	+ 5.5	0.617	− 1.3
	100	0.345	0.324	− 6.1	0.365	+ 5.8	0.363	+ 5.2
	140	0.254	0.242	− 4.7	0.273	+ 7.4	0.264	+ 3.9
m-Xylene.............	0	0.808	0.851	+ 5.3	0.794	− 1.7		
	40	0.492	0.570	+16	0.493	0.0	0.602	+ 22
	80	0.340	0.356	+ 4.7	0.345	+ 1.5	0.417	+ 23
	140	0.218	0.227	+ 4.1	0.229	+ 5.1	0.230	+ 5.5

* Experimental values were taken from American Petroleum Institute, "Selected Values of Physical and Thermodynamic Properties of Hydrocarbons and Related Compounds," Project 44, Carnegie Press, Pittsburgh, Pa., 1953, and "Landolt-Börnstein Tables," vol. 4, pt. 1, Springer-Verlag OHG, Berlin, 1955.

† [(Calculated − experimental)/experimental] × 100.

between layers. A molecule moving in this manner is treated as if it were undergoing a chemical reaction, and the pushing or squeezing of this moving molecule requires that it overcome a potential- (free-) energy barrier ΔF^* in the process. This descriptive mechanism leads, after simplification, to an equation similar to Eq. (9-48).

$$\nu_L = (\mu/\rho)_L = (hN_0/M) \exp (\Delta F^*/RT) \qquad (9\text{-}54)$$
$$\nu_L = (\mu/\rho)_L = (hN_0/M) \exp (-\Delta S^*/R) \exp (\Delta H^*/RT) \qquad (9\text{-}55)$$

The grouping $(\rho_L h N_0/M)$ exp $(-\Delta S^*/R)$ is the equivalent of A and $\Delta H^*/R$ of B in Eq. (9-48). Here the ΔF^*, ΔH^*, ΔS^* are the respective free energies, enthalpies, and entropies of activation in the process of moving a molecule from one layer to another. There is no reliable way at present to determine such energy quantities, but the descriptive picture allows one to postulate a mixture model.

For a mixture of A and B, as molecule A moves over the energy barrier, it may interact predominantly with A, with B, or with some combination of A and B, depending on the local concentration. Moreover, the interaction could be taken as a binary type or, more realistically, as a three-body type, four-body type, etc. Perhaps the simplest to visualize is the two-dimensional three-body type assumed by McAllister.* The sketch below shows the basic idea:

Here molecule Z is jumping or flowing between molecules X and Y, where, for a binary, Z, X, and Y may be A or B. If all are A, the interaction is the A-A-A type; in general, for a binary, there would be six types, that is, A-A-A, B-B-B, A-B-A, B-A-B, A-A-B, A-B-B. The ΔF^* for the viscous interaction is assumed to be expressed in general as

$$\Delta F_m^* = \sum_{i=1}^{2} \sum_{j=1}^{2} \sum_{k=1}^{2} x_i x_j x_k \, \Delta F_{ijk}^* \qquad (9\text{-}56)$$

where x represents the mole fraction. Furthermore,

$$\Delta F_{AAB}^* = \Delta F_{ABA}^* \equiv \Delta F_{AB}^*$$
$$= \Delta F_{BAB}^* \equiv \Delta F_{BA}^* \qquad (9\text{-}57)$$

By combining Eqs. (9-56) and (9-57) into (9-54) and defining a mixture kinematic viscosity ν_{AB} (and ν_{BA}) by Eq. (9-54),† there results

$$\ln \nu = x_A{}^3 \ln \nu_A + 3x_A{}^2 x_B \ln \nu_{AB} + 3x_A x_B{}^2 \ln \nu_{BA}$$
$$+ x_B{}^3 \ln \nu_B + R^0 \qquad (9\text{-}58)$$

where

$$R^0 = x_B{}^3 \ln (M_B/M_A) + 3x_A x_B{}^2 \ln [(1 + 2M_B/M_A)/3]$$
$$+ 3x_A{}^2 x_B \ln [(2 + M_B/M_A)/3] - \ln (x_A + x_B M_B/M_A) \qquad (9\text{-}59)$$

Equation (9-58) contains two undetermined parameters, ν_{AB} and ν_{BA}. They are assumed independent of composition and vary with tempera-

---

* If the ratio of the molecular diameters is large (>1.5), McAllister suggests that a four-body type or higher interaction model is necessary.

† Here it is assumed that $M_{AB} = (2M_A + M_B)/3$, $M_{BA} = (2M_B + M_A)/3$.

ture as shown in Eq. (9-54). Thus, once these constants are established for a given binary, viscosities at other temperatures and compositions may be determined. Expressions of a similar type, but with more undetermined parameters, are obtained if four-body interactions, eight-body interactions, etc., are considered.

The value of R^0 in Eq. (9-59) vanishes if $M_A = M_B$ and is negative except for large or small ratios of M_A/M_B.

McAllister applied Eq. (9-58) to the systems benzene-toluene, cyclohexane-heptane, methanol-toluene, and acetone-water, at various temperatures. The parameters ν_{AB} and ν_{BA} were fitted by a least-squares technique from the experimental data (actually ΔS^* and ΔH^* values were found for A-A, A-B, B-A, B-B), and with these values the data were well correlated. The most nonideal case, acetone-water, showed the greatest errors, i.e., an average deviation of 6.4 per cent and a maximum deviation of 15.8 per cent. McAllister showed, however, with a similar type of analysis using a four-body interaction, that the three-parameter result correlated even this system to within 2 to 4 per cent.

McAllister's approach has also been shown to apply to ternary systems containing various mixtures of water, ethyl alcohol, ethylene glycol, methyl alcohol, and acetone (37, 110). The only parameters needed were the ν_{AB}, ν_{BA} values for the three constituent binaries and pure-component viscosities.

This treatment by McAllister is evidently the best correlating technique available. In addition to pure-component values, only two binary viscosity data points are necessary at each of two different temperatures to define the entire composition-temperature range over which Eq. (9-54) is applicable, though obviously the more data used, the better the resulting correlation.

Many other equations for liquid viscosity have been suggested. They can be, in most cases, generalized to the types

$$f(\mu_m)_L = \sum_i \sum_j x_i x_j f(\mu_{ij})_L \tag{9-60}$$

or
$$f(\mu_m)_L = \sum_i x_i f(\mu_i)_L \tag{9-61}$$

In these relations $f(\mu)_L$ may be μ_L, $\ln \mu_L$, $1/\mu_L$, etc., and x_i may be the liquid volume, weight, or mole fraction (134). Some investigators claim good results with simple equations of the type of (9-61) (61), but it is obvious that such a form cannot accurately account for systems containing maximum, minimum, or both maximum and minimum viscosities as composition is varied. Acetone-water (101), N,N-dimethylacetamide–water (161), and methanol-toluene (91) are good examples of such systems. In another modification, Tamura and Kurata (202) assumed that the relaxation time for each collision was proportional to the probability of collision and, by assuming small volume changes on mixing, arrived at the following equation for binary mixtures,

$$\mu_{L_m} = x_1\varphi_1\mu_{L_1} + x_2\varphi_2\mu_{L_2} + 2(x_1x_2\varphi_1\varphi_2)^{\frac{1}{2}}\mu_{L_{12}} \qquad (9\text{-}62)$$

where x_1, x_2 = mole fractions of components
   μ_{L_m} = viscosity of mixture, centipoises
   μ_{L_1}, μ_{L_2} = viscosities of pure substances, centipoises
   $\mu_{L_{12}}$ = viscosity of interacting substances, centipoises
   φ_1, φ_2 = volume fractions of components

Equation (9-62) is actually a one-constant equation in that $\mu_{L_{12}}$ is an empirical constant at each temperature level and may be considered to vary with temperature in the same way as a pure viscosity [i.e., by Eq. (9-48)]. A test of this equation with some 30 mixtures of polar-polar, polar-nonpolar and nonpolar-nonpolar mixtures showed that maximum errors were usually less than 5 to 7 per cent, even for mixtures containing polar substances and for cases where the viscosity at intermediate compositions was greater or smaller than the viscosities of the pure components. This excellent agreement, of course, rests on the chosen values of $\mu_{L_{12}}$, which must be determined from experimental viscosity data for at least one composition. If more than one datum point is available, an average of the calculated values of $\mu_{L_{12}}$ should be used.

To predict the viscosity of mixtures with no experimental data is sometimes possible if the constituents are not too dissimilar or too polar. Lima (172) has suggested that Souders's equation (9-51) be modified to allow for two components, i.e.,

$$\log (\log 10\mu_{L_m}) = \rho_{L_m}[(x_1I_1 + x_2I_2)/(x_1M_1 + x_2M_2)] - 2.900 \qquad (9\text{-}63)$$

where μ_{L_m} = viscosity of mixture, centipoises
   x_1, x_2 = mole fractions of components
   I = viscosity constant calculated from Table 9-6
   M = molecular weight

Tests made with alcohol-nonpolar, acid-nonpolar, and nonpolar mixtures usually agreed within 10 per cent of the experimental values when the equation checked exactly for the pure components. Equation (9-63) is subject to the same disadvantages as the parent equation (9-51), namely, the requirement that ρ_{L_m} and I must be known very precisely.

Various other methods are available for estimating or correlating liquid-mixture viscosities (11, 15, 22, 96, 100, 119, 120, 124, 132, 151, 186, 208), but none show real advantages over those discussed here. Gambill (79) has recently reviewed the subject. Very little work has been done with liquid mixtures under pressure (52).

Recommendations: Viscosities of Liquid Mixtures. To estimate liquid viscosity for mixtures of two components, it is recommended that, if sufficient viscosity data points and mixture volume data are available,

Eq. (9-58) be used. ν_{AB} and ν_{BA} may be determined and viscosities at other compositions and temperatures calculated. If only one datum point is available at each of two temperatures, Eq. (9-62) or (9-60) is to be used; a convenient form for the latter is $f(\mu)_L = \ln \mu_L$ and $x = $ mole fraction. $\mu_{L_{ij}}$ is determined at each temperature and assumed to behave as indicated by Eq. (9-48). If no viscosity data are available for the mixture, Eq. (9-61) or (9-63) should be used. If the latter method is employed, one should be careful to check the validity of the equation for the pure substances. Errors to be expected may vary widely; estimates are more reliable for mixtures composed of chemically similar materials. Large interaction viscosities $\mu_{L_{AB}}, \ldots$ tend to make μ_{L_m} nonlinear in composition. This nonlinearity has been correlated in an approximate manner with the excess entropy of mixing of the solution (199). Regular solutions, i.e., those with no excess entropy of solution, would be expected to yield linear μ_L-x plots. The relationship of mixture viscosities to thermodynamic properties is also discussed by Reed and Taylor (168).

NOMENCLATURE FOR CHAPTER 9

A = constant in Eqs. (9-48) and (9-50)

A_{ij} = collision-integral ratio in Eq. (9-32)

b = constant in Eq. (9-20)

b_0 = hard-sphere volume, $\frac{2}{3}\pi N_0 \sigma^3$

B = constant in Eqs. (9-48) and (9-50)

C = constant in Eq. (9-50)

C_v = heat capacity at constant volume, cal/(g mole)(°K)

D = diffusion coefficient; D_{ij}, between i and j, cm^2/sec

$f_1(T^*) = T^{*\frac{1}{2}}/\Omega_v$

ΔF^* = free energy of activation [Eq. (9-54)]

h = Planck's constant

ΔH^* = enthalpy of activation [Eq. (9-54)]

I = Souders's viscosity constant (Table 9-6)

k = thermal conductivity, cal/(sec)(°K)(cm); Boltzmann's constant

m = I/ρ_L; mass of molecule

M = molecular weight

n = number density of molecules

N_0 = Avogadro's number

P = pressure, atm; P_c, critical pressure; P_r, reduced pressure, P/P_c; P_{c_m}, pseudocritical pressure of mixture

R = gas constant

R^0 = parameter defined in Eq. (9-59)

S = Sutherland constant in Eq. (9-20)

ΔS^* = entropy of activation in Eq. (9-54)

T = temperature, °K; T_c, critical temperature; T_r, reduced temperature, T/T_c; T_{c_m}, pseudocritical temperature of mixture

$T^* = kT/\epsilon_0$

v = molecular velocity; v_y, y component of velocity

V = volume, cm^3/g mole; V_c, critical volume; V_r, reduced volume, V/V_c; V_{r_m}, pseudocritical volume of mixture

x = mole fraction, liquid; exponent in Eq. (9-49)
y = mole fraction, vapor; exponent in Eq. (9-49)
Z = compressibility factor; Z_c, critical compressibility factor; Z_{c_m}, critical compressibility factor for mixture

Greek

δ = polar potential parameter defined in Eq. (9-11)
Δ = correction term in Eq. (9-27)
ϵ_0 = energy-potential parameter
Θ = Thomas viscosity constant (Table 9-7)
μ = viscosity, centipoises; μ^0, special notation designating value at pressure around 1 atm; μ_L, liquid; μ_K, kinetic contribution in Eq. (9-47); μ_F, intermolecular contribution in Eq. (9-47); μ_c, at the critical point; μ_m, for the mixture; μ_p dipole moment in Eq. (9-11)
ν = kinematic viscosity, μ/ρ
ξ = $T_c^{1/6}/M^{1/2}P_c^{2/3}$; ξ_m for the mixture
ρ = density, usually g moles/cm^3; ρ_c, critical density; ρ_r, reduced density, ρ/ρ_c; ρ_m, density of mixture; ρ_L, density of liquid
ρ^* = ρb_0
σ = molecular diameter, A
ϕ = mixture viscosity parameter in Eq. (9-32) or in Eq. (9-35) for Wilke's method
$\varphi(r)$ = intermolecular potential energy as a function of distance r
φ = volume fraction
χ = correction factor for Enskog's relation [Eq. (9-21)]
ω = acentric factor (Sec. 2-7)
Ω_v = collision integral for viscosity; Ω_D, collision integral for diffusion

Subscripts

i, j = components i, j
A, B = components A, B
L = liquid

REFERENCES FOR CHAPTER 9

1. Agaev, N. A., and I. F. Golubev: *Khim. i Tekhnol. Topliva i Masel*, **8**(6):28 (1963); *Chem. Abstr.*, **60**:11,399 (1964).
2. Albright, L. F., and J. Lohrenz: *AIChE J.*, **2**:290 (1956).
3. Amdur, I.: *AIChE J.*, **8**:521 (1962).
4. Amdur, I., and E. A. Mason: *Phys. Fluids*, **1**:370 (1958).
5. Anderson, R. L.: Ph.D. thesis, Pennsylvania State University, 1961; *Dissertation Abstr.*, **23**:264 (1962).
6. Andrade, E. N. daC.: *Endeavour*, **13**:117 (1954).
7. Andrade, E. N. daC.: *Nature*, **125**:309 (1930).
8. Andrade, E. N. daC.: *Phil. Mag.*, **17**:497, 698 (1934).
9. Andrussow, L.: *Z. Èlectrochem.*, **61**:253 (1957).
10. Arnold, J. H.: *J. Chem. Phys.*, **1**:170 (1933).
10a. Babb, S. E., and G. J. Scott: *J. Chem. Phys.*, **40**:3666 (1964).
11. Bak, T. A., and K. Anderson: *Acta Chem. Scand.*, **12**:1367 (1958).
12. Barker, J. A.: "Lattice Theories of the Liquid State," The Macmillan Company, New York, 1963.
13. Baron, J. D., J. G. Root, and F. W. Wells: *J. Chem. Eng. Data*, **4**:283 (1959).
14. Barrer, R. M.: *Trans. Faraday Soc.*, **39**:48 (1943).

15. Bhagwat, W. V., and M. V. Subnis: *J. Indian Chem. Soc.*, **25**:165 (1948).
16. Bicher, L. B.: Ph.D. thesis, University of Michigan, 1943.
17. Bingham, E. C., and L. W. Spooner: *Physics*, **4**:387 (1933).
18. Bingham, E. C., and S. D. Stookey: *J. Am. Chem. Soc.*, **61**:1625 (1939).
19. Bird, R. B., J. O. Hirschfelder, and C. F. Curtiss: *Trans. ASME*, **76**:1011 (1954).
20. Bondi, A.: *Ann. N.Y. Acad. Sci.*, **53**:870 (1951).
21. Bondi, A.: *Ind. Eng. Chem. Fundamentals*, **2**:95 (1963); *J. Phys. Chem.*, **68**:441 (1964); *J. Polymer Sci.*, (A)**2**:3159 (1964).
22. Boon, J. P., and G. Thomaes: *Physica*, **28**:1074 (1962).
23. Boon, J. P., and G. Thomaes: *Physica*, **29**:208 (1963).
24. Bradley, R. S. (ed.): "High Pressure Physics and Chemistry," p. 18, Academic Press, New York, 1963.
25. Brandt, W. W.: Ph.D. thesis, Polytechnic Institute of Brooklyn, 1956.
26. Brebach, W. J., and G. Thodos: *Ind. Eng. Chem.*, **50**:1095 (1958).
27. Bridgman, P. W.: *Proc. Am. Acad. Arts Sci.*, **61**:57 (1926).
28. Brokaw, R. S.: *J. Chem. Phys.*, **29**:391 (1958).
29. Brokaw, R. S.: *NASA Tech. Rept.* R-81, 1961.
30. Bromley, L. A., and C. R. Wilke: *Ind. Eng. Chem.*, **43**:1641 (1951).
31. Brush, S. G.: *Chem. Revs.*, **62**:513 (1962).
32. Buddenberg, J. W., and C. R. Wilke: *Ind. Eng. Chem.*, **41**:1345 (1949).
33. Carmichael, L. T., H. H. Reamer, and B. H. Sage: *J. Chem. Eng. Data*, **8**:400 (1963).
34. Carr, N. L.: *Inst. Gas Technol. Research Bull.* 23, June, 1953.
35. Carr, N. L., R. Kobayashi, and D. B. Burroughs: *J. Petrol. Technol.*, **6**(10):47 (1954).
36. Carr, N. L., J. D. Parent, and R. E. Peck: *Chem. Eng. Progr., Symposium Ser.*, **51**(16):91 (1955).
37. Chandramoule, V. V., and G. S. Laddha: *Indian J. Technol.*, **1**:199 (1963).
38. Chapman, S., and T. G. Cowling: "The Mathematical Theory of Non-uniform Gases," Cambridge University Press, New York, 1939.
39. Cheung, H.: *Univ. Calif. Radiation Lab. Rept.* 8230, Berkeley, Calif., April, 1958.
40. Codegone, C.: *Allgem. Wärmetech.*, **8**:49 (1957).
41. Comings, E. W., and R. S. Egly: *Ind. Eng. Chem.*, **32**:714 (1940).
42. Comings, E. W., and B. J. Mayland: *Chem. Met. Eng.*, **52**(3):115 (1945).
43. Comings, E. W., B. J. Mayland, and R. S. Egly: "The Viscosity of Gases at High Pressures," *Univ. Illinois Eng. Expt. Sta. Bull. Ser.*, 354, Urbana, Ill., 1944–1945.
44. Coremans, J. M. J., and J. J. M. Beenakker: *Physica*, **26**:653 (1960).
45. Cornelissen, J., and H. I. Waterman: *Chem. Eng. Sci.*, **4**:238 (1955).
46. Dahler, J. S.: "Thermodynamic and Transport Properties of Gases, Liquids and Solids," pp. 14–24, McGraw-Hill Book Company, New York, 1959.
47. Damasius, G., and G. Thodos: *Ind. Eng. Chem. Fundamentals*, **2**:73 (1963).
48. Davis, D. S.: *Ind. Eng. Chem.*, **33**:1537 (1941).
49. Dean, D. E., and L. I. Stiel: *AIChE J.*, **11**:526 (1965).
50. Dolan, J. P.: M.S. thesis, Illinois Institute of Technology, 1962.
51. Dolan, J. P., K. E. Starling, A. L. Lee, B. E. Eakin, and R. T. Ellington: *J. Chem. Eng. Data*, **8**:396 (1963).
52. Dow, R. B.: *Physics*, **6**:71 (1935).
53. Dullien, F. A. L.: *Trans. Faraday Soc.*, **59**:856 (1963).
54. Eakin, B. E., and R. T. Ellington: *J. Petrol. Technol.*, **15**:210 (1963).
55. Eakin, B. E., K. E. Starling, J. P. Dolan, and R. T. Ellington: *J. Chem. Eng. Data*, **7**:33 (1962).

56. Edmister, W. C.: "Applied Hydrocarbon Thermodynamics," Gulf Publishing Co., Houston, Tex., 1961.
57. Ellington, R. T.: Ph.D. thesis, Illinois Institute of Technology, 1962.
58. Eversteijn, F. C., J. M. Stevens, and H. I. Waterman: *Chem. Eng. Sci.*, **11**:267 (1960).
59. Ewell, R. H., and H. Eyring: *J. Chem. Phys.*, **5**:726 (1937).
60. Eyring, H., and R. P. Marchi: *J. Chem. Ed.*, **40**:562 (1963).
61. Fialkov, U. Y.: *Zhur. Fiz. Khim.*, **37**:1745, 2149, 2539 (1963).
62. Flynn, L. W., and G. Thodos: *AIChE J.*, **8**:362 (1962).
63. Flynn, L. W., and G. Thodos: *J. Chem. Eng. Data*, **6**:457 (1961).
64. Francis, W. E.: *Trans. Faraday Soc.*, **54**:1492 (1958).
65. Frenkel, Y. I.: "Kinetic Theory of Liquids," Oxford University Press, New York, 1946.
66. Friend, J. N.: *Trans. Faraday Soc.*, **31**:542 (1935).
67. Friend, J. N., and W. D. Hargreaves: *Phil. Mag.*, **34**:643 (1943).
68. Friend, J. N., and W. D. Hargreaves: *Phil. Mag.*, **34**:810 (1943).
69. Friend, J. N., and W. D. Hargreaves: *Phil. Mag.*, **35**:136 (1944).
70. Friend, J. N., and W. D. Hargreaves: *Phil. Mag.*, **35**:631 (1944).
71. Friend, J. N., and W. D. Hargreaves: *Phil. Mag.*, **36**:731 (1945).
72. Furth, R.: *Proc. Cambridge Phil. Soc.*, **37**:281 (1941).
73. Gambhir, R. S., and S. C. Saxena: *Trans. Faraday Soc.*, **60**:38 (1964).
74. Gambill, W. R.: *Chem. Eng.*, **65**(19):169 (1958).
75. Gambill, W. R.: *Chem. Eng.*, **65**(21):157 (1958).
76. Gambill, W. R.: *Chem. Eng.*, **65**(23):157 (1958).
77. Gambill, W. R.: *Chem. Eng.*, **66**(1):127 (1959).
78. Gambill, W. R.: *Chem. Eng.*, **66**(3):123 (1959).
79. Gambill, W. R.: *Chem. Eng.*, **66**(5):151 (1959).
80. Gandhi, J. M., and S. C. Saxena: *Indian J. Pure Appl. Phys.*, **2**:83 (1964).
81. Gemant, A.: *J. Appl. Phys.*, **12**:827 (1941).
82. Giddings, J. G., and R. Kobayashi: Paper submitted to *AIChE J.*, 1964.
83. Girifalco, L. A.: *J. Chem. Phys.*, **23**:2446 (1955).
84. Glasstone, S., K. J. Laidler, and H. Eyring: "The Theory of Rate Processes," McGraw-Hill Book Company, New York, 1941.
85. Godridge, A. M.: *Brit. Coal Utilisation Research Assoc. Monthly Bull.*, **18**(1): (1954).
86. Griest, E. M., W. Webb, and R. W. Schiessler: *J. Chem. Phys.*, **29**:711 (1958).
87. Grunberg, L., and A. H. Nissan: *Ind. Eng. Chem.*, **42**:885 (1950).
88. Grunberg, L., and A. H. Nissan: *Trans. Faraday Soc.*, **44**:1013 (1948).
89. Gutman, F., and L. M. Simmons: *J. Appl. Phys.*, **23**:977 (1952).
90. Halulov, H. M.: *Zhur. Fiz. Khim.*, **36**:2474 (1961).
91. Hammond, L. W., K. S. Howard, and R. A. McAllister: *J. Phys. Chem.*, **62**:637 (1958).
92. Heiks, J. R., and E. Orban: *J. Phys. Chem.*, **60**:1025 (1956).
93. Helfand, E., and S. A. Rice: *J. Chem. Phys.*, **32**:1642 (1960).
94. Helland, E. J.: *J. Chem. Phys.*, **24**:1173 (1956).
95. Herning, F., and L. Zipperer: *Gas u. Wasserfach*, **79**:49 (1936).
96. Hind, R. K., E. McLaughlin, and A. R. Ubbelohde: *Trans. Faraday Soc.*, **56**:328, 331 (1960).
97. Hirschfelder, J. O., R. B. Bird, and E. L. Spotz: *Trans. ASME*, **71**:921 (1949).
98. Hirschfelder, J. O., C. F. Curtiss, and R. B. Bird: "Molecular Theory of Gases and Liquids," John Wiley & Sons, Inc., New York, 1954.
99. Hirschfelder, J. O., M. H. Taylor, and T. Kihara: WIS-OOR-29, Theoretical Chemistry Laboratory, University of Wisconsin, Madison, Wis., July 8, 1960.

100. Horrocks, J. K., and E. McLaughlin: *Trans. Faraday Soc.*, **58**:1357 (1962).
101. Howard, J. S., and R. A. McAllister: *AIChE J.*, **4**:362 (1958).
102. Innes, K. K.: *J. Phys. Chem.*, **60**:817 (1956).
103. Irany, E. P.: *J. Am. Chem. Soc.*, **60**:2106 (1938).
104. Irany, E. P.: *J. Am. Chem. Soc.*, **61**:1734 (1939).
105. Irany, E. P.: *J. Am. Chem. Soc.*, **65**:1392 (1943).
106. Iyer, M. P. V.: *Indian J. Phys.*, **5**:371 (1930).
107. Jobling, A., and A. S. C. Laurence: *Proc. Roy. Soc. (London)*, **A206**:257 (1951).
108. Jones, W. J., and S. T. Bowden: *Phil. Mag.*, **36**:705 (1945).
109. Jossi, J. A., L. I. Stiel, and G. Thodos: *AIChE J.*, **8**:59 (1962).
110. Kalidas, R., and G. S. Laddha: *J. Chem. Eng. Data*, **9**:142 (1964).
111. Kerrisk, J. F., J. D. Rogers, and E. F. Hammel: "Transport Properties of He³, He⁴, H₂, D₂, T₂, and Ne in the Liquid State According to the Quantum Mechanical Principle of Corresponding States," University of California, Los Alamos Scientific Laboratory, Los Alamos, N.M., 1964.
112. Kestin, J., and W. Leidenfrost: *Physica*, **25**:525 (1959).
113. Kestin, J., and J. R. Moszynski: "Thermodynamic and Transport Properties of Gases, Liquids, and Solids," pp. 70–77, McGraw-Hill Book Company, New York, 1959.
114. Kestin, J., J. H. Whitelaw, and T. F. Zien: *Physica*, **30**:161 (1964).
115. Kierstead, H. A., and J. Turkevitch: *J. Chem. Phys.*, **12**:24 (1944).
116. Kobeko, P. P., E. V. Kuvshinskii, and N. I. Shishken: *Akad. Nauk S.S.S.R., Otdel. Tekh. Nauk*, **2**:71 (1944); *Chem. Abstr.*, **40**:3316 (1946).
117. Konowalow, D. D., and J. O. Hirschfelder: WIS-AF-17, Theoretical Chemistry Laboratory, University of Wisconsin, Madison, Wis., Oct. 18, 1960.
118. Kotišek, J., and J. Marek: *Chem. prümysl*, **5**:330 (1955); *Chem. Abstr.*, **54**:6239 (1960).
119. Kottler, F.: *J. Phys. Chem.*, **47**:277 (1943).
120. Kottler, F.: *J. Phys. Chem.*, **48**:76 (1944).
121. Kuss, E.: *Z. angew. Phys.*, **7**:372 (1955).
122. Lagemann, R. T.: *Ind. Eng. Chem.*, **37**:600 (1945).
123. "Landolt-Börnstein Tables," vol. 4, pt. 1, Springer-Verlag OHG, Berlin, 1955.
124. Lederer, E. L.: *Nature*, **139**:27 (1937).
125. Lewis, W. K., and L. Squires: *Refiner Natural Gasoline Mfr.*, **13**(12):448 (1934).
126. Licht, W., and D. G. Stechert: *J. Phys. Chem.*, **48**:23 (1944).
127. Liley, P. E.: "Progress in International Research on Thermodynamics and Transport Properties," pp. 313–330, Academic Press Inc., New York, 1962.
128. Liley, P. E.: *Symposium on Thermal Properties*, Purdue University, Feb. 23–26, 1959, pp. 40–69, Purdue University, Lafayette, Ind., 1959.
129. Lovell, S. E., and J. O. Hirschfelder: WIS-AF-19, Theoretical Chemistry Laboratory, University of Wisconsin, Madison, Wis., Dec. 20, 1961.
130. Lowitz, D. A., J. W. Spencer, W. Webb, and R. W. Schiessler: *J. Chem. Phys.*, **30**:73 (1959).
131. Luft, N. W., and O. P. Kharbanda: *Research Correspondence*, **7**(6):536 (1954).
132. MacLeod, D. B.: *Trans. Faraday Soc.*, **30**:482 (1934).
133. McAllister, R. A.: *AIChE J.*, **6**:427 (1960).
134. McLaughlin, E.: *Quart. Rev.*, **14**:236 (1960).
135. McLaughlin, E.: *Trans. Faraday Soc.*, **55**:28 (1962).
136. Majumdar, D. K.: *J. Phys. Chem.*, **67**:1374 (1963).
137. Marks, G. W.: *J. Phys. Chem.*, **43**:549 (1939).
138. Marks, L. S. (ed.): "Mechanical Engineers' Handbook," 4th ed., p. 773, McGraw-Hill Book Company, New York, 1941.
139. Marschalko, B., and J. Barna: *Acta Tech. Acad. Sci. Hung.*, **19**:85 (1957).

454   THE PROPERTIES OF GASES AND LIQUIDS

140. Mason, E. A.: *J. Chem. Phys.*, **27**:75 (1957).
141. Mason, E. A., and L. Monchick: *J. Chem. Phys.*, **36**:3746 (1962).
142. Mason, E. A., and L. Monchick: *Ninth International Symposium on Combustion,* p. 713, Academic Press, New York, 1963.
143. Mathur, G. P., and G. Thodos: *AIChE J.*, **9**:596 (1963).
144. Matsen, J. M., and E. F. Johnson: *J. Chem. Eng. Data*, **5**:531 (1960).
145. Michaels, A., A. Bolzen, and W. Schuurman: *Physica*, **20**:1141 (1941).
146. Michels, A., J. A. M. Cox, A. Botzen, and A. S. Friedman: *J. Appl. Physics,* **26**:843 (1955).
147. Miller, A. A.: *J. Chem. Phys.*, **38**:1568 (1963).
148. Miller, A. A.: *J. Phys. Chem.*, **67**:1031 (1963).
149. Miller, A. A.: *J. Phys. Chem.*, **67**: 2809 (1963).
150. Minard, R. A.: An Industrial Rotational Viscometer and Its Use with Materials of Varying Complexity, paper delivered at the First International Instrument Congress and Exposition, Philadelphia, Pa., Sept. 13–23, 1954, Instrument Society of America.
151. Misra, B. N., and Y. P. Varshni: *J. Chem. Eng. Data*, **6**:194 (1961).
152. Monchick, L., and E. A. Mason: CM-993, Johns Hopkins University Applied Physics Laboratory, February, 1961; *J. Chem. Phys.*, **35**:1676 (1961).
153. Nikul'shin, R. K., and N. I. Pyatnitskaya: *Tr. Odessk. Tekhnol. Inst. Pishchevoi i Kholodil'n. Prom.*, **12**:139 (1962); *Chem. Abstr.*, **59**:9351 (1963).
154. Nissan, A. H.: *Nature*, **144**:383 (1939).
155. Nissan, A. H., and L. V. W. Clark: *Nature*, **143**:722 (1939).
156. Nissan, A. H., L. V. W. Clark, and A. W. Nash: *J. Inst. Petrol. Technol.*, **26**:155 (1940).
157. Othmer, D. F., and J. W. Conwell: *Ind. Eng. Chem.*, **37**:1112 (1945).
158. Palit, S. R.: *J. Indian Chem. Soc.*, **40**:721 (1963).
159. Papkov, S.: *Z. physik. Chem.*, **A174**:445 (1935).
160. Perry, J. H. (ed.): "Chemical Engineers' Handbook," McGraw-Hill Book Company, New York, 1950.
161. Petersen, R. C.: *J. Phys. Chem.*, **64**:184 (1960).
162. Powell, R. E., W. E. Rosveare, and H. Eyring: *Ind. Eng. Chem.*, **33**:430 (1941).
163. Prasad, B.: *Phil. Mag.*, **39**:884 (1948).
164. Pratap, R., and G. Narsimhan: *Brit. Chem. Eng.*, **7**:757 (1962).
165. Ranz, W. E., and H. A. Brodowsky: *Chemical Engineering Department, Univ. Minnesota, Tech. Rept.* 1, OOR Project 2340, Minneapolis, Minn., Mar. 15, 1962.
166. Raw, C. J. G., and H. Tang: *J. Chem. Phys.*, **39**:2616 (1963).
167. Reamer, H. H., G. Cokelet, and B. H. Sage: *Anal. Chem.*, **31**:1422 (1959).
168. Reed, T. M., III, and T. E. Taylor: *J. Phys. Chem.*, **63**:58 (1959).
169. Reid, R. C., and L. I. Belenyessy: *J. Chem. Eng. Data*, **5**:150 (1960).
170. Ross, J. F., and G. M. Brown: *Ind. Eng. Chem.*, **49**:2026 (1957).
171. Rutherford, R., M. H. Taylor, and J. O. Hirschfelder: WIS-OOR-29a, Theoretical Chemistry Laboratory, University of Wisconsin, Madison, Wis., Aug. 23, 1960.
172. Samu, B., and F. W. Lima: *Eng. e. quim.* (Rio de Janeiro), **4**(2):21 (1952); *Chem. Abstr.*, **46**:8444 (1952).
173. Sanin, P. I., A. A. Petrov, S. R. Sergienko, and E. A. Nikitskaya: *Zhur. Priklad. Khim.*, **33**:919 (1960); *Chem. Abstr.*, **54**:14,849 (1960).
174. Saxena, S. C., and R. S. Gambhir: *Brit. J. Appl. Phys.*, **14**:436 (1963).
175. Saxena, S. C., and R. S. Gambhir: *Proc. Phys. Soc.* (*London*), **81**:788 (1963).
176. Saxena, S. C., and R. K. Joshi: *Indian J. Phys.*, **37**:479 (1963).
177. Saxena, S. C., and R. K. Joshi: *Physica*, **29**:870 (1963).

178. Saxena, S. C., and T. K. S. Narayanan: *Ind. Eng. Chem. Fundamentals*, **1**:191 (1962).
179. Schulz, G. V.: *Z. Elektrochem.*, **50**:122 (1944).
180. Shimotake, H., and G. Thodos: *AIChE J.*, **4**:257 (1958).
181. Shukla, B. P., and R. P. Bhatnagu: *J. Phys. Chem.*, **59**:988 (1955); *ibid.*, **60**:809 (1956).
182. Silverman, D., and W. E. Roseveare: *J. Am. Chem. Soc.*, **54**:4460 (1932).
183. Smith, A. S., and G. G. Brown: *Ind. Eng. Chem.*, **35**:705 (1943).
184. Souders, M.: *J. Am. Chem. Soc.*, **59**:1252 (1937).
185. Souders, M.: *J. Am. Chem. Soc.*, **60**:154 (1938).
186. Srinivasan, M. K.: *J. Indian Chem. Soc.*, **16**:305 (1939).
187. Srinivasan, M. K., and B. Prasad: *Phil. Mag.*, **33**:258 (1942).
188. Starling, K. E.: M.S. thesis in gas engineering, Illinois Institute of Technology, January, 1960.
189. Starling, K. E., B. E. Eakin, and R. T. Ellington: *AIChE J.*, **6**:438 (1960).
190. Starling, K. E., and R. T. Ellington: *AIChE J.*, **10**:11 (1964).
191. Staveley, L. A. K., and P. F. Taylor: *J. Chem. Soc. (London)*, **1956**:200.
192. Stiel, L. I., and G. Thodos: "Progress in International Research on Thermodynamics and Transport Properties," pp. 352–365, Academic Press, New York, 1962.
193. Stiel, L. I., and G. Thodos: *AIChE J.*, **7**:611 (1961).
194. Stiel, L. I., and G. Thodos: *AIChE J.*, **8**:229 (1962).
195. Stiel, L. I., and G. Thodos: *AIChE J.*, **10**:266 (1964).
196. Stiel, L. I., and G. Thodos: *AIChE J.*, **10**:275 (1964).
196a. Strunk, M. R., W. G. Custead, and G. L. Stevenson: *AIChE J.*, **10**:483 (1964).
197. Svehla, R. A.: Estimated Viscosities and Thermal Conductivities at High Temperatures, *NASA-TRR*-132, 1962.
198. Svehla, R. A.: Private communication, May, 1964.
199. Swensen, R. D.: Ph.D. thesis, State University of Iowa, 1961.
200. Swift, G. W., J. A. Christy, and F. Kurata: *AIChE J.*, **5**:98 (1959).
201. Swift, G. W., J. Lohrenz, and F. Kurata: Paper presented at the American Institute Chemical Engineers Meeting, San Francisco, Calif., December, 1959.
202. Tamura, M., and M. Kurata: *Bull. Chem. Soc. Japan*, **25**:32 (1952).
203. Telang, M. S.: *J. Chem. Phys.*, **17**:536 (1949).
204. Telang, M. S.: *J. Phys. Chem.*, **49**:579 (1945), **50**:373 (1946).
205. Thomaes, G., and J. van Itterbeek: *Mol. Phys.*, **2**:372 (1959).
206. Thomas, L. H.: *J. Chem. Soc.*, **1946**:573.
207. Titani, T.: *Bull. Inst. Phys. Chem. Res. (Tokyo)*, **8**:433 (1929).
208. Trevoy, D. J., and H. G. Drickamer: *J. Chem. Phys.*, **17**:582 (1949).
209. Uyehara, O. A., and K. M. Watson: *Natl. Petrol. News*, **36**:R-714 (1944).
210. Van Wyk, W. R., J. H. Van der Veen, H. C. Brinkman, and W. A. Seeder: *Physica*, **7**:45 (1940).
211. Vanderslice, J. T., S. Weissman, E. A. Mason, and R. J. Fallon: *Phys. Fluids*, **5**:155 (1962).
212. Vermesse, J., and B. Vodar: *J. chim. Phys.*, **60**:1407 (1963).
213. Watson, K. M., F. R. Wien, and G. B. Murphy: *Ind. Eng. Chem.*, **28**:605 (1936).
214. Whalley, E.: *Can. J. Chem.*, **32**:485 (1954).
215. Wilke, C. R.: *J. Chem. Phys.*, **18**:517 (1950).
216. Winning, W. C.: *J. Inst. Petrol.*, **45**:9 (1959).
217. Wobser, R., and Fr. Müller: *Kolloid-Beihefte*, **52**:165 (1941).
218. Wright, F. J.: *J. Chem. Eng. Data*, **6**:454 (1961).
219. Wright, P. G., and P. Gray: *Trans. Faraday Soc.*, **58**:1 (1962).

CHAPTER 10

THERMAL CONDUCTIVITY

10-1 Scope

Thermal conductivities of both gases and liquids are considered in this chapter. The theory of thermal conduction in gases is discussed in Sec. 10-2 and in liquids in Sec. 10-9. Estimation techniques for gases at low pressure are covered in Sec. 10-3 and temperature and pressure effects in Secs. 10-4 and 10-5. Similar topics for liquids are dealt with in Secs. 10-10 to 10-12. Thermal conductivities of gas and liquid mixtures are covered in Secs. 10-6, 10-7, and 10-13. Chemically reacting gas mixtures are discussed in Sec. 10-8 and Prandtl numbers in Sec. 10-14.

The units used for thermal conductivity throughout this chapter are cal/(cm)(sec)(°K). To convert these units to Btu/(ft)(hr)(°R), multiply by 241.9; to convert to watts/(cm)(°K) or joules/(cm)(sec)(°K), multiply by 4.186.

10-2 Theory of Thermal Conduction in Gases

The conduction of heat is due to the interaction of molecules from regions of different temperature. A very elementary kinetic picture was given in Sec. 9-3 for molecules which were idealized as noninteracting hard spheres of diameter σ moving at a constant velocity v with a mean free path L, that is,

$$\text{Energy flux} = q = -k \, dT/dz = (-vL/3)C_v\rho \qquad (9\text{-}4)^*$$

Upon comparing Eq. (9-4) with the equation for viscosity [Eq. (9-6)], it is easily shown that

$$(k/\mu)(M/C_v) = kM\gamma/\mu C_p = \gamma/N_{\text{Pr}} = 1.0 \qquad (10\text{-}1)$$

In Eq. (10-1), k is in cal/(cm)(sec)(°K), μ in poises [g/(cm)(sec)], and

---

* As written, the heat flux refers only to the z direction; similar equations could be written for other directions. As liquids and gases are almost always isotropic, however, k has the same value in all directions. Commonly the equation is written in the more general form $\vec{q} = -k \, \text{grad} \, T$. Also, in a mixture of gases some energy is transferred by thermal-diffusion processes; this latter effect rarely exceeds 1 per cent or so of the energy transfer due to molecular collisions and is usually neglected.

C_v (or C_p) in cal/(g mole)(°K) and M is the molecular weight, γ the ratio C_p/C_v, and N_{Pr}, the Prandtl number. Although, as discussed below, Eq. (10-1) is very inaccurate, it is still a remarkable result of kinetic theory in that the three properties k, μ, C_v are related in a simple way; since each can be independently measured, the accuracy of Eq. (10-1) may be readily determined. In actual fact, the ratio $kM/\mu C_v$ is found experimentally to be larger than 1, but by a considerably more sophisticated kinetic-theory analysis (34, 81, 90), with the assumptions of inelastic molecules interacting in a spherical symmetric force field still retained, the following result is obtained:

$$k = [(1.9891)(10^{-4})(T/M)^{\frac{1}{2}}]/\sigma^2\Omega_v \qquad (10\text{-}2)$$

σ is a characteristic dimension of the molecule, and Ω_v is a collision integral relative to a hard, noninteracting sphere model. If the intermolecular potential-energy function chosen is that of Lennard-Jones, then σ becomes the Lennard-Jones distance parameter (Sec. 2-10 or Appendix G) and Ω_v is the same collision integral tabulated in Table 9-1 as a function of kT/ϵ_0. ϵ_0 is the characteristic Lennard-Jones energy parameter, and values of ϵ_0/k are tabulated in Appendix G or may be estimated by means discussed in Sec. 2-10.

To compare Eq. (10-2) with (10-1), the former may be divided by Eq. (9-9) to yield

$$kM/\mu = 15R/4 \qquad (10\text{-}3)$$

For the molecular model chosen, the only energy-storage mode is translational (the hard sphere is assumed not to rotate, vibrate, etc.); so $C_v = \frac{3}{2}R$. Incorporating this in Eq. (10-3),

$$kM/\mu C_v \equiv f = (15R/4)(2/3R) = 2.5 \qquad (10\text{-}4)$$

Comparing Eq. (10-4) with (10-1), it is apparent that a substantial change has been effected in the estimated value of k. The choice of the Lennard-Jones potential was not particularly important in obtaining Eq. (10-4); in fact just about any molecular model would have given almost identical results, since k and μ depend linearly on the same collision cross section. Chapman and Cowling (34) have shown that one obtains a value of f equal to 2.5 as a first approximation for all smooth, spherically symmetrical molecules.*

The relation $f = 2.5$, as given in Eq. (10-4), is definitely limited to spherically symmetric molecules which possess only translational energy. It is therefore applicable for the monatomic gases, and, in fact, it does represent the data for such gases very well. Figure 10-1 shows a few

* Further approximations for rigid spheres indicate that $f = 2.522$; for molecules repelling with a force varying inversely as the nth power of the intermolecular distance, the values of f vary from 2.500 for $n = 5$ to 2.522 for $n = \infty$ (34).

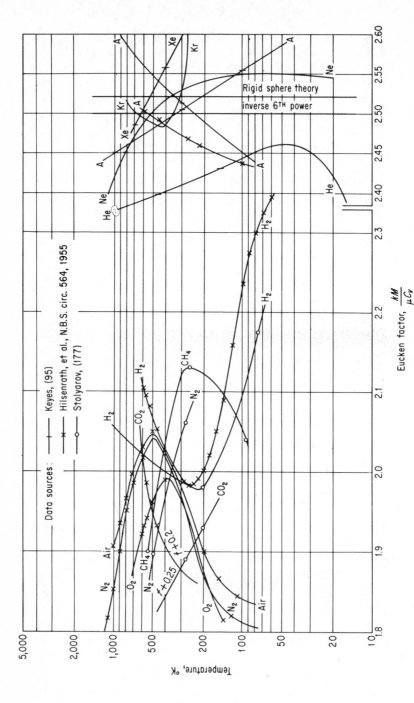

FIG. 10-1. Variation of the Eucken factor $kM/\mu C_v$ with temperature. (P. E. Liley, *Symposium on Thermal Properties, Purdue University, Lafayette, Ind.*, Feb. 23–26, 1959, pp. 40–69.)

values of f (called the *Eucken factor* in the plot) for the monatomic gases between 50 and 1000°K (106). It is apparent that Eq. (10-4) is applicable in such cases, with little error even over wide temperature ranges.

It is also apparent from this plot that f is considerably less than 2.5 for gases other than the monatomic type. The qualitative reason for the decrease is easy to visualize. The theory thus far has considered only energy carried and transferred by translational motion, though the fact that heat capacities of polyatomic gases often greatly exceed monatomic values clearly indicates that a substantial fraction of molecular energy is contained in storage modes other than translational. Molecules moving between different temperature regions also carry and transfer this internal energy upon interacting. Both the heat capacity and thermal conductivity of polyatomic gases are larger than for monatomic gases. This increase is not in proportion, since the mechanism of internal-energy transfer is apparently less efficient than for translational exchange and thus the ratio $kM/\mu C_v \equiv f$ decreases, the viscosity being essentially unaffected. This has been shown quantitatively for a molecular model consisting of "rough" spheres which have rotational energy (34) and is inferred for other, more realistic molecular models.

10-3 Estimation of the Thermal Conductivity of Polyatomic Gases

Eucken and Modified Eucken Models. Eucken proposed to correct Eq. (10-4) for the case of polyatomic molecules by splitting the thermal conductivity into two parts, one to account for the exchange of translational energy and the other for internal energy. In general form, Eq. (10-4) can then be written as,

$$kM/\mu = f_{tr}C_{tr} + f_{int}C_{int} \qquad (10\text{-}5)$$

The physical interpretation of this formulation is that there is no interaction between translational-energy exchange and the simultaneous process of internal energy exchange (44a, 98a, 113, 126, 160, 174, 191, 192) though interpretations often differ (79, 155, 167, 178).

Equation (10-5) has proved useful in estimating thermal conductivities. Invariably, f_{tr} is set equal to 2.5 to force the equation to reduce to Eq. (10-4) for a monatomic gas, C_{tr} is taken as the classical value $\frac{3}{2}R$, and C_{int} is conveniently expressed as $C_v - C_{tr}$. Inserting these,

$$kM/\mu = 15R/4 + f_{int}(C_v - 3R/2) \qquad (10\text{-}6)$$

Eucken chose $f_{int} = 1.0$, whereby Eq. (10-6) reduces to

$$kM/\mu = 9R/4 + C_v = 4.47 + C_v = [(9 - 5/\gamma)/4]C_p \qquad (10\text{-}7)$$

where $\gamma = C_p/C_v$. This is the well-known Eucken correlation for polyatomic gases at low pressures.

The many intuitive assumptions that led to Eq. (10-6) are open to question and have been thoroughly discussed in the literature; the most serious criticism (other than the splitting of k into discrete parts) appears to be the assumption that $f_{int} = 1.0$. Ubbelohde (185), Chapman and Cowling (34), Hirschfelder (79), and Schäfer (161) have suggested that the flow of internal energy should be regarded as a type of diffusional transport, and their analyses indicate that $f_{int} = 1/N_{Sc} = M\rho D/\mu$. Here N_{Sc} is the Schmidt number, ρ the density, and D the self-diffusion coefficient. Rather than evaluate the individual terms in N_{Sc}, it can be shown from Eqs. (9-9) and (11-11) with Tables 9-1 and 11-1 that $M\rho D/\mu$ is about 1.32 and almost independent of temperature. (This is also true for intermolecular potential functions other than the Lennard-Jones.) By using this value, Eq. (10-6) becomes

$$kM/\mu = 1.77R + 1.32C_v = (1.77 - 0.45/\gamma)C_p \qquad (10\text{-}8)$$

Equation (10-8) is often referred to as the *modified Eucken correlation* and was used by Svehla (178) in his compilation of high-temperature gas properties.

Experimental data for nonpolar polyatomic gases seem to indicate that Eucken factors ($f \equiv kM/\mu C_v$) lie between those calculated from Eqs. (10-7) and (10-8); Eq. (10-7) yields low values, but closer to experimental values at the lower temperatures, whereas Eq. (10-8) yields high values, but closer to experimental data at the higher temperatures. For polar gases, both predict f values considerably in excess of those calculated from experimental data.

Equations (10-7) and (10-8) indicate the limit one can attain with the simple Eucken treatment. Further studies have proceeded via three routes: (1) a more detailed theoretical analysis of the conduction process as exemplified by the Mason and Monchick treatment, (2) a more complex splitting of k into various terms in a method proposed by Bromley, and (3) empirical modifications of Eqs. (10-7) and (10-8). Each of these techniques is discussed briefly below.

Mason and Monchick Analysis. In a pioneer paper published in 1962, Mason and Monchick (113) discussed the rigorous kinetic-theory approach to estimate thermal conductivities of polyatomic molecules, allowing for inelastic collisions wherein internal- and translational-energy exchange occurs during collision. They made use of the formal dynamical treatments of Wang Chang and Uhlenbeck (194) and Taxman (180). As the theoretical expressions of these last two studies lead to equations which are almost impossible to solve, Mason and Monchick introduced several simplifying approximations and showed that, if one neglected the inelastic-collision concept, then one would obtain Eq. (10-6) with f_{int} as $M\rho D/\mu$. Next, by considering the inelastic-collision processes, they obtained Eq. (10-5). However, whereas in the modified Eucken analysis $f_{tr} = \frac{5}{2}$ and $f_{int} = M\rho D/\mu$, in the more elaborate kinetic-theory analysis these coefficients become

$$f_{tr} = \frac{5}{2}\{1 - \frac{5}{6}[1 - \frac{2}{5}(M\rho D/\mu)(C_{int}/R)(\mu/P\tau)]\} \qquad (10\text{-}9)$$
$$f_{int} = (M\rho D/\mu)\{1 + \frac{5}{4}[1 - \frac{2}{5}(M\rho D/\mu)(\mu/P\tau)]\} \qquad (10\text{-}10)$$

The key to Eqs. (10-9) and (10-10) lies in determining the relaxation time τ, which is a measure of the time required to exchange translational energy with internal energy. Commonly the relaxation time is expressed as a collision number Z, which is indicative of the number of collisions required to interchange a quantum of internal energy with translational energy. Thus,

$$Z = \tau/\tau_{coll} \qquad (10\text{-}11)$$

where τ_{coll} = mean time between collisions = $4\pi\mu/P$. Upon inserting Eq. (10-11) in Eqs. (10-9) and (10-10) and rearranging, with $M\rho D/\mu$ assumed as 1.32, $C_{tr} = \frac{3}{2}R$, and $C_{int} = C_v - C_{tr}$, then Eq. (10-5) becomes

$$kM/\mu = 1.32C_v + 1.77R - (2/\pi)(\frac{5}{2} - M\rho D/\mu)^2 \sum_k C_{vk}/Z_k$$
$$= 1.32C_v + 1.77R - 0.917 \sum_k C_{vk}/Z_k \qquad (10\text{-}12)$$

In this expansion the index k refers to the specific mode of energy storage considered, and Z_k is then the collision number to transfer energy from the kth mode to translational energy. The two principal storage modes are rotational and vibrational. For the former, values of Z_{rot} are about 10 or less (except for hydrogen),* and for the latter Z_{vib} is as high as 10^3 to 10^7 [except perhaps for some flexible molecules (127)]. It is obvious that rotational-translational energy exchange is more important.

Many authors have discussed the use of correlations similar or equal to Eq. (10-12) (25, 46, 114, 126, 127, 134, 155, 160, 174) and values of Z_{rot} determined by back calculating from experimental k, μ, and C_v values or by very approximate theoretical methods.

In summary, Eq. (10-12) is the best theoretical method to determine thermal conductivity for polyatomic gases.† Values of kM/μ calculated from this equation (with $Z_{vib} \sim \infty$ and $Z_{rot} \sim 1$ to 10) usually lie between the Eucken correlation (10-7) and the modified Eucken correlation (10-8). Z_{rot} varies somewhat with temperature [see Eq. (49) of Ref. 113] but this variation is often neglected. The relation is applicable to polar and non-polar gases but has only been tested with gases of simple structure. Judging from the current literature, one could, however, predict that Eq. (10-12) will be used more and more and modified accordingly as

* For example, O'Neal and Brokaw (127) report recent values of Z_{rot} as CH_4, 9.4; CF_4, 3.0; SF_6, 2.5; C_2H_4, 2.4; C_2H_6, 4.0; O_2, 12; N_2, 7.3; CO_2, 2.4; and C_2H_2, 1.8.

† A recent paper by L. Monchick, A. N. G. Pereira and E. A. Mason, *J. Chem. Phys.*, **42**, 3241 (1965) has validated many of the assertions made in the earlier paper (113).

TABLE 10-1. INTERNAL-ROTATIONAL HEAT-CAPACITY CONTRIBUTION
$C_{int\,rot}$ in cal/(g mole)(°C)

Temperature, °K	CH₃—C=O | R	—CH₂—OH	RCH₂—O—CH₂R
200	1.79	1.4	2.24
298	1.52	1.35	2.33
400	1.34	1.25	2.26
500	1.24	1.20	2.09
600	1.18	1.18	1.91
700	1.10	1.16	1.71
800	1.09	1.15	1.66
900	1.08	1.14	1.55
1000	1.06	1.13	1.47

NOTE: For additional bond contributions, refer to Table 5-5.

experimental data are analyzed in the light of the relaxation phenomena between internal- and translational-energy modes.*

Bromley Analysis. Bromley (26) started with Eq. (10-5) but modified f_{tr} and expanded the term $f_{int}C_{int}$ as follows:

$$kM/\mu = (2.5 - \alpha)C_{tr} + \beta C_{vib} + \psi C_{rot} + C_{int\,rot} \qquad (10\text{-}13)$$

C_{tr} and C_{rot} were taken equal to the classical values $\frac{3}{2}R$ and $F_{ir}R/2$, where R is the gas constant and F_{ir} is the number of degrees of freedom for external rotation. C_{vib} was taken to be $C_v - \frac{5}{2}R$ for linear molecules and $C_v - 3R - C_{int\,rot}$ for nonlinear molecules. The internal-rotational heat-capacity contribution $C_{int\,rot}$ was calculated from the magnitude of the potential barrier to internal rotation and the reduced moment of inertia of the rotating groups. Table 10-1 lists values of $C_{int\,rot}$ as a function of temperature for three types of bonds; other values may be obtained from Table 5-5.

The coefficient α makes allowance for the increased interaction on each collision which results from the polar character of the colliding molecules. Although noting that this might better be expressed as a function of a dimensionless group involving the dipole moment, Bromley found it convenient to relate α empirically to the difference between the actual entropy of vaporization per unit volume and the ideal entropy of vaporization given by the Kistiakowsky equation [see Eq. (4-70) with $K_F = 1.0$]. The proportionality constant was found empirically to be 3.0,

$$\alpha = 3.0\rho_b(\Delta S_{v_b} - 8.75 - R \ln T_b) \qquad (10\text{-}14)$$

* No mention has been made of relaxation phenomena from electronic-energy modes, e.g., in NO, or the rotational relaxation quantum phenomenon for H_2. These are discussed in some detail by Mason and Monchick (113).

where ρ_b = liquid density at normal boiling temperature, g mole/cm^3

ΔS_{v_b} = actual entropy of vaporization at T_b, cal/(g mole)(°K)

R = 1.986 cal/(g mole)(°K)

T_b = normal boiling point, °K

α has the units calorie per gram mole per degree Kelvin. Typical values of α are water, 0.90; ammonia, 0.51; methanol, 0.33; n-propyl alcohol, 0.24; acetone, 0.06; benzene, 0.00. Values of ρ_b may be estimated from Chap. 3 and $\Delta S_{v_b} = \Delta H_{v_b}/T_b$ from Chap. 4.

Vibrational energy is assumed to be transferred by a diffusional mechanism in the case of linear molecules, and β should be approximately the same as the self-diffusion group $M\rho D_{11}/\mu$, which as noted previously is close to a value of 1.3; for nonlinear molecules, β may be less than 1.30. Bromley attempted to relate β to the group

$$(C_v - 3R - C_{int\ rot})/(3n - 6 - F_{ir}) = Y$$

Bromley's plot of this relation shows β constant at about 1.30 for $Y < 0.6$ and then dropping rapidly to 1.0 at $Y > 0.85$. The correlation is poor, however, and it would appear that β might be taken as constant at about 1.30.

The coefficient ψ was found empirically to increase with temperature,

$$\psi = \begin{cases} 1.25 - (0.35/T_r) & \text{for linear molecules} \\ 1.32 - (0.23/T_r) & \text{for nonlinear molecules} \end{cases}$$

Bromley's correlation may then be summarized:

For monatomic gases: $\qquad Mk/\mu = 2.5C_v$

For linear molecules (considered nonpolar):

$F_{ir} = 2 \qquad C_{rot} = R \qquad C_{vib} = C_v - \tfrac{5}{2}R \qquad \beta = 1.30$
$$\alpha = 0 \qquad \psi = 1.25 - 0.35/T_r$$
$$Mk/\mu = 1.30C_v + 3.40 - 0.70/T_r \qquad (10\text{-}15)$$

For nonlinear molecules:

$F_{ir} = 3 \qquad C_{rot} = 3R/2 \qquad C_{vib} = C_v - 3R - C_{int\ rot} \qquad \beta = 1.30$
$$Mk/\mu = 1.30C_v + 3.60 - 0.3C_{int\ rot} - 0.69/T_r - 3\alpha \qquad (10\text{-}16)$$

In these three equations,

k = thermal conductivity at low pressure, cal/(cm)(sec)(°K)

μ = viscosity, poises

C_v = heat capacity at constant volume, cal/(g mole)(°C)

M = molecular weight

T_r = reduced temperature, T/T_c

α = collision-interaction coefficient from Eq. (10-14)

$C_{int\ rot}$ = internal heat capacity, cal/(g mole)(°C), obtained from Tables 10-1 and 5-5

Equations (10-15) and especially (10-16) bear a striking similarit;
to Eq. (10-12) and may be considered as providing an empirical metho
to estimate the last term in Eq. (10-12), which contains the collisio
number, i.e.,

$$0.886 \sum_k C_{v_k}/Z_k \sim \frac{0.20 + 0.70/T_r}{0.3C_{int\ rot} + 3\alpha + 0.69/T_r} \qquad \begin{array}{l} \text{linear} \\ \text{nonlinear} \end{array}$$

The semiempirical form of Eq. (10-16) also provides a means to handl
nonlinear polar molecules. The accuracy of the Bromley technique i
discussed later under Recommendations.

Empirical Approximations to the Eucken Form. Various writers hav
attempted to express kM/μ in a simple fashion to obtain values of thi
ratio larger than those predicted by the Eucken correlation [Eq. (10-7)]
but less than the modified Eucken correlation [Eq. (10-8)]. Some o
these are shown in the accompanying tabulation to indicate the type o
empirical results obtained. Others of a similar nature are given by Lile

	kM/μ
Kinetic theory, monatomic gases	$2.5C_v$
Eucken	$C_v + 4.47$
Modified Eucken	$1.32C_v + 3.52$
Stiel and Thodos (175)	$1.15C_v + 4.04$

(106). Brokaw (18) presents a nomograph of the modified Eucken, forn
and Svehla (178) calculated values of thermal conductivity for 200 gase
from 100 to 5000°K. Figure 10-2 shows some of these relations plotte
against experimental values for ethyl chloride as given by Vines anc
Bennett (192) (who have tabulated such data for many gases). It is clea
that the monatomic kinetic-theory value [Eq. (10-4)] yields far too high
ratio; the modified Eucken relation [Eq. (10-8)] and the Eucken relation
[Eq. (10-7)] form the upper and lower bands, with the former better a
the higher temperatures and the latter at the lower temperatures. Th
temperature range for this plot is about 40 to 140°C. The empirica
form of Stiel and Thodos represents a compromise. Bromley's methoc
would also have represented such a compromise. Although not evident
from the plot, the dimensionless group $kM/\mu C_v$ is nearly independent
of temperature, varying from 1.40 at 40°C to 1.49 at 140°C; this insen-
sitivity of the group $kM/\mu C_v$ to temperature is, over small temperature
ranges, typical of most materials, polar and nonpolar (192). Grilly (72)
however, has pointed out exceptions (notably hydrogen) and has studied
the temperature effect on $kM/\mu C_v$ over wider temperature ranges.

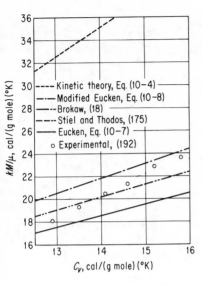

FIG. 10-2. Variation of kM/μ for ethyl chloride.

Misic and Thodos Estimation Technique. The theoretical and semi-theoretical methods outlined in the preceding all originated from the kinetic theory of gases and resulted in a correlation of the group $kM/\mu C_v$ rather than one for k itself. To eliminate the necessity for knowing μ at the temperature of interest, Misic and Thodos (121, 122) have proposed an empirical method based simply on dimensional analysis. By assuming

$$k = \alpha(M^a T_c{}^b T^c P_c{}^d V_c{}^e C_p{}^f R^g) \tag{10-17}$$

then by means of dimensional analysis it is easily shown that

$$k\gamma = \alpha[T_r{}^c (C_p/R)^f Z_c{}^{5\!/\!6 - g - f} R^{5\!/\!6}] \tag{10-18}$$

where γ is defined as

$$\gamma \equiv T_c{}^{1\!/\!6} M^{1\!/\!2}/P_c{}^{2\!/\!3} \tag{10-19}$$

The Misic and Thodos method then reduces to finding the best functional relationship between $k\gamma$ and T_r, C_p, and Z_c. There were found to be several equations for various types of compounds and for different reduced-temperature ranges. These equations are summarized in Table 10-2, and since $k\gamma$ is not dimensionless, the consistent set of units given in this table must be used. The critical constants may be found in Appendix A, or if not there, they may be estimated by methods described in Chap. 2. The low-pressure heat capacity C_p may be estimated as shown in Chap. 5. The accuracy and limitation of these equations are discussed under Recommendations.

TABLE 10-2. SUMMARY OF MISIC AND THODOS LOW-PRESSURE-GAS
THERMAL-CONDUCTIVITY ESTIMATING EQUATIONS

Equation*	Eq. No.	Remarks
$\dfrac{k\gamma}{C_p} = (0.445)(10^{-5})T_r$	(10-20)	Methane, naphthenes, and aromatic hydrocarbons below $T_r = 1.0$
$\dfrac{k\gamma}{C_p} = (10^{-6})(14.52T_r - 5.14)^{2/3}$	(10-21)	All hydrocarbon gases at all temperatures except for cases shown in Eq. (10-20)
$\dfrac{k\gamma}{C_p{}^{3/4}} = (10^{-6})(20.0Z_c + 1.08)T_r{}^{(1.810-2.604Z_c)}$	(10-22)	Nonhydrocarbons, $T_r < 1.0$
$\dfrac{k\gamma}{C_p{}^{3/4}} = (10^{-6})[(195Z_c - 31.94)T_r + 16.83 - 82.5Z_c]^{(1.524-2.800Z_c)}$	(10-23)	Nonhydrocarbons $1.0 \leq T_r \leq 3.0$
$\dfrac{k\gamma}{C_p{}^{3/4}} = (10^{-5})[(7.18 - 18.25Z_c)T_r + 10.21Z_c - 4.91]^{(1.079-1.97Z_c)}$	(10-24)	Nonhydrocarbons, $3 < T_r < 15$

* Units are as follows: k, cal/(cm)(sec)(°K); γ, $T_c{}^{1/6}M^{1/2}/P_c{}^{2/3}$; T_c, °K; T_r, T/T_c; P_c, atm; M, molecular weight; C_p, cal/(g mole)(°K).

The Misic and Thodos method is illustrated in Examples 10-1 and 10-2. The method was devised only for hydrocarbons and nonhydrocarbons of simple molecular structure. Applying the Misic and Thodos correlation for ethyl alcohol as in Example 10-2 illustrates the large errors possible with other molecules. It is also important to note that the Misic and Thodos correlation is *not* applicable to helium, hydrogen, or neon.

Example 10-1. Estimate the low-pressure thermal conductivity of chlorine gas at 0°C. From Appendix A, $T_c = 417°K$, $P_c = 76.1$ atm, $Z_c = 0.276$, and $M = 70.9$; Bromley (26) quotes experimental values of μ, C_v, and k as 119.8×10^{-6} poise, 6.05 cal/(g mole)(°K), and $(17.8)(10^{-6})$ cal/(cm)(sec)(°K).

Solution. Several estimating techniques will be illustrated.

(a) *Bromley.* From Eq. (10-15), since chlorine is diatomic,

$$k = (\mu/M)(1.30C_v + 3.40 - 0.70/T_r)$$
$$= [(119.8)(10^{-6})/70.9][(1.30)(6.05) + 3.40 - (0.70)(417)/(273)]$$
$$= 17.2 \times 10^{-6} \text{ cal/(cm)(sec)(°K)}$$
$$\text{Error} = [(17.2 - 17.8)(10^{-6})/(17.8)(10^{-6})] \times 100 = -3.4\%$$

(b) *Eucken Correlation.* Equation (10-7) yields

$$k = (\mu/M)(C_v + 4.5) = 17.8 \times 10^{-6} \text{ cal/(cm)(sec)(°K)}$$
$$\text{Error} = 0\%$$

(c) *Modified Eucken Correlation.* Equation (10-8) yields

$$k = (\mu/M)(1.30C_v + 3.60) = 19.3 \text{ cal/(cm)(sec)(°K)}$$
$$\text{Error} = [(19.3 - 17.8)(10^{-6})/(17.8)(10^{-6})] \times 100 = +8.4\%$$

(d) *Misic and Thodos Correlation.* Since $T_r = {}^{273}\!/_{417} = 0.655$ is less than unity, Eq. (10-22) is to be used.

$$\gamma = T_c^{1/6} M^{1/2} / P_c^{2/3} = (417)^{1/6}(70.9)^{1/2}/(76.1)^{2/3} = 1.28$$
$$C_p \sim C_v + R = 6.05 + 1.99 = 8.04 \text{ cal/(g mole)(°K)}$$
$$k\gamma/C_p^{3/4} = (10^{-6})(20.0Z_c + 1.08)T_r^{(1.810-2.604Z_c)}$$
$$k = [(8.04)^{3/4}/1.28](10^{-6})[(20.0)(0.276) + 1.08](0.655)^{[1.810-(2.604)(0.276)]}$$
$$= 15.5 \times 10^{-6} \text{ cal/(cm)(sec)(°K)}$$
$$\text{Error} = [(15.5 - 17.8)(10^{-6})/(17.8)(10^{-6})] \times 100 = -12\%$$

(Misic and Thodos report an average error of 2.5 per cent for Cl_2 when T_r varies from 0.47 to 1.62.)

Example 10-2. Estimate the thermal conductivity of ethyl alcohol vapor at 100°C at atmospheric pressure. From Appendix A, $T_c = 516.3°K$, $T_b = 351.7°K$, $P_c = 63.0$ atm, $Z_c = 0.248$, and $M = 46.07$. Bromley (26) reports that experimental values of μ, C_v, and k are $(108.5)(10^{-6})$ poise, 16.4 cal/(g mole)(°K) and $(49.8)(10^{-6})$ cal/(cm)(sec)(°K). The entropy of vaporization at the normal boiling point is 26.3 cal/(g mole)(°K).

Solution. (a) *Bromley Method.* Ethyl alcohol is nonlinear; so Eq. (10-16) is to be used. The liquid density at the normal boiling point must be estimated to determine the polar parameter α. An approximation from Schroeder's method (Sec. 3-18) yields 0.73 g/cm³. From Eq. (10-14),

$$\alpha = (3.0)(0.73/46.07)(26.3 - 8.75 - 1.986 \ln 351.7) = 0.27$$

The value of $C_{int\ rot}$ is to be obtained from the values for the bonds CH_3—CH_2OH and CH_3CH_2—OH from Tables 5-5 and 10-1, respectively. Values obtained by interpolation are 2.15 and 1.28 cal/(g mole)(°K). Thus $C_{int\ rot} = 2.15 + 1.28 = 3.43$ cal/(g mole)(°K). From Eq. (10-16)

$$k = [(108.5)(10^{-6})/(46.07)][(1.30)(16.4) + 3.60 - (0.3)(3.43)$$
$$- (0.69)/(373/516.3) - (3)(0.27)]$$
$$= 52.1 \times 10^{-6} \text{ cal/(cm)(sec)(°K)}$$
$$\text{Error} = [(52.1 - 49.8)(10^{-6})/(49.8)(10^{-6})] \times 100 = +4.6\%$$

(b) *Misic and Thodos.* As $T_r = 373/516.3 = 0.722$ is less than 1, Eq. (10-22) is to be used.

$$\gamma = [(516.3)^{1/6}(46.07)^{1/2}]/(63.0)^{2/3} = 0.444$$
$$C_p \sim C_v + R = 18.4 \text{ cal/(g mole)(°K)}$$
$$k = [(18.4)^{3/4}/0.444](10^{-6})[(20.0)(0.248) + 1.08](0.722)^{[1.810-(2.604)(0.248)]}$$
$$= 83 \times 10^{-6} \text{ cal/(cm)(sec)(°K)}$$

The error is very large, and this technique is not suitable.

Discussion and Recommendations. Several review articles dealing with the problem of estimating gas thermal conductivities have been published (10, 63, 106). The translational contribution for polar gases has been treated by Monchick and Mason (123) and for very high-temperature gases by Amdur and Mason (4).

Three low-pressure estimating techniques have been presented here. The most commonly used is the Eucken correlation [Eq. (10-7)]; this simple form reduces to Eq. (10-4) for monatomic gases where $C_v = \frac{3}{2}R$. Estimations using Eq. (10-7) usually predict low values of thermal conductivity (except for polar molecules). Modification of this equation leads to Eq. (10-8), which usually predicts values of k higher than experimental. More rigorous treatment of the heat-conduction phenomenon has been carried out only for nonpolar gases and leads to predicted values between those given by Eqs. (10-7) and (10-8); unfortunately, to use the more rigorous form, some independent knowledge of the translational-rotational energy relaxation times is required. Various "practical" rules have been suggested in an attempt to "split the difference," and these often yield estimated values of k very close to experimental data.

The second method, that of Bromley, accepts the general Eucken form and empirically fits constants and temperature-dependent parameters to give the best fit to experimental data; as arranged, linear, nonlinear, and even polar molecules can be treated.

The third method, that of Misic and Thodos, avoids the Eucken form and by dimensional analysis attempts a correlation among the thermal conductivity, the heat capacity, and the critical constants. Only hydrocarbons and simple nonhydrocarbons can be treated (but not He, H_2, or Ne). Errors reported for hydrocarbons of various structures average about 2.4 per cent; for simple nonhydrocarbons, the error is only slightly smaller.

Table 10-3 illustrates the type of errors one might encounter using the Eucken correlation [Eq. (10-7)] and the Bromley method [Eqs. (10-15) and (10-16)]. Thirty-nine very diverse compounds are considered. It is surprising that the Bromley method is as accurate as shown considering the diversity of materials covered; i.e., average per cent errors of 3.7 (linear), 3.4 (nonlinear), and 7.5 (polar) were found in the ratio $kM/\mu C_v$. Errors by the Eucken method averaged considerably higher.

It is recommended that, to estimate the low-pressure thermal conductivity of pure gases:

1. For hydrocarbons, use the Misic and Thodos method [Eqs. (10-20) and (10-21)]. Required data are T_c, P_c, and C_p. Errors for the simpler structures will usually be less than 5 per cent. The method has not been tested fully with high-molecular-weight hydrocarbons to allow an error estimate for this class.

2. For all nonhydrocarbons, use the Bromley technique [Eq. (10-15) or (10-16)]. The data required are heat capacity C_v and viscosity at the same temperature, critical temperature, and, if the molecule is polar, the liquid density, normal boiling point, and entropy of vaporization at the normal boiling point. Errors for nonpolar materials should be less than 5 per cent; for polar materials, less than 10 per cent.

TABLE 10-3. COMPARISON BETWEEN CALCULATED AND EXPERIMENTAL
VALUES OF $Mk/\mu C_v$

Compound	$T,$ °K	Exp. $Mk/\mu C_v$ (refs. 26, 192)	Calculated by method of			
			Eucken		Bromley	
			$\dfrac{Mk}{\mu C_v}$	% Error*	$\dfrac{Mk}{\mu C_v}$	% Error*
Nonpolar (or Slightly Polar) Nonlinear Molecules						
Acetone...............	273	1.28	1.29	+ 0.8	1.39	+ 8.6
	339	1.32	1.25	− 5.3	1.40	+ 5.7
	373	1.25	1.23	− 1.6	1.40	+11
	457	1.30	1.19	− 8.5	1.40	+ 7.2
	353	1.30	1.24	− 4.6	1.40	+ 7.2
	393	1.33	1.22	− 8.3	1.40	+ 5.0
	413	1.34	1.21	− 9.7	1.40	+ 4.2
Benzene...............	273	1.51	1.28	−15	1.45	− 4.0
	339	1.44	1.22	−15	1.44	0.0
	373	1.48	1.19	−19	1.43	− 3.4
	486	1.49	1.15	−23	1.41	− 4.7
	353	1.39	1.21	−13	1.43	+ 2.9
	393	1.40	1.18	−16	1.42	+ 1.4
	433	1.41	1.16	−18	1.41	0.0
n-Butane...............	273	1.35	1.22	− 9.7	1.34	− 0.7
	373	1.31	1.17	−11	1.34	+ 2.3
i-Butane...............	273	1.37	1.23	−10	1.35	− 1.5
	373	1.31	1.17	−11	1.35	+ 3.0
Carbon tetrachloride......	273	1.38	1.26	− 8.6	1.40	+ 1.5
	373	1.30	1.23	− 5.4	1.30	0.0
	457	1.28	1.22	− 4.7	1.25	− 2.3
Chloroform..............	273	1.48	1.34	− 9.5	1.48	0.0
	358	1.45	1.29	−11	1.47	+ 1.4
	457	1.42	1.27	−10	1.45	+ 2.1
	333	1.42	1.31	− 7.7	1.48	+ 4.2
	373	1.44	1.29	−10	1.47	+ 2.1
	413	1.48	1.28	−13	1.46	− 1.3
Cyclohexane.............	339	1.40	1.16	−17	1.41	+ 0.7
	375	1.29	1.14	−12	1.40	+ 8.6
	353	1.34	1.15	−14	1.40	+ 4.5
	393	1.36	1.13	−17	1.40	+ 3.0
	433	1.38	1.12	−19	1.38	0.0
Dichlorodifluoromethane..	273	1.52	1.32	−13	1.50	− 1.3
	373	1.56	1.27	−19	1.47	− 5.8
	473	1.57	1.24	−21	1.38	−12
Ethane.................	203	1.57	1.54	− 1.9	1.55	− 1.3
	239	1.58	1.50	− 5.1	1.54	− 2.5
	273	1.57	1.45	− 8.3	1.53	− 2.5
	373	1.57	1.35	−14	1.50	− 4.4
	373	1.53	1.35	−12	1.50	− 2.0
	393	1.52	1.33	−12	1.49	− 2.0

TABLE 10-3. COMPARISON BETWEEN CALCULATED AND EXPERIMENTAL
VALUES OF $Mk/\mu C_v$ (Continued)

Compound	T, °K	Exp. $Mk/\mu C_v$ (refs. 26, 192)	Calculated by method of			
			Eucken		Bromley	
			$\dfrac{Mk}{\mu C_v}$	% Error*	$\dfrac{Mk}{\mu C_v}$	% Error*
Nonpolar (or Slightly Polar) Nonlinear Molecules						
Ethyl acetate............	319	1.24	1.18	− 4.9	1.28	+ 3.2
	373	1.24	1.15	− 7.3	1.29	+ 4.1
	457	1.27	1.13	−11	1.31	+ 3.1
Ethyl ether..............	273	1.35	1.18	−13	1.30	− 3.7
	358	1.46	1.16	−21	1.31	−10
	486	1.45	1.13	−23	1.32	− 9.0
	333	1.36	1.16	−15	1.31	− 3.7
	393	1.38	1.14	−17	1.31	− 5.1
Ethylene..............	273	1.57	1.57	0.0	1.68	+ 7.0
	323	1.53	1.50	− 2.0	1.63	+ 6.5
	373	1.46	1.44	− 1.4	1.61	+10
Hexane................	273	1.21	1.14	− 5.8	1.28	+ 5.8
	293	1.17	1.14	− 2.6	1.28	+ 8.6
	358	1.28	1.12	−13	1.29	+ 0.8
	353	1.34	1.12	−16	1.29	− 3.7
	393	1.35	1.11	−18	1.29	− 4.4
	433	1.37	1.10	−20	1.30	− 5.1
Methane...............	90	1.68	1.75	+ 4.2	1.67	− 0.6
	140	1.73	1.75	+ 1.2	1.75	+ 1.1
	200	1.79	1.74	− 3.0	1.80	+ 0.6
	273	1.78	1.71	− 3.9	1.80	+ 1.1
	320	1.79	1.66	− 7.3	1.78	− 0.6
	380	1.78	1.60	−10	1.75	− 1.7
Methyl chloride..........	273	1.55	1.60	+ 3.2	1.63	+ 5.2
	373	1.57	1.52	− 3.2	1.60	+ 1.9
	486	1.59	1.41	−11	1.57	− 1.3
Methylene chloride.......	273	1.42	1.45	+ 2.1	1.54	+ 8.5
	373	1.40	1.37	− 2.1	1.52	+ 8.5
	485	1.40	1.32	− 5.7	1.51	+ 7.8
n-Pentane..............	273	1.32	1.17	−11	1.30	− 1.5
	293	1.32	1.17	−11	1.30	− 1.5
Propane................	273	1.47	1.31	−11	1.35	− 8.2
	373	1.42	1.23	−13	1.36	− 4.2
	373	1.45	1.23	−15	1.36	− 6.2
	413	1.46	1.21	−17	1.37	− 6.2
Uranium hexafluoride.....	322	1.15	1.15	0.0	1.18	+ 2.6
	362	1.16	1.15	− 0.8	1.15	− 0.8
Average error..........	....	....	....	8.2	....	3.4

TABLE 10-3. COMPARISON BETWEEN CALCULATED AND EXPERIMENTAL
VALUES OF $Mk/\mu C_v$ (*Continued*)

Compound	T, °K	Exp. $Mk/\mu C_v$ (refs. 26, 192)	Calculated by method of			
			Eucken		Bromley	
			$\dfrac{Mk}{\mu C_v}$	% Error*	$\dfrac{Mk}{\mu C_v}$	% Error*
Linear Molecules						
Acetylene..............	198	1.63	1.70	+ 4.3	1.68	+ 3.1
	273	1.51	1.55	+ 2.6	1.64	+ 8.6
	323	1.52	1.50	− 1.3	1.62	+ 6.6
	373	1.52	1.46	− 3.9	1.61	+ 5.9
Carbon dioxide...........	195	1.80	1.79	− 0.6	1.72	− 4.4
	200	1.67	1.76	+ 5.4	1.72	+ 3.0
	273	1.67	1.67	0.0	1.71	+ 2.4
	380	1.75	1.58	− 9.7	1.68	− 4.0
	473	1.56	1.52	− 2.6	1.67	+ 7.1
	598	1.55	1.47	− 5.2	1.64	+ 5.8
	631	1.79	1.47	−18	1.64	− 8.4
	1273	1.58	1.38	−13	1.60	+ 1.3
Carbon disulfide.........	273	1.58	1.52	− 3.8	1.55	− 1.9
	280	1.61	1.51	− 6.2	1.55	− 3.7
Carbon monoxide.........	100	1.76	1.90	+ 8.0	1.81	+ 2.8
	200	1.85	1.90	+ 2.7	1.90	+ 2.7
	273	1.86	1.90	+ 2.1	1.93	+ 3.8
	380	1.94	1.90	− 2.0	1.95	+ 0.5
Chlorine................	˙273	1.74	1.74	0.0	1.70	− 2.3
Hydrogen..............	91	2.35	2.35	0.0	2.38	+ 1.3
	200	2.08	2.02	− 2.9	2.13	+ 2.4
	273	2.03	1.91	− 5.9	2.04	+ 0.5
	473	2.12	1.89	−10	2.02	− 4.7
	673	2.19	1.88	−14	2.02	− 7.8
Nitric oxide.............	100	1.63	1.80	+10	1.70	+ 4.3
	200	1.76	1.85	+ 5.1	1.82	+ 3.4
	273	1.83	1.87	+ 2.2	1.88	+ 2.7
	380	1.92	1.86	− 3.1	1.90	− 1.0
Nitrogen................	273	1.95	1.90	− 2.6	1.94	− 0.5
	500	1.86	1.88	+ 1.1	1.95	+ 4.8
	700	1.74	1.84	+ 5.8	1.93	+11
	873	1.83	1.79	− 2.2	1.90	+ 3.8
	1273	1.73	1.73	0.0	1.86	+ 7.5
Nitrous oxide...........	200	1.62	1.71	+ 5.5	1.69	+ 4.3
	300	1.68	1.61	+ 4.2	1.69	+ 0.5
	380	1.72	1.55	−10	1.67	− 2.9
Oxygen.................	100	1.81	1.90	+ 5.0	1.78	− 1.7
	200	1.91	1.90	− 0.5	1.89	− 1.0
	273	1.92	1.89	− 1.6	1.91	− 0.5
	380	2.00	1.87	− 6.5	1.92	− 4.0
Average error...........	....	....	....	4.8	....	3.7

TABLE 10-3. COMPARISON BETWEEN CALCULATED AND EXPERIMENTAL
VALUES OF $Mk/\mu C_v$ (*Continued*)

Compound	T, °K	Exp. $Mk/\mu C_v$ (refs. 26, 192)	Calculated by method of			
			Eucken		Bromley	
			$\dfrac{Mk}{\mu C_v}$	% Error*	$\dfrac{Mk}{\mu C_v}$	% Error*
Polar Nonlinear Molecules						
Acetaldehyde	313	1.26	1.38	+ 9.6	1.50	+19
	353	1.29	1.36	+ 5.4	1.49	+15
	393	1.31	1.33	+ 1.5	1.48	+13
Acetonitrile	353	1.22	1.38	+13	1.44	+18
	393	1.23	1.35	+10	1.43	+16
Ammonia	213	1.51	1.74	+15	1.49	− 1.3
	273	1.54	1.70	+11	1.48	− 3.9
	373	1.42	1.64	+15	1.47	+ 3.5
Ethyl alcohol	293	1.44	1.34	− 6.9	1.36	− 5.5
	326	1.41	1.30	− 7.8	1.36	− 3.5
	401	1.35	1.26	− 6.6	1.35	0.0
Hydrogen sulfide	273	1.53	1.75	+14	1.50	− 2.0
Methyl alcohol	273	1.45	1.54	+ 6.2	1.46	+ 0.7
	358	1.37	1.46	+ 6.6	1.44	+ 5.1
	400	1.39	1.42	+ 2.1	1.43	+ 2.9
	373	1.36	1.45	+ 6.6	1.44	+ 5.9
	433	1.37	1.40	+ 2.2	1.43	+ 4.4
n-Propyl alcohol	304	1.46	1.27	−13	1.31	−10
	378	1.39	1.21	−13	1.31	− 5.8
	402	1.36	1.20	−12	1.31	− 3.7
Isopropyl alcohol	304	1.54	1.27	−18	1.31	− 8.5
	376	1.44	1.22	−15	1.31	− 9.1
	400	1.41	1.20	−15	1.31	− 7.1
Sulfur dioxide	273	1.48	1.61	+18	1.58	+ 6.8
	288	1.52	1.60	+ 5.3	1.58	+ 3.9
Water	373	1.41	1.73	+23	1.30	− 7.8
	473	1.40	1.70	+22	1.30	− 7.1
	573	1.41	1.68	+19	1.30	− 7.8
	673	1.42	1.65	+26	1.30	− 8.4
	373	1.35	1.73	+28	1.30	− 3.7
	413	1.39	1.72	+24	1.30	− 6.4
Average error	....	....	....	13.0	....	7.5

* % Error = [(calculated − experimental)/experimental] × 100.

10-4   Effect of Temperature on the Low-pressure Thermal Conductivity of Gases

Thermal conductivities of low-pressure gases increase with temperature in nearly a linear manner.   Values of k as a function of T for a number of different gases are shown in Fig. 10-3 (192).   The rate of change of k with temperature, dk/dT, for the various gases ranges from about 0.1 to 0.3×10^{-6} cal/(cm)(sec)(°K)^2; usually, the compound with the larger value of k has a larger value of the slope dk/dT.   Many investigators have given plots of k (at low pressure) as a function of temperature.   All have an appearance similar to Fig. 10-3, although in some cases, especially when wide temperature ranges are considered, dk/dT decreases somewhat with an increase in temperature (53, 60, 76, 86, 93, 106, 108, 137, 162, 189, 190).

Various empirical means have been suggested to relate k and T; in most cases, the representation can be reduced to a polynomial in temperature.   The coefficients of the T^2 and higher terms are, however, usually small and become important only at high temperatures.   All monatomic gases could be plotted as the same function of temperature with Eq. (10-2) since Ω_v is given as a function of temperature in Table 9-1.   For di- and polyatomic gases, the temperature dependence cannot be generalized since, as pointed out in Sec. 10-2, the theoretical representation of $kM/\mu C_v$ always contains some function of C_v (besides other properties).   This same fact precludes any success in generalizing k as a function of T_r since functions such as k/k_c^0, where k_c^0 is the low-pressure thermal conductivity at T_c, also depend on C_v and this latter property is not amenable to being represented as a function of T_r.

Thus there seems to be no simple reliable way to utilize a single thermal-conductivity datum point to obtain values at other temperatures.   Often (see Table 10-3) the ratio $kM/\mu C_v$ is assumed to be relatively independent of temperature; so

$$k_2 \cong k_1(\mu_2/\mu_1)(C_{v_2}/C_{v_1}) \qquad (10\text{-}25)$$

and variations in viscosity and heat capacity with temperature must be evaluated from recommended equations in Chaps. 9 and 5, respectively. Equation (10-25) is probably accurate to about 5 per cent for every 100°C temperature interval.   Since the per cent errors of the Eucken method [Eq. (10-7)] are approximately constant for any given compound (see Table 10-3), then one could use even a single value of k_{exp} and T_1 and determine the per cent error using the Eucken method.   This same error could then be assumed to apply at T_2, where the thermal conductivity is desired.   Owens and Thodos (129) suggest that

$$k_{T_2}/k_{T_1} = (T_2/T_1)^{1.786} \qquad (10\text{-}26)$$

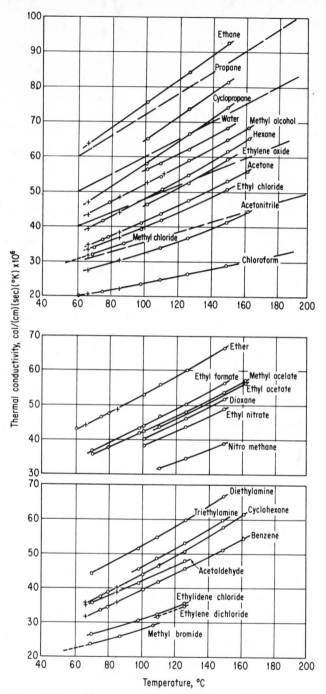

FIG. 10-3. The variation of thermal conductivity with temperature at low pressure. NOTE: Dashed lines in top drawing are from Eq. (10-26).

$$k_{T_2}/k_{T_1} = (T_2/T_1)^{1.786}$$

[R. G. Vines and L. A. Bennett, J. Chem. Phys., **22**:360 (1954).]

except for cyclic compounds. This relation would produce a slope as shown by the dashed lines in the top part of Fig. 10-3; note that these lines vary in slope depending upon the value of k_{T_1} chosen as a base. None of these techniques is particularly accurate. If, however, one has available more than one experimental datum point, representation of k as a polynomial in T is an excellent approximation. This is true even if only two points are available; i.e., in this case assume that k is linear with variations in T.

10-5 Effect of Pressure on the Thermal Conductivity of Gases

The thermal conductivity of all gases increases with pressure, although the effect is relatively small at low and moderate pressures. Three pressure regions are discussed below in which the effect of pressure is distinctly different.

Very Low Pressure (below 1 mm Hg). In this region, often called the *Knudsen domain*, the mean free path of the molecules is large compared with the dimensions of the measuring cell, and there is an important effect of pressure; i.e., at pressures below 0.1 mm Hg, k is often proportional to P. The theory of thermal conductivity in this region is discussed by Kennard (90), and experimental measurements for H_2, O_2, He, and A are reported by Prigogine and Waelbroeck (136); in the latter paper, the effect of the dimensions of the measuring cell is clearly shown. Often in reported thermal-conductivity data, the term *zero-pressure value* is used; this refers to values extrapolated from higher pressures (above a few millimeters of mercury) and not to values in the very-low-pressure region.

Low Pressure. This region extends approximately from 1 mm Hg to perhaps 10 atm and includes the domain discussed in Secs. 10-3 and 10-4. The thermal conductivity increases about 1 per cent per atmosphere. Such increases are often ignored in the literature, and either the 1-atm value or zero-pressure extrapolated value may be referred to as the *low-pressure conductivity*.

Most of the existing data on k have been obtained in the second region of pressure, but the experimental variable studied has usually been temperature and not pressure. Vines and Bennett (192) and Vines (189, 191) report data on k for a variety of organic vapors from 30 to 110°C over the pressure range 10 to 100 mm Hg and record that values of B, defined as the per cent increase in zero-pressure k per atmosphere, increase in pressure. For polar compounds, B varied from 0.5 to 4.3, with the very high values of 10.9 and 4.3 for methanol at 79 and 110°C. For the other compounds, B was less than 2. Data on both polar and nonpolar compounds showed B to decrease with increase in temperature. Working at subatmospheric pressures, Kannuliuk and Donald (89) found negligible effects of pressure on k for A, He, air, CO_2, N_2O, and CH_4.

A more quantitative picture of the variation of k with pressure in this region may be obtained from Fig. 10-4, based on the data of Keyes (95, 96). The plot shows the pressure effect on the ratio of k to $k°$, the low-pressure value of k at the same temperature. Only in the case of ammonia is k at $P_r = 0.3$ as much as 8 per cent greater than at low pressure; the more pronounced effect of pressure for this polar gas is evidently due primarily to the fact that the reduced temperatures are lower than for the other gases.

The data shown in Fig. 10-4 indicate values of B, the per cent increase per atmosphere, to be less than 1.0 in each case. The higher values in a

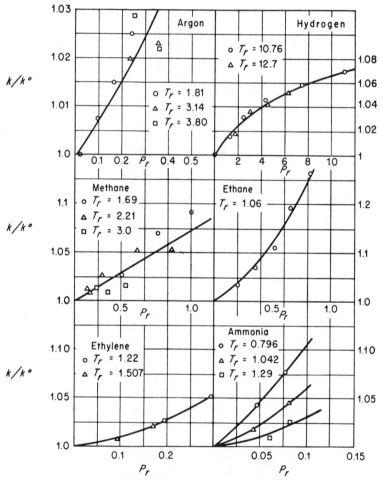

Fig. 10-4. Effect of pressure on the thermal conductivity of several gases. [*Data from* F. G. Keyes, *Trans. ASME,* **76**:809 (1954), **77**:1395 (1955).]

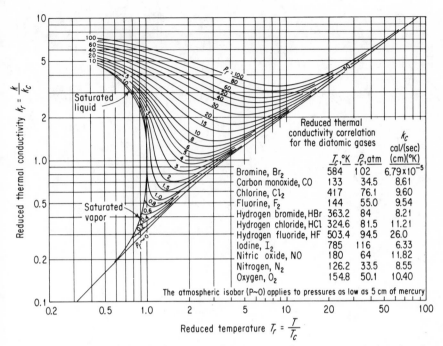

FIG. 10-5. Schaefer and Thodos reduced thermal-conductivity correlation for the diatomic gases. [*C. A. Schaefer and G. Thodos, AIChE J.*, **5**:367 (1959).]

few cases reported by Vines may be explained by the fact that B is larger near the saturation curve than at somewhat higher temperatures.

High Pressure. Many recent papers have reported or correlated high-pressure thermal-conductivity data; a number of these record both high-pressure liquid and vapor values and data near or on the saturation curve. Liley (106) has published an excellent survey of the data, and more recent papers cover nitrous and nitric oxides (142, 143), CO_2 (75), steam (92), ammonia (144), ethane (29), propane (101), butane (97), and miscellaneous gases (41).

Until recently most high-pressure thermal-conductivity correlations were based on the corresponding-state principle wherein either k/k^0 or k/k_c was plotted as a function of reduced pressure at constant reduced temperature. k^0 is the low-pressure value of k at T, and k_c is the value at T_c and P_c. k/k^0 plots were suggested first by Comings and Mayland (42) and k/k_c plots by Gamson (66).* They provide a convenient way to summarize data for a single substance or even for a homologous series (43, 104, 105, 119, 176). However, even for the simple series ethane,

* Occasionally the ratio k/k_c^0 is used; k_c^0 is the value of k at low pressure and at T_c.

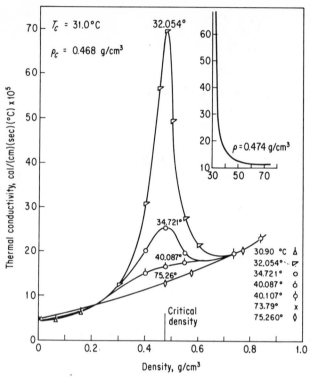

FIG. 10-6. Thermal conductivity of carbon dioxide near the critical point. [*L. A. Guildner, Proc. Natl. Acad. Sci.*, **44**:1149 (1958).]

propane, and *n*-butane, Kramer and Comings (97) have shown that the two parameters T_r and P_r are insufficient to correlate the ratio k/k^0. They suggest the use of C_p^0 as a third correlating parameter, but this technique does not seem to have been developed. A typical two-parameter plot is shown for the *diatomic* gases (162) in Fig. 10-5; while not exceptionally accurate, it is often sufficiently good for engineering calculations. Figure 10-5 indicates the very rapid variation in *k* in the critical region. Often very pronounced anomalous behavior occurs in this region (29, 75, 97, 102, 144), with *k* showing distinct humps along an isotherm as the pressure (or density) is changed. Figure 10-6 shows the CO_2 data of Guildner (75) at ρ_c; $(dk/dT)_{\rho_c}$ becomes very large as the critical temperature is approached. The explanation for this phenomenon is not clear; it may be due to a transition molecular ordering (97) or to a small-scale circulation effect resulting from the migration of small clusters of molecules (101). In any case, when generalized charts of the effect of pressure on *k* are drawn, these irregularities are usually smoothed out and are not shown.

Most recent papers dealing with the pressure effect on k have used a remarkably simple correlating suggestion made by Abas-Zade (2).* In this scheme the residual thermal conductivity, $k - k^0$, is plotted as a function of density (or reduced density), i.e.,

$$k - k^0 = f(\rho) \qquad (10\text{-}27)$$

This technique has been shown applicable to ammonia (73, 144), ethane (29), n-butane (30, 97), nitrous oxide (143), ethylene (129), methane (130), diatomic gases (162), hydrogen (163), inert gases (128), carbon dioxide (91), and many others (187). Temperature and pressure do not enter explicitly, but their effects are included in the parameters k^0 (temperature only) and density ρ.

Stiel and Thodos (175) have generalized Eq. (10-27) by reasoning that $f(\rho)$ depends only on T_c, P_c, V_c, M, and ρ. By dimensional analysis they obtain a correlation between $k - k^0$, Z_c, γ, and ρ_r, where γ is defined in Eq. (10-19). From data on 20 nonpolar substances, including inert gases, diatomic gases, CO_2, and hydrocarbons, they established the correlation shown in Fig. (10-7). Actual experimental data are shown plotted; a tabulation of the various substances used and the values of γ as calculated is also given. Approximate analytical expressions for this curve are

$$
\begin{aligned}
(k - k^0)\gamma Z_c{}^5 &= (14.0)(10^{-8})(e^{-0.535\rho_r} - 1) & \rho_r &< 0.5 & (10\text{-}28) \\
(k - k^0)\gamma Z_c{}^5 &= (13.1)(10^{-8})(e^{0.67\rho_r} - 1.069) & 0.5 &< \rho_r < 2.0 & (10\text{-}29) \\
(k - k^0)\gamma Z_c{}^5 &= (2.976)(10^{-8})(e^{1.155\rho_r} + 2.016) & 2.0 &< \rho_r < 2.8 & (10\text{-}30)
\end{aligned}
$$

Figure 10-7 should not be used for polar substances or for hydrogen or helium. Its general accuracy is in doubt, but the scatter as shown will indicate that errors of ± 10 to 20 per cent are possible. It appears, however, to be the best generalized correlation at present.

Recommendations. Use Fig. 10-7 or Eqs. (10-28) to (10-30) to determine $k - k^0$ for nonpolar materials. Critical constants may be obtained from Appendix A or estimated by the techniques given in Chap. 2. Experimental densities are preferable, but when not known, they may be found by the techniques described in Chap. 3. Low-pressure k^0 values may be determined as shown in Sec. 10-3. The accuracy of this plot is difficult to assess. Near the critical point, the accuracy is probably poor, and, in other high-density regions, probably no better than 10 to 20 per cent accuracy should be expected.

* Prof. Tsederberg (Moscow Energetics Inst.) has kindly pointed out that this type of correlation was originally suggested by N. B. Bargaftik, "Thermal Conductivities of Compressed Gases and Steam at High Pressures," Izvestiia Vsesouznovo Teplotehniches-Kovo Instituta, Nov. 7, 1951.

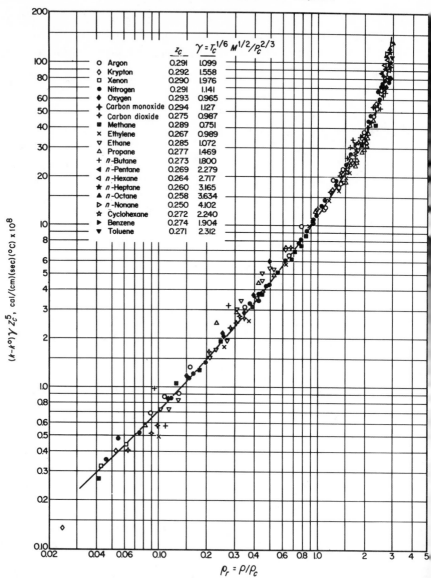

FIG. 10-7. Stiel and Thodos correlation for dense-gas thermal conductivities. [*L. I. Stiel and G. Thodos, AIChE J.*, **10**:26 (1964).]

Polar compounds should not be treated according to Fig. 10-7, nor may hydrogen or helium be so treated. In the ill-defined range of slightly polar compounds, no guide lines have been established.

Other empirical methods have been suggested, but these do not appear as suitable for general use as Fig. 10-7 (59, 63, 177).

Example 10-3. Estimate the thermal conductivity of nitrous oxide at 105°C and 2,000 psia (136 atm). At this pressure and temperature, the experimental value reported is $(93.2)(10^{-6})$ cal/(cm)(sec)(°K) (143). At 1 atm and 105°C, $k^0 = (55.8)(10^{-6})$ cal/(cm)(sec)(°K) (143). Appendix A lists $T_c = 309.7$°K, $P_c = 71.7$ atm, $V_c = 96.3$ cm³/(g mole), $Z_c = 0.271$, and $M = 44.02$. At 105°C and 2,000 psia, Z for nitrous oxide is 0.63 (45).

Solution

$$\gamma = T_c^{1/6} M^{1/2}/P_c^{2/3} = [(309.7)^{1/6}(44.02)^{1/2}]/(71.7)^{2/3} = 1.01$$
$$V = ZRT/P = [(0.63)(82.06)(378)]/136 = 144 \text{ cm}^3/\text{g mole}$$
$$\rho_r = V_c/V = 96.3/144 = 0.668$$

From Fig. 10-7, $(k - k^0)\gamma Z_c^5 = (6.5)(10^{-8})$ cal/(cm)(sec)(°K) or, from Eq. (10-29),

$$(k - k^0)\gamma Z_c^5 = (13.1)(10^{-8})[e^{(0.67)(0.668)} - 1.069] = (6.5)(10^{-8}) \text{ cal/(cm)(sec)(°K)}$$

Thus

$$k - k^0 = [(6.5)(10^{-8})]/[(1.01)(0.271)^5] = (44)(10^{-6})$$
$$k = (44 + 55.8)(10^{-6}) = (99.8)(10^{-6}) \text{ cal/(cm)(sec)(°K)}$$
$$\text{Error} = [(99.8 - 93.2)/93.2] \times 100 = +7.1\%$$

10-6 Low-pressure Gas-mixture Thermal Conductivities

The thermal conductivity of a gas mixture is usually not a linear function of composition. Generally, if the constituent molecules differ greatly in polarity, the mixture conductivity is larger than would be predicted from a mole-fraction average; for nonpolar molecules, the opposite trend is noted and is more pronounced the greater the difference in molecular weights or sizes of the constituent species (121). Some of these trends are clearly evident in Fig. 10-8, which shows experimental thermal conductivities for four systems. The argon-benzene system typifies a nonpolar case with rather different molecular sizes, and the methanol-n-hexane system is a case representing a difference in polarity. The linear systems benzene-hexane and ether-chloroform represent a balance between the minimizing effect of size and the maximizing effect of polarity.

A number of reviews have been published in the past few years summarizing the various methods of calculating mixture thermal conductivities (63, 100, 106, 138, 184), and a large number of theoretical papers have also appeared discussing the problems, approximations, and limitations of the various methods. The theory for calculating the conductivity for rare-gas mixtures has been worked out in considerable detail and has been well summarized elsewhere (124); the problems encountered in using this theory arise when one attempts to simplify the rather complex mathematical form, to choose a representative intermolecular potential to evaluate the collision integrals, and to extend the formulation to polyatomic-gas mixtures. The first problem has been discussed by many workers who, by various techniques, truncate the infinite equation set

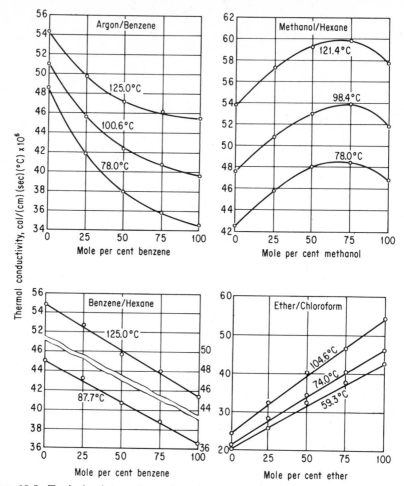

FIG. 10-8. Typical mixture thermal-conductivity data. [L. A. Bennett and R. G. Vines, J. Chem. Phys., **23**:1587 (1955).]

resulting from rigorous theory to yield a first (monatomic) approximation, a second, etc. (19, 21, 81, 112, 115, 116, 117, 124).   In general, the first approximation is sufficient, as the uncertainties in determining the correct intermolecular potential function and the polyatomic corrections usually negate the effort to calculate the monatomic term with high accuracy. Brokaw (19, 21) does, however, carry through the second approximation in some detail.   Most authors choose the Lennard-Jones 6-12 potential, but the calculated results would not be much different if other, similar potentials were chosen.

The most difficult problem however, is correcting the monatomic value for polyatomic molecules.   A very large number of techniques have been proposed; all involve approximations and are justified only by comparing the calculated results with experimental values. Several of the more useful forms are discussed in detail below.

Wassiljewa Equation. The first approximation to the monatomic-mixture conductivity reduces to a form similar to Eq. (9-31) except that k replaces μ and the functions ϕ_{ij} are not necessarily identical. Also, it has been suggested that the "internal" correction to energy transport for polyatomic gases have a similar form (21, 80), so that a very common way to express k_m is

$$k_m = \sum_{i=1}^{n} k_i \Big/ \Big[1 + \sum_{\substack{j=1 \\ j \neq i}}^{n} A_{ij}(y_j/y_i)\Big] \tag{10-31}$$

where k_m = thermal conductivity of mixture
$\quad k_i$ = thermal conductivity of pure component i
$\quad y_i, y_j$ = mole fractions of components i and j
$\quad A_{ij}$ = a function, as yet unspecified

This type of equation for k_m was proposed in 1904 by Wassiljewa (195).

Mason and Saxena Formulation. By simplifying the rigorous monatomic expression for k_m and using a suggestion made by Hirschfelder to estimate the Eucken factor for a mixture, Mason and Saxena (116) found that the value of A_{ij} in Eq. (10-31) could be expressed as,*

$$A_{ij} = (1.065/8^{1/2})\{[1 + (k_i'/k_j')^{1/2}(M_i/M_j)^{1/4}]^2/[1 + (M_i/M_j)]^{1/2}\} \tag{10-32}$$

where M is the molecular weight and k' the monatomic value of the thermal conductivity. However, from Eq. (10-4) for monatomic gases, $C_{v_i} = C_{v_j}$; so

$$k_i'/k_j' = (\mu_i/\mu_j)(M_j/M_i) \tag{10-33}$$

Upon inserting Eq. (10-33) into (10-32) and comparing with Eq. (9-35), it is seen that

$$A_{ij} = 1.065\phi_{ij} \tag{10-34}$$

This is an extremely interesting result in that it relates the Wilke viscosity equation for gas mixtures to the Wassiljewa gas-mixture thermal-conductivity correlation. The accuracy of Eq. (10-31), with A_{ij} from Eq. (10-34), is discussed later.

Lindsay and Bromley Formulation. Lindsay and Bromley (107), using a Sutherland model of a gas, proposed,

$$A_{ij} = \tfrac{1}{4}(1 + \{(\mu_i/\mu_j)(M_j/M_i)^{3/4}[(1 + S_i/T)/(1 + S_j/T)]\}^{1/2})^2$$
$$[(1 + S_{ij}/T)/(1 + S_i/T)] \tag{10-35}$$

---

* In a recent private communication, Prof. Mason indicates that the 1.065 factor can be deleted without much loss in overall accuracy.

In this equation, μ is the pure-gas viscosity, T the absolute temperature, and S the Sutherland constant.*

The parameter A_{ji} is expressed in a similar manner, but with all subscripts reversed. S for a pure component may be determined by fitting the Sutherland viscosity equation to experimental data (90), but it is usually estimated from some empirical rule. The one chosen by Lindsay and Bromley was

$$S_i = 1.5T_{b_i} \qquad (10\text{-}36)$$

where T_{b_i} is the normal boiling point of component i.† This rule is similar to the one suggested by Vogel (193). Other ways to estimate S_i are discussed by Gambill (63) and a tabulation of S for various compounds is available (133). Actually, although these rules are not accurate, the value of k_m is relatively insensitive to variations in S; for example, a variation of 20 per cent in S affects the calculated value of k_m by only about 1 per cent.

The interaction Sutherland constant S_{ij} is estimated as

$$S_{ij} = S_{ji} = C_s(S_iS_j)^{1/2} \qquad (10\text{-}37)$$

where C_s is about unity unless one of the gases is very polar, when a value of 0.733 has been suggested (107), though other values have been proposed. For nonpolar-polar systems C_s is reported to vary widely (9).‡

A_{ij} is relatively insensitive to temperature whether calculated from Eq. (10-32) or Eq. (10-35).

The accuracy and applicability of Eq. (10-31), with A_{ij} from Eq. (10-35), are discussed later.

Wassiljewa Expansion. Several of the more recent estimation techniques have been written in the Wassiljewa form, but broken into two sets of terms, the first to allow for monatomic or translational contributions and the second for internal contributions. Hirschfelder suggested and developed this technique in 1957 (80), and it has been successfully expanded by Brokaw (21) among others. A recent investigation which has used this type of expression and which has produced an estimating technique that appears quite reliable is discussed below.

Cheung, Bromley, and Wilke Method (36–38). The thermal conductiv-

---

* The Sutherland viscosity model yields $\mu \propto [T^{3/2}/(T + S)]$.

† For He, H₂, and Ne, Eq. (10-36) should not be used, and S taken as 79°K (107).

‡ As Bennett and Vines state, "There does not appear to be any systematic variation in the constant which can be correlated with the properties of the individual mixtures. The selected constants are as follows: acetone/benzene 0.85, methanol/argon 0.93, methanol/hexane 0.60, water vapor/nitrogen 0.7, water vapor/carbon dioxide 0.7. Thus, deviations from the recommended value of 0.733 are sometimes considerable."

ity for all pure components is broken into two parts, k_i^* and k_i^{**} These
are defined as

$$k_i^* = k_i\{(2.5C_{tr} + C_{ext\ rot})/[2.5C_{tr} + C_{ext\ rot} + 1.32(C_v - C_{tr} - C_{ext\ rot})]\}_i$$
$$\text{(10-38)}$$
$$k_i^{**} = k_i - k_i^* \tag{10-39}$$

The numerator in Eq. (10-38) is proportional to the energy transfer by
translation [see Eq. (10-4)] and external rotation, whereas the denominator is proportional to the energy transfer by all modes [the value 1.32
comes from the same reasoning that led to Eq. (10-8)]. C_{tr} is the
constant-volume translational heat capacity $\frac{3}{2}R$; $C_{ext\ rot}$ the constant-
volume external rotational heat capacity, $\frac{3}{2}R$ for nonlinear molecules
and R for linear molecules. Thus k_i^* may be simplified as

$$k_i^* = \begin{cases} k_i\{1/[1 + 0.25(C_{v_i}/R - 1)]\} & \text{nonlinear molecules} \\ k_i\{1/[1 + 0.35(C_{v_i}/R - 1)]\} & \text{linear molecules} \\ k_i & \text{monatomic molecules} \end{cases} \tag{10-40}$$

Upon using this breakdown of k_i, the mixture thermal conductivity is
expressed as

$$k_m = \sum_{i=1}^{n} k_i^*/\left[1 + \sum_{\substack{j=1 \\ j \neq i}}^{n} (M_{ij}/M_i)^{\frac{1}{6}}\phi_{ij}(y_j/y_i)\right] + \sum_{i=1}^{n} k_i^{**}/\left[1 + \sum_{\substack{j=1 \\ j \neq i}}^{n} \phi_{ij}(y_j/y_i)\right]$$
$$\text{(10-41)}$$

where ϕ_{ij} is defined in Eq. (9-35), y is the mole fraction, and

$$M_{ij} = (M_i + M_j)/2 \tag{10-42}$$

Note that, except for the term $(M_{ij}/M_i)^{\frac{1}{6}}$ in the denominator of the first
sum, Eq. (10-41) would collapse to the Wassiljewa form and become
identical, except for the numerical factor of 1.065, to Mason and Saxena's
form [Eq. (10-34)]. Equation (10-41) is satisfactory only for nonpolar-
nonpolar mixtures; for polar-nonpolar mixtures, the equation form
remains the same, but ϕ_{ij} is replaced by $\phi_{ij_{p-np}}$, where

$$\phi_{ij_{p-np}} = (M_i/M_{ij})^{\frac{1}{2}}\{\frac{1}{2}[1 + (V_{b_j}/V_{b_i})^{\frac{1}{3}}]\}^2[(T + FS_{ij})/(T + S_i)] \tag{10-43}$$

where $\phi_{ji_{p-np}}$ is determined by interchanging subscripts and M_{ij} is defined
in Eq. (10-42) and S_i and S_{ij} in Eqs. (10-36) and (10-37). V_b is the liquid
molal volume of the pure component at the normal boiling point, and F
is a function of V_{b_j}/V_{b_i} (or the inverse, whichever ratio > 1), as in the

accompanying tabulation (6). The accuracy of the Cheung, Bromley, and Wilke method is discussed later.

V_{b_j}/V_{b_i}	1	2	3	4	6	8	10	
F	1.00	0.98	0.953	0.920	0.875	0.838	0.805	(10-44)

Discussion of the Wassiljewa Form. A number of papers have been published in the past few years discussing the Wassiljewa equation and, in particular, giving some physical significance to the parameters A_{ij} and A_{ji} and to relating A_{ij} to ϕ_{ij} [of Eq. (9-31)] (47, 48, 62, 67, 156, 157, 158, 174, 202). No clear-cut connection between A_{ij} and ϕ_{ij} has been shown, although many of the equations given in this section certainly hint that they are related.

Particularly interesting reviews by Cowling (47), Cowling, Gray, and Wright (48), and by the last two authors (70, 202) relate A_{ij} to the efficiencies by which molecules of one component impede the transport of energy by molecules of the other component. From simple postulates the above authors then can derive the Wassiljewa equation.

Brokaw Empirical Method. Brokaw (20) noted that in most nonpolar mixtures k_m is less than a linear mole-fraction average but larger than a reciprocal average. He then suggested that, for binary mixtures,

$$k_m = qk_{m_L} + (1 - q)k_{m_R} \tag{10-45}$$

where
$$k_{m_L} = y_1k_1 + y_2k_2$$
$$1/k_{m_R} = y_1/k_1 + y_2/k_2$$

q is a parameter which is given in Table 10-4 as a function of the mole fraction of the light component. If q is assumed constant at 0.5, the

TABLE 10-4. VARIATION OF THE BROKAW FACTOR q WITH COMPOSITION OF LIGHT COMPONENT

Factor q for Eq. (10-45)	Mole fraction light component
0.32	0
0.34	0.1
0.37	0.2
0.39	0.3
0.42	0.4
0.46	0.5
0.50	0.6
0.55	0.7
0.61	0.8
0.69	0.9
0.74	0.95
0.80	1.0

rule reduces to one similar to that suggested by Burgoyne and Weinberg (27). The accuracy of the method is discussed below.

Applicability and Accuracy of the Gas-mixture Estimation Techniques. Four principal estimating techniques have been discussed above. Other proposed methods were rejected, either from an error criterion or from a combination of error criterion and the desire to choose simple techniques (44, 81, 90). Of all the four methods, the Lindsay-Bromley method, being the oldest, has received the most extensive testing. The authors themselves tested the equation with 16 binary mixtures and found an average error of 1.9 per cent. The mixtures included polar (NH_3, H_2O)-nonpolar mixtures, but no polar-polar mixtures. Temperatures ranged from 0 to 80°C. Experimental values of the pure components were used in the correlation (and in all the testing described in this section). In a very comprehensive test of both the Cheung et al. and Lindsay-Bromley method, Cheung reported the results in the accompanying tabulation (38).

	Cheung et al.	Lindsay-Bromley
Nonpolar-nonpolar mixtures:		
Binary, 38 mixtures, 177 datum points		
Average % error	2.1	2.6
Maximum % error	10.5	10.5
Ternary, 6 mixtures, 16 datum points		
Average % error	2.2	3.9
Maximum % error	6.0	8.2
Polar-nonpolar mixtures:		
Binary, 10 mixtures, 49 datum points		
Average % error	2.2	2.1
Maximum % error	5.4	6.9

This testing covered virtually all the reliable low-pressure gas-mixture viscosity data up to 1959 and indicates that both methods are reliable and capable of yielding estimations within engineering accuracy.

Brokaw tested his empirical method with 18 nonpolar mixtures and found an average error of about 2.6 per cent, with a maximum of 11.4 per cent, errors close to those found by Cheung for nonpolar mixtures. Brokaw's method cannot predict k_m larger than the linear mole-fraction average; so it cannot be used for mixtures containing a polar component.

The Mason-Saxena method has not been so thoroughly tested, but, in the comparison between calculated and experimental results for nine binary and five ternary nonpolar mixtures, average errors of 2 to 3 per cent have been reported (116).

Gray and Wright (68) assessed both the Lindsay-Bromley and Mason-Saxena methods for general reliability and applicability to the system N_2-H_2-NH_3. The Lindsay-Bromley technique was accurate within about

2 per cent for the possible binaries and the ternary mixture; the Mason-Saxena method was applicable only to the H_2-N_2 binary and in this case yielded somewhat less reliable results. These workers concluded from studies on other systems that the Lindsay-Bromley method was not particularly good for mixtures of complicated polyatomic molecules (unless the molecular weights were similar) and, in fact, was not reliable even for the argon–n-hexane system (9) or for mixtures of rare gases (errors up to 5 per cent) (154, 172, 173).

In a recent study of the methane-propane system, between 50 and 150°C, good agreement was obtained between experimental and calculated values of k_m for the Mason-Saxena method (170). Other tests have been reported, but these do not change any of the relative conclusions which can be reached from the comments given above (7, 52, 69, 125, 134, 153, 159, 171, 182).

Recommendations. Based on the extensive testing of the methods described, the following recommendations are presented to estimate k_m at low pressure:

Rare-gas mixtures. Use either the Mason-Saxena or the Cheung et al. method, i.e., Eq. (10-31) [with A_{ij} from Eq. (10-32)] or Eq. (10-41). A similar recommendation was made by Ranz (138), who suggested that the Mason-Saxena constant of 1.065 be increased to 1.09 in Eq. (10-34). Errors should be less than 2 per cent with either of these methods.

Nonpolar mixtures. The Cheung et al., Lindsay-Bromley, and empirical Brokaw methods are all suitable; the first two are, perhaps, somewhat more accurate though more complex; the last method is suitable only for binary mixtures and has not been so extensively tested. Typical errors are 1 to 3 per cent, but in some cases, e.g., argon–n-hexane, errors up to 10 per cent are possible. The Cheung et al. method comprises Eqs. (10-41), (10-38), and (10-39); the Lindsay-Bromley method, Eqs. (10-31) and (10-35); and the empirical Brokaw method, Eq. (10-45).

Polar-nonpolar mixtures. The same recommendation is made as for nonpolar mixtures except that the empirical Brokaw method is inapplicable and the Cheung et al. calculation of ϕ_{ij} is to be made from Eq. (10-43). The expected errors are summarized in the previous section, where the testing of the various methods was discussed.

Polar-polar mixtures. No test has been made of any of the methods for polar-polar mixtures, and no error estimation can be given. As a very tentative recommendation, the Lindsay-Bromley method might be used, but with no guarantee of its success.

Example 10-4. Estimate the thermal conductivity of a gas mixture of methane and propane at 1 atm and 95°C. The mixture has a mole fraction methane of 0.486. The experimental mixture value is reported as $(7.64)(10^{-5})$ cal/(cm)(sec)(°K) (38, 170).

Solution. The properties of the pure components which are required in one or all of the estimation techniques illustrated below are as follows:

	Methane	Propane
Molecular weight.......................	16.04	44.09
Pure-gas k, cal/(cm)(sec)(°K) (38, 170).....	10.49×10^{-5}	6.34×10^{-5}
Pure-gas μ, centipoises (49, 99)............	1.32×10^{-2}	1.00×10^{-2}
Normal boiling point, °K.................	111.7	231.1
C_v, cal/(g mole)(°K) (5).................	7.44	19.5

Empirical Brokaw Method. From Eq. (10-45)

$$k_{m_L} \times 10^5 = (0.486)(10.49) + (0.514)(6.34) = 8.35$$
$$k_{m_R} \times 10^5 = (0.486/10.49 + 0.514/6.34)^{-1} = 7.84$$

From Table 10-4, with the mole fraction methane = 0.486, $q = 0.45$; thus

$$k_m = [(0.45)(8.35) + (0.55)(7.84)] \times 10^{-5} = 8.0 \times 10^{-5} \text{ cal/(cm)(sec)(°K)}$$
Error $= [(8.0 - 7.64)/7.64] \times 100 = +4.7\%$

Lindsay-Bromley Method. First the Sutherland constants have to be estimated. Letting 1 denote methane and 2 propane, then, from Eqs. (10-36) and (10-37),

$$S_1 = 1.5(111.7) = 167°\text{K}$$
$$S_2 = 1.5(231.1) = 347°\text{K}$$
$$S_{12} = [(167)(347)]^{1/2} = 240°\text{K}$$

The A_{12} and A_{21} parameters are determined from Eq. (10-35); for example,

$$A_{12} = \tfrac{1}{4}(1 + \{[(1.32/1.00)(44.09/16.04)^{3/4}][(1 + {}^{167}\!/_{368})/(1 + {}^{347}\!/_{368})]\}^{1/2})^2$$
$$[(1 + {}^{240}\!/_{368})/(1 + {}^{167}\!/_{368})] = 1.71$$

Similarly $A_{21} = 0.61$. Then, with Eq. (10-31),

$$k_m = k_1/[1 + A_{12}(y_2/y_1)] + k_2/[1 + A_{21}(y_1/y_2)]$$
$$= [(10.49)(10^{-5})]/[1 + (1.71)(0.514)/0.486]$$
$$+ (6.34)(10^{-5})/[1 + (0.61)(0.486)/0.514]$$
$$= (7.75)(10^{-5}) \text{ cal/(cm)(sec)(°K)}$$
Error $= [(7.75 - 7.64)/7.64] \times 100 = +1.4\%$

Mason-Saxena Method. First the ϕ_{12} and ϕ_{21} values must be calculated from Eq. (9-35),

$$\phi_{12} = [1 + (1.32/1.00)^{1/2}(44.09/16.04)^{1/4}]^2/8^{1/2}(1 + 16.04/44.09)^{1/2} = 1.86$$

Likewise, reversing subscripts, $\phi_{21} = 0.51$. Then from Eq. (10-34)

$$A_{12} = (1.065)(1.86) = 1.98$$
$$A_{21} = (1.065)(0.51) = 0.54$$

and, inserting these into Eq. (10-31),

$$k_m = (10.49)(10^{-5})/[1 + (1.98)(0.514)/0.486]$$
$$+ (6.34)(10^{-5})/[1 + (0.54)(0.486)/0.514]$$
$$= (7.56)(10^{-5}) \text{ cal}/(\text{cm})(\text{sec})(°\text{C})$$
$$\text{Error} = [(7.56 - 7.64)/7.64] \times 100 = -1.1\%$$

Cheung-Bromley-Wilke Method. Both methane and propane are nonlinear nonpolar molecules; so from Eq. (10-40)

$$k_1^* = k_1\{1/[1 + 0.25(7.44/1.986 - 1)]\} = 0.592k_1$$
$$k_2^* = k_2\{1/[1 + 0.25(19.5/1.986 - 1)]\} = 0.313k_2$$
Thus
$$k_1^{**} = (1 - 0.592)k_1 = 0.418k_1$$
$$k_2^{**} = (1 - 0.313)k_2 = 0.687k_2$$

The ϕ_{ij} values were determined above as

$$\phi_{12} = 1.86 \qquad \phi_{21} = 0.51$$

Substituting in Eq. (10-41), with $M_{12} = (16.04 + 44.09)/2 = 30.05$

$$k_m = (10.49)(10^{-5})\left[\frac{0.592}{1 + (30.05/16.05)^{1/8}(1.86)(0.514/0.486)}\right.$$
$$\left.+ \frac{0.418}{1 + (1.86)(0.514/0.486)}\right] + (6.34)(10^{-5})\left[\frac{0.313}{1 + (30.05/44.09)^{1/8}(0.51)(0.486/0.514)}\right.$$
$$\left.+ \frac{0.687}{1 + (0.51)(0.486/0.514)}\right]$$
$$= (10.49)(10^{-5})(0.592/3.12 + 0.418/2.96)$$
$$+ (6.34)(10^{-5})(0.313/1.46 + 0.687/1.48)$$
$$= (7.77)(10^{-5}) \text{ cal}/(\text{cm})(\text{sec})(°\text{K})$$
$$\text{Error} = [(7.77 - 7.64)/7.64] \times 100 = +1.7\%$$

10-7 Effect of Temperature and Pressure on the Thermal Conductivity of Gas Mixtures

Temperature Effects. Generally the shape of the mixture thermal-conductivity–composition curves is not appreciably altered by changes in temperature (see Fig. 10-8). However, occasionally a mixture which shows a negative deviation at low temperatures may show a positive deviation at higher temperatures, the term *deviation* referring to a mole-fraction linear average curve. N_2-CO_2 seems to show such a behavior, and this has been discussed by Brokaw (22).

If one lacks evidence that there is such unusual behavior, the effect of temperature on the mixture viscosity is absorbed in the change of pure-component conductivities. This variation is discussed in Sec. 10-4; no change in the functional form of the selected mixture correlation is then necessary.

Pressure Effects. Very few experimental data are available on the thermal conductivity of high-pressure gas mixtures. Keyes (94) studied the nitrogen–carbon dioxide system and Junk and Comings (87) the ethylene-nitrogen and carbon dioxide–ethylene systems. Certainly these are insufficient data to formulate a reliable estimation method. However, reasonable estimations may be made by using the Stiel and Thodos pure-component plot (Fig. 10-7) [or Eqs. (10-28) to (10-30)] and treating the mixture as a hypothetical pure component with pseudocritical properties. By use of Prausnitz and Gunn's modified rules to determine such pseudocritical constants (see Sec. 7-9), Table 10-5 has been prepared so as to compare calculated and experimental thermal conductivities for

TABLE 10-5. COMPARISON BETWEEN CALCULATED AND EXPERIMENTAL
GAS-MIXTURE THERMAL CONDUCTIVITIES AT HIGH PRESSURE
All thermal conductivity values in cal/(cm)(sec)(°K) $\times 10^6$

Mixture	Mole % first component	T, °K	P, atm	k_m exp.	k_m^0 (1 atm), exp.	Ref.	k calc.	% Error*
Ethylene–carbon dioxide...........	55.5	315.1	50.0	63.3	49.6	87	64	+ 1.1
	....	.....	104.8	137	....	...	144	+ 4.9
	....	.....	155.9	168	....	...	191	+14
	....	.....	198.1	192	....	...	211	+10
Ethylene–carbon dioxide...........	79.8	315.1	52.1	68.6	51.6	87	70	+ 2.0
	....	.....	114.4	151	....	...	170	+14
	....	.....	155.3	168	....	...	195	+16
	....	.....	199.9	198	....	...	218	+10
Ethylene-nitrogen....	67.5	315.1	43.6	64.5	56.3	87	66	+ 2.3
	....	.....	101.9	88.5	....	...	89	+ 0.6
	....	.....	156.5	119	....	...	120	+ 0.8
	....	.....	196.9	130	....	...	135	+ 3.7
Ethylene-nitrogen....	38.8	315.1	51.1	67.9	58.2	87	67	− 1.3
	....	.....	102.4	79.5	....	...	78	− 1.9
	....	.....	154.9	94.3	....	...	95	+ 1.8
	....	.....	197.8	104	....	...	111	+ 6.7
Nitrogen–carbon dioxide...........	34.1	323.2	19.8	53.0	49.9	94	53	0
	....	.....	48.8	58.8	....	...	58	− 1.4
	....	.....	51.2	59.8	....	...	59	− 1.3
	....	.....	81.0	68.5	....	...	66	− 3.6
Nitrogen–carbon dioxide...........	52.9	323.2	20.0	56.6	53.7	94	56	− 1.0
	....	.....	42.7	59.8	....	...	63	+ 5.3
	....	.....	68.7	67.0	....	...	64	− 4.5
	....	.....	84.3	72.1	....	...	69	− 4.3

* Error = [(calculated-experimental)/experimental] $\times$ 100.

most of the available data. Surprisingly good results are obtained, even at rather high pressures, except for the C_2H_4-CO_2 system, where errors as high as $+16$ per cent were found. The pseudoreduced temperatures for the two C_2H_4-CO_2 mixtures tested were 1.08 and 1.10 (the P_{r_m} range was about 0.8 to 3.7) so that the calculations were made in a very non-ideal region where most corresponding-state correlations are least accurate. The technique is illustrated in detail in Example 10-5.

In general, therefore, to estimate the thermal conductivity of a gas mixture at high pressure, the Stiel and Thodos correlation should be used as shown in Example 10-5. Errors usually less than 5 per cent may be expected for simple nonpolar-gas mixtures at pseudoreduced tempera-tures* greater than 1.3. The method may be used for polar- and/or polyatomic-gas mixtures or at lower pseudoreduced temperatures, but considerably larger errors may be anticipated.

Example 10-5. Estimate the thermal conductivity of a nitrogen-ethylene gas mixture containing 67.5 mole % ethylene at 315°K and 101.9 atm. Junk and Comings (87) report an experimental value of $(88.5)(10^{-6})$ cal/(cm)(sec)(°K); these same inves-tigators also report that, for the same mixture at 315°K but 1 atm, $k = (56.3)(10^{-6})$ cal/(cm)(sec)(°K).

Solution. From Appendix A the critical properties are available in the accompany-ing table for nitrogen and ethylene. The modified Prausnitz and Gunn pseudocritical

	Nitrogen	Ethylene
T_c, °K	126.2	283.1
V_c, cm³/g mole	90.1	124
M	28	28
Z_c	0.291	0.270

rules [Eqs. (7-30) and (7-53)] indicate that T_{c_m}, V_{c_m}, and Z_{c_m} be calculated as linear mole-fraction averages and that P_{c_m} be determined as $P_{c_m} = Z_{c_m}RT_{c_m}/V_{c_m}$. For example,

$$T_{c_m} = (0.675)(283.1) + (0.325)(126.2) = 232°K$$

Similarly $V_{c_m} = 113$ cm³/g mole, $Z_{c_m} = 0.277$, and

$$P_{c_m} = (0.277)(82.06)(232)/113 = 46.6 \text{ atm}$$

At the conditions specified this leads to

$$T_{r_m} = {}^{315}\!/_{232} = 1.36$$
$$P_{r_m} = 101.9/46.6 = 2.19$$

With these reduced conditions and with $Z_{c_m} = 0.277$, the Lydersen compressibility-factor correlation in Appendix B leads to a value of $Z_m = 0.75$; the mixture molal

* As shown in Example 10-5, the pseudoreduced temperature is defined here as $T/\Sigma y_i T_{c_i}$.

olume is then

$$V_m = Z_m RT/P = (0.75)(82.06)(315)/101.9$$
$$= 190 \text{ cm}^3/\text{g mole}$$

r
$$\rho_{r_m} = V_{c_m}/V_m = {}^{113}\!/_{190} = 0.59$$

'rom the Stiel and Thodos plot (Fig. 10-7),

ut
$$(k - k^0)\gamma Z_c{}^5 = (5.4)(10^{-8}) \text{ cal}/(\text{cm})(\text{sec})(°\text{K})$$
$$Z_{c_m} = (0.277)^5 = (1.63)(10^{-3})$$
$$\gamma_m = T_{c_m}^{\frac{1}{6}} M_m^{\frac{1}{2}}/P_{c_m}^{\frac{2}{3}} = [(232)^{\frac{1}{6}}(28)^{\frac{1}{2}}]/(46.6)^{\frac{2}{3}} = 1.01$$

In this case M_m is independent of composition; in other cases a mole-fraction average molecular weight is to be used for M_m.) Thus

$$(k - k^0)_m = [(5.4)(10^{-8})]/[(1.63)(10^{-3})(1.01)] = (33)(10^{-6}) \text{ cal}/(\text{cm})(\text{sec})(°\text{K})$$
$$k_m = (33 + 56.3)(10^{-6}) = (89)(10^{-6}) \text{ cal}/(\text{cm})(\text{sec})(°\text{K})$$
$$\text{Error} = [(89 - 88.5)/88.5] \times 100 = +0.6\%$$

10-8 Thermal Conductivity of Reversible Chemically Reacting Gas Mixtures

The discussion up to this point has been concerned with the thermal conductivity of pure gases or of gas mixtures in which no chemical reactions occur.   If, however, a gas mixture reacts as a result of the temperature gradient and produces simultaneously a composition gradient, then heat flow will result, not only by molecular collisions, but also from a diffusion flux.   The flow of heat is then the result of two factors,

$$q = -k(dT/dz) + \sum_i H_i N_i \qquad (10\text{-}46)$$

where H_i is the molal (actually a partial molal) enthalpy of the component i and N_i represents the flux of i resulting from the concentration gradient in the z direction.
From the multicomponent diffusion equation,

$$dy_k/dz = (1/\rho) \sum_{j \neq k} (y_k N_j - y_j N_k)/D_{jk} \qquad (10\text{-}47)$$

Solving for N_i, and introducing the multicomponent diffusion coefficient $\mathfrak{D}_{ik}$,*

$$N_i = -(\rho/M_m) \sum_{\substack{k=1 \\ k \neq i}}^{n} \mathfrak{D}_{ik} M_k (dy_k/dz) \qquad (10\text{-}48)$$

* The multicomponent diffusion coefficient $\mathfrak{D}_{ik}$ is a function of the binary diffusion coefficients, composition, and molecular weight.   Explicit expressions are shown on page 541 of Ref. 81.

and noting* that $y_k = f(T)$ so that

$$dy_k/dz = (dy_k/dT)(dT/dz) \qquad (10\text{-}49)$$

then, inserting (10-48) and (10-49) in (10-46),

$$q = - \left[k + \sum_{i=1}^{n} \sum_{k=1}^{n} (\rho/M_m)\mathfrak{D}_{ik}M_kH_i(dy_k/dT) \right] (dT/dz)$$

$$= -(k + k_R)(dT/dz) = -k_{\text{eff}}(dT/dz) \qquad (10\text{-}50)$$

Equation (10-50), derived by Hirschfelder (77), has been used to study the thermal conductivity of chemically reacting mixtures by Butler and Brokaw (28). k is the ordinary thermal conductivity (often referred to as the *frozen* conductivity), and k_R is the contribution due to counter-diffusion of the reacting species. ρ is the mixture molal density, M_m the mole-fraction average molecular weight, $\mathfrak{D}_{ik}$ the multicomponent diffusion coefficient, and y the mole fraction. The sum of k and k_R is often called the *effective* thermal conductivity k_{eff}.

Before discussing the use of Eq. (10-50) it is well to point out that there are three general cases to be considered. If the chemical reaction rates are very slow, then only negligibly small composition gradients can be established and $N_i \cong 0$. In this case there is no appreciable contribution of the chemical reaction to the thermal conductivity. At the other extreme, if reaction rates are very high, then local chemical equilibrium may be assumed to exist throughout the gas and, as will be illustrated below, the dy/dT terms in Eq. (10-49) can be evaluated by the van't Hoff equation.

Intermediate between the frozen and equilibrium cases is the situation in which the reaction-rate kinetics are sufficiently rapid to increase significantly the thermal conductivity but are not fast enough to produce local chemical equilibrium. This intermediate case is treated briefly after considering the equilibrium case.

Equilibrium Case. Butler and Brokaw (28) have treated the general case and employed the van't Hoff isochore to relate the equilibrium constant to temperature, thus relating y_k to T,

$$d(\ln K)/dT = \Delta H/RT^2 \qquad (10\text{-}51)$$

The final expressions are rather complex. To illustrate the chemical-reaction contribution for the simple case $A \rightleftharpoons gB$, it can be shown that

$$k_R = \rho D_{AB}[(\Delta H)^2/(RT^2)]\{[y_A(1 - y_A)]/[gy_A + (1 - y_A)]^2\} \qquad (10\text{-}52)$$

* This assumes that reaction rates are sufficiently rapid to produce chemical equilibrium at every point in the gas. The more general case, in which the thermal conductivity is limited by chemical kinetics, is briefly discussed later.

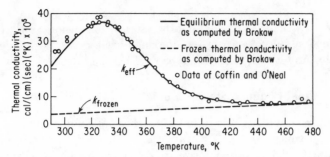

FIG. 10-9. Thermal conductivity of $N_2O_4 \rightleftharpoons 2NO_2$ mixtures at 1 atm. [*Experimental data from K. P. Coffin and C. O'Neal, NACA Tech. Note* 4209, *February, 1958. Calculated curves from J. N. Butler and R. S. Brokaw, J. Chem. Phys.,* **26**:1636 (1957).]

D_{AB} is the usual binary diffusion coefficient, and ΔH is the enthalpy of decomposition of 1 mole of A. If ΔH is large, it is evident that k_R is large; also, k_R is seen to be sensitive to both temperature and pressure. By noting that $M_A = gM_B$, Eq. (10-52) may be rewritten in terms of weight fractions x_A, x_B or extent of reaction ξ,

$$k_R = \rho D_{AB}[(\Delta H)^2/(RT^2)](x_Ax_B/g) = \rho D_{AB}[(\Delta H)^2/(RT^2)]\xi(1 - \xi) \tag{10-53}$$

which shows clearly that k_R is maximized at $x_A = x_B = 0.5$. As an example of Eq. (10-53), Fig. 10-9 has been drawn for the equilibrium system $N_2O_4 \rightleftharpoons 2 NO_2$. It is easily seen that k_{eff} may be much larger than k in those temperature regions where the equilibrium composition differs greatly from either pure reactant or products; e.g., at temperatures above about 425°K (at 1 atm) the "mixture" is essentially pure NO_2, and the effect of the chemical reaction on k is very slight (85, 166, 181).

Many other interesting comments could be made about equilibrium chemically reacting systems, e.g., the relationship between the effective heat capacity $C_{p_{eff}}$, the effective thermal conductivity k_{eff},* the effect of the energy-diffusion flux on convective heat-transfer coefficients, etc. The interested reader can find many recent articles in this field (23, 32, 39, 61, 78–80, 98, 140, 186, 197, 201).

Nonequilibrium Case. If the chemical-reaction rate is not rapid enough to maintain local chemical equilibrium, then Eq. (10-49) is not valid. The mathematics become very complicated because of the nonlinear nature of the reaction-rate expression. Usually a specific reaction-rate expression must be known before a solution is possible, but reasonable solutions are available for the general case when it is permissible to

* For a binary mixture, the relationship is approximately $k_{eff}/k \cong C_{p_{eff}}/C_p$ if the Lewis number is near unity.

linearize the expression.   This linearization is accomplished by expanding the expression in a Taylor's (or other series) expansion and truncating after the first derivative term.   Pertinent references dealing with the nonequilibrium case include Refs. 3, 12, 14, 15, 17, 24, 54, 77.

10-9   Thermal Conductivity of Liquids

For many simple organic liquids, the thermal conductivity is between 10 and 100 times as large as that of the low-pressure gas at the same temperature.   There is little pressure dependence, and usually the effect of increasing the temperature is to decrease the thermal conductivity These characteristics are very similar to those noted for liquid viscosity though the temperature dependence of the latter is nearly exponential whereas for thermal conductivity it is more nearly linear.

Values of k_L for most common organic liquids range between 200 and 500 $\times$ 10^{-6} cal/(cm)(sec)(°K) at temperatures below the normal boiling point, but water, NH_3, and other highly polar molecules have values two to three times as large.   Also, in many cases the dimensionless ratio $Mk/R\mu$ is nearly constant (for nonpolar liquids) between a value of 2 and 3 so that highly viscous liquids often have a correspondingly larger thermal conductivity.   Liquid metals and some organosilicon compounds have large values of k_L, the former often are 100 times as large as normal organic liquids.   Very approximately, the solid thermal conductivity at the melting point is 20 to 40 per cent larger than that of the liquid.

The theory of heat conduction in liquids is one which is receiving intensive study by many groups, though no reliable, general estimation techniques have been developed completely from theory.   The various theories and results to 1964 have been discussed in an excellent review article by McLaughlin (110).

There is one important point to note in dealing with liquid thermal conductivities (and also viscosities or diffusion coefficients).   The difference between values in the gas and liquid phases indicates a distinct change in mechanism of energy (or momentum or mass) transfer, i.e.,

$$k_L/k_g \sim 10 \text{ to } 100$$
$$\mu_L/\mu_g \sim 10 \text{ to } 100$$
$$D_L/D_g \sim 10^{-4}$$

In the gas phase, the molecules are relatively free to move about and transfer momentum and energy by a "collisional" mechanism.   The intermolecular force fields, though not insignificant, do not drastically affect the values of k, μ, or D.   That is, from Eq. (10-2), (9-9), or (11-11), the intermolecular forces are reflected solely in the collision-integral terms Ω_v or Ω_D, which are really a ratio of collision integrals for a real force field and an artificial case where the molecules are rigid, noninteracting spheres. The variation of Ω_v or Ω_D from unity then yields a rough quantitative measure of the importance of intermolecular forces in affecting gas-phase transport coefficients. Reference to Table 9-1 (for Ω_v) or Table 11-1 (for Ω_D) shows that Ω values are often near unity. One then concludes that a rigid noninteracting spherical molecular model will yield low-pressure transport coefficients ($k\dagger$, μ, or D) not too greatly different from values computed when intermolecular forces (such as the Lennard-Jones) are included.

In the liquid, however, this hypothesis is not even approximately true. The close proximity of molecules to one another emphasizes strongly the intermolecular forces of attraction. There is little actual wandering of the individual molecules, as evidenced by the low value of liquid diffusion coefficients, and often a liquid is modeled as a lattice with each molecule caged by its nearest neighbors. Energy and momentum are now primarily exchanged by oscillations of molecules in the mutual force fields surrounding each molecule. Scheffy (164) has pointed out an illuminating description of such processes given by Green (71): ". . . Imagine the molecules tied together by elastic strings, the tension in which varies in a rather eccentric way so as to simulate the attractive forces. Then, as the molecules move, the elastic energy of the strings will vary and by this means energy can be transported from one part of the assembly to another without actually being carried by the molecules themselves."

This problem of the difference in transport mechanisms of a dense gas or liquid compared with a low-pressure gas is discussed in considerable detail by McLaughlin (110) among others. Enskog has made a similar breakdown of the mechanisms (using only the hard-sphere model) into convective and collisional terms, the former predominating at low pressure and the latter at high gas densities or for the liquid phase (34, 110).

These theories, while holding exciting promise for the future, do not yield simple estimating techniques for liquid thermal conductivity; less rigorous (or frankly empirical) means are of more interest to an engineer. These estimation techniques are discussed in Sec. 10-10. Later sections cover the variation of thermal conductivity with temperature (Sec. 10-11) and pressure (Sec. 10-12); the conductivity of liquid mixtures is discussed in Sec. 10-13.

10-10 Estimation of the Thermal Conductivity of Pure Liquids

A large number of estimation techniques have been proposed to calculate the thermal conductivity of a pure liquid; most are empirical, though a few rest upon rather tenuous theoretical models. The criteria

---

$\dagger$ k in this case is the monatomic value, *not* including contributions from internal energy-transfer mechanisms.

used to decide which methods should be presented in this section were accuracy, generality, and ease of use. Two methods were finally selected for detailed presentation, i.e., those of Sheffy and Johnson and of Robbins and Kingrea. Others are discussed very briefly at the end of the section.

Method of Sheffy and Johnson. In an experimental and theoretical study of liquid thermal conductivities, Sheffy and Johnson (164, 165) proposed a method, very approximate but easy to use, which is given in Eq. (10-54),

$$k_L = \{(4.66)(10^{-3})[1 - 0.00126(T - T_m)]/T_m^{0.216}M^{0.300}\} \quad (10\text{-}54)$$

where T_m = melting point, °K
T = temperature, °K
M = molecular weight
k_L = liquid thermal conductivity, cal/(cm)(sec)(°K)

This equation is essentially empirical, though based originally upon a theoretical equation relating k_L at T_m to fundamental molecular properties such as vibrational frequency and intermolecular distances. It predicts a linear decrease of k_L with T and is not suitable for highly polar or inorganic molecules such as water or for reduced temperatures greater than about 0.7. Values of k_L calculated from Eq. (10-54) have been calculated for 69 different liquids with 141 data points and are presented in Table 10-7. The average per cent error is 13, though often much larger errors are noted. Particularly poor results were found for branched-chain hydrocarbons, naphthenes, and high-molecular-weight compounds. In a similar test with 66 liquids Sheffy concluded that average errors would be about 10 to 12 per cent. The method is illustrated in Example 10-6.

Method of Robbins and Kingrea. Weber in 1880 (196) suggested that k_L was proportional to the product $C_p\rho^{4/3}$, and this general type of correlation has been modified and republished several times (132, 168, 169, 187). The best modification, however, appears to be due to Robbins and Kingrea (147), who have proposed the following relation:

$$k_L = \{[(88.0 - 4.94H)(10^{-3})]/\Delta S^*\}(0.55/T_r)^N C_p\rho^{4/3} \quad (10\text{-}55)$$

where k_L = liquid thermal conductivity, cal/(cm)(sec)(°K)
T_r = reduced temperature, T/T_c
C_p = molal heat capacity of the liquid, cal/(g mole)(°K)
ρ = molal liquid density, g moles/cm³
ΔS^* = modified Everett entropy of vaporization (see Sec. 4-20)

$$= \Delta H_{v_b}/T_b + R \ln (273/T_b) \quad (10\text{-}56)$$

ΔH_{v_b} = molal heat of vaporization at the normal boiling point, cal/g mole
T_b = normal boiling point, °K

The parameters H and N are obtained from Table 10-6; H depends upon molecular structure and N upon the liquid density at 20°C. Equation (10-55) is relatively easy to use, but ΔH_{v_b}, T_b, ρ, C_p values are required. These may be obtained from experimental data or by estimation techniques described earlier in this book.

Robbins and Kingrea tested Eq. (10-55) with 70 organic liquids, using 142 data points; their test compounds and results are shown in Table 10-7. The average deviation was 3.7 per cent; rarely did the errors exceed 10 per cent. These workers state that the range of applicability is from a T_r of 0.4 to 0.9, but the testing in Table 10-7 was invariably

TABLE 10-6. H AND N FACTORS FOR EQ. (10-55)*

Functional group	Number of groups	H†
Unbranched hydrocarbons:		
Paraffins.......................	....	0
Olefins........................	....	0
Rings..........................	....	0
CH₃ branches..................	One	1
	Two	2
	Three	3
C₂H₅ branches.................	One	2
iso-C₃H₇ branches..............	One	2
C₄H₉ branches.................	One	2
F substitutions.................	One	1
	Two	2
Cl substitutions................	One	1
	Two	2
	Three or four	3
Br substitutions................	One	4
	Two	6
I substitutions..................	One	5
OH substitutions................	One (iso-)	1
	One (normal)	−1
	Two	0
	One (tert-)	5
Oxygen substitutions:		
—C̵=O (ketones, aldehydes).... O	....	0
—C̵—O— (acids, esters)..........	....	0
—O— (ethers)...............	....	2
NH₂ substitutions................	One	1

Liquid density, g/cm^3	N
<1	1
>1	0

* L. A. Robbins and C. L. Kingrea, *Hydrocarbon Proc. and Petrol. Refiner*, **41**(5):133 (1962).

† For compounds containing multiple functional groups, the H factor contributions are additive.

carried out only from about 0.5 to 0.7. Sulfur-containing compounds and inorganics cannot be treated. The abrupt change in the exponent N from zero to unity for compounds with mass densities greater or less than 1.0 g/cm^3 is difficult to accept in many instances; often more reliable results are obtained with $N = 1.0$ even for compounds with $\rho > 1$ g/cm^3 (35).

Other Liquid-thermal-conductivity Estimating Techniques. Figure 10-7, which correlates $k - k^0$ as a function of reduced density, is presumably applicable for the liquid phase; there is some difficulty in obtaining accurate values of $k - k^0$ at the high reduced densities corresponding to the liquid phase. At high reduced temperatures, however, the estimation methods described above are not reliable, and the Stiel and Thodos plot of Fig. 10-7 or Eqs. (10-28) to (10-30) are probably more reliable.

Of the other suggested estimation techniques for k_L (11, 13, 109, 111, 135) one which deserves some note is the method of Sakiadis and Coates (149, 150). The method is summarized in detail elsewhere (139), but in essence the model chosen for energy transfer involves the propagation of heat across isothermal molecule chains at sonic velocity. The detailed analysis predicts that

$$k_L = C_p\rho U_s L \qquad (10\text{-}57)$$

where $C_p\rho$ = volumetric heat capacity, cal/(cm^3)($^\circ$K)

U_s = sonic velocity, cm/sec

L = characteristic intermolecular clearance, cm

The method predicts k_L values of the same order of accuracy as those described above but requires sonic velocities, and a somewhat involved technique is necessary to estimate L; either an approximate structural estimating technique is necessary, or X-ray diffraction data are used. The relative complexity of the method and the requirement of often unavailable auxiliary data were the principal reasons for omitting it from the detailed comparison as shown in Table 10-7.

Discussion and Recommendations. One of the most important points to note about reported liquid thermal conductivities is that there are often marked differences in the literature values; such differences often are of the same order as the errors reported for the estimation techniques. Two groups of investigators have contributed notably to the determination of k_L, that is, Riedel in Germany (145) and Sakiadis and Coates in the United States (149–152). Unfortunately, the results of these two groups often do not agree well with each other, Sakiadis and Coates usually reporting values 5 to 10 per cent higher than Riedel. These differences certainly cast some doubt on the acceptability of any estimating method. Challones and Powell (33) discuss these and other studies and conclude that, in general, Riedel's values are more acceptable. Other recent experimental papers that may prove interesting are Refs. 55,

TABLE 10-7. COMPARISON BETWEEN CALCULATED AND EXPERIMENTAL VALUES OF LIQUID THERMAL CONDUCTIVITY*

All values of thermal conductivity in $cal/(cm)(sec)(°K) \times 10^6$

Compound	T, °K	k exp.	T_m, °K	k calc.	% Error†	H	N	k calc.	% Error†
			Method of Sheffy and Johnson			Method of Robbins and Kingrea			
Paraffins—straight chain:									
Propane....................	323	187	85.5	395	+111	0	1	188	+ 0.5
Pentane....................	293	272	143.5	356	+ 31	0	1	267	− 1.8
	303	265	.....	350	+ 32	0	1	257	− 3.0
Hexane....................	293	313	177.8	336	+ 7.3	0	1	297	− 5.1
	303	303	.....	331	+ 9.2	0	1	292	− 3.6
	311	295	.....	327	+ 9.8	0	1	281	− 4.7
	330	275	.....	318	+ 16	0	1	264	− 3.3
	333	271	.....	316	+ 17	0	1	262	− 3.3
Heptane....................	293	317	182.6	322	+ 1.6	0	1	309	− 2.5
	303	299	.....	317	+ 5.7	0	1	303	+ 1.3
	311	300	.....	314	+ 4.7	0	1	298	− 0.7
	333	277	.....	303	+ 11	0	1	277	0
	350	262	.....	295	+ 12	0	1	265	+ 1.1
Octane....................	293	326	216.4	314	− 3.7	0	1	321	− 1.5
	311	310	.....	306	− 1.3	0	1	307	− 1.0
	350	277	.....	289	+ 4.3	0	1	274	− 1.1
Nonane....................	293	339	219.7	307	− 6.5	0	1	325	− 4.1
	311	321	.....	299	+ 6.8	0	1	307	− 4.4
	350	284	.....	283	− 0.3	0	1	273	− 3.9
Decane....................	314	315	243.6	295	− 6.3	0	1	328	+ 4.1
	349	278	.....	281	+ 1.1	0	1	292	+ 5.0
Dodecane..................	311	329	263.6	285	− 13	0	1	322	− 2.1
Tetradecane...............	316	328	279.1	275	− 16	0	1	317	− 3.3
Paraffins—branched chain:									
2-Methylpentane.............	305	259	119.5	330	+ 27	+1	1	263	+ 1.5
	322	247	.....	321	+ 30	+1	1	247	0
3-Methylpentane.............	311	260	.....	327	+ 26	+1	1	261	+ 0.4
2,2-Dimethylbutane..........	293	244	173.3	336	+ 38	+2	1	253	+ 3.7
	302	237	.....	332	+ 40	+2	1	247	+ 4.2
	316	228	.....	325	+ 42	+2	1	237	+ 3.9
2,3-Dimethylbutane..........	305	248	144.7	330	+ 33	+2	1	243	− 2.0
	322	238	.....	322	+ 35	+2	1	231	− 2.9
2,4-Dimethylpentane.........	311	243	154.0	326	+ 34	+2	1	248	+ 2.1
2,2,4-Trimethylpentane.......	311	231	164.0	302	+ 31	+3	1	228	− 1.3
	350	201	.....	284	+ 41	+3	1	204	+ 1.5
Unsaturated hydrocarbons:									
Heptene-2..................	311	309	163.7 (trans)	315	+ 1.9	0	1	316	+ 2.3
	350	271	.....	296	+ 9.2	0	1	279	+ 2.9
Saturated ring hydrocarbons:									
Cyclopentane...............	293	316	179.3	358	+ 13	0	1	299	− 5.4
Cyclohexane................	293	297	279.7	356	+ 20	0	1	333	+12
Methylcyclopentane..........	293	289	130.8	339	+ 17	+1	1	292	+ 1.0
	311	275	.....	329	+ 20	+1	1	279	+ 1.4
Methylcyclohexane...........	293	273	146.7	323	+ 18	+1	1	309	+13

TABLE 10-7. COMPARISON BETWEEN CALCULATED AND EXPERIMENTAL VALUES
OF LIQUID THERMAL CONDUCTIVITY* (*Continued*)

Compound	T, °K	k exp.	Method of Sheffy and Johnson			Method of Robbins and Kingrea			
			T_m, °K	k calc.	% Error†	H	N	k calc.	% Error†
Aromatic hydrocarbons:									
Benzene	293	353	278.7	361	+ 2.3	0	1	369	+ 4.5
	323	327	.....	348	+ 6.4	0	1	335	+ 2.4
	349	311	.....	336	+ 8.0	0	1	311	0
	389	272	.....	317	+ 16	0	1	279	+ 2.6
Toluene	293	325	178.3	330	+ 1.5	+1	1	337	+ 3.7
o-Xylene	353	283	.....	301	+ 6.3	+1	1	289	+ 2.1
	303	316	248.1	319	+ 0.9	+2	1	320	+ 1.3
Ethylbenzene	293	316	178.3	317	+ 0.3	+2	1	328	+ 3.8
	353	281	.....	289	+ 2.8	+2	1	271	− 3.6
Alcohols—straight chain:									
Methanol	308	494	175.4	445	− 9.9	−1	1	487	− 1.4
	313	487	.....	442	− 9.2	−1	1	489	+ 0.4
	330	465	.....	431	− 7.3	−1	1	467	+ 0.4
	333	461	.....	428	− 7.2	−1	1	466	+ 1.1
	391	425	.....	389	− 8.5	−1	1	425	0
Ethanol	293	413	155.9	404	− 2.1	−1	1	426	+ 3.1
	303	406	.....	398	− 2.0	−1	1	418	+ 3.0
	313	402	.....	391	− 2.7	−1	1	415	+ 3.2
	333	385	.....	379	− 1.6	−1	1	411	+ 6.7
	347	373	.....	370	− 0.8	−1	1	411	+10
	389	353	.....	344	− 2.5	−1	1	396	+12
	445	326	.....	310	− 4.9	−1	1	344	+ 5.5
Propanol	293	389	146.2	375	− 3.6	−1	1	385	− 1.0
	308	379	.....	366	− 3.4	−1	1	368	− 2.9
	347	351	.....	344	− 2.0	−1	1	342	− 2.6
Butanol	293	367	184	355	− 3.2	−1	1	382	+ 4.1
	311	366	.....	345	− 5.7	−1	1	374	+ 2.2
	313	363	.....	344	− 5.2	−1	1	372	+ 2.5
	333	349	.....	334	− 4.3	−1	1	367	+ 5.2
Pentanol	293	369	194.7	336	− 8.9	−1	1	392	+ 6.2
	311	356	.....	327	− 8.1	−1	1	366	+ 2.8
Octanol	293	396	256.9	307	− 23	−1	1	390	− 1.5
	311	383	.....	300	− 22	−1	1	398	+ 3.9
Alcohols—branched end ring:									
Isopropanol	293	349	184.7	378	+ 8.3	+1	1	331	− 5.2
	311	336	.....	368	+ 9.5	+1	1	336	0
	350	309	.....	347	+ 12	+1	1	334	+ 8.1
Isobutanol	293	343	165.2	351	+ 2.3	+1	1	331	− 3.5
	311	332	.....	341	+ 2.7	+1	1	341	+ 2.7
tert-Butanol	311	277	298.7	362	+ 31	+5	1	269	− 2.9
	350	255	.....	344	+ 35	+5	1	254	− 0.4
Ethylene glycol	293	619	255.8	384	− 38	0	0	611	− 1.3
	311	624	.....	375	− 40	0	0	629	+ 0.8
	350	635	.....	355	− 44	0	0	676	+ 6.5
m-Cresol	293	358	284	329	− 8.1	+2	0	362	+ 1.1
	353	347	.....	304	− 12	+2	0	391	+13

TABLE 10-7. COMPARISON BETWEEN CALCULATED AND EXPERIMENTAL VALUES OF LIQUID THERMAL CONDUCTIVITY* (*Continued*)

Compound	T, °K	k exp.	Method of Sheffy and Johnson			Method of Robbins and Kingrea			
			T_m, °K	k calc.	% Error†	H	N	k calc.	% Error†
Nitrogen compounds:									
Aniline....................	290	424	267.0	347	− 18	+1	0	444	+ 4.7
Dimethylaniline..............	293	340	275.7	317	− 6.8	+3	1	378	+11
Acids:									
Acetic acid..................	296	930	289.8	393	− 58	0	0	830	−11
Propionic acid...............	285	413	251.2	366	− 11	0	0	406	− 1.7
Butyric acid.................	285	389	254	351	− 9.8	0	0	366	− 5.9
Isobutyric acid..............	285	374	226.2	346	− 7.5	+1	1	389	+ 4.0
Halogenated paraffins:									
Methylene chloride...........	258	382	176.5	350	− 8.3	+2	0	358	− 6.3
	273	380	.....	343	− 9.7	+2	0	346	− 8.9
	293	368	.....	333	− 9.5	+2	0	339	− 7.9
	313	359	.....	323	− 10	+2	0	334	− 7.0
Chloroform..................	289	289	209.7	312	+ 8.0	+3	0	281	− 2.8
	293	284	.....	310	+ 9.1	+3	0	281	− 1.1
	322	266	.....	297	+ 11.6	+3	0	273	+ 2.6
Carbon tetrachloride.........	253	274	250.4	308	+ 12	+3	0	272	− 0.7
	273	263	.....	300	+ 14	+3	0	269	+ 2.3
	311	251	.....	285	+ 13	+3	0	259	+ 3.2
	333	243	.....	277	+ 14	+3	0	251	+ 3.3
Dichlorodifluoromethane.......	273	231	113	314	+ 36	+4	0	243	+ 5.2
Ethylene dichloride...........	273	331	237.9	341	+ 3.0	+2	0	332	− 0.3
	333	298	.....	314	+ 5.4	+2	0	320	+ 7.4
	352	285	.....	306	+ 7.3	+2	0	321	+13
1,1,2,2-Tetrachloroethane......	293	269	229.4	282	+ 4.8	+3	0	282	+ 4.8
Trichloroethylene.............	293	278	200	303	+ 9.0	+3	0	282	+ 1.4
Ethyl bromide................	293	246	154	361	+ 47	+4	0	250	+ 1.6
Amyl bromide...............	291	234	185.2	287	+ 23	+4	0	231	− 1.3
Hexyl bromide...............	311	254	188.2	272	+ 7.1	+4	0	234	− 7.9
	349	225	.....	257	+ 14	+4	0	228	+ 1.3
Ethylene dibromide...........	293	244	283.2	280	+ 15	+6	0	241	− 1.2
Ethyl iodide.................	293	213	164.7	288	+ 35	+5	0	241	+13
Halogenated aromatics:									
Fluorobenzene...............	332	327	231.3	316	− 3.4	+1	0	323	− 1.2
Chlorobenzene...............	233	336	218	344	+ 2.4	+1	0	320	− 4.8
	293	301	.....	318	+ 5.6	+1	0	320	+ 6.3
	353	266	.....	291	+ 9.4	+1	0	314	+18
Bromobenzene...............	293	267	242.6	288	+ 7.9	+4	0	262	− 1.9
	353	242	.....	264	+ 9.0	+4	0	249	+ 2.9
Iodobenzene.................	253	255	241.8	280	+ 9.8	+5	0	234	− 8.2
	293	236	.....	266	+ 13	+5	0	231	− 2.1
	353	207	.....	244	+ 18	+5	0	222	+ 7.2
Esters:									
Ethyl formate................	284	403	192.7	357	− 11	0	1	395	− 2.0
Propyl formate...............	284	386	180.3	339	− 12	0	1	390	+ 1.0
Methyl acetate...............	293	410	175.1	350	− 15	0	1	434	+ 5.8

TABLE 10-7. COMPARISON BETWEEN CALCULATED AND EXPERIMENTAL VALUES
OF LIQUID THERMAL CONDUCTIVITY* (*Continued*)

Compound	T, °K	k exp.	Method of Sheffy and Johnson			Method of Robbins and Kingrea			
			T_m, °K	k calc.	% Error†	H	N	k calc.	% Error†
Esters (*cont.*)									
Ethyl acetate................	289	355	189.6	338	− 4.8	0	1	365	+ 2.8
	293	363	.....	336	− 7.4	0	1	359	− 1.1
	311	341	.....	327	− 4.1	0	1	336	− 1.5
	333	315	.....	316	+ 0.3	0	1	321	+ 1.9
Propyl acetate...............	293	348	180.7	321	− 7.8	0	1	358	+ 2.9
Butyl acetate...............	293	345	196.4	311	− 9.8	0	1	372	+ 7.8
Methyl propionate...........	311	351	185.7	325	− 7.4	0	1	360	+ 2.6
Ethyl propionate...........	293	353	199.3	322	− 8.8	0	1	355	+ 0.6
Propyl propionate...........	293	329	197.3	300	− 8.8	0	1	351	+ 6.7
Ethyl butyrate..............	311	323	179.9	302	− 6.5	0	1	336	+ 4.0
Other oxygenated compounds:									
Acetone....................	273	409	178	393	− 3.9	0	1	410	+ 0.2
	293	385	.....	382	− 0.8	0	1	382	− 0.8
	313	361	.....	371	+ 2.8	0	1	352	− 2.4
Diethyl ether..............	273	308	156.9	360	+ 17	2	1	327	+ 6.1
	293	308	.....	350	+ 14	2	1	307	− 0.3
Acetaldehyde...............	294	408	149.7	409	+ 0.2	0	1	376	− 7.8
Average error..............	...	...	.....	...	13	...	...	...	3.7

* Experimental and calculated values of thermal conductivity for the Robbins-Kingrea method have been reproduced from L. A. Robbins and C. L. Kingrea, paper presented to a session on chemical engineering during the twenty-seventh Midyear Meeting of the American Petroleum Institutes, Division of Refining, San Francisco, Calif., May 14, 1962.

Hydrocarbon melting points from R. A. Dreisbach, Physical Properties of Chemical Compounds, I, *Advances in Chem. Ser.* 15, 1955; II, *Ser.* 22, 1959; III *Ser.* 29, 1961.

Other melting points from C. D. Hodgman (ed.), "Handbook of Chemistry and Physics," 30th ed., Chemical Rubber Publishing Co., Cleveland, Ohio, 1948.

† Per cent error = [(calculated-experimental)/experimental] × 100.

57, 65, 74, 188. With these facts in mind, the best recommendations that can be made at the present time are as follows:

For organic liquids only:

1. Use Sheffy and Johnson's method [Eq. (10-54)] if a *quick, approximate* value is necessary. The method is not applicable, however, for highly polar liquids, branched-chain and naphthenic hydrocarbons, and inorganic liquids or for temperatures much above the normal boiling point. Only the molecular weight and melting point need be known.

2. Use the method of Robbins and Kingrea [Eq. (10-55)] for a more accurate estimation between reduced temperatures of about 0.4 and 0.8. Liquid densities and heat capacities are required, as are the boiling point and latent heat of vaporization at this latter point. Inorganic or sulfur-

containing compounds cannot be treated. Errors usually are within 5 per cent of reported values.

3. If the liquid is at a T_r of greater than 0.8, refer to the high-pressure-gas thermal-conductivity recommendations in Sec. 10-5.

Example 10-6. Estimate the thermal conductivity of liquid acetone at 20°C. The experimental value is $(385)(10^{-6})$ cal/(cm)(sec)(°K) (118, 145).

Solution. *Scheffy and Johnson Method.* The melting point is 178°K, and $M = 58.08$; from Eq. (10-54),

$$k_L = (4.66)(10^{-3})[1 - 0.00126(293 - 178)]/(178^{0.216})(58.08^{0.300})$$
$$= 382 \times 10^{-6} \text{ cal/(cm)(sec)(°K)}$$
$$\text{Error} = [(382 - 385)/385] \times 100 = 0.8\%$$

Robbins and Kingrea Method. At 20°C, $\rho = 0.79$ g/cm³ (84) $= 0.79/58.08 = 13.6 \times 10^{-3}$ g mole/cm³; $C_p = 30.2$ cal/(g mole)(°K) (199); $H = 0$, $N = 1$. From Appendix A, $T_c = 509°K$; so $T_r = {}^{293}\!/_{509} = 0.575$.

To determine ΔS^*, $H_{v_b} = 6952$ cal/g mole (120), and $T_b = 330°K$ (Appendix A); so, from Eq. (10-56),

$$\Delta S^* = 6,952/330 + 1.986 \ln {}^{273}\!/_{330} = 20.69 \text{ cal/(g mole)(°K)}$$

and, from Eq. (10-55),

$$k_L = \{[88.0 - (4.94)(0)]/20.69\}(10^{-3})(0.55/0.575)(30.2)(13.6)^{4/3}(10^{-3})^{4/3}$$
$$= 394 \times 10^{-6} \text{ cal/(cm)(sec)(°K)}$$
$$\text{Error} = [(394 - 385)/385] \times 100 = +2.3\%$$

(Note that this calculated value differs slightly from the calculated value of Robbins and Kingrea in Table 10-7, as a newer value of ΔH_{v_b} was used.)

10-11 Effect of Temperature on the Thermal Conductivity of Liquids

Except for some aqueous solutions, water, and a few multihydroxy molecules, the thermal conductivity of liquids decreases with temperature.* Below or near the normal boiling point, the decrease is nearly linear and is often represented as

$$k_L = k_{L_0}[1 + \alpha(T - T_0)] \tag{10-58}$$

where k_{L_0} is the thermal conductivity at temperature T_0 and α is a constant for a given compound which varies between -0.0005 and $-0.002°K^{-1}$ (8, 11, 31, 33, 50, 131, 149, 150, 179, 188, 198). At temperatures near the melting point, the slope dk/dT often becomes very small (150), and near the critical point the slope becomes large (145).

* At low temperatures, but very high pressures, dk/dT is often positive even for nonpolar liquids.

Figure 10-10 shows the general trend of k_L with T for methanol, benzene, acetone, and glycerol, the last showing an increase in k_L with temperature, although the data scatter considerably (165).

The estimation techniques for k_L discussed in Sec. 10-10 may also be used to determine the variation of k_L with T, and, especially at $T_r > 0.8$, the Stiel and Thodos plot (Fig. 10-7, Sec. 10-5) may be used to advantage. The liquid is at a high pressure and temperature and resembles a dense fluid rather than a liquid (1).

Vargaftik (187) argues that, for nonpolar liquids, k_L is proportional to $\rho_L^{4/3}$ but this is only approximate. Horrocks and McLaughlin (83, 110) in a careful study of the problem show that there is a theoretical basis for relating d (ln k_L)/dT with the coefficient of thermal expansion of the liquid, i.e., approximately,

$$d(\ln k_L)/dT = -2.75[d(\ln V)/dT]_p + 0.0015 \qquad (10\text{-}59)$$

A plot of this relation is shown in Fig. 10-11 (83), and approximate data points for a number of compounds are also shown. It is interesting to

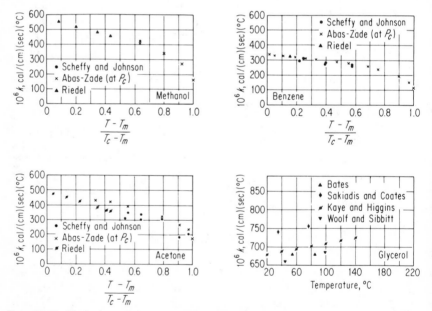

FIG. 10-10. Variation of liquid thermal conductivity with temperature. [*Plots are from* W. J. Scheffy *and* E. F. Johnson, J. Chem. Eng. Data, **6**:245 (1961). *See also* A. K. Abas-Zade, Doklady. Akad. Nauk. S.S.S.R., **99**:227 (1954); L. Riedel, Chem. -Ing. -Tech., **23**:321, 465 (1951); O. K. Bates, Ind. Eng. Chem., **28**:494 (1936); B. Sakiadis *and* J. Coates, AIChE J., **1**:275 (1955); G. Kaye *and* W. Higgins, Proc. Roy. Soc. (London), **A117**:459 (1927); J. Woolf *and* W. Sibbitt, Ind. Eng. Chem., **46**:1947 (1954).]

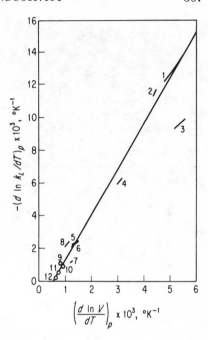

Fig. 10-11. Relation between temperature coefficient of liquid thermal conductivity and compressibility. [J. K. Horrocks and E. M. McLaughlin, Trans. Faraday Soc., **59**:1709 (1963).] Key: 1. Carbon monoxide. 2. Argon. 3. Nitrogen. 4. Methane. 5. Benzene. 6. Cyclohexane. 7. Carbon tetrachloride. 8. Toluene. 9. Diphenyl. 10. o-Terphenyl 11. p-Terphenyl. 12. m-Terphenyl.

note from this correlation that the simple liquids are the more temperature-dependent (they usually have larger values of $[d(\ln V)/dT]_p$) and that the particular structure of complex molecules is not of much importance (74). For example, as noted by Horrocks and McLaughlin (83), the temperature coefficients of o-terphenyl and p-terphenyl are almost the same. The viscosity temperature coefficients and absolute viscosities are considerably different; for the former the viscosity at the melting point is about 350 millipoises, while for the latter it is only about 8 millipoises. Clearly, liquid viscosity is much more temperature-sensitive and structurally sensitive than thermal conductivity.

In summary, therefore, the thermal conductivity of liquids usually varies linearly with temperature over wide ranges; except for highly polar, multihydroxyl compounds, increasing T decreases k_L. The effect is not large, and simple liquids are more temperature-sensitive than complex ones. These comments hold for saturated liquids or subcooled liquids up to pressures around 30 to 40 atm; i.e., over this pressure range the effect of pressure on k_L is small (except near the critical point, when Fig. 10-7 should be used).

10-12 Effect of Pressure on the Thermal Conductivity of Liquids

At moderate pressures, up to 30 to 40 atm, the effect of pressure upon the thermal conductivity of liquids is usually neglected, except near the

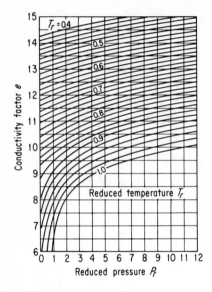

FIG. 10-12. Effect of pressure on liquid thermal conductivities. [*J. M. Lenoir, Petrol. Refiner,* **36**(8):162 (1957).]

critical point, where the liquid behaves somewhat as a dense fluid (see Sec. 10-5). At lower temperatures, the classical experiments of Bridgman (16) constitute nearly all the available data on the effect of pressure on k_L. These data show that k_L increases with pressure, although only slightly, and the rate of change is smaller at the higher pressures. An interesting result is that, above about 3,000 atm, k_L often decreases with increasing temperature, whereas the opposite is usually found at low pressures (see Sec. 10-11). This reversal in the temperature coefficient may be estimated from Eq. (10-59) or Fig. 10-11 since, at high pressures, $[d(\ln V)/dT]_P$ also decreases (88).

A convenient way to estimate the effect of pressure on k_L is by Eq. (10-60),

$$k_2/k_1 = e_2/e_1 \qquad (10\text{-}60)$$

where k_2 and k_1 refer to liquid thermal conductivities at T and pressures P_2 and P_1 and e_2, e_1 are functions of the reduced temperature and pressure as shown in Fig. 10-12 (103). This correlation was devised by Lenoir and was based primarily on Bridgman's data. In testing with 12 liquids, both polar and nonpolar, errors of only 2 to 4 per cent were noted. The use of Eq. (10-60) and Fig. 10-12 is illustrated in Example 10-7 with liquid NO_2, a material *not* used in formulating the correlation.

Example 10-7. Estimate the thermal conductivity of nitrogen dioxide at 100°F (311°K) and 4,000 psia (272 atm). The experimental value quoted is $(319)(10^{-6})$ cal/(cm)(sec)(°K) (141). The value of k_L at the bubble point of 100°F (30.7 psia) is $(296)(10^{-6})$ cal/(cm)(sec)(°K) (141).

Solution. From Appendix A, $T_c = 431°K$, $P_c = 100$ atm; so $T_r = 311/431 = 0.721$, $P_r = 272/100 = 2.72$. From Fig. 10-12, $e_2 = 11.75$, and $e_1 = 11.17$; thus, from Eq. (10-60),

$$k \text{ (at 4,000 psia)} = (296)(10^{-6})(11.75)/(11.17)$$
$$= (312)(10^{-6}) \text{ cal/(cm)(sec)(°K)}$$
$$\text{Error} = [(312 - 319)/319] \times 100 = -2.2\%$$

10-13 Thermal Conductivity of Liquid Mixtures

Thermal conductivities of mixtures of organic liquids are usually less than what one would predict using a mole- (or weight-) fraction average. The principal sources of experimental data are in publications not readily available (56, 58, 146, 183), but a few new systems have been studied by Rodriguez (148) and Horrocks and McLaughlin (82).

Generally, the correlating equations proposed for binary solutions have been of the form,

$$k_{L_m} = k_{L_1}x_1 + k_{L_2}x_2 - Cx_1x_2 \qquad (10\text{-}61)$$

where C is a constant, specific for a given mixture. In the Filippov rule (56) [or the Filippov and Novoselova rule (58)], x refers to weight fractions, and $C = 0.72|k_{L_2} - k_{L_1}|$, whereas in the Bondi rule (13) x refers to mole fractions and C is an additive group function which may be determined by a group-contribution technique. Bondi points out that Eq. (10-61) with C given by Filippov's rule is often inaccurate and fails to show any concave curvature when $k_{L_1} = k_{L_2}$. However, Filippov's rule was verified in many cases by Tsederberg (183). The experimental data for liquid thermal conductivities need a careful, critical analysis before any error limits can be placed on Eq. (10-61).

Example 10-8. Estimate the thermal conductivities of 50 mole % solutions of (a) n-propyl alcohol and water and (b) ethyl ether and chloroform at 25°C and 1 atm. Rodriguez reports the following experimental data (148):

$$k_L, \, cal/(cm)(sec)(°K) \times 10^6$$

n-propyl alcohol.................	376
Water.........................	1450
50 mole % solution..............	492

Ethyl ether.....................	330
Chloroform.....................	292
50 mole % solution..............	280

Solution. (a) n-Propyl alcohol–water. A 50 mole % solution has a weight fraction alcohol = 0.77. From Eq. (10-61) with Filippov's rule,

$$k_{L_m}(10^6) = (0.77)(376) + (0.23)(1,450) - (0.72)(1,450 - 376)(0.77)(0.23)$$
$$= 487 \text{ cal/(cm)(sec)(°K)}$$
$$\text{Error} = [(487 - 492)/492] \times 100 = -1.0\%$$

(b) Ethyl ether–chloroform. The 50 mole % solution has a weight fraction ethyl ether = 0.38. As above

$$k_{L_m}(10^6) = (0.38)(330) + (0.62)(292) - (0.72)(330 - 292)(0.38)(0.62)$$
$$= 300 \text{ cal}/(\text{cm})(\text{sec})(°K)$$
$$\text{Error} = [(300 - 280)/280] \times 100 = +7.1\%$$

10-14   Prandtl Numbers

The dimensionless group $C_p\mu/kM$, called the *Prandtl number*, plays an important role in many heat-transfer correlations.* The Prandtl number can always be calculated by obtaining individual values of C_p, μ, and k for the particular temperature, pressure, and composition of interest; from these, the Prandtl-number ratio is easily determined. This procedure is preferable to any of the techniques described below which allow direct estimation of the ratio; however, expediency often favors direct approximations.

Low-pressure Pure Gases. In Sec. 10-3, many of the estimation techniques for low-pressure-gas thermal conductivity were found to be of the form of Eqs. (10-7) or (10-8). From these equations, and the usually excellent approximation that $C_p - C_v = R$, they may be rearranged to yield

From Eq. (10-7), $N_{\text{Pr}} = C_p\mu/kM = C_p/(2.48 + C_p)$ (10-62)
From Eq. (10-8), $N_{\text{Pr}} = C_p\mu/kM = C_p/(0.90 + 1.32C_p)$ (10-63)

or perhaps, in a more general form,

$$N_{\text{Pr}} = f(C_p) \tag{10-64}$$

For monatomic gases, Eq. (10-4) is applicable, and since, in this special case, $C_p/C_v = 5/3$, then

$$N_{\text{Pr}} = C_p\mu/kM = 2/3 \tag{10-65}$$

For simple diatomic gases, near room temperature, C_p is often near 7 cal/(g mole)(°K). The Prandtl numbers calculated from both Eqs. (10-62) and (10-63) are then 0.74 and 0.69, respectively. These values agree with the general engineering assumption that for such gases $N_{\text{Pr}} \sim 0.7$.

For polyatomic gases, or for diatomic gases at high temperatures (where vibrational-energy storage becomes important) Eqs. (10-62) or (10-63) predict that larger Prandtl numbers should result. In one of the

* Often the group is written as $C_p\mu/k$, where in this case C_p is the heat capacity per unit mass; in keeping with the definition of C_p used in this book as the molal heat capacity, then the molecular weight M is required.

few studies of the influence of C_p on N_{Pr} (64), Gambill did find that there was an increase in N_{Pr} with increases in C_p, but the scatter of the data prevented the development of a reliable functional relationship expressed generally in Eq. (10-64). The Prandtl number is not ordinarily very sensitive to temperature in that C_p, μ, and k all increase with temperature. From Table 10-3, it is seen that the similar grouping $C_v\mu/kM$ is also temperature-insensitive.

In general, therefore, if one needs a rapid estimation of the Prandtl number of a pure gas at temperatures well below the critical, then:

1. *Monatomic gases.* Use $N_{Pr} = 0.67$.

2. *Nonpolar gases.* Use an average value calculated from Eqs. (10-62) and (10-63); ordinarily these will yield values of 0.73 ± 15 per cent for linear nonpolar gases and 0.79 ± 15 per cent for nonlinear nonpolar gases (64).

3. *Polar gases.* Values vary rather widely, but if water, ammonia, and other very highly polar gases are excluded, then $N_{Pr} = 0.86 \pm 8$ per cent; for water and ammonia, $N_{Pr} \sim 1$ (64).

High-pressure Pure Gases. No quick estimation technique is available. The effect of pressure on C_p, μ, and k should be estimated individually and the Prandtl-number ratio calculated.

Gas Mixtures. The Prandtl number of a gas mixture may be appreciably different from the mole-fraction average of the Prandtl numbers of the constituent gases, even if the values of C_p, M, μ, and k are essentially linear functions of composition. This nonlinearity is especially probable for mixtures of light and heavy gases. The classic example is the hydrogen-nitrogen mixture studied by Colburn and Coghlan (40). In this case the Prandtl number of both pure components is about 0.73 (at 20°C); however the Prandtl number of the mixture decreases to a distinct minimum value of 0.45 at about 30 mole % nitrogen. In this case, which is typical of many important industrial-gas mixtures, the viscosity increases and thermal conductivity decreases with an increase in nitrogen content. Thus the ratio μ/k increases rapidly with per cent nitrogen; the ratio C_p/M decreases very rapidly as the nitrogen content increases, especially at low nitrogen contents [even though $C_p(H_2) = C_p(N_2) = C_p(\text{mix}) \cong 7$ cal/(g)(mole)(°K)]. The product $(C_p/M)(\mu/k)$ has then a definite minimum, as pointed out above.

It is recommended that gas-mixture Prandtl numbers be calculated by estimating separately the values of C_p, μ, M, and k for the mixture and then the Prandtl ratio determined.

Liquids. Values for N_{Pr} for liquids vary widely with temperature, since viscosity is a strong function of temperature. Values range from around 2 for water and light organics to several thousand for heavy, viscous liquids; liquid-metal values are very low, varying from 0.003 for potassium to 0.07 for lithium (64). About the only approximate rule yet suggested is due to Denbigh (51), who found that, for low-pressure pure liquids,

$$\log N_{Pr} = A(\Delta H_v/T) - 1.80 \tag{10-66}$$

Denbigh suggested a value of 0.10 for the constant A, but Gambill (64) found better results with $A = 0.113$.* In Eq. (10-66), the logarithm is to the base 10, T is in degrees Kelvin, and ΔH_v in calories per gram mole. Equation (10-66) should not be used if $M > 150$. This correlation extends over a 10^4-fold range of N_{Pr}, though errors as great as 100 per cent may be encountered.

It is recommended that liquid Prandtl numbers be obtained whenever possible from experimental values of C_p, μ, and k; if these are not available, then each term should be estimated independently and N_{Pr} calculated; Eq. (10-66) is to be used only as a last effort to obtain an approximate value rapidly.

Example 10-9. Estimate the Prandtl number of ethyl ether at 30°C, using Denbigh's method. The value reported by Denbigh is 3.6.

Solution. ΔH_v at 30°C is 6200 cal/g mole (51). From Eq. (10-66), using Gambill's value for A,

$$\log N_{Pr} = (0.113)(6{,}200/303) - 1.80 = 0.51$$
$$N_{Pr} = 3.2$$
$$\text{Error} = [(3.2 - 3.6)/3.6] \times 100 = -11\%$$

NOMENCLATURE FOR CHAPTER 10

A_{ij} = interaction parameter for Eq. (10-31)

B = per cent increase in low-pressure k per atm

C = constant in Eq. (10-61)

C_p = heat capacity at constant pressure, cal/(g mole)(°K); C_v, at constant volume; $C_{p_{eff}}$, effective heat capacity including contribution due to chemical reaction; C_{int}, contribution due to internal-energy storage modes; $C_{int\ rot}$, due to internal rotation; C_{rot}, due to external rotation; C_{vib}, due to vibration; C_{tr}, due to translational energy

C_s = interaction Sutherland "constant" in Eq. (10-37)

D = diffusion coefficient, cm²/sec; D_{11}, self-diffusion coefficient

$\mathfrak{D}$ = multicomponent diffusion coefficient

e = parameter shown as a function of reduced conditions in Fig. 10-12

f = $kM/C_v\mu$, Eucken factor; f_{tr}, contribution due to translational energy, = 2.5; f_{int}, contribution due to internal energy [see Eq. (10-5)]

F = parameter for Eq. (10-43) and defined in Eq. (10-44)

F_{ir} = number of degrees of freedom for external rotation, = 2 for linear molecules, = 3 for nonlinear molecules

H = parameter for Eq. (10-55), shown in Table 10-6

H_i = (partial) molal enthalpy of component i, cal/g mole

ΔH = heat of reaction, cal/g mole

---

* Gambill also suggests that, for water,

$$\log N_{Pr} = 0.102(\Delta H_v/T) - 2.20$$

ΔH_v = heat of vaporization, cal/g mole; ΔH_{v_b}, at T_b

k = thermal conductivity, cal/(cm)(sec)(°K); k^0, at low pressure; k_c, at T_c and P_c; k_c^0, at T_c and low pressure; k', refers to monatomic value; k_m, for a mixture; k_L, for a liquid; k_R, contribution due to a chemical reaction; k_{eff}, $k + k_R$

k = Boltzmann's constant (when in product kT)

k_i^*, k_i^{**} = Cheung, Bromley, and Wilke thermal-conductivity expansion terms in Eqs. (10-38), (10-39), (10-40)

k_{m_L} = linear mole-fraction average k for a mixture [Eq. (10-45)]

k_{m_R} = reciprocal mole-fraction average k for a mixture [Eq. (10-45)]

K = chemical-reaction equilibrium constant

L = mean free path, cm, or characteristic intermolecular clearance in Eq. (10-57)

M = molecular weight; $M_{ij} = (M_i + M_j)/2$; M_m, mole-fraction average for a mixture

n = number of atoms in molecule

N = parameter in Eq. (10-55), Table 10-6; N_i, flux of component i, g moles/ (cm²)(sec)

N_{Pr} = Prandtl number, $C_p\mu/kM$

N_{Sc} = Schmidt number, $\mu/M\rho D$

P = pressure, atm; P_c, critical pressure; P_r, reduced pressure, P/P_c; P_{r_m}, pseudoreduced mixture pressure (note that units of P in Eqs. (10-9) and (10-10) are g/(cm)(sec²)

q = heat flux, cal/(cm²)(sec); Brokaw factor in Eq. (10-45) and Table 10-4

R = gas constant, 1.987 cal/(g mole)(°K) or 82.06 atm-cm³/(g mole)(°K)

S = Sutherland constant [Eqs. (10-36) and (10-37)]

ΔS_{v_b} = entropy of vaporization at T_b, cal/g mole-°K

ΔS^* = modified Everett entropy of vaporization in Eq. (10-56)

T = temperature, °K; T_c, critical temperature; T_r, reduced temperature, T/T_c; T_{r_m}, pseudoreduced mixture temperature; T_m, melting point; T_b, boiling point at 1 atm

U_s = sonic velocity, cm/sec

v = velocity, cm/sec

V = volume, cm³/g mole; V_c, critical volume; V_r, reduced volume, V/V_c; V_b, liquid at normal boiling point

x = weight or mole fraction

y = vapor mole fraction

Y = parameter = $(C_v - 3R - C_{int\ rot})/(3n - 6 - F_{ir})$

z = distance in z direction

Z = compressibility factor PV/RT; Z_c, at the critical point; collision number [Eq. (10-11)]

Greek

α = constant in Eq. (10-58) or polar parameter in Eqs. (10-13), (10-14)

β = vibrational-energy parameter in Eq. (10-13), $\cong 1.30$

γ = C_p/C_v or parameter $T_c^{1/6}M^{1/2}/P_c^{2/3}$

ϵ_0 = characteristic energy parameter, e.g., in Lennard-Jones potential

ξ = extent of reaction

μ = viscosity, poises or centipoises

ρ = molal density, g moles/cm³; ρ_c, at critical point

σ = characteristic molecular dimension, e.g., as in Lennard-Jones potential

τ = relaxation time; τ_{coll}, mean time between collisions [see Eq. (10-11)]

ϕ_{ij} = interaction parameter for mixture viscosity [Eq. (9-35)]; $\phi_{ij_{p\text{-}np}}$ for polar-nonpolar mixtures [see Eq. (10-43)]

ψ = rotational-energy parameter in Eq. (10-13)

Ω_v = collision integral (Table 9-1)

REFERENCES FOR CHAPTER 10

1. Abas-Zade, A. K.: *Doklady Akad. Nauk. S.S.S.R.*, **68**:665 (1949).
2. Abas-Zade, A. K.: *Doklady Akad. Nauk. S.S.S.R.*, **99**:227 (1954); *Chem. Abstr.*, **49**:12,898 (1955).
3. Altman, D., and H. Wise: *J. Am. Rocket Soc.*, **26**:256 (1956).
4. Amdur, I., and E. A. Mason: *Phys. Fluids*, **1**:370 (1958).
5. American Petroleum Institute: "Selected Values of Physical and Thermodynamic Properties of Hydrocarbons and Related Compounds," Project 44, Carnegie Press, Pittsburgh, Pa., 1953, and supplements.
6. Arnold, J. H.: *Ind. Eng. Chem.*, **22**:1091 (1930).
7. Barua, A. K.: *Indian J. Physics*, **34**:169 (1960).
8. Bates, O. K., G. Hazzard, and G. Palmer: *Ind. Eng. Chem.*, **33**:375 (1941).
9. Bennett, L. A., and R. G. Vines: *J. Chem. Phys.*, **23**:1587 (1955).
10. Bird, R. B.: *Ingenieur Nr.*, **35**:1 (1958).
11. Bird, R. B., and J. R. Brock: *AIChE J.*, **5**:436 (1959).
12. Bodman, S. W.: Sc.D. thesis in chemical engineering, Massachusetts Institute of Technology, October, 1964.
13. Bondi, A.: *AIChE J.*, **8**:610 (1962).
14. Brian, P. L. T., and S. W. Bodman: *Ind. Eng. Chem. Fundamentals*, **3**:339 (1964).
15. Brian, P. L. T., and R. C. Reid: *AIChE J.*, **8**:322 (1962).
16. Bridgman, P. W.: *Proc. Am. Acad. Arts Sci.*, **59**:154 (1923).
17. Broadwell, J. E.: *J. Fluid Mech.*, **4**:113 (1958).
18. Brokaw, R. S.: Alignment Charts for Transport Properties, Viscosity, Thermal Conductivity, and Diffusion Coefficients for Nonpolar Gases and Gas Mixtures at Low Density, *NASA Tech. Rept.* R-81, Lewis Research Center, Cleveland, Ohio, 1961.
19. Brokaw, R. S.: Approximate Formulas for Viscosity and Thermal Conductivity of Gas Mixtures, *NASA Tech. Note* D-2502, Lewis Research Center, Cleveland, Ohio, 1964.
20. Brokaw, R. S.: *Ind. Eng. Chem.*, **47**:2398 (1955).
21. Brokaw, R. S.: *J. Chem. Phys.*, **29**:391 (1958).
22. Brokaw, R. S.: *J. Chem. Phys.*, **31**:571 (1959).
23. Brokaw, R. S.: *J. Chem. Phys.*, **32**:1005 (1960).
24. Brokaw, R. S.: *J. Chem. Phys.*, **35**:1569 (1961).
25. Brokaw, R. S., and C. O'Neal, Jr.: Rotational Relaxation and the Relation between Thermal Conductivity and Viscosity for Some Nonpolar Polyatomic Gases, *Ninth International Symposium on Combustion*, p. 725, Academic Press Inc., New York, 1963.
26. Bromley, L. A.: Thermal Conductivity of Gases at Moderate Pressures, *Univ. Calif. Radiation Lab.*, UCRL-1852, Berkeley, Calif., June, 1952.
27. Burgoyne, J. H., and F. Weinberg: *Fourth Symposium on Combustion*, p. 294, The Williams & Williams Company, Baltimore, 1953.
28. Butler, J. N., and R. S. Brokaw: *J. Chem. Phys.*, **26**:1636 (1957).
29. Carmichael, L. T., V. Berry, and B. H. Sage: *J. Chem. Eng. Data*, **8**:281 (1963).
30. Carmichael, L. T., and B. H. Sage: *J. Chem. Eng. Data*, **9**:511 (1964).
31. Cecil, O. B., and R. H. Munch: *Ind. Eng. Chem.*, **48**:437 (1956).

32. Chakraborti, P. K.: *J. Chem. Phys.*, **38**:575 (1963).
33. Challoner, A. R., and R. W. Powell: *Proc. Roy. Soc. (London)*, **A238**:90 (1956).
34. Chapman, S., and T. G. Cowling: "The Mathematical Theory of Non-uniform Gases," Cambridge University Press, New York, 1961.
35. Chase, J. D.: Private communication, May, 1964.
36. Cheung, H.: Thermal Conductivity and Viscosity of Gas Mixtures, *Univ. Calif. Radiation Lab.* UCRL-8230, Berkeley, Calif., April, 1958.
37. Cheung, H., L. A. Bromley, and C. R. Wilke: *AIChE J.*, **8**:221 (1962).
38. Cheung, H., L. A. Bromley, and C. R. Wilke: Thermal Conductivity and Viscosity of Gas Mixtures, *Univ. Calif. Radiation Lab.* UCRL-8230 rev., Berkeley, Calif., April, 1959.
39. Coffin, K. P.: *J. Chem. Phys.*, **31**:1290 (1959).
40. Colburn, A. P., and C. A. Coghlan: *Trans. ASME*, **63**:561 (1941).
41. Comings, E. W., W. B. Lee, and F. R. Kramer: *Proc. Joint Conf. on Thermodynamics and Transport Properties of Fluids*, London, July, 1957, pp. 188–192, Institute of Mechanical Engineers, Westminster, London, 1958.
42. Comings, E. W., and B. J. Mayland: *Chem. Met. Eng.*, **52**(3):115 (1945).
43. Comings, E. W., and M. F. Nathan: *Ind. Eng. Chem.*, **39**:964 (1947).
44. Cotton, J. E.: Ph.D. thesis, University of Oregon, 1962.
44a. Cottrell, T. L., and J. C. McCoubrey: "Molecular Energy Transfer in Gases," Butterworth & Co. (Publishers), Ltd., London, 1961.
45. Couch, E. J., and K. A. Kobe: *J. Chem. Eng. Data*, **6**:229 (1961).
46. Cowling, T. G.: *Brit. J. Appl. Physics*, **15**:959 (1964).
47. Cowling, T. G.: *Proc. Roy. Soc. (London)*, **A263**:186 (1961).
48. Cowling, T. G., P. Gray, and P. G. Wright: *Proc. Roy. Soc. (London)*, **A276**:69 (1963).
49. Craven, P. M., and J. D. Lambert: *Proc. Roy. Soc. (London)*, **A205**:439 (1951).
50. Davis, A. H.: *Phil. Mag.*, **47**:972 (1924).
51. Denbigh, K. G.: *J. Soc. Chem. Ind.*, **65**:61 (1946).
52. Dognin, A.: *Compt. rend.*, **243**:840 (1956).
53. El Nadi, M., and E. Salam: *Z. physik. Chem.*, **215**:121 (1960).
54. Fay, J. A., and F. R. Riddell: *J. Aeronaut. Sci.*, **25**:73 (1958); *Research Rept. No.* 1, Avco Corporation, Everett, Mass. April, 1957.
55. Filippov, L. P.: *Vestnik Moskov. Univ.*, **9**(12), *Ser. Fiz.-Mat. i Estestven. Nauk*, (8):45–48 (1954); *Chem. Abstr.*, **49**:15,430 (1955).
56. Filippov, L. P.: *Vestnik Moskov. Univ.*, **10**(8), *Ser. Fiz.-Mat. i Estestven. Nauk*, (5):67–69 (1955); *Chem. Abstr.*, **50**, 8276 (1956).
57. Filippov, L. P.: *Vestnik Moskov. Univ., Fiz., Astron.*, **1960**(3):61–68.
58. Filippov, L. P., and N. S. Novoselova: *Vestnik Moskov. Univ.*, **10**(3), *Ser. Fiz.-Mat. i Estestven. Nauk*, (2):37–40 (1955); *Chem. Abstr.*, **49**:11,366 (1955).
59. Franck, E. U.: *Chem.-Ing.-Tech.*, **25**:238 (1953).
60. Franck, E. U.: *Z. Electrochem.*, **55**:636 (1951).
61. Furguson, R. R., and J. M. Smith: *AIChE J.*, **8**:654 (1962).
62. Gambhir, R. S., and S. C. Saxena: *Trans. Faraday Soc.*, **60**:38 (1964).
63. Gambill, W. R.: *Chem. Eng.*, **64**(4):277 (1957).
64. Gambill, W. R.: *Chem. Eng.*, **65**(17):121 (1958).
65. Gambill, W. R.: *Chem. Eng.*, **66**(16):129 (1959).
66. Gamson, B. W.: *Chem. Eng. Progr.*, **45**:154 (1949).
67. Gandhi, J. M., and S. C. Saxena: *Indian J. Pure Appl. Phys.*, **2**:83 (1964).
68. Gray, P., and P. G. Wright: *Proc. Roy. Soc. (London)*, **A263**:161 (1961).
69. Gray, P., and P. G. Wright: *Proc. Roy. Soc. (London)*, **A267**:408 (1962).
70. Gray, P., and P. G. Wright: "Progress in International Research on Thermo-

dynamic and Transport Properties," pp. 395–403, Academic Press Inc., New York, 1962.

71. Green, H. S.: "The Molecular Theory of Fluids," p. 135, Interscience Publishers, Inc., New York, 1952.
72. Grilly, E. R.: $Am. J. Phys.$, 20:447 (1952).
73. Groenier, W. S., and G. Thodos: $J. Chem. Eng. Data$, 6:240 (1961).
74. Gudzinowicz, B. J., R. H. Campbell, and J. S. Adams, Jr.: $J. Chem. Eng. Data$, $9(1)$:79 (1964).
75. Guildner, L. A.: $Proc. Natl. Acad. Sci.$, 44:1149 (1958).
76. Hilsenrath, J., and Y. S. Touloukian: $Trans. ASME$, 76:967 (1954).
77. Hirschfelder, J. O.: Heat Conductivity in Polyatomic, Electronically Excited or Chemically Reacting Mixtures, III, $Univ. Wisconsin$ CM-880, NOrd-15884, August, 1956.
78. Hirschfelder, J. O.: $J. Chem. Phys.$, 26:274 (1957).
79. Hirschfelder, J. O.: $J. Chem. Phys.$, 26:282 (1957).
80. Hirschfelder, J. O.: $Proc. Joint Conf. on Thermodynamic and Transport Properties of Fluids$, London, July, 1957, pp. 133–141, Institute of Mechanical Engineers, Westminster, London, 1958.
81. Hirschfelder, J. O., C. F. Curtiss, and R. B. Bird: "Molecular Theory of Gases and Liquids," John Wiley & Sons, Inc., New York, 1954.
82. Horrocks, J. K., and E. McLaughlin: $Trans. Faraday Soc.$, 58:1357 (1962).
83. Horrocks, J. K., and E. McLaughlin: $Trans. Faraday Soc.$, 59:1709 (1963).
84. "International Critical Tables," McGraw-Hill Book Company, New York, 1926–1930.
85. Irving, J. P., and J. M. Smith: $AIChE J.$, 7:91 (1961).
86. Johnston, H. L., and E. R. Grilly: $J. Chem. Phys.$, 14:233 (1946).
87. Junk, W. A., and E. W. Comings: $Chem. Eng. Progr.$, 49:263 (1953).
88. Kamal, I., and E. McLaughlin: $Trans. Faraday Soc.$, 60:809 (1964).
89. Kannuliuk, W. G. and H. B. Donald: $Australian J. Sci. Research$, $3A$:417 (1950).
90. Kennard, E. H.: "Kinetic Theory of Gases," McGraw-Hill Book Company, New York, 1938.
91. Kennedy, J. T. and G. Thodos: $AIChE J.$, 7:625 (1961).
92. Kestin, J., J. H. Whitelaw, and T. F. Zien: Thermal Conductivity of Superheated Steam, report prepared on behalf of the U.S. delegation for the Third Formal Conference of the International Commission on the Properties of Steam, Brown University, Providence, R.I., October, 1963.
93. Keyes, F. G.: $Trans. ASME$, 73:589 (1951).
94. Keyes, F. G.: $Trans. ASME$, 73:597 (1951).
95. Keyes, F. G.: $Trans. ASME$, 76:809 (1954).
96. Keyes, F. G.: $Trans. ASME$, 77:1395 (1955).
97. Kramer, F. R., and E. W. Comings: $J. Chem. Eng. Data$, 5:462 (1960).
98. Krieve, W. F., and D. M. Mason: $AIChE J.$, 7:277 (1961).
98a. Lambert, J. D.: "Atomic and Molecular Processes," D. R. Bates (ed.), Academic Press, Inc. New York, 1962.
99. "Landolt-Börnstein Tables," vol. 4, pt. 1, Springer-Verlag OHG, Berlin, 1955.
100. Lehmann, H.: $Chem. Technol.$, 9:530 (1957).
101. Leng, D. E., and E. W. Comings: $Ind. Eng. Chem.$, 49:2042 (1957).
102. Leng, D. E., and E. W. Comings: Thermal Conductivity of Propane, paper presented at The American Chemical Society Meeting, Miami, Fla., April, 1957.
103. Lenoir, J. M.: $Petrol. Refiner$, $36(8)$:162 (1957).
104. Lenoir, J. M., and E. W. Comings: $Chem. Eng. Progr.$, 47:223 (1951).
105. Lenoir, J. M., W. A. Junk, and E. W. Comings: $Chem. Eng. Progr.$, 49:539 (1953).

THERMAL CONDUCTIVITY 517

106. Liley, P. E.: *Symposium on Thermal Properties*, Purdue University, Feb. 23–26, 1959, pp. 40–69, Lafayette, Ind., 1959.
107. Lindsay, A. L., and L. A. Bromley: *Ind. Eng. Chem.*, **42**:1508 (1950).
108. Losenicky, Z.: *Czechoslov. J. Phys.*, **9**:399 (1959).
109. McLaughlin, E.: *Quart. Revs. (London)*, **14**:236 (1960).
110. McLaughlin, E.: *Chem. Revs.*, **64**:389 (1964).
111. Marcus, R. J.: Calculation of Thermal Conductivities, ONR 017-627, Office of Naval Research, Washington, D.C., 1961.
112. Mason, E. A.: *J. Chem. Phys.*, **28**:1000 (1958).
113. Mason, E. A., and L. Monchick: *J. Chem. Phys.*, **36**:1622 (1962).
114. Mason, E. A., and L. Monchick: Theory of Transport Properties of Gases, *Ninth International Symposium on Combustion*, Academic Press Inc., New York, 1963.
115. Mason, E. A., and S. C. Saxena: *J. Chem. Phys.*, **31**:511 (1959).
116. Mason, E. A., and S. C. Saxena: *Phys. Fluids*, **1**:361 (1958).
117. Mason, E. A., and H. von Ubisch: *Phys. Fluids*, **3**:355 (1960).
118. Mason, H. L.: *Trans. ASME*, **76**:817 (1954).
119. Michels, A., and A. Botzen: *Physica*, **19**:585 (1953).
120. Miller, D. G.: *Ind. Eng. Chem.*, **56**(3):46 (1964).
121. Misic, D., and G. Thodos: *AIChE J.*, **7**:264 (1961).
122. Misic, D., and G. Thodos: *J. Chem. Eng. Data*, **8**:540 (1963).
123. Monchick, L., and E. A. Mason: *J. Chem. Phys.*, **35**:1676 (1961).
124. Muckenfuss, C., and C. F. Curtiss: *J. Chem. Phys.*, **29**:1273 (1958).
125. Novotny, J. L., and T. F. Irvine, Jr.: *J. Heat Transfer*, **83**:125 (1961).
126. O'Neal, C., Jr., and R. S. Brokaw: *Phys. Fluids*, **5**:567 (1962).
127. O'Neal, C., Jr., and R. S. Brokaw: *Phys. Fluids*, **6**:1675 (1963).
128. Owens, E. J., and G. Thodos: *AIChE J.*, **3**:454 (1957).
129. Owens, E. J., and G. Thodos: *AIChE J.*, **6**:676 (1960).
130. Owens, E. J., and G. Thodos: *Proc. Joint Conf. on Thermodynamic and Transport Properties of Fluids*, London, July, 1957, pp. 163–168, Institute of Mechanical Engineers, Westminster, London, 1958.
131. Pagerey, P. R., C. R. St. Clair, and W. L. Sibbitt: *Trans. ASME*, **78**:1169 (1956).
132. Palmer, G.: *Ind. Eng. Chem.*, **40**:89 (1948).
133. Partington, J.: "An Advanced Treatise on Physical Chemistry," vol. 1, Fundamental Principles—The Properties of Gases, Longmans, Green & Co., Inc., New York, 1949.
134. Pereira, A. N. G., and C. J. G. Raw: *Phys. Fluids*, **6**:1091 (1963).
135. Powell, R. E., W. E. Roseveare, and H. Eyring: *Ind. Eng. Chem.*, **33**:430 (1941).
136. Prigogine, I., and F. Waelbroeck: *Proc. Joint Conf. on Thermodynamic and Transport Properties of Fluids*, London, July, 1957, pp. 128–132, Institute of Mechanical Engineers, Westminster, London, 1958.
137. Przybycien, W. M., and D. W. Linde: Thermal Conductivities of Gases, Metals, and Liquid Metals, *Rept.* KAPL-M-WMP-1, General Electric Co., Knolls Atomic Power Laboratory, Schenectady, N.Y., August, 1957.
138. Ranz, W. E.: Mass and Heat Transfer Rates for Large Gradients of Concentration and Temperature, *Tech. Rept.* 1, OOR Project 2340, D. A. Project 5B 99-01-004, Department of Chemical Engineering, University of Minnesota, Minneapolis, Minn., March, 1962.
139. Reid, R. C., and T. K. Sherwood: "Properties of Gases and Liquids," 1st ed., p. 249, McGraw-Hill Book Company, New York, 1958.
140. Richardson, J. L., F. P. Boynton, K. Y. Eng, and D. M. Mason: *Chem. Eng. Sci.*, **13**:130 (1961).

141. Richter, G. N., and B. H. Sage: *J. Chem. Eng. Data,* **2**:61 (1957).
142. Richter, G. N., and B. H. Sage: *J. Chem. Eng. Data,* **4**:36 (1959).
143. Richter, G. N., and B. H. Sage: *J. Chem. Eng. Data,* **8**:221 (1963).
144. Richter, G. N., and B. H. Sage: *J. Chem. Eng. Data,* **9**:75 (1964).
145. Reidel, L.: *Chem.-Ing.-Tech.,* **21**:349 (1949); *ibid.,* **23**:321, 465 (1951).
146. Riedel, L.: *Mitt. kältech. Inst. u. Reichsforsch-Anstalt Lebensmittelfrischhalt. tech. Hochschule Karlsruhe,* no. 2, 1948.
147. Robbins, L. A., and C. L. Kingrea: *Hydrocarbon Processing and Petrol. Refiner,* **41**(5):133 (1962); preprint of paper presented at the Session on Chemical Engineering at the twenty-seventh Midyear Meeting of the American Petroleum Institute, Division of Refining, San Francisco, Calif., May 14, 1962.
148. Rodriguez, H. V.: Ph.D. thesis in chemical engineering, Louisiana State University, 1962; University Microfilms 62-3663.
149. Sakiadis. B. C., and J. Coates: *AIChE J.,* **1**:275 (1955).
150. Sakiadis, B. C., and J. Coates: *AIChE J.,* **3**:121 (1957).
151. Sakiadis, B. C., and J. Coates: A Literature Survey of the Thermal Conductivity of Liquids, *Louisiana State Univ., Eng. Expt. Sta. Bull.* 34, 1952.
152. Sakiadis, B. C., and J. Coates: Studies of Thermal Conductivity of Liquids, *Louisiana State Univ. Eng. Expt. Sta. Bull.* 46, 1954.
153. Saxena, S. C.: *Indian J. Phys.,* **31**:597 (1957).
154. Saxena, S. C.: *J. Chem. Phys.,* **25**:360 (1956).
155. Saxena, S. C., and J. P. Agrawal: *J. Chem. Phys.,* **35**:2107 (1961).
156. Saxena, S. C., and R. S. Gambhir: *Brit. J. Appl. Phys.,* **14**:436 (1963).
157. Saxena, S. C., and R. S. Gambhir: *Indian J. Pure Appl. Phys.,* **1**:318 (1963).
158. Saxena, S. C., and R. S. Gambhir: *Proc. Phys. Soc.,* **81**:788 (1963).
159. Saxena, S. C., and J. M. Gandhi: *Rev. Mod. Physics,* **35**:1022 (1963).
160. Saxena, S. C., M. P. Saksena, and R. S. Gambhir: *Brit. J. Appl. Physics,* **15**:843 (1964).
161. Schäfer, K.: *Z. physik. Chem.,* **B53**:149 (1943).
162. Schaefer, C. A., and G. Thodos: *AIChE J.,* **5**:367 (1959).
163. Schaefer, C. A., and G. Thodos: *Ind. Eng. Chem.,* **50**:1585 (1958).
164. Scheffy, W. J.: "Thermal Conduction in Liquids," Project Squid, *Tech. Rept.* P.R-85-R, Princeton University, Princeton, N.J., October, 1958.
165. Scheffy, W. J., and E. F. Johnson: Thermal Conductivities of Liquids at High Temperatures, paper presented at the Annual Meeting of the American Institute of Chemical Engineers, St. Paul, Minn., September, 1959.
166. Schotte, W.: *Ind. Eng. Chem.,* **50**:683 (1958).
167. Schrock, V. E.: The Status of Transport Properties of Air, *Univ. California Radiation Lab.,* UCRL 7052, Livermore, Calif., September, 1962.
168. Smith, J. F.: *Ind. Eng. Chem.,* **22**:1246 (1930).
169. Smith, J. F.: *Trans. ASME,* **58**:719 (1936).
170. Smith, W. J. S., L. D. Durbin, and R. Kobayashi: *J. Chem. Eng. Data,* **5**:316 (1960).
171. Srivastava, B. N., and A. K. Barua: *J. Chem. Phys.,* **32**:427 (1960).
172. Srivastava, B. N., and S. C. Saxena: *J. Chem. Phys.,* **27**:583 (1957).
173. Srivastava, B. N., and S. C. Saxena: *Proc. Phys. Soc.,* **70B**:369 (1957).
174. Srivastava, B. N., and R. C. Srivastava: *J. Chem. Phys.,* **30**:1200 (1959).
175. Stiel, L. I., and G. Thodos: *AIChE J.,* **10**:26 (1964).
176. Stiel, L. I., and G. Thodos: "Progress in International Research on Thermodynamic and Transport Properties," pp. 352–365, Academic Press, Inc., New York, 1962.
177. Stolyarov, E. A.: *Zhur. Fiz. Khim.,* **24**:279 (1950); *Chem. Abstr.,* **44**:6694 (1950).

178. Svehla, R. A.: Estimated Viscosities and Thermal Conductivities of Gases at High Temperatures, *NASA Tech. Rept.* R-132, Lewis Research Center, Cleveland, Ohio, 1962.
179. Tarzimanov, A. A., and A. G. Usmanov: *Izvest. Vysschikh Uchebn. Zavedenii, Neft i Gaz.*, 7(1):73–75 (1964); *Chem. Abstr.*, 60:15,159 (1964).
180. Taxman, N.: *Phys. Rev.*, 110:1235 (1958).
181. Thievon, W. J., G. A. Sterbutzel, and J. L. Beal: *Wright Air Development Center Tech. Rept.* 59-450, June, 1959.
182. Thornton, E.: *Proc. Phys. Soc. (London)*, 76:104 (1960).
183. Tsederberg, N. V.: *Teploenergetika*, 3(9):42–48 (1956); *Chem. Abstr.*, 51·2350 (1957).
184. Tsederberg, N. V.: "Thermal Conductivity of Gases and Liquids," The M.I.T. Press, Cambridge, Mass., 1965.
185. Ubbelohde, A. R.: *J. Chem. Phys.*, 3:219 (1935).
186. Vanderslice, J. T., S. Weissman, E. A. Mason, and R. J. Fallon: *Phys. Fluids*, 5:155 (1962).
187. Vargaftik, N. B.: *Proc. Joint Conf. on Thermodynamic and Transport Properties of Fluids*, London, July, 1957, pp. 142–149, Institute of Mechanical Engineers, Westminster, London, 1958.
188. Varlashkin, P. G., and J. C. Thompson: *J. Chem. Eng. Data*, 8:526 (1963).
189. Vines, R. G.: *Australian J. Chem.*, 6:1 (1953).
190. Vines, R. G.: *J. Heat Transfer*, 82:48 (1960).
191. Vines, R. G.: *Proc. Joint Conf. on Thermodynamic and Transport Properties of Fluids*, London, July, 1957, pp. 120–123, Institute of Mechanical Engineers, Westminster, London, 1958.
192. Vines, R. G., and L. A. Bennett: *J. Chem. Phys.*, 22:360 (1954).
193. Vogel, H.: *Ann. Physik*, 43:1235 (1914).
194. Wang Chang, C. S., and G. E. Uhlenbeck: *Univ. Michigan Eng. Research Rept.* CM-681, Ann Arbor, Mich., 1951.
195. Wassiljewa, A.: *Physik. Z.*, 5:737 (1904).
196. Weber, H. F.: Wiedemann's Ann., *Ann. Phys. Chem.*, 10:103 (1880).
197. Whalley, E.: *Discussions Faraday Soc.*, 22:54 (1956).
198. Woolf, J. R., and W. L. Sibbitt: *Ind. Eng. Chem.*, 46:1947 (1954).
199. Works Laboratory Tables of Physical Properties, Carbide and Carbon Chemical Co., South Charleston, W.Va., Feb. 1, 1945.
200. Wright, J. M.: Calculated Thermal Conductivities of Pure Gases and Gaseous Mixtures at Elevated Temperatures, AECD-4197, General Electric Co., Hanford Works, Richland, Wash., July, 1951.
201. Wright, P. G.: *Proc. Leeds Phil. Lit. Soc. Sci. Sec.*, (III) 9:93 (1963).
202. Wright, P. G., and P. Gray: *Trans. Faraday Soc.*, 58:1 (1962).

CHAPTER 11

DIFFUSION COEFFICIENTS

11-1 Scope

The first part of this chapter presents the general equation for diffusion in gases and liquids and defines the reference frame usually employed in order that diffusion coefficients may have a clear and unambiguous meaning. The next several sections deal with diffusion in gases, for which modern theory provides a useful basis for the prediction of diffusion coefficients in both binary and multicomponent mixtures. The final sections deal with the theories of diffusion in liquid mixtures and with the available methods of predicting diffusion coefficients in such systems.

11-2 Diffusion Coefficients: Definitions

Diffusion is the net transport of a substance from one region to another within a single phase (gas, liquid, or solid), in the absence of mixing. Transport may be due to thermal diffusion, pressure diffusion, or "ordinary," or molecular, diffusion or to convection or mixing. This chapter will be limited to a discussion of isothermal isobaric molecular diffusion.

The diffusion coefficient, sometimes called the *diffusivity*, is the proportionality constant between the flux density of the diffusing species and the gradient of the appropriate potential, or *driving force*. Coefficients based on concentration gradients are now almost universally employed for both gas and liquid systems. Accordingly, the diffusion coefficient D_{12} for the isothermal diffusion of species 1 through a constant-pressure binary mixture of 1 and 2 is defined by the relation

$$J_1 = -D_{12} \text{ grad } c_1 \qquad (11\text{-}1)$$

or, for unidirectional diffusion along the z axis,

$$J_1 = -D_{12}(dc_1/dz) \qquad (11\text{-}2)$$

Here J_1 is the molal flux of species 1, g moles/(sec)(cm)^2; c_1 is the concentration of the diffusing species, g moles/cm^3; and z is the distance in the direction of diffusion. The coefficient D_{12} then has the units cm^2/sec.

To complete the definition of D_{12}, it is necessary to specify the reference

520

plane to which the flux J_1 is related. Though several alternatives exist, the usual choice is the plane (normal to the z axis) across which there is no net *volume* flux. In ideal-gas and ideal-liquid mixtures this is also the plane of no net *molal* flux.

It follows from simple kinetic theory that D_{12} is equal to D_{21} and independent of concentration, so that D_{12} (or D_{21}) is a *property* of the gas pair. It is found experimentally that D_{12} does vary with concentration, but for binary gas systems the variation is sufficiently small to be ignored in most engineering calculations. In liquid systems, however, D_{12} often varies widely with concentration.

Equation (11-1), often called *Fick's first law*, may be better understood in terms of molecular theory by following a simple derivation. In a binary mixture the volume fluxes $J_1 \bar{V}_1$ and $J_2 \bar{V}_2$ across the plane of no net volume flux will be equal but opposite in direction,

$$J_1 \bar{V}_1 + J_2 \bar{V}_2 = 0 \qquad (11\text{-}3)$$

where $\bar{V}_1$ and $\bar{V}_2$ are the partial molal volumes of the two constituents. Let it be assumed that the gradient of the chemical potential of the first species provides the force to overcome the friction between the streams of molecules making up the two fluxes and that this force is proportional not only to the relative velocity $u_1 - u_2$ but also to the concentration c_2 of interfering molecules of species 2,

$$d\mathbf{\mu}_1/dz = -\xi_{12}c_2(u_1 - u_2) = -\xi_{12}c_2(u_1 - u_0) + \xi_{12}c_2(u_2 - u_0) \qquad (11\text{-}4)$$

where ξ_{12} is a *friction coefficient*, dependent on the molecular properties of the two substances. The chemical potential is given by

$$\mathbf{\mu}_1 = \mathbf{\mu}_1{}^0(T,P) + RT \ln a_1 \qquad (11\text{-}5)$$

where $\mathbf{\mu}_1{}^0$ is that of the pure constituent at T and P, R is the gas constant, and $a_1(=\gamma_1 c_1)$ is the activity of 1 in the mixture. The velocities u_0, u_1, and u_2 are in relation to the apparatus; u_0 is the velocity of the plane of no net volume flux. Combining Eqs. (11-3), (11-4), and (11-5), and noting that $c_2 \bar{V}_2 + c_1 \bar{V}_1 = 1$, we have

$$J_1 = (-RT\bar{V}_2/\xi_{12})[\partial(\ln a_1)/\partial(\ln c_1)]_{T,P}(dc_1/dz) \qquad (11\text{-}6)$$

whence, from Eq. (11-1),

$$D_{12} = (RT\bar{V}_2/\xi_{12})[\partial(\ln a_1)/\partial(\ln c_1)]_{T,P}$$
$$= (RT\bar{V}_2/\xi_{12})[1 + \partial(\ln \gamma_1)/\partial(\ln c_1)]_{T,P} \qquad (11\text{-}7)$$

Following the same procedure for J_2, the corresponding relation for D_{21} is obtained; introduction of the Gibbs-Duhem relation then shows the identity of D_{12} and D_{21} (at the same temperature, pressure, and binary composition).

Equation (11-7) is evidently no more than a small start on the problem of predicting D_{12}, but modern theoretical studies are being directed with considerable success to the description of ξ_{12} in terms of molecular properties in liquid systems. As will be shown later, the theory for low-pressure gas systems is well in hand.

Diffusion in a gas or liquid mixture is called *mutual diffusion;* D_{12} is the mutual-diffusion coefficient in a binary system, and D_{1m} is the mutual-diffusion coefficient of species 1 in a multicomponent mixture. The D_{1m} for gases, to be discussed in Sec. 11-7, can be expressed in terms of mixture composition and the individual coefficients for the several binaries which constitute the mixture. *Self-diffusion* is the diffusion of a substance through itself: the coefficient is D_{11} or D_{ii}. Self-diffusion cannot be measured, since the molecules are indistinguishable by analytical procedures.

Approximate values of D_{11} may be obtained experimentally by measuring the diffusion of a radioactive isotope of the substance. Thus the isotope $C^{14}O_2$ has been used as a tracer to obtain data on self-diffusion in CO_2, the physical behavior of the two isotopes in the mixture being assumed to be essentially identical. The diffusion of a tracer of species 1 in a *mixture* containing other components is often referred to as self-diffusion, but it would seem best to call this *tracer diffusion*, since the tracer-diffusion coefficient $D_1^{\star}$, unlike the self-diffusion coefficient D_{ii}, may vary with mixture composition. Evidently D_{11} can be obtained by measuring $D_1^{\star}$ as a function of c_1 in a binary of 1 and 2 and extrapolating to $c_1 = 1$, $c_2 = 0$.

The kinetic theory relates the mutual-, self-, and tracer-diffusion coefficients in binary gas systems (28, 75),

$$1/D_1^{\star} = y_1/D_{11} + y_2/D_{12} \qquad (11\text{-}8)$$
$$1/D_2^{\star} = y_2/D_{22} + y_1/D_{12} \qquad (11\text{-}9)$$

where y_1 and y_2 are mole fractions of the two constituents. For tracer diffusion of CO_2, Kr, and CF_2Cl_2 in mixtures of these gases with hydrogen, $1/D_1^{\star}$ was found (81) to be linear in y_1, as called for by Eq. (11-8), since D_{11} is constant and D_{12}, in gas systems, is independent of concentration. Equations (11-8) and (11-9) do not apply to liquids; the corresponding relations for liquid systems will be discussed in Sec. 11-9.

Experimental Determination of Diffusion Coefficients. It is not within the province of this book to describe experimental techniques for the measurement of diffusion coefficients. Geddes (40) and Johnson and Babb (62) discuss several of the standard methods for both gases and liquids: Tyrell (116) provides a detailed discussion of experimental methods for liquids.

It is difficult to assess the accuracy of the published values of D_{12}. Many of the recent data appear to be precise to within 1 per cent, but the precision of the older data is often poor, evidently being reliable to only about 10 per cent; the experimental errors probably result in values of D_{12} which are high rather than low.

11-3 Diffusion Coefficients for Binary Gas Systems at Low Pressures: Prediction from Theory

Earlier empirical correlations of diffusion coefficients have been largely displaced in recent years by equations based on the modern mathematical theory of nonuniform gases. This theory, described in earlier chapters, leads to theoretical equations for diffusion coefficients in gases which are in remarkable agreement with experimental observations, especially for mixtures of spherical, nonpolar molecules.

Various expressions for the potential function have been proposed, but the Lennard-Jones relation has been the one most widely used for nonpolar molecules,

$$\varphi(r) = 4\epsilon_0[(\sigma/r)^{12} - (\sigma/r)^6] \qquad (3\text{-}29)$$

Equation (3-29) provides a basis for the calculation of the collision integral Ω_D in the fundamental equation for the binary diffusion coefficient, which is

$$D_{12} = \tfrac{3}{16}\{[2\pi kT(M_1 + M_2)/M_1M_2]^{1/2}f_D/n\pi\sigma_{12}^2\Omega_D\} \qquad (11\text{-}10)$$

where M_1 and M_2 are the molecular weights, n is the number density of the molecular mixture, and σ_{12} is the Lennard-Jones force constant for the mixture, corresponding to the parameter σ for a pure gas. In the case of the Lennard-Jones potential function, Ω_D depends only on the dimensionless ratio $kT/\epsilon_{0_{12}}$, k being Boltzmann's constant. Values of Ω_D as a function of kT/ϵ_0 are given in Table 11-1; this function has been expressed by Chen (23) in the form of an equation which may have application in computer calculations. The term f_D is a second-order correction, usually between 1.00 and 1.03.

Upon converting to usual technical units and dropping f_D, with n expressed by the ideal-gas law and σ_{12} in angstrom units, Eq. (11-10) becomes

$$D_{12} = 0.001858T^{3/2}[(M_1 + M_2)/M_1M_2]^{1/2}/P\sigma_{12}^2\Omega_D \qquad (11\text{-}11)$$

where D_{12} is in square centimeters per second, P is in atmospheres, and T is in degrees Kelvin. This is the most convenient form of the theoretical equation for use in estimating values of D_{12} at low pressures.

In order to use this relation, it is necessary to have values of $\epsilon_{0_{12}}$ and σ_{12} for the gas pair. These are usually estimated from the force constants for the pure gases by use of the *combining rules* (see Sec. 7-4).

$$\epsilon_{0_{12}} = (\epsilon_{0_1}\epsilon_{0_2})^{1/2} \quad \text{or} \quad \epsilon_{0_{12}}/k = [(\epsilon_{0_1}/k)(\epsilon_{0_2}/k)]^{1/2} \qquad (11\text{-}12)$$

and

$$\sigma_{12} = \tfrac{1}{2}(\sigma_1 + \sigma_2) \qquad (11\text{-}13)$$

Values of ϵ_0 and σ for the pure gases may be obtained from experimental measurements of viscosity or from the second-virial coefficient or derived from crystal properties. Values of ϵ_0/k and σ obtained from viscosity data are listed in Appendix G for a number of pure substances; estimation techniques are discussed in Sec. 2-10.

The procedure in using Eq. (11-11) for the estimation of D_{12} is straightforward: $\sigma_1, \sigma_2, \epsilon_{0_1}/k$, and ϵ_{0_2}/k are obtained from Appendix G; Eqs. (11-12) and (11-13) are then used to obtain $\epsilon_{0_{12}}/k$ and σ_{12}; $kT/\epsilon_{0_{12}}$ is calculated

TABLE 11-1. VALUES OF THE COLLISION INTEGRAL Ω_D BASED ON THE LENNARD-JONES POTENTIAL[†]

kT/ϵ_0[‡]	Ω_D[‡]	kT/ϵ_0	Ω_D	kT/ϵ_0	Ω_D
0.30	2.662	1.65	1.153	4.0	0.8836
0.35	2.476	1.70	1.140	4.1	0.8788
0.40	2.318	1.75	1.128	4.2	0.8740
0.45	2.184	1.80	1.116	4.3	0.8694
0.50	2.066	1.85	1.105	4.4	0.8652
0.55	1.966	1.90	1.094	4.5	0.8610
0.60	1.877	1.95	1.084	4.6	0.8568
0.65	1.798	2.00	1.075	4.7	0.8530
0.70	1.729	2.1	1.057	4.8	0.8492
0.75	1.667	2.2	1.041	4.9	0.8456
0.80	1.612	2.3	1.026	5.0	0.8422
0.85	1.562	2.4	1.012	6	0.8124
0.90	1.517	2.5	0.9996	7	0.7896
0.95	1.476	2.6	0.9878	8	0.7712
1.00	1.439	2.7	0.9770	9	0.7556
1.05	1.406	2.8	0.9672	10	0.7424
1.10	1.375	2.9	0.9576	20	0.6640
1.15	1.346	3.0	0.9490	30	0.6232
1.20	1.320	3.1	0.9406	40	0.5960
1.25	1.296	3.2	0.9328	50	0.5756
1.30	1.273	3.3	0.9256	60	0.5596
1.35	1.253	3.4	0.9186	70	0.5464
1.40	1.233	3.5	0.9120	80	0.5352
1.45	1.215	3.6	0.9058	90	0.5256
1.50	1.198	3.7	0.8998	100	0.5130
1.55	1.182	3.8	0.8942	200	0.4644
1.60	1.167	3.9	0.8888	400	0.4170

[†] From J. O. Hirschfelder, C. F. Curtiss, and R. B. Bird, "Molecular Theory of Gases and Liquids," John Wiley & Sons, Inc., New York, 1954.

[‡] Hirschfelder uses the symbols T^* for kT/ϵ_0 and $\Omega^{(1,1)*}$ in place of Ω_D.

and Ω_D found in Table 11-1. Appropriate substitutions are then made in Eq. (11-11). Estimates of D_{12} based on Eq. (11-11) will be referred to as *theoretical* values, though obvious empiricisms are involved in the calculation.

In cases where the force constants are not given in Appendix G they may be estimated by the following rules:

$$\epsilon_0/k = 0.75T_c; \qquad kT/\epsilon_0 = 1.33T_r \qquad (11\text{-}14)$$

or

$$\epsilon_0/k = 1.21T_b \qquad (11\text{-}15)$$

and

$$\sigma = \tfrac{5}{6}V_c^{\frac{1}{3}} \qquad (11\text{-}16)$$

or

$$\sigma = 1.18V_b^{\frac{1}{3}} \qquad (11\text{-}17)$$

These and other rules for estimating ϵ_0/k and σ are discussed in Sec. 2-10. Values of T_c, V_c, and T_b are listed in Appendix A; these may also be estimated by the methods of Chap. 2. The molal volume V_b is obtained by the method of Le Bas (see Table 3-4).

Since Ω_D is relatively insensitive to variations in kT/ϵ_0, uncertainties as to $\epsilon_{0_{12}}/k$ are not necessarily serious. The term σ_{12} in Eq. (11-11) is squared, however, and errors in estimating σ_1 and σ_2 can lead to appreciable errors in D_{12}. Erroneously low values of σ and high values of ϵ_0/k, or vice versa, can offset each other; so it is important to use values of the force constants from the same source, where this is possible.

Example 11-1. Estimate the value of the binary diffusion coefficient for the system CO-N_2 at $100°C$ and atmospheric pressure. The reported experimental value is 0.318 cm^2/sec (7).

Solution. From Appendix G, $\sigma_1(CO) = 3.690$, $\sigma_2(N_2) = 3.798$, $\epsilon_{0_1}/k = 91.7$, and $\epsilon_{0_2}/k = 71.4$. Using Eqs. (11-12) and (11-13), $\epsilon_{0_{12}}/k = 80.6$, and $\sigma_{12} = 3.744$. At $T = 373°K$, $kT/\epsilon_{0_{12}}$ is 4.63, and, from Table 11-1, Ω_D is 0.8557. Substituting in Eq. (11-11),

$$D_{12} = (0.001858)(373)^{\frac{3}{2}}[(28 + 28)/28 \times 28]^{\frac{1}{2}}/(1.0 \times 3.744^2 \times 0.8557)$$
$$= 0.299 \text{ cm}^2/\text{sec}$$
$$\text{Error} = [(0.299 - 0.318)/0.318] \times 100 = -5.3\%$$

In this case the force constants were found in Appendix G; had they not been available, it would have been necessary to use the approximate rules (11-14) to (11-17). From Eqs. (11-14) and (11-16),

$$\epsilon_{0_1}/k = 0.75 \times 133 = 99.75 \qquad \epsilon_{0_2}/k = 0.75 \times 126.2 = 94.7$$
$$\sigma_1 = 0.833(93.1)^{\frac{1}{3}} = 3.78 \qquad \sigma_2 = 0.833(90.1)^{\frac{1}{3}} = 3.74$$
$$\epsilon_{0_{12}}/k = (99.75 \times 94.7)^{\frac{1}{2}} = 97 \qquad \sigma_{12} = (3.78 + 3.74)/2 = 3.76$$
$$kT/\epsilon_{0_{12}} = 3.85 \qquad \Omega_D(\text{Table 11-1}) = 0.8915$$

Substituting Eq. (11-11), $D_{12} = 0.284$ cm^2/sec.

$$\text{Error} = [(0.284 - 0.318)/0.318] \times 100 = -10.7\%$$

The theory on which Eq. (11-11) is based, developed through statistical mechanics, has many serious faults yet serves remarkably well. It is derived for dilute gases consisting of nonpolar spherical monatomic molecules, and the potential function (3-29) is partly empirical, as are the combining rules (11-12) and (11-13). Yet Eq. (11-11) gives good results over a wide range of temperatures and provides useful approximate values of D_{12} even for polar gases. The general nature of the errors to be expected by this estimation procedure is indicated by the comparison of calculated and experimental values shown in Table 11-4.

Fortunately, the calculated value of D_{12} is relatively insensitive to the value of $\epsilon_{0_{12}}$ employed and to the form of the assumed potential function. Values of ϵ_0 and σ are available from viscosity measurements; values from diffusion data would clearly be preferable, but few are available.* The error found in Example 11-1 could have been much less if other values of $\epsilon_{0_{12}}$ and σ_{12} had been employed. Amdur and Shuler (7) obtained a nearly perfect fit of their diffusion data for CO-N_2 from 195 to 373°K by using $\epsilon_{0_{12}}/k = 37.2$ (instead of 80.6) and $\sigma_{12} = 3.9$ (instead of 3.744).

Low-pressure Diffusion Coefficients from Viscosity Data. Since the equations for low-pressure gas viscosity [Eq. (9-9)] and diffusion [Eq. (11-11)] have a common basis in the Chapman-Enskog theory, they can be combined to relate the two gas properties.

The *self-diffusion* coefficient D_{11} is easily obtained,

$$D_{11} = 1.20(RT/MP)(\Omega_v/\Omega_D)\mu_1 \qquad (11\text{-}18)$$

where μ is now expressed in poises. The ratio of collision integrals, Ω_v/Ω_D, is but a weak function of kT/ϵ_0 and is approximately 1.1 at ordinary temperatures.† This means that the relation between D_{11} and μ_1 is almost independent of the choice of force-law model and potential function. This also explains why the Schmidt number for gases at low pressure is nearly independent of temperature. Equation (11-18) has been shown (125, 126) to provide reliable predictions of D_{11}, not only for simple gases, but for HCl, HBr, BF_3, UF_6, CH_4, CO, and CO_2.

The same theory also provides a relation between the viscosity of a binary gas mixture and its composition. Experimental data on viscosity as a function of composition at constant temperature can be employed, therefore, as a basis for calculating the *binary* diffusion coefficient D_{12} (54, 125). Weissman and Mason (125, 126) compare the method with a very large collection of experimental diffusion data and find excellent agreement. Values of D_{12} obtained by this procedure are, in fact, in better agreement with experimental values than those calculated by the use of Eq. (11-11). As shown below, Eq. (11-11) predicts values of D_{12} averaging several per cent low.

---

* Scott and Cox, in an ADI table referred to in their article (100), list force constants calculated from diffusion data for 15 gas pairs.

† The ratio Ω_v/Ω_D is Hirschfelder's $\Omega^{(2,2)\star}/\Omega^{(1,1)\star}$, values of which are tabulated as a function of $T^* = kT/\epsilon_0$ in table I-N, page 1128 of Ref. 54.

Theoretical Predictions of D_{12} at High Temperatures. The use of Eqs. (11-11) to (11-13), together with force constants obtained from viscosity (Appendix G), gives values of D_{12} which are sufficiently accurate for the purposes of most engineering calculations. This appears to be true for nonpolar-gas pairs over the temperature range of perhaps 200 to 1000°K.

Almost no diffusion data above about 600°K were available until quite recently. The new experimental technique of Westenberg and Walker has made it possible to measure D_{12} to 1700°K and to compare the data with values calculated from the theory (35, 122–124, 127–129).

Another important development is the work of Amdur and his associates, who have derived values of the force constants from molecular beam-scattering experiments and calculated gas-transport properties to 15,000°K (1–4). Diffusion data at 200 to 1000°K yield force constants in the region of the potential minimum; scattering data provide information as to the nature of $\varphi(r)$ at small values of r, where the curve is very steep. This is the region of importance at high temperatures: the intermolecular forces are repulsive, and the potential-energy–distance curve is very steep. Consequently, the attractive force (or energy) term becomes unimportant, and the approximate, but useful, function is that for *point centers of repulsion*,

$$\varphi(r) = a_1/r^s \tag{11-19}$$

Values of s calculated from high-temperature gas-diffusion data range from 6 to 40, in contrast with the Lennard-Jones value of 12.

Amdur and Mason (3) give values of s ranging from 5.94 to 9.99 for self-diffusion of nitrogen and several of the rare gases and very large values for more complicated molecules, ranging up to 39.27 for CF_4. Walker and Westenberg obtained values of s for the mutual diffusion of oxygen in CO_2, H_2, CH_4, CO, and H_2O ranging from 6.54 to 11.41. The first set of values was calculated from scattering data, the second set from experimental diffusion data over the range 300 to 1000°K.

In summary, the use of a collision integral based on the Lennard-Jones potential function (Table 11-1), together with force constants from viscosity at low and moderate temperatures, gives reasonably good results to about 1000°K, and the same calculation with force constants from low-temperature diffusion data is useful up to temperatures several hundred degrees higher. The scattering data, however, evidently provide the best basis for prediction of diffusion coefficients above about 1800°K. Experimental data on He-N_2 are compared in Fig. 11-1 with curves calculated by two of the methods described (128).

Theoretical Predictions of Diffusion Coefficients for Polar Gases. *Polar-Nonpolar.* The forces of interaction between the unlike molecules

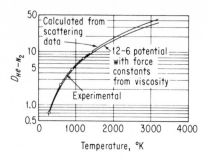

FIG. 11-1. D_{12} for helium in nitrogen at elevated temperatures.

of a polar-nonpolar gas pair are represented by the same potential-energy function as for the case of two nonpolar gases, but the combining laws are modified (54),

$$\sigma_{np} = \frac{1}{2}(\sigma_n + \sigma_p)f_c^{-\frac{1}{6}} \qquad (11\text{-}20)$$

and

$$\epsilon_{0_{np}} = (\epsilon_{0_n}\epsilon_{0_p})^{\frac{1}{2}}f_c^{2} \qquad (11\text{-}21)$$

where

$$f_c = 1 + (1/\sqrt{2})(\alpha_n t_p^*/\sigma_n^3)\sqrt{\epsilon_{0_p}/\epsilon_{0_n}} \qquad (11\text{-}22)$$

The subscripts n and p refer to the nonpolar and polar constituents and the subscript np designates a nonpolar and polar pair; α_n is the polarizability of the nonpolar molecule, and

$$t_p^* = (1/\sqrt{8})(\mu_p^2/\epsilon_{0_p}\sigma_p^3) \qquad (11\text{-}23)$$

where μ_p is the dipole moment of the polar gas. Values of α_n and t_p^* for a number of common gases are given in Tables 11-2 and 3-1, respectively; Denbigh (31) (quoted in Ref. 54) describes a method for estimating α_n from bond contributions.

Example 11-2. Estimate the binary diffusion coefficient for $H_2O\text{-}CO_2$ at 92.4°C and 1.0 atm. The experimental value is 0.248 cm^2/sec.

Solution. From Table 3-1, σ_p is 2.52 A, and ϵ_{op}/k is 775°K. From Appendix G, σ_n is 3.941 A, and ϵ_{0_n}/k is 195°K. From Tables 11-2 and 3-1, α_n is 26.5×10^{-25} cm^3, and t_p^* is 0.71,

$$f_c = 1 + (1/\sqrt{2})[(26.5 \times 10^{-25} \times 0.71)/(3.941 \times 10^{-8})^3]\sqrt{775/195} = 1.043$$
$$\sigma_{np} = \frac{1}{2}(3.941 + 2.52)(1.043)^{-\frac{1}{6}} = 3.22 \text{ A}$$
$$\epsilon_{0np}/k = (775 \times 195)^{\frac{1}{2}}(1.043)^2 = 415°K$$
$$kT/\epsilon_{0np} = 365.5/415 = 0.88; \qquad \Omega_D = 1.535 \qquad \text{(from Table 11-1)}$$

Substituting in Eq. (11-11),

$$D_{12} = \{0.001858(365.5)^{\frac{3}{2}}[(18 + 44)/18 \times 44]^{\frac{1}{2}}\}/(1.0 \times 3.22^2 \times 1.535)$$
$$= 0.228 \text{ cm}^2/\text{sec}$$

$$\text{Error} = [(0.228 - 0.248)/0.248] \times 100 = -8\%$$

(Omission of the f_c correction makes little difference in this case.)

Polar-Polar Gas Pairs. The Stockmayer potential [Eq. (3-37)] discussed in Sec. 3-13 makes allowance for dipole-dipole interactions and provides a basis for the estimation of D_{12} for polar-polar gas pairs.

Monchick and Mason (79, 82) develop the theory for the transport properties and tabulate the collision integral Ω_D as a function of kT/ϵ_{0_p} and $(\delta)_{max}$ for polar gases (79), where

$$(\delta)_{max} = \tfrac{1}{2}\mu_p^2/\sigma_p^3\epsilon_{0_p} = \sqrt{2}\,t_p^* \qquad (11\text{-}24)$$

Mason and Monchick employ the combining rules (11-12) and (11-13) to obtain $\epsilon_{0_{12}}$ and σ_{12} and the following for $(\delta_{12})_{max}$:

$$(\delta_{12})_{max} = \tfrac{1}{2}\mu_1\mu_2/\epsilon_{0_{12}}\sigma_{12}^3 = [(\delta_1)_{max}(\delta_2)_{max}]^{1/2}[(\sigma_1\sigma_2)^{1/2}/\sigma_{12}]^3 \qquad (11\text{-}25)$$

Unfortunately, there are almost no data on mutual diffusion of polar-polar gas pairs, and so the theory has never been adequately tested.

TABLE 11-2. POLARIZABILITY OF MOLECULES*

Compound	$10^{25}\alpha_n$, cm^3	Compound	$10^{25}\alpha_n$, cm^3
H_2	7.9	$C_6H_5CH_3$	122.6
N_2	17.6	$p\text{-}C_6H_4(CH_3)_2$	142
O_2	16.0	$m\text{-}C_6H_4(CH_3)_2$	141.8
Cl_2	46.1	$o\text{-}C_6H_4(CH_3)_2$	141
HF	24.6	CH_3Cl	45.6
HCl	26.3	CH_3Br	55.5
HBr	36.1	CH_2Cl_2	64.8
HI	54.5	$CHCl_3$	82.3
N_2O	30.0	CCl_4	105
CO	19.5	C_2H_5Cl	64
CO_2	26.5	C_6H_5Cl	122.5
SO_2	37.2	$p\text{-}C_6H_4Cl_2$	144.7
H_2S	37.8	$m\text{-}C_6H_4Cl_2$	142.3
CS_2	87.4	$o\text{-}C_6H_4Cl_2$	141.7
NH_3	22.6	CH_3OH	32.3
$(CN)_2$	50.1	CH_3OCH_3	51.6
HCN	25.9	$C_2H_5OC_2H_5$	87.3
$SnCl_4$	137.7	$C_3H_7OC_3H_7$	125
CH_4	26.0	$C_4H_8O_2$	94.4
C_2H_6	44.7	CH_3COCH_3	63.3
C_2H_4	42.6	$CH_3COC_2H_5$	81.3
C_2H_2	33.3	$C_2H_5COC_2H_5$	99.3
C_3H_8	62.9	$CH_3COC_3H_7$	99.3
C_6H_{12}	108.7	$C_6H_5NO_2$	129.2
C_6H_6	103.2	C_6H_5N	95

* Landolt-Börnstein Tables, "Zahlenwerte und Funktionen, vol. 1, pt. 3, p. 510, Springer-Verlag OHG, Berlin, 1952.

11-4 Diffusion Coefficients for Binary Gas Systems at Low Pressures: Empirical Correlations

Wilke and Lee (132).   These investigators employed Eq. (11-11), with the constant 0.001858 replaced by

$$0.00214 - 0.000492[(M_1 + M_2)/M_1M_2]^{1/2}$$

This reduced the average deviation of calculated and experimental values of D_{12} for 64 binary gas pairs from 7 to 4 per cent.   They retained the second-order term f_D of Eq. (11-10), which varied from 1.00 to about 1.03, and which they expressed as a function of $kT/\epsilon_{0_{12}}$ and M_1/M_2.   The estimates based on Eqs. (11-14) and (11-16) averaged about 4 per cent better than those based on Eqs. (11-15) and (11-17).

The Wilke-Lee correlation may be closely approximated by taking f_D to be a constant equal to 1.015, in which case the modified form of Eq. (11-11) becomes

$$D_{12} = \{0.00217 - 0.00050[(M_1 + M_2)/M_1M_2]^{1/2}\}$$
$$\{T^{3/2}[(M_1 + M_2)/M_1M_2]^{1/2}/P\sigma^2_{12}\Omega_D\} \quad (11\text{-}26)$$

Slattery and Bird (106).   The equation proposed is

$$D_{12} = [(2.74 \times 10^{-4}/P][(M_1 + M_2)/M_1M_2]^{1/2}$$
$$(P_{c_1}P_{c_2})^{1/3}(T_{c_1}T_{c_2})^{-0.495}T^{1.823} \quad (11\text{-}27)$$

where M_1, M_2, P_{c_1}, P_{c_2}, T_{c_1}, and T_{c_2} are the molecular weights, critical pressures in atmospheres, and critical temperatures in degrees Kelvin of the two gases. P is the total pressure in atmospheres, and T is the temperature in degrees Kelvin.

Values of D_{12} calculated from Eq. (11-27) showed an average deviation of 7 per cent when compared with experimental data on 50 systems, including 20 pairs involving CO_2 and organic compounds.   The correlation did not work well for mixtures containing helium, hydrogen, or water vapor and was not tested for systems containing air as one gas. The range of temperatures and pressures in which it is applicable was not indicated.

Slattery and Bird suggest that Eq. (11-27) may be used for low-pressure binary gas systems in which one component is *water* if the constant 2.74 is replaced by 3.64, the exponent -0.495 replaced by -0.75, and the exponent 1.823 replaced by 2.334.

Chen and Othmer (24).   These workers estimated the collision integral empirically, obtaining

$$D_{12} = \{0.0150T^{1.81}[(M_1 + M_2)/M_1M_2]^{1/2}\}/$$
$$[P(T_{c_1}T_{c_2})^{c.1405}(V_{c_1}^{0.4} + V_{c_2}^{0.4})^2] \quad (11\text{-}28)$$

where P is in atmospheres, T in degrees Kelvin, and V_c in cubic centimeters per gram mole. This was shown to give slightly better results than Eq. (11-11) (force constants from viscosity data being used) when calculated values of D_{12} were compared with experimental data on 66 binary gas pairs at low pressure. The temperature function was shown to agree well with limited diffusion data at elevated temperatures.

Othmer and Chen (87). These investigators noted that D_{12} for a number of binary systems varies with temperature as the 2.74 power of the viscosity of air. Using this fact as a basis for the development of a temperature function, and letting molecular weights and critical volumes take care of the molecular properties, they obtained the relation

$$D_{12} = 2.52 \times 10^7 \mu_{AIR}^{2.74} \{ [(M_1 + M_2)M_1M_2]^{1\!/\!2} / (V_{c1}^{0.4} + V_{c2}^{0.4})^2 \}^{1.23} \quad (11\text{-}29)$$

where μ_{AIR} is the viscosity of *air* at T in *centipoises*. Values of μ_{AIR} are tabulated as a function of temperature in Ref. 53. Comparison of calculated and observed values of D_{12} for 50 or more binary gas systems gave results quite similar to those of Eq. (11-28). Othmer and Chen provide an alignment chart to simplify the use of Eq. (11-29)

Fuller, Schettler, and Giddings (38a). The empirical correlation proposed is not unlike the early equations of Arnold and of Gilliland but is based on a large amount of relatively recent data. The equation proposed is

$$D_{12} = \frac{0.00100 T^{1.75} (1/M_1 + 1/M_2)^{1\!/\!2}}{P[(\Sigma v)_1^{1\!/\!3} + (\Sigma v)_2^{1\!/\!3}]^2} \quad (11\text{-}29a)$$

Values of the atomic diffusion volumes to be summed for each of the gas species are listed in Table 11-3. These are similar to the LeBas atomic volumes, but different numerically.

The constants and the tabulated values of the diffusion volumes were obtained by machine calculation to give a best fit of the general form of the equation to some 340 experimental points on 153 different binary gas pairs, the data being selected from experimental studies published since 1930.

Corresponding States. The principle of corresponding states may be applied to diffusion coefficients in two ways (54). If a dimensionless diffusion coefficient is defined by

$$D_{12}^* \equiv (D_{12}/\sigma_{12}) \sqrt{M_{12}/\epsilon_{0_{12}}} \quad (11\text{-}30)$$

then Eq. (11-10) can be rewritten as

$$D^*P^*(kT/\epsilon_{0_{12}})^{-3\!/\!2} = f(kT/\epsilon_{0_{12}}) \quad (11\text{-}31)$$

In the above, M_{12} is the reduced molecular weight of the binary $[=2M_1M_2/(M_1 + M_2)]$, and P^* represents $P\sigma_{12}^3/\epsilon_{0_{12}}$.

TABLE 11-3. ATOMIC DIFFUSION VOLUMES FOR USE IN ESTIMATING D_{12}
BY THE METHOD OF FULLER, SCHETTLER, AND GIDDINGS

A. Atomic and Structural Diffusion Volume Increments, v

C	16.5	(Cl)	19.5
H	1.98	(S)	17.0
O	5.48	Aromatic ring	−20.2
(N)	5.69	Heterocyclic ring	−20.2

B. Diffusion Volumes for Simple Molecules, Σv

H$_2$	7.07	CO	18.9
D$_2$	6.70	CO$_2$	26.9
He	2.88	N$_2$O	35.9
N$_2$	17.9	NH$_3$	14.9
O$_2$	16.6	H$_2$O	12.7
Air	20.1	(CCl$_2$F$_2$)	114.8
Ar	16.1	(SF$_6$)	69.7
Kr	22.8	(Cl$_2$)	37.7
(Xe)	37.9	(Br$_2$)	67.2
		(SO$_2$)	41.1

NOTE: Parentheses indicate that the value listed is based on only a few data points.

Hirschfelder, Curtiss, and Bird (54) give data on self-diffusion of 10 gases plotted as suggested by Eq. (11-31), with a curve representing Eq. (11-10). The agreement is good. Rowlinson and Townley (97) and Carswell and Stryland (19) show similar graphs.

A modification of this procedure is to eliminate the force constants ϵ_0 and σ by the use of Eqs. (11-14) and (11-16) and eliminate V_c by the approximation $P_c V_c = \text{const} \times T_c$. This leads to

$$D_r \equiv D_{12}M_{12}^{1/2}P_c^{1/3}T_c^{-5/6} = f(P_r, T_r) \tag{11-32}$$

This suggests a correlation based on a graph of D_r versus P_r with T_r as a parameter, though the applicable value of T_c for a mixture is uncertain, since it appears differently in the elimination of V_c and in the expression for Ω_D as a function of T_r. The relation (11-32) is the basis for the empirical correlation of Slattery and Bird, presented earlier as Eq. (11-27).

Fair and Lerner (37) describe a form of corresponding-state correlation which is based on a graphical representation of a reduced diffusion coefficient. The method appears to give results similar to those obtained by the use of Eq. (11-11), but in most instances it is more difficult to employ.

11-5 Comparison of Estimation Methods for Binary Gas-diffusion Coefficients at Low Pressures

Several of the estimation procedures available at the time were compared with some 80 experimental values of $D_{12}P$ in the first edition of this book. This comparison indicated the theoretical method [Eq. (11-11)], with an average error of 6 per cent, to be the best. It has been pointed out recently by Scott (101), however, that many of the "experimental" values used in this comparison, as well as by other workers (24, 132), were calculated and not original data.

Table 11-4 compares the experimental data with values obtained by use of several of the more recent estimation procedures. With the exception of several values quoted by Mason and Monchick (79), all the 114 experimental points were obtained from original sources. No attempt was made to judge the accuracy of the experimental measurements, though the selection of data was almost wholly from recent studies, and the results presumably were reliable. Inspection of the table indicates, however, that different experimenters may disagree by several per cent. The two values for helium-nitrogen at 298°K suggest the small effect of mixture composition, which is generally ignored. Values obtained by four quite different experimental techniques are included. A slide rule was used in parts of the procedures used to obtain the calculated values of $D_{12}P$, which have been rounded off to two significant figures when the first digit is 2 or larger.

Inspection of Table 11-4 suggests that the several empirical methods offer no improvement over the theoretical equation. The average error by the latter method is 8 per cent, but the calculated values average 3.7 per cent low. This may compensate roughly for the fact that experimental values are often high because of failure to eliminate convection. In systems containing water the theoretical values run rather consistently low by about 10 per cent, suggesting the empirical introduction of a multiplying factor of 1.09 in Eq. (11-11) for such cases. The temperature functions incorporated in the several equations are not adequately tested by Table 11-4; as brought out in an earlier section, that of the theoretical method appears to be quite good.

Slattery and Bird do not recommend their procedure [Eq. (11-27)] for systems containing hydrogen or helium. Comparison of values calculated by their method with experimental data on systems containing helium (not shown) supports this conclusion, but the calculated values for the hydrogen systems (tabulated) agree fairly well with the data in most cases. With hydrogen and helium omitted, this method is at least as good as the theoretical, but evidently little easier to use and not as general.

TABLE 11-4. COMPARISON OF METHODS OF ESTIMATING GAS-DIFFUSION COEFFICIENTS AT LOW PRESSURES

$D_{12}P$ in cm²/(sec) × (atm)

System	T, °K	$D_{12}P$ (obs.)	Ref.	Errors as per cent of observed values					
				Theoretical	Wilke-Lee	Slattery and Bird	Chen-Othmer	Othmer-Chen	Fuller-Schettler-Giddings
Air–carbon dioxide	276.2	0.142	56	− 6	+ 4	− 4	0	− 3	− 3
Air–carbon dioxide	317.2	0.177	56	− 3	+ 8	− 2	+ 3	+ 4	− 1
Air–ethanol	313	0.145	79	−10	0	−15	−13	−11	− 8
Air–helium	276.2	0.624	56	0	+ 3	.....	+ 9	−25	− 7
Air–helium	317.2	0.765	56	+ 2	+ 5	.....	+13	−18	− 3
Air–helium	346.2	0.902	56	0	+ 3	.....	+13	−17	− 4
Air–n-hexane	294	0.0800	18	− 6	+ 5	− 2	− 2	−18	− 6
Air–n-hexane	328	0.0930	18	− 1	+11	+ 2	− 5	−11	− 3
Air–n-heptane	294	0.071	18	+15	+28	+21	− 2	+ 3	+15
Air–n-heptane	361	0.0985	18	+21	+35	+27	+25	+15	+19
Air–water	313	0.288	79	−18	−11	+ 3	−16	+ 5	− 5
Ammonia–diethyl ether	288.3	0.0999	109	−23	−16	−12	− 8	+ 2	+11
Ammonia–diethyl ether	337.5	0.137	109	−23	−16	−15	− 7	+ 6	+ 7
Argon–ammonia	254.7	0.150	108	+ 3	+13	− 4	+11	+20	+26
Argon–ammonia	333	0.253	108	+ 3	+12	− 7	+ 7	+27	+19
Argon–carbon dioxide	276.2	0.133	56	−17	− 8	− 5	+ 4	+ 1	+ 1
Argon–helium	276.2	0.646	56	− 1	+ 2	.....	+ 9	−23	− 3
Argon–helium	288	0.696	19	− 2	+ 1	.....	+17	−22	− 3
Argon–helium	298	0.729	102	− 1	+ 3	.....	+11	−19	− 2
Argon–helium	418	1.398	19	−10	− 8	.....	+ 7	−17	− 7
Argon–hydrogen	242.2	0.562	89	− 4	+ 3	− 1	+ 9	− 7	− 2

Argon-hydrogen	295.4	0.83	127	− 9	− 1	− 4	+ 6	− 3	− 7
Argon-hydrogen	448	1.76	127	−13	− 6	− 3	+ 6	+ 6	− 9
Argon-hydrogen	628	3.21	127	−15	− 8	− 1	+ 7	+ 8	−10
Argon-hydrogen	806	4.86	127	−15	− 9	+ 2	+11	+10	− 8
Argon-hydrogen	958	6.81	127	−19	−13	0	+ 9	+ 5	−11
Argon-hydrogen	1069	8.10	127	−19	−13	− 3	+11	+ 5	−11
Argon-krypton	273	0.119	107	− 1	+11		+ 5	− 6	+ 3
Argon-methane	298	0.202	19	+ 5	+15	+ 4	+ 9	+10	+ 6
Argon-neon	273	0.276	107	− 3	+ 6	+12	+13	− 8	
Argon-sulfur dioxide	263	0.077	79	+24	+38	+18	+27	+22	+25
Argon-xenon	195	0.0518	19	− 1	+11	+ 1	+ 7	−17	+ 2
Argon-xenon	194.7	0.508	6	0	+12	+ 3	+ 8	−15	+ 4
Argon-xenon	329.9	0.137	6	− 1	+11	0	+ 4	+ 1	− 2
Argon-xenon	378	0.178	19	− 2	+10	− 2	+ 2	+ 2	− 5
Carbon dioxide-carbon dioxide	194.8	0.0516	5	− 7	+ 1	+ 1	+14	+ 3	+16
Carbon dioxide-carbon dioxide	312.8	0.125	5	− 3	+ 5	− 1	+11	+22	+10
Carbon dioxide-helium	276.2	0.531	56	− 2	+ 1		+ 5	−17	− 6
Carbon dioxide-helium	298	0.612	102	− 3	0		+ 5	−16	− 7
Carbon dioxide-helium	299	0.611	120	− 5	− 2		+ 5	−15	− 6
Carbon dioxide-helium	346.2	0.765	56	− 1	+ 2		+10	− 7	− 4
Carbon dioxide-helium	498	1.414	102	− 2	0		+15	+ 1	− 1
Carbon dioxide-nitrogen	298	0.167	121	− 9	+ 1	− 7	− 1	− 2	− 2
Carbon dioxide-nitrogen	299	0.171	120	−11	− 1	− 9	− 2	− 4	− 4
Carbon dioxide-nitrous oxide	194.8	0.0531	5	−11	0	− 2	+ 9	− 2	+ 3
Carbon dioxide-nitrous oxide	312.8	0.128	5	− 6	+ 4	− 4	+ 8	+17	− 2
Carbon dioxide-oxygen	293.2	0.153	124	− 3	+ 7	− 1	+ 6	+ 7	+ 3
Carbon dioxide-sulfur dioxide	263	0.064	79	+ 5	+12	+12	+24	+28	+27
Carbon dioxide-sulfur dioxide	473	0.195	79	+ 8	+21	+ 7	+21	+39	+16
Carbon dioxide-water	307.2	0.198	27	−20	−13	−13	− 3	+31	+12
Carbon dioxide-water	328.6	0.257	27	−30	−23	−19	−15	+17	− 3
Carbon dioxide-water	352.3	0.245	99	−14	− 6	− 3	+ 1	+41	+11

System	T, °K	$D_{12}P$ (obs.)	Ref.	Errors as per cent of observed values					
				Theoretical	Wilke-Lee	Slattery and Bird	Chen-Othmer	Othmer-Chen	Fuller-Schettler-Giddings
Carbon monoxide–carbon monoxide	194.7	0.109	7	−14	− 6	−17	−14	−35	−13
Carbon monoxide–carbon monoxide	373	0.323	7	− 7	+ 2	− 8	− 4	−10	− 8
Carbon monoxide–nitrogen	194.7	0.105	7	− 9	0	−12	−13	−32	− 8
Carbon monoxide–nitrogen	373	0.318	7	− 6	+ 3	− 5	− 3	− 6	− 5
Ethane–n-hexane	294	0.0375	18	+37	+52	+50	+18	+41	+80
Ethylene–water	328.4	0.233	99	− 7	+ 1	−12	−21	+17	− 3
Helium–benzene	423	0.610	102	+ 8	+12	...	+14	− 7	− 6
Helium–n-butanol(a)(c)	423	0.587	102	+10	+12	...	+14	− 7	− 2
Helium–ethanol	423	0.821	102	+ 3	+ 7	...	+ 9	− 7	− 5
Helium–n-hexanol(c)(d)	423	0.469	102	+16	+19	...	+19	− 7	+ 1
Helium–methane	298	0.675	19	+ 3	+ 5	...	+ 7	−19	− 6
Helium–methanol	423	1.032	102	+ 7	+10	...	+ 4	− 7	− 1
Helium–neon	242.2	0.792	89	− 6	− 4	...	+10	−33	
Helium–neon	341.2	1.405	89	− 7	− 3	...	+15	−22	
Helium–nitrogen	298	0.687	102	+ 1	+ 3	...	+13	−21	+ 1
Helium–nitrogen (He trace)	298	0.730	128	− 5	− 3	...	+ 7	−26	− 5
Helium–nitrogen (N₂ trace)	298	0.688	128	0	+ 3	...	+13	−21	+ 1
Helium–oxygen	298	0.729	102	+ 2	+ 5	...	+12	−18	− 2
Helium–n-pentanol(a)(b)	423	0.507	102	+16	+18	...	+18	− 5	+ 2
Helium–i-propanol	423	0.677	102	+ 7	+ 9	...	+13	− 6	− 4
Helium–n-propanol(a)(b)	423	0.676	102	+18	+20	...	+13	− 5	− 3

Mixture	Temp.							
Helium-water	307.1	0.902	99	-1	+2	…	-8	-15	-3
Helium-water	352.4	1.121	99	+1	+3	…	-6	-11	-4
Hydrogen-acetone	296	0.424	79	0	-3	+1	0	+6	+17
Hydrogen-ammonia	263	0.57	79	+4	+1	+6	+7	+15	+17
Hydrogen-ammonia	273	0.745	100	-15	-17	-24	-15	-3	-5
Hydrogen-ammonia	298	0.783	79	-4	-7	-14	+5	+10	+6
Hydrogen-ammonia	358	1.093	79	-4	-7	-14	+5	+15	+4
Hydrogen-ammonia	473	1.86	79	+5	-8	-16	+7	+17	0
Hydrogen-ammonia	533	2.149	100	+2	-1	-10	0	+26	+7
Hydrogen-benzene	311.3	0.404	59	0	-2	-10	+8	+8	-1
Hydrogen-cyclohexane	288.6	0.319	59	+3	+6	+15	+3	+6	+4
Hydrogen-methane	288	0.694	19	-5	-8	+42	+3	-2	-7
Hydrogen-nitrogen	294	0.763	100	+5	-8	+1	+1	-4	-3
Hydrogen-nitrogen	298	0.784	79	+6	-8	0	0	-4	-3
Hydrogen-nitrogen	358	1.052	79	+3	-5	+4	+4	+5	-1
Hydrogen-nitrogen	573	2.417	100	-8	-10	+7	+6	+12	-1
Hydrogen-piperidine(c)(d)	315	0.403	59	-2	-5	+9	+3	+4	-8
Hydrogen-pyridine(a)(c)	318	0.437	59	-5	+7	+10	+3	+7	+2
Hydrogen-sulfur dioxide	285.5	0.525	79	-5	-7	-1	0	+9	-6
Hydrogen-sulfur dioxide	473	1.23	79	0	-2	+6	+8	+27	-3
Hydrogen-thiophene(a)(b)	302	0.400	59	0	-3	+10	+2	+8	+6
Hydrogen-water	307.1	0.915	27	-12	-14	+47	-10	+13	-1
Hydrogen-water	328.5	1.121	99	-17	-20	+40	-18	+7	-8
Hydrogen-xenon	341.2	0.751	89	-1	-3	+5	+5	+13	-8
Methane-water	352.3	0.356	99	-11	-5	0	-11	+17	0
Neon-krypton	273	0.223	107	-2	+8	+4	+6	-10	
Nitrogen-ammonia	298	0.230	79	-5	+3	-13	+3	+8	+10
Nitrogen-ammonia	358	0.328	79	-6	+2	-15	+5	+10	+6
Nitrogen-benzene	311.3	0.102	59	-4	+6	-4	+6	-10	-2

TABLE 11-4. COMPARISON OF METHODS OF ESTIMATING GAS-DIFFUSION COEFFICIENTS AT LOW PRESSURES (Continued)

System	T, °K	$D_{12}P$ (obs.)	Ref.	Errors as per cent of observed values					
				Theoretical	Wilke-Lee	Slattery and Bird	Chen-Othmer	Othmer-Chen	Fuller-Schettler-Giddings
Nitrogen-cyclohexane	288.6	0.0731	59	+ 1	+12	+11	+ 4	− 5	+ 5
Nitrogen-piperidine(c)(d)	315	0.0953	59	− 3	+ 7	− 1	+ 2	− 9	− 2
Nitrogen-sulfur dioxide	263	0.104	79	− 3	+ 8	− 3	− 9	− 2	+ 1
Nitrogen-water	307.5	0.256	99	−11	− 3	+ 7	− 7	+13	+ 8
Nitrogen-water	328.9	0.313	27	−17	−11	+ 2	−14	+ 7	0
Nitrogen-water	349.1	0.354	27	−17	−10	+ 5	−16	+ 6	− 2
Nitrogen-water	352.1	0.359	99	−17	−10	+ 6	−15	+ 6	− 2
Oxygen-benzene	311.3	0.101	59	− 9	+ 1	− 5	− 7	− 8	− 3
Oxygen-carbon tetrachloride	296	0.0749	79	− 5	+ 6	+ 7	+ 3	+17	+35
Oxygen-cyclohexane(c)(d)	288.6	0.0746	59	− 7	+ 4	+ 5	− 1	− 7	0
Oxygen-piperidine	315	0.0953	59	− 7	+ 4	+ 3	− 7	− 9	− 5
Oxygen-water	352.3	0.352	99	−15	− 8	+ 2	−10	+19	0
Average error	……	……	……	7.5	8.0	9.0	8.5	12.6	6.9

NOTES: (a) The theoretical values are calculated by the use of Eqs. (11-11) to (11-13), with values of force constants from Appendix G; exceptions are cases (a) ϵ_0/k from Eq. (11-14), T_c from Appendix A; (b) ϵ_0/k from Eq. (11-16), V_c by the methods of Chap. 2; (c) σ from Eq. (11-16), V_c from Appendix A, and (d) ϵ_0/k from Eq. (11-14), T_c by the methods of Chap. 2.

(b) The values of D_{12} calculated by the Wilke-Lee method are based on the slightly modified form of their correlation, as represented by Eq. (11-26).

(c) Slattery and Bird state that their method is not applicable to binaries containing hydrogen or helium. The values of D_{12} are not calculated for systems containing helium, but the calculated values for hydrogen systems are listed since they compare reasonably well with the observed values, in spite of the authors' statement.

(d) Values of the viscosity of air employed in using the Othmer-Chen method were obtained from Ref. 53.

Fuller, Schettler, and Giddings show a table of computed mean errors for the six methods compared in Table 11-4. Using 340 data points, they find mean errors of 6.4, 6.8, 14.0, 8.9, 13.9, and 4.3 per cent, which are to be compared with the corresponding values of 7.5, 8.0, 9.0, 8.5, 12.6, and 6.9 per cent listed at the bottom of Table 11-4. It is evident that this empirical method gives results for simple molecules which are as good or better than the theoretical method, and is easier to use. It is clearly the best of the empirical correlations, but the table of atomic diffusion volumes is incomplete and the simple power-temperature function is suspect.

As noted earlier, correlations based on the principle of corresponding states have been represented in the form of graphs of $D^*P^*(kT/\epsilon_{0_{12}})^{-3/2}$ versus $kT/\epsilon_{0_{12}}$, as suggested by Eq. (11-31). This procedure is illustrated in a simpler way by rewriting Eq. (11-11),

$$(D_{12}P\sigma_{12}^2)/T^{3/2}[(M_1 + M_2)/M_1M_2]^{1/2} = 0.001858/\Omega_D = f(kT/\epsilon_{0_{12}}) \quad (11\text{-}33)$$

The data of Table 11-4 are plotted in Fig. 11-2 as suggested by this form.

Table 11-4 gives more detail as to the validity of Eq. (11-11) than the graph, but the latter gives a better overall picture of the spatter of the data than the single value of the average per cent deviation. The solid curve marked "Theoretical" represents Eq. (11-11); it is evident that the use of the collision integral based on the Lennard-Jones potential function provides a good correlation.

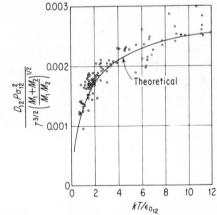

FIG. 11-2. Comparison of experimental and theoretical diffusion coefficients for binary gas systems at low pressures.

Recommendation. Use Eq. (11-11) for the estimation of diffusion coefficients in binary gas systems at low pressure. This is generally valid for pressures less than about 20 atm (see Sec. 11-6). The force constants used should be those obtained from viscosity data, as tabulated in Appendix G. Use the combining rules (11-12) and (11-13) to obtain $\epsilon_{0_{12}}/k$ and σ_{12}. If ϵ_0/k and σ for the pure gases are not available from viscosity measurements, use values estimated from the critical properties by means of Eqs. (11-14) and (11-16). Values of Ω_D are given as a function of $kT/\epsilon_{0_{12}}$ in Table 11-1. Example 11-1 illustrates the calculation procedure.

There is some support, though perhaps inadequate, for the conclusion that, for binaries containing water as one constituent, the value of D_{12} estimated by the above procedure should be multiplied by 1.09.

The method of Fuller, Schettler, and Giddings is simple to use and gives excellent results within the range of the experimental data on which it is based (simple molecules, moderate temperatures).

11-6   The Effect of Pressure on Diffusion in Gases

The product $D_{12}P$ is essentially independent of pressure from a few millimeters of mercury to some tens of atmospheres, and Eq. (11-11) serves well for the prediction of binary gas-diffusion coefficients in the range of pressures ordinarily employed in industry. This relation fails at high pressures, however, since the theory on which it is based includes no allowance for the effect of molecular size on the frequency of molecular collisions. This effect is important at pressures which cause the molecules to become closely packed, as in dense fluids.

The Enskog theory of gases made up of rigid spherical molecules provides a correction applicable to a fluid of low or medium density. The correction factor χ is defined by the relation

$$\frac{D_{12}\rho \text{ (at } T \text{ and } P)}{(D_{12}\rho)^0 \text{ (at } T \text{ and at low pressure)}} = D_{12}\rho/(D_{12}\rho)^0 = 1/\chi$$

$$= D_{12}P/Z(D_{12}P)^0 \quad (11\text{-}34)$$

The product $D_{12}\rho$ is independent of pressure at low pressures, and $(D_{12}\rho)^0$ may conveniently be based on values of ρ and D_{12} at 1 atm. Recent developments in the theory of dense gases are reviewed by Henderson (51).

Enskog's theory relates χ [the χ of Eq. (9-21)] to the molecular size and number density as follows:

$$\chi = 1.0 + 0.6250(b_0/V) + 0.2869(b_0/V)^2 + 0.115(b_0/V)^3 + \cdots$$
$$= 1.0 + 1.31n\sigma^3 + 1.26(n\sigma^3)^2 + 1.06(n\sigma^3)^3 + \cdots \quad (11\text{-}35)$$

Here V is the molal volume at the specified T and P; b_0 represents $\frac{2}{3}\pi N_0\sigma^3$; n is the molecular number density, N_0/V; N_0 is Avogadro's number; Z is the compressibility factor for the gas; and σ is the molecular collision diameter. The value of $n\sigma^3$ is given by

$$n\sigma^3 = N_0 P\sigma^3/ZRT = 0.00735P\sigma^3/ZT = 0.602\rho\sigma^3 \quad (11\text{-}36)$$

where σ is in angstrom units, as are the values in Appendix G, and ρ is the density in moles per cm^3. Values of Z may be estimated by the methods of Chaps. 3 and 7.

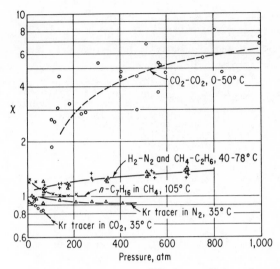

FIG. 11-3. Effect of pressure on diffusion coefficients in gases.

The Enskog theory is properly applied only to *self-diffusion* of molecules which are rigid spheres, for which three-body collisions are not possible. Attempts to extend the theory to diffusion in real-gas binaries, e.g., Thorne (22, 54), have not been very successful, though the parallel development of a theory of viscosity of dense gases has shown great promise. The general situation as regards this theoretical development is reviewed in Refs. 12 and 54. For self-diffusion, however, Lennert and Thodos (68) have suggested that both $b_0\rho/M$ and $b_0\rho\chi/M$ might be represented graphically as functions of T_r and P_r and that χ might be obtained from such correlations and used with Eq. (11-34). The two graphs presented were based on data for argon ($Z_c = 0.290$), with values of χ calculated from data for the viscosity of argon, but their use was shown to give good predictions of the self-diffusion coefficients in argon, nitrogen ($Z_c = 0.291$), and carbon dioxide ($Z_c = 0.275$).

Data on binary diffusion coefficients for gases at high pressures are relatively scarce and have not been correlated in such a way as to provide a valid prediction method. Representative data (11, 34, 94, 114) are plotted in Fig. 11-3 as χ versus pressure, to show the trends. In each case the values of $(D_{12}P)^0$ were calculated by the use of Eq. (11-11); so deviations of the intercepts from unity are attributable to errors in estimating the low-pressure values. The CO_2-CO_2 data are for self-diffusion; the other points represent binary data, including systems with substantial as well as trace amounts of the diffusing substance. It is not safe to conclude from this graph that χ lies between 0.8 and 1.4 up to pressures of several hundred atmospheres, but it seems likely that the use of $\chi = 1$

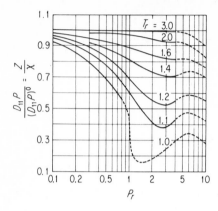

FIG. 11-4. Generalized chart for the coefficient of self-diffusion of gases at high densities.

will not introduce additional errors [over those inherent in Eq. (11-11)] of more than 10 per cent up to pressures of perhaps 100 atm. It follows from Eq. (11-34) that when χ can be taken as unity $D_{12}P$ is estimated by multiplying $D_{12}P$, as found using Eq. (11-11), by Z for the mixture.

Little is gained by plotting these data as χ versus $n\sigma^3$, as suggested by the Enskog theory for rigid spheres. It is noted, however, that the densities were greater for the CO_2 measurements and that for all the data shown, including CO_2-CO_2, χ lies between 0.8 and 1.3 for conditions where the molar density was less than 15 g moles/liter.

Correlations of data on gas viscosity at high pressure have been reasonably successful, and these may be used as a basis for estimating diffusion coefficients. Slattery and Bird (106) combined Enskog's relations for dense real-gas viscosity and diffusion coefficients with existing correlations of Z and μ/μ^0 to obtain Fig. 11-4, which relates Z/χ to P_r and T_r. It is suggested that pseudocritical properties be employed in calculating P_r and T_r for a binary system. It can easily be seen that this graph cannot represent the data shown in Fig. 11-3 but evidently does a fair job for self-diffusion, as shown by Fig. 8-2 of the first edition of this book. Though quite unreliable for binary systems, it is the only correlation now available which purports to provide rough values of D_{12} at high pressures.

11-7 Diffusion in Multicomponent Gas Mixtures

The equations developed for diffusion in multicomponent gas mixtures are more or less complex, depending on the geometry of the system and the boundary conditions. They are generally written, however, in forms which employ the binary diffusion coefficients to represent the molecular properties of the gas system. The methods for estimating D_{12} are directly applicable, therefore, to problems of multicomponent diffusion.

It is not within the scope of this book to develop the equations for diffusion applicable to the many geometries and mixtures of interest. The simplest case, however, is worth noting. If only one component diffuses in a mixture of n components, then the steady-state equation for a binary system may be employed, with D_{12} replaced by D_{1m},

$$D_{1m} = \frac{(1 - y_1)}{\sum\limits_{j=2}^{n} (y_j/D_{1j})} \tag{11-37}$$

where y_1 is the mole fraction of the diffusing component, y_j the mole fraction of component j, and D_{1j} the binary gas-diffusion coefficient for 1 and j.

The basic theory of diffusion in multicomponent gas systems is given by Hirschfelder, Curtiss, and Bird (28, 54). Approximate calculation methods were developed by Wilke (130) in 1950. Integration of the basic equations for the steady-state diffusion of two gases through a third, nondiffusing gas had been carried out earlier by Gilliland (42). The problem of diffusion in three-component gas systems has been generalized by Toor (115) and checked experimentally by Fairbanks and Wilke (38), Walker, de Haas, and Westenberg (120), and Duncan and Toor (33). Other relevant articles include Refs. 12, 32, 58, 65, 80, 103, and 112.

11-8 Diffusion in Liquids

Diffusion coefficients in liquids as well as gases are defined by Eq. (11-1). Because of the greater molecular packing density in the condensed phase, D_{12} in a typical liquid system is usually of the order of 10^{-4} times D_{12} in common gas systems at normal temperature and pressure. This does not necessarily mean that diffusion rates are correspondingly less in liquids, however, since concentration gradients may be very large.

In contrast with the situation for gases, the theory of the liquid state is only partly developed, and the existing theories do not provide as good a basis for the prediction of diffusion coefficients as the available empirical equations. Consequently, these theories will be given but a brief review. [For a more complete description of the earlier theories see the discussion by Johnson and Babb (62) and the book by Tyrell (116).] A useful theory of the liquid state can be expected to yield equations for both viscosity and diffusion, and it is natural, therefore, to find theoretical relations between D_{12} and the viscosity of the liquid mixture. As in so many other cases, even a fragmentary theory can provide a valuable *form* for an empirical correlation.

Einstein. The well-known Einstein relation (also attributed to Sutherland and to Nernst) is

$$D_{12} = kT/\xi_{12} \tag{11-38}$$

which is of the form of Eq. (11-7). If the diffusing molecule is thought of as a sphere moving through a continuum, then ξ_{12} may be evaluated by the Stokes equation, to give

$$D_{12} = kT/6\pi\mu r \tag{11-39}$$

where μ is the liquid viscosity and r is the radius of the diffusing molecule. This has been shown to apply well to the diffusion of very large molecules in a low-molecular-weight solvent. Thus, for large unhydrated molecules ($M > 1,000$) in water at room temperature, Polson (91) finds good agreement with the simple form

$$D_{12} = 2.74 \times 10^{-5} M^{-\frac{1}{3}} \tag{11-40}$$

where M is the molecular weight of the large molecule.

Attempts to relate the radius r of Eq. (11-39) with molecular radii obtained by various methods have met with only indifferent success. In this connection, however, the interesting studies of Stokes and coworkers (47, 111) suggest a possible basis for a correlation of diffusion coefficients. These authors report D_{12}^0 for iodine and for carbon tetrachloride in a number of different solvents. Here D_{12}^0 is the limiting diffusion coefficient at infinite dilution of solute 1 in solvent 2. Figure 11-5 shows the results for carbon tetrachloride, plotted as $D_{12}^0\mu_2$ versus the molal volume V_2 of the solvent. This suggests that D_{12}^0 is linear in V_2, with separate lines for alcohols, cyclic hydrocarbons, and straight-chain hydrocarbons. An interesting feature of this graph is that the intercept, representing the diffusion of carbon tetrachloride in a medium of solvent molecules infinitely

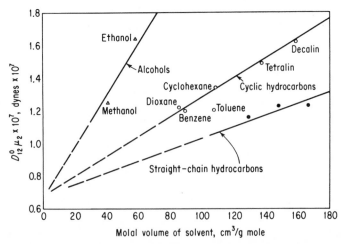

FIG. 11-5. Diffusion of carbon tetrachloride in various solvents at 25°C. [H. J. V. Tyrell, "Diffusion and Heat Flow in Liquids," Butterworth & Co. (Publishers), Ltd., London, 1961; B. R. Hammond and R. H. Stokes, Trans. Faraday Soc., **51**:1641 (1955).]

small in size, i.e., a continuum, is identical with the value calculated by means of Eq. (11-39) with $r = r_1 = 3.2$ A, which is the radius of the carbon tetrachloride molecule as calculated from data on the scattering of X rays in the liquid.

Eyring. The *absolute-reaction-rate theory* of Eyring and coworkers (10, 15, 36, 41, 70, 76, 95, 116) is based on a model of a liquid as a quasi-crystalline substance with diffusing molecules "jumping" through ordered layers of solvent molecules. It has not provided a basis for the reliable quantitative prediction of diffusion coefficients.

Holmes, Wilke, and Olander (55) and Olander (86) have recently modified the Eyring theory by suggesting a method of evaluating the difference between the free energies of activation for viscosity and for diffusion, which Eyring took to be zero. The resulting graphical correlation, involving a certain amount of empiricism, shows some 40 experimental points falling within about ± 15 per cent of the best line. This is a distinct improvement, but still not adequate for general use in predicting D_{12}.

Statistical Mechanical Theory. The modern statistical-mechanical theory of liquids, due to Kirkwood, Bearman, Rice, and others (52, 72, 74), provides the basis for a sophisticated approach to the problem of relating molecular friction coefficients to the properties of the liquid. It promises to displace the earlier but simpler theories of Einstein and of Hartley and Crank (50), though it has not been developed to the point where quantitative predictions of D_{12} can be made. Its present development is restricted to regular solutions involving molecules having similar sizes, shapes, and interaction potentials. For such systems it provides useful relations between mutual- and self-diffusion coefficients and viscosity. Bearman (10), in an excellent summary, shows that the statistical theory and the theories of Eyring and of Hartley and Crank all relate mutual- and self-diffusion coefficients by equations of the same form. These are summarized in the next section.

Kamal and Canjar (64) have recently employed the statistical-mechanical theory as a basis for the development of a method of correlating and predicting mutual-diffusion coefficients in liquids. When tested by comparison with data on 56 binary systems, it proved to be nearly as reliable as the empirical Wilke-Chang correlation [Eq. (11-45)]. It suffers, however, from the necessity of knowing values of the ratio of the total volume to the occupied volume of the solvent molecule. This ratio must be obtained from data on the velocity of sound in the liquid or from other diffusion data involving the same solvent.

The theory as developed by Kamal and Canjar is especially interesting as a basis for an empirical correlation, since it indicates that D_{12} at infinite dilution of the diffusing species is given by a product of two quantities, one a function of the properties of the solute and the other dependent only on the properties of the solvent. This approach is developed in Sec. 11-11.

11-9 Concentration Dependence of Diffusion Coefficients in Liquids

In binary solutions at constant temperature and pressure the self-diffusion coefficients D_{11} and D_{22} are constants, but the mutual-diffusion coefficient D_{12} and the tracer-diffusion coefficients $D_1^\star$ and $D_2^\star$ often vary greatly with composition. Most of the published data are for D_{12} at low concentrations of species 1, which is approximately the same as $D_1^\star$ at $c_1 = 0$.

By assuming constituent volumes to be additive, Bearman (9, 10) shows that the statistical-mechanical theory leads to the following equations:

$$D_1^\star/D_2^\star = V_2/V_1 \qquad (11\text{-}41)$$

$$D_{12} = D_1^\star[\partial(\ln a_1)/\partial(\ln c_1)]_{T,P}$$
$$= (D_2^\star x_1 + D_1^\star x_2)[\partial(\ln a_1)/\partial(\ln x_1)]_{T,P} \qquad (11\text{-}42)$$

$$D_{12}\mu = (D_1^\star)_{c_1=0}\mu_2[1 + \partial(\ln \gamma_1)/\partial(\ln c_1)]_{T,P}$$
$$= (D_1^\star)_{c_1=0}\mu_2[(V_1/V_2 - 1)x_1 + 1][\partial(\ln a_1)/\partial(\ln x_1)]_{T,P} \qquad (11\text{-}43)$$

where x_1 and x_2 are the mole fractions of the two constituents, V_1 and V_2 are the molal volumes of the pure constituents, μ is the viscosity of the solution, and μ_2 the viscosity of the pure constituent 2, and the activity coefficient γ is defined by $a_1 = \gamma_1 c_1$. The theory also suggests that $D_1^\star \mu$ should be independent of composition for regular solutions.

Equation (11-42) was first derived by Darken (29); the equivalent form is given by Hartley and Crank (50) and discussed at length by Carman and Stein (17). Bearman shows that the first equality of Eq. (11-42) is also a consequence of the Eyring theory, as is the conclusion from Eq. (11-43) that $D_{12}\mu[\partial(\ln a_1)/\partial(\ln x_1)]_{T,P}^{-1}$ should be linear in x_1 or x_2. These relations, stemming from each of the principal theories, have been compared with data on various binary liquid systems. McCarty and Mason (75) conclude that Eq. (11-42) does not hold for gas mixtures, to which Eqs. (11-8) and (11-9) apply.

In brief, Eqs. (11-42) and (11-43) are found to hold for binary ideal solutions but to be unreliable for nonideal mixtures. The deviations become very large in cases where molecular association of either component is appreciable. Figure 11-6 illustrates the variation of $D_1^\star$, $D_2^\star$, and D_{12} in the essentially ideal system (117) n-octane (1)–n-dodecane (2) at 60°C. The mutual-diffusion coefficient D_{12} is seen to be nearly linear in x_1, and extrapolation of the D_{12} data checks the tracer-diffusion data in the pure liquids ($D_{12} = D_1^\star$ at $x_1 = 0$, and $D_{12} = D_2^\star$ at $x_2 = 0$). The products $D_1^\star \mu$ and $D_2^\star \mu$ were found to vary some 30 per cent over the range of compositions. Since V_2/V_1 is $228/163 = 1.4$, Eq. (11-41) evidently holds to within 4 to 8 per cent. Carman and Stein obtained very similar

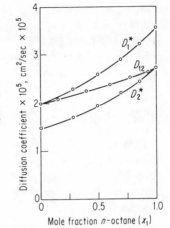

FIG. 11-6. Mutual- and tracer-diffusion coefficients for the system n-octane–n-dodecane. [*A. L. Van Geet and A. W. Adamson, J. Phys. Chem.*, **68**:238 (1964).]

results for the nearly ideal system ethyl iodide–butyl iodide; the products $D_1^* \mu$ and $D_2^* \mu$ were constant within 2 per cent in this case.

Nonideal systems show wide deviations from Eq. (11-43), as illustrated by Fig. 11-7. This shows the mutual-diffusion data of Anderson, Hall, and Babb (8) for the system acetone-water at 25.15°C. D_{12} is far from linear in composition, and $D_{12}\mu$ is more nearly linear than when corrected for activity variation, as called for by Eq. (11-43). The variation of D_{12} with composition for this and three other systems containing acetone is shown in Fig. 11-8. All but one exhibit minima in the D_{12}-x_1 curve; the exception is chloroform-acetone, a classic example of a system showing negative deviations from Raoult's law.

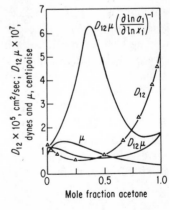

FIG. 11-7. Mutual diffusion, viscosity, uncorrected and activity-corrected $D_{12}\mu$ product for acetone-water system at 25.15°. [*D. K. Anderson, J. R. Hall, and A. L. Babb, J. Phys. Chem.*, **62**:404 (1958).]

In other cases the activity term helps the correlation, though it often overcorrects. Carman and Miller (16) obtained data on both mutual and tracer diffusion in the highly nonideal system CH_3NO_2-CCl_4. In this case D_{12} passes through a minimum value less than 15 per cent of the limiting values $D_1^{\star}$ and $D_2^{\star}$. Values calculated by the use of Eq. (11-42) followed the data moderately well in the light of the extreme curvature, though the discrepancy was nearly twofold at the minimum. Again, the activity term tended to overcorrect. Carman and Miller attributed the discrepancy to molecular association with the formation of "kinetic units," not single molecules.

11-10 Pressure Dependence of Diffusion Coefficients in Liquids

This subject has been studied very little, but, as might be expected, increased pressure decreases D_{12} as the molecular spacing is forcibly reduced. Self-diffusion in water and in several liquid metals has been measured at high pressures; the self-diffusion coefficients decrease with increase in pressure whether melting temperature increases (Hg, Ga) or decreases (H_2O, Bi). For self-diffusion in mercury Nachtrieb and Petit (83) found the product $D_{11}\mu$ to be almost exactly constant at 30°C over the pressure range from 1 to 8,366 kg/cm². D_{11} decreased from 1.63 × 10^{-5} cm²/sec to 1.35 × 10^{-5} cm²/sec, while μ increased from 1.516 to 1.838 centipoises.

11-11 Estimation of Diffusion Coefficients in Dilute Solutions

Several empirical correlations are available for the estimation of diffusion coefficients in binary solutions at infinite dilution (very low concentration of the diffusing solute). The effect of concentration must be estimated by the use of Eq. (11-42), with $(D_1^{\star})_{c_1=0}$ replaced by D_{12}^0, the mutual-diffusion coefficient at infinite dilution. (The superscript zero indicates zero concentration of solute 1; the subscript 2 refers to the solvent.) As noted in Sec. 11-9, this latter procedure, though the best available, may introduce serious errors in distinctly nonideal systems.

The best estimation methods give average errors of about 15 per cent. Many of the older data, however, are not good to better than ±5 per cent; so not much better correlations are to be expected. Furthermore, D_{12} for systems such as water-acetone (see Fig. 11-8) change rapidly with concentration in the region of low solute concentrations, and so the evaluation of D_{12}^0 from limited experimental data is not precise.

Self-diffusion Coefficients. Nagarajan, Ryan, and Shemilt (84) show an excellent correlation of data on isotope-tracer diffusion data for 10 liquids from 0 to 55°C. This can be represented by the equation

$$D_1^{\star} = 1.39 \times 10^{-7}/\mu \tag{11-44}$$

where μ is the liquid viscosity in poises.

Mutual-diffusion Coefficients. Numerous empirical correlations are available; only those which have been well tested and appear most generally useful will be described.

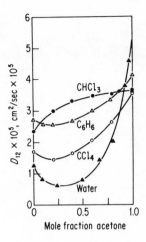

FIG. 11-8. Mutual-diffusion data for acetone systems at 25.15°: ●, acetone-chloroform; Δ, acetone-benzene, ○, acetone–carbon tetrachloride; ▲, acetone-water. [*D. K. Anderson, J. R. Hall, and A. L. Babb, J. Phys. Chem.*, **62**:404 (1958).]

Wilke and Chang (131). This empirical form of Eq. (11-39) is written

$$D_{12}^0 = 7.4 \times 10^{-8}[(\phi M_2)^{\frac{1}{2}} T / \mu_2 V_1^{0.6}] \qquad (11\text{-}45)$$

where D_{12}^0 = mutual diffusion of solute 1 in solvent 2 at very low solute concentration, cm²/sec

M_2 = molecular weight of solvent

T = temperature, °K

μ_2 = viscosity of solution (solvent), *centipoises*

V_1 = molal volume of the solute at its normal boiling point, cm³/g mole

ϕ = "association parameter" of solvent

Note that this equation is not dimensionally correct and that solvent viscosity in centipoises is used.

The values of ϕ recommended by Wilke and Chang are water, 2.6; methanol, 1.9; ethanol, 1.5; benzene, 1.0; ether, 1.0; heptane, 1.0; other unassociated solvents, 1.0. The molal volume V_1 of the solute is obtained by using the LeBas group contributions (Table 3-4).

Figure 11-9 is a graphical representation of Eq. (11-45), with a dotted line representing Eq. (11-39). The latter is assumed to represent the maximum value of the ordinate for any value of V_1.

Scheibel (98) has proposed a modification of the Wilke-Chang relation with the elimination of ϕ,

$$D_{12}^0 = KT / \mu_2 V_1^{\frac{1}{3}} \qquad (11\text{-}46)$$

where the symbols have the same meaning as above. In the general case, K is given by

$$K = 8.2 \times 10^{-8}[1 + (3V_2/V_1)^{\frac{2}{3}}] \qquad (11\text{-}47)$$

However, the following recommendations are made for several solvents:

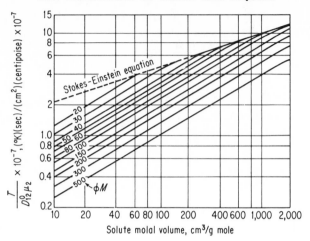

Fig. 11-9. Graphical representation of Wilke-Chang correlation of diffusion coefficients in dilute solutions. [*From C. R. Wilke and Pin Chang, AIChE J., 1(2): 270 (1955).*]

for *water*, if $V_1 < V_2$, use $K = 25.2 \times 10^{-8}$; for *benzene*, if $V_1 < 2V_2$, use $K = 18.9 \times 10^{-8}$; for other solvents, if $V_1 < 2.5V_2$, use $K = 17.5 \times 10^{-8}$. As before, μ_2 is the viscosity of the solvent in *centipoises; V_2* is the molal volume of the solvent at T_b (see Table 3-4).

Olander (85) reports that experimental values of D_{12}^0 for water as the *solute* in eight different solvents are considerably lower than predicted by Eq. (11-45); the ratio of calculated to observed values of D_{12}^0 was found to be roughly constant at 2.3.

Othmer and Thakar (88). These authors note that log D_{12}^0 is essentially linear in log μ_2, the relation holding in a given binary as temperature is varied. The slope of the line is the ratio of the activation energies for diffusion and for viscosity. Starting with this observation, the following empirical relation for D_{12}^0 was developed,

$$D_{12}^0 = 14.0 \times 10^{-5}(V_1^{0.6}\mu_2\mu_w^{1.1\Delta H_2/\Delta H_w})^{-1} \tag{11-48}$$

where μ_2 = viscosity of the solvent at 20°C, *centipoises*

μ_w = viscosity of *water* at T, *centipoises*

ΔH_2 = latent heat of vaporization of the solvent at T, cal/g mole

ΔH_w = latent heat of vaporization of water at T, cal/g mole

This amounts to a replacement of $(\phi M)^{1/2}T$ of Eq. (11-45) by $\mu_w^{-1.1\Delta H_2/\Delta H_w}$.

For dilute *aqueous* solutions Eq. (11-48) reduces to

$$D_{12}^0 = 14.0 \times 10^{-5}\mu_w^{-1.1}V_1^{-0.6} \tag{11-49}$$

Othmer and Thakar report that this agrees with a large number of data on aqueous solutions with an average deviation of about 5 per cent. The agreement of Eq. (11-48) with data for other solvents is considerably poorer.

Sitaraman, Ibrahim, and Kuloor (105). Following the earlier development of limited correlations by Ibrahim and Kuloor, these writers develop a general empirical equation, which, unlike that of Wilke and Chang, is said to hold for the diffusion of water at low concentrations in organic solvents. This is

$$D_{12}^0 = 5.4 \times 10^{-8}(M_2^{1/2}\,\Delta H_{b_2}^{1/3}\,T/\mu_2 V_1^{0.5}\,\Delta H_{b_1}^{0.3})^{0.93} \quad (11\text{-}50)$$

where ΔH_{b_1} and ΔH_{b_2} are the latent heats of vaporization of the solute and solvent, respectively, in *calories per gram* at the normal boiling point, and the other symbols have the same meanings as above. Again, μ_2 is the viscosity of the solvent in *centipoises*. When compared with experimental

TABLE 11-5. VALUES OF K_1 FOR DIFFERENT SOLUTES*

Solute	Temperature, °C	$K_1 \times 10^3$
Acetic acid	15	2.312
Acetone	15	3.546
Allyl alcohol	15	2.328
Aniline	15	2.178
Benzaldehyde	15	2.364
Benzene	25	3.460
Bromobenzene	15	2.403
n-Butanol	15	2.049
Carbon tetrachloride	25	3.576
Chloral hydrate	15	2.033
Chlorobenzene	15	2.591
Chloroform	15	3.328
Ethanol	15	2.456
Ethyl bromide	15	4.025
Ethyl ether	15	3.833
Ethylene bromide	15	2.913
Formic acid	6	4.159
Furfural	15	2.178
Isoamyl alcohol	15	2.282
Methanol	15	2.861
Methyl iodide	7.5	3.912
Nitrobenzene	15	2.322
Phenol	5	1.889
Propanol	15	2.243
Propionic acid	15	3.008
Pyridine	20	2.723
Toluene	25	3.037
Water	25	2.591

* M. R. Kamal and L. N. Canjar, *Chem. Eng.*, Dec. 10, 1962, p. 159.

TABLE 11-6. VALUES OF K_2 FOR DIFFERENT SOLVENTS*

Solvent	Temperature, °C	$K_2 \times 10^3$
Benzene......................	15	5.925
	25	5.807
Carbon tetrachloride..........	25	4.239
Chlorobenzene................	25	5.676
Bromobenzene................	25	5.094
Toluene......................	25	6.109
Methanol.....................	15	6.745
Ethanol......................	25	3.831
Water........................	15	4.050
	25	4.151

* M. R. Kamal and L. N. Canjar, *Chem. Eng.*, Dec. 10, 1962, p. 159.

values of D_{12}^0 for some 76 systems at 7 to 25°C, the average error was found to be about ± 13 per cent.

Kamal and Canjar (63, 64). As noted in Sec. 11-8, these workers developed a correlation of D_{12} in liquids, using the statistical-mechanical theory of liquids. Their result can be condensed and written as

$$D_{12}^0 = K_1 K_2 \qquad (11\text{-}51)$$

where K_1 is a function of solute properties only and K_2 depends only on the solvent. Tables 11-5 and 11-6 list the values proposed by Kamal and Canjar for use in this way. Both K_1 and K_2 are complicated functions of temperature, and so it is difficult to use this method to predict D_{12} for temperatures other than those for which K_1 and K_2 are tabulated. Where both K_1 and K_2 are tabulated at the same temperature T_1, D_{12} at T_2 can be estimated by multiplying D_{12} at T_1 by $[T_2 \times (\mu_2 \text{ at } T_1)]/[T_1 \times (\mu_2 \text{ at } T_2)]$.

It may be noted that $D_{12}^0 \mu_2 / T$ is also represented as a product of two functions, one dependent only on the solute and the other dependent only on the solvent, by Eqs. (11-45), (11-48), and (11-49).

11-12 The Effect of Temperature on Diffusion in Liquids

Experimental values of D_{12}^0 in liquids are largely confined to the temperature range 15 to 25°C, and the temperature effects suggested by the several empirical equations discussed in the preceding section have never been adequately tested. Innes and Albright (60) show that the proportionality of D_{12}^0 to T/μ_2, as called for by Eqs. (11-39), (11-45), and (11-46), is only approximately correct.

In this connection the careful study of Longsworth (71) is of interest. Accurate measurements of D_{12}^0 in water for seven solutes covering a very wide range of molecular weights and the temperature range 1 to 37°C showed a uniform trend in D_{12}^0 with the size of the solute molecule. Longsworth reports the following activation energies in calories per gram mole at 19°C: urea, 4470; glycine, 4627; alanine, 4783; dextrose, 4959; cycloheptaamylose, 4931; bovine plasma albumin, 4969. The value for alanine corresponds to the T/μ_2 function.

11-13   Comparison of Experimental and Estimated Values of Diffusion Coefficients in Liquids

Aqueous Solutions.   Table 11-7 compares experimental and estimated values of D_{12}^0 for 40 representative systems, the estimations being made by the five procedures which have been described. The first three methods reduce to essentially the same equation, with water as solvent, and, as might be expected, give nearly the same results. Confirming the more extensive calculations of Wilke and Chang, Othmer and Thakar, and Sitaraman et al., the mean absolute error by these three methods is between 10 and 15 per cent. The method of Sitaraman et al. appears to be as reliable as the others but is more difficult to use because of the need for values of the latent heat of vaporization of the solute. The theory-based method of Kamal and Canjar needs further development.

There are remarkably few data on the variation of D_{12}^0 with temperature. The trend of D_{12}^0 with temperature shown by Table 11-7 for ethyl alcohol, i-butyl alcohol, and acetone suggests that the temperature function T/μ_2 may be too sharp and that the function used by Othmer and Thakar may be more reliable. As noted in Sec. 11-12, however, the temperature variation appears to depend on properties of the solute.

Nonaqueous Solvents.   Table 11-8 compares experimental values of diffusion coefficients at infinite dilution of the solute for more than 50 systems, with values calculated by four of the empirical estimation procedures. Both old and new data were selected from the literature, and a wide variety of systems are included. Unfortunately, the data are limited to a very narrow temperature range. The tabulation of errors shows that all four methods give poor results, the average absolute error ranging from 20 to 28 per cent, with quite large errors in many individual cases.

The several estimation errors need not be judged on the basis of Table 11-8 alone, since more thorough comparisons with experimental data have been made by the authors of the several correlations. Wilke and Chang (131) report the average deviation from their equation (11-45) to be 12 per cent for 123 different systems involving unassociated solvents ($\phi = 1$) and 6 per cent for over 100 observations of D_{12}^0 where the solvent was water, ethanol, or methanol. Sitaraman, Ibrahim, and Kuloor (105) found average absolute errors of 13 per cent for 120 systems (about one-

TABLE 11-7. DIFFUSION COEFFICIENTS IN AQUEOUS SOLUTIONS AT INFINITE DILUTION

Values are D_{12}°, cm^2/sec $\times 10^5$

	T, °C	D_{12}° (exp.)	Ref.	Wilke-Chang		Scheibel		Othmer-Thakar		Sitaraman, Ibrahim, and Kuloor		Kamal-Canjar	
				Calc.	% Error[a]	Calc.	% Error[a]	Calc.	% Error[a]	Calc.	% Error[a]	Calc.	% Error[a]
Helium	25	6.3	119										
Hydrogen	25	4.8	119	3.42	−29	3.19	−34	3.25	−32				
Oxygen	25	2.41	119	2.40	0	2.50	+4	2.29	−5				
Carbon dioxide	25	2.00	119	2.02	+1	2.03	+2	1.92	−4				
Ammonia	12	1.64	61	1.65	+1	1.73	+5	1.57	−4	1.69	+2		
Nitrous oxide	25	2.67	30	1.95	−27	1.93	−28	1.86	−30				
Chlorine	25	1.25*	66	1.64	+27	1.77	+42	1.56	+25	1.48	+18		
Propylene	25	1.44	119	1.36	−6	1.27	−12	1.29	−10	1.01	−30		
Benzene	25	1.09	92	1.08	−1	1.02	−6	1.03	−5	1.09	0	1.44	+32
Methyl alcohol	15	1.26	62	1.34	+6	1.32	+5	1.28	+2	1.20	−5	1.16	−8
Ethyl alcohol	10	0.84	62	0.74	−12	0.90	+7	0.90	+7	0.790	−6		
	15	1.00	61	1.10	+10	1.04	+4	1.05	+5	0.930	−7	0.99	−1
	25	1.24	46, 62	1.45	+17	1.38	+11	1.37	+11	1.21	−2		
n-Propyl alcohol	15	0.87	61, 62	0.88	+1	0.82	−6	0.83	−5	0.75	−14	0.91	+5
i-Propyl alcohol	15	0.87	62	0.88	+1	0.82	−6	0.83	−5	0.76	−13		
n-Butyl alcohol	15	0.77	61, 62	0.86	+12	0.80	+4	0.81	+5	0.78	+1	0.83	+8
i-Butyl alcohol	15	0.77	62	0.86	+12	0.80	+4	0.81	+5	0.80†	+4		
	20	0.792	39	0.99	+25	0.93	+17	0.94	+19	0.92†	+16		
	20	0.84	69	0.99	+18	0.93	+11	0.94	+12	0.92†	+10		
i-Amyl alcohol	15	0.69	61	0.70	+1	0.66	−4	0.66	−4	0.70†	+1	0.92	+33
Allyl alcohol	15	0.90	61	0.96	+7	0.89	−1	0.91	+1	0.82	−9	0.94	+4
Ethylene glycol	20	1.04	39	1.18	+13	1.11	+7	1.12	+7	0.92	−12		
1,2-Propylene glycol	20	0.88	39	1.00	+14	0.93	+6	0.94	+7	0.83†	−6		

Glycerol	15	0.72	61	0.82	+14	0.76	+6	0.78	+8	0.67†	-8		
	20	0.825	39	0.94	+14	0.88	+7	0.89	+8	0.76†	-8		
Mannitol	20	0.56	61	0.67	+20	0.64	+16	0.63	+12				
	20	0.673	71	0.75	+11	0.71	+5	0.72	+7				
Benzyl alcohol	20	0.82	39	0.81	-1	0.76	-7	0.77	-6	0.81	-1		
Acetic acid	20	1.19	69	1.20	+1	1.05	-12	1.14	-4	1.01	-15	1.08‡	+9
Oxalic acid	20	1.53	61	1.02	-33	0.96	-37	0.96	-37				
Tartaric acid	15	0.61	61	0.65	+7	0.60	-2	0.61	0				
Benzoic acid	25	1.21	21	1.05	-13	0.98	-19	0.99	-19				
Glycine	25	1.055	71	1.17	+11	1.10	+4	1.12	+6				
Ethyl acetate	20	1.00	69	0.89	-11	0.84	-16	0.84	-16	0.94	-6		
Acetone	15	1.22	62	0.96	-21	0.91	-25	0.91	-25	0.89	-27	1.43	+17
	20	1.16	69	1.11	-4	1.04	-10	1.05	+9	1.01	-13		
	25	1.28	8	1.27	-1	1.20	-6	1.21	-5	1.14	-11		
Furfural	20	1.04	69	0.91	-12	0.85	-18	0.86	-17	0.89	-14	1.01‡	-3
Acetamide	15	0.96	61	1.01	+5	0.93	-3	0.96	0				
Urea	20	1.20	61	1.24	+3	1.18	-2	1.17	-3				
	25	1.378	71	1.42	+3	1.36	-1	1.36	-1				
Urethane	15	0.80	61	0.81	+1	0.77	-4	0.77	-4				
Diethylamine	20	0.97	69	0.86	-11	0.81	-17	0.82	-15	0.89	-12		
Aniline	20	0.92	69	0.81	-12	0.75	-18	0.76	-17	0.79	-14		
Acetonitrile	15	1.26	61	1.13	-10	1.07	-15	1.07	-15	0.89	-29		
Pyridine	15	0.58	61	0.76	+31	0.71	+23	0.72	+24	0.78	+34	0.97‡	+68
Water	25	2.44	96	2.87	+16	3.16	+30	2.74	+12	1.43	-42	1.08	-56
Average absolute error		......	......	......	11	......	11	......	11	......	12	......	(20)

NOTE: Values of V_1 employed were estimated by the use of the LeBas additive volume increments (Table 3-4).

* The value of D_{12}° for chlorine is for an equilibrium mixture of hydrolyzed and unhydrolyzed chlorine.

† The latent heat of vaporization is estimated by Eq. (4-59), with critical properties estimated by the methods of Chap. 2 if not known.

‡ Small temperature adjustment made in proportion to T/μ_2.

^{a} % Error = [(calculated−experimental)/experimental] × 100.

TABLE 11-8. COMPARISON OF METHODS OF ESTIMATING DIFFUSION COEFFICIENTS IN LIQUIDS

Solute	Solvent	Temp., °C	$D_{12}^{\circ} \times 10^5$ (obs.)	Ref.	$D_{12}^{\circ} \times 10^5$ (calc.) Wilke-Chang	% Error[†]	$D_{12}^{\circ} \times 10^5$ (calc.) Othmer-Thakar	% Error[†]	$D_{12}^{\circ} \times 10^5$ (calc.) Sitaraman, Ibrahim, Kuloor	% Error[†]	$D_{12}^{\circ} \times 10^5$ (calc.) Scheibel	% Error[†]
Acetic acid	Acetone	25	3.31	20	4.41	+33	4.16	+26	3.49	+5	4.18	+26
Benzoic acid	Acetone	25	2.62	20	3.34	+27	3.16	+21	....	....	3.57	+36
Formic acid	Acetone	25	3.77	20	5.37	+42	5.09	+35	2.98	−21	4.66	+24
Water	Aniline	20	0.70	69	0.81	+16	0.53	−24	0.41	−41	0.44	−37
Acetic acid	Benzene	25	2.09	20	2.64	+26	1.95	−7	2.17	+4	2.33	+11
Benzoic acid	Benzene	25	1.38	20	2.00	+45	1.48	+7	....	....	1.99	+44
Bromobenzene	Benzene	7.5	1.45	110	1.22	−16	0.86	−41	1.34	−7	1.82	+25
Carbon tetra-chloride	Benzene	25	1.92	57	1.89	−2	1.39	−28	2.17	+13	1.93	+1
Carbon tetra-chloride	Benzene	20	1.76	15	1.73	−2	1.26	−28	1.89	+7	1.77	+1
Cinnamic acid	Benzene	25	1.12	20	1.47	+31	1.08	−4	....	....	1.68	+50
Ethylene chloride	Benzene	7.5	1.77	110	1.89	+7	1.33	−25	1.70	−4	2.32	+31
Ethanol	Benzene	15	2.25	62	2.32	+3	1.67	−26	1.56	−31	2.39	+6
Formic acid	Benzene	25	2.28	20	3.23	+38	2.37	+4	2.38	+4	2.61	+14
Methanol	Benzene	25	3.82	26	3.43	−10	2.53	−34	2.00	−48	2.99	−22
Methyl iodide	Benzene	7.5	2.06	110	1.93	−6	1.36	−34	2.11	+2	2.34	+13
Naphthalene	Benzene	7.5	1.19	110	1.10	−8	0.77	−35	....	....	1.71	+43
1,2,4-Trichloro-benzene	Benzene	7.5	1.34	110	1.11	−17	0.78	−32	1.28	−4	1.73	+29
Acetone	iso-Butanol	20	0.74	69	0.45	−39	0.36	−51	0.37	−50	0.31	−48
Acetone	Carbon tetrachloride	20	1.86	69	2.08	+12	1.07	−42	1.33	−28	1.25	−33

Solute	Solvent											
Benzene	Chlorobenzene	20	1.25	15	1.85	+48	1.12	−10	1.51	+21	1.40	+12
Acetone	Chloroform	15	2.36	62	2.97	+26	1.61	−32	2.15	− 9	1.25	−47
Benzene	Chloroform	15	2.51	62	2.52	0	1.37	−45	1.87	−26	1.86	−26
Ethanol	Chloroform	15	2.20	62	3.38	+53	1.84	−16	1.89	−14	2.18	− 1
Ethyl ether	Chloroform	15	2.07	62	2.36	+14	1.28	−38	2.51	+21	1.79	−13
Carbon tetrachloride	Cyclohexane	25	1.49	57	1.23	−17	1.03	−31	1.31	−12	1.12	−25
Allyl alcohol	Ethanol	20	0.98	61	1.13	+15	0.87	−11	0.82	−16	1.19	+21
iso-Amyl alcohol	Ethanol	20	0.81	61	0.82	+ 1	0.63	−22	0.77	− 5	0.85	+ 5
Azobenzene	Ethanol	20	0.74	113	0.61	−17	0.47	−35	...	...	0.62	−16
Bromoform	Ethanol	20	0.97	61	1.06	+ 9	0.92	− 5	1.34	+38	1.03	+ 6
Camphor	Ethanol	20	0.70	61	0.61	−13	0.47	−33	...	...	0.62	−11
Carbon dioxide	Ethanol	17	3.2	61	1.59	−50	1.23	−62	...	...	1.16	−64
Glycerol	Ethanol	20	0.51	61	0.96	+89	0.74	+45	0.73	+43	0.93	+82
Iodine	Ethanol	25	1.32	20	1.29	+ 2	1.11	−16	...	...	1.15	−13
Iodobenzene	Ethanol	20	1.00	61	0.81*	−19	0.62	−38	0.98	− 2	0.84	−16
Pyridine	Ethanol	20	1.10	61	0.90*	−18	0.69	−37	0.83	−25	0.89	−19
Urea	Ethanol	12	0.54	61	1.06*	+96	0.68	+26	...	...	0.91	+68
Water	Ethanol	25	1.132	46	2.87	+153	2.47	+118	1.33	+17	1.80	+59
Acetic acid	Ethyl acetate	20	2.18	69	3.64	+67	2.50	+15	2.88	+32	2.81	+29
Water	Ethylene glycol	20	0.18	39	0.17*	+ 6	0.111	−38	0.102	−43	0.091	−49
Water	Glycerol	20	0.0083	39	0.005*	...	0.0028	...	0.004	...	0.0023	
Carbon tetrachloride	n-Hexane	25	3.70	47	3.72	0	2.71	−27	3.17	−14	3.36	− 9
n-Hexane	n-Hexane	25	4.21	73	3.27	−22	2.39	−43	2.81	−33	3.13	−26
Toluene	n-Hexane	25	4.21	20	3.63	−14	2.65	−37	2.98	−29	3.32	−21
Mercury	Mercury	234.3	1.63	83								
Tin	Mercury	30	1.60	69								
Water	n-Propanol	15	0.87	62	1.26	+45	0.80	+ 8	0.91	− 4	0.74	−15
Water	1,2-Propylene glycol	20	0.075	39	0.088*	+17	0.052	−30	0.052	−30	0.043	−43

TABLE 11-8. COMPARISON OF METHODS OF ESTIMATING DIFFUSION COEFFICIENTS IN LIQUIDS (Continued)

Solute	Solvent	Temp., °C	$D_{12}^{\circ} \times 10^5$ (obs.)	Ref.	$D_{12}^{\circ} \times 10^5$ (calc.) Wilke-Chang	% Error†	$D_{12}^{\circ} \times 10^5$ (calc.) Othmer-Thakar	% Error†	$D_{12}^{\circ} \times 10^5$ (calc.) Sitara-man, Ibrahim, Kuloor	% Error†	$D_{12}^{\circ} \times 10^5$ (calc.) Scheibel	% Error†
Tin	Tin	485	5.9	77								
Acetic acid	Toluene	20	2.00	69	2.93	+46	1.96	−2	2.33	+16	2.20	+10
Acetic acid	Toluene	25	2.26	20	3.14	+39	2.20	−3	2.46	+9	2.36	+5
Acetone	Toluene	20	2.93	69	2.71	−7	1.80	−38	2.04	−30	2.10	−28
Benzoic acid	Toluene	20	1.74	69	2.22	+28	1.48	−15	.....	.....	1.88	+8
Benzoic acid	Toluene	25	1.49	20	2.38	+60	1.66	+11	.....	.....	2.02	+36
Chlorobenzene	Toluene	20	2.06	15	2.06	0	1.37	−33	1.87	−9	1.80	−13
Diethylamine	Toluene	20	2.36	69	2.10	−11	1.40	−41	1.79	−24	1.83	−22
Ethanol	Toluene	15	3.00	62	2.82	−6	1.94	−35	1.79	−40	2.42	−19
Formic acid	Toluene	25	2.65	20	3.83	+45	2.68	+1	2.70	+2	2.64	0
Average error						27		28		26		25

* The Wilke-Chang association parameter ϕ was assumed to be unity except for ethanol, i-butanol, ethylene glycol, propylene glycol, and glycerol; ϕ was taken as 1.5 for these solvents.

† % Error = [(calculated−experimental)/experimental] × 100.

fifth of which were aqueous) with Eq. (11-50). Othmer and Thakar (88) found average errors of about 20 per cent in testing their method with some 120 experimental values. The first edition of this book reported average errors of 10 to 16 per cent for 87 data points with methanol and benzene as solvents, the Wilke-Chang, Scheibel, and Othmer-Thakar methods being used. Table 11-8 does not show an evaluation of the Kamal-Canjar method, since too few values of K_1 and K_2 are furnished by Tables 11-5 and 11-6 to provide a valid test; the average deviation was about 20 per cent in the few cases tested.

The several published comparisons referred to tested much the same data. The principal value of Table 11-8, which includes many new data points, is to suggest that the errors to be expected may be somewhat larger than they were previously believed to be.

As noted above, none of the several estimation procedures is very good. The Othmer-Thakar method is the most difficult to use and is generally found to be somewhat less reliable than the others. The method of Sitaraman, Ibrahim, and Kuloor shows up best in Table 11-8 but is awkward to use and has been the least tested. The Wilke-Chang and Scheibel methods give quite similar results, the latter requiring slightly less calculation.

Recommendations: Diffusion Coefficients in Liquids. *Aqueous Solutions.* For the estimation of D_{12}^0 at infinite dilution of the solute in water, use the Othmer-Thakar equation (11-49). Errors averaging 12 to 14 per cent can be expected in the temperature range 10 to 30°C.

Nonaqueous Solvents. Use the Scheibel equations (11-46) and (11-47), which may be expected to predict values of D_{12}^0 with an average absolute error of less than 20 per cent. It should not be used outside the temperature range 10 to 30°C. Within these restrictions, the error will almost never be greater than ± 50 per cent. For *water* in organic solvents, D_{12}^0 may be estimated by calculating its value by the Wilke-Chang method and dividing the result by 2.3.

Mixtures. Equation (11-42) provides the best basis for the estimation of the effect of concentration in binary solutions. Values of D_{12}^0 and D_{21}^0 must be known or estimated. The activity term can often be obtained from vapor-liquid equilibrium data, through the relation

$$[\partial(\ln a_1)/\partial(\ln c_1)]_{T,P} \cong [d(\ln a_1)/d(\ln x_1)]_T (V/V_2)$$
$$= (x_1 V/V_2)[d(\ln p_1)/dx_1]_T \quad (11\text{-}52)$$

where V is the molal volume of the mixture, V_2 the molal volume of constituent 2, and p_1 the partial pressure of the first constituent at T and x_1 (see Example 11-4).

Example 11-3. Estimate the diffusion coefficient at 15°C for isoamyl alcohol at infinite dilution in water. The experimental value (61) is 0.69×10^{-5} cm²/sec.

Solution. By employing the LeBas increments listed in Table 3-4, the molecular volume V_1 for i-amyl alcohol is found to be 126 cm^3/g mole. The viscosity of water at 15°C is 1.145 centipoises, and $\mu_w{}^{1.1}$ is 1.161. Substitution in Eq. 11-49 gives $D_{12}^0 = 0.66 \times 10^{-5}$, which is 4 per cent less than the experimental value.

Example 11-4. Estimate the mutual-diffusion coefficients for the system ethanol-water over the complete range of compositions at 25°C.

Solution. Equation (11-42) will be employed, where $D_1^{\star}$ is the coefficient of diffusion of ethanol in water at essentially zero ethanol concentration (D_{12}^0) and $D_2^{\star}$ is the diffusion coefficient for water in pure ethanol (D_{21}^0).

Use the Othmer-Thakar correlation to obtain $D_1^{\star}$ (ethanol in water),

$$D_1^{\star} = 14.0 \times 10^{-5} \times (0.895)^{-1.1}(59.2)^{-0.6} = 1.37 \times 10^{-5} \ \text{cm}^2/\text{sec}$$

The value of $D_2^{\star}$ (water at infinite dilution in ethanol) cannot be estimated with confidence. Based on Olander's result, an approximate value may be obtained by using the Wilke-Chang correlation and dividing the result by 2.3. Thus, with $M_2 = 46$, $\phi = 1.5$, $\mu_2 = 1.10$ centipoises (ethanol at 25°C), and V_1(water) = 18.9,

$$D_2^{\star} = [7.4 \times 10^{-8}(1.5 \times 46)^{\frac{1}{2}} \times 298]/[1.10(18.9)^{0.6} \times 2.3] = 1.24 \times 10^{-5} \ \text{cm}^2/\text{sec}$$

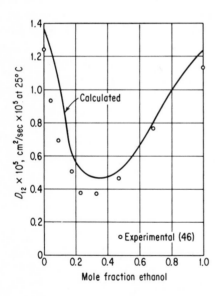

FIG. 11-10. Variation of D_{12} with composition for ethanol-water at 25°C.

Guggenheim (45) tabulates values of $x_1[d(\ln p_1)/dx_1] = [d(\ln a_1)/d(\ln x_1)]$ for ethanol in water at 25°C. At x_1 = mole fraction ethanol = 0.2, the value is 0.41. At this composition, with Eq. (11-42),

$$D_{12} = (1.24 \times 0.2 + 1.37 \times 0.8) \times 0.41 \times 10^{-5} = 0.55 \times 10^{-5} \ \text{cm}^2/\text{sec}$$

The experimental value (46) at this composition is 0.43×10^{-5} cm^2/sec. Figure 11-10 shows D_{12} as a function of x_1 calculated in this way. The agreement is better than can generally be expected for nonideal solutions.

11-14 Diffusion in Multicomponent Liquid Systems

Diffusion in liquid mixtures has been studied very little, though data on a few ternary systems have been published.

Holmes, Olander, and Wilke (55) studied the diffusion of toluene at low concentration in binary mixtures of n-hexane–n-tetradecane, n-hexane–cyclohexane, and cyclohexane–n-decane. The ratio $D\mu/T$ was found to be approximately linear in the binary solvent composition when expressed as mole fraction. The results fell some 20 per cent higher than calculated by Eq. (11-45), M_2 being taken to be the mole fraction–average molecular weight of the binary solvent. The ratio $D\mu/T$ increased approximately as the square root of the mean molecular weight of the solvent, as called for by Eq. (11-45).

In another recent study, Burchard and Toor (14) studied diffusion in the ternary toluene, chlorobenzene, bromobenzene over a wide range of compositions. In the three nearly ideal binaries D_{12} was linear in mole fraction. It was found that the theoretical equations for multicomponent diffusion in gas systems could be employed if the binary coefficients (independent of concentration in gases) were taken to be the mole-fraction average of D_{12}^0 and D_{21}^0 for each binary. Thus the diffusion in the ternary system could be represented by a single coefficient for use in Eq. (11-1), this value being simply the molal average value of the three binary diffusion coefficients at infinite dilution. This is based on the fact that in this system $D_{13}^0 = D_{23}^0$, $D_{12}^0 = D_{32}^0$, and $D_{21}^0 = D_{31}^0$, whence the required single diffusion coefficient is $x_1 D_{21}^0 + x_2 D_{12}^0 + x_3 D_{13}^0$. This rule is supported by the data of Holmes, Olander, and Wilke, who found the toluene diffusion coefficient at low concentrations in a binary to be essentially linear in the molal concentration of the binary.

11-15 Diffusion in Electrolytic Solutions

The properties of electrically conducting solutions have been studied intensively for more than 75 years so that today both theory and data are more complete than in most areas of science. Even so, the relations among electrical conduction, freezing-point depression, vapor pressure, osmotic pressure, viscosity, and diffusion are generally valid only for dilute solutions of salts in water. Concentrations encountered in industrial practice are frequently greater than the dilute range in which the theories apply, making it necessary to resort to empirical correlations. The general approach is to apply empirical corrections to the theoretical values for dilute solutions.

The diffusion coefficient D_{12}^0 in very dilute solutions of completely ionized simple univalent electrolytes is given by the Nernst equation

$$D_{12}^0 = 2RT/[(1/\lambda_+{}^0 + 1/\lambda_-{}^0)F_a{}^2] \qquad (11\text{-}53)$$

where D_{12}^0 = diffusion coefficient at infinite dilution, based on molecular concentration, cm^2/sec

T = temperature, $°K$

λ_+^0, λ_-^0 = limiting (zero concentration) ionic conductances, $amp/(cm^2)$ $(volt/cm)(g\ equivalent/cm^3)$

F_a = Faraday = 96,500 coulombs/g equivalent

R = gas constant, joules/(°K)(g mole) = 8.316

This equation has been extended to polyvalent ions by replacing 2 on the right-hand side by $1/n_+ + 1/n_-$, where n_+ and n_- are the valences of cation and anion, respectively. Table 11-9, taken from Harned and Owen (49), lists values of λ^0 at 25°C, from which D_{12}^0 at this temperature may be calculated; Robinson and Stokes (96) provide a similar table.

As the salt concentration becomes finite and increases, the diffusion coefficient decreases rapidly and then usually rises, often becoming greater than D_{12}^0 at high normalities. Figure 11-11 illustrates the typical trend for three simple salts. The initial decrease at low concentrations is proportional to the square root of the concentration, but deviations from this trend are usually significant above 0.1 N.

The modern theory of diffusion in electrolytic solution is described by

TABLE 11-9. LIMITING IONIC CONDUCTANCES IN WATER AT 25°C*
Amp/(cm^2)(volt/cm)(g equivalent/cm^3)

Cation	λ_+^0	Anion	λ_-^0
H^+	349.8	OH^-	197.6
Li^+	38.7	Cl^-	76.3
Na^+	50.1	Br^-	78.3
K^+	73.5	I^-	76.8
NH_4^+	73.4	NO_3^-	71.4
Ag^+	61.9	ClO_4^-	68.0
Tl^+	74.7	HCO_3^-	44.5
$\frac{1}{2}Mg^{++}$	53.1	HCO_2^-	54.6
$\frac{1}{2}Ca^{++}$	59.5	$CH_3CO_2^-$	40.9
$\frac{1}{2}Sr^{++}$	50.5	$ClCH_2CO_2^-$	39.8
$\frac{1}{2}Ba^{++}$	63.6	$CNCH_2CO_2^-$	41.8
$\frac{1}{2}Cu^{++}$	54	$CH_3CH_2CO_2^-$	35.8
$\frac{1}{2}Zn^{++}$	53	$CH_3(CH_2)_2CO_2^-$	32.6
$\frac{1}{3}La^{3+}$	69.5	$C_6H_5CO_2^-$	32.3
$\frac{1}{3}Co(NH_3)_6^{3+}$	102	$HC_2O_4^-$	40.2
		$\frac{1}{2}C_2O_4^-$	74.2
		$\frac{1}{2}SO_4^-$	80
		$\frac{1}{3}Fe(CN)_6^{3-}$	101
		$\frac{1}{4}Fe(CN)_6^{4-}$	111

* From H. S. Harned and B. B. Owen, The Physical Chemistry of Electrolytic Solutions, *ACS Monograph* 95, Reinhold Publishing Corporation, New York, 1950.

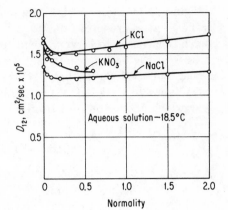

FIG. 11-11. Effect of concentration on diffusivity. [*After A. R. Gordon, J. Chem. Phys.*, **5**:522 (1937).]

Harned (48) and by Harned and Owen (49). This leads to an equation for D_{12} in the form

$$D_{12} = 16.632 \times 10^{10} T\psi\{1 + c[\partial(\ln \gamma_{\pm})/\partial(\ln c)]\} \qquad (11\text{-}54)$$

where c = molal concentration, moles/1,000 cm^3 solution

$\gamma_{\pm}$ = mean molal activity coefficient

ψ = complicated function of limiting ionic conductances and other properties of the solution

At infinite dilution, ψ is $1/F_a{}^2$, and since $2R = 16.632$, this then reduces to Eq. (11-53). Equation (11-54) provides an adequate prediction of the variation of D_{12} with concentrations up to about 0.1 to 0.2 N; for the evaluation of ψ for this purpose the reader is referred to Harned and Owen (49). In most cases the minimum value of D_{12} occurs at 0.2 to 0.5 N and is seldom less than 70 per cent of D_{12}^0.

The theory breaks down at the high concentrations encountered in many practical applications, since poorly understood ion-solvent interactions become of major importance. Gordon (44) has proposed the following semiempirical equation, which has been shown to apply to some systems at concentrations up to 2 N, or even higher,

$$D_{12} = D_{12}^0 (V/n_1 \bar{V}_1)(\mu_s/\mu)\{1 + m[\partial(\ln \gamma_{\pm})/\partial m]\} \qquad (11\text{-}55)$$

where D_{12}^0 = diffusion coefficient at infinite dilution [Eq. (11-53)], cm^2/sec

n_1 = moles solvent in V cm^3 solution

$\bar{V}_1$ = partial molal volume of solvent, cm^3/g mole

μ_s = viscosity of solvent, poises

μ = viscosity of solution, poises

m = molality, g moles/1,000 g solvent

Values of $\gamma_{\pm}$ as a function of m are tabulated by Harned and Owen (49) for a number of aqueous solutions.

Figure 11-11, after Gordon, compares the data of Clack (25), as shown by the points representing data to 2 N, with Eq. (11-55) (solid lines). The correlation is seen to be very good, though the equation is difficult to use because of the need for data on viscosities, activity coefficients, and the partial molal volume of the solvent.

Wishaw and Stokes (133) have described an equation attributed to Agar which allows for ion hydration,

$$D = D_{12}^{01}\{(\mu_s/\mu)[1 + m[\partial(\ln \gamma_\pm)/\partial m]\}$$
$$(1 + 0.018n'm)[1 + 0.018m(\nu D_{H_2O}^*/D^0 - n')] \quad (11\text{-}56)$$

where $D_{12}^{01} = D_{12}^0$, with a small correction (49) for electrophoretic effect

$\quad n' =$ "hydration number"

$\quad \nu =$ number of ions formed from one molecule of solute

$\quad D_{H_2O}^* =$ self-diffusion coefficient of water, taken as 2.43×10^{-5} cm^2/sec at 25°C

Equation (11-56) is shown to represent the data very well for three salts at concentrations of 0 to 4 N, employing the following values of n': ammonium chloride, 0.6; lithium chloride, 2.8; lithium nitrate, 2.5. An additional correction for ion-pair formation was found necessary in fitting the data for strong solutions of ammonium nitrate. The two terms involving n' are evidently but weak functions of n'; their omission affects the calculation of D for NaCl by less than 2 per cent up to 4 m.

Values of the limiting ionic conductances, as given in Table 11-9, are not readily available for temperatures other than 25°C. It is suggested that values of either D_{12} or D_{12}^0 for other temperatures be obtained by assuming them to be proportional to T/μ_2, as called for by Eq. (11-39).

Recommendations. For very dilute solutions of electrolytes, employ Eq. (11-53) with the suggested modification for polyvalent ions. Where values of the limiting ionic conductances in water are not available at the desired temperature, use those given in Table 11-9 for 25°C, and multiply D_{12}^0 at 25°C by $T/334\mu_w$, where μ_w is the viscosity of water at T, in centipoises.

For concentrated solutions, use Eq. (11-55). If values of $\gamma_\pm$ and λ^0 are not available at T, calculate D_{12} at 25°C, and multiply this by $(T/298) \times (\mu$ at 25°/μ at $T)$. If necessary, the ratio of the solution viscosity at 25° to that at T may be assumed to be the same as the corresponding ratio for water.

It is worth noting that Robinson and Stokes (96) give quite complete tables of the properties of electrolytes, including a tabulation of D_{12} at 25°C as a function of concentration for 17 salts.

Example 11-5. Estimate the diffusion coefficient of NaOH in a 2 N aqueous solution at 15°C.

Solution. From the data on densities of aqueous solutions of NaOH given in Perry (90), it is evident that, up to 12 wt % NaOH (about 3 N), the density increases almost exactly in inverse proportion to the weight fraction of water; i.e., the ratio of moles of water per 1,000 cm^3 is essentially constant at 55.5. Thus both V/n_1 and $\bar{V}_1$ are very nearly 55.5 and cancel in Eq. (11-55). In this case the molality m is essentially identical with the normality.

In plotting the values of $\gamma_{\pm}$ for NaOH at 25°C (49) vs. the molality m, the slope at 2 m is approximately 0.047. Hence

$$m[d(\ln \gamma_{\pm})/dm] = (m/\gamma_{\pm})(d\gamma_{\pm}/dm) = (2/0.698) \times 0.047 = 0.135$$

The value 0.698 is the mean activity coefficient at $m = 2$.

The viscosities of water and 2 N NaOH solution at 25°C are 0.894 and 1.42 centipoises, respectively. Substituting in Eqs. (11-53) and (11-55),

$$D_{12}^0 = (2 \times 8.316 \times 298)/[(\tfrac{1}{50} + \tfrac{1}{198})(96,500)^2] = 2.14 \times 10^{-5} \text{ cm}^2/\text{sec}$$
$$D_{12} = 2.14 \times 10^{-5} \times (55.5/55.5) \times (0.894/1.42)(1 + 2 \times 0.135)$$
$$= 1.71 \times 10^{-5} \text{ cm}^2/\text{sec at } 25°C$$

At 15°C the viscosity of water is 1.144 centipoises, and so the estimated value of D at 15°C is

$$1.71 \times 10^{-5} + [288/(334 \times 1.144)] = 1.29 \times 10^{-5} \text{ cm}^2/\text{sec}$$

which may be compared with the ICT (61) value of 1.36×10^{-5} cm^2/sec.

Diffusion of Gases in Electrolyte Solutions.

Data on the diffusion of CO_2 in aqueous solutions of NaCl, NaNO$_3$, Na$_2$SO$_4$, MgCl$_2$, Mg(NO$_3$)$_2$, and MgSO$_4$ are reported by Ratcliff and Holdcroft (93). The diffusion coefficient is found to decrease linearly with increase in salt concentration.

Diffusion in Mixed Electrolytes.

The diffusion of a single salt, even though highly dissociated by ionization, is treated as molecular diffusion since the requirement of electrical neutrality causes anions and cations to move at the same rate, where flux is expressed as chemical equivalents per unit time. In a system of mixed ions, as in the simultaneous diffusion of hydrogen chloride and sodium chloride in water, the faster-moving H$^+$ may move ahead of its Cl$^-$ partner, the required electrical neutrality being maintained by the fact that the slower-moving Na$^+$ ions lag behind the Cl$^-$ ions.

The theory of diffusion in solutions of mixed ions is outlined by Vinograd and McBain (118) as an extension of the Nernst theory, with the simplifying assumptions that activity coefficients, collision effects, ion complexes, and ion pairs may be ignored. This development leads to two equations, the first for cations and the second for anions,

$$n_+J_+ = -(RT/F_a{}^2)(\lambda_+/n_+)\{G_+$$
$$- n_+c_+[(\Sigma\lambda_+G_+/n_+ - \Sigma\lambda_-G_-/n_-)/(\Sigma\lambda_+c_+ + \Sigma\lambda_-c_-)]\} \quad (11\text{-}57)$$
$$n_-J_- = -(RT/F_a{}^2)(\lambda_-/n_-)\{G_-$$
$$+ n_-c_-[(\Sigma\lambda_+G_+/n_+ - \Sigma\lambda_-G_-/n_-)/(\Sigma\lambda_+c_+ + \Sigma\lambda_-c_-)]\} \quad (11\text{-}58)$$

where n_+, n_- = valences of cation, anion

c_+, c_- = concentrations, g equivalents/cm^3

F_a = Faraday = 96,500 coulombs/g equivalent

R = gas constant, joules/($°$K)(g mole) = 8.316

λ_+, λ_- = ion conductances, amp/(cm^2)(volt/cm)(g equivalent/cm^3)

N_+, N_- = diffusion flux of cation, anion, g equivalents/(sec)(cm^2)

G_+, G_- = concentration gradients, dc/dz, in direction of diffusion

These relations were shown by Vinograd and McBain to describe their experimental data on diffusion in several systems of mixed salts. When a mixture of barium chloride and hydrogen chloride was used, D_{12} for the hydrogen ion was found to decrease from 12.2 to 4.9 $\times$ 10^{-5} cm^2/sec as the ratio of H$^+$ to Ba^{++} was increased from zero to 1.3. These values may be compared with 9.03 $\times$ 10^{-5} for the free H$^+$ ion and 3.3 $\times$ 10^{-5} for dilute HCl alone in water, at the same temperature.

It is evident that the effect of the presence of other ions on the diffusion of one particular ion is far from trivial. The magnitude of the effect is given by Eqs. (11-57) and (11-58); for an example of the use of these equations, see Sherwood and Wei (104).

NOMENCLATURE FOR CHAPTER 11

a = activity

b_0 = $\frac{2}{3}\pi N_0\sigma^3$

c = concentration, g moles/cm^3

D = diffusion coefficient, cm^2/sec

D^0 = diffusion coefficient at infinite dilution in liquids, or in gases at low pressure, cm^2/sec

$D^\star$ = tracer diffusion coefficient, tracer in a mixture, cm^2/sec

D^* = dimensionless diffusion coefficient, defined by Eq. (11-30)

D_r = reduced diffusion coefficient, defined by Eq. (11-32)

f_c = defined by Eq. (11-22)

f_D = second-order correction [Eq. (11-10)]

F_a = Faraday, 96,500 coulombs/g equivalent

G = concentration gradient, g equivalents/(cm^3)(cm)

ΔH_w = latent heat of vaporization of water at T, cal/g mole

ΔH_2 = latent heat of vaporization of solvent at T, cal/g mole

J = diffusion flux density, g moles (or g equivalents)/(sec)(cm^2)

k = Boltzmann's constant

K_1, K_2 = functions of solute and solvent, respectively, in Eq. (11-51)

m = molality

M = molecular weight

n = molecular number density, molecules/cm^3

n_+, n_- = valence of cation, anion, respectively

n' = hydration number

N_0 = Avogadro's number

p = partial pressure, atm

P = pressure, atm

P^* = $P\sigma_{12}^3/\epsilon_{0_{12}}$

P_c = critical pressure, atm
P_r = reduced pressure, = P/P_c
r = distance between molecular centers, A; radius, cm
R = gas constant, $(cm^3)(atm)/(g\,mole)(°K)$, or joules/$(°K)(g\,mole)$ where so noted
t_p^* = defined by Eq. (11-23)
T = temperature, °K
T_b = normal boiling temperature, °K
T_c = critical temperature, °K
u = diffusion velocity, cm/sec
u_0 = velocity of plane of no net volume transport, cm/sec
V = volume, cm^3/g mole
$\bar{V}$ = partial molal volume, cm^3/g mole
x = mole fraction in liquid
y = mole fraction in gas
z = distance in direction of diffusion, cm
Z = compressibility coefficient
Z_c = compressibility coefficient at the critical point

Greek

α_n = polarizability
γ = activity coefficient
$(\delta)_{max}$ = defined by Eq. (11-24)
ϵ_0 = Lennard-Jones force constant
λ_0 = limiting (zero concentration) ionic conductance, amp/$(cm^2)(volt/cm)$ (g equivalent/cm^3)
$\mathbf{y}$ = chemical potential
μ = viscosity, poises (or centipoises where so specified); dipole moment
μ^0 = viscosity at low pressure
μ_{AIR} = viscosity of air at T, centipoises
μ_w = viscosity of water at T, centipoises
ξ = coefficient of friction between diffusing molecules
ρ = density, g/cm^3
σ = Lennard-Jones force constant
Ω_D = collision integral for diffusion
Ω_v = collision integral for viscosity
ϕ = association parameter
$\varphi(r)$ = potential energy of molecular interaction
χ = $D_{12}\rho/(D_{12}\rho)^0$, ratio of $D_{12}\rho$ at P, T, to $D_{12}\rho$ at T at low pressure
ψ = function of properties of electrolytic solution, appearing in Eq. (11-54)

REFERENCES FOR CHAPTER 11

1. Amdur, I.: "Conference on Physical Chemistry in Aerodynamics and Space Flight," p. 228, Pergamon Press, New York, 1961.
2. Amdur, I.: *AIChE J.*, **8**:521 (1962).
3. Amdur, I., and E. A. Mason: *Phys. Fluids*, **1**:370 (1958).
4. Amdur, I., and J. Ross: *Combustion and Flame*, **2**:412 (1958).
5. Amdur, I., J. Ross, and E. A. Mason: *J. Chem. Phys.*, **20**:1620 (1952).
6. Amdur, I., and T. F. Schatzki: *J. Chem. Phys.*, **27**:1049 (1957).
7. Amdur, I., and L. M. Shuler: *J. Chem. Phys.*, **38**:188 (1963).
8. Anderson, D. K., J. R. Hall, and A. L. Babb: *J. Phys. Chem.*, **62**:404 (1958).
9. Bearman, R. J.: *J. Chem. Phys.*, **32**:1308 (1960).
10. Bearman, R. J.: *J. Phys. Chem.*, **65**:1961 (1961).

11. Berry, V. J., Jr., and R. C. Koeller: *AIChE J.*, **6**:274 (1960).
12. Bird, R. B.: In T. B. Drew and J. W. Hoopes (eds.), "Advances in Chemical Engineering," vol. 1, p. 156, Academic Press Inc., New York, 1956.
13. Bird, R. B., W. E. Stewart, and E. N. Lightfoot: "Transport Phenomena," John Wiley & Sons, Inc., New York, 1960.
14. Burchard, J. K., and H. L. Toor: *J. Phys. Chem.*, **66**:2015 (1962).
15. Caldwell, C. S., and A. L. Babb: *J. Phys. Chem.*, **60**:14, 56 (1956).
16. Carman, P. C., and L. Miller: *Trans. Faraday Soc.*, **55**:1838 (1959).
17. Carman, P. C., and L. H. Stein: *Trans. Faraday Soc.*, **52**:619 (1956).
18. Carmichael, L. T., B. H. Sage, and W. N. Lacey: *AIChE J.*, **1**:385 (1955).
19. Carswell, A. J., and J. C. Stryland: *Can. J. Phys.*, **41**:708 (1963).
20. Chang, Pin, and C. R. Wilke: *J. Phys. Chem.*, **59**:592 (1955).
21. Chang, S. Y.: S. M. thesis in chemical engineering, Massachusetts Institute of Technology, 1959.
22. Chapman, S. and T. G. Cowling: "Mathematical Theory of Non-uniform Gases," Cambridge University Press, New York, 1951.
23. Chen, N. H.: *Ind. Eng. Chem.*, **51**:1494 (1959).
24. Chen, N. H., and D. F. Othmer: *J. Chem. Eng. Data*, **7**:37 (1962).
25. Clack, B. W.: *Proc. Phys. Soc. (London)*, **36**:313 (1924).
26. Cram, R. R., and A. W. Adamson: *J. Phys. Chem.*, **64**:199 (1960).
27. Crider, W. L.: *J. Am. Chem. Soc.*, **78**:924 (1956).
28. Curtiss, C. F., and J. O. Hirschfelder: *J. Chem. Phys.*, **17**:550 (1949).
29. Darken, L. S.: *Trans. AIMME* **175**:184 (1948).
30. Davidson, J. F., and E. J. Cullen: *Trans. Inst. Chem. Eng. (London)*, **35**:51 (1957).
31. Denbigh, K. G.: *Trans. Faraday Soc.*, **36**:936 (1940).
32. Dole, M.: *J. Chem. Phys.*, **25**:1082 (1956).
33. Duncan, J. B., and H. L. Toor: *AIChE J.*, **8**:38 (1962).
34. Durbin, S., and R. Kobayashi: *J. Chem. Phys.*, **37**:1643 (1962).
35. Ember, G., J. R. Ferron, and K. Wohl: *J. Chem. Phys.*, **37**:891 (1962).
36. Eyring, H., and T. Ree: *Proc. Natl. Acad. Sci.*, **47**:526 (1961).
37. Fair, J. R., and B. J. Lerner: *AIChE J.*, **2**:13 (1956).
38. Fairbanks, D. F., and C. R. Wilke: *Ind. Eng. Chem.*, **42**:471 (1950).
38a. Fuller, E. N., P. D. Schettler, and J. C. Giddings: Paper submitted for publication in *Ind. Eng. Chem. Fundamentals*, November, 1965.
39. Garner, F. H., and P. J. M. Marchant: *Trans. Inst. Chem. Eng. (London)*, **39**:397 (1961).
40. Geddes, A. L.: In A. Weissberger (ed.), "Techniques of Organic Chemistry," 2d ed., vol. I, pt. 1, p. 551; Interscience Publishers, Inc., New York, 1949.
41. Glasstone, S., K. J. Laidler, and H. Eyring: "The Theory of Rate Processes," McGraw-Hill Book Company, New York, 1941.
42. Gilliland, E. R.: In T. K. Sherwood, "Absorption and Extraction," 1st ed., p. 11, McGraw-Hill Book Company, New York, 1937.
43. Goddard, R. R., G. H. F. Gardner, and M. R. J. Wyllie: *Proc. Symposium on the Interaction between Fluids and Particles,* London, June 20–22, 1962, p. 326, Institute of Chemical Engineers.
44. Gordon, A. R.: *J. Chem. Phys.*, **5**:522 (1937).
45. Guggenheim, E. A.: "Thermodynamics," 3d ed., p. 229, North Holland Publishing Company, Amsterdam, 1957.
46. Hammond, B. R., and R. H. Stokes: *Trans. Faraday Soc.*, **49**:890 (1953).
47. Hammond, B. R., and R. H. Stokes: *Trans. Faraday Soc.*, **51**:1641 (1955).
48. Harned, H. S.: *Chem. Revs.*, **40**:461 (1947).
49. Harned, H. S., and B. B. Owen: The Physical Chemistry of Electrolytic Solutions, *ACS Monograph* 95, 1950.

50. Hartley, G. S., and J. Crank: *Trans. Faraday Soc.*, **45**:801 (1949).
51. Henderson, D.: *Ann. Rev. Phys. Chem.*, **15**:31 (1964).
52. Hill, N.: *Proc. Phys. Soc. (London)*, **67B**:149 (1954); *ibid.*, **68B**:209 (1955).
53. Hilsenrath, J., et al.: *U.S. Natl. Bur. Standards Circ.* 564, 1955.
54. Hirschfelder, J. O., C. F. Curtiss, and R. B. Bird: "Molecular Theory of Gases and Liquids," John Wiley & Sons, Inc., New York, 1954.
55. Holmes, J. T., D. R. Olander, and C. R. Wilke: *AIChE J.*, **8**:646 (1962).
56. Holsen, J. N., and M. R. Strunk: *Ind. Eng. Chem. Fundamentals* **3**:163 (1964).
57. Horrocks, J. K., and E. McLaughlin: *Trans. Faraday Soc.*, **58**:1357 (1962).
58. Hsu, H-W, and R. B. Bird: *AIChE J.*, **6**:516 (1960).
59. Hudson, G. H., J. C. McCoubrey, and A. R. Ubbelohde: *Trans. Faraday Soc.*, **56**:1144 (1960).
60. Innes, K. K., and L. F. Albright: *Ind. Eng. Chem.*, **49**:1793 (1957).
61. "International Critical Tables," McGraw-Hill Book Company, New York, 1926–1930.
62. Johnson, P. A., and A. L. Babb: *Chem. Revs.*, **56**:387 (1956).
63. Kamal, M. R., and L. N. Canjar: *Chem. Eng.*, Dec. 10, 1962, p. 159.
64. Kamal, M. R., and L. N. Canjar: *AIChE J.*, **8**:329 (1962).
65. Knuth, E. L.: *Phys. Fluids*, **2**:340 (1959).
66. Kramers, H., R. A. Douglas, and R. M. Ulmann: *Chem. Eng. Sci.*, **10**:190 (1959).
67. Landolt-Börnstein Tables: "Zahlenwerte und Funktionen," vol. 1, pt. 3, p. 510, Springer Verlag, OHG Berlin, 1952.
68. Lennert, D. A., and G. Thodos: *Ind. Eng. Chem. Fundamentals*, **4**:139 (1965).
69. Lewis, J. B.: *J. Appl. Chem.*, **5**:228 (1955).
70. Li, J. C. M., and P. Chang: *J. Chem. Phys.*, **23**:518 (1955).
71. Longsworth, L. G.: *J. Phys. Chem.*, **58**:770 (1954).
72. Longuet-Higgins, H. C., and J. A. Pople: *J. Chem. Phys.*, **25**:884 (1956).
73. McCall, D. W., and D. C. Douglas: *Phys. Fluids*, **2**:87 (1959).
74. McCall, D. W., D. C. Douglas, and E. W. Anderson: *J. Chem. Phys.*, **31**:1555 (1959).
75. McCarty, K. P., and E. A. Mason: *Phys. Fluids*, **3**:908 (1960).
76. McLaughlin, E.: *Trans. Faraday Soc.*, **55**:28 (1959).
77. Ma, C. A., and R. A. Swalin: *J. Chem. Phys.*, **36**:3014 (1962).
78. Mason, E. A.: *Phys. Fluids*, **4**:1504 (1961).
79. Mason, E. A., and L. Monchick: *J. Chem. Phys.*, **36**:2746 (1962).
80. Mickley, H. S., R. C. Ross, A. L. Squyers, and W. E. Stewart: *NACA Tech. Note*, 3208, 1954.
81. Miller, L., and P. C. Carman: *Trans. Faraday Soc.*, **57**:2143 (1961).
82. Monchick, L., and E. A. Mason: *J. Chem. Phys.*, **35**:1676 (1961).
83. Nachtrieb, N. H., and J. Petit: *J. Chem. Phys.*, **24**:746 (1956).
84. Nagarajan, R., E. J. Ryan, and L. W. Shemilt: Paper presented at the Thirteenth Chemical Engineers Conference, Montreal, Oct. 19–23, 1963, Chemical Institute of Canada.
85. Olander, D. R.: *AIChE J.*, **7**:175 (1961).
86. Olander, D. R.: *AIChE J.*, **9**:207 (1963).
87. Othmer, D. F., and H. T. Chen: *Ind. Eng. Chem. Proc. Design and Develop.*, **1**:249 (1962).
88. Othmer, D. F., and M. S. Thakar: *Ind. Eng. Chem.*, **45**:589 (1953).
89. Paul, R., and I. B. Srivastava: *J. Chem. Phys.*, **35**:1621 (1961).
90. Perry, J. H.: "Chemical Engineers' Handbook," 3d ed., McGraw-Hill Book Company, New York, 1950.
91. Polson, A.: *J. Phys. Colloid Chem.*, **54**:649 (1950).
92. Ratcliff, G. A., and N. J. Reid: *Trans. Inst. Chem. Eng. (London)*, **39**:423 (1961).

93. Ratcliff, G. A., and J. G. Holdcroft: *Trans. Inst. Chem. Eng. (London)*, **41**:315 (1963).
94. Reamer, H. H., and B. H. Sage: *J. Chem. Eng. Data*, **8**:34 (1963).
95. Ree, F. H., T. Ree, and H. Eyring: *Ind. Eng. Chem.*, **50**:1036 (1958).
96. Robinson, R. A., and R. H. Stokes: "Electrolyte Solutions," 2d ed., Academic Press Inc., New York, 1959.
97. Rowlinson, J. S., and J. R. Townley: *Trans. Faraday Soc.*, **49**:20 (1953).
98. Scheibel, E. G.: *Ind. Eng. Chem.*, **46**:2007 (1954).
99. Schwertz, F. A., and J. E. Brow: *J. Chem. Phys.*, **19**:640 (1951).
100. Scott, D. S., and K. E. Cox: *Can. J. Chem. Eng.*, **38**:201 (1960).
101. Scott, D. S.: *Ind. Eng. Chem. Fundamentals*, **3**:278 (1964).
102. Seager, S. L., L. R. Geertson, and J. C. Giddings: *J. Chem. Eng. Data*, **8**:168 (1963).
103. Shain, S. A.: *AIChE J.*, **7**:17 (1961).
104. Sherwood, T. K., and J. C. Wei: *AIChE J.*, **1**:522 (1955).
105. Sitaraman, R., S. H. Ibrahim, and N. R. Kuloor: *J. Chem. Eng. Data*, **8**:198 (1963).
106. Slattery, J. C., and R. B. Bird: *AIChE J.*, **4**:137 (1958).
107. Srivastava, B. N., and K. P. Srivastava: *J. Chem. Phys.*, **30**:984 (1959).
108. Srivastava, B. N., and I. B. Srivastava: *J. Chem. Phys.*, **36**:2616 (1962).
109. Srivastava, B. N., and I. B. Srivastava: *J. Chem. Phys.*, **38**:1183 (1963).
110. Stearn, A. E., E. M. Irish, and H. Eyring: *J. Phys. Chem.*, **44**:981 (1940).
111. Stokes, R. N., P. J. Dunlop, and J. R. Hall: *Trans. Faraday Soc.*, **49**:886 (1953).
112. Sundelöf, L-O, and I. Södervi: *Arkiv Kemi*, **21**:143 (1963).
113. Taylor, H. S.: *J. Chem. Phys.*, **6**:331 (1938).
114. Timmerhaus, K. D., and H. G. Drickamer: *J. Chem. Phys.*, **20**:981 (1952).
115. Toor, H. L.: *AIChE J.*, **3**:198 (1957).
116. Tyrell, H. J. V.: "Diffusion and Heat Flow in Liquids," Butterworth & Co., (Publishers), Ltd., London, 1961.
117. Van Geet, A. L., and A. W. Adamson: *J. Phys. Chem.*, **68**:238 (1964).
118. Vinograd, J. R., and J. W. McBain: *J. Am. Chem. Soc.*, **63**:2008 (1941).
119. Vivian, J. E., and C. J. King: *AIChE J.*, **10**:220 (1964).
120. Walker, R. E., N. de Haas, and A. A. Westenberg: *J. Chem. Phys.*, **32**:1314 (1960).
121. Walker, R. E., and A. A. Westenberg: *J. Chem. Phys.*, **29**:1139 (1958).
122. Walker, R. E., and A. A. Westenberg: *J. Chem. Phys.*, **29**:1147 (1958).
123. Walker, R. E., and A. A. Westenberg: *J. Chem. Phys.*, **31**:519 (1959).
124. Walker, R. E., and A. A. Westenberg: *J. Chem. Phys.*, **32**:436 (1960).
125. Weissman, S., and E. A. Mason: *J. Chem. Phys.*, **37**:1289 (1962).
126. Weissman, S.: *J. Chem. Phys.*, **40**:3397 (1964).
127. Westenberg, A. A., and G. Frazier: *J. Chem. Phys.*, **36**:3499 (1962).
128. Westenberg, A. A., and R. E. Walker: Thermodynamic and Transport Properties of Gases, Liquids, and Solids, *ASME Symposium at Purdue University*, McGraw-Hill Book Company, New York, 1959.
129. Westenberg, A. A., and R. E. Walker: *J. Chem. Phys.*, **36**:3499 (1962).
130. Wilke, C. R.: *Chem. Eng. Progr.*, **46**:95 (1950).
131. Wilke, C. R., and P. Chang: *AIChE J.*, **1**:264 (1955).
132. Wilke, C. R., and C. Y. Lee: *Ind. Eng. Chem.*, **47**:1253 (1955).
133. Wishaw, B. F., and R. H. Stokes: *J. Am. Chem. Soc.*, **76**:2065 (1954).
134. Young, R. A.: *J. Chem. Phys.*, **34**:1295 (1961).
135. Yun, K. S., and E. A. Mason: *Phys. Fluids*, **5**:380 (1962).

APPENDIX A

TABULATION OF PURE - COMPONENT CONSTANTS

Compound	Mol. wt.	T_b °K	Ref.	T_c °K	Ref.	P_c Atm	Ref.	V_c Cm³/g mole	Ref.	Z_c	ω	α_c
Inert gases:												
Helium	4.003	4.3	9	5.3	9	2.26	9	57.8	9	0.300	0[j]	4.74
Helium^3	3.00	....		3.34	13	1.15	13					
Neon	20.183	27.3	10	44.5	13	26.9	13	41.7	13	0.296	0[j]	5.66
Argon	39.944	87.5	10	151	13	48.0	13	75.2	13	0.290	−0.002	5.76
Krypton	83.7	121.4	9	209.4	13	54.3	13	92.2	13	0.291	−0.002	5.94
Xenon	131.3	164.1	9	289.75	13	58.0	13	118.8	13	0.290	0.002	5.83
Radon	226.05	211.4	10	377.2	9	62.0	9			0.281[f]	−0.022[h]	5.72[i]
Elementary gases:												
Hydrogen (normal)	2.016	20.4	6	33.3	13	12.80	13	65.0	13	0.304	0[j]	4.74
Hydrogen (equilibrium)	2.016	....	...	33.0	13	12.8	13	61.8	13	0.292	0[j]	
Deuterium (normal)	4.00	23.6	9	38.4	13	16.4	13			0.296[f]	0[j]	5.06[i]
Deuterium (equilibrium)	4.00	....		38.3	13	16.3	13					
Hydrogen deuteride	3.00	22.1	9	35.9	9	14.6	9	62.8	9	0.300[f]	0[j]	4.92[i]
Oxygen	32.000	90.0	9	154.8	13	50.1	13	74.4	9	0.292	0.021	5.92
Nitrogen	28.016	77.3	6	126.2	13	33.5	13	90.1	13	0.291	0.040	5.98
Air (max. temp. point)	29.2	78.8 (dew pt.)	...	132.5	...	37.17	...	90.52				
Air (max. press. point)	29.2	81.8 (bubble pt.)	...	132.4	...	37.25	...	88.28				
Fluorine	38.00	86.2	9	144	9	55	9		...	0.292[f]	0.115[h]	6.33[i]
Chlorine	70.91	238.6	9	417	13	76.1	13	124	13	0.276	0.074[h]	6.18

TABLE OF PURE-COMPONENT CONSTANTS (*Continued*)

Table title: TABULATION OF PURE-COMPONENT CONSTANTS (*Continued*)

Compound	Mol. wt.	T_b °K	T_b Ref.	T_c °K	T_c Ref.	P_c Atm	P_c Ref.	V_c Cm³/g mole	V_c Ref.	Z_c	ω	α_c
Bromine	159.83	331.9	6	584	13	102	13	144	13	0.306	0.132[h]	6.63[i]
Iodine	253.82	457.5	9	785	9	116	9	......	...	0.248[f]	0.229[h]	6.86[i]
Ozone	48.00	161	10	268	13	67	13	89.4	13	0.272	0.185[h]	6.64[i]
Paraffins:												
Methane	16.04	111.7	6	190.7	16	45.8	13	99.5	16	0.290	0.013	5.86
Ethane	30.07	184.6	6	305.4	13	48.2	13	148	13	0.285	0.105	6.28
Propane	44.09	231.1	6	369.9	1, 13	42.0	5, 13	200	13	0.277	0.152	6.54
n-Butane	58.12	272.7	6	425.2	13	37.5	13	255	13	0.274	0.201	6.77
Isobutane	58.12	261.5	6	408.1	13	36.0	13	263	13	0.283	0.192	6.71
n-Pentane	72.15	309.3	6	469.5	2	33.3	13	311	13	0.269	0.252	7.03
2-Methylbutane	72.15	301.0	6	460.4	2	32.9	13	308	13	0.268	0.206	6.87
Neopentane	72.15	282.7	6	433.8	13	31.6	2	303	13	0.269	0.195	6.78
n-Hexane	86.17	341.9	6	507.3	2	29.9	2	368	13	0.264	0.290	7.27
2-Methylpentane	86.17	333.5	6	496.5	2	30.0	2	367	13	0.270	0.295[h]	7.18
3-Methylpentane	86.17	336.5	6	504.7	13	30.8	2	367	13	0.273	0.277[h]	7.15
2,2-Dimethylbutane	86.17	322.9	6	488.7	2	30.7	2	359	13	0.273	0.266[h]	6.94
2,3-Dimethylbutane	86.17	331.2	6	499.9	2	30.9	2	358	13	0.270	0.257[h]	7.01
n-Heptane	100.20	371.6	6	540.3	2	27.0	2	426	13	0.259	0.352	7.27
2-Methylhexane	100.20	363.2	6	530.3	2	27.2	2	428	13	0.267	0.340[h]	7.45[i]
3-Methylhexane	100.20	365.0	6	535.6	13	28.1	13	418	13	0.267	0.327[h]	7.39[i]
3-Ethylpentane	100.20	366.7	6	540.8	13	28.6	13	416	13	0.268	0.314[h]	7.33[i]
2,2-Dimethylpentane	100.20	352.4	6	520.9	13	28.4	13	404	13	0.268	0.300[h]	7.36[i]
2,3-Dimethylpentane	100.20	363.0	6	537.8	13	29.2	13	405	13	0.268	0.305[h]	7.28[i]

Compound												
2,4-Dimethylpentane	100.20	353.7	6	520.3	13	27.4	13	420	13	0.270	0.307[h]	7.31[i]
3,3-Dimethylpentane	100.20	359.2	6	536	13	30	13	411[d]		0.271[g]	0.284[h]	7.18[i]
2,2,3-Trimethylbutane	100.20	354.1	6	531.5	13	29.8	13	394	13	0.269	0.260[h]	7.05[i]
n-Octane	114.22	398.9	6	568.6	2	24.6	13	486	16	0.256	0.408[h]	7.76
2-Methylheptane	114.22	390.8	6	559.6	2	24.8	13	488	13	0.263	0.384[h]	7.68[i]
3-Methylheptane	114.22	392.1	6	565	13	25.6	13	478	13	0.264	0.369[h]	7.58[i]
4-Methylheptane	114.22	390.9	6	563	13	25.6	13	476	13	0.264	0.369[h]	7.58[i]
3-Ethylhexane	114.22	391.7	6	567	13	26.4	13	466	13	0.264	0.364[h]	7.58[i]
2,2-Dimethylhexane	114.22	380.7	6	552	13	25.6	13	466	13	0.264	0.343[h]	7.49[i]
2,3-Dimethylhexane	114.22	388.8	6	566	13	26.6	13	461	16	0.264	0.340[h]	7.47[i]
2,4-Dimethylhexane	114.22	382.6	6	555	13	25.8	13	466	13	0.264	0.341[h]	7.47[i]
2,5-Dimethylhexane	114.22	382.3	6	552	16	24.6	13	478	16	0.260	0.346[h]	7.50[i]
3,3-Dimethylhexane	114.22	385.2	6	564	13	27.2	13	450	13	0.264	0.326[h]	7.18[i]
3,4-Dimethylhexane	114.22	390.1	6	571	13	27.4	13	452	16	0.264	0.327[h]	7.40[i]
3-Ethyl-2-methylpentane	114.22	388.8	6	568	13	27.4	13	450	13	0.265	0.340[h]	7.47[i]
3-Ethyl-3-methylpentane	114.22	391.4	6	578	13	28.9	13	435	16	0.265	0.292[h]	7.32[i]
2,2,3-Trimethylpentane	114.22	383.0	6	567	16	28.2	16	437	16	0.265	0.297[h]	7.25[i]
2,2,4-Trimethylpentane	114.22	372.4	6	543.6	2	25.4	13	482	16	0.274	0.310[h]	7.37
2,3,3-Trimethylpentane	114.22	387.9	6	576	16	29.0	16	433	16	0.266	0.290[h]	7.28[i]
2,3,4-Trimethylpentane	114.22	386.7	6	568	13	27.6	13	477	13	0.265	0.320[h]	7.35[i]
2,2,3,3-Tetramethylbutane	114.22	379.7	6	544	13	24.5	13	480	16	0.263	0.377[h]	7.65[i]
n-Nonane	128.25	424.0	6	594.6	2	22.5	16	543	16	0.250	0.441[h]	7.94[i]
n-Decane	142.28	447.3	6	617.6	2	20.8	16	602	16	0.247	0.586[h]	8.18
n-Undecane (hendecane)	156.30	469.0	6	640	16	19.2	16	660	16	0.241	0.530[h]	8.37[i]
n-Dodecane	170.33	489.5	6	659	16	17.9	16	718	16	0.238	0.553[h]	8.54[i]
n-Tridecane	184.36	508.6	6	677	16	17	16	780	16	0.239	0.593[h]	8.81[i]
n-Tetradecane	198.38	526.8	6	694	1	16	16	830	16	0.233	0.626[h]	8.31[i]
n-Pentadecane	212.41	543.8	6	710	16	15	16	890	16	0.229	0.650[h]	9.14[i]
n-Hexadecane	226.44	560.0	6	717	1	14	16	950	16	0.226	0.704[h]	9.79[i]
n-Heptadecane	240.46	575.0	6	735	16	13	16	1000	16	0.216	0.763[h]	9.50[i]
n-Octadecane	254.49	589.3	6	756	1	13	16	1100	16	0.230	0.685[h]	9.41[i]

TABLE OF PURE-COMPONENT CONSTANTS *(Continued)*

TABULATION OF PURE-COMPONENT CONSTANTS *(Continued)*

Compound	Mol. wt.	T_b °K	Ref.	T_c °K	Ref.	P_c Atm	Ref.	V_c Cm³/g mole	Ref.	Z_c	ω	α_c
n-Nonadecane	268.51	602.9	6	760	16	12	16	1100	16	0.212	0.772[h]	9.81[i]
n-Eicosane	282.54	615.9	6	775	16	11	16	1200	16	0.208	0.710[h]	9.61[i]
Olefins:												
Ethylene	28.05	169.5	6	283.1	16	50.5	16	124	13	0.270	0.073[h]	6.18
Propene	42.08	225.5	6	365.1	16	45.4	16	181	13	0.274	0.143	6.40
1-Butene	56.10	266.9	6	419.6	13	39.7	13	240	13	0.277	0.203	6.74
2-Butene (cis)	56.10	276.9	6	434.6	2	40.5	16	236	16	0.268	0.273	6.74[i]
2-Butene (trans)	56.10	274.1	6	428.6	2	41.5	16	240	16	0.283	0.234	6.99[i]
Isobutylene	56.10	266.3	6	417.9	13	39.5	13	235	16	0.270	0.201	6.76[i]
1-Pentene	70.13	303.2	6	464.8	2	39.9	16	295[d]		0.266[a]	0.238[i]	7.16[i]
2-Pentene (cis)	70.13	310.1	6	475.6	13	40.4	13	295[d]		0.266[a]	0.280[h]	7.18[i]
2-Pentene (trans)	70.13	309.5	6	475.6	13	40.4	13	295[d]		0.266[a]	0.285[h]	7.15[i]
3-Methyl-1-butene	70.13	293.2	6	464.8	13	33.9	16	291[d]		0.274[a]	0.123[h]	6.38[i]
2-Methyl-2-butene	70.13	311.8	6	470	16	34	16	286[d]		0.266[a]	0.293[h]	7.26[i]
Hexene	84.16	336.7	6	504.0	2	31.1[c]		350[d]		0.261[a]	0.308[h]	7.19[i]
Octene	112.21	394.5	6	578	13	25.5[c]		460[d]		0.254[a]	0.399[h]	7.19[i]
Cyclopentene	68.11	317.4	6	506.1	3	47.2[c]		248[d]		0.272[a]	0.207[h]	6.76[i]
Diolefins:												
Propadiene	40.06	238.7	6	393.3	16	45.9[c]		166[d]		0.281[a]	0.086[h]	6.21[i]
1,3-Butadiene	54.09	268.8	6	425	13	42.7	13	221	13	0.271	0.179[h]	6.74
1,5-Hexadiene	82.14	332.6	6	507.6	13	32.6[c]		330[d]		0.272[a]	0.233[h]	6.91[i]
1,3-Decadiene	138.3	442 ± 1	10	614.7	16	22.2[c]		550[d]		0.253[a]	0.478[h]	8.15[i]

Acetylenes:												
Acetylene	26.04	189.6[b]	10	309.5	13	61.6	13	113	13	0.274	0.186	6.94
Propyne	40.06	250.0	6	401	13	52.8	13	167[d]		0.270[g]	0.222[h]	6.83[i]
Ethylacetylene	54.09	281.3	6	463.7	13	37.5[c]		222[d]		0.266[g]	0.043[h]	6.01[i]
Dimethylacetylene	54.09	300.2	6	488.7	13	37.5[c]		222[d]		0.266[g]	0.073[h]	6.15[i]
Propylacetylene	68.11	313.4	6	493.5	13	38.7[c]		277[d]		0.262[g]	0.184[h]	6.67[i]
Cycloparaffins:												
Cyclopentane	70.13	322.4	6	511.8	16	44.6	13	260	13	0.276	0.193	6.76[i]
Methylcyclopentane	84.16	345.0	6	532.7	2	37.4	13	319	13	0.273	0.234	6.96[i]
Ethylcyclopentane	98.18	376.7	6	569.5	16	33.5	13	375	13	0.269	0.275[h]	7.12[i]
Cyclohexane	84.16	353.9	6	553.2	16	40	13	308	13	0.271	0.186[h]	6.85[i]
Methylcyclohexane	98.18	374.1	6	572.1	2	34.3	13	344	13	0.251	0.244[h]	6.97[i]
cis-Decalin	138.3	467.8	10	691.7	16	28.7[c]		488[d]		0.267[a]	0.304[h]	7.28[i]
trans-Decalin	138.3	458.7	10	681.5	16	28.7[c]		488[d]		0.267[a]	0.286[h]	7.16[i]
Aromatics:												
Benzene	78.11	353.3	6	562.1	2	48.6	13	260	13	0.274	0.215	6.83
Toluene	92.13	383.8	6	592.0	17	41.6	13	316	16	0.271	0.279[h]	7.12[i]
o-Xylene	106.16	417.6	6	631.6	16	35.7	16	369	16	0.254	0.300[h]	7.23[i]
m-Xylene	106.16	412.3	6	616.8	16	34.7	16	376	16	0.258	0.330[h]	7.02[i]
p-Xylene	106.16	411.5	6	618.8	16	33.9	16	378	16	0.252	0.303[h]	7.26[i]
Ethylbenzene	106.16	409.4	6	617.1	2	36.9	13	374	16	0.272	0.322[h]	7.35[i]
1,2,3-Trimethylbenzene	120.19	449.3	6	664.5	2	31	13	430	13	0.244	0.335[h]	7.42[i]
1,2,4-Trimethylbenzene	120.19	442.5	6	649.0	2	32	13	430	13	0.258	0.385[h]	7.67[i]
1,3,5-Trimethylbenzene	120.19	437.9	6	637.3	2	32	16	430	13	0.263	0.417[h]	7.83[i]
2-Ethyl-1-methylbenzene	120.19	438.3	6	653.2	16	31	16	430	13	0.249	0.266[h]	7.27[i]
3-Ethyl-1-methylbenzene	120.19	434.5	6	636.2	16	31	16	430	16	0.255	0.379[h]	7.19[i]
4-Ethyl-1-methylbenzene	120.19	435.2	6	636.2	2	31	13	430	16	0.255	0.383[h]	7.67[i]
n-Propylbenzene	120.19	432.4	6	638.4	16	31.2	16	440	16	0.262	0.343[h]	7.46[i]
Isopropylbenzene	120.19	438.6	6	635.9	16	31.2	16	440	16	0.263	0.428[h]	7.89[i]
1,2,3,5-Tetramethylbenzene	134.21	471.2	6	662.2	16	28.4[c]		481[d]		k	0.541[h]	8.49[i]
1,2,4,5-Tetramethylbenzene	134.21	470.0	6	676	16	28.6	16	481[d]	16	k	0.425[h]	7.88[i]

TABULATION OF PURE-COMPONENT CONSTANTS (Continued)

Compound	Mol. wt.	T_b °K	Ref.	T_c °K	Ref.	P_c Atm	Ref.	V_c Cm³/g mole	Ref.	Z_c	ω	α_c
Cymene (4-isopropyl-1-methylbenzene)	134.21	450.3	15	658.7	16	27.7	16	476^d	...	0.255^g	0.340^h	7.48^i
n-Butylbenzene	134.21	456.5	6	661.0	16	28.4^c	...	498	16	0.257^g	0.394^h	7.73^i
Isobutylbenzene	134.21	445.9	6	657.9	2	30.1	16	477^d	...	0.257^g	0.424^h	7.42^i
Pentamethylbenzene	148.24	505.0	6	691.2	16	25.8^c	...	532^d	...	0.252^g	0.645^h	9.05^i
Hexamethylbenzene	162.27	538	10	767.2	16	23.5^c	...	586^d	...	0.246^g	0.480^h	7.67^i
Diphenyl	154.20	527 ± 1	10	768.8	16	31.8	16	482^d	...	0.257^g	0.402^h	7.75^i
Diphenylmethane	168.23	537.9	10	770.2	16	28.2	16	527^d	...	0.253^g	0.348^h	7.95^i
Naphthalene	128.16	491.1	6	748.4	2	40.6	16	408^d	...	k	0.315^h	7.31^i
1-Methylnaphthalene	142.19	518.0	15	772	1	32.1^c	...	462^d	...	k	0.279^h	7.34^i
2-Methylnaphthalene	142.19	514.3	15	761	1	32.1^c	...	462^d	...	k	0.347^h	7.92^i
Alcohols:												
Methyl alcohol	32.04	337.8	10	513.2	13	78.5	13	118	13	0.222	0.556	8.48
Ethyl alcohol	46.07	351.7	10	516.3	16	63.0	13	167	13	0.248	0.635	8.98
n-Propyl alcohol	60.09	370.4	10	536.7	4	51.0	4	218.2	4	0.252	0.600	8.85
Isopropyl alcohol	60.09	355.5	10	508.2	4	47.0	4	220.4	4	0.248	0.773^h	9.12^i
Allyl alcohol	58.08	369 ± 1	10	545.1	16	55.5^c	...	203^c	...	0.249^f	0.568^h	8.16^i
n-Butyl alcohol	74.12	390.8	10	563.0	4	43.6	4	274.6	4	0.259	0.596^h	8.17^i
sec-Butyl alcohol	74.12	372.7	10	536.0	4	41.4	4	269.0	4	0.253	0.579^h	9.18^i
tert-Butyl alcohol	74.12	356.0	10	506.2	4	39.2	4	274.5	4	0.259	0.619^h	8.84^i
Isobutyl alcohol	74.12	381.6	10	547.7	4	42.4	4	272.2	4	0.257	0.604^h	8.77^i
n-Amyl alcohol	88.15	411	10	582.9	16	37.4^c	...	333^d	...	0.260^f	0.513^h	8.92^i
tert-Amyl alcohol	88.15	375.0	10	544.9	16	38.3^c	...	319^d	...	0.268^f	0.496^h	8.22^i

1-Heptyl alcohol	116.20	449	10	638.5	16	29.4[c]		443[d]		k	0.490[h]	8.22[i]
1-Octyl alcohol	130.23	468	10	658.7	16	26.5[c]		498[d]		k	0.452[h]	8.29[i]
2-Octyl alcohol	130.23	452	10	637.3	16	27.0[c]		494[d]		k	0.495[h]	8.26[i]
Phenol	94.11	454.9	6	694.3	1	60.5	13	264[d]		0.244[f]	0.453[h]	7.94[i]
o-Cresol	108.13	464.1	6	697.6	1	49.4	13	315[d]		0.249[f]	0.443[h]	7.92[i]
m-Cresol	108.13	475.4	16	705.8	1	45.0	13	320	16	0.248	0.464[h]	8.05[i]
p-Cresol	108.13	475.1	6	704.6	1	50.8	13	315[d]		0.246[f]	0.515[h]	8.28[i]
Thymol (3-p-cymenol)	150.21	506.7	10	698.3	16	33.0[c]		478[d]		k	0.726[h]	8.87[i]
o-Ethyl phenol	122.16	480.7	10	703.0	1	34.7[c]		373[d]		k	0.429[h]	7.90[i]
m-Ethyl phenol	122.16	487	10	716.5	1	34.7[c]		373[d]		k	0.402[h]	7.76[i]
p-Ethyl phenol	122.16	492	10	716.5	1	34.7[c]		373[d]		k	0.450[h]	7.99[i]
2,3-Xylenol	122.16	491	15	722.9	1	56.4[c]		372[d]		k	0.589[h]	8.65[i]
2,4-Xylenol	122.16	484.7	10	707.6	1	56.4[c]		372[d]		k	0.658[h]	8.78[i]
2,5-Xylenol	122.16	486	15	723.1	1	56.4[c]		372[d]		k	0.439[h]	8.39[i]
2,6-Xylenol	122.16	485	15	701.0	1	56.4[c]		372[d]		k	0.687[h]	8.16[i]
3,4-Xylenol	122.16	498	15	729.9	1	56.4[c]		372[d]		k	0.610[h]	8.77[i]
3,5-Xylenol	122.16	492.7	15	715.6	1	56.4[c]		372[d]		k	0.666[h]	9.04[i]
Ethers:												
Dimethyl ether	46.07	249.5	10	400.1	16	52.6	16	178	16	0.285	0.226[h]	6.85[i]
Ethylmethyl ether	60.09	281.1	10	437.9	16	43.4	13	221	13	0.267	0.265[h]	7.03[i]
Diethyl ether	74.12	307.8	10	465.8	14	35.6	14	274	14	0.255	0.230[h]	7.23[i]
Ethylpropyl ether	88.15	335	10	500.6	16	32.1	13	339	13	0.265	0.306[h]	7.28[i]
Isopropyl ether	102.17	342	10	500.1	13	28.4	14	382[d]		0.266[g]	0.350[h]	7.51[i]
p-Dioxane	88.10	374.7	10	588	14	51.4	14	238	14	0.253	0.288[h]	7.15[i]
Allylethyl ether	86.13	340.8	10	518.2	16	34.9[c]		315[d]		0.258[g]	0.276[h]	7.11[i]
Methylphenyl ether (anisole)	108.13	428	15	641.7	16	41.3	16	336[d]		0.263[g]	0.388[h]	7.67[i]
1,2-Dimethoxyethane	90.12	357	15	536	14	35.7[c]		300[d]		0.260[g]	0.329[h]	7.38[i]
1,1-Diethoxyethane (acetal)	118.17	376	15	527.6	16	29.5[c]		406[d]		0.249[g]	0.572[h]	8.62[i]
Ethylphenyl ether (phenetole)	122.16	445	15	647.2	16	33.8	16	391[d]		0.258[g]	0.445[h]	7.98[i]
Diphenyl ether	170.20	531.1	6	767.2	16	30.9[c]		502[d]		0.260[g]	0.435[h]	7.93[i]
Dimethoxymethane (methylal)	76.09	317	10	488.4	16	42.3[c]		245[d]		0.264[g]	0.290[h]	7.18[i]

TABULATION OF PURE-COMPONENT CONSTANTS (*Continued*)

Compound	Mol. wt.	T_b °K	Ref.	T_c °K	Ref.	P_c Atm	Ref.	V_c Cm³/g mole	Ref.	Z_c	ω	α_c
Vinyl ethyl ether	72.10	308.7	15	475	14	40.2	14	260[d]	....	0.263[g]	0.277[h]	7.12[i]
Ketones:												
Acetone	58.08	329.7	10	509.1	12	47	12	211	12	0.237	0.318	7.30
Ethylmethyl ketone	72.10	352.8	10	535	12	41.0	12	267	12	0.249	0.337[h]	7.41[i]
Diethyl ketone	86.13	375.9	10	561.0	12	36.9	12	336	12	0.269	0.365[h]	7.56[i]
Methyl-n-propyl ketone	86.13	374.9	10	564.0	12	38.4	12	302	12	0.250	0.349[h]	7.54[i]
Methyl isopropyl ketone	86.13	366	10	553.4	12	38.0	12	310	12	0.259	0.283[h]	7.34[i]
Methyl isobutyl ketone	100.16	391 ± 1	10	571.5	12	32.3	12	371[d]	....	k	0.400[h]	7.76[i]
Aldehydes:												
Acetaldehyde	44.05	294	10	461	13	54.7[c]	....	168[d]	....	0.257[f]	0.314[h]	7.27[i]
Paracetaldehyde	132.16	398	15	563	16	34.6[c]	....	403[d]	....	k	0.482[h]	8.74[i]
Organic acids:												
Acetic acid	60.05	391.1	6	594.8	13	57.1	13	171	13	0.200	0.450[h]	7.94
Acetic anhydride	102.09	413	10	569.2	16	46.2	13	290[d]	....	k	0.400[h]	10.28[i]
Propionic acid	74.08	414.2	6	612.7	16	53.0	13	230	13	0.242	0.545[h]	8.33[i]
n-Butyric acid	88.10	436.7	6	628.0	16	52	13	290	13	0.293	0.677[h]	9.12[i]
Isobutyric acid	88.10	426.4	6	609.5	16	40	13	292	13	0.234	0.603[h]	8.77[i]
n-Valeric acid	102.13	459.2	6	651.5	16	37.6[c]	....	340[d]	....	k	0.614[h]	8.83[i]
Isovaleric acid	102.13	426.4	6	633.5	16	38.4[c]	....	336[d]	....	k	0.398[h]	7.73[i]
Esters:												
Methyl formate	60.05	304.7	10	487.2	13	59.2	13	172	13	0.255	0.272[h]	7.04
Ethyl formate	74.08	327.5	10	508.5	13	46.3	16	229	16	0.257	0.291[h]	7.14

Compound	Mol. wt.											
Propyl formate	88.10	354.5	10	538.1	13	40.1	16	285	16	0.259	0.329[h]	7.37
Isobutyl formate	102.13	371.4	10	551.4	13	38.3	16	355	16	0.301	0.404[h]	7.58[i]
n-Amyl formate	116.16	403.6	10	575.8	16	34.1	16	381[d]		k	0.541[h]	8.47[i]
Isoamyl formate	116.16	396.7	10	577.8	16	31.2[c]		391[d]		k	0.407[h]	7.78[h]
Methyl acetate	74.08	330.3	10	506.9	13	46.3	13	228	16	0.254	0.339[h]	7.40
Ethyl acetate	88.10	350.3	10	523.3	13	37.8	13	286	16	0.252	0.365[h]	7.60
n-Propyl acetate	102.13	374.8	10	549.4	13	32.9	13	345	16	0.252	0.395[h]	7.74
n-Butyl acetate	116.16	399	10	579.1	16	30.7[c]		395[c]		k	0.377[h]	7.82[i]
Isobutyl acetate	116.16	389	10	561.5	16	31.4	16	413	16	0.281	0.450[h]	8.00[i]
Isoamyl acetate	130.18	412	10	599.3	16	28[c]		446[d]		k	0.363[h]	7.57[i]
Methyl propionate	88.10	353.1	10	530.6	16	39.3	16	282	16	0.255	0.363[h]	7.50
Ethyl propionate	102.13	372.3	10	546.1	16	33.0	16	345	16	0.254	0.396[h]	7.63
Propyl propionate	116.16	397	10	578.0	16	30.7[c]		395[d]		k	0.399[h]	7.75[i]
Isobutyl propionate	130.18	410.0	10	591.9	16	28[c]		446[d]		k	0.400[h]	7.76[i]
Isoamyl propionate	144.21	433.4	10	611.4	16	25.4[c]		501[d]		k	0.469[h]	8.12[i]
Methyl butyrate	102.13	375.5	10	554.5	13	34.3	16	340	16	0.256	0.380[h]	7.64[i]
Ethyl butyrate	116.16	394	10	566.2	16	30.2	16	420	16	0.273	0.455[h]	8.03[i]
n-Propyl butyrate	130.18	416	10	599.8	16	27.6[c]		450[d]		k	0.403[h]	7.78[i]
Isobutyl butyrate	144.21	430.1	10	611.4	16	25.4[c]		501[d]		k	0.427[h]	7.91[i]
Isoamyl n-butyrate	158.23	452	15	618.8	16	23.2[c]		556[d]		k	0.587[h]	8.74[i]
Methyl isobutyrate	102.13	365.8	10	540.8	16	33.9	16	339	16	0.259	0.370[h]	7.53
Ethyl isobutyrate	116.16	384.9	10	553.6	16	30.1	16	421	16	0.279	0.345[h]	7.99[i]
n-Propyl isobutyrate	130.18	408.6	10	589.2	16	28[c]		446[d]		k	0.457[h]	7.76[i]
Isobutyl isobutyrate	144.21	421.9	10	601.9	16	25.8[c]		497[d]		k	0.420[h]	7.87[i]
Methyl n-valerate	116.16	400.5	10	566.9	16	31.5	16	417	16	0.282	0.543[h]	8.48[i]
Ethyl n-valerate	130.18	419	10	570.2	16	28.0[c]		446[d]		k	0.406[h]	7.81[i]
Ethyl isovalerate	130.18	408	10	588.0	16	25.4[c]		501[d]		k	0.440[h]	7.67[i]
n-Propyl isovalerate	144.21	429.1	10	609.1	16	23.6[c]		552[d]		k	0.448[h]	8.03[i]
Isobutyl isovalerate	158.24	441.7	10	621.4	16	21.2[c]		615[d]		k	0.537[h]	8.69[i]
Ethyl n-caprylate	172.26	481	10	658.7	16	19.6[c]		607[d]		k	0.601[h]	8.85[i]
Ethyl pelargonate	186.29	500.7	10	674.0	16							
Methyl laurate	214.34			712	1							

TABULATION OF PURE-COMPONENT CONSTANTS (Continued)

Compound	Mol. wt.	T_b °K	Ref.	T_c °K	Ref.	P_c Atm	Ref.	V_c Cm³/g mole	Ref.	Z_c	ω	α_c
Nitrogen compounds:												
Ammonia	17.03	239.8	6	405.6	13	112.5	6a	72.5	13	0.242	0.250	7.00
Hydrazine	32.05	386.3	6	653.2	13	145	13	96^d		0.284^g	0.337^g	7.31^i
Cyanogen	52.02	252.5	6	400	13	50.0	6a	200^d		0.275^f	0.299^h	7.20^i
Hydrogen cyanide	27.03	298.9	6	456.7	13	48.9	6a	139	13	0.197	0.399^h	7.73
Methylamine	31.06	266.7	6	430.2	16	73.1	16	123^d		0.279^g	0.374^h	7.20^i
Dimethylamine	45.08	280.1	6	437.8	16	52.4	16	187^d		0.280^g	0.310^h	7.25^i
Trimethylamine	59.11	276.1	6	433.3	13	40.2	13	254	13	0.287	0.206^h	6.78^i
Ethylamine	45.08	289.8	6	456.5	16	55.5	13	185	16	0.274	0.303^h	7.21^i
Diethylamine	73.14	328.7	6	496.7	16	36.6	13	301	16	0.270	0.315^h	7.31
Triethylamine	101.19	362.7	6	535.4	16	30.0	13	394	16	0.269	0.328^i	7.39^i
Propylamine	59.11	321.0	6	497	16	46.8	13	233^d		0.270^g	0.306^h	7.25^i
Dipropylamine	101.19	382.4	6	550	13	31	13	407^d		0.259^g	0.456^h	8.05^i
Acetonitrile	41.05	354.8	6	548	13	47.7	13	173	16	0.184	0.319^h	7.31^i
Propionitrile	55.08	370.5	6	564	13	41.3	13	230	16	0.205	0.328^h	7.36^i
n-Propylcyanide	69.10	391.1	6	582	13	37.4	13	285^d		0.232^f	0.382^h	7.64^i
n-Heptylcyanide	125.21	478.4	6	622	13	32.2	16	505^d		k	1.150^h	11.85^i
Benzonitrile	103.12	463.9	6	699.4	13	41.6	13	341^d		k	0.365^h	7.56^i
N,N-Dimethyl-o-toluidine	135.20	457.8	6	668	16	30.8	16	468^d		k	0.389^h	7.70^i
Aniline	93.12	457.3	6	698.8	13	52.3	13	274	13	0.250	0.392^h	7.67^i
Methylaniline	107.15	468.9	6	701.6	13	51.3	13	353^d		0.256^g	0.475^h	8.09^i
Dimethylaniline	121.18	466	10	687.6	16	35.8	16	413^d		k	0.401^h	7.76^i
Pyridine	79.10	388.7	15	620.0	3	e		e		k	e	e
3-Methylpyridine (β-picoline)	93.12	416.7	10	644.9	3	e		e		k	e	e
4-Methylpyridine (γ-picoline)	93.12	416.3	10	645.7	3	e		e		k	e	e

Compound												
2,4-Dimethylpyridine (2,4-lutidine)	107.15	431 ± 1	10	647.2	3	e	e			k	e	e
2,6-Dimethylpyridine (2,6-lutidine)	107.15	416	10	623.8	3	e	e			k	e	e
2,5-Dimethylpyridine (2,5-lutidine)	107.15	429.7	10	644.2	2	e	e			k	e	e
3,5-Dimethylpyridine (3,5-lutidine)	107.15	...	...	667.3	2	e	e			k	e	e
Nitromethane	61.04	374	10	588	13	62.3	173	13	16	0.223	0.346^h	7.41^i
Pyrrolidine	71.12	361	15	570	14	56.3	249	14	14	0.300	0.296^h	7.18^i
(See also Miscellaneous)												

Sulfur and sulfur compounds:

Compound												
Sulfur	32.06	717.8	10	1313	9	116	e	9		k	0.070^h	6.10^i
Carbonyl sulfide	60.07	223.0	15	378	13	65	134^d	16		k	0.120^h	6.54^i
Carbon disulfide	76.13	319.4	6	552	13	78	170	16	16	k	0.123	6.32
Hydrogen sulfide	34.08	211.4	6	373.6	13	88.9	95^d	13		0.268^f	0.100	6.25
Dimethyl sulfide	62.13	310.5	6	503.1	13	54.6	201	13	16	0.266	0.199^h	6.73^i
Methyl ethyl sulfide	76.15	339	6	532.8	16	41.9	260^d	13		0.271^g	0.216^h	6.82^i
Methyl mercaptan	48.10	280.8	10	470	16	71.4	149	13	16	0.276	0.177^h	6.61
Ethyl mercaptan	62.13	308.2	6	499	16	54.2	207	13	16	0.274	0.173^h	6.72
Diethyl sulfide	90.18	365.3	6	557	13	39.1	323	13	16	0.276	0.303^h	7.24
Allyl sulfide	114.20	411	10	653.6	16	33.2^c	385^d			0.263^g	0.105^h	6.31^i
Diethyl disulfide	122.24	427.2	6	642.1	16	38.2^c	370^d			0.258^g	0.347^h	6.54^i
Diisoamyl sulfide	174.34	489	10	664.4	16	21.5^c	637^d			0.248^g	0.593^h	8.80^i
Thiophene	84.13	357.3	6	580	14	56.2	233^d	14		k	0.205^h	6.74^i

Inorganic halides:

Compound												
Hydrogen fluoride	20.01	292.7	6	461	7	64 ± 4	69 ± 5	7	7	0.223^f	0.358^h	7.60^i
Hydrogen chloride	36.49	188.2	6	324.6	13	82.1	87.6	6a	8	0.266	0.133^h	6.39^i
Hydrogen bromide	80.92	206.4	6	363.2	13	84.5	110^d	6a		k	0.083^h	6.18^i
Hydrogen iodide	127.93	237.7	15	424.2	16	81.9	135^d	6a		k	0.043^h	6.00^i

Tabulation of Pure-Component Constants (*Continued*)

Compound	Mol. wt.	T_b °K	Ref.	T_c °K	Ref.	P_c Atm	Ref.	V_c Cm³/g mole	Ref.	Z_c	ω	$α_c$
Boron trifluoride	67.82	172	10	260.9	13	49.2	13	e		k	0.392[h]	7.71[i]
Boron trichloride	117.19	285.7	10	452.0	13	38.2	13	e		k	0.164[h]	6.58[i]
Boron tribromide	250.57	363.8	15	573	13	e	13	280	13	k	e	e
Phosgene	98.92	280.7	6	455	13	56	13	190	13	0.285	0.206[h]	6.76[i]
Germanium tetrachloride	214.43	356.3	10	550.1	13	38	13	e		k	0.247[h]	6.98[i]
Silicon tetrafluoride	104.06	208[a]	15	259.1	13	36.7	13	e		k	1.740[h]	15.02[i]
Chlorotrifluorosilane	120.52			307.7	13	34.2	13	e		e	e	e
Dichlorodifluorosilane	136.97			369.0	13	34.5	13	e		e	e	e
Trichlorofluorosilane	153.43			438.5	13	35.3	13	e		e	e	e
Silicon tetrachloride	169.89	330.7	10	506	13	e		e		e	e	e
Stannic chloride	260.53	387.3	15	591.9	13	37.0	13	351	13	0.268	0.269[h]	7.09[i]
Sulfur hexafluoride	146.06	209.7[b]	15	318.7	13	37.1	13	194	13	0.275	0.257[h]	7.21[i]
Organic halides:												
Methyl fluoride	34.03	194.8	6	317.8	13	58.0	13	113	13	0.251	0.198[h]	6.71[i]
Methyl chloride	50.49	249.0	6	416.3	13	65.9	13	143	13	0.276	0.158[h]	6.55
Methyl bromide	94.95	276.7	6	467.2	16	83.4[c]		165[d]		k	0.195[h]	6.68[i]
Methyl iodide	141.95	315.7	10	528	13	72.7[c]		190[d]		k	0.187[h]	6.65[i]
Methylene chloride	89.94	312.9	6	510	13	60	13	193[d]		k	0.213[h]	6.78[i]
Fluoroform	70.02			298.2	16	46.9[c]		145[d]		k	e	e
Chloroform	119.39	334.9	6	536.6	13	54	13	240	13	0.294	0.214	6.86
Carbon tetrafluoride	88.01	145	16	227.7	13	41.4[c]		153[d]		0.272	0.191	6.75
Carbon tetrachloride	153.84	349.7	6	556.4	13	45.0	13	276	16	k	0.202[h]	6.78[i]
Ethyl fluoride	48.06	235.5	10	375.4	13	49.6	16	168[d]		k	-0.238[h]	4.85[i]
Ethyl chloride	64.52	285.5	6	460.4	13	52.0	16	199[d]		k	-0.022[h]	6.37
Ethyl bromide	108.98	311.5	6	503.9	13	61.5	13	215	13	0.320	0.310[h]	6.91[i]

Compound											
1,1-Dichloroethane	98.97	330.5	6	523	13	50	13	244^d	..	k	−0.018^h	7.04
1,2-Dichloroethane	98.97	356.7	6	561	13	53	13	225	16	0.259	0.291^h	7.17^i
Dibromomethane	173.86	370.1	6	583.0	13	70.6	13	235^d	13	k	0.379^h	7.57^i
Chlorodifluoromethane	86.48	232.4	10	369.6	13	48.5	13	165	13	0.264	0.237^h	7.14^i
Dichlorofluoromethane	102.93	282.1	10	451.7	13	51.0	13	197	13	0.271	0.221^h	7.17^i
Bromotrifluoromethane	148.9	..	..	339.8	16	50.3^c	16	205^d	..	e	e	e
Chlorotrifluoromethane	104.47	193	10	302.0	13	38.2	13	180	16	0.278	0.202^h	6.75^i
Dichlorodifluoromethane	120.92	245	10	384.7	13	39.6	13	218	16	0.273	0.203^h	6.66
Trichlorofluoromethane	137.38	297.3	10	471.2	13	43.2	13	248	13	0.277	0.200^h	6.74^i
Tetrafluoroethylene	100.02	194.8	10	306.5	16	38.9	16	172	16	0.274	−0.065^h	6.71^i
Chlorotrifluoroethylene	116.48	245.3	11	379	13	40	13	210	16	0.270	0.259^h	7.03^i
1,2-Dichlorotetrafluoroethane	170.93	277.0	10	419	16	32.3	16	292^a	..	k	0.262^h	7.60^i
1,1,2,2-Tetrachlorodifluoroethane	203.85	..	..	551.2	16	32.9^c	16	354^d	..	e	e	e
Trichlorotrifluoroethane	187.39	366.0	10	487.3	16	33.7	13	325	13	0.274	0.976^h	10.38^i
n-Propyl chloride	78.54	319.9	15	503.2	16	45.2	16	254^d	16	k	0.241^h	6.93^i
Perfluoro-n-propane	169	..	..	343.7	16	26.5	16	307^d	16	e	e	e
Perfluoro-n-butane	238.04	..	..	386.5	16	23	16	384^d	13	e	e	e
Perfluoro-n-heptane	388.07	..	..	474.8	16	16.0	16	664	13	0.273	e	e
Perfluoromethylcyclohexane	350.07	..	..	486.6	13	16.5^c	13	519^d	..	e	e	e
Allyl chloride	76.53	317.8	10	513.5	16	46.5^c	16	234^d	..	e	0.161^h	6.55^i
Fluorobenzene	96.10	358.3	6	560.1	2	44.6	2	271	13	0.263	0.255^h	7.02
Chlorobenzene	112.56	404.9	6	632.4	13	44.6	13	308	13	0.265	0.255^h	7.04
Bromobenzene	157.06	429.2	6	670.2	16	44.6	16	324	16	0.263	0.255^h	6.99
Iodobenzene	204.02	461.5	6	721	13	44.6	13	351	13	0.265	0.255^h	7.02

Oxides:

Compound											
Carbon dioxide	44.01	194.7	6	304.2	13	72.9	13	94.0	13	0.274	0.420^h	6.92
Carbon monoxide	28.01	81.7	6	133	13	34.5	13	93.1	13	0.294	0.041	6.04
Ethylene oxide	44.05	283.9	10	468	13	71.0	13	138	13	0.255	0.157	6.83^i
1,2-Propylene oxide	58.08	308	15	482.3	14	48.6	14	186	13	0.228	0.280^h	7.12^i
Nitrous oxide	44.02	183.7	6	309.7	13	71.7	13	96.3	13	0.271	0.160^h	6.59
Nitric oxide	30.01	121.4	10	180	13	64	13	58	13	0.251	0.600^h	8.88

TABLE OF PURE-COMPONENT CONSTANTS (*Continued*)

Compound	Mol. wt.	T_b °K	T_b Ref.	T_c °K	T_c Ref.	P_c Atm	P_c Ref.	V_c Cm³/g mole	V_c Ref.	Z_c	ω	α_c
Nitrogen dioxide	46.01	294.5	10	431	13	100	13	82	13	0.232	0.850[h]	9.91
Sulfur dioxide	64.06	263.2	6	430.7	13	77.7	16	122	13	0.268	0.273[h]	8.55
Sulfur trioxide	80.06	318.0	10	491.4	13	81.4	6a	126	13	0.262	0.510[h]	8.22[i]
Water	18.02	373.2	6	647	13	218.3	13	56	13	0.230	0.348	7.39
Furan	68.07	305	15	487	14	52.5	14	218	14	0.286	0.235[h]	6.89[i]
2-Methylfuran	82.10	336.8	14	528	14	46.6	14	246	14	0.265	0.271[h]	7.01[i]
Tetrahydrofuran	72.10	339	15	541	14	51.2	14	224	14	0.258	0.211[h]	6.78[i]
2-Methyltetrahydrofuran	86.13	353	14	537	14	37.1	14	267	14	0.225	-0.003[h]	7.18[i]
Miscellaneous:												
Phosphine	34.00	185.8	10	324.5	13	64.5	13	113	8	0.274	0.043[h]	6.00[i]
Silane	32.09	161.4	10	269.7	13	47.8	13	e		0.281[f]	0.067[h]	6.14[i]
Quinoline	129.15	511	10	782	1	e		e		k	e	e
Isoquinoline	129.15	516	10	803	1	e		e		k	e	e
Piperidine	85.15	379.6	15	594	1	44.1[c]		294.5[d]		k	0.248[h]	6.97[i]

[a] At 1,810 mm Hg.
[b] Sublimes.
[c] Calculated from Eq. (2-21) and Table 2-1.
[d] Calculated from Eq. (2-25) and Table 2-1.
[e] No method available for the calculation.
[f] Read from Fig. 2-2.
[g] Calculated from Eq. (2-24).
[h] Calculated from Eq. (2-28).
[i] Calculated from Eq. (2-32).
[j] Assumed zero.
[k] Off scale in Fig. 2-2.
[l] Calculated by equation $Z_c = P_c V_c / R T_c$.

584

APPENDIX A 585

REFERENCES FOR APPENDIX A

1. Ambrose, D.: *Trans. Faraday Soc.*, **59**:1988 (1963).
2. Ambrose, D., J. D. Cox, and R. Townsend: *Trans. Faraday Soc.*, **56**:1452 (1960).
3. Ambrose, D., and D. G. Grant: *Trans. Faraday Soc.*, **53**:771 (1957).
4. Ambrose, D., and R. Townsend: *J. Chem. Soc.*, **1963**:3614.
5. Beattie, J. A., N. Poffenberger, and C. Hadlock: *J. Chem. Phys.*, **3**:96 (1935).
6. Dreisbach, R. R.: Physical Properties of Chemical Compounds, I, *Advances in Chem. Ser.* 15, 1955; II, *ibid.*, 22, 1959; III, *ibid.* 29, 1961, American Chemical Society, Washington, D.C.
6a. Edwards, D. G.: The Vapor Pressures of 30 Inorganic Liquids between One Atmosphere and the Critical Point, *Univ. California Radiation Lab.*, UCRL-7167 rev. 1, Livermore, Calif., June 17, 1964.
7. Frank, E. U., and W. Spalthoff: *Z. physik. Chem.*, **8**:255 (1956).
8. Gambill, W. R.: *Chem. Eng.*, **66**(21):195 (1959).
9. Gates, D. S., and G. Thodos: *AIChE J.*, **6**:50 (1960).
10. Hodgman, C. D. (ed.): "Handbook of Chemistry and Physics," 30th edition, Chemical Rubber Publishing Co., Cleveland, Ohio, 1948.
11. Jordan, T. E.: "Vapor Pressures of Organic Compounds," Interscience Publishers, Inc., New York, 1954.
12. Kobe, K. A., H. R. Crawford, and R. W. Stephenson: *Ind. Eng. Chem.*, **47**:1767 (1955).
13. Kobe, K. A., and R. E. Lynn: *Chem. Revs.*, **52**:117 (1953).
14. Kobe, K. A., A. E. Ravicz, and S. P. Vohra: *J. Chem. Eng. Data*, **1**:50 (1956).
15. Lange, N. A. (ed.): "Handbook of Chemistry," 10th ed., McGraw-Hill Book Company, New York, 1961.
16. Lydersen, A. L.: Estimation of Critical Properties of Organic Compounds, *Coll. Eng., Univ. Wisconsin, Eng. Expt. Sta. Rept.* 3, Madison, Wis., April, 1955.
17. Partington, E. J., J. S. Rowlinson, and J. F. Weston: *Trans. Faraday Soc.*, **56**:479 (1960).

APPENDIX B

COMPRESSIBILITY FACTORS, ENTHALPY DEVIATIONS, AND FUGACITY COEFFICIENTS FOR GASES AND LIQUIDS*

* Tables from A. L. Lydersen, R. A. Greenkorn, and O. A. Hougen, Generalized Thermodynamic Properties of Pure Liquids, *Univ. Wisconsin Coll. Eng. Rept.* 4, October, 1955.

(Values above broken lines are for liquids; below, for gases)

T_r	$P_r = 0.01$				$P_r = 0.10$				$P_r = 0.20$			
	W $Z_c=0.23$	I $Z_c=0.25$	II $Z_c=0.27$	III $Z_c=0.29$	W $Z_c=0.23$	I $Z_c=0.25$	II $Z_c=0.27$	III $Z_c=0.29$	W $Z_c=0.23$	I $Z_c=0.25$	II $Z_c=0.27$	III $Z_c=0.29$
$T_{r,s}$					0.758	0.758	0.743	0.714	0.819	0.817	0.805	0.781
Sat. gas					0.895	0.886	0.898	0.900	0.820	0.830	0.833	0.839
Sat. liquid					0.0116	0.014	0.015	0.018	0.0227	0.028	0.030	0.034
0.50	0.0015	0.985	0.986	0.988	0.0150	0.017	0.018	0.021	0.0299	0.032	0.037	0.042
0.60	0.0013	0.987	0.988	0.990	0.0130	0.0145	0.016	0.019	0.0260	0.028	0.033	0.038
0.70	0.988	0.989	0.990	0.993	0.0119	0.0140	0.015	0.018	0.0238	0.027	0.030	0.035
0.80	0.993	0.991	0.992	0.994	0.0114	0.912	0.921	0.925	0.0228	0.026	0.030	0.854
0.90	0.997	0.993	0.994	0.995	0.949	0.940	0.947	0.950	0.886	0.884	0.890	0.900
0.92	0.997	0.994	0.994	0.995	0.954	0.945	0.951	0.955	0.897	0.888	0.901	0.910
0.94	0.998	0.994	0.994	0.995	0.958	0.950	0.955	0.959	0.907	0.907	0.909	0.916
0.96	0.998	0.994	0.995	0.995	0.962	0.954	0.958	0.963	0.915	0.913	0.915	0.923
0.98	0.998	0.994	0.995	0.996	0.964	0.959	0.962	0.965	0.922	0.918	0.922	0.929
1.00	0.998	0.995	0.995	0.996	0.967	0.963	0.965	0.969	0.928	0.923	0.927	0.934
1.01	0.999	0.995	0.996	0.996	0.968	0.964	0.966	0.970	0.931	0.925	0.930	0.937
1.02	0.999	0.995	0.996	0.996	0.970	0.965	0.967	0.971	0.934	0.929	0.933	0.939
1.03	0.999	0.995	0.996	0.996	0.971	0.967	0.968	0.972	0.936	0.931	0.935	0.941
1.04	0.999	0.995	0.996	0.996	0.972	0.969	0.970	0.973	0.939	0.934	0.938	0.943
1.05	0.999	0.996	0.996	0.996	0.973	0.971	0.971	0.974	0.940	0.936	0.940	0.946
1.06	0.999	0.996	0.996	0.997	0.974	0.972	0.972	0.975	0.942	0.939	0.942	0.948
1.07	0.999	0.996	0.996	0.997	0.975	0.973	0.973	0.976	0.945	0.941	0.944	0.950
1.08	0.999	0.996	0.996	0.997	0.976	0.974	0.974	0.977	0.946	0.943	0.946	0.952
1.09	0.999	0.996	0.997	0.997	0.977	0.975	0.975	0.978	0.949	0.945	0.948	0.954
1.10	0.999	0.996	0.997	0.997	0.978	0.976	0.976	0.979	0.951	0.948	0.950	0.955
1.12	0.999	0.996	0.997	0.998	0.979	0.977	0.977	0.980	0.954	0.951	0.953	0.957
1.14	0.999	0.997	0.997	0.998	0.980	0.979	0.979	0.981	0.958	0.953	0.957	0.959
1.16	1.000	0.997	0.998	0.998	0.982	0.981	0.980	0.982	0.960	0.957	0.960	0.962
1.18	1.000	0.997	0.998	0.998	0.983	0.982	0.982	0.983	0.963	0.960	0.963	0.964
1.20	1.000	0.997	0.998	0.998	0.984	0.983	0.983	0.984	0.965	0.963	0.965	0.967
1.30	1.000	0.998	0.998	0.998	0.989	0.987	0.987	0.988	0.974	0.970	0.974	0.975
1.40	1.000	0.998	0.998	0.999	0.992	0.989	0.990	0.991	0.981	0.980	0.982	0.982
1.50	1.000	0.998	0.999	0.999	0.995	0.991	0.991	0.992	0.986	0.985	0.986	0.986
1.60	1.000	0.998	0.999	1.000	0.997	0.992	0.992	0.992	0.990	0.988	0.988	0.988
1.70	1.001	0.998	0.999	1.000	0.998	0.992	0.992	0.992	0.992	0.989	0.989	0.989
1.80		0.999	1.000	1.000		0.993	0.993	0.993		0.991	0.991	0.991
1.90		0.999	1.000	1.000		0.993	0.993	0.993		0.993	0.993	0.993
2.00		0.999	1.000	1.000		0.994	0.994	0.994		0.994	0.994	0.994
3.00		1.000	1.000	1.000		1.000	1.000	1.000		1.000	1.000	1.000
4.00		1.000	1.000	1.000		1.000	1.000	1.000		1.000	1.000	1.000
6.00		1.000	1.000	1.000		1.000	1.000	1.000		1.000	1.000	1.000
8.00		1.000	1.000	1.000		1.000	1.000	1.000		1.000	1.000	1.000
10.00		1.000	1.000	1.000		1.000	1.000	1.000		1.000	1.000	1.000
15.00		1.000	1.000	1.000		1.000	1.000	1.000		1.000	1.000	1.000

587

COMPRESSIBILITY FACTORS OF PURE GASES AND LIQUIDS (Continued)

T_r	$P_r = 0.30$				$P_r = 0.40$				$P_r = 0.50$			
	W $Z_c=0.23$	I $Z_c=0.25$	II $Z_c=0.27$	III $Z_c=0.29$	W $Z_c=0.23$	I $Z_c=0.25$	II $Z_c=0.27$	III $Z_c=0.29$	W $Z_c=0.23$	I $Z_c=0.25$	II $Z_c=0.27$	III $Z_c=0.29$
T_{rs}	0.858	0.856	0.846	0.826	0.889	0.885	0.876	0.861	0.914	0.910	0.900	0.892
Sat. gas	0.760	0.780	0.783	0.790	0.700	0.732	0.738	0.746	0.650	0.681	0.693	0.698
Sat. liquid	0.0347	0.040	0.045	0.051	0.047	0.052	0.060	0.068	0.060	0.069	0.077	0.086
0.50	0.0448	0.048	0.055	0.063	0.0597	0.062	0.073	0.084	0.0745	0.080	0.093	0.105
0.60	0.0389	0.043	0.049	0.056	0.0519	0.057	0.065	0.075	0.0648	0.071	0.082	0.094
0.70	0.0356	0.040	0.046	0.052	0.0474	0.053	0.061	0.070	0.0591	0.066	0.076	0.087
0.80	0.0342	0.039	0.044	0.051	0.0456	0.051	0.059	0.067	0.0568	0.064	0.073	0.084
0.90	0.813	0.822	0.826	0.840	0.721	0.745	0.764	0.775	0.0590	0.068	0.077	0.705
0.92	0.836	0.835	0.842	0.852	0.756	0.767	0.783	0.789	0.662	0.692	0.710	0.729
0.94	0.851	0.853	0.856	0.862	0.786	0.790	0.798	0.806	0.712	0.721	0.735	0.752
0.96	0.865	0.864	0.868	0.876	0.809	0.805	0.817	0.820	0.746	0.750	0.761	0.773
0.98	0.877	0.873	0.879	0.885	0.826	0.824	0.832	0.832	0.774	0.772	0.782	0.793
1.00	0.888	0.882	0.889	0.893	0.844	0.838	0.846	0.852	0.798	0.792	0.801	0.808
1.01	0.893	0.886	0.893	0.897	0.851	0.844	0.852	0.858	0.805	0.800	0.809	0.816
1.02	0.898	0.890	0.897	0.902	0.858	0.852	0.858	0.864	0.817	0.808	0.817	0.824
1.03	0.901	0.894	0.901	0.906	0.863	0.856	0.863	0.869	0.825	0.818	0.825	0.831
1.04	0.906	0.898	0.905	0.910	0.870	0.861	0.868	0.874	0.834	0.824	0.832	0.838
1.05	0.910	0.902	0.908	0.913	0.875	0.868	0.873	0.879	0.842	0.833	0.838	0.845
1.06	0.912	0.906	0.911	0.918	0.880	0.873	0.878	0.886	0.848	0.840	0.845	0.852
1.07	0.916	0.910	0.916	0.920	0.885	0.878	0.883	0.889	0.855	0.846	0.850	0.857
1.08	0.920	0.913	0.918	0.923	0.890	0.882	0.886	0.891	0.861	0.851	0.856	0.860
1.09	0.922	0.918	0.920	0.926	0.893	0.886	0.890	0.893	0.866	0.855	0.862	0.865
1.10	0.925	0.919	0.923	0.927	0.898	0.889	0.894	0.899	0.872	0.860	0.866	0.870
1.12	0.930	0.924	0.928	0.931	0.905	0.896	0.901	0.904	0.882	0.870	0.876	0.878
1.14	0.934	0.928	0.933	0.936	0.913	0.903	0.907	0.912	0.890	0.878	0.884	0.887
1.16	0.940	0.934	0.937	0.939	0.918	0.911	0.913	0.917	0.898	0.886	0.891	0.894
1.18	0.943	0.937	0.942	0.943	0.923	0.915	0.918	0.924	0.905	0.893	0.898	0.903
1.20	0.946	0.942	0.946	0.948	0.928	0.920	0.924	0.931	0.911	0.901	0.905	0.916
1.30	0.961	0.959	0.961	0.963	0.948	0.944	0.945	0.946	0.937	0.931	0.931	0.932
1.40	0.968	0.970	0.972	0.973	0.960	0.957	0.959	0.961	0.954	0.948	0.949	0.950
1.50	0.974	0.978	0.980	0.980	0.971	0.968	0.970	0.973	0.966	0.961	0.963	0.965
1.60	0.984	0.984	0.984	0.985	0.979	0.978	0.978	0.978	0.975	0.970	0.973	0.976
1.70	0.988	0.988	0.989	0.989	0.984	0.984	0.984	0.984	0.981	0.978	0.980	0.980
1.80		0.991	0.991	0.991		0.987	0.987	0.987		0.985	0.985	0.985
1.90		0.993	0.993	0.993		0.991	0.991	0.991		0.989	0.989	0.989
2.00		0.994	0.994	0.994		0.994	0.994	0.994		0.993	0.993	0.993
3.00		1.000	1.000	1.000		1.000	1.000	1.000		1.000	1.000	1.000
4.00		1.000	1.000	1.000		1.000	1.000	1.000		1.000	1.000	1.000
6.00		1.000	1.000	1.000		1.000	1.000	1.000		1.000	1.000	1.000
8.00		1.000	1.000	1.000		1.000	1.000	1.000		1.000	1.000	1.000
10.00		1.000	1.000	1.000		1.000	1.000	1.000		1.000	1.000	1.000
15.00		1.000	1.000	1.000		1.000	1.000	1.000		1.000	1.000	1.000

COMPRESSIBILITY FACTORS OF PURE GASES AND LIQUIDS (Continued)

	$P_r = 0.60$				$P_r = 0.70$				$P_r = 0.80$			
	W ($Z_c=0.23$)	I ($Z_c=0.25$)	II ($Z_c=0.27$)	III ($Z_c=0.29$)	W ($Z_c=0.23$)	I ($Z_c=0.25$)	II ($Z_c=0.27$)	III ($Z_c=0.29$)	W ($Z_c=0.23$)	I ($Z_c=0.25$)	II ($Z_c=0.27$)	III ($Z_c=0.29$)
T_{rs}	0.940	0.932	0.928	0.919	0.954	0.952	0.949	0.942	0.971	0.969	0.967	0.963
Sat. gas	0.602	0.628	0.641	0.650	0.548	0.570	0.583	0.596	0.486	0.505	0.519	0.536
Sat. liquid	0.0749	0.086	0.096	0.103	0.091	0.103	0.114	0.125	0.110	0.124	0.136	0.150
T_r												
0.50	0.0894	0.096	0.110	0.126	0.104	0.112	0.128	0.147	0.119	0.128	0.147	0.168
0.60	0.0776	0.086	0.098	0.112	0.0904	0.100	0.113	0.131	0.103	0.114	0.130	0.149
0.70	0.0709	0.079	0.092	0.104	0.0826	0.092	0.106	0.121	0.0942	0.105	0.121	0.138
0.80	0.0679	0.077	0.088	0.101	0.0790	0.089	0.102	0.117	0.0900	0.102	0.116	0.133
0.90	0.0706	0.080	0.091	0.103	0.0817	0.092	0.105	0.120	0.0927	0.105	0.120	0.136
0.92	0.0721	0.082	0.093	0.652	0.0834	0.095	0.108	0.123	0.0946	0.107	0.122	0.139
0.94	0.0748	0.655	0.660	0.684	0.0866	0.098	0.111	0.126	0.0961	0.111	0.126	0.143
0.96	0.638	0.684	0.700	0.708	0.0933	0.598	0.613	0.630	0.105	0.117	0.133	0.150
0.98	0.675	0.712	0.731	0.736	0.632	0.636	0.665	0.669	0.528	0.555	0.580	0.598
1.00	0.709	0.744	0.755	0.760	0.680	0.690	0.704	0.710	0.605	0.616	0.640	0.652
1.01	0.728	0.756	0.766	0.772	0.700	0.706	0.718	0.726	0.634	0.642	0.661	0.671
1.02	0.744	0.765	0.776	0.782	0.718	0.720	0.732	0.738	0.659	0.664	0.679	0.689
1.03	0.754	0.778	0.785	0.792	0.732	0.735	0.745	0.751	0.679	0.682	0.696	0.701
1.04	0.767	0.786	0.794	0.800	0.746	0.745	0.756	0.760	0.697	0.699	0.709	0.715
1.05	0.777	0.798	0.802	0.808	0.760	0.758	0.766	0.770	0.715	0.716	0.723	0.727
1.06	0.785	0.805	0.809	0.818	0.771	0.769	0.775	0.780	0.728	0.728	0.734	0.739
1.07	0.795	0.811	0.817	0.824	0.782	0.776	0.782	0.788	0.743	0.738	0.745	0.750
1.08	0.805	0.818	0.824	0.829	0.793	0.786	0.790	0.797	0.756	0.748	0.755	0.762
1.09	0.813	0.823	0.830	0.834	0.801	0.792	0.798	0.802	0.766	0.758	0.764	0.769
1.10	0.822	0.831	0.837	0.840	0.810	0.800	0.805	0.808	0.779	0.766	0.773	0.776
1.12	0.840	0.842	0.849	0.852	0.826	0.814	0.818	0.822	0.800	0.785	0.789	0.791
1.14	0.855	0.852	0.859	0.863	0.839	0.827	0.830	0.832	0.815	0.800	0.804	0.806
1.16	0.868	0.861	0.870	0.874	0.850	0.840	0.842	0.844	0.827	0.815	0.817	0.819
1.18	0.878	0.870	0.878	0.880	0.862	0.848	0.852	0.856	0.838	0.825	0.830	0.831
1.20	0.889	0.880	0.905	0.888	0.871	0.860	0.862	0.864	0.848	0.839	0.840	0.842
1.30	0.921	0.916	0.91	0.918	0.909	0.900	0.900	0.902	0.890	0.886	0.888	0.890
1.40	0.940	0.934	0.937	0.940	0.932	0.926	0.928	0.930	0.922	0.920	0.921	0.922
1.50	0.954	0.950	0.953	0.956	0.949	0.947	0.948	0.949	0.941	0.944	0.945	0.946
1.60	0.965	0.960	0.965	0.970	0.963	0.963	0.964	0.965	0.958	0.960	0.960	0.960
1.70	0.973	0.971	0.974	0.977	0.972	0.974	0.974	0.975	0.968	0.970	0.972	0.972
1.80		0.982	0.982	0.982		0.982	0.982	0.982		0.980	0.980	0.980
1.90		0.987	0.987	0.987		0.987	0.987	0.987		0.981	0.987	0.987
2.00		0.992	0.992	0.992		0.992	0.992	0.992		0.990	0.990	0.990
3.00		1.000	1.000	1.000		1.000	1.000	1.000		1.000	1.000	1.000
4.00		1.000	1.000	1.000		1.000	1.000	1.000		1.000	1.000	1.000
6.00		1.000	1.000	1.000		1.000	1.000	1.000		1.000	1.000	1.000
8.00		1.000	1.000	1.000		1.000	1.000	1.000		1.000	1.000	1.000
10.00		1.000	1.000	1.000		1.000	1.000	1.000		1.000	1.000	1.000
15.00		1.000	1.000	1.000		1.000	1.000	1.000		1.000	1.000	1.000

Compressibility Factors of Pure Gases and Liquids (Continued)

T_r	$P_r = 0.9$				$P_r = 1.0$				$P_r = 1.05$			
	W $Z_c = 0.23$	I $Z_c = 0.25$	II $Z_c = 0.27$	III $Z_c = 0.29$	W $Z_c = 0.23$	I $Z_c = 0.25$	II $Z_c = 0.27$	III $Z_c = 0.29$	W $Z_c = 0.23$	I $Z_c = 0.25$	II $Z_c = 0.27$	III $Z_c = 0.29$
Sat. gas	0.986	0.985	0.984	0.982	1.000	1.000	1.000	1.000				
Sat. liquid	0.415	0.427	0.443	0.460	0.232	0.250	0.270	0.290				
	0.136	0.152	0.164	0.177	0.232	0.250	0.270	0.290				
T_r												
0.50	0.134	0.144	0.165	0.189	0.148	0.160	0.183	0.210	0.156	0.168	0.192	0.220
0.60	0.116	0.128	0.147	0.168	0.129	0.142	0.163	0.186	0.136	0.149	0.171	0.196
0.70	0.106	0.118	0.136	0.155	0.117	0.130	0.151	0.171	0.123	0.138	0.158	0.181
0.80	0.101	0.114	0.131	0.150	0.112	0.126	0.145	0.165	0.117	0.133	0.152	0.177
0.90	0.104	0.117	0.134	0.153	0.122	0.129	0.148	0.169	0.120	0.136	0.155	0.168
0.92	0.105	0.120	0.137	0.155	0.116	0.133	0.151	0.170	0.121	0.139	0.158	0.179
0.94	0.109	0.124	0.141	0.159	0.120	0.136	0.155	0.175	0.125	0.143	0.162	0.183
0.96	0.115	0.130	0.147	0.166	0.126	0.143	0.161	0.182	0.132	0.149	0.169	0.190
0.98	0.127	0.143	0.161	0.180	0.136	0.157	0.174	0.195	0.140	0.161	0.181	0.204
1.00	0.515	0.500	0.520	0.544	0.232	0.250	0.270	0.290	0.194	0.218	0.230	0.237
1.01	0.556	0.550	0.568	0.580	0.442	0.360	0.424	0.464	0.343	0.272	0.365	0.380
1.02	0.591	0.592	0.602	0.619	0.508	0.484	0.509	0.522	0.454	0.410	0.463	0.466
1.03	0.618	0.620	0.627	0.640	0.547	0.538	0.555	0.564	0.505	0.486	0.505	0.518
1.04	0.643	0.646	0.650	0.662	0.581	0.577	0.585	0.596	0.546	0.537	0.546	0.558
1.05	0.665	0.664	0.670	0.678	0.610	0.600	0.611	0.620	0.581	0.566	0.577	0.587
1.06	0.683	0.683	0.687	0.694	0.632	0.625	0.633	0.639	0.607	0.595	0.603	0.609
1.07	0.701	0.696	0.703	0.708	0.655	0.646	0.654	0.658	0.631	0.620	0.627	0.630
1.08	0.713	0.710	0.715	0.723	0.675	0.665	0.671	0.676	0.653	0.639	0.647	0.653
1.09	0.729	0.721	0.726	0.730	0.691	0.680	0.686	0.689	0.670	0.657	0.662	0.668
1.10	0.743	0.731	0.738	0.742	0.707	0.694	0.700	0.702	0.689	0.675	0.678	0.682
1.12	0.765	0.753	0.756	0.760	0.734	0.718	0.723	0.726	0.718	0.702	0.704	0.708
1.14	0.785	0.772	0.773	0.777	0.756	0.740	0.745	0.748	0.742	0.724	0.731	0.735
1.16	0.803	0.786	0.790	0.793	0.780	0.758	0.764	0.766	0.765	0.746	0.750	0.752
1.18	0.817	0.801	0.805	0.808	0.795	0.776	0.780	0.782	0.783	0.765	0.771	0.772
1.20	0.831	0.817	0.818	0.822	0.810	0.792	0.795	0.799	0.800	0.782	0.787	0.788
1.30	0.883	0.872	0.874	0.876	0.866	0.855	0.857	0.860	0.860	0.848	0.849	0.851
1.40	0.912	0.910	0.912	0.914	0.902	0.897	0.899	0.900	0.897	0.892	0.892	0.894
1.50	0.934	0.937	0.938	0.939	0.926	0.926	0.929	0.930	0.923	0.920	0.922	0.926
1.60	0.952	0.955	0.955	0.956	0.946	0.948	0.948	0.952	0.944	0.943	0.943	0.948
1.70	0.963	0.967	0.968	0.968	0.959	0.963	0.964	0.965	0.957	0.958	0.958	0.962
1.80		0.977	0.978	0.978		0.970	0.974	0.974		0.970	0.970	0.972
1.90		0.985	0.985	0.985		0.983	0.983	0.983		0.978	0.978	0.980
2.00		0.990	0.990	0.990		0.988	0.988	0.988		0.986	0.986	0.987
3.00		1.000	1.000	1.000		1.000	1.000	1.000		1.000	1.000	1.000
4.00		1.000	1.000	1.000		1.000	1.000	1.000		1.000	1.000	1.000
6.00		1.000	1.000	1.000		1.000	1.000	1.000		1.000	1.000	1.000
8.00		1.000	1.000	1.000		1.000	1.000	1.000		1.000	1.000	1.000
10.00		1.000	1.000	1.000		1.000	1.000	1.000		1.000	1.000	1.000
15.00		1.000	1.000	1.000		1.000	1.000	1.000		1.000	1.000	1.000

Compressibility Factors of Pure Gases and Liquids *(Continued)*

T_r	$P_r = 1.10$ W $Z_c = 0.23$	I $Z_c = 0.25$	II $Z_c = 0.27$	III $Z_c = 0.29$	$P_r = 1.15$ W $Z_c = 0.23$	I $Z_c = 0.25$	II $Z_c = 0.27$	III $Z_c = 0.29$	$P_r = 1.20$ W $Z_c = 0.23$	II $Z_c = 0.27$
0.50	0.163	0.176	0.201	0.231	0.170	0.184	0.211	0.241	0.178	0.220
0.60	0.142	0.156	0.179	0.205	0.148	0.163	0.187	0.214	0.154	0.195
0.70	0.129	0.144	0.165	0.190	0.135	0.151	0.173	0.198	0.140	0.180
0.80	0.123	0.139	0.159	0.182	0.128	0.145	0.166	0.190	0.134	0.173
0.90	0.125	0.142	0.162	0.185	0.130	0.148	0.169	0.193	0.135	0.176
0.92	0.127	0.145	0.165	0.187	0.132	0.151	0.172	0.195	0.137	0.179
0.94	0.130	0.149	0.169	0.191	0.136	0.155	0.176	0.199	0.141	0.183
0.96	0.136	0.155	0.176	0.198	0.142	0.161	0.183	0.206	0.146	0.189
0.98	0.145	0.168	0.189	0.212	0.150	0.174	0.195	0.210	0.153	0.202
1.00	0.163	0.214	0.224	0.228	0.166	0.215	0.223	0.223	0.164	0.220
1.01	0.214	0.245	0.256	0.290	0.191	0.239	0.246	0.252	0.183	0.242
1.02	0.381	0.353	0.360	0.398	0.282	0.314	0.316	0.325	0.227	0.295
1.03	0.458	0.430	0.461	0.470	0.400	0.395	0.408	0.415	0.329	0.369
1.04	0.511	0.498	0.505	0.510	0.466	0.459	0.471	0.475	0.419	0.422
1.05	0.549	0.536	0.541	0.551	0.510	0.505	0.513	0.520	0.479	0.478
1.06	0.578	0.560	0.568	0.578	0.546	0.540	0.545	0.545	0.515	0.517
1.07	0.606	0.590	0.594	0.603	0.580	0.570	0.573	0.574	0.551	0.548
1.08	0.631	0.611	0.616	0.628	0.607	0.593	0.597	0.600	0.581	0.573
1.09	0.650	0.635	0.637	0.644	0.628	0.615	0.618	0.620	0.605	0.598
1.10	0.670	0.654	0.655	0.660	0.653	0.636	0.639	0.641	0.629	0.618
1.12	0.701	0.685	0.686	0.690	0.684	0.668	0.672	0.674	0.666	0.654
1.14	0.728	0.709	0.712	0.716	0.713	0.694	0.698	0.700	0.698	0.683
1.16	0.752	0.732	0.735	0.738	0.739	0.720	0.724	0.726	0.725	0.707
1.18	0.771	0.753	0.756	0.757	0.759	0.742	0.745	0.748	0.747	0.730
1.20	0.789	0.772	0.773	0.774	0.778	0.761	0.763	0.765	0.767	0.751
1.30	0.853	0.841	0.841	0.843	0.846	0.834	0.835	0.837	0.838	0.827
1.40	0.893	0.886	0.888	0.888	0.885	0.880	0.882	0.884	0.881	0.875
1.50	0.919	0.915	0.918	0.921	0.915	0.912	0.914	0.916	0.911	0.911
1.60	0.941	0.938	0.940	0.944	0.938	0.938	0.938	0.940	0.935	0.935
1.70	0.955	0.956	0.956	0.958	0.953	0.954	0.954	0.955	0.951	0.951
1.80		0.968	0.968	0.969		0.965	0.966	0.966		0.963
1.90		0.976	0.977	0.978		0.973	0.974	0.976		0.974
2.00		0.984	0.984	0.986		0.982	0.982	0.985		0.981
3.00		1.000	1.000	1.000						1.000
4.00		1.000	1.000	1.000						1.000
6.00										1.000
8.00		1.000	1.000	1.000						1.004
10.00		1.000	1.000	1.000						1.005
15.00		1.000	1.000	1.000						1.010

COMPRESSIBILITY FACTORS OF PURE GASES AND LIQUIDS (*Continued*)

T_r	$P_r = 1.25$ W, $Z_c = 0.23$	$P_r = 1.25$ II, $Z_c = 0.27$	$P_r = 1.30$ W, $Z_c = 0.23$	$P_r = 1.30$ II, $Z_c = 0.27$	$P_r = 1.35$ W, $Z_c = 0.23$	$P_r = 1.35$ II, $Z_c = 0.27$	$P_r = 1.40$ W, $Z_c = 0.23$	$P_r = 1.40$ II, $Z_c = 0.27$	$P_r = 1.45$ W, $Z_c = 0.23$	$P_r = 1.45$ II, $Z_c = 0.27$
0.50	0.185	0.229	0.192	0.238	0.200	0.247	0.207	0.256	0.214	0.265
0.60	0.160	0.203	0.167	0.211	0.173	0.219	0.180	0.227	0.186	0.235
0.70	0.146	0.188	0.152	0.195	0.158	0.202	0.163	0.210	0.169	0.217
0.80	0.139	0.180	0.144	0.187	0.150	0.194	0.155	0.201	0.161	0.208
0.90	0.141	0.183	0.146	0.190	0.151	0.197	0.156	0.203	0.162	0.210
0.92	0.143	0.185	0.148	0.192	0.153	0.199	0.158	0.206	0.163	0.213
0.94	0.147	0.190	0.152	0.197	0.156	0.203	0.161	0.210	0.166	0.217
0.96	0.151	0.196	0.156	0.203	0.162	0.210	0.166	0.217	0.172	0.223
0.98	0.159	0.209	0.164	0.216	0.169	0.222	0.174	0.228	0.179	0.235
1.00	0.171	0.223	0.174	0.225	0.178	0.230	0.182	0.234	0.187	0.241
1.01	0.183	0.242	0.185	0.242	0.188	0.246	0.190	0.246	0.195	0.259
1.02	0.209	0.282	0.207	0.271	0.206	0.267	0.202	0.264	0.205	0.270
1.03	0.268	0.343	0.254	0.336	0.238	0.302	0.220	0.288	0.221	0.292
1.04	0.368	0.396	0.333	0.364	0.298	0.345	0.254	0.323	0.251	0.316
1.05	0.438	0.444	0.400	0.415	0.359	0.389	0.311	0.366	0.299	0.346
1.06	0.485	0.488	0.450	0.455	0.414	0.430	0.370	0.403	0.351	0.380
1.07	0.525	0.529	0.496	0.493	0.465	0.467	0.427	0.438	0.405	0.415
1.08	0.559	0.552	0.534	0.522	0.507	0.500	0.474	0.472	0.452	0.447
1.09	0.590	0.579	0.562	0.550	0.538	0.531	0.507	0.507	0.488	0.481
1.10	0.611	0.599	0.591	0.574	0.569	0.553	0.541	0.534	0.524	0.512
1.12	0.651	0.636	0.634	0.615	0.616	0.600	0.592	0.577	0.578	0.559
1.14	0.685	0.667	0.670	0.649	0.655	0.632	0.633	0.615	0.621	0.600
1.16	0.715	0.694	0.702	0.678	0.689	0.663	0.669	0.647	0.659	0.632
1.18	0.738	0.718	0.728	0.706	0.715	0.692	0.697	0.677	0.690	0.667
1.20	0.758	0.741	0.749	0.728	0.738	0.719	0.721	0.705	0.715	0.694
1.30	0.833	0.819	0.827	0.811	0.821	0.803	0.808	0.795	0.806	0.790
1.40	0.878	0.872	0.874	0.865	0.869	0.860	0.859	0.855	0.859	0.852
1.50	0.909	0.907	0.907	0.902	0.903	0.899	0.894	0.894	0.895	0.892
1.60	0.934	0.932	0.933	0.928	0.931	0.926	0.922	0.923	0.924	0.926
1.70	0.950	0.949	0.949	0.947	0.950	0.949	0.941	0.945	0.943	0.949
1.80		0.962		0.962		0.962		0.960		0.962
1.90		0.973		0.972		0.972		0.972		0.972
2.00		0.981		0.981		0.980		0.979		0.978
3.00		1.000		1.000		1.000		1.000		1.000
4.00		1.000		1.000		1.000		1.000		1.000
6.00		1.000		1.000		1.000		1.004		1.000
8.00		1.004		1.004		1.004		1.008		1.004
10.00		1.007		1.007		1.007		1.010		1.010
15.00		1.010		1.010		1.010		1.020		1.020

Compressibility Factors of Pure Gases and Liquids (Continued)

T_r	$P_r = 1.50$ W ($Z_c = 0.23$)	$P_r = 1.50$ II ($Z_c = 0.27$)	$P_r = 1.60$ W ($Z_c = 0.23$)	$P_r = 1.60$ II ($Z_c = 0.27$)	$P_r = 1.70$ W ($Z_c = 0.23$)	$P_r = 1.70$ II ($Z_c = 0.27$)	$P_r = 1.8$ II ($Z_c = 0.27$)	$P_r = 1.9$ II ($Z_c = 0.27$)	$P_r = 2.0$ II ($Z_c = 0.27$)	$P_r = 2.2$ II ($Z_c = 0.27$)
0.50	0.221	0.274	0.236	0.293	0.251	0.311	0.329	0.347	0.365	0.402
0.60	0.192	0.243	0.205	0.259	0.217	0.275	0.291	0.307	0.323	0.355
0.70	0.175	0.224	0.186	0.239	0.196	0.254	0.268	0.282	0.297	0.326
0.80	0.166	0.215	0.177	0.229	0.187	0.243	0.257	0.270	0.284	0.311
0.90	0.167	0.217	0.177	0.230	0.187	0.244	0.257	0.270	0.283	0.309
0.92	0.169	0.219	0.179	0.233	0.189	0.246	0.259	0.272	0.284	0.311
0.94	0.171	0.223	0.182	0.237	0.192	0.249	0.262	0.275	0.287	0.313
0.96	0.177	0.230	0.187	0.242	0.197	0.255	0.267	0.279	0.291	0.317
0.98	0.184	0.241	0.191	0.253	0.203	0.265	0.276	0.287	0.298	0.323
1.00	0.191	0.247	0.200	0.254	0.209	0.268	0.279	0.293	0.306	0.328
1.01	0.198	0.258	0.206	0.262	0.215	0.277	0.287	0.300	0.312	0.333
1.02	0.208	0.273	0.214	0.276	0.222	0.288	0.296	0.308	0.318	0.338
1.03	0.222	0.288	0.224	0.289	0.229	0.300	0.307	0.319	0.326	0.344
1.04	0.246	0.308	0.239	0.305	0.241	0.312	0.317	0.326	0.333	0.351
1.05	0.286	0.332	0.262	0.323	0.258	0.328	0.332	0.338	0.341	0.358
1.06	0.333	0.368	0.293	0.347	0.278	0.346	0.347	0.349	0.351	0.366
1.07	0.387	0.398	0.334	0.370	0.307	0.365	0.365	0.364	0.361	0.375
1.08	0.429	0.431	0.378	0.396	0.342	0.387	0.380	0.375	0.372	0.384
1.09	0.466	0.464	0.418	0.424	0.380	0.409	0.398	0.390	0.386	0.394
1.10	0.504	0.496	0.460	0.455	0.419	0.432	0.416	0.408	0.400	0.404
1.12	0.563	0.542	0.526	0.505	0.486	0.480	0.454	0.439	0.432	0.426
1.14	0.609	0.580	0.577	0.549	0.541	0.521	0.494	0.479	0.466	0.454
1.16	0.649	0.619	0.621	0.588	0.588	0.565	0.540	0.521	0.503	0.488
1.18	0.680	0.653	0.651	0.622	0.626	0.606	0.583	0.561	0.542	0.525
1.20	0.707	0.682	0.685	0.653	0.652	0.638	0.620	0.600	0.573	0.562
1.30	0.801	0.783	0.784	0.768	0.770	0.755	0.742	0.731	0.716	0.697
1.40	0.856	0.846	0.843	0.837	0.832	0.829	0.819	0.812	0.801	0.786
1.50	0.895	0.888	0.883	0.872	0.874	0.877	0.869	0.861	0.852	0.842
1.60	0.926	0.919	0.914	0.916	0.909	0.904	0.904	0.896	0.888	0.880
1.70	0.952	0.940	0.935	0.932	0.931	0.932	0.929	0.922	0.915	0.908
1.80		0.956		0.953		0.949	0.946	0.940	0.935	0.930
1.90		0.968		0.965		0.962	0.960	0.956	0.952	0.947
2.00		0.976		0.974		0.972	0.971	0.969	0.966	0.960
3.00		0.999		0.997		0.997	0.995	0.991	0.986	0.984
4.00		1.000		1.000		1.000	0.997	0.993	0.990	0.988
6.00		1.004		1.003		1.005	1.000	0.994	0.995	0.993
8.00		1.008		1.008		1.008	1.005	0.998	0.998	0.996
10.00		1.010		1.010		1.012	1.008	1.000	1.000	0.998
15.00		1.020		1.020		1.020	1.020	1.020	1.020	1.020

COMPRESSIBILITY FACTORS OF PURE GASES AND LIQUIDS (Continued)

T_r	$P_r = 2.4$ II $Z_c = 0.27$	$P_r = 2.6$ II $Z_c = 0.27$	$P_r = 2.8$ II $Z_c = 0.27$	$P_r = 3.0$ II $Z_c = 0.27$	$P_r = 3.5$ II $Z_c = 0.27$	$P_r = 4.0$ II $Z_c = 0.27$	$P_r = 4.5$ II $Z_c = 0.27$	$P_r = 5.0$ II $Z_c = 0.27$	$P_r = 6.0$ II $Z_c = 0.27$	$P_r = 7.0$ II $Z_c = 0.27$
0.50	0.438	0.474	0.510	0.546	0.636	0.726	0.817	0.905	1.083	1.262
0.60	0.387	0.419	0.451	0.482	0.562	0.640	0.719	0.797	0.952	1.108
0.70	0.355	0.384	0.413	0.441	0.513	0.584	0.654	0.724	0.862	1.001
0.80	0.339	0.365	0.392	0.419	0.484	0.549	0.614	0.678	0.804	0.931
0.90	0.335	0.361	0.386	0.411	0.471	0.532	0.592	0.652	0.768	0.888
0.92	0.336	0.362	0.387	0.412	0.472	0.530	0.590	0.649	0.763	0.881
0.94	0.339	0.364	0.389	0.413	0.473	0.530	0.590	0.647	0.760	0.877
0.96	0.343	0.368	0.392	0.416	0.475	0.531	0.590	0.647	0.757	0.873
0.98	0.349	0.374	0.398	0.421	0.478	0.532	0.590	0.647	0.755	0.868
1.00	0.352	0.375	0.401	0.422	0.479	0.536	0.590	0.645	0.756	0.865
1.01	0.357	0.379	0.405	0.426	0.481	0.538	0.592	0.646	0.757	0.864
1.02	0.361	0.384	0.409	0.430	0.484	0.540	0.593	0.648	0.758	0.864
1.03	0.366	0.387	0.414	0.434	0.487	0.543	0.595	0.649	0.759	0.864
1.04	0.372	0.393	0.417	0.439	0.491	0.546	0.596	0.651	0.760	0.864
1.05	0.377	0.399	0.421	0.444	0.495	0.548	0.598	0.653	0.761	0.864
1.06	0.384	0.404	0.426	0.449	0.499	0.552	0.601	0.655	0.762	0.864
1.07	0.389	0.410	0.431	0.455	0.504	0.554	0.604	0.657	0.763	0.864
1.08	0.396	0.416	0.436	0.461	0.508	0.558	0.606	0.660	0.764	0.864
1.09	0.405	0.423	0.443	0.467	0.513	0.562	0.608	0.662	0.766	0.865
1.10	0.413	0.431	0.450	0.474	0.518	0.565	0.611	0.665	0.768	0.866
1.12	0.432	0.448	0.468	0.488	0.529	0.572	0.617	0.671	0.772	0.868
1.14	0.456	0.466	0.484	0.504	0.540	0.581	0.624	0.678	0.776	0.870
1.16	0.488	0.488	0.504	0.521	0.553	0.589	0.631	0.685	0.780	0.873
1.18	0.521	0.518	0.529	0.539	0.567	0.599	0.640	0.692	0.786	0.876
1.20	0.550	0.540	0.554	0.556	0.582	0.609	0.649	0.701	0.792	0.880
1.30	0.682	0.670	0.666	0.660	0.671	0.687	0.712	0.749	0.824	0.904
1.40	0.776	0.768	0.762	0.755	0.754	0.763	0.780	0.807	0.863	0.928
1.50	0.832	0.824	0.819	0.813	0.813	0.813	0.829	0.849	0.893	0.952
1.60	0.872	0.863	0.859	0.855	0.852	0.852	0.867	0.881	0.918	0.972
1.70	0.901	0.893	0.890	0.886	0.885	0.883	0.895	0.908	0.940	0.990
1.80	0.923	0.916	0.914	0.909	0.908	0.909	0.919	0.929	0.960	1.004
1.90	0.941	0.936	0.934	0.930	0.931	0.932	0.940	0.948	0.977	1.017
2.00	0.956	0.953	0.953	0.946	0.951	0.952	0.957	0.965	0.993	1.028
3.00	0.984	0.984	0.984	0.984	0.985	0.986	0.989	0.996	0.995	1.032
4.00	0.988	0.988	0.988	0.988	0.989	0.990	0.992	0.997	0.997	1.035
6.00	0.993	0.993	0.993	0.993	0.994	0.995	0.996	0.998	0.999	1.037
8.00	0.996	0.996	0.996	0.996	0.997	0.997	0.998	0.999	1.000	1.039
10.00	0.998	0.998	0.998	0.998	0.999	0.999	0.999	1.000	1.010	1.042
15.00	1.020	1.020	1.020	1.025	1.030	1.030	1.035	1.040	1.045	1.050

COMPRESSIBILITY FACTORS OF PURE GASES AND LIQUIDS (*Continued*)

T_r	$P_r = 8.0$ II $Z_c = 0.27$	$P_r = 9.0$ II $Z_c = 0.27$	$P_r = 10$ II $Z_c = 0.27$	$P_r = 15$ II $Z_c = 0.27$	$P_r = 20$ II $Z_c = 0.27$	$P_r = 25$ II $Z_c = 0.27$	$P_r = 30$ II $Z_c = 0.27$
0.50	1.439	1.616	1.791	2.673	3.551	4.41	5.28
0.60	1.262	1.415	1.568	2.337	3.098	3.85	4.59
0.70	1.139	1.277	1.413	2.096	2.769	3.43	4.08
0.80	1.056	1.180	1.305	1.922	2.525	3.12	3.70
0.90	1.005	1.119	1.233	1.796	2.341	2.88	3.40
0.92	0.997	1.110	1.222	1.774	2.310	2.83	3.35
0.94	0.991	1.100	1.201	1.753	2.278	2.79	3.30
0.96	0.985	1.090	1.202	1.734	2.250	2.76	3.25
0.98	0.980	1.080	1.195	1.715	2.224	2.72	3.20
1.00	0.975	1.074	1.193	1.704	2.200	2.69	3.15
1.01	0.974	1.072	1.188	1.697	2.188	2.67	3.14
1.02	0.973	1.069	1.184	1.688	2.175	2.66	3.11
1.03	0.972	1.068	1.181	1.681	2.164	2.63	3.08
1.04	0.972	1.066	1.177	1.672	2.153	2.61	3.06
1.05	0.972	1.065	1.174	1.666	2.142	2.60	3.04
1.06	0.971	1.064	1.171	1.658	2.130	2.58	3.02
1.07	0.970	1.062	1.168	1.652	2.119	2.57	3.00
1.08	0.970	1.061	1.165	1.646	2.109	2.55	2.96
1.09	0.970	1.060	1.162	1.638	2.098	2.53	2.95
1.10	0.970	1.060	1.160	1.631	2.088	2.51	2.93
1.12	0.970	1.058	1.156	1.618	2.068	2.50	2.89
1.14	0.970	1.058	1.153	1.606	2.049	2.46	2.85
1.16	0.972	1.057	1.151	1.594	2.030	2.44	2.81
1.18	0.973	1.056	1.150	1.584	2.013	2.41	2.78
1.20	0.975	1.057	1.148	1.573	1.995	2.39	2.74
1.30	0.984	1.063	1.144	1.528	1.921	2.27	2.63
1.40	0.996	1.071	1.144	1.496	1.862	2.19	2.56
1.50	1.012	1.081	1.146	1.476	1.818	2.15	2.49
1.60	1.028	1.092	1.150	1.461	1.790	2.12	2.44
1.70	1.041	1.100	1.154	1.448	1.767	2.09	2.39
1.80	1.052	1.108	1.156	1.435	1.744	2.05	2.33
1.90	1.061	1.115	1.158	1.420	1.714	2.02	2.29
2.00	1.070	1.120	1.159	1.400	1.691	1.99	2.24
3.00	1.068	1.107	1.130	1.310	1.500	1.67	1.84
4.00	1.065	1.099	1.120	1.255	1.400	1.53	1.66
6.00	1.064	1.089	1.100	1.200	1.300	1.42	1.50
8.00	1.063	1.082	1.085	1.170	1.250	1.32	1.40
10.00	1.062	1.077	1.080	1.130	1.185	1.24	1.30
15.00	1.061	1.070	1.070	1.100	1.140	1.17	1.20

Enthalpy Deviations of Gases and Liquids From Ideal-gas Behavior, $(H^0 - H)/T_c$, cal/(g mole)(°K)

T_r,	$P_r = 0.01$				$P_r = 0.10$				$P_r = 0.20$			
	W	I	II	III	W	I	II	III	W	I	II	III
	$Z_c = 0.23$	$Z_c = 0.25$	$Z_c = 0.27$	$Z_c = 0.29$	$Z_c = 0.23$	$Z_c = 0.25$	$Z_c = 0.27$	$Z_c = 0.29$	$Z_c = 0.23$	$Z_c = 0.25$	$Z_c = 0.27$	$Z_c = 0.29$
Sat. gas					0.758	0.758	0.743	0.714	0.819	0.817	0.805	0.781
—					0.758	0.550	0.430	0.430	1.275	0.920	0.810	0.66
Sat. liquid					13.193	12.68	12.08	10.04	12.480	11.85	11.28	9.60
T_r												
0.50	15.843	15.75	14.81	11.20	15.830	15.75	14.81	11.20	15.817	15.80	14.82	11.20
0.60	14.854	14.79	0.057	0.055	14.845	14.80	13.75	10.76	14.834	14.80	13.76	10.76
0.70	0.078	0.066	0.047	0.044	13.810	13.60	12.52	10.07	13.801	13.60	12.53	10.12
0.80	0.060	0.050	0.038	0.034	0.601	0.50	0.38	0.34	12.674	12.06	11.36	0.67
0.90	0.036	0.036	0.030	0.025	0.362	0.36	0.30	0.25	0.796	0.73	0.64	0.50
0.92	0.033	0.034	0.028	0.023	0.335	0.34	0.28	0.23	0.773	0.68	0.60	0.46
0.94	0.031	0.032	0.027	0.022	0.312	0.32	0.27	0.22	0.676	0.64	0.57	0.44
0.96	0.029	0.030	0.025	0.020	0.291	0.30	0.25	0.20	0.621	0.60	0.54	0.41
0.98	0.027	0.028	0.024	0.019	0.271	0.28	0.24	0.19	0.600	0.56	0.51	0.38
1.00	0.025	0.026	0.023	0.018	0.252	0.26	0.23	0.18	0.536	0.52	0.48	0.36
1.01	0.025	0.025	0.022	0.017	0.246	0.25	0.22	0.17	0.518	0.50	0.47	0.34
1.02	0.024	0.024	0.021	0.016	0.240	0.24	0.21	0.16	0.502	0.49	0.45	0.33
1.03	0.023	0.023	0.020	0.016	0.233	0.235	0.20	0.16	0.490	0.47	0.44	0.32
1.04	0.023	0.023	0.020	0.015	0.227	0.23	0.20	0.15	0.475	0.46	0.43	0.31
1.05	0.022	0.022	0.019	0.015	0.220	0.22	0.19	0.15	0.458	0.44	0.41	0.30
1.06	0.022	0.021	0.018	0.014	0.216	0.21	0.18	0.14	0.445	0.42	0.40	0.29
1.07	0.021	0.021	0.018	0.014	0.207	0.205	0.18	0.14	0.430	0.41	0.39	0.28
1.08	0.020	0.020	0.018	0.013	0.201	0.20	0.18	0.13	0.417	0.39	0.38	0.27
1.09	0.020	0.019	0.017	0.013	0.198	0.19	0.17	0.13	0.408	0.38	0.37	0.26
1.10	0.019	0.018	0.016	0.013	0.193	0.185	0.16	0.13	0.397	0.37	0.36	0.25
1.12	0.018	0.017	0.016	0.012	0.182	0.175	0.16	0.12	0.376	0.35	0.34	0.24
1.14	0.017	0.016	0.015	0.011	0.175	0.165	0.15	0.11	0.359	0.33	0.32	0.22
1.16	0.017	0.016	0.014	0.011	0.167	0.16	0.14	0.11	0.340	0.31	0.30	0.21
1.18	0.016	0.015	0.013	0.010	0.161	0.15	0.135	0.10	0.325	0.30	0.29	0.20
1.20	0.015	0.014	0.013	0.009	0.155	0.14	0.13	0.10	0.311	0.28	0.27	0.19
1.30	0.012	0.011	0.011	0.008	0.125	0.11	0.11	0.08	0.252	0.22	0.21	0.16
1.40	0.010	0.010	0.010	0.008	0.104	0.10	0.10	0.08	0.206	0.18	0.17	0.14
1.50	0.009	0.009	0.008	0.007	0.091	0.09	0.08	0.07	0.172	0.14	0.14	0.13
1.60	0.008	0.008	0.007	0.006	0.077	0.08	0.07	0.06	0.155	0.125	0.12	0.12
1.70	0.006	0.006	0.006	0.006		0.06	0.06	0.05	0.133	0.11	0.10	0.10
1.80		0.005	0.005	0.005		0.05	0.05	0.04		0.10	0.07	0.09
1.90		0.004	0.004	0.004		0.04	0.04	0.03		0.08	0.07	0.08
2.00		0.003	0.003	0.003		0.03	0.03			0.07	0.06	0.07
3.00												
4.00												
6.00												
8.00												
10.00												
15.00												

ENTHALPY DEVIATIONS OF GASES AND LIQUIDS FROM IDEAL-GAS BEHAVIOR, $(H^0 - H)/T_c$, cal/(g mole)(°K) (Continued)

T_r	$P_r = 0.3$ W $Z_c=0.23$	I $Z_c=0.25$	II $Z_c=0.27$	III $Z_c=0.29$	$P_r = 0.4$ W $Z_c=0.23$	I $Z_c=0.25$	II $Z_c=0.27$	III $Z_c=0.29$	$P_r = 0.5$ W $Z_c=0.23$	I $Z_c=0.25$	II $Z_c=0.27$	III $Z_c=0.29$
T_r	0.858	0.856	0.846	0.826	0.889	0.885	0.876	0.861	0.914	0.910	0.900	0.892
Sat. gas	1.760	1.300	1.15	1.01	2.21	1.710	1.52	1.35	2.722	2.11	1.91	1.70
Sat. liquid	11.912	11.30	10.79	9.29	11.474	10.80	10.34	8.93	11.035	10.31	9.86	8.58
0.50	15.805	15.75	14.82	11.20	15.794	15.75	14.82	11.20	15.781	15.72	14.82	11.15
0.60	14.825	14.82	13.76	10.76	14.814	14.81	13.76	10.76	14.804	14.81	13.76	10.77
0.70	13.796	13.60	12.54	10.12	13.788	13.60	12.55	10.12	13.780	13.62	12.55	10.12
0.80	12.676	12.07	11.37	9.46	12.677	12.08	11.38	9.46	12.676	12.09	11.39	9.46
0.90	1.349	1.14	1.00	0.75	2.053	1.62	1.48	1.20	11.271	10.51	9.90	1.64
0.92	1.218	1.06	0.94	0.70	1.800	1.50	1.36	1.10	10.921	2.13	1.78	1.51
0.94	1.097	0.98	0.89	0.66	1.597	1.38	1.25	1.02	2.211	1.90	1.64	1.39
0.96	0.993	0.91	0.84	0.61	1.441	1.27	1.16	0.94	1.956	1.72	1.52	1.28
0.98	0.919	0.85	0.79	0.57	1.311	1.18	1.08	0.86	1.756	1.57	1.41	1.20
1.00	0.850	0.79	0.74	0.53	1.200	1.10	1.00	0.80	1.591	1.45	1.32	1.10
1.01	0.819	0.76	0.71	0.50	1.153	1.07	0.96	0.77	1.521	1.40	1.28	1.07
1.02	0.790	0.73	0.69	0.48	1.113	1.04	0.93	0.74	1.455	1.35	1.24	1.03
1.03	0.764	0.71	0.66	0.47	1.067	1.00	0.91	0.72	1.398	1.30	1.20	1.00
1.04	0.739	0.68	0.64	0.45	1.030	0.98	0.88	0.69	1.342	1.25	1.16	0.96
1.05	0.714	0.66	0.62	0.44	0.993	0.95	0.85	0.66	1.289	1.21	1.12	0.93
1.06	0.693	0.63	0.60	0.43	0.960	0.92	0.82	0.64	1.244	1.17	1.09	0.90
1.07	0.669	0.61	0.58	0.41	0.926	0.89	0.80	0.62	1.197	1.13	1.06	0.88
1.08	0.648	0.59	0.56	0.40	0.890	0.86	0.78	0.60	1.154	1.08	1.02	0.85
1.09	0.631	0.57	0.55	0.39	0.869	0.84	0.76	0.59	1.119	1.05	1.00	0.82
1.10	0.614	0.55	0.53	0.37	0.843	0.81	0.74	0.57	1.081	1.02	0.97	0.80
1.12	0.588	0.52	0.50	0.35	0.790	0.77	0.70	0.54	1.016	0.95	0.92	0.75
1.14	0.551	0.49	0.48	0.33	0.751	0.72	0.66	0.51	0.959	0.89	0.87	0.71
1.16	0.521	0.47	0.45	0.31	0.710	0.68	0.62	0.49	0.905	0.85	0.82	0.68
1.18	0.498	0.44	0.42	0.30	0.705	0.65	0.59	0.47	0.875	0.80	0.78	0.66
1.20	0.477	0.42	0.40	0.29	0.646	0.62	0.56	0.45	0.818	0.77	0.75	0.64
1.30	0.384	0.33	0.32	0.25	0.516	0.47	0.42	0.37	0.651	0.61	0.60	0.51
1.40	0.317	0.27	0.26	0.22	0.427	0.37	0.34	0.31	0.536	0.50	0.48	0.43
1.50	0.265	0.22	0.21	0.19	0.356	0.30	0.28	0.26	0.450	0.41	0.38	0.36
1.60	0.232	0.19	0.19	0.17	0.311	0.26	0.24	0.22	0.372	0.34	0.32	0.31
1.70	0.205	0.17	0.16	0.15	0.284	0.21	0.21	0.19	0.340	0.29	0.28	0.27
1.80		0.15	0.14	0.13		0.18	0.18	0.17		0.25	0.24	0.23
1.90		0.13	0.12	0.12		0.16	0.15	0.15		0.21	0.21	0.20
2.00		0.10	0.10	0.10		0.13	0.13	0.13		0.17	0.17	0.17
3.00							0.12				0.13	
4.00												
6.00												
8.00												
10.00												
15.00												

ENTHALPY DEVIATIONS OF GASES AND LIQUIDS FROM IDEAL-GAS BEHAVIOR, $(H^0 - H)/T_c$, cal/(g mole)(°K) (Continued)

	$P_r = 0.6$				$P_r = 0.7$				$P_r = 0.8$			
	W $Z_c=0.23$	I $Z_c=0.25$	II $Z_c=0.27$	III $Z_c=0.29$	W $Z_c=0.23$	I $Z_c=0.25$	II $Z_c=0.27$	III $Z_c=0.29$	W $Z_c=0.23$	I $Z_c=0.25$	II $Z_c=0.27$	III $Z_c=0.29$
T_{r_s}	0.936	0.932	0.928	0.919	0.954	0.952	0.949	0.942	0.971	0.969	0.967	0.963
Sat. gas	3.239	2.55	2.28	2.04	3.746	3.08	2.74	2.45	4.40	3.70	3.24	2.93
Sat. liquid	10.641	9.85	9.38	8.24	10.217	9.46	8.88	7.95	9.753	8.97	8.29	7.58
T_r												
0.50	15.768	15.71	14.82	11.12	15.757	15.70	14.82	11.09	15.743	15.70	14.82	11.02
0.60	14.793	14.80	13.77	10.77	14.783	14.79	13.77	10.77	14.772	14.78	13.77	10.70
0.70	13.773	13.62	12.56	10.15	13.765	13.61	12.56	10.18	13.757	13.62	12.56	10.23
0.80	12.675	12.10	11.30	9.60	12.674	12.10	11.30	9.60	12.672	12.10	11.30	9.72
0.90	11.309	10.53	9.90	9.03	11.324	10.57	9.90	8.97	11.343	10.61	9.91	8.93
0.92	10.972	10.15	9.52	2.09	10.994	10.20	9.52	8.73	11.015	10.24	9.52	8.70
0.94	2.998	2.46	2.12	1.86	10.626	9.74	9.13	8.35	10.644	9.78	9.14	8.35
0.96	2.729	2.19	1.94	1.68	10.078	2.90	2.56	2.17	10.140	9.24	8.56	7.57
0.98	2.412	2.00	1.80	1.54	2.931	2.52	2.30	1.95	3.816	3.45	2.98	2.61
1.00	2.116	1.82	1.66	1.41	2.587	2.23	2.08	1.76	3.001	3.01	2.63	2.30
1.01	2.036	1.75	1.60	1.36	2.437	2.13	2.00	1.68	3.024	2.86	2.49	2.16
1.02	1.912	1.68	1.54	1.30	2.305	2.05	1.92	1.62	2.830	2.69	2.38	2.05
1.03	1.834	1.63	1.49	1.26	2.190	1.96	1.84	1.56	2.664	2.55	2.28	1.95
1.04	1.773	1.57	1.44	1.21	2.086	1.88	1.77	1.50	2.526	2.42	2.19	1.86
1.05	1.670	1.52	1.40	1.17	1.986	1.82	1.71	1.45	2.330	2.30	2.10	1.79
1.06	1.611	1.48	1.36	1.14	1.904	1.76	1.65	1.41	2.283	2.20	2.03	1.72
1.07	1.543	1.42	1.31	1.10	1.820	1.70	1.60	1.36	2.175	2.10	1.95	1.65
1.08	1.481	1.37	1.28	1.07	1.743	1.65	1.54	1.31	2.073	2.01	1.89	1.59
1.09	1.435	1.33	1.24	1.05	1.682	1.60	1.49	1.28	1.996	1.94	1.82	1.53
1.10	1.384	1.30	1.20	1.02	1.618	1.55	1.45	1.25	1.833	1.87	1.76	1.48
1.12	1.260	1.22	1.14	0.97	1.469	1.46	1.37	1.17	1.773	1.76	1.66	1.40
1.14	1.204	1.15	1.08	0.93	1.412	1.37	1.30	1.13	1.656	1.66	1.56	1.34
1.16	1.156	1.10	1.02	0.89	1.323	1.30	1.24	1.09	1.541	1.57	1.48	1.28
1.18	1.088	1.04	0.98	0.86	1.252	1.24	1.18	1.03	1.473	1.50	1.40	1.23
1.20	1.033	1.00	0.93	0.82	1.185	1.18	1.13	1.01	1.376	1.43	1.33	1.18
1.30	0.832	0.77	0.73	0.65	0.929	0.92	0.92	0.81	1.042	1.12	1.06	0.96
1.40	0.657	0.61	0.59	0.53	0.760	0.75	0.74	0.67	0.875	0.88	0.85	0.79
1.50	0.549	0.50	0.48	0.43	0.640	0.62	0.60	0.56	0.770	0.72	0.70	0.66
1.60	0.510	0.41	0.40	0.37	0.544	0.52	0.50	0.47	0.626	0.60	0.58	0.55
1.70	0.421	0.35	0.35	0.32	0.479	0.44	0.42	0.41	0.543	0.51	0.49	0.47
1.80		0.30	0.30	0.28		0.37	0.36	0.36		0.43	0.41	0.41
1.90		0.26	0.25	0.25		0.32	0.32	0.31		0.37	0.36	0.36
2.00		0.22	0.22	0.22		0.28	0.28	0.28		0.32	0.32	0.32
3.00			0.15				0.16				0.17	
4.00												
6.00												
8.00												
10.00												
15.00												

ENTHALPY DEVIATIONS OF GASES AND LIQUIDS FROM IDEAL-GAS BEHAVIOR, $(H^o - H)/T_c$, cal/(g mole)(°K) (Continued)

T_r	$P_r = 0.9$ W $Z_c=0.23$	I $Z_c=0.25$	II $Z_c=0.27$	III $Z_c=0.29$	$P_r = 1.0$ W $Z_c=0.23$	I $Z_c=0.25$	II $Z_c=0.27$	III $Z_c=0.29$	$P_r = 1.05$ W $Z_c=0.23$	I $Z_c=0.25$	II $Z_c=0.27$	III $Z_c=0.29$
T_r	0.986	0.983	0.984	0.982	1.000	1.000	1.000	1.000				
Sat. gas	5.156	4.50	4.02	3.61	7.478	6.50	5.80	5.40				
Sat. liquid	9.261	8.46	7.54	7.15	7.478	6.50	5.80	5.40				
0.50	15.730	15.68	14.81	11.00	15.717	15.66	14.81	11.00	15.715	15.66	14.80	10.97
0.60	14.761	14.78	13.77	10.65	14.750	14.78	13.77	10.65	14.763	14.78	13.77	10.62
0.70	13.750	13.64	12.56	10.25	13.740	13.66	12.56	10.25	13.737	13.66	12.56	10.30
0.80	12.671	12.20	11.40	9.74	12.671	12.20	11.40	9.74	12.652	12.20	11.40	9.80
0.90	11.354	10.64	9.92	8.90	11.379	10.67	9.94	8.90	11.390	10.67	9.96	9.00
0.92	11.040	10.27	9.55	8.61	11.065	10.31	9.69	8.61	11.076	10.32	9.61	8.65
0.94	10.691	9.85	9.16	8.30	10.726	9.85	9.19	8.30	10.746	9.87	9.21	8.30
0.96	10.207	9.24	8.60	7.62	10.273	9.25	8.67	7.62	10.313	9.26	8.70	7.76
0.98	9.624	8.66	7.84	7.04	9.746	8.67	7.69	7.04	9.818	8.68	8.02	7.24
1.00	4.149	3.75	3.28	3.09	7.478	6.50	5.80	5.40	8.360	7.10	6.58	5.60
1.01	3.747	3.40	3.08	2.81	4.914	4.70	4.26	4.25	6.333	5.62	5.47	4.80
1.02	3.440	3.20	2.92	2.63	4.288	4.18	3.86	3.65	4.852	4.75	4.73	4.10
1.03	3.215	3.00	2.80	2.47	3.914	3.75	3.56	3.17	4.344	4.22	4.08	3.57
1.04	3.012	2.82	2.68	2.30	3.615	3.42	3.31	2.84	3.930	3.85	3.70	3.19
1.05	2.836	2.69	2.56	2.17	3.368	3.18	3.10	2.63	3.662	3.56	3.41	2.96
1.06	2.694	2.56	2.46	2.04	3.175	2.96	2.93	2.48	3.437	3.30	3.20	2.75
1.07	2.553	2.45	2.36	1.95	2.991	2.80	2.79	2.35	3.226	3.10	3.02	2.58
1.08	2.428	2.36	2.28	1.86	2.831	2.65	2.66	2.22	3.044	2.93	2.87	2.42
1.09	2.329	2.26	2.19	1.80	2.706	2.55	2.52	2.13	2.903	2.78	2.72	2.32
1.10	2.225	2.17	2.11	1.75	2.574	2.46	2.42	2.05	2.756	2.68	2.60	2.21
1.12	2.052	2.02	1.97	1.64	2.360	2.28	2.24	1.91	2.518	2.45	2.40	2.06
1.14	1.906	1.88	1.85	1.56	2.181	2.15	2.09	1.80	2.321	2.29	2.24	1.93
1.16	1.765	1.78	1.74	1.48	2.021	2.04	1.97	1.70	2.147	2.12	2.10	1.83
1.18	1.660	1.70	1.65	1.43	1.890	1.95	1.87	1.62	2.005	2.00	1.99	1.74
1.20	1.568	1.63	1.56	1.37	1.777	1.86	1.78	1.55	1.881	1.91	1.90	1.66
1.30	1.212	1.27	1.21	1.08	1.362	1.46	1.40	1.27	1.435	1.52	1.49	1.36
1.40	0.986	1.00	0.97	0.89	1.103	1.17	1.13	1.05	1.161	1.24	1.21	1.12
1.50	0.829	0.82	0.78	0.74	0.943	0.93	0.91	0.87	0.976	1.01	0.98	0.92
1.60	0.704	0.69	0.64	0.63	0.786	0.76	0.74	0.72	0.825	0.82	0.79	0.76
1.70	0.617	0.59	0.56	0.54	0.688	0.64	0.63	0.60	0.722	0.68	0.66	0.64
1.80		0.51	0.48	0.48		0.55	0.54	0.52		0.59	0.57	0.56
1.90		0.44	0.43	0.42		0.49	0.48	0.47		0.52	0.51	0.52
2.00		0.39	0.39	0.39		0.43	0.43	0.43		0.46	0.46	0.45
3.00			0.18				0.19				0.20	
4.00												
5.00												
8.00												
10.00												
15.00												

ENTHALPY DEVIATIONS OF GASES AND LIQUIDS FROM IDEAL-GAS BEHAVIOR, $(H° − H)/T_c$, cal/(g mole)(°K) (Continued)

T_r	$P_r = 1.10$ W $Z_c = 0.23$	I $Z_c = 0.25$	II $Z_c = 0.27$	III $Z_c = 0.29$	$P_r = 1.15$ W $Z_c = 0.23$	I $Z_c = 0.25$	II $Z_c = 0.27$	III $Z_c = 0.29$	$P_r = 1.20$ W $Z_c = 0.23$	I $Z_c = 0.25$	II $Z_c = 0.27$	III $Z_c = 0.29$
0.50	15.713	15.65	14.80	10.95	15.704	15.65	14.80	10.94	15.695	15.65	14.80	10.93
0.60	14.744	14.78	13.77	10.62	14.738	14.70	13.76	10.61	14.732	14.78	13.76	10.61
0.70	13.732	13.50	12.55	10.40	13.728	13.50	12.55	10.45	13.723	13.50	12.54	10.45
0.80	12.634	12.12	11.40	9.95	12.631	12.15	11.40	10.00	12.628	12.16	11.41	10.00
0.90	11.394	10.67	9.98	9.00	11.405	10.70	10.01	9.10	11.405	10.71	10.03	9.10
0.92	11.086	10.34	9.63	8.60	11.096	10.35	9.65	8.64	11.105	10.37	9.68	8.68
0.94	10.765	9.89	9.24	8.20	10.769	9.92	9.26	8.30	10.769	9.94	9.29	8.30
0.96	10.354	9.30	8.74	7.82	10.372	9.35	8.78	7.95	10.397	9.40	8.84	7.90
0.98	9.871	8.69	8.14	7.28	9.914	8.70	8.26	7.38	9.958	8.73	8.38	7.48
1.00	9.104	7.50	7.36	6.55	9.210	7.86	7.52	6.66	9.318	8.00	7.68	6.80
1.01	7.722	6.80	6.68	6.00	8.595	7.35	6.90	6.08	8.867	7.55	7.12	6.40
1.02	5.686	5.81	5.60	5.15	6.851	6.70	6.00	5.26	7.885	7.00	6.40	5.88
1.03	4.858	4.85	4.60	4.35	5.504	5.89	5.04	4.58	6.405	6.30	5.48	5.30
1.04	4.354	4.13	4.10	3.70	4.804	4.94	4.47	4.08	5.355	5.12	4.88	4.65
1.05	3.992	3.80	3.73	3.21	4.383	4.38	4.02	3.75	4.756	4.50	4.30	4.13
1.06	3.725	3.52	3.47	2.94	4.029	3.93	3.69	3.42	4.366	4.05	3.92	3.65
1.07	3.477	3.31	3.26	2.74	3.744	3.62	3.45	3.18	4.032	3.80	3.64	3.27
1.08	3.269	3.12	3.08	2.61	3.507	3.41	3.26	2.92	3.760	3.60	3.42	3.02
1.09	3.111	2.99	2.92	2.48	3.328	3.23	3.09	2.75	3.558	3.40	3.26	2.82
1.10	2.946	2.87	2.79	2.37	3.143	3.09	2.95	2.61	3.349	3.24	3.09	2.72
1.12	2.684	2.63	2.56	2.20	2.855	2.83	2.72	2.40	3.032	3.00	2.88	2.54
1.14	2.468	2.44	2.38	2.09	2.618	2.64	2.53	2.23	2.775	2.76	2.68	2.39
1.16	2.428	2.28	2.24	1.98	2.409	2.47	2.37	2.12	2.545	2.61	2.50	2.30
1.18	2.121	2.17	2.12	1.87	2.240	2.31	2.24	2.02	2.362	2.47	2.37	2.17
1.20	1.987	2.05	2.02	1.78	2.095	2.22	2.13	1.93	2.205	2.35	2.25	2.07
1.30	1.510	1.63	1.58	1.44	1.585	1.75	1.66	1.57	1.661	1.84	1.74	1.68
1.40	1.217	1.31	1.28	1.20	1.287	1.44	1.36	1.26	1.342	1.46	1.43	1.36
1.50	1.025	1.05	1.04	0.99	1.073	1.15	1.10	1.04	1.161	1.21	1.17	1.11
1.60	0.867	0.86	0.84	0.82	0.906	0.93	0.90	0.86	0.947	0.99	0.96	0.92
1.70	0.771	0.72	0.70	0.69	0.818	0.77	0.75	0.72	0.837	0.82	0.80	0.76
1.80		0.61	0.60	0.59		0.65	0.64	0.62		0.69	0.68	0.65
1.90		0.54	0.54	0.52		0.57	0.56	0.54		0.59	0.58	0.56
2.00		0.49	0.48	0.47		0.51	0.50	0.49		0.53	0.52	0.51
3.00			0.20				0.21				0.22	
4.00												
6.00												
8.00												
10.00												
15.00												

ENTHALPY DEVIATIONS OF GASES AND LIQUIDS FROM IDEAL-GAS BEHAVIOR, $(H^\circ - H)/T_c$, cal/(g mole)(°K) (Continued)

T_r	$P_r = 1.25$ W, $Z_c = 0.23$	$P_r = 1.25$ II, $Z_c = 0.27$	$P_r = 1.30$ W, $Z_c = 0.23$	$P_r = 1.30$ II, $Z_c = 0.27$	$P_r = 1.35$ W, $Z_c = 0.23$	$P_r = 1.35$ II, $Z_c = 0.27$	$P_r = 1.40$ W, $Z_c = 0.23$	$P_r = 1.40$ II, $Z_c = 0.27$	$P_r = 1.45$ W, $Z_c = 0.23$	$P_r = 1.45$ II, $Z_c = 0.27$	$P_r = 1.50$ W, $Z_c = 0.23$	$P_r = 1.50$ II, $Z_c = 0.27$
0.50	15.687	14.80	15.681	14.80	15.675	14.80	15.682	14.80	15.661	14.80	15.655	14.80
0.60	14.724	13.76	14.719	13.76	14.715	13.76	14.709	13.76	14.704	13.76	14.698	13.75
0.70	13.720	12.54	13.715	12.54	13.865	12.54	13.707	12.53	13.704	12.53	13.700	12.52
0.80	12.626	11.40	12.625	11.40	12.623	11.40	12.622	11.40	12.618	11.40	12.614	11.40
0.90	11.411	10.06	11.416	10.08	11.420	10.10	11.425	10.12	11.431	10.15	11.436	10.16
0.92	11.113	9.70	11.120	9.74	11.128	9.76	11.137	9.80	11.144	9.83	11.150	9.87
0.94	10.780	9.32	10.803	9.36	10.672	9.42	10.848	9.48	10.854	9.50	10.862	9.52
0.96	10.420	8.90	10.440	8.96	10.462	9.03	10.482	9.10	10.504	9.13	10.527	9.16
0.98	10.000	8.46	10.032	8.55	9.910	8.60	10.097	8.64	10.117	8.69	10.139	8.73
1.00	9.435	7.84	9.502	8.00	9.571	8.08	9.625	8.16	9.659	8.20	9.693	8.24
1.01	9.023	7.35	9.127	7.58	9.225	7.70	9.139	7.83	9.379	7.89	9.428	7.96
1.02	8.378	6.73	8.571	7.06	8.756	7.26	8.596	7.45	9.029	7.54	9.104	7.64
1.03	7.308	5.82	7.712	6.16	8.097	6.52	7.763	6.89	8.624	7.08	8.738	7.28
1.04	5.998	5.12	6.600	5.40	7.174	5.79	6.676	6.18	7.953	6.48	8.115	6.78
1.05	5.200	4.57	5.770	4.84	6.314	5.20	5.841	5.56	7.207	5.86	7.514	6.16
1.06	4.717	4.19	5.191	4.46	5.644	4.79	5.251	5.12	6.494	5.40	6.858	5.68
1.07	4.325	3.89	4.706	4.15	5.069	4.43	4.754	4.70	5.822	4.94	6.184	5.19
1.08	4.013	3.66	4.335	3.89	4.640	4.15	4.374	4.40	5.282	4.62	5.597	4.84
1.09	3.788	3.46	4.072	3.66	4.342	3.88	4.107	4.11	4.911	4.32	5.191	4.52
1.10	3.557	3.30	3.803	3.47	4.038	3.67	3.834	3.88	4.536	4.08	4.781	4.28
1.12	3.207	3.03	3.412	3.17	3.607	3.34	3.438	3.51	4.017	3.69	4.216	3.88
1.14	2.925	2.82	3.099	2.96	3.265	3.10	3.121	3.23	3.613	3.40	3.785	3.56
1.16	2.678	2.64	2.830	2.77	2.974	2.89	2.849	3.01	3.275	3.15	3.423	3.28
1.18	2.481	2.50	2.615	2.62	2.744	2.72	2.634	2.83	3.010	2.95	3.138	3.08
1.20	2.312	2.36	2.433	2.47	2.548	2.58	2.448	2.68	2.791	2.78	2.909	2.89
1.30	1.733	1.84	1.814	1.93	1.891	2.00	1.824	2.08	2.047	2.16	2.121	2.23
1.40	1.402	1.48	1.464	1.54	1.523	1.60	1.462	1.65	1.643	1.72	1.699	1.79
1.50	1.168	1.21	1.220	1.24	1.331	1.28	1.228	1.35	1.613	1.40	1.414	1.46
1.60	0.984	0.99	1.027	1.03	1.067	1.08	1.032	1.13	1.148	1.19	1.186	1.24
1.70	0.870	0.84	0.907	0.88	0.948	0.92	0.902	0.96	0.965	0.99	1.363	1.03
1.80		0.71		0.74		0.77		0.79		0.83		0.86
1.90		0.62		0.66		0.68		0.69		0.72		0.75
2.00		0.54		0.56		0.58		0.60		0.63		0.66
3.00		0.22		0.23		0.24		0.24		0.25		0.26
4.00												
6.00												
8.00												
10.00												
15.00												

Enthalpy Deviations of Gases and Liquids from Ideal-gas Behavior, $(H^0 - H)/T_c$, cal/(g mole)(°K) (Continued)

T_r	$P_r=1.60$ W ($Z_c=0.23$)	$P_r=1.60$ II ($Z_c=0.27$)	$P_r=1.70$ W ($Z_c=0.23$)	$P_r=1.70$ II ($Z_c=0.27$)	$P_r=1.8$ II ($Z_c=0.27$)	$P_r=1.9$ II ($Z_c=0.27$)	$P_r=2.0$ II ($Z_c=0.27$)	$P_r=2.2$ II ($Z_c=0.27$)	$P_r=2.4$ II ($Z_c=0.27$)	$P_r=2.6$ II ($Z_c=0.27$)	$P_r=2.8$ II ($Z_c=0.27$)	$P_r=3.0$ II ($Z_c=0.27$)
0.50	15.643	14.80	15.630	14.80	14.80	14.80	14.80	14.79	14.78	14.77	14.77	14.76
0.60	14.687	13.75	14.668	13.74	13.73	13.72	13.72	13.69	13.66	13.62	13.60	13.58
0.70	13.692	12.52	13.683	12.52	12.51	12.50	12.49	12.45	12.42	12.39	12.36	12.33
0.80	12.606	11.40	12.600	11.40	11.40	11.39	11.38	11.37	11.36	11.35	11.34	11.32
0.90	11.443	10.20	11.451	10.24	10.26	10.28	10.29	10.30	10.31	10.32	10.34	10.35
0.92	11.162	9.91	11.176	9.97	10.00	10.03	10.04	10.05	10.06	10.07	10.06	10.05
0.94	10.876	9.58	10.892	9.65	9.68	9.72	9.76	9.77	9.78	9.79	9.80	9.82
0.96	10.573	9.20	10.619	9.29	9.34	9.40	9.44	9.46	9.49	9.51	9.53	9.55
0.98	10.180	8.78	10.221	8.89	8.96	9.04	9.08	9.11	9.14	9.16	9.19	9.22
1.00	9.761	8.32	9.829	8.47	8.55	8.63	8.69	8.74	8.78	8.82	8.87	8.91
1.01	9.524	8.00	9.601	8.21	8.34	8.42	8.46	8.51	8.57	8.63	8.69	8.75
1.02	9.322	7.80	9.375	7.98	8.11	8.19	8.27	8.32	8.38	8.44	8.49	8.58
1.03	8.947	7.47	9.087	7.69	7.83	7.98	8.01	8.08	8.16	8.24	8.32	8.40
1.04	8.539	7.10	8.748	7.36	7.52	7.66	7.77	7.86	7.95	8.04	8.13	8.22
1.05	8.049	6.65	8.358	6.96	7.16	7.36	7.48	7.59	7.70	7.81	7.92	8.04
1.06	7.517	6.24	7.936	6.56	6.81	7.00	7.16	7.30	7.45	7.60	7.74	7.88
1.07	6.886	5.68	7.427	6.07	6.36	6.62	6.81	6.99	7.16	7.33	7.50	7.68
1.08	6.264	5.18	6.874	5.62	5.91	6.26	6.44	6.65	6.86	7.07	7.28	7.50
1.09	5.803	4.88	6.385	5.16	5.52	5.90	6.09	6.33	6.57	6.82	7.07	7.31
1.10	5.332	4.63	5.875	4.92	5.22	5.57	5.72	6.01	6.29	6.57	6.85	7.13
1.12	4.666	4.18	5.120	4.48	4.72	5.01	5.18	5.50	5.82	6.14	6.46	6.79
1.14	4.170	3.85	4.560	4.12	4.40	4.61	4.80	5.09	5.38	5.68	5.97	6.26
1.16	3.754	3.56	4.091	3.83	4.04	4.29	4.50	4.83	5.16	5.49	5.81	6.13
1.18	3.429	3.36	3.725	3.59	3.82	4.02	4.24	4.56	4.89	5.21	5.54	5.87
1.20	3.160	3.12	3.423	3.39	3.56	3.78	4.00	4.32	4.64	4.96	5.28	5.60
1.30	2.285	2.42	2.448	2.56	2.68	2.84	3.05	3.34	3.62	3.90	4.19	4.47
1.40	1.821	1.91	1.930	2.04	2.16	2.30	2.38	2.62	2.86	3.10	3.34	3.58
1.50	1.516	1.58	1.614	1.67	1.80	1.88	1.93	2.13	2.33	2.53	2.73	2.92
1.60	1.269	1.32	1.351	1.40	1.48	1.56	1.63	1.79	1.95	2.10	2.25	2.40
1.70	1.118	1.10	1.179	1.18	1.26	1.33	1.39	1.51	1.63	1.75	1.87	1.98
1.80		0.96		1.00	1.07	1.14	1.18	1.28	1.38	1.49	1.60	1.70
1.90		0.82		0.87	0.92	0.97	1.03	1.13	1.22	1.31	1.40	1.50
2.00		0.70		0.75	0.79	0.84	0.88	0.97	1.07	1.17	1.26	1.35
4.00		0.27		0.29	0.30	0.31	0.32	0.34	0.36	0.38	0.40	0.43
6.00				0.03	0.05	0.09	0.11	0.13	0.15	0.16	0.18	0.20
8.00					0.01	0.01	0.01	0.01	0.01	0.02	0.03	0.04
10.00					0.00	0.00	0.00	0.00	0.00	0.00	0.00	0.01
15.00					0.03	0.03	0.03	0.04	0.04	0.05	0.06	0.07

ENTHALPY DEVIATIONS OF GASES AND LIQUIDS FROM IDEAL-GAS BEHAVIOR, $(H° - H)/T_c$, cal/(g mole)(°K) (Continued)

T_r	$P_r = 3.5$	$P_r = 4.0$	$P_r = 4.5$	$P_r = 5.0$	$P_r = 6.0$	$P_r = 7.0$	$P_r = 8.0$	$P_r = 9.0$	$P_r = 10.0$	$P_r = 15.0$	$P_r = 20.0$	$P_r = 25.0$	$P_r = 30.0$
	II $Z_c = 0.27$	II $Z_c = 0.27$	II $Z_c = 0.27$	II $Z_c = 0.27$	II $Z_c = 0.27$	II $Z_c = 0.27$	II $Z_c = 0.27$	II $Z_c = 0.27$	II $Z_c = 0.27$	II $Z_c = 0.27$	II $Z_c = 0.27$	II $Z_c = 0.27$	II $Z_c = 0.27$
0.50	14.75	14.73	14.71	14.68	14.64	14.57	14.52	14.45	14.40	14.00	13.57	13.10	12.57
0.60	13.53	13.48	13.44	13.40	13.30	13.21	13.14	13.06	12.96	12.49	11.90	11.27	10.58
0.70	12.28	12.22	12.17	12.12	12.03	11.94	11.82	11.68	11.57	10.96	10.36	9.60	8.94
0.80	11.26	11.21	11.16	11.11	11.02	10.96	10.84	10.68	10.57	9.97	9.34	8.62	8.00
0.90	10.28	10.26	10.24	10.22	10.14	10.08	10.02	9.93	9.83	9.32	8.74	8.12	7.58
0.92	10.04	10.04	10.04	10.04	9.97	9.89	9.85	9.77	9.68	9.17	8.62	8.02	7.47
0.94	9.81	9.80	9.80	9.80	9.80	9.73	9.69	9.60	9.52	9.06	8.51	7.93	7.37
0.96	9.58	9.60	9.60	9.60	9.60	9.56	9.50	9.42	9.37	8.91	8.38	7.80	7.24
0.98	9.31	9.40	9.40	9.40	9.40	9.36	9.31	9.25	9.22	8.75	8.24	7.64	7.10
1.00	8.99	9.08	9.11	9.13	9.17	9.15	9.12	9.02	9.02	8.57	8.06	7.49	6.94
1.01	8.83	8.94	8.98	9.01	9.06	9.04	9.02	8.92	8.92	8.48	7.94	7.40	6.84
1.02	8.68	8.80	8.85	8.89	8.95	8.93	8.91	8.82	8.82	8.36	7.82	7.31	6.70
1.03	8.52	8.66	8.72	8.77	8.83	8.82	8.80	8.70	8.70	8.24	7.71	7.21	6.60
1.04	8.36	8.51	8.59	8.65	8.71	8.71	8.69	8.60	8.60	8.10	7.60	7.12	6.50
1.05	8.21	8.37	8.45	8.53	8.60	8.60	8.58	8.48	8.48	8.00	7.51	7.02	6.40
1.06	8.04	8.20	8.29	8.38	8.45	8.47	8.45	8.36	8.36	7.88	7.40	6.92	6.30
1.07	7.86	8.03	8.13	8.22	8.30	8.33	8.31	8.22	8.22	7.73	7.29	6.84	6.20
1.08	7.68	7.87	7.96	8.07	8.16	8.19	8.18	8.14	8.14	7.64	7.20	6.74	6.11
1.09	7.51	7.70	7.80	7.91	8.02	8.05	8.04	8.00	8.00	7.51	7.06	6.64	6.01
1.10	7.33	7.53	7.64	7.76	7.88	7.92	7.91	7.90	7.90	7.41	6.94	6.53	5.91
1.12	7.05	7.26	7.40	7.52	7.66	7.70	7.70	7.64	7.66	7.20	6.74	6.33	5.74
1.14	6.77	7.00	7.16	7.29	7.44	7.49	7.50	7.43	7.45	7.00	6.56	6.15	5.55
1.16	6.49	6.74	6.92	7.06	7.22	7.28	7.30	7.22	7.23	6.82	6.36	5.93	5.37
1.18	6.21	6.49	6.67	6.83	7.00	7.07	7.10	7.02	7.03	6.62	6.18	5.76	5.19
1.20	5.92	6.24	6.42	6.60	6.78	6.86	6.89	6.84	6.86	6.44	6.00	5.59	5.00
1.30	4.82	5.18	5.38	5.58	5.82	5.98	5.98	5.94	5.96	5.64	5.16	4.77	4.18
1.40	3.92	4.26	4.47	4.68	4.94	5.10	5.10	5.11	5.18	4.95	4.44	4.04	3.45
1.50	3.24	3.50	3.75	3.90	4.17	4.36	4.36	4.42	4.48	4.30	3.78	3.39	2.80
1.60	2.65	2.91	3.10	3.28	3.56	3.75	3.78	3.84	3.90	3.76	3.25	2.81	2.23
1.70	2.22	2.45	2.62	2.80	3.08	3.27	3.32	3.37	3.44	3.30	2.80	2.32	1.80
1.80	1.90	2.11	2.27	2.42	2.71	2.89	2.97	3.02	3.07	2.93	2.45	1.92	1.43
1.90	1.71	1.91	2.05	2.20	2.45	2.61	2.71	2.75	2.79	2.66	2.18	1.59	1.14
2.00	1.55	1.76	1.90	2.05	2.28	2.43	2.54	2.56	2.62	2.47	1.98	1.35	0.94
3.00	0.48	0.53	0.57	0.61	0.65	0.66	0.67	0.66	0.63	0.27	-0.25	-0.90	-1.78
4.00	0.24	0.28	0.31	0.34	0.35	0.35	0.19	0.16	0.14	-0.02	-0.23	-0.27	-1.48
6.00	0.05	0.06	0.08	0.10	0.14	0.14	0.05	0.05	0.04	-0.03	-0.14	-0.14	-0.48
8.00	0.01	0.02	0.02	0.03	0.03	0.03	0.02	0.02	0.02	-0.02	-0.07	-0.14	-0.21
10.00	0.00	0.00	0.00	0.00	0.00	0.00	0.00	0.00	0.00	0.00	0.00	0.00	-0.03
15.00	0.08	0.09	0.10	0.11	0.13	0.15	0.16	0.17	0.17	0.15	0.14	0.10	-0.07

Fugacity Coefficients of Pure Gases and Liquids, f/p

Values of T_{r_s} and $(f/p)_s$ for P_r above 1.0 are hypothetical, obtained by extrapolation

T_r	$P_r = 0.10$				$P_r = 0.20$			
	W $Z_c=0.23$	I $Z_c=0.25$	II $Z_c=0.27$	III $Z_c=0.29$	W $Z_c=0.23$	I $Z_c=0.25$	II $Z_c=0.27$	III $Z_c=0.29$
T_{r_s} Sat. gas and liquids	0.758	0.758	0.743	0.714	0.819	0.817	0.805	0.781
$(f/p)_s$	0.887	0.944	0.946	0.948	0.840	0.885	0.887	0.890
0.50	0.0058	0.00203	0.0102	0.0509	0.0030	0.00103	0.00518	0.0266
0.60	0.0763	0.0707	0.111	0.212	0.0387	0.0358	0.0563	0.113
0.70	0.427	0.412	0.640	0.800	0.216	0.209	0.325	0.410
0.80	0.906	0.957	0.961	0.966	0.719	0.761	0.848	0.900
0.90	0.944	0.975	0.972	0.975	0.885	0.918	0.922	0.936
0.92	0.948	0.977	0.975	0.980	0.897	0.924	0.929	0.939
0.94	0.949	0.978	0.977	0.982	0.907	0.930	0.934	0.943
0.96	0.953	0.979	0.979	0.983	0.916	0.936	0.939	0.947
0.98	0.958	0.980	0.981	0.984	0.921	0.940	0.943	0.950
1.00	0.958	0.981	0.983	0.984	0.930	0.945	0.947	0.953
1.01	0.960	0.982	0.983	0.985	0.932	0.946	0.949	0.955
1.02	0.961	0.982	0.983	0.985	0.932	0.948	0.951	0.956
1.03	0.962	0.983	0.984	0.986	0.933	0.950	0.953	0.958
1.04	0.963	0.984	0.985	0.986	0.935	0.953	0.955	0.959
1.05	0.964	0.985	0.985	0.987	0.940	0.955	0.956	0.961
1.06	0.965	0.986	0.986	0.987	0.941	0.958	0.958	0.962
1.07	0.967	0.986	0.986	0.988	0.942	0.959	0.959	0.964
1.08	0.968	0.987	0.986	0.988	0.947	0.961	0.962	0.965
1.09	0.969	0.987	0.987	0.989	0.948	0.962	0.962	0.967
1.10	0.970	0.988	0.988	0.989	0.949	0.964	0.964	0.968
1.12	0.971	0.989	0.989	0.990	0.951	0.967	0.967	0.969
1.14	0.972	0.990	0.990	0.990	0.954	0.969	0.969	0.971
1.16	0.975	0.990	0.991	0.991	0.958	0.970	0.970	0.972
1.18	0.975	0.991	0.991	0.991	0.960	0.972	0.973	0.973
1.20	0.975	0.991	0.993	0.992	0.961	0.973	0.974	0.975
1.30	0.975	0.993	0.995	0.993	0.972	0.979	0.980	0.982
1.40	0.975	0.994	0.996	0.995	0.980	0.983	0.985	0.986
1.50	0.975	0.995	0.997	0.996	0.985	0.987	0.987	0.989
1.60	0.975	0.996	0.997	0.997	0.989	0.989	0.989	0.991
1.70		0.997	0.997	0.997	0.990	0.991	0.989	0.992
1.80		0.997	0.998	0.998		0.993	0.990	0.994
1.90		0.998	0.999	0.999		0.994	0.990	0.995
2.00		0.998	1.000	1.000		0.995	0.992	0.997
3.00		1.000	1.000	1.000		1.000	1.000	1.000
4.00		1.000	1.000	1.000		1.000	1.000	1.000
6.00		1.000	1.000	1.000		1.000	1.000	1.000
8.00		1.000	1.000	1.000		1.000	1.000	1.000
10.00		1.000	1.000	1.000		1.000	1.000	1.000
15.00		1.000	1.000	1.000		1.000	1.000	1.000

FUGACITY COEFFICIENTS OF PURE GASES AND LIQUIDS, f/p *(Continued)*

	$P_r = 0.30$				$P_r = 0.40$				$P_r = 0.50$			
T_r	W $Z_c=0.23$	I $Z_c=0.25$	II $Z_c=0.27$	III $Z_c=0.29$	W $Z_c=0.23$	I $Z_c=0.25$	II $Z_c=0.27$	III $Z_c=0.29$	W $Z_c=0.23$	I $Z_c=0.25$	II $Z_c=0.27$	III $Z_c=0.29$
T_{rs}	0.858	0.856	0.840	0.843	0.889	0.885	0.876	0.861	0.914	0.910	0.900	0.892
Sat. gas or liquids	0.806	0.838	0.840	0.826	0.772	0.803	0.805	0.807	0.749	0.775	0.777	0.781
0.50	0.0020	0.00070	0.00351	0.018	0.0015	0.00053	0.00268	0.0135	0.0012	0.00043	0.0029	0.015
0.60	0.0261	0.0210	0.0381	0.078	0.0198	0.0144	0.0291	0.0580	0.0161	0.0155	0.0236	0.048
0.70	0.146	0.1411	0.220	0.275	0.110	0.1072	0.168	0.210	0.0891	0.0869	0.136	0.177
0.80	0.482	0.514	0.574	0.730	0.363	0.390	0.437	0.551	0.294	0.316	0.354	0.448
0.90	0.837	0.865	0.871	0.888	0.696	0.813	0.820	0.840	0.707	0.722	0.759	0.740
0.92	0.853	0.870	0.882	0.898	0.805	0.830	0.836	0.851	0.785	0.760	0.789	0.795
0.94	0.865	0.885	0.892	0.902	0.820	0.840	0.849	0.861	0.774	0.788	0.806	0.819
0.96	0.880	0.893	0.900	0.909	0.836	0.852	0.860	0.870	0.795	0.805	0.820	0.834
0.98	0.887	0.902	0.907	0.917	0.846	0.862	0.870	0.880	0.813	0.825	0.834	0.846
1.00	0.897	0.909	0.916	0.920	0.858	0.871	0.879	0.887	0.829	0.840	0.846	0.856
1.01	0.900	0.913	0.917	0.924	0.865	0.876	0.884	0.892	0.834	0.845	0.852	0.861
1.02	0.901	0.915	0.919	0.926	0.868	0.882	0.887	0.896	0.838	0.850	0.856	0.865
1.03	0.905	0.918	0.922	0.929	0.875	0.885	0.891	0.900	0.843	0.856	0.860	0.871
1.04	0.908	0.921	0.926	0.931	0.879	0.890	0.896	0.903	0.849	0.860	0.868	0.874
1.05	0.911	0.925	0.928	0.934	0.883	0.895	0.899	0.907	0.854	0.866	0.871	0.879
1.06	0.913	0.929	0.930	0.936	0.887	0.899	0.903	0.910	0.860	0.871	0.876	0.884
1.07	0.919	0.930	0.933	0.939	0.893	0.903	0.906	0.914	0.864	0.876	0.879	0.888
1.08	0.922	0.933	0.935	0.941	0.898	0.907	0.910	0.916	0.869	0.880	0.883	0.892
1.09	0.923	0.936	0.938	0.944	0.900	0.910	0.913	0.919	0.874	0.884	0.887	0.895
1.10	0.925	0.938	0.942	0.945	0.905	0.913	0.916	0.922	0.877	0.888	0.892	0.898
1.12	0.925	0.943	0.943	0.948	0.909	0.918	0.920	0.926	0.883	0.895	0.898	0.906
1.14	0.933	0.946	0.947	0.952	0.913	0.924	0.926	0.931	0.891	0.903	0.905	0.911
1.16	0.935	0.949	0.950	0.955	0.921	0.929	0.931	0.935	0.899	0.908	0.910	0.916
1.18	0.939	0.952	0.954	0.957	0.925	0.932	0.936	0.938	0.905	0.913	0.917	0.921
1.20	0.941	0.955	0.958	0.960	0.928	0.936	0.939	0.942	0.909	0.918	0.920	0.926
1.30	0.954	0.966	0.968	0.970	0.941	0.952	0.955	0.957	0.926	0.939	0.942	0.944
1.40	0.966	0.973	0.976	0.977	0.955	0.964	0.967	0.967	0.940	0.954	0.956	0.957
1.50	0.972	0.980	0.980	0.982	0.965	0.973	0.973	0.975	0.951	0.965	0.966	0.969
1.60	0.979	0.983	0.983	0.986	0.970	0.978	0.978	0.979	0.965	0.973	0.972	0.976
1.70	0.984	0.986	0.984	0.988	0.975	0.982	0.980	0.984	0.975	0.978	0.976	0.981
1.80		0.990	0.986	0.991		0.986	0.983	0.988		0.984	0.980	0.985
1.90		0.992	0.987	0.993		0.991	0.985	0.991		0.988	0.983	0.989
2.00		0.994	0.989	0.995		0.993	0.987	0.993		0.992	0.985	0.991
3.00		1.000	1.000	1.000		1.000	1.000	1.000		1.000	1.000	1.000
4.00		1.000	1.000	1.000		1.000	1.000	1.000		1.000	1.000	1.000
6.00		1.000	1.000	1.000		1.000	1.000	1.000		1.000	1.000	1.000
8.00		1.000	1.000	1.000		1.000	1.000	1.000		1.000	1.000	1.000
10.00		1.000	1.000	1.000		1.000	1.000	1.000		1.000	1.000	1.000
15.00		1.000	1.000	1.000		1.000	1.000	1.000		1.000	1.000	1.000

FUGACITY COEFFICIENTS OF PURE GASES AND LIQUIDS, f/p (Continued)

T_r	$P_r = 0.60$ W $Z_c=0.23$	I $Z_c=0.25$	II $Z_c=0.27$	III $Z_c=0.29$	$P_r = 0.70$ W $Z_c=0.23$	I $Z_c=0.25$	II $Z_c=0.27$	III $Z_c=0.29$	$P_r = 0.80$ W $Z_c=0.23$	I $Z_c=0.25$	II $Z_c=0.27$	III $Z_c=0.29$
$T_{r,s}$	0.936	0.932	0.928	0.919	0.954	0.952	0.949	0.942	0.971	0.969	0.967	0.963
Sat. gas or liquids	0.727	0.749	0.752	0.760	0.705	0.727	0.730	0.738	0.683	0.703	0.710	0.718
0.50	0.0010	0.00037	0.00186	0.00942	0.0009	0.00032	0.00162	0.0082	0.0008	0.00028	0.00144	0.00737
0.60	0.0136	0.0126	0.0200	0.0410	0.0118	0.0110	0.0174	0.0360	0.0104	0.00976	0.0155	0.0310
0.70	0.0750	0.0734	0.115	0.145	0.0652	0.0638	0.100	0.126	0.0579	0.0565	0.0890	0.113
0.80	0.248	0.267	0.300	0.380	0.215	0.232	0.261	0.331	0.190	0.205	0.231	0.295
0.90	0.585	0.609	0.642	0.697	0.503	0.529	0.559	0.608	0.441	0.469	0.496	0.541
0.92	0.673	0.696	0.722	0.762	0.571	0.605	0.629	0.666	0.504	0.536	0.559	0.593
0.94	0.735	0.757	0.762	0.778	0.658	0.679	0.699	0.733	0.574	0.602	0.622	0.653
0.96	0.767	0.776	0.781	0.796	0.710	0.735	0.741	0.756	0.643	0.669	0.688	0.720
0.98	0.784	0.791	0.798	0.809	0.732	0.753	0.762	0.773	0.698	0.718	0.725	0.739
1.00	0.800	0.806	0.812	0.821	0.756	0.769	0.779	0.790	0.726	0.735	0.745	0.756
1.01	0.805	0.812	0.818	0.828	0.769	0.778	0.786	0.798	0.736	0.745	0.755	0.765
1.02	0.812	0.819	0.826	0.834	0.777	0.786	0.794	0.805	0.745	0.753	0.764	0.774
1.03	0.819	0.825	0.831	0.840	0.785	0.793	0.802	0.813	0.755	0.762	0.772	0.781
1.04	0.825	0.831	0.838	0.846	0.790	0.800	0.810	0.819	0.764	0.772	0.781	0.789
1.05	0.830	0.837	0.842	0.852	0.799	0.808	0.816	0.825	0.774	0.781	0.788	0.796
1.06	0.835	0.843	0.848	0.858	0.807	0.816	0.822	0.832	0.781	0.789	0.795	0.805
1.07	0.841	0.848	0.853	0.863	0.814	0.822	0.826	0.838	0.792	0.796	0.800	0.812
1.08	0.848	0.854	0.857	0.867	0.820	0.828	0.832	0.842	0.798	0.804	0.807	0.818
1.09	0.852	0.859	0.863	0.871	0.828	0.834	0.838	0.847	0.805	0.810	0.813	0.823
1.10	0.858	0.863	0.867	0.876	0.832	0.839	0.843	0.852	0.812	0.816	0.820	0.828
1.12	0.866	0.872	0.876	0.883	0.842	0.850	0.853	0.861	0.822	0.827	0.831	0.840
1.14	0.873	0.879	0.884	0.890	0.853	0.859	0.863	0.869	0.834	0.838	0.843	0.849
1.16	0.884	0.887	0.890	0.897	0.862	0.867	0.871	0.876	0.842	0.846	0.852	0.859
1.18	0.891	0.893	0.898	0.903	0.871	0.874	0.880	0.884	0.849	0.856	0.862	0.867
1.20	0.896	0.899	0.906	0.909	0.878	0.882	0.889	0.892	0.855	0.864	0.872	0.876
1.30	0.920	0.926	0.929	0.931	0.904	0.913	0.917	0.918	0.876	0.900	0.903	0.905
1.40	0.943	0.944	0.947	0.947	0.925	0.935	0.938	0.938	0.900	0.926	0.928	0.929
1.50	0.962	0.958	0.958	0.961	0.944	0.953	0.950	0.955	0.920	0.946	0.944	0.948
1.60	0.967	0.967	0.962	0.970	0.959	0.964	0.961	0.967	0.946	0.959	0.956	0.962
1.70	0.973	0.974	0.972	0.976	0.968	0.972	0.968	0.972	0.969	0.967	0.965	0.970
1.80		0.980	0.977	0.982		0.978	0.974	0.979		0.975	0.971	0.976
1.90		0.986	0.981	0.987		0.984	0.979	0.985		0.982	0.977	0.982
2.00		0.991	0.983	0.989		0.990	0.982	0.988		0.989	0.981	0.987
3.00		1.000	1.000	1.000		1.000	1.000	1.000		1.000	1.000	1.000
4.00		1.000	1.000	1.000		1.000	1.000	1.000		1.000	1.000	1.000
6.00		1.000	1.000	1.000		1.000	1.000	1.000		1.000	1.000	1.000
8.00		1.000	1.000	1.000		1.000	1.000	1.000		1.000	1.000	1.000
10.00		1.000	1.000	1.000		1.000	1.000	1.000		1.000	1.000	1.000
15.00		1.000	1.000	1.000		1.000	1.000	1.000		1.000	1.000	1.000

Fugacity Coefficients of Pure Gases and Liquids, f/p (Continued)

T_r	$P_r = 0.90$				$P_r = 1.0$				$P_r = 1.05$			
	W $Z_c = 0.23$	I $Z_c = 0.25$	II $Z_c = 0.27$	III $Z_c = 0.29$	W $Z_c = 0.23$	I $Z_c = 0.25$	II $Z_c = 0.27$	III $Z_c = 0.29$	W $Z_c = 0.23$	I $Z_c = 0.25$	II $Z_c = 0.27$	III $Z_c = 0.29$
T_{rs}	0.986	0.985	0.984	0.982	1.000	1.000	1.000	1.000		1.01	1.008	1.005
Sat. gas and liquids	0.664	0.680	0.688	0.698	0.650	0.654	0.665	0.677		0.646	0.662	0.672
0.50	0.0007	0.00026	0.00131	0.00669	0.0007	0.00023	0.00120	0.00615	0.0006	0.00023	0.00115	0.00612
0.60	0.0094	0.00880	0.0150	0.0275	0.0086	0.00803	0.0134	0.0265	0.0081	0.00770	0.0123	0.0262
0.70	0.0520	0.0531	0.0803	0.103	0.0474	0.0491	0.0734	0.0931	0.0455	0.0463	0.0704	0.0899
0.80	0.169	0.185	0.209	0.266	0.153	0.169	0.191	0.243	0.149	0.162	0.183	0.234
0.90	0.396	0.423	0.448	0.489	0.360	0.385	0.409	0.448	0.343	0.369	0.392	0.432
0.92	0.458	0.483	0.504	0.546	0.414	0.441	0.461	0.491	0.397	0.422	0.442	0.474
0.94	0.509	0.543	0.561	0.591	0.471	0.495	0.513	0.541	0.451	0.475	0.493	0.528
0.96	0.584	0.603	0.622	0.641	0.531	0.551	0.569	0.588	0.509	0.528	0.546	0.569
0.98	0.650	0.674	0.678	0.691	0.592	0.592	0.621	0.649	0.560	0.587	0.596	0.626
1.00	0.688	0.698	0.710	0.720	0.650	0.654	0.665	0.677	0.608	0.630	0.641	0.655
1.01	0.707	0.710	0.721	0.732	0.667	0.670	0.685	0.696	0.633	0.649	0.665	0.679
1.02	0.717	0.720	0.733	0.742	0.680	0.686	0.699	0.710	0.664	0.668	0.681	0.692
1.03	0.729	0.732	0.742	0.752	0.693	0.700	0.710	0.724	0.677	0.684	0.695	0.707
1.04	0.739	0.743	0.752	0.761	0.702	0.714	0.722	0.734	0.694	0.696	0.706	0.718
1.05	0.748	0.754	0.760	0.769	0.717	0.725	0.731	0.744	0.704	0.710	0.717	0.728
1.06	0.759	0.761	0.768	0.778	0.728	0.735	0.741	0.753	0.715	0.721	0.727	0.739
1.07	0.768	0.770	0.776	0.786	0.740	0.743	0.750	0.761	0.726	0.730	0.736	0.749
1.08	0.777	0.778	0.783	0.794	0.750	0.753	0.759	0.769	0.738	0.740	0.746	0.756
1.09	0.784	0.784	0.789	0.800	0.758	0.760	0.766	0.775	0.746	0.747	0.753	0.762
1.10	0.790	0.791	0.796	0.806	0.767	0.768	0.772	0.783	0.754	0.757	0.762	0.770
1.12	0.803	0.805	0.809	0.818	0.780	0.783	0.787	0.795	0.770	0.772	0.776	0.783
1.14	0.816	0.817	0.822	0.828	0.795	0.796	0.802	0.807	0.785	0.785	0.792	0.796
1.16	0.828	0.826	0.832	0.838	0.806	0.806	0.812	0.818	0.800	0.796	0.802	0.808
1.18	0.836	0.837	0.844	0.847	0.820	0.818	0.825	0.830	0.812	0.809	0.816	0.820
1.20	0.845	0.847	0.855	0.857	0.830	0.830	0.838	0.840	0.822	0.822	0.829	0.832
1.30	0.881	0.888	0.890	0.892	0.868	0.876	0.878	0.880	0.863	0.869	0.872	0.874
1.40	0.908	0.916	0.918	0.918	0.898	0.908	0.910	0.905	0.892	0.903	0.905	0.906
1.50	0.930	0.936	0.937	0.936	0.922	0.930	0.931	0.930	0.920	0.930	0.927	0.931
1.60	0.949	0.951	0.951	0.951	0.943	0.946	0.946	0.946	0.945	0.946	0.944	0.947
1.70	0.963	0.963	0.961	0.965	0.957	0.959	0.957	0.961	0.970	0.957	0.955	0.959
1.80		0.973	0.969	0.973		0.969	0.966	0.970		0.968	0.965	0.969
1.90		0.980	0.975	0.981		0.978	0.973	0.979		0.977	0.972	0.978
2.00		0.988	0.980	0.986		0.987	0.979	0.985		0.986	0.978	0.984
3.00		1.000	1.000	1.000		1.000	1.000	1.000		1.000	1.000	1.000
4.00		1.000	1.000	1.000		1.000	1.000	1.000		1.000	1.000	1.000
6.00		1.000	1.000	1.000		1.000	1.000	1.000		1.000	1.000	1.000
8.00		1.000	1.000	1.000		1.000	1.000	1.000		1.000	1.000	1.000
10.00		1.000	1.000	1.000		1.000	1.000	1.000		1.000	1.000	1.000
15.00		1.000	1.000	1.000		1.000	1.000	1.000		1.000	1.000	1.000

FUGACITY COEFFICIENTS OF PURE GASES AND LIQUIDS, f/p (Continued)

	$P_r = 1.10$				$P_r = 1.15$				$P_r = 1.20$			
T_{r_0}, (f/p), T_r	W $Z_c=0.23$	I $Z_c=0.25$	II $Z_c=0.27$	III $Z_c=0.29$	W $Z_c=0.23$	I $Z_c=0.25$	II $Z_c=0.27$	III $Z_c=0.29$	W $Z_c=0.23$	I $Z_c=0.25$	II $Z_c=0.27$	III $Z_c=0.29$
0.50		1.014	1.018	1.016		1.02	1.025	1.022		1.025	1.032	1.028
0.60		0.638	0.657	0.663		0.631	0.699	0.656		0.625	0.642	0.650
0.70	0.0006	0.00022	0.00111	0.00608	0.0006	0.00021	0.00107	0.00604	0.0006	0.00020	0.00104	0.00600
0.80	0.0078	0.00741	0.0119	0.0258	0.0076	0.00714	0.0114	0.0254	0.0073	0.00689	0.0110	0.0250
0.90	0.0438	0.0447	0.0677	0.0867	0.0421	0.0412	0.0653	0.0835	0.0405	0.0420	0.0619	0.0803
0.92	0.146	0.155	0.176	0.225	0.141	0.149	0.169	0.217	0.136	0.144	0.163	0.210
0.94	0.329	0.355	0.377	0.414	0.317	0.342	0.364	0.402	0.304	0.330	0.351	0.386
0.96	0.382	0.406	0.425	0.457	0.367	0.391	0.410	0.440	0.353	0.377	0.396	0.396
0.98	0.433	0.456	0.474	0.504	0.419	0.439	0.457	0.486	0.407	0.424	0.441	0.467
1.00	0.485	0.513	0.526	0.549	0.468	0.489	0.507	0.529	0.451	0.472	0.489	0.510
1.01	0.543	0.548	0.574	0.604	0.523	0.530	0.554	0.582	0.504	0.518	0.535	0.560
1.02	0.600	0.607	0.618	0.633	0.580	0.587	0.598	0.611	0.560	0.570	0.578	0.590
1.03	0.631	0.626	0.643	0.657	0.604	0.605	0.622	0.636	0.584	0.586	0.602	0.616
1.04	0.642	0.649	0.664	0.675	0.626	0.630	0.645	0.656	0.611	0.611	0.620	0.638
1.05	0.659	0.667	0.678	0.691	0.645	0.650	0.661	0.674	0.634	0.634	0.645	0.656
1.06	0.674	0.682	0.692	0.701	0.660	0.666	0.675	0.685	0.649	0.650	0.660	0.669
1.07	0.686	0.696	0.703	0.713	0.664	0.682	0.688	0.699	0.663	0.666	0.674	0.683
1.08	0.699	0.707	0.713	0.725	0.688	0.693	0.700	0.712	0.677	0.680	0.685	0.698
1.09	0.712	0.717	0.723	0.736	0.701	0.704	0.710	0.721	0.689	0.690	0.697	0.709
1.10	0.724	0.728	0.733	0.744	0.713	0.715	0.719	0.731	0.703	0.701	0.706	0.718
1.12	0.733	0.738	0.741	0.750	0.722	0.724	0.730	0.739	0.713	0.711	0.716	0.726
1.14	0.742	0.745	0.750	0.759	0.731	0.733	0.738	0.748	0.722	0.721	0.726	0.736
1.16	0.759	0.761	0.766	0.772	0.748	0.750	0.755	0.764	0.740	0.740	0.745	0.753
1.18	0.775	0.775	0.781	0.786	0.767	0.765	0.771	0.777	0.757	0.755	0.761	0.767
1.20	0.790	0.788	0.793	0.798	0.783	0.778	0.784	0.789	0.774	0.769	0.774	0.781
1.30	0.803	0.800	0.807	0.810	0.795	0.792	0.799	0.801	0.787	0.783	0.790	0.795
1.40	0.814	0.813	0.821	0.824	0.806	0.805	0.813	0.816	0.800	0.797	0.805	0.808
1.50	0.855	0.863	0.866	0.868	0.851	0.857	0.860	0.861	0.846	0.851	0.854	0.856
1.60	0.888	0.901	0.903	0.902	0.879	0.894	0.897	0.897	0.873	0.890	0.892	0.892
1.70	0.922	0.926	0.923	0.928	0.916	0.922	0.920	0.924	0.910	0.919	0.916	0.920
1.80	0.937	0.942	0.941	0.944	0.935	0.939	0.938	0.941	0.933	0.936	0.935	0.940
1.90	0.948	0.955	0.953	0.957	0.947	0.953	0.951	0.955	0.948	0.951	0.949	0.954
2.00		0.968	0.964	0.969		0.965	0.962	0.968		0.962	0.961	0.966
3.00		0.977	0.971	0.977		0.976	0.971	0.976		0.973	0.970	0.975
4.00		0.985	0.977	0.983		0.984	0.976	0.982		0.983	0.975	0.981
6.00		1.000	1.000	1.000		1.000	1.000	1.000		1.000	1.000	1.000
8.00		1.000	1.000	1.000		1.000	1.000	1.000		1.000	1.000	1.000
10.00		1.000	1.000	1.000		1.000	1.000	1.000		1.000	1.000	1.000
15.00		1.000	1.000	1.000		1.000	1.000	1.000		1.000	1.000	1.000

Fugacity Coefficients of Pure Gases and Liquids, f/p *(Continued)*

T_r, $(f/p)_s$	$P_r = 1.25$ W ($Z_c=0.23$)	$P_r = 1.25$ II ($Z_c=0.27$)	$P_r = 1.30$ W ($Z_c=0.23$)	$P_r = 1.30$ II ($Z_c=0.27$)	$P_r = 1.35$ W ($Z_c=0.23$)	$P_r = 1.35$ II ($Z_c=0.27$)	$P_r = 1.40$ W ($Z_c=0.23$)	$P_r = 1.40$ II ($Z_c=0.27$)	$P_r = 1.45$ W ($Z_c=0.23$)	$P_r = 1.45$ II ($Z_c=0.27$)	$P_r = 1.50$ W ($Z_c=0.23$)	$P_r = 1.50$ II ($Z_c=0.27$)
T_r		1.037		1.042		1.047		1.051		1.058		1.062
$(f/p)_s$		0.635		0.628		0.623		0.617		0.611		0.606
0.50	0.0006	0.00100	0.0005	0.00097	0.0005	0.00095	0.0005	0.00092	0.0005	0.00092	0.0005	0.00088
0.60	0.0071	0.0107	0.0069	0.0104	0.0067	0.0101	0.0065	0.00978	0.0063	0.00952	0.0061	0.00927
0.70	0.0391	0.0609	0.0378	0.0590	0.0328	0.0573	0.0355	0.0556	0.0345	0.0520	0.0335	0.0527
0.80	0.131	0.158	0.127	0.153	0.123	0.148	0.119	0.144	0.115	0.140	0.113	0.137
0.90	0.297	0.339	0.285	0.329	0.279	0.319	0.271	0.310	0.262	0.301	0.255	0.293
0.92	0.340	0.383	0.329	0.371	0.319	0.360	0.309	0.349	0.300	0.340	0.291	0.331
0.94	0.394	0.427	0.379	0.413	0.366	0.401	0.352	0.390	0.342	0.379	0.333	0.369
0.96	0.436	0.474	0.421	0.459	0.408	0.445	0.396	0.433	0.381	0.421	0.370	0.410
0.98	0.488	0.518	0.470	0.503	0.457	0.488	0.444	0.474	0.431	0.462	0.419	0.450
1.00	0.541	0.560	0.523	0.543	0.510	0.528	0.492	0.513	0.478	0.500	0.465	0.487
1.01	0.564	0.585	0.546	0.567	0.528	0.551	0.514	0.540	0.500	0.523	0.487	0.510
1.02	0.588	0.607	0.569	0.591	0.552	0.574	0.540	0.559	0.528	0.545	0.530	0.531
1.03	0.610	0.628	0.592	0.611	0.575	0.595	0.560	0.580	0.544	0.566	0.540	0.552
1.04	0.629	0.645	0.610	0.629	0.596	0.614	0.578	0.599	0.560	0.585	0.550	0.572
1.05	0.645	0.659	0.629	0.645	0.615	0.630	0.600	0.615	0.586	0.602	0.570	0.589
1.06	0.660	0.671	0.646	0.658	0.632	0.645	0.619	0.630	0.606	0.617	0.590	0.605
1.07	0.673	0.682	0.660	0.670	0.648	0.656	0.635	0.644	0.623	0.631	0.610	0.618
1.08	0.687	0.695	0.674	0.682	0.663	0.670	0.652	0.658	0.640	0.644	0.626	0.632
1.09	0.698	0.705	0.686	0.692	0.675	0.681	0.664	0.668	0.653	0.656	0.641	0.644
1.10	0.707	0.714	0.696	0.703	0.686	0.692	0.675	0.680	0.665	0.669	0.653	0.658
1.12	0.727	0.734	0.720	0.723	0.707	0.712	0.698	0.701	0.688	0.691	0.676	0.680
1.14	0.745	0.751	0.735	0.742	0.726	0.732	0.716	0.721	0.709	0.711	0.699	0.701
1.16	0.762	0.765	0.754	0.756	0.746	0.747	0.738	0.737	0.730	0.728	0.718	0.718
1.18	0.776	0.781	0.768	0.773	0.760	0.764	0.752	0.756	0.745	0.747	0.736	0.738
1.20	0.789	0.797	0.780	0.789	0.774	0.781	0.766	0.773	0.758	0.765	0.749	0.757
1.30	0.838	0.848	0.834	0.842	0.827	0.836	0.822	0.830	0.817	0.824	0.810	0.819
1.40	0.880	0.888	0.875	0.883	0.868	0.879	0.866	0.874	0.856	0.870	0.850	0.866
1.50	0.917	0.912	0.910	0.909	0.900	0.905	0.897	0.901	0.895	0.898	0.890	0.894
1.60	0.929	0.932	0.926	0.930	0.924	0.927	0.922	0.924	0.919	0.921	0.910	0.919
1.70	0.946	0.947	0.944	0.945	0.942	0.943	0.936	0.942	0.930	0.940	0.920	0.938
1.80		0.959		0.957		0.956		0.955		0.954		0.953
1.90		0.969		0.968		0.967		0.966		0.965		0.964
2.00		0.974		0.973		0.972		0.971		0.971		0.970
3.00		1.000		1.000		1.000		1.000		1.000		1.000
4.00		1.000		1.000		1.000		1.000		1.000		1.000
6.00												
8.00		1.000		1.000		1.000		1.000		1.000		1.000
10.00		1.000		1.000		1.000		1.000		1.000		1.000
15.00		1.000		1.000		1.000		1.000		1.000		1.000

FUGACITY COEFFICIENTS OF PURE GASES AND LIQUIDS, f/p *(Continued)*

T_r	$P_r=1.60$ W, $Z_c=0.23$	$P_r=1.60$ II, $Z_c=0.27$	$P_r=1.70$ W, $Z_c=0.23$	$P_r=1.70$ II, $Z_c=0.27$	$P_r=1.80$ II, $Z_c=0.27$	$P_r=1.90$ II, $Z_c=0.27$	$P_r=2.00$ II, $Z_c=0.27$	$P_r=2.20$ II, $Z_c=0.27$	$P_r=2.40$ II, $Z_c=0.27$	$P_r=2.60$ II, $Z_c=0.27$	$P_r=2.80$ II, $Z_c=0.27$	$P_r=3.00$ II, $Z_c=0.27$
		1.071		1.079	1.087	1.096	1.103	1.116	1.127	1.135	1.144	1.453
		0.597		0.588	0.578	0.570	0.562	0.548	0.536	0.528	0.517	0.509
0.50	0.0005	0.00084	0.0004	0.00080	0.00077	0.00074	0.00072	0.00068	0.00065	0.00062	0.00059	0.00058
0.60	0.0058	0.00884	0.0056	0.00845	0.00811	0.00800	0.00798	0.00708	0.00671	0.00640	0.00613	0.00591
0.70	0.0318	0.0502	0.0303	0.0479	0.0459	0.0440	0.0426	0.0399	0.0377	0.0358	0.0342	0.0329
0.80	0.107	0.130	0.102	0.124	0.119	0.114	0.110	0.103	0.0970	0.0921	0.0878	0.0844
0.90	0.242	0.279	0.231	0.266	0.255	0.245	0.236	0.221	0.208	0.198	0.189	0.181
0.92	0.276	0.315	0.262	0.301	0.288	0.277	0.267	0.249	0.235	0.223	0.213	0.204
0.94	0.324	0.351	0.301	0.335	0.321	0.309	0.298	0.279	0.263	0.249	0.238	0.229
0.96	0.360	0.391	0.335	0.373	0.358	0.344	0.332	0.310	0.293	0.278	0.266	0.255
0.98	0.398	0.429	0.379	0.410	0.393	0.378	0.365	0.341	0.322	0.306	0.293	0.281
1.00	0.442	0.464	0.420	0.444	0.426	0.410	0.396	0.371	0.350	0.333	0.318	0.306
1.01	0.462	0.485	0.440	0.465	0.446	0.429	0.414	0.388	0.365	0.350	0.333	0.320
1.02	0.465	0.507	0.465	0.485	0.465	0.447	0.433	0.405	0.384	0.365	0.350	0.335
1.03	0.504	0.529	0.490	0.505	0.485	0.469	0.451	0.425	0.400	0.381	0.364	0.350
1.04	0.526	0.546	0.505	0.525	0.505	0.485	0.470	0.441	0.416	0.395	0.380	0.365
1.05	0.546	0.563	0.525	0.540	0.520	0.504	0.485	0.455	0.432	0.411	0.393	0.378
1.06	0.566	0.580	0.544	0.557	0.536	0.519	0.499	0.472	0.447	0.425	0.407	0.392
1.07	0.585	0.594	0.561	0.572	0.552	0.533	0.515	0.485	0.460	0.438	0.420	0.405
1.08	0.603	0.610	0.580	0.588	0.566	0.548	0.531	0.500	0.474	0.452	0.433	0.417
1.09	0.618	0.622	0.596	0.601	0.581	0.561	0.545	0.514	0.488	0.466	0.446	0.430
1.10	0.632	0.636	0.610	0.614	0.594	0.576	0.555	0.527	0.500	0.478	0.460	0.443
1.12	0.658	0.660	0.638	0.639	0.620	0.602	0.585	0.555	0.527	0.504	0.484	0.466
1.14	0.681	0.682	0.663	0.663	0.645	0.627	0.611	0.579	0.553	0.529	0.511	0.492
1.16	0.704	0.700	0.686	0.682	0.664	0.648	0.632	0.602	0.576	0.553	0.538	0.516
1.18	0.721	0.721	0.705	0.705	0.689	0.673	0.658	0.630	0.604	0.581	0.561	0.544
1.20	0.738	0.741	0.720	0.725	0.710	0.695	0.681	0.654	0.629	0.606	0.586	0.569
1.30	0.801	0.806	0.789	0.794	0.783	0.773	0.762	0.741	0.721	0.703	0.685	0.669
1.40	0.850	0.857	0.845	0.848	0.840	0.832	0.824	0.808	0.792	0.778	0.765	0.752
1.50	0.895	0.888	0.895	0.882	0.876	0.870	0.863	0.856	0.844	0.833	0.822	0.812
1.60	0.912	0.913	0.910	0.908	0.903	0.898	0.893	0.883	0.874	0.864	0.856	0.847
1.70	0.920	0.933	0.920	0.929	0.925	0.921	0.918	0.910	0.903	0.896	0.889	0.882
1.80		0.949		0.946	0.943	0.940	0.937	0.932	0.926	0.920	0.915	0.909
1.90		0.962		0.960	0.958	0.956	0.954	0.949	0.945	0.940	0.935	0.930
2.00		0.968		1.000	0.964	0.962	0.960	0.956	0.952	0.948	0.946	0.943
3.00		1.000		1.000	1.000	1.000	0.999	0.998	0.998	0.997	0.996	0.994
4.00		1.000		1.000	1.000	1.000	1.000	1.000	0.999	0.998	0.997	0.995
6.00		1.000		1.000	1.000	1.000	1.000	1.000	0.999	0.999	0.999	0.998
8.00		1.000		1.000	1.000	1.000	1.001	1.001	1.001	1.001	1.001	1.001
10.00		1.000		1.003	1.003	1.003	1.003	1.003	1.003	1.003	1.003	1.003
15.00		1.000		1.007	1.006	1.007	1.008					1.017

FUGACITY COEFFICIENTS OF PURE GASES AND LIQUIDS, f/p (Continued)

T_r / $(f/p)_s$	$P_r = 3.50$	$P_r = 4.00$	$P_r = 4.5$	$P_r = 5.0$	$P_r = 6.0$	$P_r = 7.0$	$P_r = 8.0$	$P_r = 9.0$	$P_r = 10.0$	$P_r = 15.0$	$P_r = 20.0$	$P_r = 25.0$	$P_r = 30.0$
$(f/p)_s$ II	1.169	1.18	1.89	1.199	1.204	1.210	1.216	1.126	1.207	1.182	1.132	1.071	0.987
$(f/p)_s$ $Z_c = 0.27$	0.491	0.480	0.471	0.461	0.449	0.448	0.440	0.440	0.449	0.475	0.530	0.596	0.674
0.50	0.00054	0.00052	0.00050	0.00050	0.00050	0.00051	0.00053	0.00057	0.00061	0.00099	0.00182	0.00352	0.00709
0.60	0.00549	0.00520	0.00501	0.00488	0.00477	0.00510	0.00511	0.0055	0.0058	0.00840	0.0127	0.0221	0.0396
0.70	0.0304	0.0286	0.0273	0.0264	0.0255	0.0252	0.0254	0.0260	0.0270	0.0363	0.0547	0.082	0.144
0.80	0.0776	0.0727	0.0692	0.0667	0.0636	0.0623	0.0622	0.0631	0.0648	0.0824	0.121	0.175	0.271
0.90	0.166	0.155	0.148	0.142	0.135	0.131	0.131	0.132	0.134	0.164	0.222	0.318	0.469
0.92	0.188	0.175	0.167	0.160	0.152	0.148	0.146	0.147	0.150	0.182	0.245	0.348	0.508
0.94	0.210	0.196	0.186	0.172	0.169	0.165	0.163	0.164	0.167	0.202	0.269	0.379	0.550
0.96	0.234	0.219	0.208	0.200	0.189	0.184	0.182	0.183	0.186	0.223	0.296	0.413	0.595
0.98	0.258	0.241	0.229	0.220	0.209	0.203	0.201	0.201	0.204	0.244	0.322	0.447	0.638
1.00	0.281	0.263	0.250	0.240	0.228	0.221	0.219	0.220	0.223	0.265	0.348	0.479	0.679
1.01	0.294	0.275	0.261	0.251	0.238	0.231	0.228	0.229	0.232	0.274	0.358	0.493	0.697
1.02	0.308	0.288	0.274	0.263	0.248	0.241	0.238	0.240	0.242	0.286	0.372	0.510	0.721
1.03	0.323	0.303	0.288	0.276	0.261	0.253	0.250	0.251	0.255	0.300	0.392	0.534	0.750
1.04	0.336	0.316	0.300	0.284	0.272	0.264	0.262	0.262	0.265	0.312	0.403	0.548	0.769
1.05	0.348	0.327	0.310	0.298	0.282	0.274	0.272	0.272	0.276	0.324	0.418	0.561	0.786
1.06	0.362	0.339	0.322	0.310	0.294	0.285	0.282	0.283	0.286	0.335	0.430	0.583	0.815
1.07	0.373	0.351	0.334	0.321	0.304	0.296	0.292	0.293	0.296	0.346	0.444	0.599	0.835
1.08	0.385	0.362	0.344	0.331	0.314	0.305	0.302	0.302	0.306	0.356	0.457	0.615	0.855
1.09	0.398	0.374	0.355	0.341	0.324	0.315	0.312	0.313	0.315	0.367	0.470	0.630	0.875
1.10	0.410	0.385	0.366	0.352	0.334	0.325	0.322	0.323	0.325	0.378	0.484	0.648	0.894
1.12	0.433	0.408	0.388	0.374	0.356	0.345	0.342	0.342	0.346	0.401	0.509	0.676	0.934
1.14	0.457	0.431	0.411	0.396	0.376	0.366	0.362	0.363	0.366	0.424	0.536	0.708	0.966
1.16	0.479	0.453	0.432	0.416	0.396	0.386	0.382	0.382	0.386	0.446	0.561	0.742	1.004
1.18	0.504	0.481	0.460	0.443	0.422	0.412	0.408	0.408	0.412	0.474	0.594	0.781	1.051
1.20	0.526	0.504	0.484	0.466	0.445	0.433	0.429	0.430	0.434	0.496	0.620	0.811	1.088
1.30	0.636	0.609	0.587	0.570	0.548	0.537	0.533	0.534	0.540	0.616	0.756	0.961	1.248
1.40	0.724	0.700	0.682	0.667	0.647	0.637	0.634	0.636	0.643	0.727	0.881	1.103	1.420
1.50	0.788	0.768	0.754	0.740	0.722	0.714	0.712	0.716	0.724	0.814	0.976	1.214	1.545
1.60	0.828	0.813	0.798	0.788	0.766	0.754	0.753	0.758	0.768	0.863	1.030	1.265	1.595
1.70	0.866	0.852	0.841	0.832	0.820	0.816	0.817	0.824	0.834	0.933	1.106	1.349	1.688
1.80	0.897	0.886	0.877	0.870	0.862	0.859	0.862	0.869	0.882	0.986	1.164	1.410	1.753
1.90	0.920	0.912	0.905	0.899	0.893	0.892	0.897	0.906	0.919	1.025	1.201	1.440	1.775
2.00	0.935	0.929	0.923	0.920	0.916	0.918	0.923	0.933	0.947	1.053	1.224	1.455	1.784
3.00	0.991	0.989	0.987	0.986	0.986	0.988	0.994	1.004	1.016	1.107	1.242	1.413	1.621
4.00	0.993	0.991	0.990	0.989	0.989	0.992	0.999	1.008	1.019	1.096	1.204	1.334	1.476
6.00	0.997	0.996	0.995	0.995	0.995	0.998	1.005	1.014	1.024	1.089	1.171	1.266	1.372
8.00	1.001	1.001	1.001	1.001	1.001	1.004	1.010	1.018	1.027	1.080	1.148	1.223	1.306
10.00	1.003	1.001	1.003	1.003	1.004	1.008	1.015	1.023	1.031	1.074	1.124	1.177	1.224
15.00	1.021	1.025	1.029	1.034	1.042	1.049	1.057	1.064	1.071	1.107	1.145	1.183	1.220

(Each P_r heading lists two sub-columns: II and $Z_c = 0.27$.)

NOTE: To define the saturated liquid-vapor locus, a correlation $P_{vp_r} = f(T_r, Z_c)$ was used. This correlation is noted in the tables by values given for saturated vapor and liquid; the same comment holds for $\Delta H_s = f(T_r, Z_c)$. If only vapor-pressure or ΔH_s values are desired, it is preferable to use the correlations in Chap. 4.

APPENDIX C

TABLES OF m, m', AND C FOR USE WITH FIGS. 4-3 AND 4-6 TO DETERMINE VAPOR PRESSURES AND ENTHALPIES OF VAPORIZATION*

Hydrocarbons

Compound	Formula	m	C, atm	m'
Isoprene	C_5H_8	0.6173	+0.8110	0.1630
n-Pentane	C_5H_{12}	0.6274	+0.7743	0.1565
Benzene	C_6H_6	0.7688	+0.2526	0.1771
Cyclohexane	C_6H_{12}	0.7520	+0.2392	0.1608
n-Hexane	C_6H_{14}	0.7263	+0.3898	0.1516
Toluene	C_7H_8	0.8544	−0.1360	0.1669
2-Heptene	C_7H_{14}	0.8125	+0.0190	0.1489
Methylcyclohexane	C_7H_{14}	0.7992	−0.0111	0.1465
n-Heptane	C_7H_{16}	0.8235	+0.0205	0.1479
Ethylbenzene	C_8H_{10}	0.9385	−0.4739	0.1591
o-Xylene	C_8H_{10}	0.9597	−0.5882	0.1627
m-Xylene	C_8H_{10}	0.9500	−0.5142	0.1611
p-Xylene	C_8H_{10}	0.9443	−0.5017	0.1601
Ethylcyclohexane	C_8H_{16}	0.9006	−0.4042	0.1444
2-Methyl-2-heptene	C_8H_{16}	0.9330	−0.3044	0.1496
n-Octane	C_8H_{18}	0.9172	−0.3374	0.1445
α-Methylstyrene	C_9H_{10}	1.0996	−0.9246	0.1675
β-Methylstyrene	C_9H_{10}	1.0830	−1.0671	0.1536
4-Methylstyrene	C_9H_{10}	1.0790	−1.0195	0.1643
Cumene	C_9H_{12}	0.9914	−0.6937	0.1484
Nonane	C_9H_{20}	0.9810	−0.6534	0.1377
Naphthalene	$C_{10}H_8$	1.2142	−1.6290	0.1706
Tetralin	$C_{10}H_{12}$	1.1670	−1.4580	0.1589
Butylbenzene	$C_{10}H_{14}$	1.1180	−1.1471	0.1499
Isobutylbenzene	$C_{10}H_{14}$	0.9547	−0.8576	0.1280
p-Cymene	$C_{10}H_{14}$	1.1090	−1.0470	0.1487
d-Limonene	$C_{10}H_{16}$	1.0700	−1.010	0.1414
Dipentene	$C_{10}H_{16}$	1.0750	−1.0113	0.1420
Myrcene	$C_{10}H_{16}$	1.0740	−0.9759	0.1419
α-Pinene	$C_{10}H_{16}$	0.9863	−0.7194	0.1303
β-Pinene	$C_{10}H_{16}$	1.0230	−0.7841	0.1352
Terpinolene	$C_{10}H_{16}$	1.231	−1.2860	0.1626
cis-Decalin	$C_{10}H_{18}$	1.092	−1.240	0.1421
trans-Decalin	$C_{10}H_{18}$	0.996	−1.057	0.1296
Decane	$C_{10}H_{22}$	1.092	−1.009	0.1382
4-Isopropylstyrene	$C_{11}H_{14}$	1.1857	−1.432	0.1459
3-Ethylcumene	$C_{11}H_{16}$	1.140	−1.279	0.1384
4-Ethylcumene	$C_{11}H_{16}$	1.163	−1.334	0.1402
1,2-Diisopropylbenzene	$C_{12}H_{18}$	1.207	−1.529	0.1339

TABLES OF m, m', AND C (*Continued*)

Hydrocarbons

Compound	Formula	m	C, atm	m'
Triisobutylene	$C_{12}H_{24}$	1.060	−1.044	0.1133
Dodecane	$C_{12}H_{26}$	1.272	−1.670	0.1344
Heptylbenzene	$C_{13}H_{20}$	1.430	−2.094	0.1459
Tetradecane	$C_{14}H_{30}$	1.401	−2.244	0.1271
Pentadecane	$C_{15}H_{32}$	1.435	−2.509	0.1215
Hexadecane	$C_{16}H_{34}$	1.508	−2.790	0.1199

Halogenated Hydrocarbons

Compound	Formula	m	C, atm	m'
Tribromomethane	$CHBr_3$	0.972	−0.660	0.0627
Chloroform	$CHCl_3$	0.720	+0.489	0.1085
Dibromomethane	CH_2Br_2	0.833	+0.018	0.0862
Methylene chloride	CH_2Cl_2	0.668	+0.750	0.1415
Carbon tetrachloride	CCl_4	0.754	+0.294	0.0882
Tetrachloroethylene	C_2Cl_4	0.891	−0.270	0.0967
Trichloroethylene	C_2HCl_3	0.780	+0.167	0.1068
1,1-Ethylidene chloride	$C_2H_4Cl_2$	0.711	+0.540	0.1293
1,1,1,2-Tetrabromoethane	$C_2H_2Br_4$	1.515	−1.798	0.0789
1,1,2,2-Tetrabromoethane	$C_2H_2Br_4$	1.351	−2.089	0.0703
1,1,1,2-Tetrachloroethane	$C_2H_2Cl_4$	0.976	−0.608	0.1046
1,1,2-Trichloroethane	$C_2H_3Cl_3$	0.878	−0.180	0.1184
1-Bromo-2-chloroethane	C_2H_4BrCl	0.858	−0.087	0.1076
1,2-Dibromoethane	$C_2H_4Br_2$	0.919	−0.409	0.0880
1,2-Dichloroethane	$C_2H_4Cl_4$	0.812	+0.235	0.1474
Ethyl bromide	C_2H_5Br	0.641	+0.542	0.1059
Ethyl iodide	C_2H_5I	0.719	+0.336	0.0899
2,3-Dibromopropane	$C_3H_4Br_2$	0.972	−0.550	0.0875
Methyl dichloroacetate	$C_3H_4Cl_2O_2$	1.065	−0.626	0.1340
1,2,3-Tribromopropane	$C_3H_5Br_3$	1.239	−1.685	0.0795
Epichlorohydrin	$C_3H_5Cl_{10}$	0.947	−0.248	0.1841
1,2,3-Trichloropropane	$C_3H_5Cl_3$	1.066	−0.813	0.1301
1,1,1-Trichloropropane	$C_3H_5Cl_3$	0.849	−0.104	0.1035
1,2-Dibromopropane	$C_3H_6Br_2$	0.954	−0.546	0.0925
1,3-Dibromopropane	$C_3H_6Br_2$	1.038	−0.899	0.0925
Propylene dichloride	$C_3H_6Cl_2$	0.798	+0.039	0.1271
1-Bromopropane	C_3H_7Br	0.729	+0.360	0.1066
2-Bromopropane	C_3H_7Br	0.694	+0.491	0.1016
1-Chloropropane	C_3H_7Cl	0.674	+0.669	0.1545
2-Chloropropane	C_3H_7Cl	0.604	+0.742	0.1384
1-Iodopropane	C_3H_7I	0.809	−0.030	0.0855
2-Iodopropane	C_3H_7I	0.772	+0.129	0.0817
1,2,2-Tribromobutane	$C_4H_7Br_3$	1.197	−1.565	0.0731
1,2,3-Trichlorobutane	$C_4H_7Cl_3$	0.935	−0.824	0.1042
1,2-Dibromobutane	$C_4H_8Br_2$	1.025	−0.875	0.0853
1,4-Dibromobutane	$C_4H_8Br_2$	1.168	−1.360	0.0974
1,2-Dichlorobutane	$C_4H_8Cl_2$	0.840	−0.284	0.1190

TABLES OF m, m', AND C (Continued)

Halogenated Hydrocarbons

Compound	Formula	m	C, atm	m'
2,3-Dichlorobutane	$C_4H_8Cl_2$	0.857	−0.202	0.1213
Dichloroethyl ether	$C_4H_8Cl_2O$	1.148	−1.125	0.1446
1-Bromobutane	C_4H_9Br	0.833	−0.020	0.1094
n-Butyl chloride	C_4H_9Cl	0.755	+0.278	0.1468
tert-Butyl chloride	C_4H_9Cl	0.649	+0.579	0.1262
1-Bromo-3-methylbutane	$C_5H_{11}Br$	0.885	−0.263	0.1054
Pentachlorobenzene	C_6HCl_5	1.616	−2.868	0.1162
1,2,3,4-Tetrachlorobenzene	$C_6H_2Cl_4$	1.262	−2.049	0.1052
1,2,4,5-Tetrachlorobenzene	$C_6H_2Cl_4$	1.410	−2.195	0.1175
1,2,4-Trichlorobenzene	$C_6H_3Cl_3$	1.174	−1.528	0.1164
1,4-Bromochlorobenzene	C_6H_4BrCl	1.175	−1.358	0.1104
1,4-Dibromobenzene	$C_6H_4Br_2$	1.227	−1.653	0.0936
1,4-Dichlorobenzene	$C_6H_4Cl_2$	1.090	−1.017	0.1335
o-Dichlorobenzene	$C_6H_4Cl_2$	1.108	−1.033	0.1357
Bromobenzene	C_6H_5Br	0.993	−0.738	0.1138
Chlorobenzene	C_6H_5Cl	0.929	−0.421	0.1485
Fluorobenzene	C_6H_5F	0.786	+0.195	0.1472
Iodobenzene	C_6H_5I	1.089	−1.176	0.0961
Dichloroisopropyl ether	$C_6H_{12}Cl_2O$	1.201	−1.226	0.1264
2-Bromotoluene	C_7H_7Br	1.064	−1.078	0.1120
3-Bromotoluene	C_7H_7Br	1.141	−1.177	0.1201
4-Bromotoluene	C_7H_7Br	1.095	−1.139	0.1152
3-Chlorotoluene	C_7H_7Cl	1.012	−0.827	0.1439
o-Chlorotoluene	C_7H_7Cl	1.021	−0.794	0.1452
p-Chlorotoluene	C_7H_7Cl	1.012	−0.819	0.1439
3-Fluorotoluene	C_7H_7F	0.8894	−0.209	0.1453
4-Fluorotoluene	C_7H_7F	0.889	−0.221	0.1453
2-Iodotoluene	C_7H_7I	1.164	−1.494	0.0961
1-Chloro-3-ethylbenzene	C_8H_9Cl	1.091	−1.097	0.1397
2-Bromoethylcyclohexane	$C_8H_{15}Br$	1.147	−1.492	0.1082
1-Iodo-octane	$C_8H_{17}I$	1.203	−1.690	0.0902
Iodononane	$C_9H_{19}I$	1.558	−2.111	0.1103
1-Bromonaphthalene	$C_{10}H_7Br$	1.386	−2.514	0.1205
1-Chloronaphthalene	$C_{10}H_7Cl$	1.336	−2.219	0.1479

Alcohols and Polyols

Compound	Formula	m	C, atm	m'
Methanol	CH_4O	0.885	+0.543	0.4970
2-Chloroethanol	C_2H_5OCl	1.064	−0.434	0.2379
Ethyl alcohol	C_2H_6O	0.981	+0.351	0.3832
Ethylene glycol	$C_2H_6O_2$	1.476	−1.715	0.4280
2,3-Dibromo-1-propanol	$C_3H_6OBr_2$	1.365	−1.846	0.1128
Isopropyl alcohol	C_3H_8O	1.022	+0.293	0.3829
n-Propyl alcohol	C_3H_8O	1.078	+0.037	0.4035
Propylene glycol	$C_3H_8O_2$	1.408	−1.515	0.3955
1-Bromo-2-butanol	C_4H_9OBr	1.348	−0.826	0.1585

Tables of m, m', and C *(Continued)*

Alcohols and Polyols

Compound	Formula	m	C, atm	m'
Isobutyl alcohol	$C_4H_{10}O$	1.093	-0.129	0.2653
tert-Butyl alcohol	$C_4H_{10}O$	1.026	$+0.287$	0.2491
n-Butyl alcohol	$C_4H_{10}O$	1.141	-0.293	0.2770
sec-Butyl alcohol	$C_4H_{10}O$	1.081	$+0.008$	0.2787
1,3-Butanediol	$C_4H_{10}O_2$	1.297	-1.613	0.2590
Furfuryl alcohol	$C_5H_6O_2$	1.329	-1.187	0.2438
n-Amyl alcohol	$C_5H_{12}O$	1.175	-0.618	0.2399
2-Pentanol	$C_5H_{12}O$	1.129	-0.326	0.2305
tert-Amyl alcohol	$C_5H_{12}O$	1.071	-0.024	0.2187
Isoamyl alcohol	$C_5H_{12}O$	1.167	-0.505	0.2383
3-Pentanol	$C_5H_{12}O$	1.178	-0.617	0.2406
Cyclohexanol	$C_6H_{12}O$	1.204	-0.960	0.2164
2-Hexyl alcohol	$C_6H_{14}O$	1.162	-0.640	0.2047
n-Hexyl alcohol	$C_6H_{14}O$	1.250	-0.940	0.2202
2-Methyl-1-pentanol	$C_6H_{14}O$	1.192	-0.771	0.2099
2-Methyl-4-pentanol	$C_6H_{14}O$	1.192	-0.771	0.2088
Dipropylene glycol	$C_6H_{14}O_2$	1.551	-2.255	0.2081
Heptyl alcohol	$C_7H_{16}O$	1.329	-1.267	0.2057
Methylphenylcarbinol	$C_8H_{10}O$	1.384	-0.384	0.2039
Cyclohexylethanol	$C_8H_{16}O$	1.354	-1.670	0.1901
Tetraethylene glycol	$C_6H_{18}O_5$	2.316	-4.575	0.2146
Cinnamyl alcohol	$C_9H_{10}O$	1.411	-2.249	0.1893
Nonanol	$C_9H_{20}O$	1.432	-1.867	0.1787
Tripropylene glycol	$C_9H_{20}O_4$.	1.631	-2.799	0.1527
α-Terpinol	$C_{10}H_{18}O$	1.323	-1.772	0.1544
Citronellol	$C_{10}H_{20}O$	1.495	-2.051	0.1722
1-Menthol	$C_{10}H_{20}O$	1.397	-1.805	0.1609
Decyl alcohol	$C_{10}H_{22}O$	1.466	-2.125	0.1667

Aldehydes, Ketones, and Ethers

Compound	Formula	m	C, atm	m'
Bromal	C_2HBr_3O	1.134	-1.060	0.0727
Chloral	C_2HCl_3O	0.802	$+0.028$	0.0979
Chloral hydrate	$H_3Cl_3O_2$	1.175	$+0.069$	0.1279
2-Propenal	C_3H_4O	0.686	$+0.590$	0.2202
Acetone	C_3H_6O	0.729	$+0.567$	0.2259
Propylene oxide	C_3H_6O	0.653	$+0.828$	0.2024
2-Methylpropionyl bromide	C_4H_7BrO	1.106	-0.905	0.1318
1-Bromo-2-butanone	C_4H_7BrO	1.085	-0.690	0.1293
Di-2-bromoethyl ether	$C_4H_8Br_2O$	1.270	-1.645	0.0985
Methylethyl ketone	C_4H_8O	0.754	$+0.255$	0.1882
Dichloroethyl ether	$C_4H_8Cl_2O$	1.148	-1.125	0.1495
1,4-Dioxane	$C_4H_8O_2$	0.846	-0.014	0.1728
Methylpropyl ether	$C_4H_{10}O$	0.663	$+0.768$	0.1610
Diethyl ether	$C_4H_{10}O$	0.660	$+0.835$	0.1602
2-Furfurylaldehyde	$C_5H_4O_2$	1.168	-0.940	0.1216

TABLES OF m, m', AND C (Continued)

Aldehydes, Ketones, and Ethers

Compound	Formula	m	C, atm	m'
Tiglaldehyde	C_5H_8O	0.882	−0.214	0.1887
Levulinaldehyde	$C_5H_8O_2$	1.180	−1.256	0.2121
3-Pentanone	$C_5H_{10}O$	1.069	−0.043	0.2240
2-Pentanone	$C_5H_{10}O$	1.071	−0.051	0.2238
3-Methyl-2-butanone	$C_5H_{10}O$	1.054	+0.187	0.2203
2-Chloroethyl-2-chloroisopropyl ether	$C_5H_{10}Cl_2O$	1.150	−1.145	0.1318
2-Chloroethyl-2-chloropropyl ether	$C_5H_{10}Cl_2O$	1.151	−1.303	0.1318
4-Hydroxy-3-methyl-2-butanone	$C_5H_{10}O_2$	1.393	−1.454	0.2455
Ethylpropyl ether	$C_5H_{12}O$	0.657	+0.440	0.1342
Cyclohexanone	$C_6H_{10}O$	0.990	−0.729	0.1814
Mesityl oxide	$C_6H_{10}O$	0.979	−0.418	0.1796
Dichlorodiisopropyl ether	$C_6H_{12}Cl_2O$	1.203	−1.229	0.1266
Allyl propyl ether	$C_6H_{12}O$	0.809	+0.123	0.1454
Allyl isopropyl ether	$C_6H_{12}O$	0.826	+0.281	0.1484
Paraformaldehyde	$C_6H_{12}O_6$	1.004	−0.347	0.1367
Dipropyl ether	$C_6H_{14}O$	0.778	+0.130	0.1371
Diisopropyl ether	$C_6H_{14}O$	0.707	+0.396	0.1245
Acetal	$C_6H_{14}O_2$	0.934	−0.030	0.1423
Diethyl cellosolve	$C_6H_{14}O_2$	0.761	+1.304	0.1159
Benzaldehyde	C_7H_6O	1.111	−1.092	0.1884
Salicylaldehyde	$C_7H_6O_2$	1.199	−1.381	0.1767
4-Bromoanisole	C_7H_7OBr	1.243	−1.721	0.1196
Anisole	C_7H_8O	1.038	−0.773	0.1728
4-Heptanone	$C_7H_{14}O$	1.330	−0.795	0.1839
Methyl-n-amyl ketone	$C_7H_{14}O$	1.303	−0.878	0.1802
Acetophenone	C_8H_5O	1.193	−1.442	0.1787
Anisaldehyde	$C_8H_8O_2$	1.439	−2.271	0.1902
2-Octanone	$C_8H_{16}O$	1.171	−1.081	0.1644
Caprylaldehyde	$C_8H_{16}O$	2.191	−1.921	0.3076
1,2-Dipropoxyethane	$C_8H_{18}O_2$	0.617	−0.614	0.0759
Diethylene glycol butyl ether	$C_8H_{18}O_3$	1.329	−1.914	0.1475
Cinnemal aldehyde	C_9H_3O	1.480	−2.316	0.2016
Benzyl ethyl ether	$C_9H_{12}O$	1.146	−1.196	0.1515
Phorone	$C_9H_{14}O$	1.289	−1.495	0.1679
Isophorone	$C_9H_{14}O$	1.158	−1.152	0.1508
Azelaldehyde	$C_9H_{18}O$	1.233	−1.287	0.1560
2-Nonanone	$C_9H_{18}O$	1.175	−1.340	0.1487
Eugenol	$C_{10}H_{12}O_2$	1.458	−2.360	0.1598
Isoeugenol	$C_{10}H_{12}O_2$	1.497	−2.572	0.1641
Cineole	$C_{10}H_{18}O$	1.056	−1.008	0.1232
Capraldehyde	$C_{10}H_{20}O$	1.364	−1.720	0.1571
2-Decanone	$C_{10}H_{20}O$	1.244	−1.596	0.1433
Diisoamyl ether	$C_{10}H_{22}O$	1.119	−1.039	0.1272
Dipropylene glycol monobutyl ether	$C_{10}H_{22}O_3$	1.388	−1.967	0.1434
Diphenyl ether	$C_{12}H_{10}O$	1.308	−2.163	0.1383

TABLES OF m, m', AND C (*Continued*)

Aldehydes, Ketones, and Ethers

Compound	Formula	m	C, atm	m'
1-Acetonaphthalene................	$C_{12}H_{10}O$	1.723	-3.275	0.1822
2-Dodecanone....................	$C_{12}H_{24}O$	1.476	-2.314	0.1441
Lauraldehyde....................	$C_{12}H_{24}O$	1.453	-2.388	0.1419
Tripropylene glycol monoisopropyl ether..........................	$C_{12}H_{26}O_4$	1.529	-2.510	0.1175
Benzyl phenyl ether..............	$C_{13}H_{12}O$	1.516	-2.801	0.1481

Acids

Compound	Formula	m	C, atm	m'
Trichloroacetic acid..............	$C_2HO_2Cl_3$	1.419	-1.624	0.1563
Dichloroacetic acid...............	$C_2H_2O_2Cl_2$	1.334	-1.516	0.1862
Bromoacetic acid.................	$C_2H_3O_2Br$	1.404	-1.764	0.1819
Chloroacetic acid.................	$C_2H_3O_2Cl$	1.352	-1.471	0.2575
Acetic acid......................	$C_2H_4O_2$	0.961	-0.254	0.2880
Acrylic acid.....................	$C_3H_4O_2$	1.113	-0.628	0.2788
Propionic acid...................	$C_3H_6O_2$	1.104	-0.625	0.2683
Methoxyacetic acid...............	$C_3H_6O_3$	1.422	-1.739	0.2841
Succinyl chloride.................	$C_4H_4O_2Cl_2$	1.283	-1.432	0.1490
Succinic anhydride...............	$C_4H_4O_3$	1.494	-2.499	0.2687
Chloroacetic anhydride...........	$C_4H_4O_3Cl_2$	1.598	-2.132	0.1682
Metacrylic acid..................	$C_4H_6O_2$	1.260	-1.004	0.2634
Acetic anhydride.................	$C_4H_6O_3$	1.052	-0.575	0.1855
Butyric acid.....................	$C_4H_8O_2$	1.255	-1.032	0.2170
Tiglic acid......................	$C_5H_8O_2$	1.424	-1.645	0.2207
Valeric acid.....................	$C_5H_{10}O_2$	1.399	-1.453	0.2162
Isovaleric acid...................	$C_5H_{10}O_2$	1.320	-1.242	0.2011
Benzenesulfonyl chloride..........	$C_6H_5O_2ClS$	1.320	-2.119	0.1345
Propionic anhydride..............	$C_6H_{10}O_3$	1.171	-1.008	0.1620
Benzoyl chloride.................	C_7H_5OCl	1.159	-1.342	0.1484
Phenylacetic chloride.............	C_8H_7OCl	1.297	-1.653	0.1481

Esters

Compound	Formula	m	C, atm	m'
Methyl formate..................	$C_2H_4O_2$	0.668	$+0.887$	0.2002
Methyl dichloroacetate...........	$C_3H_4Cl_2O_2$	1.064	-0.627	0.1340
Ethyl formate...................	$C_3H_6O_2$	0.718	$+0.591$	0.1745
Methyl acetate..................	$C_3H_6O_2$	0.743	$+0.558$	0.1800
Methyl glycolate.................	$C_3H_6O_3$	1.109	-0.765	0.1956
Ethyl chloroglyoxylate...........	$C_4H_5ClO_3$	1.000	-0.490	0.1318
Ethyl trichloroacetate............	$C_4H_5Cl_3O_2$	1.170	-1.007	0.1098
Ethyl dichloroacetate.............	$C_4H_6Cl_2O_2$	1.085	-0.809	0.1252
2-Chloroethyl chloroacetate........	$C_4H_6Cl_2O_2$	1.292	-1.590	0.1481
Methyl acrylate..................	$C_4H_6O_2$	0.796	$+0.260$	0.1664
Dimethyl oxalate.................	$C_4H_6O_4$	1.176	-0.965	0.1792
Ethyl acetate....................	$C_4H_8O_2$	0.819	$+0.312$	0.1673
Methyl propionate...............	$C_4H_8O_2$	0.823	$+0.274$	0.1681

TABLES OF m, m', AND C (Continued)

Esters				
Compound	Formula	m	C, atm	m'
Propyl formate...............	$C_4H_8O_2$	0.812	+0.250	0.1659
Ethyl glycolate...............	$C_4H_8O_2$	1.138	−0.765	0.1968
Ethyl acrylate................	$C_5H_8O_2$	0.862	−0.006	0.1550
Isopropyl chloroacetate..........	$C_5H_9ClO_2$	1.082	−0.709	0.1426
Ethyl propionate..............	$C_5H_{10}O_2$	0.883	+0.012	0.1556
Methyl butyrate..............	$C_5H_{10}O_2$	0.892	−0.032	0.1572
Methyl isobutyrate............	$C_5H_{10}O_2$	0.856	+0.101	0.1509
Isopropyl acetate.............	$C_5H_{10}O_2$	0.829	+0.146	0.1461
n-Propyl acetate..............	$C_5H_{10}O_2$	0.887	−0.024	0.1563
Isobutyl formate..............	$C_5H_{10}O_2$	0.852	+0.023	0.1498
Butyl formate................	$C_5H_{10}O_2$	0.891	−0.081	0.1570
sec-Butyl formate.............	$C_5H_{10}O_2$	0.857	+0.087	0.1510
Diethyl carbonate.............	$C_5H_{10}O_3$	0.989	−0.365	0.1507
Dimethyl maleate.............	$C_6H_8O_4$	1.293	−1.591	0.1258
Isobutyl dichloroacetate.........	$C_6H_{10}Cl_2O_2$	1.192	−1.221	0.1159
Ethyl acetoacetate............	$C_6H_{10}O_3$	1.203	−1.207	0.1664
Glycol diacetate..............	$C_6H_{10}O_4$	1.267	−1.391	0.1560
Diethyl oxalate...............	$C_6H_{10}O_4$	1.435	−1.509	0.1767
Dimethyl-l-maleate............	$C_6H_{10}O_5$	1.480	−2.278	0.1643
Dimethyl-d-tartrate...........	$C_6H_{10}O_5$	1.636	−2.947	0.1816
Methyl isovalerate............	$C_6H_{12}O_2$	0.919	−0.226	0.1423
Ethyl butyrate...............	$C_6H_{12}O_2$	0.904	−0.277	0.1401
Ethyl isobutyrate.............	$C_6H_{12}O_2$	0.893	−0.135	0.1383
Propyl propionate.............	$C_6H_{12}O_2$	0.947	−0.308	0.1467
Isobutyl acetate..............	$C_6H_{12}O_2$	0.904	−0.239	0.1401
Isoamyl formate..............	$C_6H_{12}O_2$	0.943	−0.318	0.1461
sec-Butyl glycolate............	$C_6H_{12}O_3$	1.214	−1.177	0.1653
Dimethyl citraconate...........	$C_7H_{10}O_4$	1.343	−1.717	0.1528
trans-Dimethyl mesaconate........	$C_7H_{10}O_4$	1.310	−1.623	0.1491
Dimethyl itaconate............	$C_7H_{10}O_4$	1.640	−2.059	0.1866
Butyl acrylate...............	$C_7H_{12}O_2$	1.000	−0.654	0.1124
Diethyl malonate..............	$C_7H_{12}O_4$	1.310	−1.540	0.1227
Methyl caproate..............	$C_7H_{14}O_2$	1.0845	−0.734	0.1203
Ethyl isovalerate.............	$C_7H_{14}O_2$	0.997	−0.479	0.1106
Propyl butyrate..............	$C_7H_{14}O_2$	1.015	−0.592	0.1126
Propyl isobutyrate............	$C_7H_{14}O_2$	0.959	−0.455	0.1064
Isoamyl acetate..............	$C_7H_{14}O_2$	1.044	−0.590	0.1159
Isopropyl isobutyrate...........	$C_7H_{14}O_2$	0.928	−0.277	0.1030
Isobutyl propionate............	$C_7H_{14}O_2$	1.030	−0.527	0.1143
Triethyl orthoformate..........	$C_7H_{16}O_3$	1.082	−0.675	0.1081
Phenyl acetate...............	$C_8H_8O_2$	1.251	−1.437	0.1654
Methyl benzoate..............	$C_8H_8O_2$	1.195	−1.410	0.1580
Methyl salicylate.............	$C_8H_8O_2$	1.239	−1.717	0.1466
Diethyl maleate..............	$C_8H_{12}O_4$	1.327	−1.788	0.1387
Dipropyl oxalate..............	$C_8H_{14}O_4$	1.344	−1.753	0.1360
Diethyl fumarate.............	$C_8H_{12}O_4$	1.327	−1.788	0.1387

Esters

Compound	Formula	m	C, atm	m'
Diisopropyl oxalate	$C_8H_{14}O_4$	1.316	-1.484	0.1359
Ethyl isocaproate	$C_8H_{16}O_2$	1.081	-0.851	0.1349
Propyl isovalerate	$C_8H_{16}O_2$	1.071	-0.791	0.1337
Isobutyl isobutyrate	$C_8H_{16}O_2$	1.054	-0.679	0.1315
Isobutyl butyrate	$C_8H_{16}O_2$	1.040	-0.786	0.1298
Amyl isopropionate	$C_8H_{16}O_2$	1.067	-0.840	0.1332
Benzyl acetate	$C_9H_{10}O_2$	1.263	-1.647	0.1514
Ethyl benzoate	$C_9H_{10}O_2$	1.236	-1.612	0.1481
Ethyl salicylate	$C_9H_{10}O_2$	1.358	-1.975	0.1471
Diethyl itaconate	$C_9H_{14}O_4$	1.252	-1.782	0.1210
Diethyl glutarate	$C_9H_{16}O_4$	1.413	-2.113	0.1351
Methyl caprylate	$C_9H_{18}O_2$	1.218	-1.367	0.1385
Isobutyl isovalerate	$C_9H_{18}O_2$	1.100	-0.967	0.1251
Isoamyl butyrate	$C_9H_{18}O_2$	1.120	-1.098	0.1274
Isoamyl isobutyrate	$C_9H_{18}O_2$	1.086	-0.956	0.1235
Methyl cinnamate	$C_{10}H_{10}O_2$	1.388	-2.341	0.1540
Dimethyl phthalate	$C_{10}H_{10}O_4$	1.595	-2.912	0.1479
Propyl benzoate	$C_{10}H_{12}O_2$	1.279	-1.853	0.1402
Diethyl adipate	$C_{10}H_{18}O_4$	1.659	-2.520	0.1476
Diisobutyl oxalate	$C_{10}H_{18}O_4$	1.394	-2.003	0.1241
Isoamyl isovalerate	$C_{10}H_{20}O_2$	1.141	-1.291	0.1192
Isobutyl benzoate	$C_{11}H_{14}O_2$	1.380	-2.065	0.1394
Bornyl formate	$C_{11}H_{18}O_2$	1.278	-1.673	0.0950
Geranyl formate	$C_{11}H_{18}O_2$	1.362	-1.963	0.1012
Neryl formate	$C_{11}H_{18}O_2$	1.336	-1.868	0.0992
Menthyl formate	$C_{11}H_{20}O_2$	1.253	-1.694	0.0887
2-Ethyl hexyl acrylate	$C_{11}H_{20}O_2$	1.298	-1.721	0.0919
Octyl acrylate	$C_{11}H_{20}O_2$	1.379	-1.956	0.0976
Isoamyl benzoate	$C_{12}H_{16}O_2$	1.411	-2.370	0.0969
Geranyl acetate	$C_{12}H_{20}O_2$	1.469	-2.268	0.1008
Linalyl acetate	$C_{12}H_{20}O_2$	1.312	-1.785	0.0887
Citroneryl acetate	$C_{12}H_{22}O_2$	1.644	-2.193	0.1103
Menthyl acetate	$C_{12}H_{22}O_2$	1.319	-1.871	0.0885
Dimethyl sebacate	$C_{12}H_{22}O_4$	1.740	-3.284	0.1043
Diisoamyl oxylate	$C_{12}H_{22}O_4$	1.507	-2.562	0.1903
Bornyl propionate	$C_{13}H_{22}O_2$	1.385	-2.052	0.0889
Bornyl butyrate	$C_{14}H_{24}O_2$	1.437	-2.257	0.0879
Bornyl isobutyrate	$C_{14}H_{24}O_2$	1.412	-2.178	0.0863
Geranyl butyrate	$C_{14}H_{24}O_2$	1.706	-2.810	0.1043
Geranyl isobutyrate	$C_{14}H_{24}O_2$	1.659	-2.655	0.1015

Nitrogen Compounds

Compound	Formula	m	C, atm	m'
Formamide	CH_3NO	1.687	-2.158	0.6700
Nitromethane	CH_3NO_2	0.875	-0.015	0.2570
Tetranitromethane	CN_4O_8	0.974	-0.357	0.0815
Acetonitrile	C_2H_3N	0.760	$+0.226$	0.3323
Methyl thiocyanate	C_2H_3NS	0.914	-0.421	0.2250

TABLES OF m, m', AND C (*Continued*)

Nitrogen Compounds

Compound	Formula	m	C, atm	m'
Methyl isothiocyanate	C_2H_3NS	0.879	-0.243	0.2164
Acetamide	C_2H_5NO	1.445	-1.990	0.5526
Acetaldoxime	C_2H_5NO	1.092	-0.243	0.4179
Ethylamine	C_2H_7N	0.647	$+1.118$	0.2373
Nitroethane	$C_2H_5NO_2$	0.917	-0.191	0.2088
1,2-Ethanediamine	$C_2H_8N_2$	1.019	-0.258	0.3052
Acrylonitrile	C_3H_3N	0.731	$+0.260$	0.2480
Propionitrile	C_3H_5N	0.830	$+0.037$	0.2712
Ethyl isothiocyanate	C_3H_5NS	0.962	-0.422	0.2036
2-Bromo-2-nitrosopropane	C_3H_6BrNO	0.903	$+0.252$	0.1069
Ethyl carbamate	$C_3H_7NO_2$	1.349	-1.396	0.2725
1-Nitropropane	$C_3H_7NO_2$	0.962	-0.429	0.1943
2-Nitropropane	$C_3H_7NO_2$	0.917	-0.271	0.1853
Propylamine	C_3H_9N	0.700	$+0.663$	0.2131
3-Butene nitrile	C_4H_5N	0.900	-0.250	0.2416
cis-Crotonitrile	C_4H_5N	0.857	-0.103	0.2299
trans-Crotonitrile	C_4H_5N	0.899	-0.296	0.2412
Methacrylonitrile	C_4H_5N	0.761	$+0.118$	0.2042
Allyl isothiocyanate	C_4H_5NS	1.032	-0.702	0.1873
Diacetamide	$C_4H_7NO_2$	1.491	-2.052	0.2654
Ethylmethyl carbamate	$C_4H_9NO_2$	1.234	-1.102	0.2154
Propyl carbamate	$C_4H_9NO_2$	1.451	-1.654	0.2532
Diethylamine	$C_4H_{11}N$	0.713	$+0.569$	0.1755
3-Bromopyridine	C_5H_4BrN	1.082	-1.035	0.1187
2-Chloropyridine	C_5H_4ClN	1.076	-0.963	0.1706
Tiglonitrile	C_5H_7N	0.830	-0.265	0.1842
Angelonitrile	C_5H_7N	0.951	-0.522	0.2110
Ethyl cyanoacetate	$C_5H_7NO_2$	1.666	-2.066	0.2651
Piperidine	$C_5H_{11}N$	0.858	-0.078	0.1814
Isobutyl carbamate	$C_5H_{11}NO_2$	1.463	-1.814	0.2248
Isoamyl nitrate	$C_5H_{11}NO_3$	1.065	-0.685	0.1440
2,4,6-Trichloroaniline	$C_6H_4Cl_3N$	2.404	-4.037	0.2202
Nitrobenzene	$C_6H_5NO_2$	1.214	-1.550	0.1775
2-Chloroaniline	C_6H_6ClN	1.229	-1.551	0.1734
3-Chloroaniline	C_6H_6ClN	1.328	-1.898	0.1874
4-Chloroaniline	C_6H_6ClN	1.339	-1.932	0.1889
2-Nitroaniline	$C_6H_6N_2O_2$	1.654	-3.028	0.2156
Aniline	C_6H_7N	1.1732	-1.218	0.2267
2-Picoline	C_6H_7N	0.982	-0.403	0.1898
1,3-Phenylenediamine	$C_6H_8N_2$	1.560	-2.867	0.2983
Phenylhydrazine	$C_6H_8N_2$	1.428	-2.207	0.2731
Benzonitrile	C_7H_5N	1.159	-1.272	0.2023
Phenyl isocyanide	C_7H_5N	1.066	-0.896	0.1861
Phenyl isocyanate	C_7H_5NO	1.049	-0.889	0.1585
Phenyl isothiocyanate	C_7H_5NS	1.252	-1.687	0.1667
Benzylamine	C_7H_9N	1.179	-1.226	0.1981

TABLES OF m, m', AND C (*Continued*)

Nitrogen Compounds

Compound	Formula	m	C, atm	m'
2-Toluidine....................	C_7H_9N	1.231	−1.457	0.2068
2-Tolunitrile...................	C_8H_7N	1.181	−1.457	0.1814
Phenyl acetonitrile.............	C_8H_7N	1.327	−1.949	0.1209
2-Tolyl isocyanide..............	C_8H_7N	1.1395	−1.173	0.1750
4-Ethylaniline..................	$C_8H_{11}N$	1.319	−1.764	0.1959
2,4-Xylidine....................	$C_8H_{11}N$	1.354	−1.741	0.2011
2,6-Xylidine....................	$C_8H_{11}N$	1.223	−1.642	0.1817
Tetramethylpiperazine...........	$C_8H_{18}N_2$	1.069	−1.101	0.1353
Diisobutylamine.................	$C_8H_{19}N$	0.987	−0.539	0.1375
Quinoline.......................	C_9H_7N	1.294	−1.942	0.1803
Isoquinoline....................	C_9H_7N	1.348	−2.052	0.1879
4-Cumidine.....................	$C_9H_{13}N$	1.353	−1.918	0.1801
Triisobutylamine................	$C_{12}H_{27}N$	1.259	−1.240	0.1222

Phenols

Compound	Formula	m	C, atm	m'
2,3,4,6-Tetrachlorophenol.........	$C_6H_2Cl_4O$	1.641	−2.902	0.1274
2,4,5-Trichlorophenol..............	$C_6H_3Cl_3O$	1.3702	−2.219	0.1248
2,4,6-Trichlorophenol..............	$C_6H_3Cl_3O$	1.480	−2.317	0.1349
2,4-Dichlorophenol................	$C_6H_4Cl_2O$	1.361	−1.734	0.1503
2,6-Dichlorophenol................	$C_6H_4Cl_2O$	1.404	−1.910	0.1550
2-Chlorophenol...................	C_6H_5ClO	1.037	−0.974	0.1452
3-Chlorophenol...................	C_6H_5ClO	1.224	−1.602	0.1714
2-Nitrophenol....................	$C_6H_5NO_3$	1.290	−1.692	0.1669
Phenol..........................	C_6H_6O	1.258	−1.275	0.2406
Pyrocatechol....................	$C_6H_6O_2$	1.453	−2.267	0.2375
2-Methoxyphenol.................	$C_7H_8O_2$	1.397	−1.719	0.2026
2-Ethylphenol....................	$C_8H_{10}O$	1.297	−1.626	0.1911
3-Ethylphenol....................	$C_8H_{10}O$	1.442	−1.887	0.2125
4-Ethylphenol....................	$C_8H_{10}O$	1.415	−1.913	0.2085
4,6-Dimethylresorcinol............	$C_8H_{10}O_2$	1.294	−1.705	0.1685
2-Isopropylphenol................	$C_9H_{12}O$	1.387	−1.819	0.1833
3-Isopropylphenol................	$C_9H_{12}O$	1.404	−2.000	0.1856
4-Isopropylphenol................	$C_9H_{12}O$	1.467	−2.094	0.1939
Thymol.........................	$C_{10}H_{14}O$	1.412	−2.053	0.1692
1-Naphthol......................	$C_{10}H_8O$	1.519	−2.760	0.1896
2-Naphthol......................	$C_{10}H_8O$	1.522	−2.820	0.1900
4-Isobutylphenol.................	$C_{10}H_{14}O$	1.492	−2.231	0.1788
4-*sec*-Butylphenol................	$C_{10}H_{14}O$	1.433	−2.199	0.1717
2-*sec*-Butylphenol................	$C_{10}H_{14}O$	1.328	−1.892	0.1591

Metal Organic Compounds

Compound	Formula	m	C, atm	m'
Carbon disulfide.................	CS_2	0.631	+0.623	0.1491
Methyl trichlorosilane.............	CH_3Cl_3Si	0.687	+0.398	0.0827
Methyl dichlorosilane.............	CH_4Cl_2Si	0.620	+0.678	0.0970
2-Methyldisilazane...............	CH_9NSi_2	0.645	+0.825	0.1272

TABLES OF m, m', AND C (*Continued*)

Metal Organic Compounds

Compound	Formula	m	C, atm	m'
Trichloroethoxysilane	$C_2H_5Cl_3OSi$	0.833	-0.030	0.0835
Trichloroethylsilane	$C_2H_5Cl_3Si$	0.894	$+0.007$	0.0984
Dimethyldichlorosilane	$C_2H_6Cl_2Si$	0.737	$+0.373$	0.1028
Dimethylantimony	C_2H_6Sb	1.268	-1.627	0.0962
2-Ethyldisilazane	$C_2H_{11}NSi_2$	0.671	$+0.396$	0.1147
Allyltrichlorosilane	$C_3H_5Cl_2Si$	0.896	-0.236	0.0919
Trichloroisopropylsilane	$C_3H_7Cl_3Si$	0.859	-0.232	0.0870
Dichloroethoxymethylsilane	$C_3H_8Cl_2OSi$	0.835	-0.007	0.0944
Trimethylchlorosilane	C_3H_9ClSi	0.689	$+0.517$	0.1141
Trimethyldiborane	$C_3H_{12}B_2$	0.656	$+0.664$	0.1693
Trimethylgallium	C_3H_9Ga	0.745	$+0.593$	0.1168
Trimethyl phosphate	$C_3H_9O_4P$	1.143	-1.269	0.1469
Selenophene	C_4H_4Se	0.736	-0.156	0.1009
Diethylzinc	$C_4H_{10}Zn$	0.886	-0.234	0.1291
Dichlorodiethylsilane	$C_4H_{10}Cl_2Si$	0.968	-0.419	0.1109
Diethyldifluorosilane	$C_4H_{10}F_2Si$	0.748	$+0.559$	0.1084
Diethyl sulfate	$C_4H_{10}O_4S$	1.278	-1.624	0.1492
Diethyl sulfide	$C_4H_{10}S$	0.826	$+0.159$	0.1647
Tetramethyllead	$C_4H_{12}Pb$	0.849	-0.125	0.1657
Allyldichloroethylsilane	$C_5H_{10}Cl_2Si$	0.970	-0.654	0.1032
Trifluorophenylsilane	$C_6H_5F_3Si$	0.869	$+0.023$	0.0964
Trichlorophenylsilane	$C_6H_5Cl_3Si$	1.155	-1.380	0.0983
Benzenethiol	C_6H_6S	1.136	-0.990	0.1856
Hexamethyldisiloxane	$C_6H_8OSi_2$	0.881	$+0.010$	0.1041
Diallyldichlorosilane	$C_6H_{10}Cl_2Si$	1.035	-0.873	0.1028
Diallyl sulfide	$C_6H_{10}S$	0.939	-0.501	0.1480
Chlorotriethylsilane	$C_6H_{15}ClSi$	0.9604	-0.603	0.1147
Triethyl phosphate	$C_6H_{15}O_4P$	1.228	-1.575	0.1229
Diethoxydimethylsilane	$C_6H_{16}O_3Si_2$	0.921	-0.186	0.0694
Trimethylpropylsilane	$C_6H_{16}Si$	0.745	$+0.119$	0.1153
Hexamethylcyclotrisiloxane	$C_6H_{18}O_3Si_2$	1.066	-0.508	0.0805
Benzyldichlorosilane	$C_7H_8Cl_2Si$	1.335	-1.511	0.1257
Dichloromethylphenylsilane	$C_7H_8Cl_2Si$	1.171	-1.443	0.1103
Triethoxymethylsilane	$C_7H_{18}O_3Si$	1.008	-0.598	0.1018
Butyltrimethylsilane	$C_7H_{18}Si$	0.877	-0.195	0.1211
Triethylmethylsilane	$C_7H_{18}Si$	0.895	-0.345	0.1235
Dichloroethylphenylsilane	$C_8H_{10}Cl_2Si$	1.207	-1.739	0.1059
Chlorodimethylphenylsilane	$C_8H_{11}ClSi$	1.145	-1.292	0.1207
Dimethylphenylsilane	$C_8H_{12}Si$	1.012	-0.787	0.1337
Dibutyl sulfide	$C_8H_{18}S$	1.187	-1.204	0.1461
Tetraethoxysilane	$C_8H_{20}O_4Si$	1.073	-0.941	0.0927
Tetraethyllead	$C_8H_{20}Pb$	1.293	-1.326	0.0719
Amyltrimethylsilane	$C_8H_{20}Si$	0.940	-0.507	0.1170
Tetraethylsilane	$C_8H_{20}Si$	0.977	-0.691	0.1218
Tetraethylbistibine	$C_8H_{20}Sb_2$	1.375	-2.817	0.0687
1,3-Diethoxytetramethyldisiloxane	$C_8H_{22}O_3Si_2$	1.160	-0.884	0.0939

Tables of m, m', and C (Continued)

Metal Organic Compounds

Compound	Formula	m	C, atm	m'
1,7-Dichloroctamethyltetrasiloxane..	$C_8H_{24}Cl_2O_3Si_4$	1.307	−1.798	0.0669
Octamethoxytrisiloxane............	$C_8H_{24}O_4Si_4$	1.078	−0.727	0.0654
Octamethylcyclotetrasiloxane.......	$C_8H_{24}O_4Si_4$	1.157	−1.048	0.0702
Chloroethoxymethylphenylsilane....	$C_9H_{13}ClOSi$	1.238	−1.603	0.1110
Hexyltrimethylsilane..............	$C_9H_{22}Si$	1.019	−0.834	0.1158
Triethylpropylsilane..............	$C_9H_{22}Si$	1.079	−0.997	0.1226
Diisoamyl sulfide.................	$C_{10}H_{22}S$	1.238	−1.642	0.1278
Heptyltrimethylsilane.............	$C_{10}H_{24}Si$	1.107	−1.145	0.1156
Butyltriethylsilane...............	$C_{10}H_{24}Si$	1.129	−1.256	0.1179
Decamethylcyclopentasiloxane......	$C_{10}H_{30}O_5Si_5$	1.263	−1.609	0.0613
Decamethyltetrasiloxane...........	$C_{10}H_{30}O_3Si_4$	1.199	−1.351	0.0694
Diethoxymethylphenylsilane........	$C_{11}H_{18}O_2Si$	1.364	−1.815	0.1167
Trimethyloctylsilane..............	$C_{11}H_{26}Si$	1.264	−1.524	0.1220
Amyltriethylsilane................	$C_{11}H_{26}Si$	1.226	−1.573	0.1184
Difluorodiphenylsilane............	$C_{12}H_{10}F_2Si$	1.351	−2.178	0.1104
Tetraethoxyphenylsilane...........	$C_{12}H_{20}O_2Si$	1.461	−2.147	0.1094
Triethylhexylsilane...............	$C_{12}H_{28}Si$	1.258	−1.813	0.1130
1,7-Diethoxyoctamethyltetrasiloxane		1.443	−2.050	0.0700
Dodecamethylpentasiloxane........	$C_{12}H_{36}O_4Si_5$	1.345	−1.831	0.0629
Dodecamethylcyclohexasiloxane.....	$C_{12}H_{36}O_6Si_6$	1.394	−2.074	0.0563

* D. F. Othmer, P. W. Maurer, C. J. Molinary, and R. C. Kowalski, *Ind. Eng. Chem.*, **49**:125 (1957); D. F. Othmer and D. Zudkevitch, *Ind. Eng. Chem.*, **51**:791 (1959).

THERMODYNAMIC FUNCTIONS FROM HIRSCHFELDER, BUEHLER, McGEE, AND SUTTON EQUATION OF STATE* EQS. (3-58) AND (3-63)

Region I, all T, $\rho_r \leq 1$
Region II, $T_r > 1$, $\rho_r \geq 1$

1. $(\partial P_r/\partial \rho_r)_{T_r}$

Region I $= -2(k_0 + k_1 T_r^{-1})\rho_r + 3k_2(-T_r + T_r^{-1})\rho_r^2$
$$+ (T_r/Z_c)(1 - b^1\rho_r^2)(1 - b\rho_r + b^1\rho_r^2)^{-2}$$

Region II $= \displaystyle\sum_{j=0}^{3} T_r^{i-1} R_j(\rho_r)$

2. $(\partial P_r/\partial T_r)_{\rho_r}$

Region I $= k_1 T_r^{-2}\rho_r^2 - k_2(1 + T_r^{-2})\rho_r^3 + (\rho_r/Z_c)(1 - b\rho_r + b^1\rho_r^2)^{-1}$

Region II $= \displaystyle\sum_{j=0}^{3} (j - 1)T_r^{i-2}Q_j(\rho_r)$

3. $(H - H^0)/RT$

Region 1 $= -Z_c[\rho_r(2k_0 T_r^{-1} + 3k_1 T_r^{-2}) + k_2\rho_r^2(1 - 2T_r^{-2})]$
$$+ (b\rho_r - b^1\rho_r^2)/(1 - b\rho_r + b^1\rho_r^2)$$

At the critical density,

$(H_c - H^0)/RT = -Z_c[2k_0 T_r^{-1} + 3k_1 T_r^{-2} + k_2(1 - 2T_r^{-2})] + (b - b^1)/(1 - b + b^1)$

Region II $= Z_c \displaystyle\sum_{j=0}^{3} T_r^{i-2}\{[Q_j(\rho_r)/\rho_r] - Q_j(1) - (j - 2)[W_j(\rho_r) - W_j(1)]\}$
$$+ (H_c - H^0)/RT$$

4. $\ln (f/P_c)$

Region I $= -Z_c[2\rho_r(k_0 T_r^{-1} + k_1 T_r^{-2}) + \tfrac{3}{2}k_2\rho_r^2(1 - T_r^{-2})]$
$$+ \ln (\rho_r T_r) + (b\rho_r - b^1\rho_r^2)/(1 - b\rho_r + b^1\rho_r^2) - \tfrac{1}{2}\ln (1 - b\rho_r + b^1\rho_r^2)$$
$$+ k_3 \tan^{-1} k_3 + k_3 \tan^{-1}(k_4\rho_r - k_3) - \ln Z_c \qquad -\pi/2 < \tan^{-1} < \pi/2$$

At the critical density,

$\ln (f_c/P_c) = -Z_c[2(k_0 T_r^{-1} + k_1 T_r^{-2}) + \tfrac{3}{2}k_2(1 - T_r^{-2})]$
$$+ \ln T_r + (b - b^1)/(1 - b + b^1) - \tfrac{1}{2}\ln (1 - b + b^1)$$
$$+ k_3[\tan^{-1} k_3 + \tan^{-1}(k_4 - k_3)] - \ln Z_c$$

Region II $= Z_c \displaystyle\sum_{j=0}^{3} T_r^{i-2}\{[Q_j(\rho_r)/\rho_r] - Q_j(1) + W_j(\rho_r) - W_j(1)\} + \ln (f_c/P_c)$

*Ind. Eng. Chem., **50**:386 (1958); Ind. Eng. Chem. Fundamentals, **1**:224 (1962).*

5. $(C_v - C_v{}^0)/R$

Region I $= Z_c(2k_1\rho_r - k_2\rho_r{}^2)T_r{}^{-2}$

Region II $= Z_c(2k_1 - k_2)T_r{}^{-2} - Z_c \displaystyle\sum_{j=0}^{3} (j-1)(j-2)T_r{}^{j-2}[W_j(\rho_r) - W_j(1)]$

where $k_0 = 5.5$

$k_1 = \beta - k_0$

$k_2 = (1 - k_0 - \alpha + 2\beta)/2$

$b = (1/\beta)(3\beta^2 - 6\beta - 1)/(3\beta - 1)$

$b^1 = (\beta - 3)/(3\beta - 1)$

$k_3 = b(4b^1 - b^2)^{-\frac{1}{2}}$

$k_4 = 2b^1(4b^1 - b^2)^{-\frac{1}{2}}$

$\beta = f(Z_c)$ that is $Z_c = \beta(3\beta - 1)(1 + \beta)^{-3}$

α = Riedel factor

$Q_j(\rho_r) = (k_{0j} + k_{1j}\rho_r + k_{2j}\rho_r{}^2 + k_{3j}\rho_r{}^3 + k_{4j}\rho_r{}^4 + k_{5j}\rho_r{}^5)/\rho_r$

$R_j(\rho_r) = (-k_{0j} + k_{2j}\rho_r{}^2 + 2k_{3j}\rho_r{}^3 + 3k_{4j}\rho_r{}^4 + 4k_{5j}\rho_r{}^5)/\rho_r{}^2$

$W_j(\rho_r) = [-\frac{1}{2}k_{0j} - k_{1j}\rho_r + k_{2j}\rho_r{}^2 \ln (\rho_r) + k_{3j}\rho_r{}^3 + \frac{1}{2}k_{4j}\rho_r{}^4 + \frac{1}{3}k_{5j}\rho_r{}^5]/\rho_r{}^2$

NOTE: $R_j = dQ_j/d\rho_r$; $Q_j = \rho_r{}^2 \, dW_j/d\rho_r$.

k_{ij} CONSTANTS

	$j = 0$	$j = 1$	$j = 2$	$j = 3$
$i = 0$	0	$88.5 - 3.12\beta$	$-124.5 + 3.84\beta$ $+ 0.363\beta^2$	$44.4 - 5.22\beta$
$i = 1$	0	$-313.3 + 13.42\beta$	$429 - 9.84\beta$ $- 1.815\beta^2$	$-156.9 + 18.92\beta$
$i = 2$	0	$408.9 - 21.54\beta$	$-528.8 + 1.98\beta$ $+ 3.63\beta^2$	$204.3 - 25.44\beta$
$i = 3$	$5.5 - \beta$	$-237.4 + 15.3\beta$	$263 + 15.7\beta$ $- 3.63\beta^2$	$-115.5 + 15\beta$
$i = 4$	$-2.25 - (\alpha/2)$ $+ \beta$	$47.8 - 4.06\beta$	$(\alpha/2) - 27.05$ $-16.18\beta + 1.815\beta^2$	$23.7 - 3.26\beta$
$i = 5$	0	0	$-8.44 + 4.50\beta$ $- 0.363\beta^2$	0

NOTE:
$(C_p - C_p{}^0)/R = (C_v - C_v{}^0)/R + \{(Z_cT_r/\rho_r{}^2)[(\partial P_r/\partial T_r)_{\rho_r}]^2\}/[(\partial P_r/\partial \rho_r)_{T_r}] - 1$

BENEDICT - WEBB - RUBIN EQUATION OF STATE

Compressibility Factor

$$Z = PV/RT = 1 + (B_0 - A_0/RT - C_0/RT^3)(1/V) + (b - a/RT)(1/V^2) + (a\alpha/RT)(1/V^5) + (c/RT^3)[(1 + \gamma V^{-2})/V^{-2}]\,e^{-\gamma V^{-2}} \quad \text{(E-1)}$$

The constants are tabulated for hydrocarbons, CO_2, N_2, and SO_2 in Table E-1.

Isothermal Enthalpy Deviation for the Pure Component

$$H - H^0 = (B_0RT - 2A_0 - 4C_0T^{-2})V^{-1} + \tfrac{1}{2}(2bRT - 3a)V^{-2} + \tfrac{6}{5}a\alpha V^{-5} + cV^{-2}T^{-2}\{3[(1 - e^{-\gamma V^{-2}})/\gamma V^{-2}] - (\tfrac{1}{2} - \gamma V^{-2})e^{-\gamma V^{-2}}\} \quad \text{(E-2)}$$

Fugacity of the Pure Component

$$RT \ln f_i = RT \ln RTV^{-} + 2(B_0RT - A_0 - C_0T^{-2})V^{-1} + \tfrac{3}{2}(bRT - a)V^{-2} + \tfrac{6}{5}a\alpha V^{-5} + cT^{-2}V^{-2}[(1 - e^{-\gamma V^{-2}})/\gamma V^{-2} + (\tfrac{1}{2} + \gamma V^{-2})e^{-\gamma V^{-2}}] \quad \text{(E-3)}$$

Isothermal Entropy Deviation of the Pure Component

$(S - S_s)/R$ may be determined from Eqs. (E-2), (E-3), and (6-21).

Mixtures

The B-W-R mixture constants are approximated from the pure-component values (denoted by a subscript $i = 1$ to n), as follows:

$$B_{0_m} = \tfrac{1}{4}\sum_i y_i B_{0_i} + \tfrac{3}{4}\left(\sum_i y_i B_{0_i}^{1/3}\right)\left(\sum_i y_i B_{0_i}^{2/3}\right) \quad \text{(E-4)}$$

$$A_{0_m} = \left(\sum_i y_i A_{0_i}^{1/2}\right)^2 \quad \text{(E-5)}$$

$$C_{0_m} = \left(\sum_i y_i C_{0_i}^{1/2}\right)^2 \quad \text{(E-6)}$$

$$a_m = \left(\sum_i y_i a_i^{1/3}\right)^3 \quad \text{(E-7)}$$

$$b_m = \left(\sum_i y_i b_i^{1/3}\right)^3 \quad \text{(E-8)}$$

$$c_m = \left(\sum_i y_i c_i^{1/3}\right)^3 \quad \text{(E-9)}$$

$$\alpha_m = \left(\sum_i y_i \alpha_i^{1/3}\right)^3 \quad \text{(E-10)}$$

$$\gamma_m = \left(\sum_i y_i \gamma_i^{1/2}\right)^2 \quad \text{(E-11)}$$

TABLE E-1. CONSTANTS FOR THE EQUATION OF BENEDICT, WEBB, AND RUBIN

Substance	Ref.	A_0	B_0	$C_0 \times 10^{-6}$	a	b	$c \times 10^{-6}$	$\alpha \times 10^3$	$\gamma \times 10^2$
Methane	1	1.85500	0.042600	0.02257	0.49400	0.00338004	0.002545	0.124359	0.6000
Ethane	1	4.15556	0.0627724	0.179592	0.345160	0.0111220	0.0327670	0.243389	1.18000
Ethylene	1	3.33958	0.0556833	0.131140	0.259000	0.0086000	0.021120	0.178000	0.923000
Propane	1	6.87225	0.0973130	0.508256	0.947700	0.0225000	0.129000	0.607175	2.20000
Propene	1	6.11220	0.0850647	0.439182	0.774056	0.0187059	0.102611	0.455696	1.82900
n-Butane	1	10.0847	0.124361	0.992830	1.88231	0.0399983	0.316400	1.10132	3.40000
Isobutane	1	10.23264	0.137544	0.849943	1.93763	0.0424352	0.286010	1.07408	3.40000
1-Butene	1	8.95325	0.116025	0.927280	1.69270	0.0348156	0.274920	0.910889	2.95945
n-Pentane	1	12.1794	0.156751	2.12121	4.07480	0.0668120	0.824170	1.81000	4.75000
Isopentane	1	12.7959	0.160053	1.74632	3.75620	0.0668120	0.695000	1.70000	4.63000
n-Hexane	1	14.4373	0.177813	3.31935	7.11671	0.109131	1.51276	2.81086	6.66849
n-Heptane	1	17.5206	0.199005	4.74574	10.36475	0.151954	2.47000	4.35611	9.00000
n-Decane	5	25.2325	-0.0645222	3.88626	381.637	0.646261	5.75722	5.70791	15.3030
Benzene	6	6.51013	0.0503020	3.43016	55.7047	0.0766343	1.17652	0.700159	2.93016
3-Methylpentane	3	17.973	0.17900	1.8861	4.3546	0.08637	0.89829	3.0450	7.2131
2,3-Dimethylbutane	3	13.828	0.09209	1.8670	5.5238	0.10994	0.85505	2.2759	6.5044
2,2-Dimethylbutane	3	11.842	0.19214	3.3595	5.108	0.14000	1.7483	2.1890	6.6500
CO_2: I†	2	1.97575	0.0338945	0.0778086	1.75020	0.00527242	0.00978903	0.0698624	0.460598
II‡	2	2.46616	0.0484030	0.0841836	6.32033	0.00358992	0.00409736	0.961331	0.539386
N_2	8	1.19257	0.0458013	0.0058894	0.149013	0.00198165	0.00054811	0.291569	0.750042
SO_2	4	2.12054	0.0261827	0.793879	8.44395	0.0146542	0.113362	0.0719604	0.592390
H_2S	7	2.78413	0.0669750	0.221172	0.77460	0.0068946	0.031026	0.538738	1.90774

NOTE: Units are P, atmospheres; d, gram moles per liter; T, degrees Kelvin; R, 0.08207 (liter)(atm)/(g mole)(°K).

REFERENCES: 1. M. Benedict, G. B. Webb, and L. C. Rubin, *Chem. Eng. Progr.*, **47**:419 (1951). 2. R. T. Ellington, B. E. Eakin, J. D. Parent, D. C. Gami, and O. T. Bloomer, Thermodynamic and Transport Properties of Gases, Liquids, and Solids, papers given at the Symposium of the American Society of Mechanical Engineers, Lafayette, Ind., pp. 180, 195, McGraw-Hill Book Company, New York, 1959. 3. R. G. Griskey, and H. H. Beyer, *AIChE J.*, **9**:507 (1963). 4. T. L. Kang, and J. J. McKetta, *J. Chem. Eng. Data*, **6**:227 (1961). 5. J. B. Opfell, B. H. Sage, and K. Pitzer, *Ind. Eng. Chem.*, **48**:2069 (1956). 6. E. I. Organick, and W. R. Studhalter, *Chem. Eng. Progr.*, **44**:847 (1948). 7. R. Simon and J. E. Briggs, *AIChE J.*, **10**:548 (1964). 8. H. H. Stotler and M. Benedict, *Chem. Eng. Progr., Symposium Ser.*, **49**:25 (1953).

† Recommended for natural gases containing CO_2.
‡ To be used for mixtures containing over 40 mole % CO_2.

627

Volumes of Mixtures

Use Eq. (E-1) with constants subscripted by m from Eqs. (E-4) through (E-11) with Table E-1.

Enthalpy of Mixtures

$$H_m = \sum_i y_i H_i^0 + (B_{0_m}RT - 2A_{0_m} - 4C_{0_m}T^{-2})V^{-1}$$

$$+ \tfrac{1}{2}(2b_m RT - 3a_m)V^{-2} + \tfrac{6}{5}(a_m \alpha_m V^{-5})$$

$$+ c_m V^{-2}T^{-2}\{3[(1 - e^{-\gamma_m V^{-2}})/\gamma_m V^{-2}] - (\tfrac{1}{2} - \gamma_m V^{-2})e^{-\gamma_m V^{-2}}\} \quad \text{(E-12)}$$

H_i^0 is the enthalpy of pure component at zero pressure.

Entropy of the Mixture

$$S_m = \sum_i y_i[S_{s_i} - R \ln (RTy_i/P_s V)] - (B_{0_m}R + 2C_{0_m}T^{-3})V^{-1} - b_m RV^{-2}$$

$$+ 2c_m V^{-2}T^{-3}[(1 - e^{-\gamma_m V^{-2}})/\gamma_m V^{-2} - e^{-\gamma_m V^{-2}}/2] \quad \text{(E-13)}$$

where S_{s_i} is the pure component entropy at some standard pressure P_s.

Fugacity of a Component in the Mixture

$$RT \ln \bar{f}_i = RT \ln (RTy_i/V) + [(B_{0_m} + B_{0_i})RT - 2(A_{0_m}A_{0_i})^{1/2} - 2(C_{0_m}C_{0_i})^{1/2}T^{-2}]V^{-1}$$

$$+ \tfrac{3}{2}[RT(b_m^2 b_i)^{1/3} - (a_m^2 a_i)^{1/3}]V^{-2} + \tfrac{3}{5}[a_m(\alpha_m^2 \alpha_i)^{1/3} + \alpha_m(a_m^2 a_i)^{1/3}]V^{-5}$$

$$+ [3V^{-2}(c_m^2 c_i)^{1/3}/T^2][(1 - e^{-\gamma_m V^{-2}})/\gamma_m V^{-2} - e^{-\gamma_m V^{-2}}/2]$$

$$- (2V^{-2}c_m/T^2)(\gamma_i/\gamma_m)^{1/2}[(1 - e^{-\gamma_m V^{-2}})/\gamma_m V^{-2} - e^{-\gamma_m V^{-2}}(1 + \gamma_m V^{-2}/2)] \quad \text{(E-14)}$$

GENERAL APPLICATION OF PSEUDOCRITICAL CONCEPT TO THE ESTIMATION OF PARTIAL QUANTITIES

The definition of a partial quantity is

$$\bar{G}_i = (\partial \underline{G}/\partial N_i)_{T,P,N_j} \qquad j \neq i \tag{F-1}$$

If $\underline{G}$ is an extensive property such as total volume, total free energy, etc., then, by Euler's theorem,

$$\underline{G} = \sum_j N_j \bar{G}_j = GN \tag{F-2}$$

where G is the intensive property and N the total moles.

Differentiating with respect to N_i, keeping all other moles constant,

$$\bar{G}_i = G + N(\partial G/\partial N_i)_{T,P,N_j} \qquad j \neq i \tag{F-3}$$

Now, if G [or some function related to G such that the derivative of this function is equal to $(\partial G/\partial N_i)_{T,P,N_j}, j \neq i$] can be expressed as

$$G = f(T_r, P_r, \omega) \tag{F-4}$$

then

$$\bar{G}_i = G + [(\partial G/\partial T_r)_{P_r,\omega}\psi_{T_r} + (\partial G/\partial P_r)_{T_r,\omega}\psi_{P_r} + (\partial G/\partial \omega)_{T_r,P_r}\psi_\omega] \tag{F-5}$$

where

$$\psi_{T_r} = N(\partial T_r/\partial N_i)_{T,P,N_j} \qquad j \neq i \tag{F-6}$$
$$\psi_{P_r} = N(\partial P_r/\partial N_i)_{T,P,N_j} \qquad j \neq i \tag{F-7}$$
$$\psi_\omega = N(\partial \omega/\partial N_i)_{T,P,N_j} \qquad j \neq i \tag{F-8}$$

In Eq. (F-5) the derivatives $(\partial G/\partial)$ depend only on the property G, whereas ψ_{T_r}, ψ_{P_r}, ψ_ω depend only on the pseudocritical-constant rule chosen.

$(\partial G/\partial)$ DERIVATIVES

Property	Fugacity	Volume	Enthalpy
$\bar{G}_i$	$\ln(\bar{f}_i/y_iP)$	$\bar{V}_i$	$\bar{H}_i - H_i^0$
G	$\ln(f_m/P)$	ZRT/P	$H_m - \sum_j y_s H_j^0$
$(\partial G/\partial T_r)_{P_r,\omega}$	$-(1/T_r)(H_m - H_m^0)/RT$	$(RT/P)(Z_T - Z)/T_r$	$-RT_{c_m}(\partial\theta/\partial T_r)_{P_r,\omega}$
$(\partial G/\partial P_r)_{T_r,\omega}$	$(Z-1)/P_r$	$(RT/P)(Z - Z_p)/P_r$	$-RT_{c_m}(\partial\theta/\partial P_r)_{T_r\omega}$
$(\partial G/\partial \omega)_{T_r,P_r}$	$\ln(f/P)^1$	$(RT/P)Z$	$-RT_{c_m}[(H_m^0 - H_m)/RT_{c_m}]^1$

In this table the functions for $(\partial G/\partial\omega)_{T_r,P_r}$ have been taken from Ref. 86,* where (f/P), Z, and $(H_m - H_m{}^0)/RT$ have been expressed as linear functions of ω, for example,

$$f/P = (f/P)^0 + \omega(f/P)^1 \tag{F-9}$$

or as shown in Eq. (3-15) for Z. The terms Z_p and Z_T are derivative compressibility factors evaluated and discussed in Sec. 6-9. Finally, the term

$$\Theta \equiv (H_m{}^0 - H_m)/RT_c \tag{F-10}$$

and derivatives of Θ with respect to T_r and P_r may be obtained by differentiating the $H_m{}^0 - H_m$ values in Appendix B (at a Z_c comparable with ω for the substance in question) or, approximately, from Ref. 152.

ψ Factors

The ψ factors depend only upon the choice of the chosen pseudocritical-constant rule. Listed below are the ψ factors for all the rules given in Sec. 7-9, except the complex PG rule. In all cases ω_m is assumed equal to $\sum_j x_j\omega_j$.

Kay's Rule, Eqs. (7-30) and (7-31)

$$\psi_{T_r} = (-T/T_{c_m}^2)(T_{c_i} - T_{c_m}) \tag{F-11}$$
$$\psi_{P_r} = (-P/P_{c_m}^2)(P_{c_i} - P_{c_m}) \tag{F-12}$$
$$\psi_\omega = \omega_i - \omega_m \tag{F-13}$$

J-SBV Rules, Eqs. (7-38) to (7-41)

$$\psi_{T_r} = 2(T/T_{c_m}) \left(Q_i / \sum_i y_i Q_i - R_i / \sum_j y_j R_j \right) \tag{F-14}$$

$$\psi_{P_r} = 2(P/P_{c_m}) \left(Q_i / \sum_i y_i Q_i - R_i / \sum_i y_i R_i \right) \tag{F-15}$$

$$\psi_\omega = \text{same as Eq. (F-13)}$$
$$Q_i = \sum_j y_j[(T_{c_j}/P_{c_j})^{1/3} + (T_{c_i}/P_{c_i})^{1/3}]^3 \tag{F-16}$$
$$R_i = T_{c_i}/P_{c_i}^{1/2} \quad \text{and} \quad \text{similarly for } j$$

[Simplification equation (7-12) was not used.]

Modified Prausnitz and Gunn, Eqs. (7-30) and (7-53)

$$\psi_{T_r} = \text{same as Eq. (F-11)}$$
$$\psi_{P_r} = (P/P_{c_m})[(V_{c_i} - V_{c_m})/V_{c_m} - (Z_{c_i} - Z_{c_m})/Z_{c_m} - (T_{c_i} - T_{c_m})/T_{c_m}] \tag{F-17}$$
$$\psi_\omega = \text{same as Eq. (F-13)}$$

Leland and Mueller, Eqs. (7-32) to (7-35)

Instead of Eq. (7-36), α is defined for this rule (81) as

$$\alpha = 1 + \exp\left[-10\left(P/\sum_j y_j P_{c_j} - 1\right)^2\right] \tag{F-18}$$

$$\psi_{T_r} = \psi_{T_{r_1}} + \psi_{T_{r_2}} \tag{F-19}$$

$$\psi_{T_{r_1}} = (T_{c_m}/\alpha)(\alpha - 1)(20) \left[\left(P^2 - P\sum_j \gamma_j P_{c_j}\right) / \left(\sum_j y_j P_{c_j}\right)^3\right] \left(\sum_j y_j P_{c_j} - P_{c_i}\right)$$
$$\left(\ln T_{c_m} - \tfrac{1}{2}\sum_j \sum_k \ln T_{c_j} T_{c_k}\right) \tag{F-20}$$

* All references in this Appendix are to the publications cited at the end of Chap. 7.

$$\psi_{T_{r_2}} = (2T_{c_m}/\alpha) \left[\sum_j y_j a_j a_i \bigg/ \sum_j \sum_k y_j y_k a_j a_k \right.$$

$$\left. - \sum_j y_j (b_j + b_i)^3 \bigg/ \sum_j \sum_k y_j y_k (b_j + b_k)^3 \right] \quad \text{(F-21)}$$

$$\psi_{P_r} = \psi_{P_{r_1}} + \psi_{P_{r_2}}$$

$$\psi_{P_{r_1}} = (P_{c_m}/T_{c_m}) \psi_{T_{r_1}}$$

$$\psi_{P_{r_2}} = P_{c_m} \left\{ (2/\alpha) \left(\sum_j y_j a_j a_i \bigg/ \sum_j \sum_k y_j y_k a_j a_k \right) - (1 + \alpha)(2/\alpha) \right.$$

$$\left. \left[\sum_j y_j (b_j + b_i)^3 \bigg/ \sum_j \sum_k y_j y_k (b_j + b_k)^3 \right] + \left(1 + Z_{c_i} \bigg/ \sum_j y_j Z_{c_j} \right) \right\} \quad \text{(F-22)}$$

(NOTE: $\psi_{T_{r_1}} = \psi_{P_{r_1}} = 0$ if $\alpha = $ const.)

$$\psi_\omega = \text{same as Eq. (F-13)}$$

$$a_j = [Z T_c{}^{\alpha+1}/P_c]_j{}^{1/2}$$

$$b_j = \tfrac{1}{2}[Z_c T_c/P_c]_j{}^{1/3}$$

LENNARD - JONES POTENTIALS AS DETERMINED FROM VISCOSITY DATA*

Molecule	Compound	b_0,† cm³/g mole	σ, A	ϵ_0/k, °K
A	Argon	46.08	3.542	93.3
He	Helium	20.95	2.551‡	10.22
Kr	Krypton	61.62	3.655	178.9
Ne	Neon	28.30	2.820	32.8
Xe	Xenon	83.66	4.047	231.0
Air	Air	64.50	3.711	78.6
AsH_3	Arsine	89.88	4.145	259.8
BCl_3	Boron chloride	170.1	5.127	337.7
BF_3	Boron fluoride	93.35	4.198	186.3
$B(OCH_3)_3$	Methyl borate	210.3	5.503	396.7
Br_2	Bromine	100.1	4.296	507.9
CCl_4	Carbon tetrachloride	265.5	5.947	322.7
CF_4	Carbon tetrafluoride	127.9	4.662	134.0
$CHCl_3$	Chloroform	197.5	5.389	340.2
CH_2Cl_2	Methylene chloride	148.3	4.898	356.3
CH_3Br	Methyl bromide	88.14	4.118	449.2
CH_3Cl	Methyl chloride	92.31	4.182	350
CH_3OH	Methanol	60.17	3.626	481.8
CH_4	Methane	66.98	3.758	148.6
CO	Carbon monoxide	63.41	3.690	91.7
COS	Carbonyl sulfide	88.91	4.130	336.0
CO_2	Carbon dioxide	77.25	3.941	195.2
CS_2	Carbon disulfide	113.7	4.483	467
C_2H_2	Acetylene	82.79	4.033	231.8
C_2H_4	Ethylene	91.06	4.163	224.7
C_2H_6	Ethane	110.7	4.443.	215.7
C_2H_5Cl	Ethyl chloride	148.3	4.898	300
C_2H_5OH	Ethanol	117.3	4.530	362.6
C_2N_2	Cyanogen	104.7	4.361	348.6
CH_3OCH_3	Methyl ether	100.9	4.307	395.0
CH_2CHCH_3	Propylene	129.2	4.678	298.9
CH_3CCH	Methylacetylene	136.2	4.761	251.8
C_3H_6	Cyclopropane	140.2	4.807	248.9
C_3H_8	Propane	169.2	5.118	237.1
$n\text{-}C_3H_7OH$	n-Propyl alcohol	118.8	4.549	576.7
CH_3COCH_3	Acetone	122.8	4.600	560.2
CH_3COOCH_3	Methyl acetate	151.8	4.936	469.8
$n\text{-}C_4H_{10}$	n-Butane	130.0	4.687	531.4
$iso\text{-}C_4H_{10}$	Isobutane	185.6	5.278	330.1
$C_2H_5OC_2H_5$	Ethyl ether	231.0	5.678	313.8
$CH_3COOC_2H_5$	Ethyl acetate	178.0	5.205	521.3
$n\text{-}C_5H_{12}$	n-Pentane	244.2	5.784	341.1
$C(CH_3)_4$	2,2-Dimethylpropane	340.9	6.464	193.4

LENNARD-JONES POTENTIALS AS DETERMINED FROM
VISCOSITY DATA* *(Continued)*

Molecule	Compound	b_0,† cm^3/g mole	σ, A	ϵ_0/k, °K
C_6H_6	Benzene	193.2	5.349	412.3
C_6H_{12}	Cyclohexane	298.2	6.182	297.1
$n\text{-}C_6H_{14}$	n-Hexane	265.7	5.949	399.3
Cl_2	Chlorine	94.65	4.217	316.0
F_2	Fluorine	47.75	3.357	112.6
HBr	Hydrogen bromide	47.58	3.353	449
HCN	Hydrogen cyanide	60.37	3.630	569.1
HCl	Hydrogen chloride	46.98	3.339	344.7
HF	Hydrogen fluoride	39.37	3.148	330
HI	Hydrogen iodide	94.24	4.211	288.7
H_2	Hydrogen	28.51	2.827	59.7
H_2O	Water	23.25	2.641	809.1
H_2O_2	Hydrogen peroxide	93.24	4.196	289.3
H_2S	Hydrogen sulfide	60.02	3.623	301.1
Hg	Mercury	33.03	2.969	750
$HgBr_2$	Mercuric bromide	165.5	5.080	686.2
$HgCl_2$	Mercuric chloride	118.9	4.550	750
HgI_2	Mercuric iodide	224.6	5.625	695.6
I_2	Iodine	173.4	5.160	474.2
NH_3	Ammonia	30.78	2.900	558.3
NO	Nitric oxide	53.74	3.492	116.7
NOCl	Nitrosyl chloride	87.75	4.112	395.3
N_2	Nitrogen	69.14	3.798	71.4
N_2O	Nitrous oxide	70.80	3.828	232.4
O_2	Oxygen	52.60	3.467	106.7
PH_3	Phosphine	79.63	3.981	251.5
SF_6	Sulfur hexafluoride	170.2	5.128	222.1
SO_2	Sulfur dioxide	87.75	4.112	335.4
SiF_4	Silicon tetrafluoride	146.7	4.880	171.9
SiH_4	Silicon hydride	85.97	4.084	207.6
$SnBr_4$	Stannic bromide	329.0	6.388	563.7
UF_6	Uranium hexafluoride	268.1	5.967	236.8

* R. A. Svehla, *NASA Tech. Rept.* R-132, Lewis Research Center, Cleveland, Ohio, 1962.

† $b_0 = \frac{2}{3}\pi N_0 \sigma^3$, where N_0 is Avogadro's number.

‡ The potential σ was determined by quantum-mechanical formulas.

ESTIMATION OF PROPERTIES OF
ORGANOMETALLIC COMPOUNDS*

Few reliable data are available on the physical and thermodynamic properties of organometallic compounds, and few methods of estimating properties of such materials exist. An analogue technique recently suggested by Kapner for organometallic compounds containing tetravalent metals is summarized in this Appendix.†

The basis of the method is the *organic analogue* to the organometallic compound. This analogue is simply the identical compound, with all metallic atoms replaced by carbon, whether or not the organic compound does or does not exist as a stable entity. It is assumed, however, that the properties of any organic analogue are known or can be estimated by methods given in this book. The estimation of the properties of organometallics is then related to the corresponding property of the organic analogue. Only a few organometallic properties have been studied, but the concept may be expanded.

TABLE H-1. ESTIMATION OF CRITICAL TEMPERATURES FOR ORGANOMETALLIC COMPOUNDS, DIRECT TEST OF THE ANALOGUE METHOD

| Compound | Analogue | θ | $_mT_b$, °C | $_mT_c$, °K | | % Error |
				Calc.	Lit.	
$SiCl_4$	CCl_4	0.6304	$+ 57.3$	524.0	506	$+3.6$
$GeCl_4$	CCl_4	0.6304	$+ 84.0$	566.5	550.1	$+3.0$
$SnCl_4$	CCl_4	0.6304	$+113.0$	612.5	591.9	$+3.5$
$SiCl_3F$	CCl_3F	0.6313	$+ 12.2$	452.0	438.5	$+3.1$
$SiCl_2F_2$	CCl_2F_2	0.6321	$- 31.8$	381.7	369.0	$+3.4$
$SiClF_3$	$CClF_3$	0.6330	$- 70.0$	320.9	307.7	$+4.3$
SiF_4	CF_4	0.6338	$- 94.8(s)$	281.3	259.1	$+8.6$
SiH_4	CH_4	0.587	-111.5	275.5	269.7	$+2.2$
$(CH_3)_4Si$	$(CH_3)_4C$	0.641	$+ 24.9$	465.0	458	$+1.5$
UCl_4	CCl_4	0.6304	$+792.0$	1689.6	1598.1	$+5.7$

NOTE: (s) = solid at 760 mm. $_mT_b$ = normal boiling point of the organometallic.

* Most of this Appendix has been abstracted, with permission, from a paper by R. S. Kapner submitted to the *AIChE J*.

† The term *organometallic* also includes the inorganic type of compounds with tetravalent metallic atoms such as $TiCl_4$, SnH_4, Ge_3H_8, etc.

TABLE H-2. VAN LAAR CORRELATION OF b

Van Laar Values

$H = 59^{(4)}$
34
14   He = 105

C = 100$^{(1)}$	N = 85$^{(2)}$	O = 70$^{(3)}$	F = 55	Ne = 76
175	60	50	17†	
Si = 155	P = 140	S = 125	Cl = 115	A = 144
Ti = 177.5*				
Ge = 210	As = 195	Se = 180	Br = 165	Kr = 144
Sn = 265	Sb = 250	Te = 235	I = 220	Xe = 228
Pb = 320*				

$$U = 317.5^*$$

Van Laar Rules

(1) C = 100 for aliphatic and inorganic molecules
    = 75 for aromatic and cyclic molecules
(2) N = 85 for N_2 only
    = 60 for all other molecules
(3) O = 70 for O_2, ethers, ketones, and alcohols
    = 50 for CO_2 and double-bonded O in —COOH and —COOR
(4) H = 59 for H_2 and HCl
    = 34 for all other inorganic molecules, >NH, —NH$_2$, NH$_3$
    = 14 for all other organic compounds

NOTE: H = 34 was used for H attached to metallic atom.

* Interpolated values.
† Value recommended by J. C. Devins and A. H. Sharbaugh, unpublished, General Electric Co., Research Laboratory, Schenectady, N.Y.

Critical Temperature

First, use Lydersen's group-contribution technique to determine θ for the organic analogue [Table 2-1 and Eq. (2-3)]. Then calculate T_c (organometallic) from Eq. (2-2), using the actual boiling point of the organometallic.

A few comparisons of calculated and experimental critical temperatures are shown in Table H-1. The paucity of critical temperatures of complex organometallics limits the test to simple compounds. Similarly good agreement might be expected with more complex materials since the method should have better applicability to longer hydrocarbon groups.

Critical Pressure

Simple analogue techniques similar to Riedel's method (Sec. 2-4) were found to predict P_c values much larger than those found experimentally. However, from Eqs. (2-4) and (2-5),

$$_mP_c/_aP_c = (_mT_c/_aT_c)(_mb_ab) \tag{H-1}$$

where subscripts m and a refer to the organometallic and organic analogue, the subscript c to the critical value, and b is the van der Waals' constant. For the purposes of this technique, the addition method of van Laar* was used to estimate b for both the organometallic and organic analogue; b contributions are given in Table H-2.

* J. J. van Laar, *Z. anorg. Chem.*, **104**:57 (1918).

TABLE H-3. ESTIMATION OF CRITICAL PRESSURES FOR ORGANOMETALLIC COMPOUNDS, DIRECT TEST OF THE ANALOGUE METHOD

Compound	Analogue	$_mP_c$, atm	
		Calc.†	Lit.
$SiCl_4$	CCl_4	38.6	37.1
$GeCl_4$	CCl_4	38.3	38
$SnCl_4$	CCl_4	38.3	37.0
$TiCl_4$	CCl_4	46.2	45.7
$SiCl_3F$	CCl_3F	37.1	35.3
$SiCl_2F_2$	CCl_2F_2	34.9	34.5
$SiClF_3$	$CClF_3$	34.5	34.2
SiF_4	CF_4	39.1	36.7
SiH_4	CH_4	35.6	47.8
$(CH_3)_4Si$	$(CH_3)_4C$	31.3	33

† $_mP_c$ (calc.) $= _aP_c$ (lit.) $\times [_mT_c$ (calc.)$/_aT_c$ (lit.) $\times \Sigma b_a/\Sigma b_m]$.

By using Eq. (H-1), where $_mT_c$ was found by the critical-temperature procedure noted above, and with either experimental or estimated values of $_aT_c$, $_aP_c$, values of $_mP_c$ were calculated; a few results are shown in Table H-3. The agreement between experimental and calculated values is satisfactory, though not as good as for $_mT_c$.

Other Properties

If one has confidence in the estimated values of $_mT_c$ and $_mP_c$, then vapor pressures* liquid and vapor densities, thermodynamic-property variations with pressure, etc., may be determined by techniques given in this book. Kapner successfully correlated liquid density, using a method similar to the reduced method of Lydersen et al. (Table 3-6) and vapor pressures with an Othmer plot (Fig. 4-3). This success was achieved with compounds for which no experimental critical data were available; so the use of a reduced correlation was an indirect justification of the critical-property estimation technique.

* Usually the boiling point or some reference point must be known.

INDEX